Advanced Engineering Mathematics

ADVANCED

ENGINEERING

MATHEMATICS

Erwin Kreyszig

Professor of Mathematics

Ohio State University

Columbus, Ohio

John Wiley and Sons, Inc. New York · London

THIRD PRINTING, MARCH, 1964

Library of Congress Catalog Card Number: 62–15182
Printed in the United States of America

PREFACE

Purpose of the book. This book is intended to introduce students of engineering and physics to those fields of mathematics which, from the modern point of view, seem to be the most important in connection with practical problems. Topics are chosen according to the frequency of occurrence in applications. New ideas of modern mathematical training, as expressed in various recent symposia on engineering education, were taken into account. The book should suit those institutions that have offered extended mathematical training for a long time as well as those that intend to follow the general trend of broadening the program of instruction in mathematics.

A course in elementary calculus is the sole prerequisite.

The material included in the book has formed the basis of various lecture courses given to undergraduate and graduate students of engineering, physics, and mathematics in this country, in Canada, and in Europe.

Content and arrangement. The arrangement of the subject matter in major parts can be seen from the diagram on the next page.

Much space is devoted to ordinary differential equations and complex analysis, probably the two most important fields for engineers. But also the length of the other chapters on vectors, Fourier series, matrices, etc., is such that the representation can be used as a text for courses of the usual type.

v

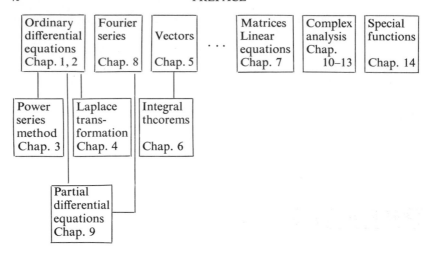

Sections which may be omitted in a shorter course are indicated at the beginning of each chapter.

To facilitate the use of parts of the book, the chapters are kept as independent of each other as possible.

The chapters are subdivided into relatively short sections. Each section includes typical examples and problems illustrating the concepts, methods, and results as well as their engineering applications.

Historical notes, references to original literature, and more than 400 figures are included in the text.

Problems and answers. The book contains more than 3500 carefully selected problems, which range from simple routine exercises to practical applications of considerable complexity. Answers to odd-numbered problems are included at the end of the book, starting on page 799.

References. A list of some books for reference and further study can be found at the end of the book, on pp. 795–798.

Suggestions for courses. The material may be taken in sequence and is then suitable for four consecutive semester courses, meeting 3–5 hours a week as follows:

First semester. Ordinary differential equations (Chap. 1–4).
Second semester. Vectors and matrices (Chap. 5–7).
Third semester. Fourier series and partial differential equations (Chap. 8, 9).
Fourth semester. Complex analysis (Chap. 10–13).

The book is also suitable for various independent one-semester courses meeting 3 hours a week; for example:

Introduction to ordinary differential equations (Chap. 1, 2).

Laplace transformation (Chap. 4).

Vector calculus (Chap. 5, 6).

Matrices and systems of linear equations (Chap. 7).

Fourier series and integrals (Chap. 8).

Partial differential equations (Chap. 9).

Complex analysis (Chap. 10–12).

Infinite series (Sec. 10.4–10.8, 8.1–8.6, 14.3, 14.4).

Special functions (Chap. 14, Sec. 3.3–3.7, 8.12, 8.13).

Numerical analysis (Sec. 0.6–0.8, 1.13, 2.17, 7.14, 7.15, 8.8, 14.3, 14.4).

Principles for selection of topics.   Which topics should be contained in a book of the present type, and how should these topics be arranged and presented?

To find some answer to these basic questions we may take a look at the historical development of engineering mathematics. This development shows the following two interesting features:

1. Mathematics has become more and more important in engineering science, and it is easy to conjecture that this trend will also continue in the future. An important reason for this tendency is that the problems in modern engineering are so complex that most of them cannot be solved solely on the basis of physical intuition and past experience. This empirical approach, which has been successful for many problems, fails as soon as high speeds, large forces, high temperatures or other abnormal conditions are involved, and the situation becomes still more critical because of the fact that various modern materials (plastics, alloys, etc.) have unusual physical properties.   Experimental work becomes complicated, time-consuming, and expensive.   Here mathematics offers help in planning constructions and experiments, and in evaluating experimental data.

2. Mathematical methods, which were developed for purely theoretical reasons, suddenly became of great importance in engineering mathematics. Examples are the theory of matrices, conformal mapping, and the theory of differential equations having periodic solutions.

What are the reflections of this situation on the teaching of engineering mathematics? Since there will be more and more mathematics needed, should we try to include more and more topics in our courses, devoting less and less time to each topic? Or should we concentrate on a few carefully selected basic things of general practical importance which are suitable for teaching the student mathematical thinking and for developing his own creative ability?

Sixty or eighty years ago no one was able to predict that conformal mapping or matrices would ever be of importance in the mathematical part of engineering work. Similarly, it is difficult to conjecture which new mathematical theories will have applications to engineering twenty or thirty years from now. But no matter what happens in that respect, if a student has a good training in the fundamentals of mathematics he will meet his future needs because he will be able to get acquainted with new methods by his own further study.

It follows that the most important objective and purpose in engineering mathematics seems to be that the student becomes familiar with mathematical thinking. He should learn to recognize the guiding principles and ideas "behind the stage," which are more important than formal manipulations. He should get the impression that mathematics is not a collection of tricks and recipes but a systematic science of practical importance, resting on a relatively small number of basic concepts and involving powerful unifying methods. He should soon convince himself of the necessity for applying mathematical procedures to engineering problems, and he will find that the theory and its applications are related to each other like a tree and its fruits.

The student will see that the application of mathematics to an engineering problem consists essentially of three phases:

1. Translation of the given physical information into a mathematical form. In this way we obtain a mathematical model of the physical situation. This model may be a differential equation, a system of linear equations, or some other mathematical expression.

2. Treatment of the model by mathematical methods. This will lead to the solution of the given problem in mathematical form.

3. Interpretation of the mathematical result in physical terms.

All three steps seem to be of equal importance, and the presentation in this book is such that it will help the student to develop skill in carrying out all these steps. In this connection, preference has been given to applications which are of a general nature.

In some considerations it will be unavoidable to rely on results whose proofs are beyond the level of a book of the present type. In any case these points are marked distinctly, because hiding difficulties and oversimplifying matters is no real help to the student in preparing him for his professional work.

These are some of the guiding principles employed in selecting and presenting the material included in this book. I made the choice with great care, using past and present teaching and research experience and resisting the temptation to consider "everything which is important" in engineering mathematics.

Particular efforts have been made in presenting the topics as simply, clearly, and accurately as possible; this refers also to the choice of the notations. In each chapter the level increases gradually, avoiding jumps and accumulations of difficult theoretical considerations.

Numerical methods. Engineering mathematics comes down ultimately to numerical results, and the engineering student should therefore supplement his mathematical equipment with a definite knowledge of some fundamental numerical procedures. For this reason, numerical work is included in the text as well as in the problems, and basic numerical methods are considered in connection with differential equations, matrices, Fourier series, etc. Preference is given to methods suitable for numerical work in a simple form (slide rule, desk calculator) as well as in connection with modern high-speed computation.

Acknowledgment. I am indebted to many of my former teachers, colleagues, and students for advice and help in preparing this book. Various parts of the manuscript were distributed to my classes in mimeographed form and returned to me, together with suggestions for improvement. Discussions with various engineers and mathematicians were of great help to me; I want to mention in particular Professors S. Bergman, P. L. Chambré, A. Cronheim, J. W. Dettman, H. Kuhn, H. B. Mann, I. Marx, W. D. Munro, T. Rado, H. A. Smith, J. Todd, H. J. Weiss, A. Wilansky, all in this country, Professor H. S. M. Coxeter of Toronto, and Professors B. Baule, H. Behnke, H. Florian, H. Graf, F. Hohenberg, K. Klotter, M. Pinl, F. Reutter, C. Schmieden, H. Unger, A. Walther, H. Wielandt, all in Europe. I can offer here only an inadequate acknowledgment of my appreciation.

Last, but not least, I want to thank John Wiley and Sons for their effective cooperation and their great care in preparing this edition of the book.

Any further comment and suggestion for improvement by the readers of the book will be gratefully received.

ERWIN KREYSZIG

Columbus, Ohio
July 1962

CONTENTS

Introduction · Review of some topics from algebra and calculus   **1**

0.1 Elementary functions, 1
0.2 Partial derivatives, 9
0.3 Second- and third-order determinants, 12
0.4 Complex numbers, 20
0.5 Polar form of complex numbers, 24
0.6 Some general remarks about numerical computations, 26
0.7 Solution of equations, 29
0.8 Approximate integration, 34

Chapter 1 · Ordinary differential equations of the first order   **42**

1.1 Basic concepts and ideas, 43
1.2 Geometrical considerations. Isoclines, 50
1.3 Separable equations, 53
1.4 Equations reducible to separable form, 61
1.5 Exact differential equations, 63
1.6 Integrating factors, 65
1.7 Linear first-order differential equations, 67
1.8 Variation of parameters, 72

1.9   Electric circuits, 74
1.10 Families of curves. Orthogonal trajectories, 79
1.11 Picard's iteration method, 83
1.12 Existence and uniqueness of solutions, 86
1.13 Numerical methods for differential equations of the first order, 91

Chapter 2 · Ordinary linear differential equations   **99**

2.1   Homogeneous linear equations of the second order, 100
2.2   Homogeneous second-order equations with constant coefficients, 104
2.3   General solution. Fundamental system, 106
2.4   Complex roots of the characteristic equation. Initial value problem, 109
2.5   Double root of the characteristic equation, 114
2.6   Free oscillations, 117
2.7   Cauchy equation, 124
2.8   Existence and uniqueness of solutions, 126
2.9   Homogeneous linear equations of arbitrary order, 133
2.10 Homogeneous linear equations of arbitrary order with constant coefficients, 136
2.11 Nonhomogeneous linear equations, 138
2.12 A method for solving nonhomogeneous linear equations, 140
2.13 Forced oscillations. Resonance, 143
2.14 Electric circuits, 150
2.15 Complex method for obtaining particular solutions, 154
2.16 General method for solving nonhomogeneous equations, 157
2.17 Numerical methods for second-order differential equations, 159

Chapter 3 · Power series solutions of differential equations   **165**

3.1   The power series method, 166
3.2   Theoretical basis of the power series method, 169
3.3   Legendre's equation. Legendre polynomials, 175
3.4   Extended power series method. Indicial equation, 180
3.5   Bessel's equation. Bessel functions of the first kind, 190

3.6   Further properties of Bessel functions of the first kind, 195

3.7   Bessel functions of the second kind, 199

Chapter 4 · Laplace transformation   205

4.1   Laplace transform. Inverse transform. Linearity, 206
4.2   Laplace transforms of derivatives and integrals, 211
4.3   Transformation of ordinary differential equations, 215
4.4   Partial fractions. Unrepeated factors, 218
4.5   Simple complex roots, 221
4.6   Multiple roots, 225
4.7   Multiple complex roots, 228
4.8   Differentiation and integration of transforms, 232
4.9   Unit step function, 235
4.10 Shifting on the t-axis, 239
4.11 Periodic functions, 243
4.12 Table 17. Some Laplace transforms, 251

Chapter 5 · Vector analysis   255

5.1   Scalars and vectors, 255
5.2   Components of a vector, 257
5.3   Vector addition. Multiplication by scalars, 260
5.4   Scalar product, 263
5.5   Vector product, 267
5.6   Vector products in terms of components, 269
5.7   Scalar triple product. Linear dependence of vectors, 274
5.8   Other repeated products, 279
5.9   Scalar fields and vector fields, 281
5.10 Vector calculus, 284
5.11 Curves, 287
5.12 Arc length, 290
5.13 Tangent. Curvature and torsion, 292
5.14 Velocity and acceleration, 296
5.15 Chain rule and mean value theorem for functions of several variables, 300
5.16 Directional derivative. Gradient of a scalar field, 304
5.17 Transformation of coordinate systems and vector components, 311
5.18 Divergence of a vector field, 315
5.19 Curl of a vector field, 319

Chapter 6 · Line and surface integrals. Integral theorems   **324**

  6.1   Line integral, 325
  6.2   Evaluation of line integrals, 327
  6.3   Double integrals, 332
  6.4   Transformation of double integrals into line integrals, 340
  6.5   Surfaces, 346
  6.6   Tangent plane. First fundamental form. Area, 349
  6.7   Surface integrals, 355
  6.8   Triple integrals. Divergence theorem of Gauss, 361
  6.9   Consequences and applications of the divergence theorem, 366
 6.10 Stokes's theorem, 372
 6.11 Consequences and applications of Stokes's theorem, 376
 6.12 Line integrals independent of path, 378

Chapter 7 · Matrices and determinants. Systems of linear equations   **386**

  7.1   Basic concepts. Addition of matrices, 387
  7.2   Matrix multiplication, 392
  7.3   Determinants, 399
  7.4   Submatrices. Rank, 410
  7.5   Systems of n linear equations in n unknowns. Cramer's rule, 412
  7.6   Arbitrary homogeneous systems of linear equations, 417
  7.7   Arbitrary nonhomogeneous systems of linear equations, 423
  7.8   Further properties of systems of linear equations, 426
  7.9   Gauss's elimination method, 430
 7.10 The inverse of a matrix, 433
 7.11 Eigenvalues. Eigenvectors, 439
 7.12 Bilinear, quadratic, Hermitian, and skew-Hermitian forms, 445
 7.13 Eigenvalues of Hermitian, skew-Hermitian, and unitary matrices, 449
 7.14 Bounds for eigenvalues, 455
 7.15 Determination of eigenvalues by iteration, 460

Chapter 8 · Fourier series and integrals 464

8.1 Periodic functions. Trigonometric series, 465
8.2 Fourier series. Euler's formulas, 467
8.3 Even and odd functions, 474
8.4 Functions having arbitrary period, 479
8.5 Half-range expansions, 482
8.6 Determination of Fourier coefficients without integration, 486
8.7 Forced oscillations, 491
8.8 Numerical methods for determining Fourier coefficients. Square error, 494
8.9 Instrumental methods for determining Fourier coefficients, 500
8.10 The Fourier integral, 502
8.11 Orthogonal functions, 510
8.12 Sturm-Liouville problem, 513
8.13 Orthogonality of Bessel functions, 520

Chapter 9 · Partial differential equations 524

9.1 Basic concepts, 524
9.2 Vibrating string. One-dimensional wave equation, 527
9.3 Separation of variables (product method), 529
9.4 D'Alembert's solution of the wave equation, 536
9.5 One-dimensional heat flow, 540
9.6 Heat flow in an infinite bar, 545
9.7 Vibrating membrane. Two-dimensional wave equation, 550
9.8 Rectangular membrane, 552
9.9 Laplacian in polar coordinates, 559
9.10 Circular membrane. Bessel's equation, 562
9.11 Laplace's equation. Potential, 568
9.12 Laplace's equation in spherical coordinates. Legendre's equation, 571

Chapter 10 · Complex analytic functions 577

10.1 Complex numbers. Triangle inequality, 578
10.2 Limit. Derivative. Analytic function, 582

10.3   Cauchy-Riemann equations. Laplace's equation, 587
10.4   Sequences, 592
10.5   Series, 599
10.6   Tests for convergence and divergence of series, 605
10.7   Operations on series, 612
10.8   Power series, 616
10.9   Functions represented by power series, 623
10.10 Rational functions. Root, 629
10.11 Exponential function, 632
10.12 Trigonometric and hyperbolic functions, 635
10.13 Logarithm. General power, 639

Chapter 11 · Complex integrals. Taylor and Laurent series   644

11.1   Line integral in the complex plane, 645
11.2   Basic properties of the complex line integral, 651
11.3   Cauchy's integral theorem, 653
11.4   Evaluation of line integrals by indefinite integration, 661
11.5   Cauchy's integral formula, 664
11.6   The derivatives of an analytic function, 666
11.7   Taylor series, 669
11.8   Practical methods for obtaining power series, 674
11.9   Uniform convergence, 677
11.10 Laurent series, 685
11.11 The "point" at infinity, 690
11.12 Zeros and singularities, 693
11.13 Residues, 697
11.14 The residue theorem, 700
11.15 Evaluation of real integrals, 703

Chapter 12 · Conformal mapping   713

12.1   Mapping, 713
12.2   Conformal mapping, 717
12.3   Linear transformations, 721
12.4   Special linear transformations, 726
12.5   Mapping by other elementary functions, 731
12.6   Riemann surfaces, 739

Chapter 13 · Complex analytic functions and potential theory   **743**

   13.1   Electrostatic fields, 744
   13.2   Two-dimensional fluid flow, 749
   13.3   Special complex potentials, 753
   13.4   General properties of harmonic functions, 758
   13.5   Poisson's integral formula, 762

Chapter 14 · Special functions. Asymptotic expansions   **767**

   14.1   Gamma and Beta functions, 768
   14.2   Error function. Fresnel integrals. Sine and cosine integrals, 774
   14.3   Asymptotic expansions, 780
   14.4   Further properties of asymptotic expansions, 787

Appendix 1 · References   **795**

Appendix 2 · Answers to odd-numbered problems   **799**

Index   **843**

Chapter 11 Complex functions, conformal and potential theory

REVIEW OF SOME TOPICS FROM ALGEBRA AND CALCULUS

This introductory chapter includes some topics which are usually covered in elementary algebra and calculus. We shall refer to sections of this chapter whenever we need some of these topics as a prerequisite for our further consideration.

References: Appendix 1, Ref. [A13].

Answers to problems: Appendix 2.

0.1 ELEMENTARY FUNCTIONS

In this section we shall present a collection of some basic formulas for reference.

Figure 1 shows the graph of the **exponential function** e^x, where

$$e = 2.7\ 1828\ 1828\ 45\ 90\ 45\ 2 \cdots.$$

Basic identities are

(1) $$e^x e^y = e^{x+y}, \qquad e^x/e^y = e^{x-y}, \qquad (e^x)^y = e^{xy}.$$

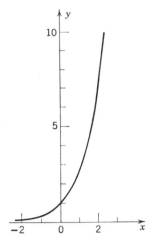

Fig. 1. Exponential function e^x. **Fig. 2.** Natural logarithm $\ln x$.

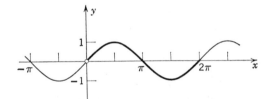

Fig. 3. Sin x.

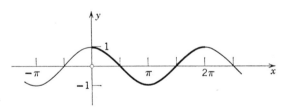

Fig. 4. Cos x.

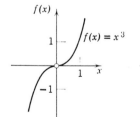 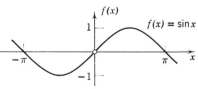

Fig. 5. Odd functions.

The inverse of e^x is the **natural logarithm** $\ln x$ (Fig. 2). It satisfies the identities

(2) $\ln(xy) = \ln x + \ln y$, $\ln \dfrac{x}{y} = \ln x - \ln y$, $\ln(x^a) = a \ln x$.

Furthermore,

$$e^{\ln x} = x, \qquad e^{-\ln x} = e^{\ln(1/x)} = \frac{1}{x}.$$

The inverse of the exponential function 10^x is the *logarithm of base 10* which is denoted by $\log_{10} x$ or simply by $\log x$. We have

$$\log x = M \ln x$$

where

$$M = \log e = 0.43429\ 44819\ 03251\ 82765$$

and conversely

$$\ln x = \frac{1}{M} \log x$$

where

$$\frac{1}{M} = \ln 10 = 2.30258\ 50929\ 94045\ 68402.$$

The **sine** and **cosine functions** $\sin x$ and $\cos x$ are defined in trigonometry for all values of x. *Throughout calculus, angles are measured in radians* so that both functions have the period 2π.

A function $w = f(x)$ which is defined for all x and has the property

(3) $f(-x) = f(x)$ for all x

is called an **even function**. The graph of such a function is symmetric with respect to the w-axis. If $f(x)$ is defined for all x and

(4) $f(-x) = -f(x)$ for all x,

then $f(x)$ is called an **odd function**. These are two quite important concepts.

Since

(5) $\sin(-x) = -\sin x$, $\cos(-x) = \cos x$

$\sin x$ is odd while $\cos x$ is even. The exponential function e^x is neither odd nor even.

The functions $\sin x$ and $\cos x$ are related by the identity

(6) $\sin^2 x + \cos^2 x = 1$.

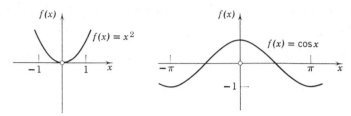

Fig. 6. Even functions.

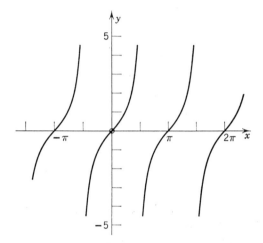

Fig. 7. Tan x.

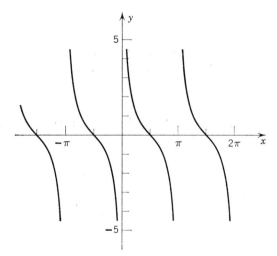

Fig. 8. Cot x.

The addition formulas of the sine function are

(7)
$$\sin (x + y) = \sin x \cos y + \cos x \sin y$$
$$\sin (x - y) = \sin x \cos y - \cos x \sin y.$$

In particular,

(7*)
$$\sin 2x = 2 \sin x \cos x.$$

The addition formulas of the cosine function are

(8)
$$\cos (x + y) = \cos x \cos y - \sin x \sin y$$
$$\cos (x - y) = \cos x \cos y + \sin x \sin y.$$

In particular,

(8*)
$$\cos 2x = \cos^2 x - \sin^2 x.$$

From (7) and (8),

(9)
$$\sin x = \cos \left(x - \frac{\pi}{2}\right) = \cos \left(\frac{\pi}{2} - x\right)$$
$$\cos x = \sin \left(x + \frac{\pi}{2}\right) = \sin \left(\frac{\pi}{2} - x\right)$$
$$\sin (\pi - x) = \sin x, \qquad \cos (\pi - x) = -\cos x.$$

From (8*) and (6),

(10) $\qquad \cos^2 x = \tfrac{1}{2}(1 + \cos 2x), \qquad \sin^2 x = \tfrac{1}{2}(1 - \cos 2x).$

From (8),

(11a)
$$\sin x \sin y = \tfrac{1}{2}[-\cos (x + y) + \cos (x - y)]$$
$$\cos x \cos y = \tfrac{1}{2}[\cos (x + y) + \cos (x - y)],$$

and from (7),

(11b) $\qquad \sin x \cos y = \tfrac{1}{2}[\sin (x + y) + \sin (x - y)].$

From this, by setting $x + y = u$ and $x - y = v$,

(12)
$$\sin u + \sin v = 2 \sin \frac{u + v}{2} \cos \frac{u - v}{2}$$
$$\cos u + \cos v = 2 \cos \frac{u + v}{2} \cos \frac{u - v}{2}$$
$$\cos v - \cos u = 2 \sin \frac{u + v}{2} \sin \frac{u - v}{2}.$$

The other trigonometric functions are defined by the identities

(13) $\quad \tan x = \dfrac{\sin x}{\cos x}, \quad \cot x = \dfrac{\cos x}{\sin x}, \quad \sec x = \dfrac{1}{\cos x}, \quad \csc x = \dfrac{1}{\sin x}.$

The addition formulas for the tangent are

$$(14) \quad \tan(x + y) = \frac{\tan x + \tan y}{1 - \tan x \tan y}, \quad \tan(x - y) = \frac{\tan x - \tan y}{1 + \tan x \tan y}.$$

In applications it is sometimes required to write $A \cos x + B \sin x$ where A and B are given constants, in the form $C \cos(x - \delta)$ where C and δ are constants. From (8) we obtain

$$C \cos(x - \delta) = C \cos \delta \cos x + C \sin \delta \sin x$$

and this is equal to $A \cos x + B \sin x$, if $C \cos \delta = A$ and $C \sin \delta = B$. Using (6), we thus obtain

(15a) $\qquad A \cos x + B \sin x = \sqrt{A^2 + B^2} \cos(x - \delta)$

where

$$\tan \delta = \frac{\sin \delta}{\cos \delta} = \frac{B}{A}.$$

Similarly,

(15b) $\qquad A \cos x + B \sin x = \sqrt{A^2 + B^2} \sin(x \pm \delta)$

where

$$\tan \delta = \frac{\sin \delta}{\cos \delta} = \pm \frac{A}{B}.$$

The **hyperbolic cosine** and **sine functions** are defined by the identities

(16) $\qquad \cosh x = \tfrac{1}{2}(e^x + e^{-x}), \qquad \sinh x = \tfrac{1}{2}(e^x - e^{-x}).$

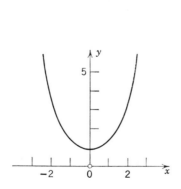

Fig. 9. Cosh x.

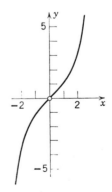

Fig. 10. Sinh x.

TABLE 1. SOME ELEMENTARY FUNCTIONS

x	$\sin x$	$\cos x$	$\tan x$	e^x	$\sinh x$	$\cosh x$
0	0.00000	1.00000	0.00000	1.00000	0.00000	1.00000
0.1	0.09983	0.99500	0.10033	1.10517	0.10017	1.00500
0.2	0.19867	0.98007	0.20271	1.22140	0.20134	1.02007
0.3	0.29552	0.95534	0.30934	1.34986	0.30452	1.04534
0.4	0.38942	0.92106	0.42279	1.49182	0.41075	1.08107
0.5	0.47943	0.87758	0.54630	1.64872	0.52110	1.12763
0.6	0.56464	0.82534	0.68414	1.82212	0.63665	1.18547
0.7	0.64422	0.76484	0.84229	2.01375	0.75858	1.25517
0.8	0.71736	0.69671	1.02964	2.22554	0.88811	1.33743
0.9	0.78333	0.62161	1.26016	2.45960	1.02652	1.43309
1.0	0.84147	0.54030	1.55741	2.71828	1.17520	1.54308
1.1	0.89121	0.45360	1.96476	3.00417	1.33565	1.66852
1.2	0.93204	0.36236	2.57215	3.32012	1.50946	1.81066
1.3	0.96356	0.26750	3.60210	3.66930	1.69838	1.97091
1.4	0.98545	0.16997	5.79788	4.05520	1.90430	2.15090
1.5	0.99750	0.07074	14.10142	4.48169	2.12928	2.35241
1.6	0.99957	−0.02920	−34.23253	4.95303	2.37557	2.57746
1.7	0.99166	−0.12884	−7.69660	5.47395	2.64563	2.82832
1.8	0.97385	−0.22720	−4.28626	6.04965	2.94217	3.10747
1.9	0.94630	−0.32329	−2.92710	6.68589	3.26816	3.41773
2.0	0.90930	−0.41615	−2.18504	7.38906	3.62686	3.76220

x	$\ln x$	x	$\ln x$	x	$\ln x$	x	$\ln x$
1.0	0.00000	2.0	0.69315	3.0	1.09861	5	1.60944
1.1	0.09531	2.1	0.74194	3.1	1.13140	7	1.94591
1.2	0.18232	2.2	0.78846	3.2	1.16315	11	2.39790
1.3	0.26236	2.3	0.83291	3.3	1.19392	13	2.56495
1.4	0.33647	2.4	0.87547	3.4	1.22378	17	2.83321
1.5	0.40547	2.5	0.91629	3.5	1.25276	19	2.94444
1.6	0.47000	2.6	0.95551	3.6	1.28093	23	3.13549
1.7	0.53063	2.7	0.99325	3.7	1.30833	29	3.36730
1.8	0.58779	2.8	1.02962	3.8	1.33500	31	3.43399
1.9	0.64185	2.9	1.06471	3.9	1.36098	37	3.61092

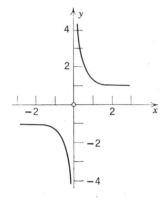

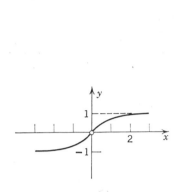

Fig. 11. Tanh x.   Fig. 12. Coth x.

The function $\cosh x$ is even, while $\sinh x$ is odd. The other hyperbolic functions are defined by the identities

(17) $$\tanh x = \frac{\sinh x}{\cosh x}, \qquad \coth x = \frac{\cosh x}{\sinh x}.$$

From the definitions we obtain

(18)
$$\cosh^2 x - \sinh^2 x = 1$$
$$\cosh x + \sinh x = e^x, \qquad \cosh x - \sinh x = e^{-x}$$

and furthermore the addition formulas

(19)
$$\sinh (x \pm y) = \sinh x \cosh y \pm \cosh x \sinh y$$
$$\cosh (x \pm y) = \cosh x \cosh y \pm \sinh x \sinh y$$
$$\tanh (x \pm y) = \frac{\tanh x \pm \tanh y}{1 \pm \tanh x \tanh y}.$$

PROBLEMS

Are the following functions even, odd, or neither even nor odd?

1. $\sin (x^2)$ **2.** $\sin^2 x$ **3.** $\sin x + \cos x$ **4.** x, x^3, x^5

5. $\tan x$ **6.** $\tanh x$ **7.** x^2, x^4, x^6 **8.** $\ln (1 + e^x) - \dfrac{x}{2}$

9. Prove that the sum and the product of even functions are even functions.
10. Prove that the sum of odd functions is odd and the product of two odd functions is even.
11. Derive (9) from (7) and (8).
12. Derive (11) from (7) and (8).

13. Prove (18).
14. Prove the addition formulas of the hyperbolic sine and cosine.
Prove the following identities.
15. $\sinh x \sinh y = \frac{1}{2}[\cosh (x + y) - \cosh (x - y)]$
16. $\cosh x \cosh y = \frac{1}{2}[\cosh (x + y) + \cosh (x - y)]$
17. $\sinh x \cosh y = \frac{1}{2}[\sinh (x + y) + \sinh (x - y)]$
18. $\sinh^2 x = \frac{1}{2}(\cosh 2x - 1),\ \cosh^2 x = \frac{1}{2}(\cosh 2x + 1)$
19. Using the differentiation formula of e^x, find the derivatives of $\sinh x$, $\cosh x$, and $\tanh x$.
20. Show that for large x, $\sinh x \approx e^x/2$, $\cosh x \approx e^x/2$.

0.2 PARTIAL DERIVATIVES

Let $z = f(x, y)$ be a real function of two independent real variables, x and y. If we hold y constant, say, $y = y_1$, and think of x as a variable, then $f(x, y_1)$ depends on x alone. If the derivative of $f(x, y_1)$ with respect to x for a value $x = x_1$ exists, then the value of this derivative is called the *partial derivative of $f(x, y)$ with respect to x at the point (x_1, y_1)* and is denoted by

$$\frac{\partial f}{\partial x}\bigg|_{(x_1, y_1)} \qquad \text{or by} \qquad \frac{\partial z}{\partial x}\bigg|_{(x_1, y_1)}$$

Other notations are

$$f_x(x_1, y_1) \qquad \text{and} \qquad z_x(x_1, y_1);$$

these may be used when subscripts are not used for another purpose and there is no danger of confusion.

We thus have, by the definition of the derivative,

$$(1) \qquad \frac{\partial f}{\partial x}\bigg|_{(x_1, y_1)} = \lim_{\Delta x \to 0} \frac{f(x_1 + \Delta x, y_1) - f(x_1, y_1)}{\Delta x}.$$

The partial derivative of $z = f(x, y)$ with respect to y is defined similarly; we now hold x constant, say, equal to x_1, and differentiate $f(x_1, y)$ with respect to y. Thus

$$(2) \qquad \frac{\partial f}{\partial y}\bigg|_{(x_1, y_1)} = \frac{\partial z}{\partial y}\bigg|_{(x_1, y_1)} = \lim_{\Delta y \to 0} \frac{f(x_1, y_1 + \Delta y) - f(x_1, y_1)}{\Delta y}.$$

Other notations are $f_y(x_1, y_1)$ and $z_y(x_1, y_1)$.

It is clear that the values of those two partial derivatives will in general depend on the point (x_1, y_1), and so the partial derivatives $\partial z/\partial x$ and $\partial z/\partial y$ at a variable point (x, y) are functions of x and y. The function $\partial z/\partial x$ is obtained as in ordinary calculus by differentiating $z = f(x, y)$ with respect to x, *treating y as a constant*, and $\partial z/\partial y$ is obtained by differentiating z with respect to y, *treating x as a constant*.

Example 1.   Let $z = f(x, y) = x^2 y + x \sin y$.   Then

$$\frac{\partial f}{\partial x} = 2xy + \sin y, \qquad \frac{\partial f}{\partial y} = x^2 + x \cos y.$$

The partial derivatives $\partial z / \partial x$ and $\partial z / \partial y$ of a function $z = f(x, y)$ have a very simple geometric interpretation.   The function $z = f(x, y)$ can be represented by a surface in space.   The equation $y = y_1$ then represents a vertical plane intersecting the surface in a curve, and the partial derivative $\partial z / \partial x$ at a point (x_1, y_1) is the slope of the tangent (i.e., $\tan \alpha$ where α is the angle shown in Fig. 13) to the curve.   Similarly, the partial derivative $\partial z / \partial y$ at (x_1, y_1) is the slope of the tangent to the curve $x = x_1$ on the surface $z = f(x, y)$ at (x_1, y_1).

The partial derivatives $\partial z / \partial x$ and $\partial z / \partial y$ are called *first partial derivatives* or *partial derivatives of the first order*.   By differentiating these derivatives once more, we obtain the four *second partial derivatives* (or *partial derivatives of the second order*):

$$(3) \quad \frac{\partial^2 z}{\partial x^2} = f_{xx}(x, y), \quad \frac{\partial^2 z}{\partial x \, \partial y} = f_{xy}(x, y), \quad \frac{\partial^2 z}{\partial y \, \partial x} = f_{yx}(x, y), \quad \frac{\partial^2 z}{\partial y^2} = f_{yy}(x, y).$$

Thus $\partial^2 z / \partial x^2$ is the partial derivative of $\partial z / \partial x$ with respect to x, $\partial^2 z / \partial x \, \partial y$ is the partial derivative of $\partial z / \partial x$ with respect to y, etc.

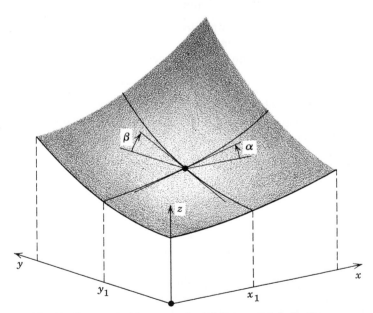

Fig. 13. Geometrical interpretation of first partial derivatives.

It can be shown[1] that if all the derivatives concerned are continuous, then

(4)
$$\frac{\partial^2 z}{\partial x\, \partial y} = \frac{\partial^2 z}{\partial y\, \partial x} ;$$

i.e., the order of differentiation is then immaterial.

Example 2. For the function in Ex. 1,

$$f_{xx} = 2y, \qquad f_{xy} = 2x + \cos y = f_{yx}, \qquad f_{yy} = -x \sin y.$$

By differentiating the second partial derivatives again with respect to x and y, respectively, we obtain the *third partial derivatives* or *partial derivatives of the third order* of f, etc.

If we consider a function $f(x, y, z)$ of three independent variables, then we have the three first partial derivatives $f_x(x, y, z), f_y(x, y, z),$ and $f_z(x, y, z)$. Here f_x is obtained by differentiating f with respect to x, *treating both y and z as constants.* Thus, in analogy to (1), we now have

$$\left. \frac{\partial f}{\partial x} \right|_{(x_1, y_1, z_1)} = \lim_{\Delta x \to 0} \frac{f(x_1 + \Delta x, y_1, z_1) - f(x_1, y_1, z_1)}{\Delta x},$$

etc. By differentiating f_x, f_y, f_z again in this fashion we obtain the second partial derivatives of f, etc.

Example 3. Let $f(x, y, z) = x^2 + y^2 + z^2 + xy\, e^z$. Then

$$\begin{aligned}
f_x &= 2x + y\, e^z, & f_y &= 2y + x\, e^z, & f_z &= 2z + xy\, e^z, \\
f_{xx} &= 2, & f_{xy} &= f_{yx} = e^z, & f_{xz} &= f_{zx} = y\, e^z, \\
f_{yy} &= 2, & f_{yz} &= f_{zy} = x\, e^z, & f_{zz} &= 2 + xy\, e^z.
\end{aligned}$$

PROBLEMS

Find the first partial derivatives of the following functions.

1. $f(x, y) = \sqrt{x^2 + y^2}$ **2.** $f(r, \theta) = r \cos \theta$ **3.** $f(x, y) = \arctan \dfrac{y}{x}$

4. $f(x, y) = e^{xy}$ **5.** $f(x,y) = \dfrac{1}{\sqrt{(x - a)^2 + (y - b)^2}}$ (a, b constant)

6. $f(r, h) = \dfrac{\pi}{3} r^2 h$ **7.** $f(R_1, R_2) = \dfrac{R_1 + R_2}{R_1 R_2}$

Find $f_x + g_y$ where
8. $f(x, y) = x^2 - y^2,$ $g(x, y) = 2xy$

9. $f(x, y) = \ln(x^2 + y^2),$ $g(x, y) = 2 \arctan \dfrac{y}{x}$

Find $f_{xx} + f_{yy}$ where
10. $f(x, y) = x^2 - y^2$ **11.** $f(x, y) = e^x \cos y$ **12.** $f(x, y) = \sin x \cosh y$

[1] Cf. Ref. [A1] in Appendix 1.

Sketch the surfaces corresponding to the following functions.

13. $z = x^2 + y^2$ **14.** $z = \ln (x^2 + y^2)$ **15.** $z = e^{xy}$

16. The curves $z = f(x, y) = const$ are called **level curves** of $f(x, y)$. Draw the level curves of the functions in Probs. 13–15.

Find the first partial derivatives of the following functions at the given points.

17. $f(x, y) = \sqrt{1 - x^2 - y^2}$, at $(0, 0)$ **18.** $f(x, y) = (x^2 + y^2)^2$, at $(1, 2)$

Find the first and second partial derivatives of the following functions.

19. $f(x, y, z) = \dfrac{1}{x^2 + y^2 + z^2}$ **20.** $f(x, y, z) = \dfrac{x + y + z}{xyz}$

0.3 SECOND- AND THIRD-ORDER DETERMINANTS

Consider the system

(1)
$$a_1 x + b_1 y = k_1$$
$$a_2 x + b_2 y = k_2$$

consisting of two linear equations in the unknowns x and y. To solve this system we may multiply the first equation by b_2, the second by $-b_1$, and add, finding

$$(a_1 b_2 - a_2 b_1)x = k_1 b_2 - k_2 b_1.$$

Then we multiply the first equation of (1) by $-a_2$, the second by a_1, and add again, finding

$$(a_1 b_2 - a_2 b_1)y = a_1 k_2 - a_2 k_1.$$

If $a_1 b_2 - a_2 b_1$ is not zero, we may divide and obtain the desired result

(2)
$$x = \frac{k_1 b_2 - k_2 b_1}{a_1 b_2 - a_2 b_1}, \qquad y = \frac{a_1 k_2 - a_2 k_1}{a_1 b_2 - a_2 b_1}.$$

The expression in the denominators is written in the form

$$\begin{vmatrix} a_1 & b_1 \\ a_2 & b_2 \end{vmatrix}$$

and is called a **determinant of the second order**; thus

(3)
$$\begin{vmatrix} a_1 & b_1 \\ a_2 & b_2 \end{vmatrix} = a_1 b_2 - a_2 b_1.$$

The four numbers a_1, b_1, a_2, b_2 are called the **elements** of the determinant. The elements in a horizontal line are said to form a **row** and the elements in a vertical line are said to form a **column** of the determinant.

We may now write the solution (2) of the system (1) in the form

(4) $$x = \frac{D_1}{D}, \qquad y = \frac{D_2}{D} \qquad (D \neq 0)$$

where
$$D = \begin{vmatrix} a_1 & b_1 \\ a_2 & b_2 \end{vmatrix}, \qquad D_1 = \begin{vmatrix} k_1 & b_1 \\ k_2 & b_2 \end{vmatrix}, \qquad D_2 = \begin{vmatrix} a_1 & k_1 \\ a_2 & k_2 \end{vmatrix}.$$

The formula (4) is called **Cramer's rule**[2]. Note that D_1 is obtained by replacing the first column of D by the column with elements k_1, k_2, and D_2 is obtained by replacing the last column of D by that column.

Each equation of the system (1) represents a straight line in the xy-plane, and a pair of numbers (x, y) is a solution of (1) if, and only if, the point P with coordinates x, y lies on both lines. Hence there are three possible cases:

(a) No solution if the lines are parallel.
(b) Precisely one solution if they intersect.
(c) Infinitely many solutions if they coincide.

Example 1.

$x + y = 1$	$x + y = 1$	$x + y = 1$
$x + y = 0$	$x - y = 0$	$2x + 2y = 2$
Case (a)	Case (b)	Case (c)

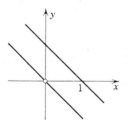 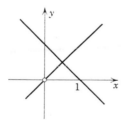 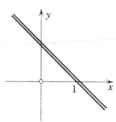

If both k_1 and k_2 are zero, the system is said to be **homogeneous**; otherwise it is said to be **nonhomogeneous**.

If the system is homogeneous, Case (a) cannot occur, because then the lines represented by the equations pass through the origin, and the system has at least the *trivial solution* $x = 0$, $y = 0$.

The homogeneous system will have further solutions if, and only if, those two lines coincide, and then each point on the line is a solution. This happens if, and only if, $D = 0$, as the reader may show.

[2] GABRIEL CRAMER (1704–1752), Italian mathematician, also known by his contributions to the theory of curves.

If the system is nonhomogeneous and $D \neq 0$, it has precisely one solution, which is obtained from (4).

A system of three linear equations in three unknowns x, y, z

$$
\begin{aligned}
a_1 x + b_1 y + c_1 z &= k_1 \\
a_2 x + b_2 y + c_2 z &= k_2 \\
a_3 x + b_3 y + c_3 z &= k_3
\end{aligned}
$$

(5)

may be considered in a similar fashion. To obtain an equation involving only x the equations are multiplied, respectively, by

$$ b_2 c_3 - b_3 c_2, \qquad -(b_1 c_3 - b_3 c_1), \qquad b_1 c_2 - b_2 c_1. $$

We see that these expressions may be written as second-order determinants:

$$ M_1 = \begin{vmatrix} b_2 & c_2 \\ b_3 & c_3 \end{vmatrix}, \qquad -M_2 = -\begin{vmatrix} b_1 & c_1 \\ b_3 & c_3 \end{vmatrix}, \qquad M_3 = \begin{vmatrix} b_1 & c_1 \\ b_2 & c_2 \end{vmatrix}. $$

Adding the resulting equations, we obtain

(6) $$ (a_1 M_1 - a_2 M_2 + a_3 M_3)x = k_1 M_1 - k_2 M_2 + k_3 M_3. $$

Two further equations containing only y and z, respectively, may be obtained in a similar manner.

To simplify our notation we now define a **determinant of the third order** by the equation

(7) $$ D = \begin{vmatrix} a_1 & b_1 & c_1 \\ a_2 & b_2 & c_2 \\ a_3 & b_3 & c_3 \end{vmatrix} = a_1 \begin{vmatrix} b_2 & c_2 \\ b_3 & c_3 \end{vmatrix} - a_2 \begin{vmatrix} b_1 & c_1 \\ b_3 & c_3 \end{vmatrix} + a_3 \begin{vmatrix} b_1 & c_1 \\ b_2 & c_2 \end{vmatrix}. $$

We see that

$$ D = a_1 M_1 - a_2 M_2 + a_3 M_3, $$

the coefficient of x in (6), and if we write the second-order determinants in (7) at length, we obtain

$$ D = a_1(b_2 c_3 - b_3 c_2) - a_2(b_1 c_3 - b_3 c_1) + a_3(b_1 c_2 - b_2 c_1) $$

or

(8) $$ D = a_1 b_2 c_3 - a_1 b_3 c_2 + a_2 b_3 c_1 - a_2 b_1 c_3 + a_3 b_1 c_2 - a_3 b_2 c_1. $$

Obviously the determinant on the right-hand side of (7) which is multiplied by a_i, $i = 1$, 2, or 3, is obtained from D by omitting the first column and the ith row of D.

We see that (6) may now be written

$$Dx = D_1$$

where

$$D_1 = \begin{vmatrix} k_1 & b_1 & c_1 \\ k_2 & b_2 & c_2 \\ k_3 & b_3 & c_3 \end{vmatrix}.$$

The aforementioned equation containing only y may be written

$$Dy = D_2$$

where

$$D_2 = \begin{vmatrix} a_1 & k_1 & c_1 \\ a_2 & k_2 & c_2 \\ a_3 & k_3 & c_3 \end{vmatrix},$$

and the equation containing only z may be written

$$Dz = D_3$$

where

$$D_3 = \begin{vmatrix} a_1 & b_1 & k_1 \\ a_2 & b_2 & k_2 \\ a_3 & b_3 & k_3 \end{vmatrix}.$$

Note that the elements of D are arranged in the same order as they occur as coefficients in the equations of (5), and $D_j, j = 1, 2,$ or 3, is obtained from D by replacing the jth column by the column with elements k_1, k_2, k_3, the expressions on the right sides of the equations of (5).

It follows that if $D \neq 0$, then system (5) has the unique solution

(9) $$x = \frac{D_1}{D}, \quad y = \frac{D_2}{D}, \quad z = \frac{D_3}{D} \qquad \text{(Cramer's rule).}$$

Each equation of system (5) represents a plane in space, and a triple of numbers (x, y, z) is a solution of (5) if, and only if, the point P with coordinates x, y, z is a common point of the three planes. As before we have three possible cases:

(a) No solution if two (or all three) planes are parallel, if two of them coincide and the third is parallel, or if the intersections of each pair of them are three parallel lines.

(b) Precisely one solution, given by (9) if the planes have just one point in common.

(c) Infinitely many solutions if they have a line in common or coincide.

If (5) is homogeneous, i.e., $k_1 = k_2 = k_3 = 0$, it has at least the trivial solution $x = y = z = 0$, and nontrivial solutions exist if, and only if, $D = 0$.

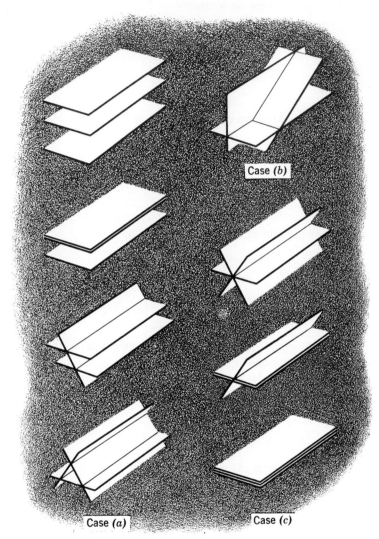

Case (b)

Case (a)   Case (c)

Fig. 14. Geometrical interpretation of three linear equations in three unknowns.

If (5) *is nonhomogeneous and* $D \neq 0$, *it has precisely one solution which is obtained from* (9).

We shall now list the most important properties of our determinants; the corresponding proofs follow from (7) by direct calculation[3].

[3] Determinants of arbitrary order n will be defined in Sec. 7.3, and we shall see that they have quite similar properties.

(A) *The value of a determinant is not altered if its rows are written as columns in the same order,*

(10)
$$\begin{vmatrix} a_1 & a_2 & a_3 \\ b_1 & b_2 & b_3 \\ c_1 & c_2 & c_3 \end{vmatrix} = \begin{vmatrix} a_1 & b_1 & c_1 \\ a_2 & b_2 & c_2 \\ a_3 & b_3 & c_3 \end{vmatrix}.$$

(B) *If any two rows (or two columns) of a determinant are interchanged, the value of the determinant is multiplied by* -1. Example:

(11)
$$\begin{vmatrix} a_1 & a_2 & a_3 \\ b_1 & b_2 & b_3 \\ c_1 & c_2 & c_3 \end{vmatrix} = -\begin{vmatrix} c_1 & c_2 & c_3 \\ b_1 & b_2 & b_3 \\ a_1 & a_2 & a_3 \end{vmatrix} = \begin{vmatrix} c_1 & c_2 & c_3 \\ a_1 & a_2 & a_3 \\ b_1 & b_2 & b_3 \end{vmatrix}.$$

The second-order determinant obtained from

$$D = \begin{vmatrix} a_1 & b_1 & c_1 \\ a_2 & b_2 & c_2 \\ a_3 & b_3 & c_3 \end{vmatrix}$$

by deleting one row and one column is called the **minor** of the element which belongs to the deleted row and column. Example: The minor of a_2 in D is

$$\begin{vmatrix} b_1 & c_1 \\ b_3 & c_3 \end{vmatrix},$$

the minor of b_2 in D is

$$\begin{vmatrix} a_1 & c_1 \\ a_3 & c_3 \end{vmatrix},$$

etc.

The **cofactor** of the element of D in the ith row and the kth column is defined as $(-1)^{i+k}$ times the minor of that element. Example: The cofactors of a_2 and b_2 are

$$-\begin{vmatrix} b_1 & c_1 \\ b_3 & c_3 \end{vmatrix} \quad \text{and} \quad \begin{vmatrix} a_1 & c_1 \\ a_3 & c_3 \end{vmatrix},$$

respectively. Furthermore we see that we may write (7) in the form

$$D = a_1 C_1 + a_2 C_2 + a_3 C_3,$$

where C_i is the cofactor of a_i in D. From this and the properties (A) and (B) we obtain the following property.

(C) *The determinant D may be developed by any row or column, that is, it may be written as the sum of the three elements of any row (or column) each* *multiplied by its cofactor.* For example, the development of D by its second row is

$$D = -a_2 \begin{vmatrix} b_1 & c_1 \\ b_3 & c_3 \end{vmatrix} + b_2 \begin{vmatrix} a_1 & c_1 \\ a_3 & c_3 \end{vmatrix} - c_2 \begin{vmatrix} a_1 & b_1 \\ a_3 & b_3 \end{vmatrix}.$$

From **(C)** we obtain

(D) *A factor of the elements of any row (or column) can be placed before the determinant.* Example:

$$\begin{vmatrix} 4 & 6 & 1 \\ 3 & -9 & 2 \\ -1 & 12 & 5 \end{vmatrix} = \begin{vmatrix} 4 & 2 \cdot 3 & 1 \\ 3 & -3 \cdot 3 & 2 \\ -1 & 4 \cdot 3 & 5 \end{vmatrix} = 3 \begin{vmatrix} 4 & 2 & 1 \\ 3 & -3 & 2 \\ -1 & 4 & 5 \end{vmatrix}.$$

From the properties **(B)** and **(D)** we may draw the following conclusion.

(E) *If corresponding elements of two rows (or columns) of a determinant are proportional, the value of the determinant is zero.*

The following property is basic for simplifying determinants to be evaluated.

(F) *The value of a determinant remains unaltered if the elements of one row (or column) are altered by adding to them any constant multiple of the corresponding elements in any other row (or column).* Example:

$$\begin{vmatrix} -6 & 21 & -30 \\ 1 & -3 & 5 \\ 2 & 7 & -4 \end{vmatrix} = \begin{vmatrix} -6+1 \cdot 7 & 21 - 3 \cdot 7 & -30 + 5 \cdot 7 \\ 1 & -3 & 5 \\ 2 & 7 & -4 \end{vmatrix}$$

$$= \begin{vmatrix} 1 & 0 & 5 \\ 1 & -3 & 5 \\ 2 & 7 & -4 \end{vmatrix} = \begin{vmatrix} 1 & 0 & 5 \\ 0 & -3 & 0 \\ 2 & 7 & -4 \end{vmatrix} = -3 \begin{vmatrix} 1 & 5 \\ 2 & -4 \end{vmatrix} = 42.$$

(G) *If each element of a row (or column) of a determinant is expressed as a binomial, the determinant can be written as the sum of two determinants.* Example:

$$\begin{vmatrix} a_1 + d_1 & b_1 & c_1 \\ a_2 + d_2 & b_2 & c_2 \\ a_3 + d_3 & b_3 & c_3 \end{vmatrix} = \begin{vmatrix} a_1 & b_1 & c_1 \\ a_2 & b_2 & c_2 \\ a_3 & b_3 & c_3 \end{vmatrix} + \begin{vmatrix} d_1 & b_1 & c_1 \\ d_2 & b_2 & c_2 \\ d_3 & b_3 & c_3 \end{vmatrix}.$$

By applying the product rule of differentiation we obtain the following property.

(II) *If the elements of a determinant are differentiable functions of a variable, the derivative of the determinant may be written as a sum of three determinants,*

$$\frac{d}{dx}\begin{vmatrix} f & g & h \\ p & q & r \\ u & v & w \end{vmatrix} = \begin{vmatrix} f' & g' & h' \\ p & q & r \\ u & v & w \end{vmatrix} + \begin{vmatrix} f & g & h \\ p' & q' & r' \\ u & v & w \end{vmatrix} + \begin{vmatrix} f & g & h \\ p & q & r \\ u' & v' & w' \end{vmatrix},$$

where primes denote derivatives with respect to x.

Determinants of higher order and more general systems of linear equations will be considered in Chap. 7.

PROBLEMS

Evaluate:

1. $\begin{vmatrix} 3 & -1 \\ 2 & 4 \end{vmatrix}$ **2.** $\begin{vmatrix} 0 & 3 \\ 5 & 7 \end{vmatrix}$ **3.** $\begin{vmatrix} \cos\theta & \sin\theta \\ -\sin\theta & \cos\theta \end{vmatrix}$

4. $\begin{vmatrix} 4.6 & -4.1 \\ -2.0 & 0.2 \end{vmatrix}$ **5.** $\begin{vmatrix} 4 & 12 \\ 40 & 20 \end{vmatrix}$ **6.** $\begin{vmatrix} \sqrt{3} & -2 \\ 0.5 & \sqrt{27} \end{vmatrix}$

7. $\begin{vmatrix} 1 & 2 & 3 \\ 4 & 5 & 6 \\ 7 & 8 & 9 \end{vmatrix}$ **8.** $\begin{vmatrix} -4 & 18 & 7 \\ 0 & -1 & 4 \\ 0 & 0 & 6 \end{vmatrix}$ **9.** $\begin{vmatrix} 9 & 0 & 0 \\ 0 & -3 & 0 \\ 0 & 0 & 1 \end{vmatrix}$

10. $\begin{vmatrix} 6 & 13 & -2 \\ 5 & 37 & -5 \\ 1 & 13 & -2 \end{vmatrix}$ **11.** $\begin{vmatrix} 1 & a & a^2 \\ 1 & b & b^2 \\ 1 & c & c^2 \end{vmatrix}$ **12.** $\begin{vmatrix} 17 & 4 & 6 \\ 8 & 0 & 5 \\ 4 & 0 & 3 \end{vmatrix}$

13. $\begin{vmatrix} 1 & c & -b \\ -c & 1 & a \\ b & -a & 1 \end{vmatrix}$ **14.** $\begin{vmatrix} a & b & c \\ c & a & b \\ b & c & a \end{vmatrix}$ **15.** $\begin{vmatrix} a+b & b & 0 \\ b & b+c & c \\ 0 & c & c+d \end{vmatrix}$

Solve the following systems of equations.

16. $17x + 4y = -24$ **17.** $3x - y = 1$ **18.** $3x - 4y = 14$
$x - 3y = 18$ $x + 3y = 7$ $-x + 3y = -8$

19. Plot the straight lines represented by the equations in Prob. 17 and determine their point of intersection.

20. Show that the equation

$$\begin{vmatrix} y & x^2 & x \\ 1 & 1 & -1 \\ 2 & 1 & 1 \end{vmatrix} = 0$$

represents a parabola passing through the points $(0, 0)$, $(-1, 1)$, and $(1, 2)$.

0.4 COMPLEX NUMBERS

The fact that there are equations such as

$$x^2 + 3 = 0, \qquad x^2 - 10x + 40 = 0,$$

which are not satisfied by any real number, leads to the introduction of complex numbers.[4] These are of the form $a + ib$ (or $a + bi$) where a and b are real numbers. The symbol i is called the **imaginary unit**; the number a is called the **real part** and b the **imaginary part** of $a + ib$. For example, the real part of $4 - 3i$ is 4, and the imaginary part is -3. To each ordered pair of real numbers a, b there corresponds one complex number $a + ib$, and conversely.

Complex numbers can be represented as points in the plane. For this purpose we choose two perpendicular coordinate axes, the horizontal x-axis and the vertical y-axis and on both axes the same unit of length (Fig. 15). The xy-coordinate system thus obtained is called a **Cartesian coordinate system**.[5] To the complex number $z = x + iy$ there corresponds the point P with Cartesian coordinates (x, y). The xy-plane in which the complex numbers are represented geometrically in this fashion is called the **complex plane** or *Argand diagram*.[6] The x-axis is called the *real axis*, and the y-axis the *imaginary axis*.

Two complex numbers

$$z_1 = x_1 + iy_1 \qquad \text{and} \qquad z_2 = x_2 + iy_2$$

are defined to be **equal** if, and only if, their real parts are equal and their imaginary parts are equal; that is,

$$z_1 = z_2 \quad \textit{if, and only if,} \quad x_1 = x_2 \text{ and } y_1 = y_2.$$

If z_1 and z_2 are different (not equal), then we may write $z_1 \neq z_2$.

Inequalities between complex numbers, such as $z_1 < z_2$ or $z_1 \geq z_2$, have no meaning. (Inequalities may hold between the *absolute values* of complex numbers; see Sec. 0.5.)

[4] First to use complex numbers for this purpose was the Italian mathematician GIROLAMO CARDANO (1501–1576) who found the formula for solving cubic equations. The term "complex number" was introduced by the great German mathematician CARL FRIEDRICH GAUSS (1777–1855) whose work was of basic importance in algebra, number theory, differential equations, differential geometry, non-Euclidean geometry, complex analysis, numerical analysis, and theoretical mechanics. He also paved the way for a general and systematic use of complex numbers.

[5] Named after the French philosopher and mathematician RENATUS CARTESIUS (latinized for RENÉ DESCARTES (1596–1650)) who invented analytic geometry.

[6] JEAN ROBERT ARGAND (1768–1822), French mathematician. His paper on the complex plane appeared in 1806, nine years after a similar memoir by the Norwegian mathematician CASPAR WESSEL (1745–1818).

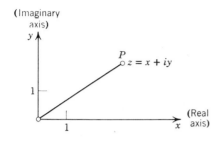

Fig. 15. The complex plane.

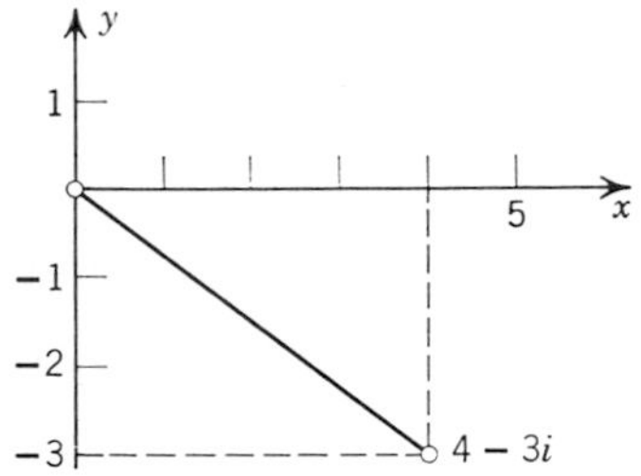

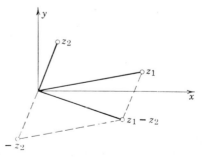

Fig. 16. The number $4-3i$ in the complex plane.

Addition. The sum $z_1 + z_2$ of z_1 and z_2 is defined as the complex number obtained by adding the real parts and the imaginary parts of z_1 and z_2, that is,

(1) $$z_1 + z_2 = (x_1 + x_2) + i(y_1 + y_2).$$

We see that addition of complex numbers is in accordance with the *"parallelogram law"* by which forces are added in mechanics (Fig. 17).

Subtraction is defined as the inverse operation of addition; that is, the difference $z_1 - z_2$ is the complex number z for which $z_1 = z + z_2$. Obviously,

(2) $$z_1 - z_2 = (x_1 - x_2) + i(y_1 - y_2).$$

Multiplication. The product $z_1 z_2$ is defined as the complex number

(3) $$z_1 z_2 = (x_1 + iy_1)(x_2 + iy_2) = (x_1 x_2 - y_1 y_2) + i(x_1 y_2 + x_2 y_1),$$

which is obtained formally by applying the ordinary rules of arithmetic for real numbers, treating the symbol i as a number, and replacing $i^2 = ii$ by -1.

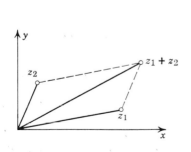

Fig. 17. Addition of complex numbers.

Fig. 18. Subtraction of complex numbers.

Division is defined as the inverse operation of multiplication; that is, the quotient $z = z_1/z_2$ is the complex number $z = x + iy$ for which

$$z_1 = zz_2 = (x + iy)(x_2 + iy_2).$$

By using (3) this can be written

$$x_1 + iy_1 = (x_2x - y_2y) + i(y_2x + x_2y).$$

By definition of equality the real parts and the imaginary parts on both sides must be equal:

$$x_1 = x_2x - y_2y$$
$$y_1 = y_2x + x_2y.$$

This is a system of two linear equations in the unknowns x and y. The determinant of the coefficients has the value $x_2^2 + y_2^2$. Assuming that $z_2 = x_2 + iy_2 \neq 0$ that determinant is not zero, and Cramer's rule (Sec. 0.3) yields the unique solution

$$x = \frac{x_1x_2 + y_1y_2}{x_2^2 + y_2^2}, \qquad y = \frac{x_2y_1 - x_1y_2}{x_2^2 + y_2^2} \qquad (z_2 \neq 0).$$

From this we see that the number $z = x + iy$ can be obtained formally by multiplying both the numerator and the denominator of the quotient z_1/z_2 by $x_2 - iy_2$; thus

(4) $\quad z = \dfrac{z_1}{z_2} = \dfrac{(x_1 + iy_1)(x_2 - iy_2)}{(x_2 + iy_2)(x_2 - iy_2)} = \dfrac{x_1x_2 + y_1y_2}{x_2^2 + y_2^2} + i\,\dfrac{x_2y_1 - x_1y_2}{x_2^2 + y_2^2}.$

Example 1. Let $z_1 = 2 - 3i$ and $z_2 = -5 + i$. Then

$$z_1 + z_2 = -3 - 2i, \qquad z_1 - z_2 = 7 - 4i, \qquad z_1z_2 = -7 + 17i,$$

$$\frac{z_1}{z_2} = \frac{(2 - 3i)(-5 - i)}{(-5 + i)(-5 - i)} = \frac{-10 - 2i + 15i - 3}{25 + 1} = -\frac{1}{2} + \frac{i}{2}.$$

For any complex numbers z_1, z_2, z_3 we have

$$z_1 + z_2 = z_2 + z_1$$
$$z_1z_2 = z_2z_1$$

(*Commutative laws*)

(5)

$$(z_1 + z_2) + z_3 = z_1 + (z_2 + z_3)$$
$$(z_1z_2)z_3 = z_1(z_2z_3)$$

(*Associative laws*)

$$z_1(z_2 + z_3) = z_1z_2 + z_1z_3 \qquad (\textit{Distributive law}).$$

These laws follow immediately from the corresponding laws for real numbers and the above definitions of the algebraic operations for complex numbers.

Let $z = x + iy$ be any complex number; then $x - iy$ is called the **conjugate** of z and is denoted by $\bar{z}$ (Fig. 19). Thus

$$z = x + iy, \qquad \bar{z} = x - iy.$$

For example, the conjugate of $4 + 7i$ is $4 - 7i$. Now

$$z + \bar{z} = 2x, \qquad z - \bar{z} = 2iy$$

and therefore

(6) $$\operatorname{Re} z = x = \frac{1}{2}(z + \bar{z}), \qquad \operatorname{Im} z = y = \frac{1}{2i}(z - \bar{z})$$

where the symbol Re denotes the real part and Im denotes the imaginary part. Obviously,

$$\overline{(z_1 + z_2)} = \bar{z}_1 + \bar{z}_2, \qquad \overline{(z_1 - z_2)} = \bar{z}_1 - \bar{z}_2,$$

(7) $$\overline{(z_1 z_2)} = \bar{z}_1 \bar{z}_2, \qquad \overline{\left(\frac{z_1}{z_2}\right)} = \frac{\bar{z}_1}{\bar{z}_2}.$$

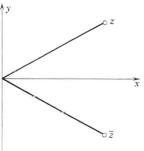

In the fundamental operations of arithmetic the complex number $x + i0$ behaves like the real number x. Indeed, equality, sum, and product as defined for two such numbers $x_1 + i0$ and $x_2 + i0$ carry over, respectively, into equality, sum, and product as defined for two real numbers x_1 and x_2. For this reason we may say that a complex number whose imaginary part is zero is a real number, and

Fig. 19. Conjugate complex numbers.

write simply x instead of $x + i0$. The complex number $0 + iy$ is written as iy and is said to be a **pure imaginary number**. Defining i to mean $0 + i1$ we have

(8) $$i^2 = (0 + i1)(0 + i1) = -1$$

and so i^2 may be replaced by -1 whenever it occurs. Consequently,

(9) $$i^2 = -1, \qquad i^3 = -i, \qquad i^4 = 1, \qquad i^5 = i, \cdots$$
$$\frac{1}{i} = \frac{i}{i^2} = -i, \qquad \frac{1}{i^2} = -1, \cdots.$$

PROBLEMS

Let $z_1 = 3 - 2i$ and $z_2 = 2 + 4i$. Reduce each of the following expressions to the form $a + ib$.

1. $z_1 z_2,\ z_1/z_2,\ z_1{}^2,\ z_1{}^2/z_2,\ (1 + i)z_1$

2. $z_1 + z_2,\ z_1 - z_2,\ z_2 - z_1,\ z_2{}^3,\ (z_1/z_2)^2,\ z_2/(1 - 2i)$

Reduce each of the following expressions to the form $a + ib$.

3. $(1 + i)^2,\ \left(\dfrac{1 + i}{1 - i}\right)^2$ \qquad **4.** $\left(\dfrac{1 + i}{1 - i}\right)^2 - \left(\dfrac{1 - i}{1 + i}\right)^2$

Solve the following equations.

5. $z^2 + 9 = 0$ **6.** $z^2 - 2z + 2 = 0$

7. $z^2 + 2z + 5 = 0$ **8.** $z^2 + z + 9 = 0$

9. Prove the first two formulas of (7).

10. Prove the last two formulas of (7).

11. If $z = \bar{z}$, show that z is real. If $z = -\bar{z}$, show that z is pure imaginary or zero.

12. If $z^2 = \bar{z}^2$, show that z is either real or pure imaginary.

13. Prove that any number is equal to the conjugate of its conjugate.

14. Plot the numbers $2 + 4i$, $2 - 4i$, $-2 + 4i$, $-2i$, and $1 - i$ as points in the complex plane.

15. If $z_1 z_2 = 0$, show that at least $z_1 = 0$ or $z_2 = 0$.

Let $z = x + iy$. Find

16. Re $(1/z)$, Im $(1/z)$ **17.** Im (z^3) **18.** Re $(1/z^2)$, Re $(z^2 + z)$

19. Re $(-iz^2)$, Im $(4iz^2 - 6z + 8i)$ **20.** Re $[1/(z - i)]$

0.5   POLAR FORM OF COMPLEX NUMBERS

If we introduce polar coordinates r, θ in the complex plane by setting

$$\text{(1)} \qquad\qquad x = r \cos \theta, \qquad y = r \sin \theta,$$

then the complex number $z = x + iy$ may be written

$$\text{(2)} \qquad\qquad z = r \cos \theta + ir \sin \theta = r(\cos \theta + i \sin \theta).$$

This is known as the **polar form** or *trigonometric form* of a complex number. r is called the **absolute value** or *modulus* of z and is denoted by $|z|$. Thus

$$\text{(3)} \qquad\qquad |z| = r = \sqrt{x^2 + y^2} = \sqrt{z\bar{z}} \qquad (\geq 0).$$

Obviously, r is the distance of the point P corresponding to z from the origin O in the complex plane (Fig. 20). The oriented angle measured from the positive x-axis to OP is called the **argument** of z and is denoted by arg z; *angles will be measured positive in the counterclockwise direction and in terms of radians.* We have, then,

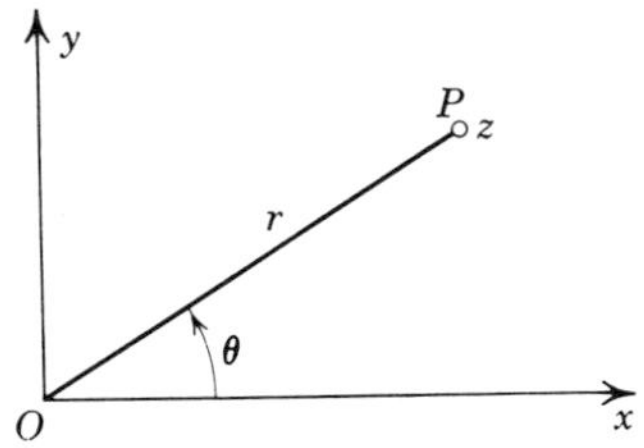

Fig. 20. Trigonometric form of complex numbers.

$$\text{(4)} \qquad \arg z = \theta = \arcsin \frac{y}{r}$$

$$= \arccos \frac{x}{r} = \arctan \frac{y}{x},$$

as in trigonometry. Note that for given z, *the argument θ is determined only up to multiples of 2π.*

Example 1. Let $z = 1 + i$. Then $|z| = \sqrt{2}$ and arg $z = \dfrac{\pi}{4} \pm 2n\pi$ where $n = 0, 1, 2, \cdots$.

The polar form of complex numbers is particularly useful in analyzing multiplication and division. Let

$$z_1 = r_1(\cos \theta_1 + i \sin \theta_1) \quad \text{and} \quad z_2 = r_2(\cos \theta_2 + i \sin \theta_2).$$

Then the product is

$$z_1 z_2 = r_1 r_2[(\cos \theta_1 \cos \theta_2 - \sin \theta_1 \sin \theta_2) + i(\sin \theta_1 \cos \theta_2 + \cos \theta_1 \sin \theta_2)].$$

By applying the familiar addition theorems of the sine and the cosine this assumes the simple form

$$(5) \qquad z_1 z_2 = r_1 r_2[\cos (\theta_1 + \theta_2) + i \sin (\theta_1 + \theta_2)].$$

We thus obtain the important rules

$$(6) \qquad |z_1 z_2| = |z_1|\, |z_2|$$

and

$$(7) \qquad \arg (z_1 z_2) = \arg z_1 + \arg z_2 \quad \text{(up to multiples of } 2\pi).$$

Similarly, from the definition of division it follows that

$$(8) \qquad \left| \frac{z_1}{z_2} \right| = \frac{|z_1|}{|z_2|}$$

and

$$(9) \qquad \arg \frac{z_1}{z_2} = \arg z_1 - \arg z_2 \quad \text{(up to multiples of } 2\pi).$$

TABLE 2. Arc tan $\dfrac{y}{x}$

$\dfrac{y}{x}$	arc tan $\dfrac{y}{x}$	$\dfrac{y}{x}$	arc tan $\dfrac{y}{x}$	$\dfrac{y}{x}$	arc tan $\dfrac{y}{x}$	$\dfrac{y}{x}$	arc tan $\dfrac{y}{x}$
0	0.00000	1.0	0.78540	2.0	1.10715	4.0	1.32582
0.1	0.09967	1.1	0.83298	2.2	1.14417	4.5	1.35213
0.2	0.19740	1.2	0.87606	2.4	1.17601	5.0	1.37340
0.3	0.29146	1.3	0.91510	2.6	1.20362	5.5	1.39094
0.4	0.38051	1.4	0.95055	2.8	1.22777	6.0	1.40565
0.5	0.46365	1.5	0.98279	3.0	1.24905	7.0	1.42890
0.6	0.54042	1.6	1.01220	3.2	1.26791	8.0	1.44644
0.7	0.61073	1.7	1.03907	3.4	1.28474	9.0	1.46014
0.8	0.67474	1.8	1.06370	3.6	1.29985	10.0	1.47113
0.9	0.73282	1.9	1.08632	3.8	1.31347	11.0	1.48014

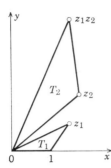

Fig. 21. Multiplication of complex numbers.

Example 2. From (6) and (7) we obtain
$$z^n = r^n(\cos \theta + i \sin \theta)^n = r^n(\cos n\theta + i \sin n\theta)$$
and from this the so-called **formula of De Moivre**[7]
$$(10) \qquad (\cos \theta + i \sin \theta)^n = \cos n\theta + i \sin n\theta.$$

From (6) and (7) it follows that the triangles T_1 and T_2 in Fig. 21 are similar. This can be used as the basis for a graphical construction of the product of complex numbers.

PROBLEMS

Represent the following complex numbers in polar form.

1. $2 - 2i, i, 3 + 4i$ **2.** $5 + 5i, -5 + 5i, -5 - 5i$

3. Show that arg $\bar{z} = -$arg z (up to multiples of 2π).

4. Show that arg $(1/z) = -$arg z (up to multiples of 2π).

5. Prove that $|a - z| = |a - \bar{z}|$ where a is any real number. Interpret geometrically.

6. Prove that $|z_1 - z_2|$ is the distance between the points z_1 and z_2 in the complex plane.

Find the absolute values of the following numbers.

7. $1 + i\sqrt{3}, -9i, 2 + i\sqrt{5}$ **8.** $2 - i\sqrt{5}, 2 + 3i, (4 + i)^3$

9. $\dfrac{(4 - 3i)(\frac{1}{2} + i)^4}{\left(1 - \dfrac{3i}{4}\right)^2(-3 + 4i)}$ **10.** $\left(\dfrac{1 + i}{1 - i}\right)^8, (3 + 4i)^3(-1 - i)^6$

What loci are represented by the following equations and inequalities? (Plot a graph in each case).

11. $|z| = 1$ **12.** $|z - 1| = 1$ **13.** Re $(z^2) = -1$ **14.** Im $(2z) = -1$

15. $0 \leq$ arg $z \leq \pi/2$ **16.** $0 \leq$ arg $(1/z) \leq \pi/2$

17. Using (10), prove the identities
$$\cos 3\theta = \cos^3 \theta - 3 \cos \theta \sin^2 \theta, \qquad \sin 3\theta = 3 \cos^2 \theta \sin \theta - \sin^3 \theta.$$

18. Find similar identities as in Prob. 17 for cos 2θ and cos 4θ.

19. Find $(3 - i)(2 + i)$ by means of a graphical construction in the complex plane.

20. For given z find $1/z$ by a graphical construction.

0.6 SOME GENERAL REMARKS ABOUT NUMERICAL COMPUTATIONS

The present section is devoted to a few simple but important general remarks about numerical computations.

[7] ABRAHAM DE MOIVRE (1667–1754), French mathematician, who introduced imaginary quantities in trigonometry and contributed to the theory of mathematical probability.

It is clear that engineering mathematics ultimately comes down to numerical results, and the engineering student should, therefore, supplement his mathematical equipment with a definite knowledge of some fundamental numerical methods.

Various examples and problems in the text will help the student to learn how to arrange computations in a suitable form. However, numerical computation is an art which requires experience. It cannot be learned solely from books; practical training is needed, just as in swimming, driving a car, or playing the piano. Consequently, the student should not only work out book examples and problems, but also set up and calculate examples of his own. Active work is more important in numerical analysis than in many other branches of mathematics. Famous mathematicians like Gauss spent a considerable part of their time with numerical computations, and the engineering student will do well in developing a similar attitude.

In many cases formally complete answers to a problem obtained by theoretical considerations may be almost useless for numerical purposes. For example, in the case of systems of linear equations we obtain the solution in the form of quotients of determinants (Secs. 0.3 and 7.5), but if the number of equations and unknowns is large, the direct evaluation of the solution in this form is certainly not the *practical* answer to the problem of finding *numerical values* of the unknowns. In other cases, the theory may yield the solution of a problem in the form of an integral which cannot be evaluated by the usual methods of calculus. Then we need an approximation method for obtaining numerical values of that solution. Moreover there are many practical problems which cannot be solved by exact methods at all, and in such cases, which arise quite frequently, we have to look for an appropriate approximation method which will yield numerical values of the solution of the problem.

Because we work with a finite number of digits and carry out a finite number of steps in computations, the methods of numerical analysis are *finite processes*, and a numerical result is an approximate value of the (unknown) exact result, except for the rare cases where the exact answer is a sufficiently simple rational number. The difference

$$E = a^* - a$$

between the exact value a and the approximate value a^* is called the *absolute* **error** of a^*, and the quotient

$$E_r = \frac{a^* - a}{a} \qquad (a \neq 0)$$

is called the *relative error* of a^*.

An error may arise by the process of *rounding off*, that is, by retaining only the more significant decimal digits of a number and rejecting the less significant beyond a certain point. This error is called a **rounding error**. Rounding errors can often be eliminated by carrying one, two or even more, extra figures, known as *guarding figures* in the intermediate steps of calculation.

Another error may result from the fact that one or several of the formulas used in numerical work are obtained by replacing an infinite series by one of its partial sums. Such an error is called a **truncation error**. It occurs, for instance, in connection with numerical integration and differentiation.

Moreover, a computation may contain **mistakes** because of the fallibility of the human computer or the mechanical and electrical equipment used in the computation. While errors cannot be avoided, mistakes are avoidable in principle. **Checking** of numerical results is quite important, and any numerical method should include checking procedures to confirm that the results contain no mistakes. This certainly applies to final results, but in a longer computation it is also advisable to check intermediate results.

Of course, *any computation should be arranged in a systematic tabular form and should contain all the intermediate results directly on the working sheet.* This will help to avoid mistakes and to locate and correct mistakes that have been made. *Numerical work should not be done on scraps of paper.* The numbers should be written in a neat and legible manner on paper that is full notebook page size.

Our last remark is concerned with approximation methods. If a problem cannot be solved by an exact method and we therefore use an approximation method, the immediate basic question is how much at most can the approximate result deviate from the (unknown) exact result. This requires the *estimation of error* involved in approximation methods. In many cases formulas for estimating the maximum possible error are known, and they should be used whenever such an approximation formula is applied. This is the only way to obtain a clear picture of the quality of an approximation and to eliminate a source of stupid mistakes which otherwise may, and actually do, occur in the mathematical part of engineering work. The determination of new and more effective methods of estimating errors is one of the important and interesting problems in modern applied mathematics. The most recent developments in this direction are influenced considerably by the increasing use of electronic computers. Older methods were brought into forms suitable for electronic computation, and new methods have been added; this development is still in progress.

0.7 SOLUTION OF EQUATIONS

A frequent task in engineering mathematics is the determination of the roots of an equation of the form

(1) $$f(x) = 0$$ (x real).

If $f(x)$ is a simple function, then there may be a formula which yields the exact values of the roots. For example, if

$$f(x) = ax^2 + bx + c \qquad (a \neq 0)$$

we have to solve a *quadratic equation*, the solutions being

(2) $$x = \frac{1}{2a}(-b \pm \sqrt{b^2 - 4ac}).$$

However, if $f(x)$ is more complicated, there may not be a formula for the exact values of the roots and in such a case we may use an approximation method which yields approximate values of the roots. Let us explain an important method of this type.

Suppose we want to determine the real roots of the equation $f(x) = 0$ where f is a differentiable function. Then we may plot a graph of $f(x)$ in the usual way. Assuming that the equation has a real root, we may obtain from the graph a first rough approximation of this root; let x_1 be this approximation. We may then determine a second approximation x_2, namely, the point of intersection of the tangent to the curve of $f(x)$ at x_1 and the x-axis (Fig. 22). Since

$$\tan \alpha = f'(x_1) = \frac{f(x_1)}{x_1 - x_2}$$

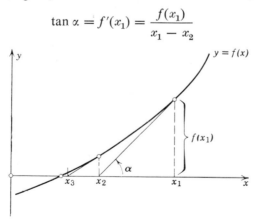

Fig. 22. Newton's method.

by solving for x_2 we obtain

$$x_2 = x_1 - \frac{f(x_1)}{f'(x_1)}.$$

In the next step we compute

$$x_3 = x_2 - \frac{f(x_2)}{f'(x_2)}$$

etc., and in general

(3) $$x_{n+1} = x_n - \frac{f(x_n)}{f'(x_n)}$$ $(n = 1, 2, \cdots)$.

This method of successive approximations is called **Newton's[8] method.**

Example 1. Given the equation

$$f(x) = x^3 + x - 1 = 0$$

we see that it has a root near $x_1 = 1$ (Fig. 23). From (3) we obtain

$$x_{n+1} = x_n - \frac{x_n^3 + x_n - 1}{3x_n^2 + 1} = \frac{2x_n^3 + 1}{3x_n^2 + 1} = \frac{N_n}{D_n}.$$

The computation may be arranged in tabular form:

n	x_n	x_n^2	x_n^3	N_n	D_n	x_{n+1}
1	1	1	1	3	4	0.75
2	0.75	0.562 5	0.421 875	1.843 750	2.687 500	0.686 047
3	0.686 047	0.470 660	0.322 895	1.645 790	2.411 980	0.682 340
4	0.682 340	0.465 588	0.317 689	1.635 378	2.396 764	0.682 328

The result seems to indicate that the desired root to four decimal places is $x = 0.6823$. (We mention that even all six decimals of x_5 are the correct first decimals of the root.)

Sometimes work may be saved by starting with a small number of digits and increasing it gradually. Our present computation may then become:

n	x_n	x_n^2	x_n^3	N_n	D_n	x_{n+1}
1	1	1	1	3	4	0.75
2	0.75	0.562 5	0.421 9	1.843 8	2.687 5	0.686
3	0.686	0.470 60	0.322 83	1.645 66	2.411 80	0.682 3
4	0.682 3	0.465 533	0.317 633	1.635 266	2.396 599	0.682 33

[8] Sir ISAAC NEWTON (1642–1727), English physicist and mathematician. Newton and the German mathematician and philosopher, GOTTFRIED WILHELM LEIBNIZ (1646–1716), invented (independently) the differential and integral calculus. Newton discovered many basic physical laws and introduced the method of investigating physical problems by means of calculus. His work is of greatest importance to both mathematics and physics.

Example 2. Find the positive root of the equation

$$2 \sin x = x.$$

Here $f(x) = x - 2 \sin x = 0$, and from (3),

$$x_{n+1} = x_n - \frac{x_n - 2 \sin x_n}{1 - 2 \cos x_n} = \frac{2(\sin x_n - x_n \cos x_n)}{1 - 2 \cos x_n} = \frac{N_n}{D_n}.$$

From the graph we conclude that the root is near $x_1 = 2$. Using tables of the sine and cosine functions, the computation yields

n	x_n	N_n	D_n	x_{n+1}
1	2	3.48	1.83	1.90
2	1.90	3.121 1	1.646 6	1.895 5
3	1.895 5	3.104 925 6	1.638 055 9	1.895 494

The root to four decimal places is $x = 1.8955$.

Newton's method approximates the curve of $f(x)$ by tangents. Complications will arise if the derivative $f'(x)$ is zero at or near a root of $f(x) = 0$, because then the denominator in (3) is small in absolute value. (For details see Ref. [A11] in Appendix 1.)

We shall now consider the so-called **regula falsi** (*method of false position*) which approximates that curve by a chord, as shown in Fig. 25. The chord intersects the x-axis at the point

(4)
$$x = \frac{af(b) - bf(a)}{f(b) - f(a)},$$

and this is an approximation for the root X_0 of the equation $f(x) = 0$.

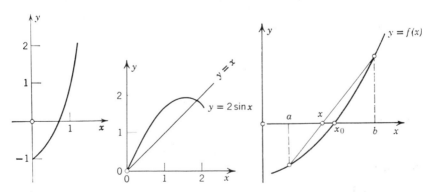

Fig. 23. Example 1.   **Fig. 24.** Example 2.   **Fig. 25.** Regula falsi.

Example 3. Find an approximate value of the root of the equation

$$f(x) = x^3 + x - 1 = 0$$

near $x = 1$ (cf. Ex. 1). We find that

$$f(0.5) = -0.375 \quad \text{and} \quad f(1) = 1.$$

Choosing $a = 0.5$ and $b = 1$, formula (4) yields

$$x_1 = \frac{0.5 \cdot 1 - 1 \cdot (-0.375)}{1 - (-0.375)} = 0.64.$$

Since $f(0.64) = -0.0979 < 0$, in the next step we may choose $a = 0.64$ and $b = 1$, and obtain from (4) the more accurate approximation $x_2 = 0.672$, and so on.

A third important method for determining the roots of an equation $f(x) = 0$ is the so-called **iteration method.**

This method is applicable if the given equation $f(x) = 0$ can be written in the form

$$x = g(x).$$

We choose a rough approximation x_1 of the root X_0 of the given equation and compute a second approximation

$$x_2 = g(x_1),$$

a third approximation

$$x_3 = g(x_2),$$

etc., and in general

(5) $$x_{n+1} = g(x_n) \qquad (n = 1, 2, \cdots).$$

It can be shown that if

$$|g'(X_0)| < 1$$

and x_1 is sufficiently accurate (sufficiently close to X_0) then $x_n \to X_0$ as $n \to \infty$, that is, (5) will yield better and better approximations as n increases.

Example 4. The equation

$$f(x) = x^3 + x - 1 = 0$$

(cf. Ex. 1) may be written

(6) $$x = \frac{1}{1 + x^2}.$$

Hence, in this case, (5) takes the form

$$x_{n+1} = \frac{1}{1 + x_n^2}.$$

Starting from $x_1 = 1$, as in Ex. 1, we thus obtain

$$x_2 = \frac{1}{1 + 1^2} = \frac{1}{2} = 0.5, \quad x_3 = \frac{1}{1 + (1/2)^2} = \frac{4}{5} = 0.8, \quad x_4 = 0.61, \quad \text{etc.}$$

Note that the right-hand side of (6) is

$$g(x) = \frac{1}{1 + x^2}, \quad \text{and} \quad g'(x) = \frac{-2x}{(1 + x^2)^2}.$$

Now $X_0 \approx 0.7$, and $|g'(0.7)| = 1.4/1.49^2 < 1$, which shows that for x_1 sufficiently close to X_0 we have $x_n \to X_0$ as $n \to \infty$. Our numerical results seem to confirm this fact.

It is clear that a given equation $f(x) = 0$ may be written in the form $x = g(x)$ in many ways. In the present example we may write

$$x = 1 - x^3$$

but then

$$g(x) = 1 - x^3, \quad |g'(x)| = 3x^2 > 1 \text{ when } x = X_0 \approx 0.7,$$

and the iteration will not work. The reader may try to start from $x_1 = 1$, $x_1 = 0.7$, $x_1 = 2$, and see what happens.

PROBLEMS

Find a root of the following equations; carry out three steps of Newton's method, starting from the given x_1.

1. $x^3 - 1.2x^2 + 2x - 2.4 = 0$, $x_1 = 1$
2. $x^3 - 1.2x^2 + 2x - 2.4 = 0$, $x_1 = 2$
3. $x^3 - 3.9x^2 + 0.9x + 5.8 = 0$, $x_1 = 3$
4. $x^3 - 3.9x^2 + 0.9x + 5.8 = 0$, $x_1 = 1$
5. $x^3 - 3.9x^2 + 4.79x - 1.881 = 0$, $x_1 = 1$

6. The roots of the equation in Prob. 5 are 0.9, 1.1, and 1.9. Although $x_1 = 1$ lies close to 0.9 and 1.1, Newton's method does not yield one of these roots. Why? Choose another x_1 such that the method yields approximations for the root 1.1.

Find all real roots of the following equations by Newton's method.

7. $x^4 - 0.1x^3 - 0.82x^2 - 0.1x - 1.82 = 0$
8. $x^3 - 4x^2 + 2x - 8 = 0$
9. $x^3 - 5x^2 + 6.64x - 1.92 = 0$ 10. $\cos x = x$
11. $x + \ln x = 2$ 12. $2x + \ln x = 1$

Find the real roots of the following equations by means of the regula falsi.

13. $x^4 = 2$ 14. $x^4 = 2x$ 15. $3 \sin x = 2x$

16. In Prob. 13 the approximate values of the positive root will always be somewhat smaller than the exact value of the root. Why?

17. Find the root of $x^5 = x + 0.2$ near $x = 0$ by the iteration method, starting from $x_1 = 0$.

18. The equation in Prob. 17 has a root near $x = 1$. Find this root by the iteration method, starting from $x_1 = 1$. *Hint:* Write the equation in the form $x = \sqrt[5]{x + 0.2}$.

19. What happens in Prob. 18 if you write the equation in the form $x = x^5 - 0.2$ and start from $x_1 = 1$?

20. Using the iteration method, show that the smallest positive root of the equation $x = \tan x$ is 4.49, approximately. *Hint:* conclude from the graphs of x and $\tan x$ that a root lies close to $x_1 = 3\pi/2$; write the equation in the form $x = \arctan x$. (Why?)

0.8   APPROXIMATE INTEGRATION

If $f(x)$ is a given function and we can find a function $F(x)$ whose derivative is $f(x)$, then we may evaluate definite integrals of $f(x)$ by using the familiar formula

$$(1) \qquad \int_a^b f(x)\, dx = F(b) - F(a) \qquad [F'(x) = f(x)].$$

Tables of integrals[9] may be helpful for this purpose. However, in engineering applications there frequently occur integrals which cannot be evaluated by familiar methods known from calculus. These may be integrals of two types, namely, integrals such as

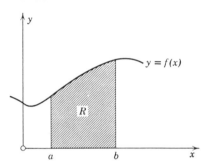

Fig. 26. Geometrical interpretation of a definite integral.

$$\int e^{-x^2} dx, \quad \int \frac{\sin x}{x}\, dx, \quad \int \cos(x^2)\, dx,$$

which cannot be represented in terms of finitely many elementary functions, or integrals whose integrands are empirical functions, given by a table of numerical values which are obtained from a physical experiment or in some other way. In many cases, integrals of the first type may be evaluated by one of the advanced methods (complex integration, use of power series, or asymptotic expansions), and in the case of an integral of the second type we may try to approximate the empirical function by a polynomial or some other elementary function.

Nevertheless, in various situations it will be preferable to apply one of the standard methods of numerical integration which we shall consider in the present section. These methods use the fact that the definite integral in (1) equals the area A of the shaded region R in Fig. 26.

To determine A we may cut R from cardboard, weight the piece and divide the result by the weight of a square of this cardboard whose side is 1.

Another simple method is to draw R on a graph paper and count squares.

More accurate results are obtained by using a **planimeter**. So let us briefly discuss this instrumental method. Planimeters are inexpensive precision instruments which measure the area of any region R bounded by a closed curve C. There are several types of planimeters.[10] Figure 27 shows a so-called *polar planimeter*. This instrument has a rod, the tracing arm (I),

---

[9] Cf. e.g., Ref. [A3] in Appendix 1.

[10] These types and the corresponding mathematical theories are considered in Ref. [A15] in Appendix 1.

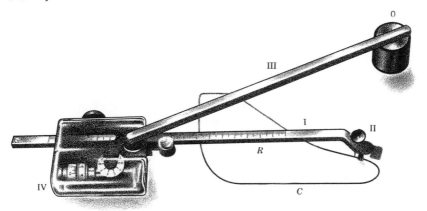

Fig. 27. Polar planimeter, made by A. Ott, Kempten, Germany, manufacturers of high precision instruments.

on one end of which is mounted the tracing pin (II) which follows the curve C. The other end of the tracing arm is moved on a circular path by means of a second rod, the pole arm (III), which can be turned about the end point 0 (the pole) and is joined to the other end of the tracing arm by means of a hinge. An integrating wheel (IV), mounted on the tracing arm, measures the area of the region R when the pin traces once around the entire boundary curve C, starting from any point of C and returning to that point; the area is obtained as the difference of the initial and final reading on the scale of the integrating wheel. The accuracy can be increased by repeating this procedure m times, adding the m results and dividing their sum by m.

We shall now consider the simplest formulas of numerical integration. We assume that $b > a$ in (1).

We subdivide the interval of integration, whose length is $b - a$, into n equal parts of length

$$\Delta x = \frac{b - a}{n}.$$

Let $x_1{}^*, \cdots, x_n{}^*$ be the midpoints of these n intervals. Then the n rectangles in Fig. 28 have the areas $f(x_1{}^*)\,\Delta x, \cdots, f(x_n{}^*)\,\Delta x$. Therefore,

$$(2) \qquad \int_a^b f(x)\,dx \approx \Delta x[f(x_1{}^*) + f(x_2{}^*) + \cdots + f(x_n{}^*)].$$

This simple formula is called the **rectangular rule**.

Example 1. Use (2) to find an approximate value of $\ln 2 (= 0.693\,15)$. We have

$$\ln 2 = \int_1^2 \frac{dx}{x}.$$

We choose $n = 5$ and $n = 10$ and arrange the work in tabular form.

j	$x_j{}^*$	$1/x_j{}^*$	j	$x_j{}^*$	$1/x_j{}^*$	j	$x_j{}^*$	$1/x_j{}^*$
1	1.1	0.909 091	1	1.05	0.952 381	6	1.55	0.645 161
2	1.3	0.769 231	2	1.15	0.869 565	7	1.65	0.606 061
3	1.5	0.666 667	3	1.25	0.800 000	8	1.75	0.571 429
4	1.7	0.588 235	4	1.35	0.740 741	9	1.85	0.540 541
5	1.9	0.526 316	5	1.45	0.689 655	10	1.95	0.512 821

Sum $S = 3.459\ 540$	Sum $S_1 = 4.052\ 342$ Sum $S_2 = 2.876\ 013$
$\ln 2 \approx \frac{1}{5}S = 0.691\ 91$	$\ln 2 \approx \frac{1}{10}(S_1 + S_2) = 0.692\ 84$
Error: $0.001\ 24\ (0.2\%)$	Error: $0.000\ 31\ (0.05\%)$
Computation for $n = 5$	Computation for $n = 10$

We see that the result for $n = 10$ is more accurate than that for $n = 5$.

We shall now derive another integration formula. We subdivide the interval $a \leq x \leq b$ into n equal parts of length $\Delta x = (b - a)/n$, as before, and denote the end points of these subintervals by $a, x_1, x_2, \cdots, x_{n-1}, b$. Then the n trapezoids in Fig. 29 have the areas

$$\tfrac{1}{2}[f(a) + f(x_1)]\,\Delta x,\ \tfrac{1}{2}[f(x_1) + f(x_2)]\,\Delta x, \cdots, \tfrac{1}{2}[f(x_{n-1}) + f(b)]\,\Delta x.$$

Thus

$$(3) \quad \int_a^b f(x)\,dx \approx \Delta x \left[\frac{f(a)}{2} + f(x_1) + f(x_2) + \cdots + f(x_{n-1}) + \frac{f(b)}{2}\right]$$

where $\Delta x = (b - a)/n$. This formula is called the **trapezoidal rule**.

Let A be the exact value of the integral under consideration, and let A^* be the approximate value obtained by the trapezoidal rule (3). Then the difference

$$E_T = A^* - A$$

is called the *error* of A^*, and

$$(4) \qquad A = \int_a^b f(x)\,dx = A^* - E_T.$$

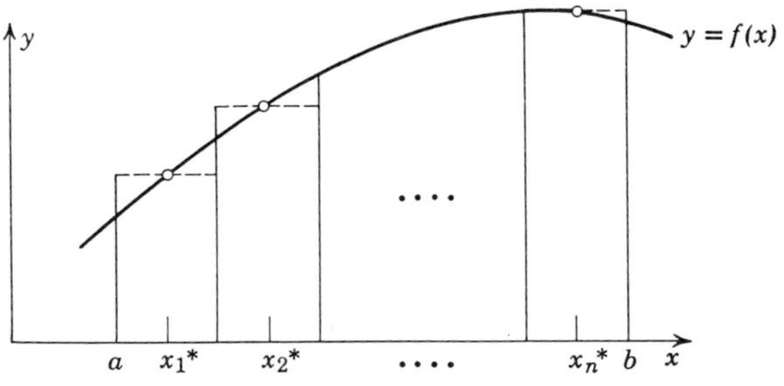

Fig. 28. Rectangular rule.

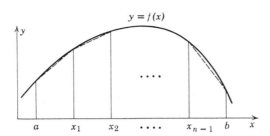

$y = f(x)$

Fig. 29. Trapezoidal rule.

Clearly, if $f(x)$ is a *linear* function, its graph is a straight line, and the trapezoidal rule will yield the exact value of the integral, that is, $E_T = 0$. Now in this case, f' is constant and f'' is zero for all x. Hence the error results from the fact that in general $f'' \neq 0$, and it seems to be plausible that its magnitude will depend on the values of f'' in the interval of integration and also on the number n of subintervals in (3). In fact, it can be shown that E_T always lies in the interval

$$(5) \qquad\qquad KM^* \leq E_T \leq KM$$

where M^* and M are the smallest and largest values of the second derivative of f in the interval of integration, and

$$K = \frac{(b - a)^3}{12n^2}.$$

Example 2. Compute the integral

$$I = \int_0^1 e^{-x^2}\, dx$$

by means of the trapezoidal rule (3), taking $n = 10$, and estimate the error.

j	x_j	x_j^2	$e^{-x_j^2}$	
0	0	0	1.000 000	
1	0.1	0.01		0.990 050
2	0.2	0.04		0.960 789
3	0.3	0.09		0.913 931
4	0.4	0.16		0.852 144
5	0.5	0.25		0.778 801
6	0.6	0.36		0.697 676
7	0.7	0.49		0.612 626
8	0.8	0.64		0.527 292
9	0.9	0.81		0.444 858
10	1.0	1.00	0.367 879	
	Sums		1.367 879	6.778 167

We have $\Delta x = 0.1$, and

$$I \approx 0.1 \left[\frac{1.363\ 879}{2} + 6.778\ 176 \right] = 0.746\ 211.$$

Estimate of error.

$$f''(x) = 2(2x^2 - 1)e^{-x^2}, \qquad M^* = f''(0) = -2, \qquad M = f''(1) = 0.735\ 758.$$

From this and (5),

$$-2K \leq E_T \leq 0.735\ 758\ K$$

where $K = 1/1200$. Thus

$$-0.001\ 667 \leq E_T \leq 0.000\ 614.$$

From this and (4) it follows that the exact value of I must lie between

$$0.746\ 211 - 0.000\ 614 = 0.745\ 597$$

and $0.746\ 211 + 0.001\ 667 = 0.747\ 878.$

(The exact value is $I = 0.746\ 824 \cdots$.)

The rectangular rule is obtained by approximating the integrand $f(x)$ by a step function (piecewise constant function). The trapezoidal rule results by approximating $f(x)$ by linear functions. We may expect to obtain a more accurate integration formula by approximating the curve of $f(x)$ by portions of parabolas.

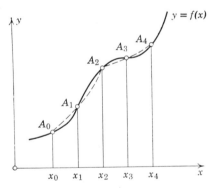

For this purpose we subdivide the interval of integration $a \leq x \leq b$ into an *even* number of equal subintervals, say, into $2n$ subintervals of length $\Delta x = (b - a)/2n$, with end points

$$x_0\ (= a),\ x_1,\ \cdots,\ x_{2n-1},\ x_{2n}\ (= b).$$

Fig. 30. Simpson's rule.

In the first two intervals we approximate the curve of $f(x)$ by the parabola of the form $\alpha x^2 + \beta x + \gamma$ passing through the points A_0, A_1, A_2 of that curve (Fig. 30). In the next two intervals we approximate that curve by another such parabola through A_2, A_3, A_4, and so on. Proceeding in this fashion, we obtain a curve consisting of n portions of parabolas, and the area under that curve is an approximation for the area under the curve of $f(x)$ between a and b. It can be shown that the integration formula thus obtained is

(6) $$\int_a^b f(x)\,dx \approx \frac{\Delta x}{3} \left[f(x_0) + 4f(x_1) + 2f(x_2) + 4f(x_3) \right.$$

$$\left. + \cdots + 2f(x_{n-2}) + 4f(x_{2n-1}) + f(x_{2n}) \right]$$

where $\Delta x = (b - a)/2n$ (cf. Ref. [A13] in Appendix 1). This important formula for approximate integration is called **Simpson's rule**.

If we write (6) in the form

(7) $$\int_a^b f(x) \, dx = \frac{\Delta x}{3} [f(x_0) + 4f(x_1) + \cdots + f(x_{2n})] - E_S,$$

then E_S is the error of the approximation. It can be shown that E_S lies in the interval

(8) $$CM_4^* \leq E_S \leq CM_4$$

where M_4^* and M_4 are the smallest and the largest value of the fourth derivative of f in the interval of integration, and

$$C = \frac{(b - a)^5}{180(2n)^4}.$$

From (8) we see that Simpson's rule yields the exact result not only for polynomials of the second degree but even for polynomials of the third degree.

Example 3. Evaluate $I = \int_0^1 e^{-x^2} \, dx$ by Simpson's rule with $2n = 10$ and estimate the error.

j	x_j	x_j^2		$e^{-x_j^2}$	
0	0	0	1.000 000		
1	0.1	0.01		0.990 050	
2	0.2	0.04			0.960 789
3	0.3	0.09		0.913 931	
4	0.4	0.16			0.852 144
5	0.5	0.25		0.778 801	
6	0.6	0.36			0.697 676
7	0.7	0.49		0.612 626	
8	0.8	0.64			0.527 292
9	0.9	0.81		0.444 858	
10	1.0	1.00	0.367 879		
Sums			1.367 879	3.740 266	3.037 901

We find, since $\Delta x = 0.1$,

$$I \approx \frac{0.1}{3} (1.367\ 879 + 4 \cdot 3.740\ 266 + 2 \cdot 3.037\ 901) = 0.746\ 825.$$

Estimate of error. The fourth derivative of the integrand is

$$f^{IV}(x) = 4(4x^4 - 12x^2 + 3)e^{-x^2}.$$

By considering the derivative of f^{IV} we find that the smallest value of f^{IV} in the interval of integration occurs at $x = x^* = 2.5 + 0.5\sqrt{10}$ and the largest value occurs at $x = 0$. Computing the corresponding values of f^{IV} we obtain in (8)

$$M_4^* = f^{IV}(x^*) = -7.359 \cdots \quad \text{and} \quad M_4 = f^{IV}(0) = 12.$$

Furthermore, since $2n = 10$ and $b - a = 1$, in (8),

$$C = 1/1\ 800\ 000 = 0.000\ 000\ 55 \cdots.$$

Therefore

$$-0.000\ 004 \cdots \leq E_S \leq 0.000\ 006 \cdots.$$

This shows that the first four decimals of the above approximation are correct and, by (7),

$$0.746\ 818 < I < 0.746\ 830.$$

The exact value to six decimal places is $I = 0.746\ 824$, and we see that even five decimals of our result are correct. Our present result is much better than that obtained in Ex. 2 by the trapezoidal rule, while the amount of work is almost the same in both cases.

PROBLEMS

Review some integration formulas and methods by integrating

1. $\displaystyle\int \frac{dx}{a^2 + x^2}, \int \frac{dx}{\sqrt{a^2 - x^2}}$ **2.** $\displaystyle\int \ln x\ dx$

3. $\displaystyle\int e^{ax} \cos bx\ dx$ **4.** $\displaystyle\int e^{ax} \sin bx\ dx$

5. $\displaystyle\int \frac{dx}{x^2(x^2 + 1)^2}$ **6.** $\displaystyle\int \cos^2 x\ dx$

7. $\displaystyle\int \sin^2 \omega x\ dx$ **8.** $\displaystyle\int \tan x\ dx, \int \cot x\ dx$

9. Compute $\displaystyle\int_0^1 x^3\ dx$ by the rectangular rule (2) with $n = 5$. What is the error?

10. Repeat the computation in Prob. 9, taking $n = 10$. What is the error?

11. Compute the integral in Prob. 9 by the trapezoidal rule (3) with $n = 5$. What error bounds are obtained from (5)? What is the actual error of the result? Why is this result larger than the exact value?

12. Compute the integral in Ex. 2 by using (2) with $n = 5$.

Using the column of $\sin x$ in Table 1 in Sec. 0.1 evaluate $\displaystyle\int_0^1 \frac{\sin x}{x}\ dx$:

13. By the rectangular rule (2) with $n = 5$.
14. By the trapezoidal rule (3) with $n = 5$.
15. By (3) with $n = 10$.
16. By Simpson's rule with $2n = 2$.
17. By Simpson's rule with $2n = 10$.

18. Evaluate $\displaystyle\int_0^1 x^5\ dx$ by Simpson's rule with $2n = 10$. What error bounds are obtained from (8)? What is the actual error of the result?

19. Find an approximate value of $\ln 2 = \displaystyle\int_1^2 \frac{dx}{x}$ by Simpson's rule with $2n = 4$. Estimate the error by (8).

20. If subintervals of different lengths $\Delta_1 x$, $\Delta_2 x$, $\cdots$, $\Delta_n x$ are chosen, show that the trapezoidal rule assumes the form

$$\int_a^b f(x)\, dx \approx \tfrac{1}{2}[f(a) + f(x_1)]\Delta_1 x + \cdots + \tfrac{1}{2}[f(x_{n-1}) + f(b)]\Delta_n x.$$

Using this formula evaluate $\int_0^{\sqrt{\pi/2}} \cos(x^2)\, dx$, choosing the subintervals with end points 0, $\sqrt{\pi/6}$, $\sqrt{\pi/3}$, $\sqrt{\pi/2}$.

chapter **1**

ORDINARY DIFFERENTIAL EQUATIONS OF THE FIRST ORDER

Differential equations are of fundamental importance in engineering mathematics. This is due to the fact that many physical laws and relations appear mathematically in the form of a differential equation. We shall consider various physical and geometrical problems which lead to differential equations and the most important standard methods for solving such equations. These methods will in general involve integration.

We shall pay particular attention to the derivation of the differential equations from given physical situations. This transition from the physical problem to a "mathematical model" is of great practical importance and will be illustrated by typical examples.

The present chapter will be devoted to the simplest ordinary differential equations, the so-called equations of the first order. It includes also numerical methods for obtaining approximate solutions of such equations (Sec. 1.13).

Prerequisite for the present chapter: integral calculus.

Sections which may be omitted in a shorter course: 1.8, 1.11–1.13.

References: Appendix 1, Part B.

Answers to problems: Appendix 2.

1.1 BASIC CONCEPTS AND IDEAS

By an **ordinary differential equation** we mean a relation which involves one or several derivatives of an unspecified function y of x with respect to x; the relation may also involve y itself, given functions of x, and constants. For example,

$$(1) \qquad y' = \cos x$$

$$(2) \qquad y'' + 4y = 0$$

$$(3) \qquad x^2 y''' y' + 2e^x y'' = (x^2 + 2)y^2$$

are ordinary differential equations.

The term *ordinary* distinguishes it from a *partial differential equation* which involves partial derivatives of an unspecified function of two or more independent variables. For example,

$$\frac{\partial^2 u}{\partial x^2} + \frac{\partial^2 u}{\partial y^2} = 0$$

is a partial differential equation. In the present chapter we shall consider only ordinary differential equations.

An ordinary differential equation is said to be of **order** n, if the nth derivative of y with respect to x is the highest derivative of y in that equation.

The notion of the order of a differential equation leads to a useful classification of the equations into equations of first order, second order, etc. Thus (1) is a first-order equation, (2) is of the second order, and (3) is of the third order.

In the present chapter we shall consider first-order equations. Equations of second and higher order will be considered in Chaps. 2–4.

A function

$$(4) \qquad y = g(x)$$

is called a **solution** of a given first-order differential equation on some interval, say, $a < x < b$ (perhaps infinite) if it is defined and differentiable throughout the interval and is such that the equation becomes an identity when y and y' are replaced by g and g', respectively.

For example, the function

$$y = g(x) = e^{2x}$$

is a solution of the first-order equation

$$y' = 2y$$

for all x, because

$$g' = 2e^{2x},$$

and by inserting g and g' the equation reduces to the identity

$$2e^{2x} = 2e^{2x}.$$

Sometimes a solution of a given differential will appear as an implicit function, that is, in the form

$$G(x, y) = 0$$

and is then called an *implicit solution*, in contrast to the *explicit solution* (4).

For example,

$$x^2 + y^2 = 1 \qquad\qquad (y \neq 0)$$

is an implicit solution of the differential equation

$$y' = -\frac{x}{y},$$

as the student may verify. In this case we may easily write the solution in explicit form, but in other cases this may be difficult or even impossible.

The principal task of the theory of differential equations is to find all the solutions of a given differential equation and investigate their properties. We shall consider various standard methods which were developed for that purpose.

A differential equation may have many solutions. Let us illustrate this fact by the following examples.

Example 1. Each of the functions

$$y = \sin x, \qquad y = \sin x + 3, \qquad y = \sin x - \tfrac{4}{5}$$

is a solution of the equation (1),

$$y' = \cos x,$$

and we know from calculus that any solution of the equation is of the form

(5) $$y = \sin x + c$$

where c is a constant. If we regard c as arbitrary, then (5) represents the totality of all solutions of the equation. Cf. Fig. 31.

Example 2. The student may verify that each of the functions

(6) $$y = e^x, \quad y = 2e^x, \quad y = -\tfrac{6}{5}e^x$$

is a solution of the equation

$$y' = y.$$

We shall see later that any solution of the equation is of the form

(7) $$y = ce^x$$

where c is a constant. Regarding c as arbitrary (7) thus represents the totality of all solutions of the equation. Cf. Fig. 32.

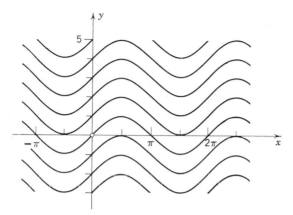

Fig. 31. Solutions of $y' = \cos x$.

Our examples illustrate that a differential equation may (and, in general, will) have more than one solution, even infinitely many solutions, which can be represented by a single formula involving an arbitrary constant c. It is customary to call such a function which contains an arbitrary[1] constant a **general solution** of the corresponding differential equation of the first order. If we assign a definite value to that constant, then the solution so obtained is called a **particular solution**.

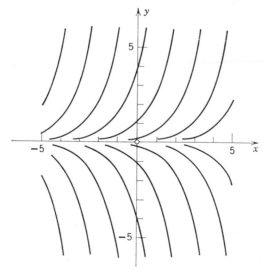

Fig. 32. Solutions of $y' = y$.

[1] The range of the constant may have to be restricted in some cases to avoid imaginary expressions or other degeneracies.

Thus (7) is a general solution of the equation $y' = y$, and (6) are particular solutions.

In the following sections we shall develop various methods for obtaining general solutions of first order equations. We shall see that each such method will yield a general solution of an equation which is unique, except for notation, and will then be called *the* general solution of that equation.

We mention that in some cases there may be further solutions of a given equation which cannot be obtained by assigning a definite value to the arbitrary constant in the general solution; such a solution is then called a **singular solution** of the equation.

For example, the equation

(8) $$y'^2 - xy' + y = 0$$

has the general solution

$$y = cx - c^2$$

representing a family of straight lines where each line corresponds to a definite value of c. A further solution is

$$y = \frac{x^2}{4},$$

and since this solution cannot be obtained by assigning a definite value to c in the general solution, it is a singular solution. Obviously, each particular solution represents a tangent to the parabola represented by the singular solution (Fig. 33).

Singular solutions will rarely occur in engineering problems.

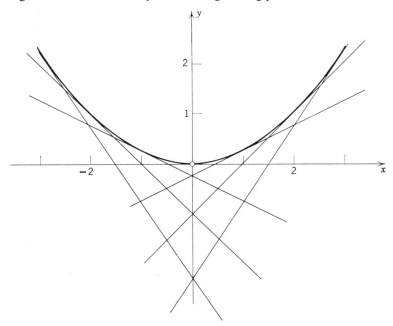

Fig. 33. Singular solution and particular solutions of the equation (8).

It should be noted that in some books the notion *general solution* means a formula which includes *all* solutions of an equation, that is, both the particular and the singular ones. We do not adopt this definition for two reasons. First of all, it is frequently quite difficult to prove that a particular formula includes all solutions, and that definition of a general solution is therefore rather useless from the practical point of view. Furthermore, we shall see that a large and very important class of equations (the so-called linear differential equations) does not have singular solutions, and our definition of a general solution can be easily generalized to equations of higher order so that the resulting notion includes all solutions of a differential equation which is linear.

We shall see that the conditions under which a given differential equation has solutions are fairly general. But we should note that there are simple equations which do not have solutions at all, and others which do not have a general solution. For example, the equation $y'^2 = -1$ does not have a solution for real y, as is obvious; the equation $|y'| + |y| = 0$ does not have a general solution, because its only solution is $y \equiv 0$.

Differential equations are of great importance in engineering, because many physical laws and relations appear mathematically in the form of differential equations.

Let us consider a simple physical example which will illustrate the typical steps leading from the physical situation to its mathematical formulation and solution. This may be the easiest way to obtain a first idea of the nature and purpose of differential equations and their applications.

Example 3 (Radioactivity). Experiments show that a radioactive substance decomposes at a rate proportional to the amount present. Starting with a given amount of substance, say, 2 grams, at a certain time, say, $t = 0$, what can be said about the amount available at a later time?

1st Step (Mathematical description of the physical process by a differential equation). We denote the amount of substance still present at time t by $y(t)$. The rate of change is dy/dt. According to the law governing the process of radiation, dy/dt is proportional to y. Thus,

(9)
$$\frac{dy}{dt} = ky$$

where k is a definite physical constant whose numerical value is known for various radioactive substances. (For example, in the case of radium, $k \approx -1.4 \cdot 10^{-11}$ sec^{-1}.) Clearly, since the amount of substance is positive and decreases with time, dy/dt is negative, and so is k. We see that the physical process under consideration is described mathematically by an ordinary linear differential equation of the first order. Whenever a physical law involves a rate of change of a function, such as velocity, acceleration, etc., it will lead to a differential equation. For this reason differential equations occur frequently in physical and engineering problems.

2nd Step (Solving the differential equation). At this early stage of our consideration no systematic method for solving (9) is at our disposal. However, we see that if (9) has a solution $y(t)$, its derivative must be proportional to y. From calculus we remember that exponential functions have this property. In fact, the function e^{kt} or more generally

$$(10) \qquad\qquad y(t) = ce^{kt}$$

where c is any constant, is a solution of (9) for all t, as can readily be verified by substituting (10) into (9). Since (10) involves an arbitrary constant, it is a general solution of the first order equation (9). [We shall see later that (10) includes all solutions of (9), that is, (9) does not have singular solutions.]

3rd Step (*Determination of a particular solution*). It is clear that our physical process has a unique behavior, and we may therefore expect that by using further given information we shall be able to select a definite numerical value of c in (10) so that the resulting particular solution will describe the process properly. The amount of substance $y(t)$ still present at time t will depend on the initial amount of substance given. This amount is 2 grams at $t = 0$. Hence we have to specify the value of c so that $y = 2$ when $t = 0$. By inserting this *initial condition*

$$(11) \qquad\qquad y(0) = 2$$

in (10) we obtain

$$y(0) = ce^0 = 2 \qquad \text{or} \qquad c = 2.$$

Using this value of c, (10) becomes

$$(12) \qquad\qquad y(t) = 2e^{kt}.$$

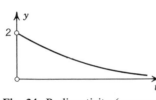

Fig. 34. Radioactivity (exponential decay).

This particular solution of (9) characterizes the amount of substance still present at any time $t \geqq 0$. The physical constant k is negative, and $y(t)$ decreases, as is shown in Fig. 34.

4th Step (*Checking*). From (12) we have

$$\frac{dy}{dt} = 2ke^{kt} = ky \qquad \text{and} \qquad y(0) = 2e^0 = 2.$$

The function (12) satisfies the equation (9) as well as the initial condition (11).

The student should never forget to carry out the important final step which shows him whether the function obtained is (or is not) the solution of the problem.

Let us illustrate that geometrical problems may also lead to differential equations.

Example 4. Find the curve through the point $(1, 1)$ in the xy-plane having at each of its points the slope $-y/x$. Clearly the function representing the desired curve must be a solution of the differential equation

$$(13) \qquad\qquad y' = -\frac{y}{x}.$$

We shall soon learn how to solve such an equation. For the time being the student may verify that

$$y = \frac{c}{x}$$

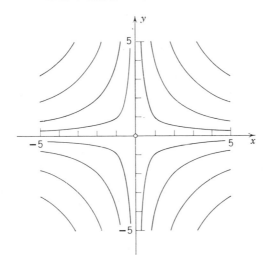

Fig. 35. Solutions of $y' = -y/x$.

is a solution of (13) for any value of the constant c. Now we must have $y = 1$ when $x = 1$, and this yields $c = 1$. Hence the solution of our problem is the hyperbola

$$y = \frac{1}{x} .$$

PROBLEMS

In each case, verify that the given function is a solution of the corresponding differential equation and graph the corresponding curves for some values of the constant c.

1. $y' = -\sin x,\ y = \cos x + c$ **2.** $y' + y \tan x = 0,\ y = c \cos x$

3. $2y' = e^{x/2},\ y = e^{x/2} + c$ **4.** $2y' = y,\ y = ce^{x/2}$

5. $y' - y + x = 0,\ y = ce^x + x + 1$ **6.** $y' + 2xy = 0,\ y = ce^{-x^2}$

7. $xy' + y + 4 = 0,\ y = \dfrac{c}{x} - 4$ **8.** $xy' + 2y = 0,\ x^2 y = c$

9. $xy' = y,\ y = cx$ **10.** $xy' + y = \sin x,\ y = \dfrac{c - \cos x}{x}$

11. $y'^2 - xy' + y = 0,\ y = cx - c^2,\ y = x^2/4$

In each case find $y = \int f(x)\, dx + c$ and determine c such that y satisfies the given condition.

12. $f = x^3$, $y = 0$ when $x = 1$

13. $f = \sin 2x$, $y = 1$ when $x = 0$

14. $f = e^{-3x}$, $y = 0$ when $x = -\tfrac{1}{3}$

15. $f = \cos^2 x$, $y = \pi/2$ when $x = \pi/2$

In each case verify that the given function is a solution of the corresponding equation and determine c such that the resulting particular solution satisfies the given condition. Graph this solution.

16. $y' = 3y$, $y = ce^{3x}$, $y = 2$ when $x = 1$

17. $xy' = 2y,$ $y = cx^2,$ $y = 2$ when $x = -1$
18. $y' + 2xy = 0,$ $y = ce^{-x^2},$ $y = -1$ when $x = 0$
19. $y' + y = 1,$ $y = 1 + ce^{-x},$ $y = 0$ when $x = 0$
20. $y' + y = 2,$ $y = 2 + ce^{-x},$ $y = 4$ when $x = 0$

21. (Falling body). If a body falls in vacuum due to the action of gravity, starting at time $t = 0$ with initial velocity 0, experiments show that its velocity is proportional to the time. State this physical law in terms of a first-order differential equation, and show that by solving it one obtains the familiar law

$$s(t) = \frac{g}{2} t^2$$

where s is the distance of the body from its initial position and g is the constant of proportionality between velocity and time.

Find a first-order differential equation involving both y' and y for which the given function y is a solution.

22. $y = 2e^{-2x}$ **23.** $y = 3x^4$ **24.** $y = xe^x$ **25.** $y = \cos x$

1.2 GEOMETRICAL CONSIDERATIONS. ISOCLINES

We shall now start with a systematic treatment of first-order differential equations. Any such equation may be written in the *implicit form*

(1) $F(x, y, y') = 0.$

Not always, but in many cases we shall be able to write a first-order equation in the *explicit form*

(2) $y' = f(x, y).$

Before we consider various standard methods for solving equations of the form (2) we shall demonstrate that (2) has a very simple geometric interpretation. This will immediately lead to a useful graphical method for obtaining a rough picture of the particular solutions of (2), without solving the equation.

We suppose that $f(x, y)$ is *single-valued*, that is, at each point (x, y) of the xy-plane where $f(x, y)$ is defined, it has just one value. The solutions of (2) can be plotted as curves in the xy-plane. We don't know the solutions, but we see from (2) that a solution passing through a point (x_0, y_0) must have the slope $f(x_0, y_0)$ at this point. This suggests the following method. We first graph some of the curves in the xy-plane along which $f(x, y)$ is constant. These curves are called *curves of constant slope*, or **isoclines** of (2). Along any such isocline, given by

$$f(x, y) = k = const$$

we draw a number of parallel short line segments (*lineal elements*) with slope k, which is the slope of solution curves of (2) at any point of that isocline. This we do for all isoclines which we graphed before. In this way we obtain a field of lineal elements, called the *direction field* of (2). With the help of the lineal elements we can now easily graph approximation curves to the (unknown) solution curves of the given equation (2) and thus obtain a qualitatively correct picture of these solution curves.

Let us consider two simple illustrative examples.

Example 1. Graph the direction field of the equation

(3)
$$y' = -\frac{x}{y}$$

and an approximation to the solution curve through the point ($\sqrt{5}$, 2). The isoclines are the straight lines

$$-\frac{x}{y} = k = const \qquad \text{or} \qquad y = -\frac{x}{k}.$$

Since the slope of any such line is $-1/k$ the lineal elements are perpendicular to the corresponding isocline. For example, along the isocline $y = x$ we have $x/y = 1$ and from (3), $y' = -1$, etc. (See Fig. 36.)

In the next section we shall see that (3) can be easily solved, so that our example merely illustrates the technical details of the method of the direction field, and the same is true for the following example.

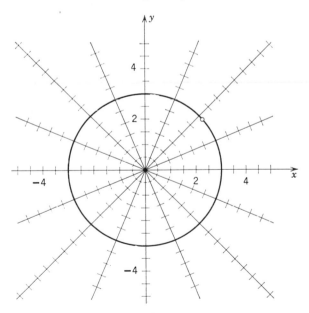

Fig. 36. Direction field of the equation (3).

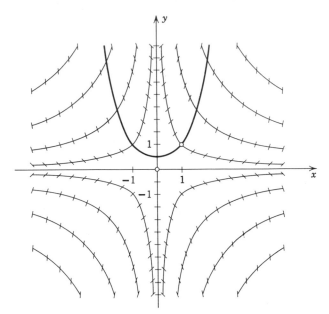

Fig. 37. Direction field of the equation (4).

Example 2. Graph the direction field of the equation

(4) $$y' = xy$$

and an approximation to the solution curve through the point (1,1). The iso-clines are the equilateral hyperbolas $xy = k$ together with the two coordinate axes. The result is shown in Fig. 37.

The method of the direction field is particularly helpful in engineering problems involving a first order equation whose solution cannot be expressed in terms of known functions or is a very complicated expression.

PROBLEMS

1. Verify that $x^2 + y^2 = c$ and $y = ce^{x^2/2}$ are the general solutions of (3) and (4), respectively. Compare the exact and the approximate solution curves obtained before.

Draw good direction fields for the following differential equations and plot several approximate solution curves.

2. $y' = x$ **3.** $y' = x^2$ **4.** $y' = 1 - x$ **5.** $y' = y$

6. $y' = x + y$ **7.** $y' = y/x$ **8.** $y' = x^2 + y$ **9.** $y' = y - x^2$

10. $y' = \dfrac{1}{x} + \dfrac{1}{y}$ **11.** $y' = 2xy$ **12.** $y' = \sin y$

13. What are the isoclines of (2), if f depends on one of the two variables only?
14. In what way can the direction field be used for approximate integration of definite integrals?

15. Using direction fields, find approximate values of $\int_0^1 x^2\, dx$ and $\int_0^1 e^{-x^2}\, dx$.

Give examples of differential equations (2) whose isoclines are:

16. Ellipses with center at the origin and principal axes in the directions of the coordinate axes.

17. Parabolas through the origin with the y-axis as common axis.

18. Congruent parabolas with the y-axis as common axis.

19. A body B moves on a straight line L. Let $s(t)$ be its distance from a fixed point 0 of L. Suppose that at each instant the velocity of B equals $1/s(t)$, and $s = 1$ when $t = 0$. Find the corresponding differential equation. Graph the direction field and plot the (approximate) solution curve $s(t)$ of the problem.

20. A body B moves on a straight line L, starting at $t = 0$ from the point $s = 1$ where $s(t)$ is the distance of B measured from a fixed point 0 of L. Suppose that the velocity of B equals $-s(t)$. Find the corresponding differential equation. Graph the direction field and plot the (approximate) solution curve of the problem.

1.3 SEPARABLE EQUATIONS

Many first-order differential equations can be reduced by algebraic manipulations to the form

$$(1) \qquad\qquad g(y)y' = f(x).$$

Since $y' = dy/dx$ we find it convenient to write (1) in the form

$$(2) \qquad\qquad g(y)\, dy = f(x)\, dx,$$

but we keep in mind that this is merely another way of writing (1). Such an equation is called an *equation with separable variables*, or a **separable equation**, because the variables x and y have been *separated* from each other in such a way that x appears only on the right while y appears only on the left. By integrating on both sides of (2) we obtain

$$(3) \qquad\qquad \int g(y)\, dy = \int f(x)\, dx + c.$$

Assuming that f and g are continuous functions, the integrals in (3) will exist, and by evaluating these integrals we obtain the general solution of (1).

Example 1. Solve

$$y' = -\frac{4x}{9y}.$$

By separating variables we have

$$y\, dy = -\frac{4}{9} x\, dx.$$

By integrating on both sides we obtain the general solution

$$\frac{y^2}{2} = -\frac{2}{9}x^2 + \tilde{c} \quad \text{or} \quad \frac{y^2}{4} + \frac{x^2}{9} = c \qquad \left(c = \frac{\tilde{c}}{2}\right).$$

The solution represents a family of ellipses.

Example 2. Find the solutions of

$$y' = -2xy$$

in the upper half plane ($y > 0$). By separating variables we have

$$\frac{dy}{y} = -2x\, dx.$$

Integration yields

(4) $$\ln y = -x^2 + \tilde{c}.$$

It is of great importance that the constant of integration is introduced immediately when the integration is carried out. From (4) we obtain

$$y = e^{-x^2 + \tilde{c}}$$

or by noting that $e^{a+b} = e^a e^b$ and setting $e^{\tilde{c}} = c$,

$$y = ce^{-x^2}.$$

The solution represents a family of so-called *bell-shaped curves* (Fig. 38).

Example 3. Solve the differential equation

$$y' = 1 + y^2.$$

By separating variables and integrating we obtain

$$\frac{dy}{1 + y^2} = dx, \qquad \text{arc tan } y = x + c, \qquad y = \tan(x + c).$$

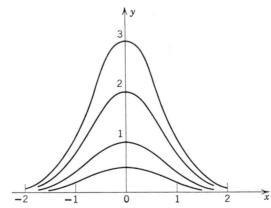

Fig. 38. Solutions of $y' = -2xy$ ("bell-shaped curves").

In many engineering applications we are not interested in the general solution of a given differential equation but only in the particular solution $y(x)$ satisfying a given **initial condition**, say, the condition that at some point x_0 the solution $y(x)$ has a prescribed value y_0, briefly

(5) $$y(x_0) = y_0.$$

A first-order differential equation together with an initial condition is called an **initial value problem**. To solve such a problem we must find the particular solution of the equation satisfying the given initial condition.

Example 4. Solve the initial value problem

$$(x^2 + 1)y' + y^2 + 1 = 0, \qquad y(0) = 1.$$

1st Step. Separating variables, we find

$$\frac{dy}{1 + y^2} = -\frac{dx}{1 + x^2}.$$

By integration,

$$\text{arc tan } y = -\text{arc tan } x + c$$

or

$$\text{arc tan } y + \text{arc tan } x = c.$$

Taking the tangent on both sides, we have

(6) $$\tan (\text{arc tan } y + \text{arc tan } x) = \tan c.$$

Now the addition formula for the tangent is

$$\tan (a + b) = \frac{\tan a + \tan b}{1 - \tan a \tan b}.$$

For $a = \text{arc tan } y$ and $b = \text{arc tan } x$ this becomes

$$\tan (\text{arc tan } y + \text{arc tan } x) = \frac{y + x}{1 - xy}.$$

Consequently, (6) may be written

(7) $$\frac{y + x}{1 - xy} = \tan c.$$

2nd Step. We determine c from the initial condition. Setting $x = 0$ and $y = 1$ in (7), we have $1 = \tan c$, so that

$$\frac{y + x}{1 - xy} = 1 \qquad \text{or} \qquad y = \frac{1 - x}{1 + x}.$$

3rd Step. Check the result.

Example 5 (Newton's law of cooling). A copper ball is heated to a temperature of $100°C$. Then at time $t = 0$ it is placed in water which is maintained at a temperature of $30°C$. At the end of 3 minutes the temperature of the ball is reduced to $70°C$. Find the time at which the temperature of the ball is reduced to $31°C$.

Physical information. Experiments show that the rate of change of the temperature T of the ball is proportional to the difference between T and the temperature of the surrounding medium (*Newton's law of cooling*).

Heat flows so rapidly in copper that at any time the temperature is practically the same at all points of the ball.

1st Step. The mathematical formulation of Newton's law of cooling in our case is

$$\text{(8)} \qquad \frac{dT}{dt} = -k(T - 30)$$

where we denoted the constant of proportionality by $-k$ in order that $k > 0$.

2nd Step. The general solution of (8) is obtained by separating variables, finding

$$T(t) = ce^{-kt} + 30.$$

3rd Step. The given initial condition is $T(0) = 100$. The particular solution satisfying this condition is

$$T(t) = 70e^{-kt} + 30.$$

4th Step. k can be determined from the given information $T(3) = 70$. Thus

$$T(3) = 70e^{-3k} + 30 = 70 \qquad \text{or} \qquad k = \tfrac{1}{3} \ln \tfrac{7}{4} = 0.1865.$$

Hence the temperature $T(t)$ of the ball is

$$T(t) = 70e^{-0.1865t} + 30,$$

and the value $T = 31°C$ is reached when

$$70e^{-0.1865t} = 1 \qquad \text{or} \qquad 0.1865\,t = \ln 70, \qquad t = \frac{\ln 70}{0.1865} = 22.78,$$

that is, after approximately 23 minutes.

5th Step. Check the result.

Example 6 (Velocity of escape from the earth). Find the minimum initial velocity of a body which is fired in radial direction from the earth and is supposed to escape from the earth. Neglect the air resistance and the gravitational pull of other celestial bodies.

1st Step. According to *Newton's law of gravitation*, the gravitational force, and therefore also the acceleration a of the body, is proportional to $1/r^2$ where r is the distance between the body and the center of the earth. Thus

$$a(r) = \frac{dv}{dt} = \frac{k}{r^2}$$

where v is the velocity and t is the time. Since v is decreasing, $a < 0$ and thus $k < 0$. Let R be the radius of the earth. When $r = R$ then $a = -g$, the acceleration of gravity at the surface of the earth. Note that the minus sign occurs because g is positive and the attraction of gravity acts in the negative direction (the direction towards the center of the earth). Thus

$$-g = a(R) = \frac{k}{R^2} \qquad \text{and} \qquad a(r) = -\frac{gR^2}{r^2}.$$

Now $v = dr/dt$ and

$$a = \frac{dv}{dt} = \frac{dv}{dr}\frac{dr}{dt} = \frac{dv}{dr}v.$$

Hence the differential equation for the velocity is

$$\frac{dv}{dr} v = -\frac{gR^2}{r^2}.$$

2nd Step. Separating variables and integrating, we obtain

(9) $\qquad v\, dv = -gR^2 \frac{dr}{r^2}$ and $\quad \frac{v^2}{2} = \frac{gR^2}{r} + c.$

3rd Step. On the earth's surface, $r = R$ and $v = v_0$, the initial velocity. For these values of r and v, (9) becomes

$$\frac{v_0^2}{2} = \frac{gR^2}{R} + c, \qquad \text{and} \qquad c = \frac{v_0^2}{2} - gR.$$

By inserting this expression for c into (9) we obtain

(10) $\qquad\qquad v^2 = \frac{2gR^2}{r} + v_0^2 - 2gR.$

4th Step. If $v^2 = 0$, then $v = 0$, the body stops, and it is clear from the physical situation that then the velocity will change from positive to negative and the body will return to the earth. Consequently, we have to choose v_0 so large that this cannot happen. If we choose

(11) $\qquad\qquad v_0 = \sqrt{2gR},$

then in (10) the expression $v_0^2 - 2gR$ is zero and v^2 is never zero for any r. However, if we choose a smaller value for the initial velocity v_0, then $v = 0$ for a certain r. The expression in (11) is called the *velocity of escape* from the earth. Since $R = 3960$ statute miles and $g = 32.17$ ft/sec² = 0.006 09 miles/sec²,

$$v_0 = \sqrt{2gR} \approx 7 \text{ miles/sec.}$$

5th Step. Check the result.

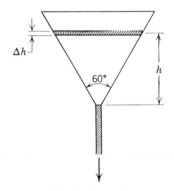

Fig. 39. Funnel.

Example 7. A funnel (Fig. 39), whose angle at the outlet is 60° and whose outlet has a cross-sectional area of 0.5 cm², contains water. At time $t = 0$ the outlet is opened and the water flows out. Determine the time when the funnel will be empty, assuming that the initial height of water is $h(0) = 10$ cm.

1st Step. The volume of water which flows out during a short interval of time Δt is

$$\Delta V = 0.5\, v\, \Delta t$$

where v is the velocity of the outflowing water. From **Torricelli's law,**[2] the velocity with which a liquid issues from an orifice is

$$v = 0.6\sqrt{2gh}$$

[2] EVANGELISTA TORRICELLI (1608–1647), Italian physicist. The "contraction factor" 0.6 was introduced by BORDA in 1766 because of the fact that the cross section of the outflowing stream of liquid is somewhat smaller than that of the orifice.

where $g = 980$ (cm/sec^2) is the acceleration of gravity at the surface of the earth and h is the instantaneous height of the liquid above the orifice. Hence

$$\Delta V = 0.3\sqrt{2gh}\,\Delta t.$$

ΔV must equal the change ΔV^* of the volume of water in the funnel. Now

$$\Delta V^* = -\pi r^2\,\Delta h$$

where Δh is the decrease of the height $h(t)$ of the water and $r = h\tan 30° = h/\sqrt{3}$ is the radius of the funnel at height $h(t)$, so that

$$\Delta V^* = -\pi\frac{h^2}{3}\,\Delta h.$$

The minus sign appears because the volume of water in the funnel decreases.
By equating ΔV and ΔV^* we obtain

$$0.3\sqrt{2gh}\,\Delta t = -\frac{\pi}{3}h^2\,\Delta h \qquad \text{or} \qquad \frac{\Delta h}{\Delta t} = -\frac{0.9\sqrt{2g}}{\pi}h^{-3/2}.$$

If we now let Δt approach zero, we obtain the differential equation

$$\frac{dh}{dt} = -kh^{-3/2}$$

where $$k = \frac{0.9\sqrt{2g}}{\pi} = 12.7.$$

2nd Step. By separating variables and integrating we have

(12) $h^{3/2}\,dh = -k\,dt \qquad \text{and} \qquad \frac{2}{5}h^{5/2} = -kt + c.$

3rd Step. The initial condition is $h(0) = 10$. Setting $t = 0$ and $h = 10$ in the general solution given by the last formula in (12), we obtain

$$\tfrac{2}{5}10^{5/2} = c.$$

Using this value of c, the last formula in (12) becomes

(13) $\frac{2}{5}h^{5/2} = -kt + \frac{2}{5}10^{5/2}.$

4th Step. By solving (13) for t and substituting $k = 12.7$ we find

$$t = \frac{2}{5k}(10^{5/2} - h^{5/2}) \approx 10 - 0.0315h^{5/2}.$$

Hence the funnel will be empty ($h = 0$) at $t \approx 10$ sec.

PROBLEMS

1. Why is it important that the constant of integration is introduced immediately when the integration is carried out?

2. Graph some particular solutions of the equation in Ex. 1. Graph the solution in Ex. 4.

3. Using (3), show that the solution of (1) satisfying (5) is obtained from

(14) $$\int_{y_0}^{y} g(y^*)\, dy^* = \int_{x_0}^{x} f(x^*)\, dx^*.$$

Apply this formula to Ex. 4.

Find the general solution of the following equations. (a, b, m, n etc., are constants.)

4. $y' = ky$ **5.** $y' + ay + b = 0\ (a \neq 0)$ **6.** $y' - n\dfrac{y}{x} = 0$

7. $2xy' = 3y$ **8.** $mxy' - ny = 0\ (m \neq 0)$

9. $(x^2 + 1)yy' = 1$ **10.** $y' + y \tan x = 0$

11. $y' - y \tanh x = 0$ **12.** $y' = 3y \coth 3x$

13. $y' = 4y \tanh x$ **14.** $y' + 3y \sin \omega x = 0$

15. $y^2 y' - \cos^2 x = 0$ **16.** $2yy' = \sin^2 \omega x$

17. $(x^2 - 1)yy' + x(y^2 - 1) = 0$ **18.** $(x + 2)y' - xy = 0$

19. $(x - 1)y' - 2x^3 y = 0$ **20.** $(x^2 - x + 1)y' + 4(1 - 2x)y = 0$

21. $xyy' = 2(y + 3)$ **22.** $\dfrac{dr}{d\theta} = b\left(\cos\theta\,\dfrac{dr}{d\theta} + r \sin\theta\right)$

Solve the following initial value problems.

23. $y' = 3y/x, \quad y(1) = 2$ **24.** $(x + 1)y' - 2y = 0, \quad y(0) = 1$

25. $y' + 2xy = 0, \quad y(0) = 1$ **26.** $y'x \ln x - y = 0, \quad y(2) = \ln 4$

27. $y' - 2y \cot x = 0, \quad y(\pi/2) = 2$ **28.** $y' + 6y \tan 2x = 0, \quad y(0) = -2$

29. $y^2 y' - x^2 = 0, \quad y(-2) = -2$ **30.** $(y^2 + 1)y' - 2 \cos x = 0,$
$$y(-\pi/2) = 0$$

31. $y' - \sec y = 0, \quad y(0) = 0$ **32.** $yy'e^{y^2} = x - 1, \quad y(2) = 0$

33. $v\dfrac{dv}{dx} = g = const, \quad v(x_0) = v_0$ **34.** $\dfrac{dr}{dt} = -2rt, \quad r(0) = r_0$

35. Find the curve through the point $(3, -4)$ having at each of its points (x, y) the slope $2y/x$.

36. Find the curve through $(1, 0)$ having at each of its points the slope $-x/y$.

37. (*Boyle-Mariotte's law for ideal gases*).[3] Experiments show that for a gas at low pressure p (and constant temperature) the rate of change of the volume $V(p)$ equals $-V/p$. Solve the corresponding differential equation.

38. A thermometer, reading $30°F$, is brought into a room whose temperature is $75°F$. One minute later the thermometer reading is $45°F$. Find the temperature reading 3 minutes after the thermometer is first brought into the room.

39. (*Radiation of radium*). Experiments show that radium disintegrates at a rate proportional to the amount of radium instantaneously present. Its *half-life*, that is, the time in which 50% of a given amount will disappear, is 1590 years. What per cent will disappear in 1 year?

---

[3] ROBERT BOYLE (1627–1691), English physicist; EDMÉ MARIOTTE (1620–1684), French physicist.

40. Determine the time in which 1% of each of the following radioactive substances disappears.

Name	Symbol	Isotope of	Discovered in	Half-life
Radium A	$^{218}_{84}Po$	polonium	1905 (Rutherford)	3.05 minutes
Radium B	$^{214}_{82}Pb$	lead	1905 (Rutherford)	26.8 minutes
Radium C	$^{214}_{83}Bi$	bismuth	1905 (Rutherford)	19.7 minutes
Radium D	$^{210}_{82}Pb$	lead	1903 (P. and M. Curie)	22 years

41. (*Atmospheric pressure*). Observations show that the rate of change of the atmospheric pressure p with altitude h is proportional to the pressure. Assuming that the pressure at 18,000 ft is $\frac{1}{2}$ of its value p_0 at sea level, find the formula for the pressure at any height.

42. (*Evaporation*). A wet porous substance in the open air loses its moisture at a rate proportional to the moisture content. If a sheet hung in the wind loses half its moisture during the first hour, when will it have lost 99%, weather conditions remaining the same?

43. Experiments show that the rate of inversion of cane sugar in dilute solution is proportional to the concentration $Y(t)$ of the unaltered sugar. If the concentration is $\frac{1}{100}$ at $t = 0$ and is $\frac{1}{250}$ at $t = 5$ [hours], find $Y(t)$.

44. A tank contains 200 gal of brine in which 100 lb of salt is dissolved. Fresh water runs into the tank at the rate of 2 gal/min, and the mixture, kept practically uniform by stirring, runs out at the same rate. How much salt will there be in the tank at the end of 1 hour?

45. If in the culture of yeast the amount of active ferment $y(t)$ doubles in 4 hours, how much can be expected at the end of 8 hours at the same rate of growth?

46. Two liquids are boiling in a vessel. It is found that the ratio of the quantities of each passing off as vapor at any instant is proportional to the ratio of the quantities x and y still in the liquid state. Show that $\dfrac{dy}{dx} = k\dfrac{y}{x}$ and solve this equation.

47. Lambert's[4] **law of absorption** states that the absorption of light in a very thin transparent layer is proportional to the thickness of the layer and to the amount incident on that layer. Formulate this in terms of a differential equation and solve it.

48. Consider the following modification of Ex. 6. The body is carried by a rocket and is separated from the rocket at a distance of 200 miles from the earth's surface. Determine the minimum velocity at this point sufficient for escape from the earth.

49. The **law of mass action** states that, if the temperature is kept constant, the velocity of a chemical reaction is proportional to the product of the concentrations of the substances which are reacting. In the bimolecular reaction

$$A + B \rightarrow M,$$

a moles per liter of a substance A and b moles of a substance B are combined.

---

[4] JOHANN HEINRICH LAMBERT (1728–1777), German physicist and mathematician.

If y is the number of moles per liter which have reacted after time t, the rate of reaction is given by

$$y' = k(a - y)(b - y).$$

Solve this equation, assuming that $a \neq b$.

50. Show that a ball thrown vertically upward with initial velocity v_0 takes twice as much time to return as to reach the highest point. Find the velocity upon return. (Air resistance is assumed negligible.)

1.4 EQUATIONS REDUCIBLE TO SEPARABLE FORM

Certain first-order differential equations are not separable but can be made separable by a simple change of variables. This holds for equations of the form[5]

$$(1) \qquad\qquad y' = g\left(\frac{y}{x}\right)$$

where g is any given function of y/x, for example $(y/x)^3$, $\sin (y/x)$, etc. The form of the equation suggests that we set

$$\frac{y}{x} = u,$$

remembering that y and u are functions of x. Then $y = ux$, and by differentiation,

$$(2) \qquad\qquad y' = u + u'x.$$

By inserting this into (1) we obtain

$$u + u'x = g(u).$$

Now we may separate variables, finding

$$\frac{du}{g(u) - u} = \frac{dx}{x}.$$

Integrating and replacing u by y/x gives us the general solution of (1).

Example 1. Solve

$$2xyy' - y^2 + x^2 = 0.$$

Dividing by x^2, we have

$$2\frac{y}{x}y' - \left(\frac{y}{x}\right)^2 + 1 = 0.$$

Setting $u = y/x$ and using (2), the equation becomes

$$2u(u + u'x) - u^2 + 1 = 0 \qquad \text{or} \qquad 2xuu' + u^2 + 1 = 0.$$

---

[5] These equations are sometimes called **homogeneous equations**. We shall not use this terminology but reserve the term "homogeneous" for a much more important purpose (cf. Sec. 1.7).

Separating variables, we find

$$\frac{2u\,du}{1 + u^2} = -\frac{dx}{x}$$

and by integration   .

$$\ln(1 + u^2) = -\ln|x| + c^* \qquad \text{or} \qquad 1 + u^2 = \frac{c}{x}.$$

Replacing u by y/x, we finally obtain

$$x^2 + y^2 = cx \qquad \text{or} \qquad \left(x - \frac{c}{2}\right)^2 + y^2 = \frac{c^2}{4}.$$

Sometime the form of a given differential equation suggests other simple substitutions, as the following example illustrates.

Example 2. Solve

$$(2x - 4y + 5)y' + x - 2y + 3 = 0.$$

We set $x - 2y = v$. Then $y' = \frac{1}{2}(1 - v')$ and the equation becomes

$$(2v + 5)v' = 4v + 11.$$

Separating variables and integrating, we find

$$\left(1 - \frac{1}{4v + 11}\right) dv = 2\,dx \qquad \text{and} \qquad v - \frac{1}{4}\ln|4v + 11| = 2x + c^*$$

or, since $v = x - 2y$,

$$4x + 8y + \ln|4x - 8y + 11| = c.$$

Further simple substitutions are illustrated by the equations in Probs. 11–14 and 16–18.

PROBLEMS

Find the general solutions of the following equations.

1. $xy' - 2y - 3x = 0$ **2.** $xy' = 3y - 4x$

3. $x^2y' - y^2 + xy = x^2$ **4.** $x^2y' = y^2 + 5xy + 4x^2$

5. $x^2y' = y^2 + 3xy + 2x^2$ **6.** $x^2y' - y^2 + 5xy - 10x^2 = 0$

7. $x^3y' = y^3 + 3xy^2 + 4x^2y + x^3$ **8.** $x^3y' - y^3 + 3xy^2 - 4x^2y + x^3 = 0$

9. $(2xy + x^2)y' = 3y^2 + 2xy$ **10.** $2xyy' = 3y^2 + x^2$

11. $y' = \dfrac{y - x + 1}{y - x + 5}$ (put $y - x = v$)

12. $y' = \dfrac{y - x}{y - x - 1}$ **13.** $y' = \dfrac{y - x}{y + x}$

14. $y' = \dfrac{y - x + 1}{y + x + 5}$ (put $x = X - 2, y = Y - 3$)

15. $2yy' = y^2 + x^2 - 2x$ **16.** $y' = \tan(x + y) - 1$

17. $e^y y' = k(x + e^y) - 1$ (put $x + e^y = z$)

18. $x^2yy' = \frac{1}{2}\tan(x^2y^2) - xy^2$ (put $x^2y^2 = z$)

19. Four flies sit at the corners of a card table, facing inward. They start walking simultaneously at the same rate, each directing its motion steadily toward the fly on its right. Find the path of each.

20. Show that the solution of the initial value problem $\dfrac{dr}{d\theta} + \dfrac{a^2}{r} \sin 2\theta = 0$, $r^2(0) = a^2$, is a *lemniscate* (a is constant; r and θ are polar coordinates).

1.5 EXACT DIFFERENTIAL EQUATIONS

A first-order differential equation

(1) $$M(x, y)\, dx + N(x, y)\, dy = 0$$

is said to be **exact** if the left-hand side is the total or exact differential

(2) $$du = \frac{\partial u}{\partial x}\, dx + \frac{\partial u}{\partial y}\, dy$$

of some function $u(x, y)$. Then (1) may be written

$$du = 0,$$

and by integration we immediately obtain the general solution of (1) in the form

(3) $$u(x, y) = c.$$

By comparing (1) and (2) we see that (1) is exact, if there is some function $u(x, y)$ such that

(4) $\qquad$ (a) $\dfrac{\partial u}{\partial x} = M$, $\qquad$ (b) $\dfrac{\partial u}{\partial y} = N$.

Suppose that M and N are defined and have continuous first partial derivatives in a region in the xy-plane whose boundary is a closed curve having no self-intersections. Then from (4),

$$\frac{\partial M}{\partial y} = \frac{\partial^2 u}{\partial x\, \partial y} \qquad \frac{\partial N}{\partial x} = \frac{\partial^2 u}{\partial y\, \partial x}$$

and by assumption of continuity the second derivatives are equal [cf. (4) in Sec. 0.2]. Thus

(5) $$\frac{\partial M}{\partial y} = \frac{\partial N}{\partial x}.$$

This condition is not only necessary but also sufficient[6] for $M\, dx + N\, dy$ to be a total differential.

---

[6] We shall prove this fact at another occasion (in Sec. 6.12); the proof can also be found in some books on elementary calculus; cf. Ref. [A13] in Appendix 1.

If (1) is exact, the function $u(x, y)$ can be found by guessing or in the following systematic way. From (4a) we have[7]

(6)
$$u = \int M \, dx + k(y);$$

in this integration, y is to be regarded as a constant, and $k(y)$ plays the role of a "constant" of integration. To determine $k(y)$, we find $\partial u/\partial y$ from (6), use (4b) to find dk/dy, and integrate.

Example 1. Solve
$$xy' + y + 4 = 0.$$

If we write the equation in the form (1),

$$(y + 4) \, dx + x \, dy = 0$$

we see that $M = y + 4$, $N = x$, and (5) holds, so that the equation is exact. Now from (4b) we have $N = \partial u/\partial y = x$, and by integration

$$u = xy + k(x).$$

To determine $k(x)$ we differentiate u and apply (4a), finding

$$\frac{\partial u}{\partial x} = y + \frac{dk}{dx} = M = y + 4.$$

Thus $dk/dx = 4$ and $k = 4x + c^*$. By inserting this into the equation $u = xy + k = const$ and solving for y, we obtain the general solution of our equation,

$$y = \frac{c}{x} - 4.$$

Intelligent students, who know that thinking is an important thing in mathematics, write the given equation in the form

$$y \, dx + x \, dy = -4 \, dx,$$

recognize the left side as the total differential of xy, and integrate, finding $xy = -4x + c$ which is equivalent to our previous result.

Example 2. Solve
$$2x \sin 3y \, dx + 3x^2 \cos 3y \, dy = 0.$$

The equation is exact, and from (6) we obtain

$$u = \int 2x \sin 3y \, dx + k(y) = x^2 \sin 3y + k(y).$$

Therefore $\partial u/\partial y = 3x^2 \cos 3y + dk/dy$, and $dk/dy = 0$ or $k = c^* = const.$ The general solution is $u = const$ or $x^2 \sin 3y = c$.

---

[7] Or from (4b), $u = \int N \, dy + k(x)$, etc; see Ex. 1.

PROBLEMS

In each case, find whether the equation is exact and solve it.

1. $(1 + x^2)\, dy + 2xy\, dx = 0$ **2.** $x^2\, dx + y^2\, dy = 0$

3. $x\, dy - 2y\, dx = 0$ **4.** $b^2 x\, dx + a^2 y\, dy = 0$

5. $4x^3 - e^{xy}(y + xy') = 0$ **6.** $x\, dy - (2y + 3x)\, dx = 0$

7. $(x + e^x)\, dx + y\, dy = 0$ **8.** $\left(x + \dfrac{1}{x}\right) dy = \left(\dfrac{1}{x^2} - 1\right) y\, dx$

9. $y' \cosh x \sin y = \sinh x \cos y$ **10.** $e^x(\cos y\, dx - \sin y\, dy) = 0$

11. $\cos y\, dx - \sin y\, dy = 0$ **12.** $\dfrac{dx}{x} + \left(1 + \dfrac{1}{y}\right) dy = 0$

Find the exact equations that have the following general solutions.

13. $\cos 3y + \sin 2x = c$ **14.** $x^3 \sin y = c$

15. $x^2 e^{2xy} = c$ **16.** $x^2 + 4y^2 = c$

17. $\arctan \dfrac{y}{x} = c$ **18.** $\ln(x^2 + y^2) + 2 \arctan \dfrac{y}{x} = c$

Find and graph the curve having the given slope y' and passing through the given point (x, y).

19. $y' = \dfrac{2 - x}{y}$, $(0, 0)$ **20.** $y' = \dfrac{1 - x}{y - 1}$, $(0, 1)$

21. $y' = \dfrac{3 - x}{9y - 9}$, $(3, 0)$ **22.** $y' = -\dfrac{x + 1}{4y}$, $(1, 0)$

Solve the following equations by integrating by inspection.

23. $x\, dy + y\, dx = 0$ **24.** $x\, dx + \dfrac{y\, dx - x\, dy}{y^2} = 0$

25. $x^2\, dx + \dfrac{dy}{1 + y^2} = 0$

Determine for what values of a and b the following equations are exact, and solve the exact equations.

26. $(y + x^3)\, dx + (ax + by^3)\, dy = 0$ **27.** $axy\, dx + (x^2 + \cos y)\, dy = 0$

28. $(ax + b)y\, dx + \left(x^2 + x + \dfrac{1}{y}\right) dy = 0$ **29.** $xy^3\, dx + ax^2 y^2\, dy = 0$

30. $ax(y - \cos y)\, dx + x^2(1 + \sin y)\, dy = 0$

31. Prove that a necessary and sufficient condition for the equation
$$f(x)\, dx + g(x)h(y)\, dy = 0 \qquad [h(y) \not\equiv 0]$$
to be exact is that $g(x)$ be constant.

32. Under what conditions is $[f(x) + g(y)]\, dx + [h(x) + l(y)]\, dy = 0$ exact?

1.6 INTEGRATING FACTORS

Sometimes a given differential equation

(1) $P(x, y)\, dx + Q(x, y)\, dy = 0$

is not exact but can be made exact by multiplying it by a suitable function $F(x, y)$ ($\not\equiv 0$). This function is then called an **integrating factor** of (1). With some experience, integrating factors can be found by inspection. For this purpose the student should keep in mind the differentials listed in Ex. 2 below. In some important special cases, integrating factors can be determined in a systematic way which is illustrated in the subsequent section.

Example 1. Solve

$$x \, dy - y \, dx = 0.$$

The equation is not exact. An integrating factor is $F = 1/x^2$, and

$$F(x)(x \, dy - y \, dx) = \frac{x \, dy - y \, dx}{x^2} = d\left(\frac{y}{x}\right) = 0, \qquad y = cx.$$

Theorem 1. *If (1) is not exact and has a general solution $u(x, y) = c$, then there exists an integrating factor (even infinitely many such factors).*

Proof. By differentiating $u(x, y) = c$ we have

$$du = \frac{\partial u}{\partial x} \, dx + \frac{\partial u}{\partial y} \, dy = 0.$$

From this and (1) it follows that

$$\frac{\partial u}{\partial x} : \frac{\partial u}{\partial y} = P : Q$$

must hold identically. Hence a function $F(x, y)$ exists such that

$$\frac{\partial u}{\partial x} = FP, \qquad \frac{\partial u}{\partial y} = FQ,$$

and then

(2) $$F(x, y)(P \, dx + Q \, dy) = du.$$

This shows that F is an integrating factor of (1). Furthermore, multiplication of (2) by a function $H(u)$ yields the expression

$$H(u)F(P \, dx + Q \, dy) = H(u) \, du$$

which is exact. Hence $H(u)F(x, y)$ is another integrating factor, and since H is arbitrary, there are infinitely many integrating factors of (1).

Example 2. Find integrating factors of $x \, dy - y \, dx = 0$; cf. Ex. 1. Since

$$d\left(\frac{x}{y}\right) = \frac{y \, dx - x \, dy}{y^2}, \qquad d\left(\ln \frac{y}{x}\right) = \frac{x \, dy - y \, dx}{xy}, \qquad d\left(\arctan \frac{y}{x}\right) = \frac{x \, dy - y \, dx}{x^2 + y^2}$$

the functions $1/y^2$, $1/xy$, and $1/(x^2 + y^2)$ are such factors. The corresponding solutions

$$\frac{x}{y} = c, \qquad \ln \frac{y}{x} = c, \qquad \arctan \frac{y}{x} = c$$

are essentially the same, because each represents a family of straight lines through the origin.

PROBLEMS

Find integrating factors F and solve:

1. $2y\,dx + x\,dy = 0$ **2.** $dx + \dfrac{x}{y}\,dy = 0$ **3.** $\cos y\,dx - \sin y\,dy = 0$

4. $2y\,dx + 3x\,dy = 0$ **5.** $y \sin xy\,dx - \left(\dfrac{\cos xy}{y} - x \sin xy\right)dy = 0$

6. $dx + e^{y-x}\,dy = 0$ **7.** $(2y + xy)\,dx + 2x\,dy = 0$

8. $2x^2\,dx - 3xy^2\,dy = 0$ **9.** $x\,dy - 2y\,dx = 0$

10. $2xy\,dx - x^2\,dy = 0$ **11.** $(y - 1)\,dx - x\,dy = 0$

Find integrating factors F and solve the following initial value problems.

12. $x\,dy - y\,dx = 0,\quad y(1) = -2$ **13.** $dx + \dfrac{y}{x}\,dy = 0,\quad y(0) = 3$

14. $\dfrac{x}{y}\,dx + 4\,dy = 0,\quad y(0) = \dfrac{1}{2}$ **15.** $2\,dx + \left(\dfrac{x}{y} - 3\dfrac{y}{x}\right)dy = 0,\quad y(0) = 2$

16. Prove that if P and Q in (1) satisfy the relation

$$(3) \qquad \frac{\partial P}{\partial y} = \frac{\partial Q}{\partial x} + \frac{k}{x}\,Q,$$

then $F = x^k$ is an integrating factor of (1).

Using the result of Prob. 16, solve

17. $4y\,dx + x\,dy = 0$ **18.** Prob. 1

19. Show that $F = y$ is an integrating factor of $y\,dx + 2x\,dy = 0$. Then find other integrating factors of this equation.

20. Show that if $\dfrac{1}{Q}\left(\dfrac{\partial P}{\partial y} - \dfrac{\partial Q}{\partial x}\right)$ is a function of x only, say, $f(x)$, then $F(x) = e^{\int f(x)\,dx}$ is an integrating factor of (1). *Hint:* Start from the assumption that $F(x)(P\,dx + Q\,dy) = 0$ is exact and use (5) of Sec. 1.5.

1.7 LINEAR FIRST-ORDER DIFFERENTIAL EQUATIONS

A first-order differential equation is said to be **linear** if it can be written in the form

$$(1) \qquad y' + f(x)y = r(x).$$

The characteristic feature of this equation is that it is linear in y and y', while f and r may be *any* given functions of x.

If $r(x) \equiv 0$, the equation is said to be **homogeneous**; otherwise, it is said to be **nonhomogeneous**. [Here, $r \equiv 0$ means $r = 0$ for all x].

Let us find a formula for the general solution of (1) in some interval I, assuming that f and r are continuous in I. For the homogeneous equation

$$(2) \qquad\qquad y' + f(x)y = 0$$

this is very simple. By separating variables we have

$$\frac{dy}{y} = -f(x)\,dx \qquad \text{and thus} \qquad \ln|y| = -\int f(x)\,dx + c^*$$

or

$$(3) \qquad\qquad y(x) = ce^{-\int f(x)\,dx} \qquad\qquad (c = e^{c^*}).$$

To solve the nonhomogeneous equation (1), let us write it in the form

$$(fy - r)\,dx + dy = 0$$

and show that we can find an integrating factor $F(x)$ *depending only on x*. If such a factor exists,

$$F(x)(fy - r)\,dx + F(x)\,dy = 0$$

must be exact. Now for this equation the condition (5) of Sec. 1.5 assumes the form

$$\frac{\partial}{\partial y}[F(fy - r)] = \frac{dF}{dx} \qquad \text{or} \qquad Ff = \frac{dF}{dx}.$$

By separating variables and integrating we obtain

$$\ln F = \int f(x)\,dx$$

and from this

$$F(x) = e^{h(x)} \qquad \text{where} \qquad h(x) = \int f(x)\,dx.$$

This shows that $F(x)$ is an integrating factor of (1). Let us now multiply (1) by this factor, finding

$$e^h(y' + fy) = e^h r.$$

Since $h' = f$ this may be written

$$\frac{d}{dx}(ye^h) = e^h r.$$

Now we can integrate on both sides and obtain

$$ye^h = \int e^h r\,dx + c.$$

By dividing both sides by e^h we have the desired formula

$$(4) \qquad y(x) = e^{-h}\left[\int e^h r\,dx + c\right], \qquad\qquad h = \int f(x)\,dx,$$

which represents the general solution of (1) in the form of an integral. (The choice of the values of the constants of integration is immaterial; cf. Prob. 2 below.)

Example 1. Solve the linear differential equation

$$y' - y = e^{2x}.$$

Here

$$f = -1, \qquad r = e^{2x}, \qquad h = \int f\, dx = -x$$

and from (4) we obtain the general solution

$$y(x) = e^x \left[\int e^{-x} e^{2x}\, dx + c \right] = e^x[e^x + c] = ce^x + e^{2x}.$$

Example 2. Solve

$$xy' + y + 4 = 0.$$

We write this equation in the form (1), that is,

$$y' + \frac{1}{x} y = -\frac{4}{x}.$$

Hence, $f = \frac{1}{x}$, $r = -\frac{4}{x}$ and, therefore,

$$h = \int f\, dx = \ln x, \qquad e^h = x, \qquad e^{-h} = \frac{1}{x}.$$

From this and (4) we obtain the general solution

$$y(x) = \frac{1}{x}\left[\int x\left(-\frac{4}{x}\right) dx + c \right] = \frac{c}{x} - 4,$$

in agreement with Ex. 1 of Sec. 1.5.

Of course, in simple cases such as Exs. 2, 3 and 5 (below) we may solve the equation without using (4).

Example 3. Solve the linear equation

$$xy' + y = \sin x.$$

We can write the equation in the form

$$d(xy) = \sin x\, dx$$

and integrate on both sides, finding

$$xy = -\cos x + c \qquad \text{or} \qquad y = \frac{1}{x}(c - \cos x).$$

The procedure of solving initial value problems may be illustrated by the following examples.

Example 4. Solve the initial value problem

$$y' + y \tan x = \sin 2x, \qquad y(0) = 1.$$

Here $f = \tan x$, $r = \sin 2x = 2 \sin x \cos x$, and

$$\int f \, dx = \int \tan x \, dx = \ln |\sec x|.$$

From this we see that in (4),

$$e^h = \sec x, \qquad e^{-h} = \cos x, \qquad e^h r = 2 \sin x$$

and the general solution of our equation is

$$y(x) = \cos x \left[2 \int \sin x \, dx + c \right] = c \cos x - 2 \cos^2 x.$$

According to the initial condition, $y = 1$ when $x = 0$, that is

$$1 = c - 2 \qquad \text{or} \qquad c = 3,$$

and the solution of our initial value problem is

$$y = 3 \cos x - 2 \cos^2 x.$$

Example 5. Solve the initial value problem

$$x^2 y' + 2xy - x + 1 = 0, \qquad y(1) = 0.$$

The equation may be written as $d(x^2 y) = (x - 1) \, dx$. By integration

$$x^2 y = \tfrac{1}{2} x^2 - x + c \qquad \text{or} \qquad y(x) = \frac{1}{2} - \frac{1}{x} + \frac{c}{x^2}.$$

From this and the initial condition, $y(1) = \tfrac{1}{2} - 1 + c = 0$ or $c = \tfrac{1}{2}$. Thus

$$y(x) = \frac{1}{2} - \frac{1}{x} + \frac{1}{2x^2}.$$

Very often the solutions of differential equations appearing in engineering applications are not elementary functions. In the case of equation (1) they appear as integrals, as can be seen from (4). If it happens that such a non-elementary integral is a tabulated function[8], that is a great convenience, but it is not vital. The essential thing is to reduce the solution to a computable form, for example, by approximate integration, such as Simpson's rule, or by developing the integrand in a power series and integrating term by term.

In applications the independent variable x will often be the time; the function $r(x)$ on the right-hand side of (1) may represent a force, and the solution $y(x)$ a displacement, a current, or some other variable physical quantity. In engineering mathematics $r(x)$ is frequently called the **input**,

---

[8] Whether tables of a certain function were computed can be found in the extremely useful book Ref. [A6], listed in Appendix 1. Some important nonelementary integrals will be considered in Chap. 14, power series in Secs. 3.2 and 10.8, and numerical methods for solving first-order differential equations in Sec. 1.13. Methods of approximate integration are included in Sec. 0.8.

and $y(x)$ is called the **output** or *response to the input* (and the initial conditions). This terminology is widely used in electrical engineering where the differential equation may govern the behavior of an electric circuit and the output $y(x)$ is obtained as the solution of that equation corresponding to the input $r(x)$. For example, in the field of analogue computers the physical system may be an

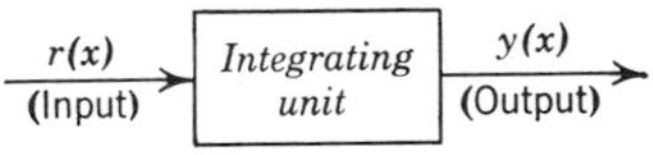

Fig. 40. Simple block diagram.

integrating unit; then the corresponding differential equation is

$$y' = r(x),$$

and the output $y(x)$ corresponding to an input $r(x)$ is the integral of $r(x)$,

$$y(x) = \int_{x_0}^{x} r(x^*)\, dx^*.$$

The system may be represented by a "block diagram" as shown in Fig. 40. Various examples will occur in our further consideration.

PROBLEMS

1. Show that $e^{-\ln x} = 1/x$ (but not $-x$) and $e^{-\ln(\sec x)} = \cos x$.
2. Show that the choice of the value of the constant of integration in $\int f\, dx$ [cf. (4)] is immaterial.

Find the general solutions of the following equations.

3. $y' + y = 5$ **4.** $y' - 4y = 1$ **5.** $y' - y = 3e^x$
6. $y' + 4y = -e^{-4x}$ **7.** $xy' + 2y - 8x^2 = 0$ **8.** $xy' = y + (x + 1)^2$
9. $xy' - 2y = x^4$ **10.** $(x + 4)y' + 3y = 3x$ **11.** $y' + y = \sin x$
12. $y' - 2y = \cos 3x$ **13.** $y' + xy = 2x$ **14.** $y' - x^3 y = -4x^3$

Solve the following initial value problems.

15. $y' - y = e^x,$ $y(0) = 0$ **16.** $y' - 2xy = 2x,$ $y(0) = 0$

17. $y' - y \cot x = 2x - x^2 \cot x,$ $y\left(\dfrac{\pi}{2}\right) = \dfrac{\pi^2}{4} + 1$

18. $xy' - 3y = 2x,$ $y(1) = 0$

19. $y' - \left(1 + \dfrac{3}{x}\right)y = x + 2,$ $y(1) = e - 1$

20. $y' - y \cot x = -\cot x,$ $y\left(\dfrac{\pi}{2}\right) = 3$

Prove the following theorems.

21. $y \equiv 0$ is a solution of the homogeneous equation (2).
22. If y_1 is a solution of (2), then $y = cy_1$, where c is any constant, is a solution of (2).
23. If y_1 and y_2 are any solutions of (1), then $y = y_1 - y_2$ is a solution of (2).
24. If y_1 and y_2 are any particular solutions of (2), then $y = y_1 + y_2$ is a solution of (2).
25. If y_1 is a solution of (1) and y_2 is a solution of (2), then $y = y_1 + y_2$ is a solution of (1).

Certain nonlinear first-order differential equations may be reduced to linear form by a suitable change in the dependent variable, as the following problems illustrate.

26. Solve $y' + y = y^2$ by setting $y = 1/u$ and solving the resulting linear equation for u.

27. The equation

$$y' + f(x)y = g(x)y^a \qquad (a \text{ any real number})$$

is called **Bernoulli's[9] equation**. For $a = 1$, the equation is linear, and for $a \neq 1$ it is nonlinear. Set $[y(x)]^{1-a} = u(x)$ and show that the equation assumes the linear form

$$u' + (1 - a)f(x)u = (1 - a)g(x).$$

Solve the following Bernoulli equations.

28. $y' + xy = \dfrac{x}{y}$ **29.** $y' = 5x^2y^5 + \dfrac{y}{2x}$

30. Solve $(y^4 + 2x)y' - y = 0$. *Hint:* Take x as the dependent variable.

1.8 VARIATION OF PARAMETERS

There is another interesting way of obtaining the general solution of the linear differential equation

$$(1) \qquad\qquad y' + f(x)y = r(x).$$

We have seen that

$$(2) \qquad\qquad v(x) = e^{-\int f(x)\,dx}$$

is a solution of the corresponding homogeneous linear equation. Let us try to determine a function $u(x)$ such that

$$(3) \qquad\qquad y(x) = u(x)v(x)$$

is the general solution of (1). This attempt is suggested by the form of the general solution $cv(x)$ of the homogeneous equation and consists in replacing the parameter c by a variable $u(x)$. Therefore, this approach, due to Lagrange,[10] is called the **method of variation of parameters**. It can be generalized to equations of higher order where it is of great importance. Our present simple case is a good occasion for getting acquainted with this basic method.

---

[9] JACOB BERNOULLI (1654–1705), Swiss mathematician, who contributed to the theory of elasticity and to the theory of mathematical probability. The method for solving Bernoulli's equation was discovered by Leibniz in 1696.

[10] JOSEPH LOUIS LAGRANGE (1736–1813), a great French mathematician, spent 20 years of his life in Prussia and then returned to Paris. His important major work was in the calculus of variations, celestial and general mechanics, differential equations, and algebra.

By substituting (3) into (1) we obtain

$$u'v + u(v' + fv) = r.$$

Since v is a solution of the homogeneous equation, this reduces to

$$u'v = r \qquad \text{or} \qquad u' = \frac{r}{v}.$$

Integration yields

$$u = \int \frac{r}{v} \, dx + c.$$

We thus obtain the result

(4) $$y = uv = v\left(\int \frac{r}{v} \, dx + c \right),$$

and from (2) we see that this is identical with (4) of the previous section.

PROBLEMS

Apply the method of variation of parameters to the following equations.
1. $y' - y = 3$ 2. $y' + 2y = x^2$ 3. $xy' - 2y = x^4$
Find substitutions which reduce the following equations to linear form. Then solve the resulting equations.
4. $y' \cos y + x \sin y = 2x$ 5. $y' + y \ln y \cot x = y$
6. $yy' + y^2 = x$ 7. $3y' + xy = x/y^2$
8. $y' - 1 = e^{-y} \sin x$ 9. $2xyy' + (x - 1)y^2 = x^2 e^x$ (put $y^2 = xz$)
10. Using the method of direction fields (cf. Sec. 1.2) find an approximate solution curve of the initial value problem $y' - 2xy = 1$, $y(1) = 1$.

11. Show that the direction field of (1) has the following interesting property: The lineal elements on any vertical line $x = x_0$ all pass through a single point with coordinates

$$\xi = x_0 + \frac{1}{f(x_0)}, \qquad \eta = \frac{r(x_0)}{f(x_0)}.$$

How can this property be used for constructing the direction field of a linear differential equation?
12. Apply the result in Prob. 11 to the construction of the direction field in Prob. 10.
13. Apply the result in Prob. 11 to the construction of the direction field of the equation (4) in Sec. 1.2.
14. Show that the transformation $y = a(x)u + b(x)$ [$a(x)$ and $b(x)$ any differentiable functions, $a(x) \neq 0$] transforms (1) into a linear differential equation involving u and du/dx.
15. Show that the transformation $x = \phi(t)$ (where ϕ has a continuous derivative) transforms (1) into a linear differential equation involving y and dy/dt.

1.9 ELECTRIC CIRCUITS

Linear first-order differential equations have various applications in physics and engineering practice. To illustrate this, let us consider some standard examples in connection with electric circuits. These and similar considerations are important, because they help all students to learn how to express physical situations in terms of mathematical relations. The transition from the physical situation to a corresponding mathematical model is always the first step in engineering mathematics, and this important step requires experience and training which can only be gained by considering typical examples from various fields.

The simplest electric circuit is a series circuit in which we have a source of electric energy (*electromotive force*) such as a generator or a battery, and a

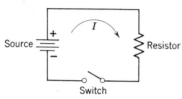

Fig. 41. Circuit.

resistor, which uses energy, for example an electric light bulb (Fig. 41). If we close the switch, a current I will flow through the resistor, and this will cause a *voltage drop*, that is, the electric potential at the two ends of the resistor will be different; this potential difference or voltage drop can be measured by a voltmeter. Experiments show that the following law holds.

The voltage drop E_R across a resistor is proportional to the instantaneous current I, say

(1) $$E_R = RI$$ (*Ohm's law*)

where the constant of proportionality R is called the **resistance** of the resistor. The current I is measured in *amperes*, the resistance R in *ohms*, and the voltage E_R in *volts*.[11]

The other two important elements in more complicated circuits are *inductors* and *capacitors*. An inductor opposes a change in current, having an inertia effect in electricity similar to that of mass in mechanics; we shall consider this analogy later (Sec. 2.14). Experiments yield the following law.

The voltage drop E_L across an inductor is proportional to the instantaneous time rate of change of the current I, say,

(2) $$E_L = L\frac{dI}{dt}$$

[11] These and the subsequent units are named after ANDRÉ MARIE AMPÈRE (1775–1836), French physicist, GEORG SIMON OHM (1789–1854), German physicist, ALLESSANDRO VOLTA (1745–1827), Italian physicist, JOSEPH HENRY (1797–1878) American physicist, MICHAEL FARADAY (1791–1867), English physicist, and CHARLES AUGUSTIN DE COULOMB (1736–1806), French physicist.

where the constant of proportionality L is called the **inductance** of the inductor and is measured in *henrys*; the time t is measured in seconds.

A capacitor is an element which stores energy. Experiments yield the following law.

The voltage drop E_C across a capacitor is proportional to the instantaneous electric charge Q on the capacitor, say,

$$(3*) \qquad E_C = \frac{1}{C} Q$$

where C is called the **capacitance** and is measured in *farads*; the charge Q is measured in *coulombs*. Since

$$(3') \qquad I(t) = \frac{dQ}{dt}$$

this may be written

$$(3) \qquad E_C = \frac{1}{C} \int_{t_0}^{t} I(t^*) \, dt^*.$$

The current $I(t)$ in a circuit may be determined by solving the equation (or equations) resulting from the application of **Kirchhoff's**[12] **second law:**

The algebraic sum of all the instantaneous voltage drops around any closed loop is zero, or the voltage impressed on a closed loop is equal to the sum of the voltage drops in the rest of the loop.

Example 1 (RL-circuit). For the "*RL*-circuit" in Fig. 42 we obtain from Kirchhoff's second law and (1), (2)

$$(4) \qquad L\frac{dI}{dt} + RI = E(t).$$

Case A (Constant electromotive force). If $E = E_0 = const$, then (4) in Sec. 1.7 yields the general solution

$$(5) \qquad \begin{aligned} I(t) &= e^{-\alpha t}\left[\frac{E_0}{L}\int e^{\alpha t}\, dt + c\right] \qquad (\alpha = R/L) \\ &= \frac{E_0}{R} + ce^{-(R/L)t}. \end{aligned}$$

The last term approaches zero as t tends to infinity, so that $I(t)$ tends to the limit value E_0/R; after a sufficiently long time, I will practically be constant. Figure 43 shows the particular solution

$$(5*) \qquad I(t) = \frac{E_0}{R}(1 - e^{-(R/L)t}),$$

which corresponds to the initial condition $I(0) = 0$.

---

[12] GUSTAV ROBERT KIRCHHOFF (1824–1887), German physicist. Later we shall also need **Kirchhoff's first law:** At any point of a circuit the sum of the inflowing currents is equal to the sum of the outflowing currents.

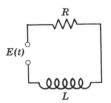

Fig. 42. RL-circuit.

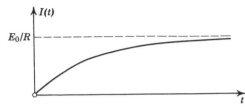

Fig. 43. Current in an RL-circuit due to a constant electromotive force.

Case B (Periodic electromotive force). If $E(t) = E_0 \sin \omega t$, then, by (4) in Sec. 1.7, the general solution of (4) in this current section is

$$I(t) = e^{-\alpha t}\left[\frac{E_0}{L}\int e^{\alpha t} \sin \omega t \, dt + c\right] \qquad (\alpha = R/L).$$

Integration by parts yields

$$I(t) = ce^{-(R/L)t} + \frac{E_0}{R^2 + \omega^2 L^2}(R \sin \omega t - \omega L \cos \omega t).$$

According to (15b) in Sec. 0.1 this may be written

(6) $\quad I(t) = ce^{-(R/L)t} + \dfrac{E_0}{\sqrt{R^2 + \omega^2 L^2}} \sin(\omega t - \delta), \qquad \delta = \arctan \dfrac{\omega L}{R}.$

The exponential term will approach zero as t approaches infinity. This means that after a sufficiently long time the current $I(t)$ executes practically harmonic oscillations. [Cf. Fig. 45]. Figure 44 shows the phase angle δ as a function of $\omega L/R$. If $L = 0$, then $\delta = 0$, and the oscillations of $I(t)$ are in phase with those of $E(t)$.

An electrical (or dynamical) system is said to be in the **steady state** when the variables describing its behavior are periodic functions of the time or constant, and it is said to be in the **transient state** (or *unsteady state*) when it is not in the steady state. The corresponding variables are called *steady state functions* and *transient functions*, respectively.

In Ex. 1, Case A, the function E_0/R is the steady state function or **steady state solution** of (4), and in Case B the steady state solution is represented by the last term in (6). Before the circuit (practically) reaches the steady state it is in the transient state. It is clear that such an interim or transient

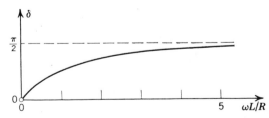

Fig. 44. Phase angle δ in (6) as a function of $\omega L/R$.

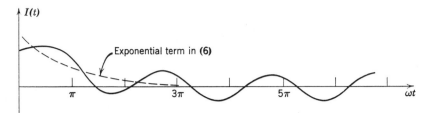

Fig. 45. Current in an *RL*-circuit due to a sinusoidal electromotive force, as given by (6) (with $\delta = \pi/4$).

period occurs because inductors and capacitors store energy, and the corresponding inductor currents and capacitor voltages cannot be changed instantly. Similar situations arise in various physical systems. For example, if a radio receiver having heater-type vacuum tubes is turned on, a transient interval of time must elapse during which the tubes change from "cold" to "hot."

Example 2 (RC-circuit). By applying Kirchhoff's second law and (1), (3) to the *RC*-circuit in Fig. 46 we obtain the equation

$$(7) \qquad RI + \frac{1}{C} \int I \, dt = E(t).$$

To get rid of the integral we differentiate with respect to *t*, finding

$$(8) \qquad R\frac{dI}{dt} + \frac{1}{C} I = \frac{dE}{dt}.$$

According to (4) in Sec. 1.7, the general solution of (8) is

$$(9) \qquad I(t) = e^{-t/RC}\left(\frac{1}{R} \int e^{t/RC} \frac{dE}{dt} \, dt + c \right).$$

Case A (Constant electromotive force). If E is constant, then $\dfrac{dE}{dt} = 0$, and (9) assumes the simple form (Fig. 47)

$$(10) \qquad I(t) = ce^{-t/RC}.$$

Case B (Sinusoidal electromotive force). If $E(t) = E_0 \sin \omega t$, then

$$\frac{dE}{dt} = \omega E_0 \cos \omega t,$$

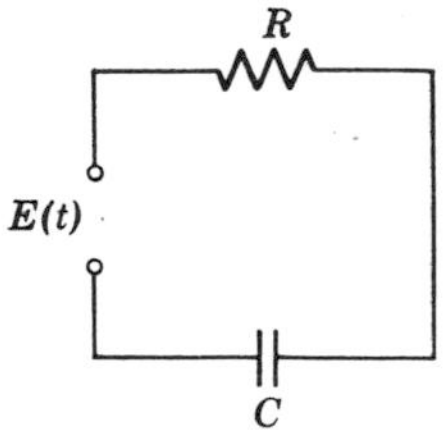

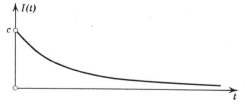

Fig. 46. *RC*-circuit.

Fig. 47. Current in an *RC*-circuit due to a constant electromotive force.

and by inserting this in (9) and integrating by parts we find

$$I(t) = ce^{-t/RC} + \frac{\omega E_0 C}{1 + (\omega RC)^2} (\cos \omega t + \omega RC \sin \omega t)$$

(11)

$$= ce^{-t/RC} + \frac{\omega E_0 C}{\sqrt{1 + (\omega RC)^2}} \sin (\omega t - \delta),$$

where $\tan \delta = -1/\omega RC$. The first term decreases steadily as t increases, and the last term represents the steady-state current, which is sinusoidal. The graph of $I(t)$ is similar to that in Fig. 45.

More complicated circuits and the analogy between electrical and mechanical vibrations will be considered in connection with second-order differential equations in Sec. 2.14.

PROBLEMS

1. Derive and check (5).   **2.** Derive and check (6).   **3.** Verify (11).

4. In (5*), the rapidity of rise of the current depends on R/L. The reciprocal L/R is called the **time constant** of the circuit. Show that when $t = L/R$ the current has reached approximately 63 % of its final value.

5. In Ex. 1, Case A, let $R = 20$ ohms, $L = 0.03$ millihenry $(3 \cdot 10^{-5}$ henry), and $I(0) = 0$. Find the time when the current reaches 99.9 % of its final value.

6. In Ex. 1, Case A, let $R = 100$ ohms, $L = 2.5$ henrys, $E_0 = 110$ volts, and $I(0) = 0$. Find the time constant and the time necessary for the current to rise from 0 to 0.6 ampere.

7. Find the current in the RC-circuit in Fig. 46 assuming that $R = 100$ ohms, $C = 0.01$ farad, $E(t) = 110 \sin 314t$, and $I(0) = 0$.

8. Using (3′), introduce $Q(t)$ as the dependent variable in (7) and solve the resulting equation for the cases of a constant and a sinusoidal electromotive force.

9. A capacitor $(C = 0.1$ farad) in series with a resistor $(R = 200$ ohms) is charged from a source $(E_0 = 12$ volts), cf. Fig. 46. Find the voltage $V(t)$ on the capacitor, assuming that at $t = 0$ the capacitor is completely uncharged.

10. In Fig. 48, $R = 20$ ohms and $C = 0.01$ farad. At $t = 0$ the switch is closed and the capacitor, whose charge is assumed to be 0.5 coulomb, starts discharging. Find the current, the charge, and the voltage on the capacitor as functions of time t.

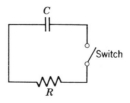

Fig. 48. Problem 10.

11. If the electromotive force in the *RL*-circuit in Ex. 1 is constant and the initial current is zero, show that the current builds up to half its theoretical maximum value in $(L \ln 2)/R$ sec.

12. Obtain from (11) the particular solution satisfying the initial condition $I(0) = 0$. Discuss the case when $\omega = 0$.

13. Find the current $I(t)$ in the *RC*-circuit shown in Fig. 46, assuming that $E = 100$ volts, $C = 0.25$ farad, R is variable according to $R = (100 - t)$ ohms when $0 \leq t \leq 100$ sec, $R = 0$ when $t > 100$ sec, and $I(0) = 1$ ampere.

14. Find the charge $Q(t)$ and the voltage $V(t)$ on the capacitor in Prob. 13.

Find the current $I(t)$ in the *RL*-circuit in Fig. 42 under the following assumptions.

15. $E = 4$ volts, $R = 2$ ohms, $L = (100 - t)$ henrys when $0 \leq t \leq 100$ sec, $L = 0$ when $t > 100$ sec, $I(0) = 0$.

16. $E = 110$ volts, $R = 22$ ohms, $L = (10 - t)$ henrys when $0 \leq t \leq 10$ sec, $L = 0$ when $t > 10$ sec, $I(0) = 5$ amperes.

17. $R = 1$ ohm, $L = 10$ henrys, $E = 6$ volts when $0 \leq t \leq 10$ sec, $E = 0$ when $t > 10$ sec, $I(0) = 6$ amperes.

18. $R = 200$ ohms, $L = 400$ henrys, $E = 100$ volts when $0 \leq t \leq 5$ sec, $E = 0$ when $t > 5$ sec, $I(0) = 0$.

19. $R = 1$ ohm, $L = 100$ henrys, E periodic as shown in Fig. 49, $I(0) = 0$.

Fig. 49. Problem 19.

20. Show that $I(0) = (e - 1)/(e^2 - 1)$ is the only initial condition for which $I(t)$ in Prob. 19 is periodic, that is, $I(t + 200) = I(t)$ for all $t \geq 0$.

1.10   FAMILIES OF CURVES. ORTHOGONAL TRAJECTORIES

If for each fixed real value of c the equation

(1) $F(x, y, c) = 0$

represents a curve in the xy-plane and if for variable c it represents infinitely many curves, then the totality of these curves is called a **one-parameter family of curves**, and c is called the *parameter* of the family.

Example 1. The equation

(2) $F(x, y, c) = x + y + c = 0$

represents a family of parallel straight lines; each line corresponds to precisely one value of c. The equation

(3) $F(x, y, c) = x^2 + y^2 - c^2 = 0$

represents a family of concentric circles of radius c with center at the origin.

The general solution of a first-order differential equation involves a parameter c and thus represents a family of curves. This yields a possibility for representing many one-parameter families of curves by such differential equations. The practical use of such representations will become obvious from our further consideration.

Example 2. By differentiating (2) we see that

$$y' + 1 = 0$$

is the differential equation of that family of straight lines. Similarly the differential equation of the family (3) is

$$y' = -x/y.$$

If the equation obtained by differentiating (1) still contains the parameter c, then we have to eliminate c from this equation by using (1).

Example 3. The differential equation of the family of parabolas

(4) $$y = cx^2$$

is obtained by differentiating (4),

(5) $$y' = 2cx,$$

and by eliminating c from (5). From (4) we have $c = y/x^2$, and by substituting this into (5) we find the desired result

(6) $$y' = 2y/x.$$

In many engineering applications, a family of curves is given, and it is required to find another family whose curves intersect each of the given curves at right angles.[13] Then the curves of the two families are said to be *mutually orthogonal*, they form an *orthogonal net*, and the curves of the family to be obtained are called the **orthogonal trajectories** of the given curves (and conversely); cf. Fig. 50.

Let us mention some familiar examples. The meridians on the earth's surface are the orthogonal trajectories of the parallels. On a map the curves of steepest descend are the orthogonal trajectories of the contour lines. Weather maps show the isobars, or curves of constant barometric pressure, and their orthogonal trajectories indicate the general direction of the wind from high to low pressure areas, at least on parts of the globe where the disturbance by mountains and other obstacles is negligible. In electrostatics the equipotential lines and the lines of electric force are orthogonal trajectories of each other. We shall see later that orthogonal trajectories play an important role in various fields of physics, for example, in hydrodynamics and heat conduction.

[13] Remember that the angle of intersection of two curves is defined as the angle between their tangents at the point of intersection.

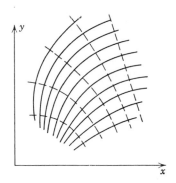

Fig. 50. Curves and their orthogonal trajectories.

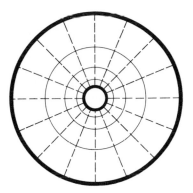

Fig. 51. Equipotential lines and lines of electric force (dashed) between two concentric cylinders.

Given a family $F(x, y, c) = 0$ which can be represented by a differential equation

$$(7) \qquad\qquad y' = f(x, y)$$

we may find the corresponding orthogonal trajectories as follows. From (7) we see that a curve of the given family which passes through a point (x_0, y_0) has the slope $f(x_0, y_0)$ at this point. The slope of the orthogonal trajectory through (x_0, y_0) at this point should be the negative reciprocal of $f(x_0, y_0)$, that is, $-1/f(x_0, y_0)$, because this is the condition for the tangents of the two curves at (x_0, y_0) to be perpendicular. Consequently, the differential

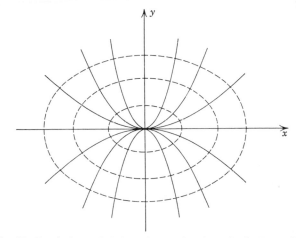

Fig. 52. Parabolas and their orthogonal trajectories in Example 4.

equation of the orthogonal trajectories is

(8)
$$y' = -\frac{1}{f(x, y)},$$

and the trajectories are obtained by solving this equation.

It can be shown that, under relatively general conditions, a family of curves has orthogonal trajectories, but we shall not consider this question here.

Example 4. Find the orthogonal trajectories of the parabolas in Ex. 3. From (6) we see that the differential equation of the orthogonal trajectories is

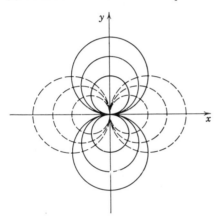

$$y' = -\frac{1}{2y/x} = -\frac{x}{2y}.$$

By separating variables and integrating we find that the orthogonal trajectories are the ellipses (Fig. 52)

$$\frac{x^2}{2} + y^2 = c^*.$$

Example 5. Find the orthogonal trajectories of the circles

(9) $$x^2 + (y - c)^2 = c^2.$$

We first determine the differential equation of the given family. By differentiating (9) with respect to x we find

Fig. 53. Circles and their orthogonal trajectories (dashed) in Example 5.

(10) $$2x + 2(y - c)y' = 0.$$

We have to eliminate c. Solving (9) for c, we have

$$c = \frac{x^2 + y^2}{2y}.$$

By inserting this into (10) and simplifying we get

$$x + \frac{y^2 - x^2}{2y}y' = 0 \quad \text{or} \quad y' = \frac{2xy}{x^2 - y^2}.$$

From this and (8) we see that the differential equation of the orthogonal trajectories is

$$y' = -\frac{x^2 - y^2}{2xy} \quad \text{or} \quad 2xyy' - y^2 + x^2 = 0.$$

The orthogonal trajectories obtained by solving this equation (cf. Ex. 1 in Sec. 1.4) are the circles (Fig. 53)

$$(x - \tilde{c})^2 + y^2 = \tilde{c}^2.$$

PROBLEMS

What families of curves are represented by the following equations?

1. $2y - x + c = 0$ **2.** $(x - c)^2 + y^2 = 1$
3. $y - (x - c)^2 = 0$ **4.** $cx^2 + y^2 = 1$
5. $xy = c$ **6.** $(x - c)^2 + (y - 2c)^2 = 4$
7. $(x - c)^2 + (y - \sqrt{1 - c^2})^2 = 1$ **8.** $y - (x - c)^3 = 0$
9. $y^2 - (x - c)^3 = 0$

Find the differential equations which represent the following families of curves.

10. $y = ce^x$ **11.** $y = e^{cx}$ **12.** $y = e^{x+c}$ **13.** $\dfrac{x^2}{c^2} + y^2 = 1$

14. $y = c \cos x$ **15.** $y = \sin(x - c)$ **16.** $y = cxe^x$ **17.** $y = \sin cx$

Find the orthogonal trajectories of the following curves and graph some of the curves and their trajectories.

18. $x^2 + y^2 = c^2$ **19.** $\dfrac{x^2}{2} + y^2 = c$ **20.** $y = \sqrt{x - c}$

21. $y = ce^{-x}$ **22.** $y = ce^x$ **23.** $y = \tan x + c$
24. $y = cx^3$ **25.** $xy = c$ **26.** $y = x^3 + c$

27. Show that the orthogonal trajectories of the family $g(x, y) = c$ can be obtained from the differential equation

$$\frac{dy}{dx} = \frac{\partial g / \partial y}{\partial g / \partial x}.$$

Using the result in Prob. 27, find the orthogonal trajectories of the curves:
28. $x^2 + y^2 = c$ **29.** $x^2 - y^2 = c$ **30.** $y - x^2 = c$
31. Show that (8) may be written in the form

$$\frac{dx}{dy} = -f(x, y).$$

32. Using the result in Prob. 31, find the orthogonal trajectories of the curves $y = x + ce^{-x}$.

33. Find the curves in the xy-plane for which the segment of every tangent between the coordinate axes is bisected by the point of tangency.

34. Find the curves in the xy-plane whose normals all pass through the origin.

35. Find the curves in the xy-plane for which the slope of the normals at all points equals the ratio of the abscissa to the ordinate.

1.11 PICARD'S ITERATION METHOD

We have seen that the solution of a *linear* first-order differential equation can be obtained by evaluating an integral; cf. (4) in Sec. 1.7. In the case of other differential equations of the first order, the situation may be more complicated. In fact, there are various such equations which cannot be solved by one of the standard methods considered before or by another elementary method.[14] Often when considering engineering problems that involve such equations it will be sufficient to obtain approximate solutions. In such cases the method which we shall now consider may be helpful. This method, which is called **Picard's iteration method**,[15] yields an approximate solution of an initial value problem of the form

$$(1) \qquad y' = f(x, y), \qquad y(x_0) = y_0.$$

Iteration methods are methods which consist of a repeated execution of the same type of steps where in each step the result of the preceding step (or steps) is used; we want to mention that these methods are of increasing importance in various branches of applied mathematics.

The basic idea of Picard's method is very simple. By integration we see that (1) may be written in the form

$$(2) \qquad y(x) = y_0 + \int_{x_0}^{x} f[t, y(t)] \, dt,$$

where t denotes the variable of integration. In fact, when $x = x_0$ the integral is zero and $y = y_0$, so that (2) satisfies the initial condition in (1); furthermore, by differentiating (2) we obtain the differential equation in (1).

To find approximations to the solution $y(x)$ of (2) we proceed as follows. We substitute the crude approximation $y = y_0 = const$ on the right; this yields the presumably better approximation

$$y_1(x) = y_0 + \int_{x_0}^{x} f(t, y_0) \, dt.$$

Then we substitute $y_1(x)$ in the same way to get

$$y_2(x) = y_0 + \int_{x_0}^{x} f[t, y_1(t)] \, dt,$$

etc. The nth step of this iteration yields

$$(3) \qquad y_n(x) = y_0 + \int_{x_0}^{x} f[t, y_{n-1}(t)] \, dt.$$

In this way we obtain a sequence of approximations

$$y_1(x), y_2(x), \cdots, y_n(x), \cdots,$$

and we shall see in the next section that the conditions under which this sequence converges to the solution $y(x)$ of (1) are relatively general.

[14] Reference [B6] in Appendix 1 includes more than 1500 important differential equations and their solutions, arranged in systematic order and accompanied by numerous references to original literature.

[15] EMILE PICARD (1856–1941), French mathematician who made important contributions to the theory of complex analytic functions and differential equations.

Let us now illustrate the practical application of Picard's method by some simple examples which can also be treated otherwise so that we can check our results.

Example 1. Find approximate solutions to the initial value problem

$$y' = 1 + y^2, \qquad y(0) = 0.$$

In this case, $x_0 = 0$, $y_0 = 0$, $f(x, y) = 1 + y^2$, and (3) becomes

$$y_n(x) = \int_0^x [1 + y_{n-1}^2(t)]\, dt = x + \int_0^x y_{n-1}^2(t)\, dt.$$

Starting from $y_0 = 0$, we thus obtain

$$y_1(x) = x + \int_0^x 0 \cdot dt = x$$

$$y_2(x) = x + \int_0^x t^2\, dt = x + \tfrac{1}{3}x^3$$

$$y_3(x) = x + \int_0^x \left(t + \frac{t^3}{3} \right)^2 dt$$

$$= x + \tfrac{1}{3}x^3 + \tfrac{2}{15}x^5 + \tfrac{1}{63}x^7$$

etc. Of course, we can obtain the exact solution of our present problem by separating variables (Ex. 3 in Sec. 1.3), finding

(4) $y(x) = \tan x = x$
  $+ \tfrac{1}{3}x^3 + \tfrac{2}{15}x^5 + \tfrac{17}{315}x^7 + \cdots$

$$\left(-\frac{\pi}{2} < x < \frac{\pi}{2} \right).$$

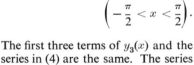

Fig. 54. Approximate solutions in Example 1.

The first three terms of $y_3(x)$ and the series in (4) are the same. The series in (4) converges for $|x| < \pi/2$, and all we may expect is that our sequence $y_1, y_2, \cdots$ converges to a function which is the solution of our problem for $|x| < \pi/2$. This illustrates that the problem of convergence is of practical importance.

Example 2. Apply Picard's method to the initial value problem

$$y' = 2xy + 1, \qquad y(0) = 0.$$

Here $x_0 = 0$, $y_0 = 0$, $f(x, y) = 1 + 2xy$, and (3) assumes the form

$$y_n(x) = \int_0^x [1 + 2t y_{n-1}(t)]\, dt.$$

Starting from $y_0 = 0$, we thus obtain

$$y_1(x) = \int_0^x dt = x$$

$$y_2(x) = \int_0^x (1 + 2t^2)\, dt = x + \tfrac{2}{3}x^3$$

$$y_3(x) = \int_0^x [1 + 2t(t + \tfrac{2}{3}t^3)]\, dt = x + \tfrac{2}{3}x^3 + \tfrac{4}{15}x^5$$

etc. These are the first terms of the Maclaurin series of the exact solution obtained from (4) in Sec. 1.7,

$$y(x) = e^{x^2} \int_0^x e^{-t^2}\, dt = x + \tfrac{2}{3}x^3 + \frac{2^2}{3 \cdot 5}x^5 + \frac{2^3}{3 \cdot 5 \cdot 7}x^7 + \cdots.$$

We mention that the integral in this formula, which cannot be evaluated by the elementary methods of calculus, will be considered later in Sec. 14.2.

PROBLEMS

Apply Picard's method to the following initial value problems.

1. $y' = xy$, $\quad y(0) = 1$ **2.** $y' = 2xy$, $\quad y(0) = 1$
3. $y' = 2xy$, $\quad y(0) = \pi$ **4.** $y' = x + y$, $\quad y(0) = 1$
5. $y' = x + y$, $\quad y(0) = 0$ **6.** $y' = xy + 1$, $\quad y(0) = 1$
7. $y' = xy + 1$, $\quad y(0) = 0$ **8.** $y' = 2xy - 1$, $\quad y(0) = 0$
9. $y' = xy + 2x - x^3$, $\quad y(0) = 0$ **10.** $y' = x - y^2$, $\quad y(0) = \tfrac{1}{2}$

11. In Prob. 1, compute y_1, y_2, y_3 for $x = 0.5$ and compare the results with the corresponding value of the exact solution $e^{0.125} = 1.133\,148 \cdots$.

12. In Prob. 2, plot graphs of the first few approximations and of the exact solution for $0 \leq x \leq 2$.

13. Show that in the case of the problem $y' = x$, $y(x_0) = a$, the approximations obtained by Picard's method are identical with the exact solution.

14. Apply Picard's method to $y' = y$, $y(0) = 1$ and show that the successive approximations tend to the limit $y = e^x$, i.e., to the exact solution.

15. Show that both $y \equiv 0$ and $y = -x^2/4$ are solutions of the problem $y' = \sqrt{\dfrac{x^2}{4} + y} - \dfrac{x}{2}$, $y(0) = 0$, in the range $x \geq 0$. Which of these solutions is obtained by Picard's method, starting from $y_0 = 0$?

1.12 EXISTENCE AND UNIQUENESS OF SOLUTIONS

The initial value problem

$$|y'| + |y| = 0, \qquad y(0) = 1$$

has no solution because $y \equiv 0$ is the only solution of the differential equation. The initial value problem

$$y' = x, \qquad y(0) = 1$$

has precisely one solution, namely, $y = \frac{1}{2}x^2 + 1$. The initial value problem

$$y' = \frac{y - 1}{x}, \qquad y(0) = 1$$

has infinitely many solutions, namely, $y = 1 + cx$ where c is arbitrary. From these examples we see that an initial value problem

$$(1) \qquad\qquad y' = f(x, y), \qquad y(x_0) = y_0$$

may have none, precisely one, or more than one solution. This leads to the following two fundamental questions.

Problem of existence.   *Under what conditions does an initial value problem of the form (1) have at least one solution?*

Problem of uniqueness.   *Under what conditions does that problem have a unique solution, that is, only one solution?*

Theorems which state such conditions are called **existence theorems** and **uniqueness theorems**, respectively.

Of course, our three examples are so simple that we can find the answer to those two questions by inspection, without using any theorems. However, it is clear that in more complicated cases—for example, when the equation cannot be solved by elementary methods—existence and uniqueness theorems will be of great importance. As a matter of fact, a more advanced course in differential equations consists mainly of considerations concerning the existence, uniqueness, and general behavior of solutions of various types of differential equations, and many of these considerations have far-reaching practical consequences. For example, results about the existence and uniqueness of periodic solutions of certain differential equations, which were obtained by Poincaré for entirely theoretical reasons about 80 years ago, are nowadays the base of many practical investigations in nonlinear mechanics.

We want to mention that in many branches of mathematics existence and uniqueness theorems are of similar importance. Let us illustrate this by a familiar example in linear algebra. The three systems of linear equations

$$(a)\ \ \begin{matrix} x + y = 1 \\ x + y = 0 \end{matrix} \qquad (b)\ \ \begin{matrix} x + y = 1 \\ x - y = 0 \end{matrix} \qquad (c)\ \ \begin{matrix} x + y = 1 \\ 2x + 2y = 2 \end{matrix}$$

have, respectively, none, precisely one, and infinitely many solutions (cf. also Ex. 1 in Sec. 0.3). This is immediately clear, without using any theorems. However, if a system of many equations in many unknowns is given, the need for existence and uniqueness theorems in this field becomes obvious because then the question of whether the system has a solution at all, and if so, how many solutions there are, cannot be answered immediately.

In connection with differential equations, a student who is exclusively interested in applications and does not like theoretical considerations (an attitude which will prevent him from having good success in the applied area) may be inclined to reason in the following manner. The physical problem corresponding to a certain differential equation has a unique solution, and the same must therefore be true for the differential equation. In simpler cases he may be right. However, he should keep in mind that the differential equation is merely an abstraction of the reality obtained by disregarding certain physical facts which seem to be of minor influence, and in complicated physical situations there may be no way of judging a priori the importance of various circumstances. In such a case there will then be no a priori guarantee that the differential equation leads to a faithful picture of the reality.

In the case of an initial value problem of the form

$$(1) \qquad y' = f(x, y), \qquad y(x_0) = y_0$$

the conditions for the existence and uniqueness of the solution are quite simple. If f is continuous in some region of the xy-plane containing the point (x_0, y_0), then the problem (1) has at least one solution. If moreover the partial derivative $\partial f/\partial y$ exists and is continuous in that region, then the problem (1) has precisely one solution. This solution can then be obtained by Picard's iteration method. Let us formulate these three statements in a precise manner.

Existence theorem. *If $f(x, y)$ is continuous at all points (x, y) in some rectangle (Fig. 55)*

$$R: \qquad |x - x_0| \leqq a, \qquad |y - y_0| \leqq b$$

and therefore bounded,[16] say,

$$(2) \qquad\qquad |f(x, y)| \leqq K \qquad\qquad \textit{for all } (x, y) \textit{ in } R,$$

then the initial value problem (1) has at least one solution $y(x)$, which is defined

---

[16] A function $f(x, y)$ is said to be **bounded** when (x, y) varies in a region in the xy-plane, if there is a number K such that $|f| \leqq K$ when (x, y) is in that region. For example, $f = x^2 + y^2$ is bounded, with $K = 2$ if $|x| < 1$ and $|y| < 1$. The function $f = \tan (x + y)$ is not bounded for $|x + y| < \pi/2$.

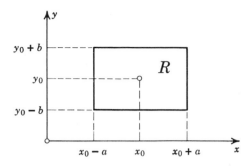

Fig. 55. Rectangle R in the existence and uniqueness theorems.

at least for all x in the interval $|x - x_0| \leq \alpha$ where α is the smaller of the two numbers a and b/K.

Uniqueness theorem.   *If $f(x, y)$ and $\partial f/\partial y$ are continuous for all (x, y) in that rectangle R and therefore bounded, say,*

$$(3) \qquad (a) \quad |f| \leq K, \qquad (b) \quad \left| \frac{\partial f}{\partial y} \right| \leq M \qquad \text{for all } (x, y) \text{ in } R$$

then the initial value problem (1) has only one solution $y(x)$, which is defined at least for all x in that interval $|x - x_0| \leq \alpha$. This solution can then be obtained by Picard's iteration method, that is, the sequence $y_0, y_1, \cdots, y_n, \cdots$ where

$$y_n(x) = y_0 + \int_{x_0}^{x} f[t, y_{n-1}(t)] \, dt, \qquad n = 1, 2, \cdots,$$

converges to that solution $y(x)$.

Since the proofs of these theorems require familiarity with uniformly convergent series and other concepts to be considered later in this book, we shall not present these proofs at this time but refer the student to Ref. [B5] in Appendix 1. However, we want to include some remarks and examples which may be helpful for a good understanding of the two theorems.

Because $y' = f(x, y)$, the condition (2) implies that $|y'| \leq K$, that is, the slope of any solution curve $y(x)$ in R is at least $-K$ and at most K. Hence a solution curve which passes through the point (x_0, y_0) must lie in the shaded region in Fig. 56 bounded by the lines l_1 and l_2 whose slopes are $-K$ and K, respectively. Depending on the form of R, two different cases may arise. In the first case, shown in Fig. 56a, we have $b/K \geq a$ and therefore $\alpha = a$ in the existence theorem, which then asserts that the solution exists for all x between $x_0 - a$ and $x_0 + a$. In the second case, shown in Fig. 56b, we

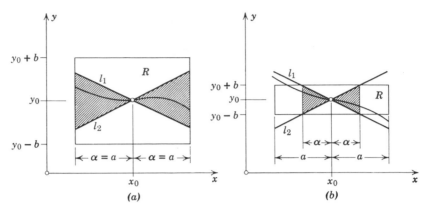

Fig. 56. The condition (2) of the existence theorem. (*a*) First case. (*b*) Second case.

have $b/K < a$. Therefore $\alpha = b/K$, and all we can conclude from the theorems is that the solution exists for all x between $x_0 - b/K$ and $x_0 + b/K$; for larger or smaller x's the solution curve may leave the rectangle R, and since nothing is assumed about f outside R, nothing can be concluded about the solution for those corresponding values of x.

Example 1. Consider the problem

$$y' = 1 + y^2, \qquad y(0) = 0 \qquad \text{(cf. Ex. 1 in Sec. 1.11)}$$

and take R: $|x| \leq 5, |y| \leq 3$. Then $a = 5, b = 3, |f| = |1 + y^2| \leq K = 10$, $|\partial f/\partial y| = 2|y| \leq M = 6, \alpha = b/K = 0.3 < a$. In fact, the solution $y = \tan x$ of the problem is discontinuous at $x = \pm \pi/2$, and there is no continuous solution valid in the entire interval $|x| \leq 5$ from which we started.

The conditions in the two theorems are sufficient conditions rather than necessary ones, and can be lessened. For example, by the mean value theorem of differential calculus we have

$$f(x, y_2) - f(x, y_1) = (y_2 - y_1) \frac{\partial f}{\partial y}\bigg|_{y = \tilde{y}}$$

where (x, y_1) and (x, y_2) are assumed to be in R, and $\tilde{y}$ is a suitable value between y_1 and y_2. From this and (3*b*) it follows that

$$(4) \qquad\qquad |f(x, y_2) - f(x, y_1)| \leq M |y_2 - y_1|,$$

and it can be shown that (3*b*) may be replaced by the weaker condition (4) which is known as a **Lipschitz condition**.[17] However, continuity of $f(x, y)$ is not enough to guarantee the *uniqueness* of the solution. This may be illustrated by the following example.

[17] RUDOLF LIPSCHITZ (1831–1903), German mathematician, who contributed also to algebra and differential geometry.

Example 2. The initial value problem

$$y' = \sqrt{|y|}, \qquad y(0) = 0$$

has the two solutions

$$y \equiv 0 \quad \text{and} \quad y^* = \begin{cases} x^2/4 & \text{when } x \geqq 0 \\ -x^2/4 & \text{when } x \leqq 0 \end{cases}$$

although $f(x, y) = \sqrt{|y|}$ is continuous for all y. The Lipschitz condition (4) is violated in any region which includes the line $y = 0$, because for $y_1 = 0$ and positive y_2 we have

$$\frac{|f(x, y_2) - f(x, y_1)|}{|y_2 - y_1|} = \frac{\sqrt{y_2}}{y_2} = \frac{1}{\sqrt{y_2}}, \qquad (\sqrt{y_2} > 0)$$

and this can be made as large as we please by choosing y_2 sufficiently small, while (4) requires that the quotient on the left does not exceed a fixed constant M.

1.13 NUMERICAL METHODS FOR DIFFERENTIAL EQUATIONS OF THE FIRST ORDER

We shall now consider some standard numerical methods for solving initial value problems of the form

$$(1) \qquad\qquad y' = f(x, y), \qquad y(x_0) = y_0.$$

Numerical methods for solving differential equations are methods which yield approximate numerical values of the solutions. They may be applied if a given differential equation cannot be solved by an exact method. This happens quite often in engineering mathematics, and these methods are therefore of great practical importance. They must also be applied if we want to solve a differential equation by the use of an electronic computer.

Many numerical methods for solving problems of the form (1) are such that we start from $y_0 = y(x_0)$ and proceed stepwise. That is, in the first step we compute a value y_1 of the solution of (1) at $x = x_0 + h$. In the second step we compute a value y_2 of that solution at $x = x_0 + 2h$, etc. Here h is some fixed number, e.g., 0.2 or 0.1 or 0.01, depending on the desired accuracy of the approximate values.

In each step the computation is done by the same formula. Such formulas can be obtained from the Taylor series

$$y(x + h) = y(x) + hy'(x) + \frac{h^2}{2} y''(x) + \cdots.$$

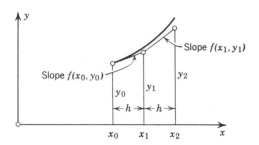

Fig. 57. Euler-Cauchy method.

From (1) we have $y' = f$. Hence $y'' = f'$, etc., and the Taylor series becomes

(2) $$y(x + h) = y(x) + hf + \frac{h^2}{2}f' + \frac{h^3}{6}f'' + \cdots,$$

where the derivatives $f', f'', \cdots$ are evaluated at $[x, y(x)]$.

Throughout this section we shall assume that f is such that (1) has a unique solution in some interval containing x_0.

For small values of h the terms containing h^2, h^3, $\cdots$ in (2) will be very small; neglecting these terms, we obtain from (2) the approximation

$$y(x + h) \approx y(x) + hf.$$

Using this formula, we may now proceed stepwise as follows. In the first step we compute
$$y_1 = y_0 + hf(x_0, y_0),$$
which approximates $y(x_1) = y(x_0 + h)$. In the second step we compute
$$y_2 = y_1 + hf(x_1, y_1),$$
which approximates $y(x_2) = y(x_0 + 2h)$, etc., and in general

(3) $$y_{n+1} = y_n + hf(x_n, y_n).$$

In this fashion we obtain approximate values to the solution $y(x)$ of the initial value problem (1) at $x = x_0$, $x_0 + h$, $x_0 + 2h$, $\cdots$. This simple procedure is called the **Euler-Cauchy method**.[18]

Geometrically speaking, this method is an approximation of $y(x)$ by a polygon (Fig. 57).

[18] LEONHARD EULER (1707–1783) was an enormously creative Swiss mathematician. He contributed to almost all branches of mathematics and its application to physical problems. His important books on algebra and calculus include numerous results of his own research work. The great French mathematician, AUGUSTIN LOUIS CAUCHY (1789–1857), is the father of modern analysis. He exercised a great influence on the theory of infinite series, complex analysis, and differential equations.

The method can also be used in graphical form, that is, in (3) only $f(x_n, y_n)$ is computed while y_{n+1} is then obtained from y_n by means of a good graph.

The method is said to be a *first-order method* because in (2) we take only the term containing the first power of h. The omission of the further terms in (2) causes an error which is called the *truncation error* of the method (cf. Sec. 0.6). For small h, the third and higher powers of h will be small compared with h^2 contained in the first neglected term, and we therefore say that *the truncation error is of order h^2*. Note that another error of the method is due to the fact that, in (3), $f(x_n, y_n)$ is an approximation of $f[x_n, y(x_n)]$.

Example 1. Apply the Euler-Cauchy method to the initial value problem

$$(4) \qquad\qquad y' = x + y, \qquad y(0) = 0,$$

choosing $h = 0.2$. Here $f(x, y) = x + y$, and (3) becomes

$$y_{n-1} = y_n + 0.2(x_n + y_n).$$

Table 3 shows a convenient arrangement of the numerical work.

Of course the exact solution of our problem is readily obtained from (4) in Sec. 1.7,

$$y = e^x - x - 1,$$

and we may determine the errors of our approximate values (cf. Table 8 in the current section).

TABLE 3. EULER-CAUCHY METHOD APPLIED TO (4).

n	x_n	y_n	$x_n + y_n$	$0.2(x_n + y_n)$	$y_n + 0.2(x_n + y_n)$
0	0	0	0	0	0
1	0.2	0	0.200	0.040	0.040
2	0.4	0.040	0.440	0.088	0.128
3	0.6	0.128	0.728	0.146	0.274
4	0.8	0.274	1.074	0.215	0.489
5	1.0	0.489			

In any practical case, when the exact solution is unknown, an indication of the accuracy of the values computed by the Euler-Cauchy method can be obtained by applying the method twice, using h and $h/2$, and then comparing corresponding values of the two approximations.

By taking more terms in (2) into account we obtain numerical methods of higher order. The corresponding formulas can be represented in such a form that the complicated computation of derivatives of $f(x, y)$ is avoided and is replaced by computing f for one or several suitably chosen auxiliary values of (x, y). Let us consider two such methods which are of great practical importance.

The first method is the so-called **improved Euler-Cauchy method**. In each step of this method we first compute the auxiliary value

(5a) $y_{n+1}^* = y_n + hf(x_n, y_n)$

and then the new value

(5b) $y_{n+1} = y_n + \dfrac{h}{2} [f(x_{n+1}, y_{n+1}^*) + f(x_n, y_n)].$

Geometrically speaking, we may say that we approximate $y(x)$ for $x \geqq x_n$ by the straight line through (x_n, y_n) with slope $f(x_n, y_n)$ until x reaches the value $x_n + \frac{1}{2}h$, and then we continue along the line with slope $f(x_{n+1}, y_{n+1}^*)$; cf. Fig. 58 (where $n = 0$).

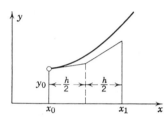

It can be shown that the truncation error of the method is of the order h^3 (cf. Ref. [B7] in Appendix 1) and the improved Euler-Cauchy method is, therefore, a second-order method.

Fig. 58. Improved Euler-Cauchy method.

Example 2. Apply the improved Euler-Cauchy method to the initial value problem (4) in Ex. 1, choosing $h = 0.2$ as before. Here (5a) becomes

$$y_{n+1}^* = y_n + 0.2(x_n + y_n),$$

and (5b) becomes

$$y_{n+1} = y_n + 0.1 [(x_{n+1} + y_{n+1}^*) + (x_n + y_n)].$$

Since in the present case the expression for y_{n+1}^* is very simple, it pays to insert it into the formula for y_{n+1}. Simplifying the resulting expression, we readily obtain

$$y_{n+1} = 0.12x_n + 0.1x_{n+1} + 1.22y_n.$$

The computations are shown in Table 4, and we see that the values are more accurate than those in Ex. 1 (cf. Table 8).

TABLE 4. IMPROVED EULER-CAUCHY METHOD APPLIED TO (4).

n	x_n	y_n	$0.12x_n$	$0.1x_{n+1}$	$1.22y_n$	y_{n+1}
0	0	0	0	0.0200	0	0.0200
1	0.2	0.0200	0.0240	0.0400	0.0244	0.0884
2	0.4	0.0884	0.0480	0.0600	0.1078	0.2158
3	0.6	0.2158	0.0720	0.0800	0.2633	0.4153
4	0.8	0.4153	0.0960	0.1000	0.5067	0.7027
5	1.0	0.7027				

A still more accurate method is the so-called **Runge-Kutta method,**[19] which is of great practical importance. In each step of this method we first compute four auxiliary quantities

(6a)
$$A_n = hf(x_n, y_n), \qquad\qquad B_n = hf\left(x_n + \frac{h}{2}, y_n + \frac{A_n}{2}\right),$$
$$C_n = hf\left(x_n + \frac{h}{2}, y_n + \frac{B_n}{2}\right), \qquad D_n = hf(x_{n+1}, y_n + C_n),$$

and then the new value

(6b)
$$y_{n+1} = y_n + \tfrac{1}{6}(A_n + 2B_n + 2C_n + D_n).$$

It can be shown that the truncation error of the method is of the order h^5 (cf. Ref. [A15], Appendix 1) and the method is, therefore, a fourth-order method. Note that if f depends only on x, this method reduces to Simpson's rule of integration (Sec. 0.8).

The computations may be arranged as shown in Table 5.

TABLE 5. RUNGE-KUTTA METHOD, FIRST STEP.

n	x	y		
	x_0	y_0	$\dfrac{A_0}{2}$	A_0
0	$x_0 + \dfrac{h}{2}$	$y_0 + \dfrac{A_0}{2}$	$\dfrac{B_0}{2}$	$2B_0$
	$x_0 + \dfrac{h}{2}$	$y_0 + \dfrac{B_0}{2}$	C_0	$2C_0$
	$x_0 + h$	$y_0 + C_0$		D_0
				Sum
			$K_0 = \dfrac{\text{Sum}}{6}$	
	x_1	$y_1(=y_0 + K_0)$		

Example 3. Apply the Runge-Kutta method to the initial value problem (4) in Ex. 1, choosing $h = 0.2$, as before. Here $f(x, y) = x + y$, and (6a) becomes

$$A_n = 0.2(x_n + y_n),$$
$$B_n = 0.2\left(x_n + 0.1 + y_n + \frac{A_n}{2}\right),$$
$$C_n = 0.2\left(x_n + 0.1 + y_n + \frac{B_n}{2}\right),$$
$$D_n = 0.2(x_n + 0.2 + y_n + C_n).$$

[19] CARL RUNGE (1856–1927) and WILHELM KUTTA (1867–1944), German mathematicians.

Table 6 shows the computations in the first step (arranged as in Table 5).

TABLE 6. EXAMPLE 3, FIRST STEP.

n	x	y		
	0	0	0	0
0	0.1	0	0.0100	0.0400
	0.1	0.0100	0.0220	0.0440
	0.2	0.0220		0.0444
				0.1284
				$K_0 = 0.0214$
	0.2	0.0214		

We note that in the present case, where A_n, B_n, C_n, and D_n are very simple expressions, it is worthwhile to insert A_n into B_n, finding

$$B_n = 0.22(x_n + y_n) + 0.02,$$

then insert this expression into C_n, finding

$$C_n = 0.222(x_n + y_n) + 0.022,$$

and finally insert this expression into D_n, finding

$$D_n = 0.2444(x_n + y_n) + 0.0444.$$

Using these expressions, (6b) becomes

$$(7) \qquad y_{n+1} = y_n + 0.2214(x_n + y_n) + 0.0214.$$

Table 7 shows the corresponding computations, and we see that the values are much more accurate than those in Ex. 1 and 2.

TABLE 7. RUNGE-KUTTA METHOD APPLIED TO (4); COMPUTATIONS
BY THE USE OF (7).

n	x_n	y_n	$x_n + y_n$	$0.2214(x_n + y_n)$	$0.2214(x_n + y_n)$ $+ 0.0214$
0	0	0	0	0	0.021 400
1	0.2	0.021 400	0.221 400	0.049 018	0.070 418
2	0.4	0.091 818	0.491 818	0.108 889	0.130 289
3	0.6	0.222 107	0.822 107	0.182 014	0.203 414
4	0.8	0.425 521	1.225 521	0.271 330	0.292 730
5	1.0	0.718 251			

TABLE 8. COMPARISON OF THE ACCURACY OF THE THREE METHODS UNDER
CONSIDERATION IN THE CASE OF THE INITIAL VALUE PROBLEM (4), WITH $h = 0.2$.
(Cf. Exs. 1–3).

x	$y = e^x - x - 1$	Absolute value of error		
		Euler-Cauchy (Table 3)	Improved Euler-Cauchy (Table 4)	Runge-Kutta (Table 7)
0.2	0.021 403	0.021	0.0014	0.000 003
0.4	0.091 825	0.052	0.0034	0.000 007
0.6	0.222 119	0.094	0.0063	0.000 011
0.8	0.425 541	0.152	0.0102	0.000 020
1.0	0.718 282	0.229	0.0156	0.000 031

PROBLEMS

1. Repeat the computations in Ex. 1, choosing $h = 0.1$ (instead of $h = 0.2$), and note that the errors of the values thus obtained are about 50% of those in Ex. 1 (which are listed in Table 8).

2. Same task as in Prob. 1, but with $h = 0.01$ (twenty steps). Compare the error of the value corresponding to $x = 0.2$ with that in Ex. 1.

3. Repeat the computations in Ex. 2, choosing $h = 0.1$, and note that the errors of the values thus obtained are about 25% of those in Ex. 2.

4. Same task as in Prob. 3, but with $h = 0.05$ (eight steps). Compare the error of the value corresponding to $x = 0.4$ with those in Ex. 2 and Prob. 3.

Apply the Euler-Cauchy method to the following differential equations. (Carry out ten steps).

5. $y' = y$, $y(0) = 1$, $h = 0.1$ **6.** $y' = y$, $y(0) = 1$, $h = 0.01$

7. $y' = 2xy + 1$, $y(0) = 0$, $h = 0.1$ **8.** $y' = 2xy$, $y(0) = 1$, $h = 0.1$

9. Compute $y = e^x$ for $x = 0, 0.1, 0.2, \cdots, 1.0$ by applying the Runge-Kutta method to the initial value problem in Prob. 5. Show that the first five decimal places of the results are correct (cf. Table 1 in Sec. 0.1).

10. In Prob. 9 insert A_n into B_n, then B_n into C_n, etc. and show that the resulting formula becomes

$$y_{n+1} = 1.105\ 170\ 833 y_n.$$

Repeat the computations in Prob. 9, using this formula.

11. Show that for $x = 0.1$

$$1 + x + \frac{x^2}{2!} + \frac{x^3}{3!} + \frac{x^4}{4!} = 1.105\ 170\ 833 \cdots,$$

the constant in Prob. 10. What is the reason for this result?

12. Using the idea of Prob. 11, show that a more accurate recursion formula for computing $y = e^x$, $x = 0, 0.1, 0.2, \cdots$ is

$$y_{n+1} = 1.105\ 170\ 917 y_n.$$

Compute nine decimal places of e^x for $x = 0.1, 0.2, 0.3$, using this formula, and compare the result with the accurate values $1.105\,170\,918$, $1.221\,402\,758$, $1.349\,858\,808$.

13. Apply the Euler-Cauchy method to the initial value problem $y' = 1 + y^2$, $y(0) = 0$, choosing $h = 0.1$. Compute five steps and compare the results with the exact values (cf. Table 1 in Sec. 0.1).

14. Apply the improved Euler-Cauchy method to the initial value problem in Prob. 13, choosing $h = 0.1$. Compute two steps and compare the errors with those of the corresponding values in Prob. 13.

15. Apply the Runge-Kutta method to the initial value problem in Prob. 13, choosing $h = 0.1$. Compute two steps. Compare the results with the exact values $0.100\,334\,672$, $0.202\,710\,036$.

16. Apply the improved Euler-Cauchy method to the initial value problem $y' = 2x$, $y(0) = 0$, choosing $h = 0.1$. Why are the errors zero?

chapter 2

ORDINARY LINEAR DIFFERENTIAL EQUATIONS

The ordinary differential equations may be divided into two large classes, the so-called linear equations and the nonlinear equations. While nonlinear equations (of the second and higher orders) are rather difficult, linear equations are much simpler in many respects, because various properties of their solutions can be characterized in a general way, and standard methods are available for solving many of these equations. In the present chapter we shall consider linear differential equations and their applications. These equations play an important role in engineering mathematics, for example, in connection with mechanical vibrations and electric circuits and networks.

Much space will be devoted to linear equations of the second order. This seems to be justified by the following facts. First of all, second-order equations are the most important ones from the practical point of view. Furthermore, the necessary theoretical considerations will become easier if we first concentrate upon second-order equations. Once the student understands what is needed to handle second-order equations, he will easily become familiar with the generalizations of the concepts, methods, and results to differential equations of the third and higher orders.

Important engineering applications in connection with mechanical and electrical oscillations will be considered in Secs. 2.6 and 2.13–2.15.

Numerical methods for solving second-order differential equations are included in Sec. 2.17.

(Legendre's, Bessel's, and the hypergeometric equations will be considered in Chap. 3.)

Prerequisite for this chapter: Chap. 1, in particular Secs. 1.7–1.9.
Sections which may be omitted in a shorter course: 2.8–2.10, 2.15–2.17.
References: Appendix 1, Part B.
Answers to problems: Appendix 2.

2.1 HOMOGENEOUS LINEAR EQUATIONS OF THE SECOND ORDER

The student has already met with linear differential equations of the first order (Secs. 1.7–1.9), and we shall now define and consider linear equations of the second order.

A second-order differential equation is said to be **linear** if it can be written in the form

(1) $$y'' + f(x)y' + g(x)y = r(x).$$

The characteristic feature of this equation is that it is linear *in y and its derivatives*, while *f*, *g*, and *r* may be any given functions of *x*. Any equation of the second order which cannot be written in the form (1) is said to be **nonlinear**. For example,

(2) $$y'' + 4y = e^{-x} \sin x$$

and

(3) $$x^2 y'' + xy' + (x^2 - 1)y = 0$$

are linear equations, while

$$y''y + y' = 0$$

and

$$y'' + \sqrt{y} = 0$$

are nonlinear equations.

Linear differential equations of the second order play a basic role in many different engineering problems. We shall see that some of these equations are very simple because their solutions are elementary functions. Others are more complicated, their solutions being important higher functions, such as Bessel and hypergeometric functions.

Our further consideration will show that equation (1) has somewhat simpler properties if the function $r(x)$ on the right-hand side is identically zero. Then equation (1) becomes

(4)
$$y'' + f(x)y' + g(x)y = 0$$

and is said to be **homogeneous**. If $r(x) \not\equiv 0$, equation (1) is said to be **nonhomogeneous**. These notions are quite similar to those in the case of linear equations of the first order in Sec. 1.7.

For example, (2) is a nonhomogeneous equation while (3) is homogeneous.

The functions f and g in (1) and (4) are called the **coefficients** of the equations.

In all our considerations x will be assumed to vary in some arbitrary fixed range, for example, in some finite interval or on the entire x-axis. All the assumptions and statements will refer to such a fixed range, which need not be specified in each case.

A function

$$y = \phi(x)$$

is said to be a **solution** of a (linear or nonlinear) differential equation of the second order *on some interval* (perhaps infinite), if $\phi(x)$ is defined and twice differentiable throughout that interval and is such that the equation becomes an identity when we replace the unspecified function y and its derivatives in the equation by ϕ and its derivatives.

This definition is analogous to that in the case of first-order equations in Sec. 1.1.

Example 1. The functions

$$y = \cos x \quad \text{and} \quad y = \sin x$$

are solutions of the homogeneous linear differential equation

$$y'' + y = 0$$

for all x, since

$$(\cos x)'' + \cos x = -\cos x + \cos x = 0$$

and similarly for $y = \sin x$. We can even go an important step further. If we multiply the first solution by a constant, for example, by 3, the resulting function $y = 3 \cos x$ is also a solution, because

$$(3 \cos x)'' + 3 \cos x = 3[(\cos x)'' + \cos x] = 0.$$

It is clear that instead of 3 we may choose any other constant, for example, -5 or $\frac{2}{9}$. We may even multiply $\cos x$ and $\sin x$ by different constants, say, by 2 and -8, respectively, and add the resulting functions, having

$$y = 2 \cos x - 8 \sin x,$$

and this function is also a solution of our homogeneous equation for all x, because

$$(2 \cos x - 8 \sin x)'' + 2 \cos x - 8 \sin x$$
$$= 2[(\cos x)'' + \cos x] - 8[(\sin x)'' + \sin x] = 0.$$

This example illustrates the very important fact that we may obtain new solutions of the homogeneous linear equation (4) from known solutions by multiplication by constants and by addition. Of course, this is a great practical and theoretical advantage, because this property will enable us to generate more complicated solutions from simple solutions. We may characterize this basic property as follows.

Fundamental Theorem 1. *If a solution of the homogeneous linear differential equation* (4) *is multiplied by any constant, the resulting function is also a solution of* (4). *If two solutions of that equation are added, the resulting sum is also a solution of that equation.*[1]

Proof. The proof follows at once from the properties of linearity of derivatives, which assert that the derivative of a constant times a function is the constant times the derivative of the function, and the derivative of a sum of functions is the sum of their derivatives.

In fact, to prove the first statement of the theorem, we assume that $\phi(x)$ is a solution of (4) and show that then $y = c\phi(x)$ is also a solution of (4). If we substitute $y = c\phi(x)$ into (4), the left-hand side of (4) becomes

$$(c\phi)'' + f(c\phi)' + gc\phi = c[\phi'' + f\phi' + g\phi].$$

Since ϕ satisfies (4), the expression in brackets is zero, and the first statement of the theorem is proved. The proof of the last statement is quite simple, too, and is left to the reader.

The student should know this highly important theorem as well as he knows his multiplication table, but he should not forget that *the theorem* **does not hold** *for nonhomogeneous linear equations or nonlinear equations*, as may be illustrated by the following two examples.

Example 2. Substitution shows that the functions

$$y = 1 + \cos x \quad \text{and} \quad y = 1 + \sin x$$

are solutions of the nonhomogeneous linear equation

$$y'' + y = 1,$$

but the functions

$$2(1 + \cos x) \quad \text{and} \quad (1 + \cos x) + (1 + \sin x)$$

are not solutions of that equation.

---

[1] This theorem is sometimes called the **superposition principle** or *linearity principle*.

Example 3. Substitution shows that the functions

$$y = x^2 \quad \text{and} \quad y = 1$$

are solutions of the nonlinear differential equation

$$y''y - xy' = 0,$$

but the functions

$$-x^2 \quad \text{and} \quad x^2 + 1$$

are not solutions of that equation.

PROBLEMS

Prove:

1. $y \equiv 0$ is a solution of the homogeneous equation (4), but not of the non-homogeneous equation (1).

2. If y_1 is a solution of (1) then $y = cy_1$ is a solution of

$$y'' + fy' + gy = cr.$$

Hence $y = cy_1$ ($c \neq 1$) is *not* a solution of (1).

3. If y_1 and y_2 are solutions of (1) then $y = y_1 + y_2$ is a solution of

$$y'' + fy' + gy = 2r.$$

Hence $y = y_1 + y_2$ is *not* a solution of (1).

4. If y_1 and y_2 are, respectively, solutions of

$$y'' + fy' + gy = r_1 \quad \text{and} \quad y'' + fy' + gy = r_2,$$

then $y = y_1 + y_2$ is a solution of

$$y'' + fy' + gy = r_1 + r_2.$$

5. If y_1 is a solution of (1) and y_2 is a solution of (4), then $y = y_1 + y_2$ is a solution of (1).

6. If y_1 and y_2 are solutions of (1), then $y = y_1 - y_2$ is a solution of (4).

7. (Second-order equations reducible to the first order). If a second-order differential equation does not contain the dependent variable y explicitly, it is of the form $F(x, y', y'') = 0$. Show that by setting $y' = z$ this equation becomes a first-order equation in z. [Clearly, from a solution z of the new equation, a solution y of the original equation can be obtained by integration].

Reduce to the first order and solve:

8. $y'' + y' = 0$ **9.** $y'' = 4y'$ **10.** $y'' + 9y' = 0$

11. $y'' = y'$ **12.** $xy'' = 2y'$ **13.** $xy'' + y' = 0$

14. $2xy'' = 3y'$ **15.** $y'' = y' \tanh x$ **16.** $y'' = 2y' \coth 2x$

17. A particle moves on a straight line in such a way that its acceleration is equal to its velocity. At the time $t = 0$ its displacement from the origin is 6 ft and its velocity is 2 ft/sec. Find its position and velocity when $t = 3$ sec.

18. A particle moves on a straight line in such a way that its acceleration is equal to three times its velocity. At $t = 0$, its displacement from the origin is 1 ft and its velocity is 1.5 ft/sec. Find the time when the displacement is 10 ft.

19. A particle moves on a straight line in such a way that its acceleration is equal to the reciprocal of its velocity. At the time $t = 0$ the displacement from the origin is 2 ft and the velocity is 2 ft/sec. Determine its displacement and velocity when $t = 6$ sec.

20. A particle moves on a straight line in such way that its acceleration is equal to twice its velocity. At $t = 1$ sec and $t = 2$ sec its displacements from the origin are 1 and 2 ft, respectively. Find its displacement when $t = 3$ sec.

21. (Second-order equations reducible to the first order). Show that a second-order equation $F(y, y', y'') = 0$, which does not involve the independent variable explicitly, can be reduced to a first-order equation in $z = y'$, in which y is the independent variable.

22. Given $y'' + a(y')^2 + f(y) = 0$ where a is a constant. Show that the substitutions $y' = z$, $v = z^2$ lead to the linear first-order equation

$$\frac{dv}{dy} + 2av + 2f(y) = 0.$$

2.2 HOMOGENEOUS SECOND-ORDER EQUATIONS WITH CONSTANT COEFFICIENTS

We shall now consider linear differential equations of the second order whose coefficients are constant. These equations have important engineering applications, especially in connection with mechanical and electrical vibrations, as will be demonstrated in Secs. 2.6, 2.13, and 2.14.

We start with homogeneous equations, that is, equations of the form

(1) $$y'' + ay' + by = 0$$

where a and b are constants.

We shall assume that a and b are real and that the range of x considered is the entire x-axis.

How to solve equation (1)? We remember that the solution of the *first-order* linear homogeneous equation with constant coefficients

$$y' + ky = 0$$

is an exponential function, namely,

$$y = ce^{-kx}.$$

It seems natural to suppose that

(2) $$y = e^{\lambda x}$$

may be a solution of (1) if λ is properly chosen. Substituting (2) and its derivatives

$$y' = \lambda e^{\lambda x} \quad \text{and} \quad y'' = \lambda^2 e^{\lambda x}$$

into our equation (1), we obtain

$$(\lambda^2 + a\lambda + b)e^{\lambda x} = 0.$$

So (2) is a solution of (1), if λ is a solution of the quadratic equation

(3) $$\lambda^2 + a\lambda + b = 0.$$

This equation is called the **characteristic equation** (or *auxiliary equation*) of (1). Its roots are

(4) $$\lambda_1 = \tfrac{1}{2}(-a + \sqrt{a^2 - 4b}), \qquad \lambda_2 = \tfrac{1}{2}(-a - \sqrt{a^2 - 4b}).$$

From our derivation it follows that the functions

(5) $$y_1 = e^{\lambda_1 x} \quad \text{and} \quad y_2 = e^{\lambda_2 x}$$

are solutions of (1). The student may check this result by substituting (5) into (1).

From elementary algebra we know that, since a and b are real, the characteristic equation may have

> (**Case I**) *two distinct real roots,*
> (**Case II**) *two complex conjugate roots,* or
> (**Case III**) *a real double root.*

These cases will be discussed separately. For the time being let us illustrate each case by a simple example.

Example 1. Find solutions of the equation

$$y'' + y' - 2y = 0.$$

The characteristic equation is

$$\lambda^2 + \lambda - 2 = 0.$$

The roots are 1 and -2, and we obtain the two solutions

$$y_1 = e^x \quad \text{and} \quad y_2 = e^{-2x}.$$

Example 2. Find solutions of the equation

$$y'' + y = 0.$$

The characteristic equation is

$$\lambda^2 + 1 = 0.$$

The roots are $i(=\sqrt{-1})$ and $-i$, and we obtain the two solutions

$$y_1 = e^{ix} \quad \text{and} \quad y_2 = e^{-ix}.$$

In Sec. 2.4 we shall see that it is quite simple to obtain real solutions from such complex solutions.

Example 3. Find solutions of the equation

$$y'' - 2y' + y = 0.$$

The characteristic equation

$$\lambda^2 - 2\lambda + 1 = 0$$

has the real double root 1, and we obtain at first only one solution

$$y_1 = e^x.$$

The case of a real double root will be discussed in Sec. 2.5.

PROBLEMS

Find solutions of the following equations.

1. $y'' - y = 0$ **2.** $y'' - 4y = 0$

3. $y'' - 3y' + 2y = 0$ **4.** $y'' - y' - 6y = 0$

5. $y'' - 2y' - 8y = 0$ **6.** $y'' + 3y' + 2y = 0$

7. $y'' + y' = 0$ **8.** $y'' + 4y' = 0$

9. $y'' + 9y = 0$ **10.** $y'' - 2y' + 2y = 0$

11. $y'' + 2y' + 2y = 0$ **12.** $y'' - 4y' + 8y = 0$

13. Let (5) be solutions of (1). Express a and b in terms of λ_1 and λ_2.

14. Show that the characteristic equation (3) has real distinct roots if, and only if, $a^2 - 4b > 0$. Find similar conditions for the occurrence of complex conjugate roots. Also for a real double root.

Find a differential equation of the form (1) for which the following functions are solutions.

15. e^x, e^{3x} **16.** e^{-x}, e^{4x} **17.** 1, e^{-5x}

18. e^{4ix}, e^{-4ix} **19.** $e^{(1+i)x}$, $e^{(1-i)x}$ **20.** $e^{(-2+3i)x}$, $e^{(-2-3i)x}$

2.3 GENERAL SOLUTION. FUNDAMENTAL SYSTEM

In our further discussion of linear equations with constant coefficients, it will be necessary to know about some important general properties of the solutions of linear differential equations to be considered in this section. We first introduce the following two concepts.

A solution of a differential equation of the second order (linear or not) is called a **general solution** if it contains two arbitrary[2] independent constants. Here *independence* means that the same solution cannot be reduced to a form containing only one arbitrary constant or none. If we assign definite values to those two constants, then the solution so obtained is called a **particular solution.**

[2] The range of the constants may have to be restricted in some cases to avoid imaginary expressions or other degeneracies.

These notions are obvious generalizations of those in the case of first-order differential equations (Sec. 1.1).

It will be shown later (in Secs. 2.8 and 2.11) that if a differential equation of the second order is linear (homogeneous or not), then a general solution includes *all* solutions of the equation; any solution containing no arbitrary constants can be obtained by assigning definite values to the arbitrary constants in that general solution (cf. also the general remark in Sec. 1.1, p. 47).

In the present section we shall consider the homogeneous linear equation

(1) $y'' + f(x)y' + g(x)y = 0,$

and we want to show that a general solution of such an equation can be readily obtained if two suitable solutions y_1 and y_2 are known.

Clearly, if $y_1(x)$ and $y_2(x)$ are solutions of (1) on some interval I, then, by Fundamental Theorem 1 in Sec. 2.1,

(2) $y(x) = c_1 y_1(x) + c_2 y_2(x)$

where c_1 and c_2 are arbitrary constants, will be a solution of (1) on I. Since it contains two arbitrary constants, it will be a general solution of (1), provided it cannot be reduced to an expression containing less than two arbitrary constants.

Under what conditions will such a reduction be possible? To consider this question, we first introduce the following basic concepts, which are important in other considerations, too.

Two functions $y_1(x)$ and $y_2(x)$ are said to be **linearly dependent** *on an interval I* where both functions are defined, if they are proportional on I, that is, if[3]

(3)   (a) $y_1 = ky_2$ or   (b) $y_2 = ly_1$

holds for all x on I; here k and l are numbers, zero or not. If the functions are not proportional on I they are said to be **linearly independent** *on I*.

Note that the concepts of linear dependence and independence always refer to an interval, but not merely to a single point.

If at least one of the functions y_1 and y_2 is identically zero on I, then the functions are linearly dependent on I. In any other case the functions are linearly dependent on I if, and only if, the quotient y_1/y_2 is constant on I. Hence, if y_1/y_2 depends on x on I, then y_1 and y_2 are linearly independent on I.

In fact, if $y_1 \equiv 0$, then (3a) holds with $k = 0$; and if $y_2 \equiv 0$, then (3b) holds with $l = 0$. This proves the first statement, and the other statements

---

[3] Note that if (3a) holds for a $k \neq 0$, we may divide by k, finding $y_2 = y_1/k$, so that in this case (3a) implies (3b) (with $l = 1/k$). However, if $y_1 \equiv 0$, then (3a) holds for $k = 0$, but does not imply (3b); in fact, in this case (3b) will not hold unless $y_2 \equiv 0$, too.

are immediate consequences of (3), too. Of course, in the last statement, we admit that y_1/y_2 may become infinite, namely, for those x for which $y_2 = 0$.

Example 1. The functions

$$y_1 = 3x \quad \text{and} \quad y_2 = x$$

are linearly dependent on any interval, because $y_1/y_2 = 3 = const$. The functions

$$y_1 = x^2 \quad \text{and} \quad y_2 = x$$

are linearly independent on any interval because $y_1/y_2 = x \neq const$, and so are the functions

$$y_1 = x \quad \text{and} \quad y_2 = x + 1.$$

If the solutions y_1 and y_2 in (2) are linearly dependent on I, then (3a) or (3b) holds and we see that we may then reduce (2) to one of the forms

$$y = Ay_2 \quad (A = c_1k + c_2)$$

and

$$y = By_1 \quad (B = c_1 + lc_2)$$

containing only one arbitrary constant. Hence in this case (2) is certainly not a general solution of (1) on I.

On the other hand, if y_1 and y_2 are linearly independent on I, then they are not proportional, and no such reduction can be performed. Hence, in this case, (2) is a general solution of (1) on I.

Two linearly independent solutions of (1) on I are called a **fundamental system** of solutions on I. Using this notion, we may formulate our result as follows.

Theorem 1. *The solution*

$$y(x) = c_1y_1(x) + c_2y_2(x) \qquad (c_1, c_2 \ arbitrary)$$

is a general solution of the differential equation (1) *on an interval I of the x-axis if, and only if, the functions y_1 and y_2 constitute a fundamental system of solutions of* (1) *on I.*

y_1 and y_2 constitute such a fundamental system if, and only if, their quotient[4] y_1/y_2 is not constant on I but depends on x.

Example 2. The functions

$$y_1 = e^x \quad \text{and} \quad y_2 = e^{-2x}$$

considered in Ex. 1, Sec. 2.2, are solutions of

$$y'' + y' - 2y = 0.$$

---

[4] Of course, here we exclude the trivial case $y_2 \equiv 0$ in which y_1 and y_2 do not constitute a fundamental system, and we also admit that y_1/y_2 may become infinite (namely, for those values of x for which $y_2 = 0$).

Since y_1/y_2 is not constant, these solutions constitute a fundamental system, and the corresponding general solution for all x is

$$y = c_1 y_1 + c_2 y_2 = c_1 e^x + c_2 e^{-2x}.$$

Example 3. The functions

$$y_1 = e^x \quad \text{and} \quad y_2 = 3e^x$$

are solutions of the equation in Ex. 2, but since their quotient is constant they do not form a fundamental system.

We are now prepared for continuing our discussion of differential equations with constant coefficients, and shall, therefore, postpone further theoretical considerations until Sec. 2.8.

PROBLEMS

Find a general solution of the following equations.

1. $y'' - y' - 6y = 0$ 2. $y'' - y' - 2y = 0$
3. $y'' - 4y = 0$ 4. $y'' - 6y' + 5y = 0$
5. $y'' + y = 0$ 6. $y'' + 25y = 0$
7. $y'' - 4y' + 5y = 0$ 8. $y'' - 2y' + 10y = 0$
9. $y'' + 3y' = 0$ 10. $y'' - 4y' + 8y = 0$

Find a differential equation of the form $y'' + ay' + by = 0$ for which the given functions constitute a fundamental system of solutions. Test linear independence by means of Theorem 1.

11. e^x, e^{-4x} 12. e^{2ix}, e^{-2ix} 13. $1, e^{3x}$
14. $e^{(3+i)x}, e^{(3-i)x}$ 15. $e^{(-1+i)x}, e^{-(1+i)x}$ 16. e^{2x}, e^{-4x}

Are the following functions linearly dependent or independent on the given interval?

17. $\cos x, \sin x$ $(-\infty < x < \infty)$ 18. x^2, x^3 $(0 < x < 1)$
19. $\ln x, \ln x^2$ $(x > 0)$ 20. $\ln x, (\ln x)^2$ $(x > 0)$
21. x, xe^x $(-\infty < x < \infty)$ 22. $1, x$ $(-1 < x < 1)$
23. e^x, e^{2x} $(0 < x < 1)$ 24. $x + 1, x - 1$ $(0 < x < 1)$

25. If $y_1(x)$ and $y_2(x)$ are linearly dependent on an interval I, show that these functions are also linearly dependent on any subinterval of I. Is the same statement with respect to linear independence generally true? *Hint:* consider $y_1 = x^2$ and $y_2 = x|x|$ on the interval $-1 < x < 1$ and on the subinterval $0 < x < 1$. Graph the two functions.

2.4 COMPLEX ROOTS OF THE CHARACTERISTIC EQUATION. INITIAL VALUE PROBLEM

In Sec. 2.2 we saw that solutions of the homogeneous linear equation with constant coefficients

(1) $$y'' + ay' + by = 0 \qquad (a, b \text{ real})$$

can be obtained by a purely algebraic procedure, namely, by determining the roots λ_1, λ_2 of the corresponding characteristic equation

(2) $$\lambda^2 + a\lambda + b = 0,$$

and these solutions are of the form

(3) $$y_1 = e^{\lambda_1 x}, \qquad y_2 = e^{\lambda_2 x}.$$

If $\lambda_1 \neq \lambda_2$, the quotient y_1/y_2 is not constant, and from Theorem 1 in Sec. 2.3 it follows that these solutions constitute a fundamental system for all x. The corresponding general solution is

(4) $$y = c_1 e^{\lambda_1 x} + c_2 e^{\lambda_2 x}.$$

If these distinct roots are real (Case I in Sec. 2.2), then the solutions (3) are real. However, if λ_1 and λ_2 are complex conjugate (Case II in Sec. 2.2), say,

$$\lambda_1 = p + iq, \qquad \lambda_2 = p - iq \qquad (p, q \text{ real}, q \neq 0)$$

then the solutions (3) are complex,

$$y_1 = e^{(p+iq)x}, \qquad y_2 = e^{(p-iq)x},$$

and it is of great practical interest to obtain real solutions from these complex solutions.

This can be done by applying the *Euler formulas*[5]

$$e^{i\theta} = \cos\theta + i\sin\theta, \qquad e^{-i\theta} = \cos\theta - i\sin\theta,$$

taking $\theta = qx$. In this way y_1 becomes

$$y_1 = e^{(p+iq)x} = e^{px}e^{iqx} = e^{px}(\cos qx + i\sin qx),$$

and by applying the second Euler formula,

$$y_2 = e^{(p-iq)x} = e^{px}e^{-iqx} = e^{px}(\cos qx - i\sin qx).$$

From these two expressions for y_1 and y_2 we now obtain

$$\tfrac{1}{2}(y_1 + y_2) = e^{px}\cos qx,$$

$$\frac{1}{2i}(y_1 - y_2) = e^{px}\sin qx.$$

We see that these two functions on the right-hand sides are real, and from Theorem 1 in Sec. 2.1 it follows that they are solutions of the differential equation (1). Furthermore, since their quotient is not a constant, they are linearly independent on any interval and thus constitute a fundamental

---

[5] Students not familiar with these important formulas from elementary calculus will find a proof in Sec. 10.11. Of course, once we got (5) we may verify directly that it satisfies (1) in the present case.

system of solutions of (1) on the entire x-axis. The corresponding general solution is

(5) $$y(x) = e^{px}(A \cos qx + B \sin qx)$$

where A and B are arbitrary constants.

Example 1. Find a general solution of the equation

$$y'' - 2y' + 10y = 0.$$

The characteristic equation

$$\lambda^2 - 2\lambda + 10 = 0$$

has the roots $\lambda_1 = p + iq = 1 + 3i$ and $\lambda_2 = p - iq = 1 - 3i$. Thus $p = 1$, $q = 3$, and the answer is

$$y = e^x(A \cos 3x + B \sin 3x).$$

Example 2. A general solution of the equation

$$y'' + \omega^2 y = 0 \qquad\qquad (\omega \text{ constant, not zero})$$

is

$$y = A \cos \omega x + B \sin \omega x.$$

In many practical cases it is required to find a particular solution $y(x)$ of (1) which has a given value K at a point $x = x_0$ and whose derivative has a given value L at $x = x_0$; that is,

$$y = K \qquad \text{and} \qquad y' = L \qquad \text{when } x = x_0,$$

or more briefly,

(6) $$y(x_0) = K, \qquad y'(x_0) = L.$$

The equation (1), together with the two conditions (6), constitutes what is called an **initial value problem**. To solve such a problem we must find a particular solution of (1) satisfying (6). We shall see later (in Sec. 2.8) that such a problem has a unique solution; practically speaking, this means that by the use of the conditions (6) we can assign definite values to the arbitrary constants in a general solution of (1), the result being a unique particular solution satisfying (1) and (6). Let us illustrate the simple practical procedure, which is quite similar to that in the case of a differential equation of the first order.

Example 3. Solve the initial value problem

$$y'' - 2y' + 10y = 0, \qquad y(0) = 4, \qquad y'(0) = 1.$$

A fundamental system of solutions is

$$e^x \cos 3x \qquad \text{and} \qquad e^x \sin 3x,$$

cf. Ex. 1. The corresponding general solution is

$$y(x) = e^x(A \cos 3x + B \sin 3x),$$

and $y(0) = A$. By differentiation,

$$y'(x) = e^x[(A + 3B) \cos 3x + (B - 3A) \sin 3x],$$

and $y'(0) = A + 3B$. From this and the given initial conditions,

$$y(0) = A = 4,$$

$$y'(0) = A + 3B = 1.$$

Hence $A = 4$, $B = -1$, and the answer is

(7) $$y = e^x(4 \cos 3x - \sin 3x).$$

Do we obtain the same result if we start from another fundamental system? Let us take

$$e^{(1+3i)x} \qquad \text{and} \qquad e^{(1-3i)x}.$$

The corresponding general solution is

$$y(x) = c_1 e^{(1+3i)x} + c_2 e^{(1-3i)x},$$

and $y(0) = c_1 + c_2$. By differentiation,

$$y'(x) = (1 + 3i)c_1 e^{(1+3i)x} + (1 - 3i)c_2 e^{(1-3i)x},$$

and $y'(0) = (1 + 3i)c_1 + (1 - 3i)c_2$. From this and the initial conditions,

$$y(0) = c_1 + c_2 = 4$$

$$y'(0) = (1 + 3i)c_1 + (1 - 3i)c_2 = 1.$$

Hence $c_1 = 2 + \dfrac{i}{2}$, $c_2 = 2 - \dfrac{i}{2}$ and, therefore,

$$y = \left(2 + \frac{i}{2}\right)e^{(1+3i)x} + \left(2 - \frac{i}{2}\right)e^{(1-3i)x}$$

$$= \left(2 + \frac{i}{2}\right)e^x(\cos 3x + i \sin 3x) + \left(2 - \frac{i}{2}\right)e^x(\cos 3x - i \sin 3x).$$

By performing the multiplications and simplifying the resulting expression we obtain (7).

Example 4. Solve the initial value problem

$$y'' + y' - 2y = 0, \qquad y(0) = 3, \qquad y'(0) = 0.$$

A general solution is

$$y(x) = c_1 e^x + c_2 e^{-2x},$$

and

$$y'(x) = c_1 e^x - 2c_2 e^{-2x}.$$

From this and the initial conditions,

$$y(0) = c_1 + c_2 = 3, \qquad y'(0) = c_1 - 2c_2 = 0.$$

Hence $c_1 = 2$, $c_2 = 1$, and the answer is

$$y = 2e^x + e^{-2x}.$$

PROBLEMS

Show that the following functions are solutions of the corresponding equations.

1. $y = A \cos 2x + B \sin 2x$, $y'' + 4y = 0$
2. $y = 4 \cos 4x - \sin 4x$, $y'' + 16y = 0$
3. $y = e^x(\cos 3x + 2 \sin 3x)$, $y'' - 2y' + 10y = 0$
4. $y = e^{-2x}(A \cos 2x + B \sin 2x)$, $y'' + 4y' + 8y = 0$
5. $y = e^{-2x} + 2e^{2x}$, $y'' - 4y = 0$
6. $y = e^x - e^{-4x}$, $y'' + 3y' - 4y = 0$

Show that the following functions are solutions of the corresponding equations and represent them in the form (5).

7. $y = c_1 e^{ix} + c_2 e^{-ix}$, $y'' + y = 0$
8. $y = c_1 e^{4ix} + c_2 e^{-4ix}$, $y'' + 16y = 0$
9. $y = c_1 e^{(1+i)x} + c_2 e^{(1-i)x}$, $y'' - 2y' + 2y = 0$
10. $y = c_1 e^{(-1+2i)x} + c_2 e^{(-1-2i)x}$, $y'' + 2y' + 5y = 0$
11. $y = c_1 e^{(-5+3i)x} + c_2 e^{(-5-3i)x}$, $y'' + 10y' + 34y = 0$
12. $y = c_1 e^{(0.5+i\sqrt{2})x} + c_2 e^{(0.5-i\sqrt{2})x}$, $y'' - y' + 2.25y = 0$

13. Suppose that (5) is a solution of (1). Express a and b in terms of p and q.
14. Use the result of Prob. 13 for deriving the equations in Probs. 1–4 having the given solutions y.

In each case find a general solution.

15. $y'' + 4y = 0$ 16. $y'' + 25y = 0$
17. $y'' - 25y = 0$ 18. $y'' + y' - 2y = 0$
19. $y'' + 2y' + 10y = 0$ 20. $y'' - 6y' + 10y = 0$
21. $y'' - 4y' + 8y = 0$ 22. $y'' - 4y' - 12y = 0$
23. $y'' + 8y' + 18y = 0$ 24. $y'' + y' + 0.5y = 0$
25. $y'' + 3y = 0$ 26. $y'' - 3y = 0$

In each case write the solution in the form (5) and determine A and B such that the given conditions are satisfied.

27. $y = c_1 e^{3ix} + c_2 e^{-3ix}$, $y(0) = 0$, $y'(0) = 6$
28. $y = c_1 e^{ix} + c_2 e^{-ix}$, $y(0) = 1$, $y'(0) = -1$
29. $y = c_1 e^{(1+2i)x} + c_2 e^{(1-2i)x}$, $y(0) = 1$, $y'(0) = 1$

30. $y = c_1 e^{ix} + c_2 e^{-ix}$, $y(0) = 2$, $y\left(\dfrac{\pi}{2}\right) = 0$

31. $y = c_1 e^{(2+i)x} + c_2 e^{(2-i)x}$, $y(0) = 1$, $y\left(\dfrac{\pi}{2}\right) = e^\pi$

Solve the following initial value problems.

32. $y'' + y = 0$, $y(0) = 1$, $y'(0) = -1$
33. $y'' - y = 0$, $y(0) = 0$, $y'(0) = 2$
34. $y'' - 2y' + 5y = 0$, $y(0) = 0$, $y'(0) = 2$
35. $y'' + 6y' + 25y = 0$, $y(0) = 2$, $y'(0) = -6$
36. $y'' - y' - 12y = 0$, $y(0) = 4$, $y'(0) = -5$
37. $y'' + 2y' + 2y = 0$, $y(0) = 1$, $y'(0) = -3$
38. $y'' - 4y' + 20y = 0$, $y(0) = 0$, $y'(0) = 16$
39. $y'' - 4y = 0$, $y(0) = 4$, $y'(0) = 0$
40. $y'' + 4y = 0$, $y(0) = 2$, $y'(0) = -8$

2.5   DOUBLE ROOT OF THE CHARACTERISTIC EQUATION

To complete our discussion of the solutions of homogeneous linear differential equations with constant coefficients

$$(1) \qquad\qquad y'' + ay' + b = 0$$

we shall now consider the case when the characteristic equation

$$(2) \qquad\qquad \lambda^2 + a\lambda + b = 0$$

has a double root. This case is sometimes called the **critical case**. It arises if, and only if, the discriminant of (2) is zero:

$$a^2 - 4b = 0, \qquad \text{and then} \qquad b = \tfrac{1}{4}a^2.$$

The root is $\lambda = -a/2$, and we obtain at first only one solution

$$(3) \qquad\qquad y_1 = e^{\lambda x} \qquad\qquad \left(\lambda = -\frac{a}{2}\right)$$

Theorem 1.   *In the case of a double root of* (2) *another solution of* (1) *is*

$$(4) \qquad\qquad y_2 = xe^{\lambda x} \qquad\qquad \left(\lambda = -\frac{a}{2}\right);$$

the two solutions (3) *and* (4) *constitute a fundamental system, and the corresponding general solution is, therefore,*

$$(5) \qquad\qquad y = (c_1 + c_2 x)e^{\lambda x}.$$

Proof.   By differentiating (4) we obtain

$$y_2' = (1 + \lambda x)e^{\lambda x}, \qquad y_2'' = \lambda(2 + \lambda x)e^{\lambda x}.$$

By inserting this and (4) into the equation (1) we get

$$(6) \qquad\qquad [(\lambda^2 + a\lambda + b)x + 2\lambda + a]e^{\lambda x} = 0.$$

Since λ is a solution of (2), the coefficient of x in this equation is zero. Since $\lambda = -a/2$ we also have $2\lambda + a = 0$. Hence (6) reduces to $0 = 0$ which proves that (4) is a solution of (1). The two solutions y_1 and y_2 constitute a fundamental system for all x, as follows from Theorem 1 in Sec. 2.3, because the quotient y_1/y_2 is not constant (but equal to $1/x$). The corresponding general solution is (5), and the theorem is proved.

It is well for the student to note that if λ is a *simple* root of (2) then (4) is *not* a solution of (1).

Example 1. Solve

$$y'' + 8y' + 16y = 0.$$

The characteristic equation has the double root $\lambda = -4$. Hence a fundamental system of solutions is

$$e^{-4x} \quad \text{and} \quad xe^{-4x}$$

and the corresponding general solution is

$$y = (c_1 + c_2 x)e^{-4x}.$$

Example 2. Solve the initial value problem

$$y'' - 4y' + 4y = 0, \quad y(0) = 3, \quad y'(0) = 1.$$

A general solution of the differential equation is

$$y(x) = (c_1 + c_2 x)e^{2x}.$$

By differentiation we obtain

$$y'(x) = c_2 e^{2x} + 2(c_1 + c_2 x)e^{2x}.$$

From this and the initial conditions it follows that

$$y(0) = c_1 = 3, \quad y'(0) = c_2 + 2c_1 = 1.$$

Hence $c_1 = 3$, $c_2 = -5$, and the answer is

$$y = (3 - 5x)e^{2x}.$$

How did we find the solution (4)? One way of obtaining (4) is the method of variation of parameters (Prob. 23 at the end of this section). Another way is to start from the differential equation

(7) $$y'' + (a - s)y' + \frac{a}{2}\left(\frac{a}{2} - s\right)y = 0 \qquad (s \neq 0)$$

having the solutions

$$e^{-ax/2} \quad \text{and} \quad e^{(2s-a)x/2}.$$

By Theorem 1 in Sec. 2.1 the function

$$Y = \frac{e^{(2s-a)x/2} - e^{-ax/2}}{s}$$

is a solution of (7). We now let s approach zero. Then (7) becomes identical with (1) where $b = a^2/4$, and by applying l'Hospital's rule to Y, *considered as a function of s* (not x) we obtain (4).

This completes the discussion of all three cases, and we may sum up our result in tabular form:

Case	Roots of (2)	Fundamental system of (1)	General solution of (1)
I	Distinct real λ_1, λ_2	$e^{\lambda_1 x}, e^{\lambda_2 x}$	$y = c_1 e^{\lambda_1 x} + c_2 e^{\lambda_2 x}$
II	Complex conjugate $\lambda_1 = p + iq, \lambda_2 = p - iq$	$e^{px} \cos qx$ $e^{px} \sin qx$	$y = e^{px}(A \cos qx + B \sin qx)$
III	Real double root $\lambda \, (= -a/2)$	$e^{\lambda x}, x e^{\lambda x}$	$y = (c_1 + c_2 x)e^{\lambda x}$

PROBLEMS

Verify that the given function is a solution of the corresponding equation.
1. $y = xe^{2x}$, $y'' - 4y' + 4y = 0$
2. $y = (3 + x)e^{-x}$, $y'' + 2y' + y = 0$
3. $y = (4x - 7)e^{3x}$, $y'' - 6y' + 9y = 0$
4. $y = (c_1 + c_2 x)e^{-4x}$, $y'' + 8y' + 16y = 0$
5. $y = (x - 1)e^{x-1}$, $y'' - 2y' + y = 0$
6. $y = 4(x + 3)e^{-2x}$, $y'' + 4y' + 4y = 0$
Find a general solution of the following equations.
7. $y'' - y' + \frac{1}{4}y = 0$ 8. $y'' + 6y' + 9y = 0$
9. $y'' - 9y = 0$ 10. $y'' + 2y' + 5y = 0$
11. $y'' + 2\pi y' + \pi^2 y = 0$ 12. $y'' + 4y' + 4y = 0$
Solve the following initial value problems.
13. $y'' - 2y' + y = 0$, $y(0) = 1$, $y'(0) = 2$
14. $y'' + 4y' + 4y = 0$, $y(0) = 0$, $y'(0) = 3$
15. $y'' + 6y' + 9y = 0$, $y(0) = -6$, $y'(0) = 18$
16. $y'' - 4y' + 4y = 0$, $y(0) = -4$, $y'(0) = -6$
17. $y'' + y' - 2y = 0$, $y(0) = 0$, $y'(0) = 3$
18. $y'' - 2y' + 5y = 0$, $y(0) = 1$, $y'(0) = 1$
19. $y'' + ay' + by = 0$, $y(0) = 0$, $y'(0) = 0$
Applying the method explained in the text, find a second solution of the following equations.
20. $y'' - 2y' + y = 0$ 21. $y'' + 4y' + 4y = 0$
22. Verify that $y = e^{3x}$ satisfies $y'' - 6y' + 9y = 0$. Using the method of variation of parameters, find another independent solution.
23. Suppose that the characteristic equation of (1) has a double root. Use the method of variation of parameters for finding a second independent solution.

2.6 FREE OSCILLATIONS

We shall now consider an important engineering application of linear homogeneous differential equations with constant coefficients. The problem will be taken from mechanics, but we shall see later that it has a complete analogue in electric circuits.

Consider an ordinary spring, which resists compression as well as extension. Suppose that the spring is suspended vertically from a fixed support (Fig. 59). At the lower end of the spring we attach a body whose mass m is so large in comparison with the mass of the spring that we may disregard the latter. If the body is pulled down a certain distance and then released it will undergo a motion. We assume that the motion takes place strictly in vertical direction.

We want to determine the motion of our mechanical system, that is, the displacement of the body as a function of the time. For this purpose we shall consider the forces[6] acting on the body during the motion. This will lead to a differential equation, and by solving this equation we shall then obtain the displacement as a function of the time.

We choose the downward direction as the positive direction and regard forces which act downward as positive and upward forces as negative.

The most obvious force acting on the body is the *attraction of gravity*

$$(1) \qquad\qquad F_1 = mg$$

where m is the mass of the body and g ($= 980 \text{ cm/sec}^2$) is the acceleration of gravity.

The next force to be considered is the *spring force* exerted by the spring, if the spring is stretched. Experiments show that this force is proportional to the stretch, say,

$$F = ks \qquad\qquad \textbf{(Hooke's}^7 \textbf{ law)}$$

[6] The most important systems of units are as follows.

System of units	length	mass	time	force
Cgs system	centimeter (cm)	gram (gm)	second (sec)	dyne
Mks system	meter	kilogram (kg)	second (sec)	newton (nt)
Engineering system	foot (ft)	slug	second (sec)	pound (lb)

1 ft $= 30.4800$ cm $= 0.304800$ meter,   1 slug $= 14,594$ g $= 14.594$ kg,
1 lb $= 444,822$ dynes $= 4.44822$ nt

For further details see, e.g., D. Halliday and R. Resnick, *Physics*. New York: Wiley 1961.

[7] ROBERT HOOKE (1635–1703), English physicist.

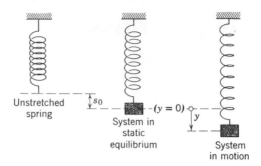

Unstretched
spring

System in
static
equilibrium

System
in motion

Fig. 59. Mechanical system under consideration.

where s is the stretch; the constant of proportionality k is called the *spring modulus*.

If $s = 1$, then $F = k$. The stiffer the spring, the larger k is.

When the body is at rest we describe its position as the *static equilibrium position*. Clearly in this position the spring is stretched by an amount s_0 such that the resultant of the corresponding spring force and the gravitational force (1) is zero. Hence this spring force acts upward and its magnitude ks_0 is equal to that of F_1; that is,

$$(2) \qquad\qquad ks_0 = mg.$$

Let $y = y(t)$ denote the displacement of the body from the static equilibrium position, with the positive direction downward (Fig. 59).

From Hooke's law it follows that the spring force corresponding to a displacement y is

$$(3) \qquad\qquad F_2 = -ks_0 - ky,$$

the resultant of the spring force $-ks_0$ when the body is in static equilibrium position and the additional spring force $-ky$ caused by the displacement. Note that the sign of the last term in (3) is properly chosen, because when y is positive, $-ky$ is negative and, according to our agreement, represents an upward force, while for negative y the force $-ky$ represents a downward force.

The resultant of the forces F_1 and F_2 given by (1) and (3) is

$$F_1 + F_2 = mg - ks_0 - ky,$$

and because of (2) this becomes

$$(4) \qquad\qquad F_1 + F_2 = -ky.$$

Undamped system. If the damping of the system is so small that it can be disregarded, then (4) is the resultant of all the forces acting on the body.

The differential equation will now be obtained by the use of **Newton's second law**

$$\text{Mass} \times \text{Acceleration} = \text{Force}$$

where *force* means the resultant of the forces acting on the body at any instant. In our case, the acceleration is $\ddot{y} = d^2y/dt^2$ and that resultant is given by (4). Thus

$$m\ddot{y} = -ky.$$

Hence the motion of our system is governed by the linear equation with constant coefficients

(5) $$m\ddot{y} + ky = 0.$$

The general solution is

(6) $$y(t) = A \cos \omega_0 t + B \sin \omega_0 t \qquad \text{where } \omega_0 = \sqrt{k/m}.$$

We know that this may be written (cf. Sec. 0.1)

(6*) $$y(t) = C \cos (\omega_0 t - \delta) \qquad \left(\tan \delta = \frac{B}{A}\right).$$

The corresponding motion is called a **harmonic oscillation.** Figure 60 shows typical forms of (6) corresponding to various initial conditions.

Since the period of the trigonometric functions in (6) is $2\pi/\omega_0$, the body executes $\omega_0/2\pi$ cycles per second. The quantity $\omega_0/2\pi$ is called the **frequency** of the oscillations. The larger k is, the higher is the frequency, in agreement with our intuition that the stiffer the spring is, the more rapidly the body oscillates.

Damped system.   If we connect the mass to a dashpot (Fig. 61), then we have to take the corresponding viscous damping into account. The corresponding damping force has the direction opposite to the instantaneous

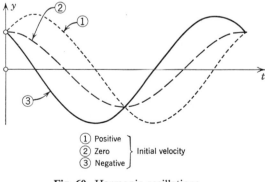

① Positive ⎫
② Zero ⎬ Initial velocity
③ Negative ⎭

Fig. 60. Harmonic oscillations.

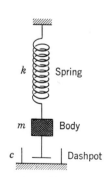

Fig. 61. Damped system.

motion, and we shall assume that it is proportional to the velocity $\dot{y} = dy/dt$ of the body. This is generally a good approximation, at least for small velocities. Thus the damping force is of the form

$$F_3 = -c\dot{y}.$$

Let us show that the *damping constant c* is positive. If $\dot{y}$ is positive, the body moves downward (in the positive y-direction) and $-c\dot{y}$ must be an upward force, that is, by agreement, $-c\dot{y} < 0$, which implies $c > 0$. For negative $\dot{y}$ the body moves upward and $-c\dot{y}$ must represent a downward force, that is, $-c\dot{y} > 0$ which implies $c > 0$.

The resultant of the forces acting on the body is now [cf. (4)]

$$F_1 + F_2 + F_3 = -ky - c\dot{y}.$$

Hence, by Newton's second law,

$$m\ddot{y} = -ky - c\dot{y},$$

and we see that the motion of the damped mechanical system is governed by the linear differential equation with constant coefficients

(7) $$m\ddot{y} + c\dot{y} + ky = 0.$$

The corresponding characteristic equation is

$$\lambda^2 + \frac{c}{m}\lambda + \frac{k}{m} = 0.$$

The roots are

$$\lambda_{1,2} = -\frac{c}{2m} \pm \frac{1}{2m}\sqrt{c^2 - 4mk}.$$

Using the abbreviated notations

(8) $$\alpha = \frac{c}{2m} \quad \text{and} \quad \beta = \frac{1}{2m}\sqrt{c^2 - 4mk},$$

the roots can be written in the form

$$\lambda_1 = -\alpha + \beta \quad \text{and} \quad \lambda_2 = -\alpha - \beta.$$

The form of the solution of (7) will depend on the damping, and, as in Sec. 2.2, we may now distinguish between the following three cases:

Case I. $c^2 > 4mk$.   *Distinct real roots λ_1, λ_2. (Overdamping)*
Case II. $c^2 < 4mk$.   *Complex conjugate roots. (Underdamping)*
Case III. $c^2 = 4mk$.   *A real double root. (Critical damping)*

Let us discuss these three cases separately.

Case I. Overdamping. When the damping constant c is so large that $c^2 > 4mk$, then λ_1 and λ_2 are distinct real roots, the general solution of (7) is

$$(9) \qquad y(t) = c_1 e^{-(\alpha - \beta)t} + c_2 e^{-(\alpha + \beta)t},$$

and we see that in this case the body does not oscillate. For $t > 0$ both exponents in (9) are negative because $\alpha > 0$, $\beta > 0$, and $\beta^2 = \alpha^2 - k/m < \alpha^2$. Hence both terms in (9) approach zero as t approaches infinity. Practically speaking, after a sufficiently long time the mass will be at rest in the static equilibrium position ($y = 0$). Figure 62 shows (9) for some typical initial conditions.

Case II. Underdamping. This is the most interesting case. If the damping constant c is so small that $c^2 < 4mk$, then β in (8) is purely

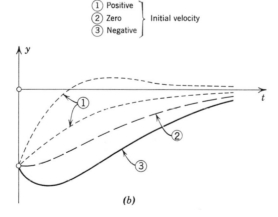

(a)

① Positive ⎫
② Zero   ⎬ Initial velocity
③ Negative ⎭

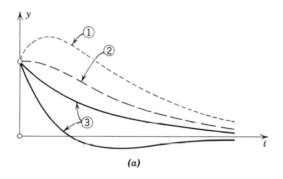

(b)

Fig. 62. Typical motions in the overdamped case. (a) Positive initial displacement. (b) Negative initial displacement.

imaginary, say

(10) $\beta = i\omega^*$ where $\omega^* = \dfrac{1}{2m} \sqrt{4mk - c^2}$ (>0).

The roots of the characteristic equation are complex conjugate,

$$\lambda_1 = -\alpha + i\omega^*,$$
$$\lambda_2 = -\alpha - i\omega^*,$$

and the general solution is

(11) $y(t) = e^{-\alpha t}(A \cos \omega^* t$
$\qquad\qquad + B \sin \omega^* t)$
$\qquad = Ce^{-\alpha t} \cos (\omega^* t - \delta)$

where $C^2 = A^2 + B^2$ and $\tan \delta = B/A$ (cf. Sec. 0.1).

This solution represents damped oscillations. Since $\cos (\omega^* t - \delta)$ varies between -1 and 1, the curve of the solution lies between the curves $y = Ce^{-\alpha t}$ and $y = -Ce^{-\alpha t}$ in Fig. 63, touching these curves when $\omega^* t - \delta$ is an integral multiple of π.

The frequency is $\omega^*/2\pi$ cycles per second. From (10) we see that the smaller c (>0) is, the larger ω^* and the more rapid the oscillations be-

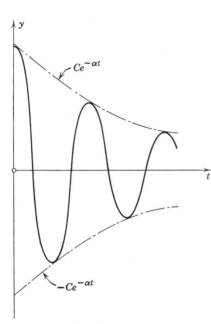

Fig. 63. Damped oscillation in Case II.

come. As c approaches zero, ω^* approaches the value $\omega_0 = \sqrt{k/m}$, corresponding to the harmonic oscillation (6).

Case III. Critical damping. If $c^2 = 4mk$, then $\beta = 0$, $\lambda_1 = \lambda_2 = -\alpha$, and the general solution is

(12) $y(t) = (c_1 t + c_2)e^{-\alpha t}.$

Since the exponential function is never zero and $c_1 t + c_2$ can have at most one positive zero, it follows that the motion can have at most one passage through the equilibrium position ($y = 0$). If the initial conditions are such that c_1 and c_2 have the same sign, there is no such passage at all. This is similar to Case I. Figure 64 shows typical forms of (12).

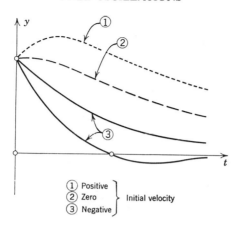

Fig. 64. Critical damping.

PROBLEMS

Determine the motions of the mechanical system described by (7), starting from $y = 1$ with initial velocity 0. Choose $m = 1$, $k = 1$, and various values of the damping constant, namely,

1. $c = 0$ **2.** $c = 0.5$ **3.** $c = 1$ **4.** $c = 1.5$ **5.** $c = 2$
6. $c = 2.5$ **7.** $c = 10$

8. Does the frequency of a harmonic motion or a damped motion depend on the initial conditions?

9. In what manner does the frequency of a damped oscillation depend on the damping?

10. Consider the harmonic oscillation $y = A \cos t + B \sin t$. Determine A and B such that the initial displacement is 1 in. and the initial velocity is

(*a*) 0   (*b*) 1 in./sec   (*c*) -1 in./sec

Represent the resulting functions in the form

$$y = C \cos (t - \delta).$$

Graph and compare the curves. What are the displacements and velocities when $t = \pi$ and $t = 2\pi$?

11. Consider the harmonic oscillation $y = A \cos \omega^* t + B \sin \omega^* t$ for various values of ω^*, say, (*a*) π, (*b*) 2π, (*c*) 3π, (*d*) 4π. In each case, determine A and B such that the initial displacement and the initial velocity are equal to 1, represent the resulting functions in the form $y = C \cos (\omega^* t - \delta)$, and graph their curves. In what manner does C (for the chosen initial conditions) depend on ω^*?

12. Consider the damped oscillation

$$y = e^{-t}(A \cos t + B \sin t).$$

Determine A and B such that the initial displacement is equal to 1 and the initial velocity is equal to (*a*) 0, (*b*) 1, (*c*) -1. Represent the resulting functions in the form $y = Ce^{-t} \cos(t - \delta)$, graph them, and compare the behavior of the motions with those in Prob. 10.

13. Determine the values of t corresponding to the maximum and minimum displacements of the damped oscillation $y = e^{-t} \cos t$. To check your result, graph $y(t)$.

14. In what manner does the position of the maximum and minimum displacements of the oscillation $y = e^{-\alpha t} \cos \omega^* t$ depend on α (that is, on the damping)?

15. Show that the maxima and minima of a damped oscillation [cf. (11)] occur at equidistant values of t, the distance between two consecutive maxima being $2\pi/\omega^*$.

16. Show that the ratio of two consecutive maximum amplitudes of a damped oscillation [cf. (11)] is constant, the natural logarithm of this ratio being $\Delta = 2\pi\alpha/\omega^*$. ($\Delta$ is called the **logarithmic decrement** of the oscillation.)

17. Determine A and B such that (11) satisfies the initial conditions $y(0) = y_0$, $\dot{y}(0) = v_0$.

18. Determine c_1 and c_2 such that the overdamped motion (9) starts from the displacement y_0 with initial velocity v_0.

Prove that the overdamped motion has the following properties.

19. The mass cannot pass through $y = 0$ more than once (Fig. 62).

20. If the initial conditions are such that both constants c_1 and c_2 in (9) have the same sign, then the mass does not pass through $y = 0$.

21. If the mass starts from $y = 0$, it cannot pass through $y = 0$ again.

22. Determine c_1 and c_2 such that the critical motion (12) starts from y_0 with initial velocity v_0.

23. For what initial conditions does the critical motion (12) have a maximum or minimum at some instant $t > 0$?

24. Express the maximum or minimum amplitude in Prob. 23 in terms of the initial values y_0 and v_0.

2.7   CAUCHY EQUATION

The so-called **Cauchy equation** or **Euler equation**

$$(1) \qquad\qquad x^2 y'' + axy' + by = 0 \qquad\qquad (a, b \text{ constant})$$

can also be solved by purely algebraic manipulations. By substituting

$$(2) \qquad\qquad y = x^m$$

and its derivatives into the equation (1) we find

$$x^2 m(m-1)x^{m-2} + axmx^{m-1} + bx^m = 0.$$

By omitting the common power x^m, which is not zero when $x \neq 0$, we obtain the auxiliary equation

$$(3) \qquad\qquad m^2 + (a-1)m + b = 0.$$

If the roots m_1 and m_2 of this equation are different, then the functions

$$y_1(x) = x^{m_1} \qquad \text{and} \qquad y_2(x) = x^{m_2}$$

constitute a fundamental system of solutions of (1) for all x for which these functions are real and finite. The corresponding general solution is

$$(4) \qquad\qquad y = c_1 x^{m_1} + c_2 x^{m_2} \qquad\qquad (c_1, c_2 \text{ arbitrary}).$$

Example 1. Solve

$$x^2 y'' - \tfrac{3}{2} x y' - \tfrac{3}{2} y = 0.$$

The auxiliary equation is

$$m^2 - \tfrac{5}{2} m - \tfrac{3}{2} = 0.$$

The roots are $m_1 = -\tfrac{1}{2}$ and $m_2 = 3$. Hence a fundamental system of solutions for all positive x is

$$y_1 = \frac{1}{\sqrt{x}}, \qquad y_2 = x^3$$

and the corresponding general solution for all those x is

$$y = \frac{c_1}{\sqrt{x}} + c_2 x^3.$$

The auxiliary equation (3) has a *double root* $m_1 = m_2$ if, and only if,

$$b = \tfrac{1}{4}(a - 1)^2, \qquad \text{and then} \qquad m_1 = m_2 = \frac{1 - a}{2}.$$

In this *critical case* a second solution may be obtained in several ways. One way is to consider the Cauchy equation satisfied by x^{m_1} and x^{m_1+s}, that is,

$$(5) \qquad x^2 y'' + (1 - 2m_1 - s) x y' + m_1(m_1 + s) y = 0.$$

Since the equation is linear and homogeneous, another solution is

$$Y = \frac{x^{m_1+s} - x^{m_1}}{s} \qquad\qquad (s \neq 0).$$

By letting s approach zero and applying l'Hospital's rule to Y, as a function of s (not x) we obtain

$$\lim_{s \to 0} Y = \lim_{s \to 0} \frac{x^{m_1+s} - x^{m_1}}{s} = \lim_{s \to 0} \frac{x^{m_1+s} \ln x}{1} = x^{m_1} \ln x.$$

It may readily be verified that this is a solution of Cauchy's equation in the critical case. Thus, writing m in place of m_1,

$$(6) \qquad\qquad y_1 = x^m \qquad \text{and} \qquad y_2 = x^m \ln x \qquad \left(m = \frac{1 - a}{2} \right)$$

are solutions of (1) in the case of a double root m of (3). Since these solutions are linearly independent they constitute a fundamental system of solutions of (1) for all positive x, and the corresponding general solution is

(7) $$y = (c_1 + c_2 \ln x)x^m \qquad (c_1, c_2 \text{ arbitrary}).$$

Example 2. Solve $x^2 y'' - 3xy' + 4y = 0.$

The auxiliary equation has the double root $m = 2$. Hence a fundamental system of solutions is x^2, $x^2 \ln x$, and the corresponding general solution for all positive x is

$$y = (c_1 + c_2 \ln x)\, x^2.$$

PROBLEMS

Find a general solution of the following equations.
1. $x^2 y'' - 2xy' + 2y = 0$ 2. $x^2 y'' + xy' - y = 0$
3. $x^2 y'' - 6y = 0$ 4. $x^2 y'' - xy' + \frac{3}{4}y = 0$
5. $x^2 y'' - xy' + y = 0$ 6. $x^2 y'' + 5xy' + 4y = 0$
7. $xy'' + y' = 0$ 8. $xy'' - 2y' = 0$
9. $x^2 y'' + \frac{1}{4}y = 0$ 10. $x^2 y'' + xy' - \frac{9}{4}y = 0$

Find a solution of the following differential equations satisfying the given conditions.
11. $x^2 y'' - 4xy' + 4y = 0,$ $y(1) = 4,$ $y'(1) = 13$
12. $x^2 y'' - 6y = 0,$ $y(1) = 4,$ $y'(1) = -8$
13. $x^2 y'' - 3xy' + 3y = 0,$ $y(1) = 0,$ $y'(1) = -2$
14. $x^2 y'' - 5xy' + 8y = 0,$ $y(1) = 5,$ $y'(1) = 18$
15. $x^2 y'' - 3xy' + 4y = 0,$ $y(1) = 1,$ $y'(1) = 3$
16. Show that if the roots m_1, m_2 of (3) are different, $x^{m_1} \ln x$ and $x^{m_2} \ln x$ are not solutions of (1).
17. Show that by setting $x = e^t$ $(x > 0)$ the Cauchy equation (1) can be transformed into an equation with constant coefficients.
18. Show that under the transformation in Prob. 17, the function in (2) transforms into an expression of the form (2) in Sec. 2.2.
19. Find y_2 in (6) by the method of variation of parameters, that is, by substituting $y_2 = u(x)y_1 = u(x)x^m$ into (1).
20. Using the transformation in Prob. 17, derive (6) from the fundamental system of solutions of the linear equation with constant coefficients in the critical case.

2.8 EXISTENCE AND UNIQUENESS OF SOLUTIONS

An *initial value problem for a second-order differential equation* consists of the equation and two initial conditions, one for the solution $y(x)$ and one for its derivative $y'(x)$. We shall now consider initial value problems of the form

(1) $y'' + f(x)y' + g(x)y = 0,$ $y(x_0) = K_1,$ $y'(x_0) = K_2$

involving a second-order linear homogeneous differential equation; K_1 and K_2 are given constants. The important result will be that continuity of the coefficients f and g is sufficient for the existence and uniqueness of the solution of the problem (1).

Existence and uniqueness theorem. *If $f(x)$ and $g(x)$ are continuous functions on a closed interval I and x_0 is in I, then the initial value problem (1) has a unique solution $y(x)$ on I.*

The *proof of existence* uses the same prerequisites as those of the existence theorem in Sec. 1.12 and will not be presented here; it can be found in Ref. [B5] in Appendix 1.

Proof of uniqueness.[8]   Assuming that (1) has two solutions $y_1(x)$ and $y_2(x)$ on I, we show that their difference

$$y(x) = y_1(x) - y_2(x)$$

is identically zero on I; then $y_1 \equiv y_2$ on I, which implies uniqueness.

Since the equation in (1) is homogeneous and linear, y is a solution of that equation on I, and since y_1 and y_2 satisfy the same initial conditions, y satisfies the conditions

(2) $y(x_0) = 0,$ $y'(x_0) = 0.$

We consider the function

$$z(x) = y(x)^2 + y'(x)^2$$

and its derivative

$$z' = 2yy' + 2y'y''.$$

From the differential equation we have

$$y'' = -fy' - gy.$$

By substituting this in the expression for z' we obtain

(3) $z' = 2yy' - 2fy'^2 - 2gyy'.$

Now, since y and y' are real,

$$(y \pm y')^2 = y^2 \pm 2yy' + y'^2 \geq 0,$$

[8] This proof was suggested by my colleague, Prof. A. D. Ziebur.

and from this we immediately obtain the two inequalities

(4)   (a) $2yy' \leq y^2 + y'^2 = z,$ (b) $-2yy' \leq y^2 + y'^2 = z.$

For the last term in (3) we now have

$$-2gyy' \leq |-2gyy'| = |g| \, |2yy'| \leq |g| \, z.$$

Using this result and applying (4a) to the term $2yy'$ in (3), we find

$$z' \leq z + 2 \, |f| \, y'^2 + |g| \, z.$$

Since $y'^2 \leq y^2 + y'^2 = z$ we obtain from this

$$z' \leq (1 + 2 \, |f| + |g|) \, z$$

or, denoting the function in parentheses by h,

(5) $z' \leq hz$ for all x on I.

Similarly, from (3) and (4) it follows that

(6) $-z' = -2yy' + 2fy'^2 + 2gyy'$
$$\leq z + 2 \, |f| \, z + |g| \, z = hz.$$

The inequalities (5) and (6) are equivalent to the inequalities

(7) $z' - hz \leq 0,$ $z' + hz \geq 0.$

Integrating factors for the two expressions on the left are

$$F_1 = e^{-\int h(x) \, dx} \quad \text{and} \quad F_2 = e^{\int h(x) \, dx}.$$

The integrals in the exponents exist since h is continuous. Since F_1 and F_2 are positive we thus obtain from (7)

$$F_1(z' - hz) = (F_1 z)' \leq 0 \quad \text{and} \quad F_2(z' + hz) = (F_2 z)' \geq 0,$$

which means that $F_1 z$ is nonincreasing while $F_2 z$ is nondecreasing on I. Since by (2), $z(x_0) = 0$ we thus obtain when $x \leq x_0$

$$F_1 z \geq (F_1 z)_{x_0} = 0, \qquad F_2 z \leq (F_2 z)_{x_0} = 0$$

and similarly, when $x \geq x_0$,

$$F_1 z \leq 0, \qquad F_2 z \geq 0.$$

Dividing by F_1 and F_2 and noting that these functions are positive, we altogether have

$$z \geq 0, \qquad z \leq 0 \qquad\qquad \text{for all } x \text{ on } I.$$

This implies $z = y^2 + y'^2 \equiv 0$ on I. Hence $y \equiv 0$ or $y_1 \equiv y_2$ on I, and the proof is complete.

The remaining part of the present section will be devoted to some important consequences of this theorem.

To prepare for this consideration let us return to the concepts of linear dependence and independence of functions introduced in Sec. 2.3. Let $y_1(x)$ and $y_2(x)$ be given functions defined on an interval I and consider the relation

$$k_1 y_1(x) + k_2 y_2(x) = 0$$

on I, where k_1 and k_2 are constants to be determined. This relation certainly holds for $k_1 = 0$, $k_2 = 0$. It may happen that we can find a $k_1 \neq 0$ such that the relation holds on I. Then we may divide by k_1 and solve for y_1:

$$y_1 = -\frac{k_2}{k_1} y_2.$$

Similarly, if that relation holds for a $k_2 \neq 0$ on I we may solve for y_2:

$$y_2 = -\frac{k_1}{k_2} y_1.$$

We see that in both cases y_1 and y_2 are linearly dependent on I.

However if $k_1 = 0$ $k_2 = 0$ is the only pair of numbers for which that relation holds on I, we cannot solve for y_1 or y_2, and the functions are linearly independent on I.

Consequently, *two functions $y_1(x)$ and $y_2(x)$ are linearly dependent on an interval I where both functions are defined if, and only if, we can find constants k_1, k_2, not both zero such that*

$$k_1 y_1(x) + k_2 y_2(x) = 0$$

for all x on I.

This result will be used in the subsequent proof.

In our further consideration we shall need another criterion for testing linear dependence and independence of two solutions $y_1(x)$ and $y_2(x)$ of the differential equation

$$(8) \qquad\qquad y'' + f(x)y' + g(x)y = 0.$$

This criterion uses the determinant

$$W(y_1, y_2) = \begin{vmatrix} y_1 & y_2 \\ y_1' & y_2' \end{vmatrix} = y_1 y_2' - y_2 y_1',$$

which is called the *Wronski determinant*[9] or briefly the **Wronskian** of y_1 and y_2. It can be stated as follows.

Theorem 2. *Suppose that the coefficients $f(x)$ and $g(x)$ of the differential equation (8) are continuous functions on an interval I. Then any two solutions of (8) on I are linearly dependent on I if, and only if, their Wronskian W is zero for some $x = x_0$ in I. (If $W = 0$ for $x = x_0$, then $W \equiv 0$ on I).*

Proof.   (a) Let $y_1(x)$ and $y_2(x)$ be linearly dependent solutions of (8) on I. Then there are constants k_1 and k_2, not both zero, such that

$$k_1 y_1 + k_2 y_2 = 0$$

holds on I. By differentiation we obtain

$$k_1 y_1' + k_2 y_2' = 0.$$

Suppose that $k_1 \neq 0$. Then by multiplying the first equation by y_2'/k_1 and the last by $-y_2/k_1$ and adding the resulting equations, we obtain

$$y_1 y_2' - y_2 y_1' = 0, \qquad \text{that is,} \qquad W(y_1, y_2) = 0.$$

If $k_1 = 0$, then $k_2 \neq 0$, and the argument is similar.

(b) Conversely, suppose that $W(y_1, y_2) = 0$ for some $x = x_0$ in I. Consider the system of linear equations

(9)
$$\begin{aligned} k_1 y_1(x_0) + k_2 y_2(x_0) &= 0 \\ k_1 y_1'(x_0) + k_2 y_2'(x_0) &= 0 \end{aligned}$$

in the unknowns k_1, k_2. Since the system is homogeneous and the determinant of the system is just the Wronskian $W[y_1(x_0), y_2(x_0)]$ and $W = 0$, the system has a solution k_1, k_2 where k_1 and k_2 are not both zero (cf. Sec. 0.3). Using these numbers k_1, k_2, we introduce the function

$$y(x) = k_1 y_1(x) + k_2 y_2(x).$$

By Fundamental Theorem 1 in Sec. 2.1 the function $y(x)$ is a solution of (8) on I. From (9) we see that it satisfies the initial conditions $y(x_0) = 0$, $y'(x_0) = 0$. Now another solution of (8) satisfying the same initial conditions is $y^* \equiv 0$. Since f and g are continuous, the uniqueness theorem is applicable and we conclude that $y^* \equiv y$, that is,

$$k_1 y_1 + k_2 y_2 \equiv 0$$

on I. Since k_1 and k_2 are not both zero, this means that y_1 and y_2 are linearly dependent on I. Furthermore, from this and the first part of the proof it follows that $W(y_1, y_2) \equiv 0$ on I.

---

[9] Introduced by HÖNE (1778–1853) who changed his name to Wronski.

Example 1. The functions $y_1 = \cos \omega x$ and $y_2 = \sin \omega x$ are solutions of the equation

$$y'' + \omega^2 y = 0 \qquad\qquad (\omega \neq 0).$$

Since their Wronskian has the value ω, they constitute a fundamental system of solutions for all x.

Further examples are included in Secs. 2.3–2.5.

The following example illustrates the fact that *the assumption of continuity of the coefficients in Theorem 2 cannot be omitted.*

Example 2. The functions

$$y_1 = x^3 \quad\text{and}\quad y_2 = \begin{cases} x^3 & \text{when } x \geq 0 \\ -x^3 & \text{when } x \leq 0 \end{cases}$$

are solutions of the differential equation

(10) $$y'' - \frac{3}{x} y' + \frac{3}{x^2} y = 0$$

for all x, as can be readily verified by substituting each of the functions and its derivatives into (10). The reader may show that the functions are linearly independent on the x-axis, although their Wronskian is identically zero. This does not contradict Theorem 2, because the coefficients of (10) are not continuous at $x = 0$.

Of course, Ex. 2 also illustrates the fact that *if u_1 and u_2 are any differentiable functions of x, the condition $W(u_1, u_2) = 0$ is only necessary for linear dependence of u_1 and u_2* (as follows from part **(a)** of the proof of Theorem 2), *but not sufficient.*

Let us now show that *an equation of the form* (8), *whose coefficients are continuous on an interval I, has a fundamental system of solutions on I, and, in fact, infinitely many such systems.*

Proof. From the existence theorem it follows that (8) has a solution $y_1(x)$ satisfying the initial conditions

$$y_1(x_0) = 1, \qquad y_1'(x_0) = 0$$

and a solution $y_2(x)$ satisfying the initial conditions

$$y_2(x_0) = 0, \qquad y_2'(x_0) = 1$$

where x_0 is any fixed point in I. At x_0, $W(y_1, y_2) = 1$. Hence, by Theorem 2, the two solutions are linearly independent on I and form a fundamental system of (8) on I. Another fundamental system is ay_1, by_2 where $a \neq 0$, $b \neq 0$ are any constants, so that there are infinitely many such systems. This completes the proof.

We shall now prove the important fact that a general solution of an equation of the form (8) with continuous coefficients includes the totality of all solutions of (8).

Theorem 3. *Let*

$$(11) \qquad\qquad y(x) = c_1 y_1(x) + c_2 y_2(x)$$

be a general solution of the differential equation (8) on an interval I where the coefficients f and g are continuous. Let $Y(x)$ be any solution of (8) on I containing no arbitrary constants. Then $Y(x)$ is obtained from (11) by assigning suitable values to the constants c_1 and c_2.

Proof. Let $Y(x)$ be any solution of (8) on I containing no arbitrary constants, and let $x = x_0$ be any fixed point in I. We first show that we can find values of c_1 and c_2 in (11) such that

$$y(x_0) = Y(x_0), \qquad y'(x_0) = Y'(x_0)$$

or at length

$$(12) \qquad \begin{aligned} c_1 y_1(x_0) + c_2 y_2(x_0) &= Y(x_0), \\ c_1 y_1'(x_0) + c_2 y_2'(x_0) &= Y'(x_0). \end{aligned}$$

In fact, this is a system of linear equations in the unknowns c_1, c_2. Its determinant is the Wronskian of y_1 and y_2 at $x = x_0$. Since (11) is a general solution, y_1 and y_2 are linearly independent on I, and from Theorem 2 it follows that their Wronskian is not zero. Hence the system has a unique solution $c_1 = c_1{}^*$, $c_2 = c_2{}^*$ which can be obtained by Cramer's rule (Sec. 0. 3). By using these constants we obtain from (11) the particular solution

$$y^*(x) = c_1{}^* y_1(x) + c_2{}^* y_2(x).$$

From (12) we see that

$$(13) \qquad\qquad y^*(x_0) = Y(x_0), \qquad y^{*\prime}(x_0) = Y'(x_0).$$

From this and the uniqueness theorem we conclude that y^* and Y must be identical on I, and the proof is complete.

PROBLEMS

In each case find a linear homogeneous differential equation of the second order satisfied by the pair of given functions. Find the Wronskian of the functions. Using Theorem 2, show that the functions are linearly independent.

1. e^x, e^{-x} 2. $\cos 2x$, $\sin 2x$
3. $e^{-x} \cos x$, $e^{-x} \sin x$ 4. 1, e^{3x}
5. e^{2x}, xe^{2x} 6. 1, x
7. $\sqrt{x}$, $1/\sqrt{x}$ 8. x, $x \ln x$

Find the Wronskian of:

9. $y_1 = e^{\lambda_1 x}$, $y_2 = e^{\lambda_2 x}$ 10. $y_1 = e^{\lambda x}$, $y_2 = xe^{\lambda x}$
11. $y_1 = x^{m_1}$, $y_2 = x^{m_2}$ 12. $y_1 = x^m$, $y_2 = x^m \ln x$

2.9 HOMOGENEOUS LINEAR EQUATIONS OF ARBITRARY ORDER

A differential equation of nth order is said to be **linear** if it can be written in the form

(1) $\qquad y^{(n)} + f_{n-1}(x)y^{(n-1)} + \cdots + f_1(x)y' + f_0(x)y = r(x)$

where the function r on the right-hand side and the *coefficients* $f_0, f_1, \cdots, f_{n-1}$ are any given functions of x, and $y^{(n)}$ is the nth derivative of y with respect to x, etc. Any differential equation of order n which cannot be written in the form (1) is said to be **nonlinear**.

If $r(x) \equiv 0$, equation (1) becomes

(2) $\qquad y^{(n)} + f_{n-1}(x)y^{(n-1)} + \cdots + f_1(x)y' + f_0(x)y = 0$

and is said to be **homogeneous**. If $r(x)$ is not identically zero, the equation is said to be **nonhomogeneous**.

A function $y = \phi(x)$ is said to be a **solution** of a (linear or nonlinear) differential equation of nth order *on an interval I*, if $\phi(x)$ is defined and n times differentiable on I and is such that the equation becomes an identity when we replace the unspecified function y and its derivatives in the equation by ϕ and its derivatives.

We shall now see that our considerations in Secs. 2.3 and 2.8 can be readily extended to linear homogeneous equations of arbitrary order n.

Existence and uniqueness theorem. *If $f_0(x), \cdots, f_{n-1}(x)$ in (2) are continuous functions on a closed interval I, then the initial value problem consisting of the equation (2) and the n initial conditions*

$$y(x_0) = K_1, \qquad y'(x_0) = K_2, \qquad \cdots, \qquad y^{(n-1)}(x_0) = K_n$$

has a unique solution $y(x)$ on I; here x_0 is any fixed point in I, and $K_1, \cdots, K_n$ are given numbers.

The proof of existence can be found in Ref. [B5] in Appendix 1, and uniqueness can be proved by a slight generalization of the proof in Sec. 2.8.

To extend the considerations of Sec. 2.3 we need the concepts of linear dependence and independence of n functions, say, $y_1(x), \cdots, y_n(x)$. These functions are said to be **linearly dependent** *on some interval I* where they are defined, if (at least) one of them can be represented on I as a sum of the other functions, each multiplied by some constant (zero or not). If none of the functions can be represented in this way, they are said to be **linearly independent** *on I*.

This definition includes that in Sec. 2.3 for two functions as a particular case.

For example, the functions $y_1 = x$, $y_2 = x^2$, $y_3 = x^3$ are linearly independent on any interval. The functions $y_1 = x$, $y_2 = 3x$, $y_3 = x^2$ are linearly dependent on any interval, because $y_2 = 3y_1 + 0y_3$.

The n functions $y_1(x), \cdots, y_n(x)$ are linearly dependent on an interval I where they are defined if, and only if, we can find constants $k_1, \cdots, k_n$, not all zero, such that the relation

$$(3) \qquad k_1 y_1(x) + \cdots + k_n y_n(x) = 0$$

holds for all x on I.

In fact, if (3) holds for some $k_1 \neq 0$, we may divide by k_1 and express y_1 as a linear function of $y_2, \cdots, y_n$:

$$y_1 = -\frac{1}{k_1}(k_2 y_2 + \cdots + k_n y_n),$$

which proves linear dependence. Similarly, if (3) holds for some $k_i \neq 0$, we may express y_i as a linear function of the other functions. On the other hand, if $k_1 = 0, \cdots, k_n = 0$ is the only set of constants for which (3) holds on I, then we cannot solve for any of the functions in terms of the others, and the functions are linearly independent. This proves the statement.

A solution of a differential equation of the order n (linear or not) is called a **general solution** if it contains n arbitrary[10] independent constants. Here *independence* means that the same solution cannot be reduced to a form containing less than n arbitrary constants. If we assign definite values to the n constants, then the solution so obtained is called a **particular solution** of that equation.

A set of n linearly independent solutions $y_1(x), \cdots, y_n(x)$ of the linear homogeneous equation (2) on I is called a **fundamental system** of solutions of (2) on I.

If $y_1, \cdots, y_n$ is such a fundamental system, then

$$(4) \qquad y(x) = c_1 y_1(x) + \cdots + c_n y_n(x) \qquad (c_1, \cdots, c_n \text{ arbitrary})$$

is a general solution of (2) on I. In fact, since (2) is linear and homogeneous, (4) is a solution of (2), and since $y_1, \cdots, y_n$ are linearly independent functions on I, none of them can be expressed as a linear function of the others, that is, (4) cannot be reduced to a form containing less than n arbitrary constants.

The test for linear dependence and independence of solutions (Theorem 2 in Sec. 2.8) can be generalized to nth order equations as follows.

[10] Cf. footnote 2, in Sec. 2.3.

Theorem 2. *Suppose that the coefficients $f_0(x), \cdots, f_{n-1}(x)$ of (2) are continuous on an interval I. Then n solutions $y_1, \cdots, y_n$ of (2) on I are linearly dependent on I if, and only if, their* **Wronskian**

$$(5) \qquad W(y_1, \cdots, y_n) = \begin{vmatrix} y_1 & y_2 & \cdots & y_n \\ y_1' & y_2' & \cdots & y_n' \\ & & \cdots & \\ y_1^{(n-1)} & y_2^{(n-1)} & \cdots & y_n^{(n-1)} \end{vmatrix}$$

is zero for some $x = x_0$ in I. (If $W = 0$ at $x = x_0$, then $W \equiv 0$ on I).

The idea of the proof is similar to that of Theorem 2 in Sec. 2.8.

A general solution of an equation of the form (2) with continuous coefficients includes the totality of all solutions of (2). In fact, the following generalization of Theorem 3 in Sec. 2.8 holds true.

Theorem 3. *Let (4) be a general solution of (2) on an interval I where $f_0(x), \cdots, f_{n-1}(x)$ are continuous, and let $Y(x)$ be any solution of (2) on I involving no arbitrary constants. Then $Y(x)$ is obtained from (4) by assigning suitable values to the arbitrary constants $c_1, \cdots, c_n$.*

The idea of the proof is similar to that of Theorem 3 in Sec. 2.8.

Example 1. The functions $y_1 = e^{-x}$, $y_2 = e^x$, and $y_3 = e^{2x}$ are solutions of the equation

$$(6) \qquad y''' - 2y'' - y' + 2y = 0.$$

The Wronskian is

$$W(e^{-x}, e^x, e^{2x}) = \begin{vmatrix} e^{-x} & e^x & e^{2x} \\ -e^{-x} & e^x & 2e^{2x} \\ e^{-x} & e^x & 4e^{2x} \end{vmatrix} = 6e^{2x} \neq 0,$$

which shows that the functions constitute a fundamental system of solutions of (6) for all x, and the corresponding general solution is

$$y = c_1 e^{-x} + c_2 e^x + c_3 e^{2x}.$$

PROBLEMS

Are the following functions linearly dependent or independent on the x-axis?
1. x^2, x^4, x^8 2. $\cos x, \sin x, 1$ 3. $\cos^2 x, \sin^2 x, 1$
4. $e^x, xe^x, x^2 e^x$ 5. $e^x, e^{-x}, 1$ 6. e^x, e^{2x}, e^{3x}
7. $x, x+1, x+2$ 8. $e^x, e^{-x}, 0$ 9. $1, 2, x$
Prove:
10. Any set of functions is linearly dependent, if $y \equiv 0$ is a function of the set.
11. Any set of functions is linearly dependent, if one of the functions is a constant multiple of another function of the set.

12. A set of n functions is linearly dependent, if it contains a set of m ($<n$) functions which is linearly dependent.

13. In Prob. 12, replace "linearly dependent" by "linearly independent." Is the resulting statement true?

Using Theorem 2, show that the given functions form a fundamental system of solutions of the corresponding equation.

14. $e^x, e^{-x}, 1,$ $\qquad y''' - y' = 0$

15. $e^{-x}, e^x, e^{2x},$ $\qquad y''' - 2y'' - y' + 2y = 0$

16. $e^x, xe^x, x^2e^x,$ $\qquad y''' - 3y'' + 3y' - y = 0$

17. $e^x, \cos x, \sin x,$ $\qquad y''' - y'' + y' - y = 0$

18. $\cos x, \sin x, \cos 2x, \sin 2x,$ $\qquad y^{(4)} + 5y'' + 4y = 0$

19. $x, x^2, x^3,$ $\qquad x^3y''' - 3x^2y'' + 6xy' - 6y = 0$

20. $x^{-1}, x, x^2,$ $\qquad x^3y''' + x^2y'' - 2xy' + 2y = 0$

2.10 HOMOGENEOUS LINEAR EQUATIONS OF ARBITRARY ORDER WITH CONSTANT COEFFICIENTS

The method in Sec. 2.2 may easily be extended to a linear homogeneous equation of any order n with constant coefficients

(1) $\qquad y^{(n)} + a_{n-1}y^{(n-1)} + \cdots + a_1y' + a_0y = 0.$

Substituting $y = e^{\lambda x}$ and its derivatives into (1), we obtain the *characteristic equation*

(2) $\qquad \lambda^n + a_{n-1}\lambda^{n-1} + \cdots + a_1\lambda + a_0 = 0.$

If this equation has n distinct roots $\lambda_1, \cdots, \lambda_n$, then the n solutions

(3) $\qquad y_1 = e^{\lambda_1 x}, \cdots, y_n = e^{\lambda_n x}$

constitute a fundamental system for all x, and the corresponding general solution of (1) is

(4) $\qquad y = c_1 e^{\lambda_1 x} + \cdots + c_n e^{\lambda_n x}.$

If a *double root* occurs, say, $\lambda_1 = \lambda_2$, then $y_1 = y_2$ in (3) and we take y_1 and $y_2 = xy_1$ as two linearly independent solutions corresponding to that root; this is as in Sec. 2.5.

If a *triple root* occurs, say, $\lambda_1 = \lambda_2 = \lambda_3$, then $y_1 = y_2 = y_3$ in (3), and three linearly independent solutions corresponding to that root are

$$y_1, \qquad xy_1, \qquad x^2y_1;$$

these solutions are obtained by a slight generalization of the method in

Sec. 2.5, or by the method of variation of parameters. More generally, if λ is a *root of order m*, then

$$e^{\lambda x}, \qquad xe^{\lambda x}, \qquad \cdots, \qquad x^{m-1}e^{\lambda x}$$

are m linearly independent solutions of (1) corresponding to that root. Let us illustrate these simple facts by two examples.

Example 1. Solve the differential equation

$$y''' - 2y'' - y' + 2y = 0.$$

The roots of the characteristic equation

$$\lambda^3 - 2\lambda^2 - \lambda + 2 = 0$$

are -1, 1, and 2, and the corresponding general solution (4) is

$$y = c_1 e^{-x} + c_2 e^x + c_3 e^{2x}.$$

Example 2. Solve the differential equation

$$y^{(5)} - 3y^{(4)} + 3y''' - y'' = 0.$$

The characteristic equation

$$\lambda^5 - 3\lambda^4 + 3\lambda^3 - \lambda^2 = 0$$

has the roots $\lambda_1 = \lambda_2 = 0$ and $\lambda_3 = \lambda_4 = \lambda_5 = 1$, and the answer is

$$(5) \qquad y = c_1 + c_2 x + (c_3 + c_4 x + c_5 x^2)e^x.$$

This result can also be obtained by noting that y and y' do not occur in the equation and setting $y'' = z$. Then the equation becomes

$$z''' - 3z'' + 3z' - z = 0.$$

Since the corresponding characteristic equation has the triple root 1, we first obtain

$$z = (C_1 + C_2 x + C_3 x^2)e^x.$$

By integrating this twice we obtain an expression for y which may be written in the form (5). Obviously, the first way is simpler than the present one.

PROBLEMS

Find a general solution of the following equations.

1. $y''' - 6y'' + 11y' - 6y = 0$ 2. $y''' + 6y'' + 11y' + 6y = 0$
3. $y''' - 6y'' + 12y' - 8y = 0$ 4. $y''' + 3y'' + 3y' + y = 0$
5. $y''' - y'' - y' + y = 0$ 6. $y''' + y'' - y' - y = 0$
7. $y''' + y' = 0$ 8. $y''' - 2y'' + 2y' = 0$
9. $y''' - y'' + y' - y = 0$ 10. $y''' - y'' - y' + y = 0$
11. The **Cauchy equation** or *Euler equation* of the third order is

$$x^3 y''' + ax^2 y'' + bxy' + cy = 0.$$

Show that $y = x^m$ is a solution of the equation if, and only if, r is a root of the auxiliary equation

$$m^3 + (a - 3)m^2 + (b - a + 2)m + c = 0.$$

Solve:

12. $x^3 y''' - 3x^2 y'' + 6xy' - 6y = 0$

13. $x^3 y''' + x^2 y'' - 2xy' + 2y = 0$

14. $xy''' + 3y'' = 0$

15. Show that the Wronskian of $y_1 = e^{\lambda_1 x}$, $y_2 = e^{\lambda_2 x}$, $y_3 = e^{\lambda_3 x}$ may be written

$$W = (\lambda_2 - \lambda_1)(\lambda_3 - \lambda_1)(\lambda_3 - \lambda_2)e^{(\lambda_1 + \lambda_2 + \lambda_3)x}.$$

2.11 NONHOMOGENEOUS LINEAR EQUATIONS

So far we have considered *homogeneous* linear equations. We shall now discuss linear equations which are *nonhomogeneous*. For the sake of simplicity we concentrate on second-order equations

(1) $$y'' + f(x)y' + g(x)y = r(x),$$

but it will be obvious that the results in this section can easily be generalized to linear equations of any order.

We shall first show that a general solution $y(x)$ of (1) can be obtained in a simple way from a general solution $y_h(x)$ of the corresponding homogeneous equation

(2) $$y'' + f(x)y' + g(x)y = 0,$$

namely, by adding to y_h any solution $\tilde{y}$ of (1) involving no arbitrary constant:

(3) $$y(x) = y_h(x) + \tilde{y}(x).$$

In fact, since y_h involves two arbitrary constants, so does y and will therefore be a general solution of (1) as defined in Sec. 2.3, provided y is a solution of (1) at all. To show this, we substitute (3) into (1). Then the left-hand side of (1) becomes

$$(y_h + \tilde{y})'' + f(y_h + \tilde{y})' + g(y_h + \tilde{y}).$$

This may be written

$$(y_h'' + fy_h' + gy_h) + \tilde{y}'' + f\tilde{y}' + g\tilde{y}.$$

Because y_h is a solution of (2), the expression in parentheses is zero. Since $\tilde{y}$ satisfies (1), the remaining expression equals $r(x)$, and the statement is proved.

The remaining practical question is how to obtain a solution $\tilde{y}$ of (1). This problem will be considered in Secs. 2.12 and 2.16.

We shall now prove that a general solution of an equation (1) with continuous functions f, g, and r represents the totality of all solutions of (1) as follows.

Theorem 1. *Suppose that $f(x)$, $g(x)$, and $r(x)$ in (1) are continuous[11] functions of x on some interval I. Let $Y(x)$ be any solution of (1) on I containing no arbitrary constants. Then $Y(x)$ is obtained from (3) by assigning suitable values to the two arbitrary constants contained in the general solution $y_h(x)$ of (2). In (3), the function $\tilde{y}(x)$ is any solution of (1) on I containing no arbitrary constants.*

Proof. We set $Y - \tilde{y} = y^*$. Then

$$y^{*\prime\prime} + fy^{*\prime} + gy^* = (Y^{\prime\prime} + fY^{\prime} + gY) - (\tilde{y}^{\prime\prime} + f\tilde{y}^{\prime} + g\tilde{y}) = r - r = 0,$$

that is, y^* is a solution of (2). Now y^* does not contain arbitrary constants. Hence, by Theorem 3, Sec. 2.8, (with Y replaced by y^*), it can be obtained from y_h by assigning suitable values to the arbitrary constants in y_h. From this, since $Y = y^* + \tilde{y}$, the statement follows.

This theorem shows that any solution of (1) containing no arbitrary constants is a particular solution of (1) in the sense of our definition in Sec. 2.3, and we may now formulate our result as follows.

Theorem 2. *A general solution $y(x)$ of the linear nonhomogeneous differential equation (1) is the sum of a general solution $y_h(x)$ of the corresponding homogeneous equation (2) and an arbitrary particular solution $y_p(x)$ of (1):*

(4) $$y(x) = y_h(x) + y_p(x).$$

PROBLEMS

In each case verify that $y_p(x)$ is a solution of the given equation and find a general solution.

1. $y'' + y = 2e^x$, $y_p = e^x$
2. $y'' - y = 3e^{2x}$, $y_p = e^{2x}$
3. $y'' + y = -3 \sin 2x$, $y_p = \sin 2x$
4. $y'' + y' - 2y = 14 + 2x - 2x^2$, $y_p = x^2 - 6$
5. $y'' + y = -6 \sin 2x$, $y_p = 2 \sin 2x$
6. $y'' - y = 2e^x$, $y_p = xe^x$
7. $y'' + 4y = -12 \sin 2x$, $y_p = 3x \cos 2x$
8. $y'' - 4y' + 3y = 4e^{3x}$, $y_p = 2xe^{3x}$
9. Extend Theorem 1 to a third-order equation. To an equation of any order n.
10. Extend Theorem 2 to a third-order equation. To an equation of any order n.

---

[11] This suffices for the existence of y_h on I, as we know, and for the existence of $\tilde{y}$ on I, as will become obvious in Sec. 2.16.

2.12   A METHOD FOR SOLVING NONHOMOGENEOUS LINEAR EQUATIONS

In the last section we have shown that for obtaining a general solution of a linear nonhomogeneous equation we need a particular solution $y_p(x)$ of the equation. How can we find such a function y_p?

One method is the so-called **method of undetermined coefficients**. The advantage of this method is that it is much simpler and more economical than another general method to be discussed later (in Sec. 2.16). The disadvantage is that it is only applicable to certain linear equations. But since some of these equations are of great practical importance—for example, in connection with vibrational problems—the method is frequently used in engineering mathematics.

The method is suitable for equations with constant coefficients

(1) $$y'' + ay' + by = r(x)$$

when $r(x)$ is such that the form of a particular solution $y_p(x)$ of (1) may be guessed;[12] for example, r may be a single power of x, a polynomial, an exponential function, a sine or cosine, or a sum of such functions. The method consists in assuming for y_p an expression similar to that of $r(x)$ containing unknown coefficients which are to be determined by inserting y_p and its derivatives into (1).

Let us start with some illustrative examples.

Example 1. Solve the nonhomogeneous equation

(2) $$y'' + 4y = 12.$$

We try $y_p = K$, a constant. Then $y_p'' = 0$. By substitution, $4K = 12$. Thus $y_p = K = 3$. A general solution of the corresponding homogeneous equation is

$$y_h = A \cos 2x + B \sin 2x.$$

Hence, by Theorem 2 in the preceding section, a general solution of (2) is

$$y = y_h + y_p = A \cos 2x + B \sin 2x + 3.$$

Example 2. Solve the nonhomogeneous equation

(3) $$y'' + 4y = 8x^2.$$

We try $y_p = Kx^2$, but this attempt will fail. We have $y_p'' = 2K$. By substitution in (3) we obtain

$$2K + 4Kx^2 = 8x^2.$$

[12] The student will see in Sec. 2.16 that our present method actually results from the general method.

In order that this holds for all x, the coefficients of each power of x on both sides (x^2 and x^0) must be the same:

$$4K = 8 \quad \text{and} \quad 2K = 0,$$

which has no solution. Let us try

$$y_p = Kx^2 + Lx + M. \quad \text{Then} \quad y_p'' = 2K.$$

Substitution in (3) yields

$$2K + 4(Kx^2 + Lx + M) = 8x^2.$$

Equating the coefficients of x^2, x, and x^0 on both sides, we have $4K = 8$, $4L = 0$, $2K + 4M = 0$. Thus $K = 2$, $L = 0$, $M = -1$. Hence, $y_p = 2x^2 - 1$, and a general solution of (3) is

$$y = A \cos 2x + B \sin 2x + 2x^2 - 1.$$

Example 3. Solve the nonhomogeneous equation

(4) $$y'' - y' - 2y = 10 \cos x.$$

The student may try $y_p = K \cos x$ and see that this attempt fails. We try

$$y_p = K \cos x + M \sin x.$$

Then

$$y_p' = -K \sin x + M \cos x,$$

$$y_p'' = -K \cos x - M \sin x.$$

By inserting this into (4) we obtain

$$(-3K - M) \cos x + (K - 3M) \sin x = 10 \cos x.$$

By equating the coefficients of $\cos x$ and $\sin x$ on both sides we have

$$-3K - M = 10, \quad K - 3M = 0.$$

Hence $K = -3$, $M = -1$, and $y_p = -3 \cos x - \sin x$. A general solution of the corresponding homogeneous equation is

$$y_h = c_1 e^{-x} + c_2 e^{2x}.$$

Altogether,

$$y = y_h + y_p = c_1 e^{-x} + c_2 e^{2x} - 3 \cos x - \sin x.$$

TABLE 9. METHOD OF UNDETERMINED COEFFICIENTS.

Term in $r(x)$	Choice for y_p	
$kx^n \ (n = 0, 1, \ldots)$	$K_n x^n + K_{n-1} x^{n-1} + \cdots + K_1 x + K_0$	0
ke^{px}	Ce^{px}	p
$k \cos qx$	$K \cos qx + M \sin qx$	iq
$k \sin qx$		iq

In the first column of Table 9 are listed some of the possible terms of $r(x)$. The second column gives the form of y_p, provided the number listed in the last column is not one of the roots of the characteristic equation of the homogeneous equation corresponding to (1).

If $r(x)$ is a sum of functions in the first column, choose for y_p the sum of the functions in the corresponding lines.

Example 4. Find a particular solution of the equation

$$y'' - 3y' + 2y = 4x + e^{3x}.$$

We start from

$$y_p = K_1 x + K_0 + Ce^{3x}.$$

By substitution we find $K_1 = 2$, $K_0 = 3$, $C = 1/2$, and therefore

$$y_p = 2x + 3 + \tfrac{1}{2}e^{3x}.$$

Modification rule. *If the number listed in the last column of Table 9 is a root of the characteristic equation of the homogeneous equation corresponding to (1), the function in the second column of the table must be multiplied by x^m where m is the multiplicity of that root in that equation.*

This rule, most likely first discovered by experimenting, can be justified by the general method to be discussed in Sec. 2.16.

Example 5. Solve the nonhomogeneous equation

(5) $$y'' - 2y' + y = e^x + x.$$

The characteristic equation of the corresponding homogeneous equation is

(6) $$\lambda^2 - 2\lambda + 1 = 0.$$

Since 0 is not a root of (6), the function x in the right-hand side of (5) indicates the particular solution choice

$$K_1 x + K_0.$$

Since 1 is a root of (6) of multiplicity 2, according to the modification rule the function e^x calls for the particular solution

$$Cx^2 e^x \qquad\qquad \text{(instead of } Ce^x\text{)}.$$

Altogether,

$$y_p = K_1 x + K_0 + Cx^2 e^x.$$

Substituting this into (5), we obtain

$$y_p'' - 2y_p' + y_p = 2Ce^x + K_1 x - 2K_1 + K_0 = e^x + x.$$

Hence $C = 1/2$, $K_1 = 1$, $K_0 = 2$, and a general solution of (5) is

$$y = y_h + y_p = (c_1 x + c_2)e^x + \tfrac{1}{2}x^2 e^x + x + 2.$$

PROBLEMS

Find a particular solution of the following equations.

1. $y'' + 2y' + 3y = 9x$ **2.** $y'' + 3y' - 4y = 5x$
3. $y'' + y' + y = x^4 + 4x^3 + 12x^2$ **4.** $y'' + 3y' - 2y = -2x^2 + 11$

5. $y'' - 2y' - 6y = -12(1 + x)x^2 - 4$

6. $y'' - 3y' + y = x^2 - 6x - 2$

7. $y'' - y' + y = e^x + x - 1$

8. $y'' + 2y' - y = 2e^x + 2x^2 - 8x - 4$

9. $y'' + 5y' + y = 1 - 5 \sin x$

10. $y'' - 4y' + 9y = 10e^{2x} - 12 \cos 3x$

Find a general solution of the following equations.

11. $y'' + y' - 2y = 14 + 2x - 2x^2$

12. $y'' - 2y' - 3y = 4 \sin 2x - 7 \cos 2x$

13. $y'' + y = -6 \sin 2x$

14. $y'' + 4y = 5e^{-x}$

15. $y'' - y = 2e^x$

16. $y'' + 4y' + 4y = 4 \cos x + 3 \sin x$

17. $y'' + 4y = -12 \sin 2x$

18. $y'' + y = -4 \cos x$

19. $y'' - 4y' + 3y = 4e^{3x}$

20. $y'' + y' - 2y = 3e^x$

Solve the following initial value problems.

21. $y'' + y = x^2 + 2,$ $y(0) = 0,$ $y'(0) = 2$

22. $y'' - 4y = 6e^x,$ $y(0) = -1,$ $y'(0) = 0$

23. $y'' + y = -9 \cos 2x,$ $y(0) = 2,$ $y'(0) = 1$

24. $y'' + y = -60 \sin 4x,$ $y(0) = 8,$ $y'(0) = 14$

25. $y'' + 2y' + 2y = -2 \cos 2x - 4 \sin 2x,$ $y(0) = 1,$ $y'(0) = 1$

26. $y'' + 4y' + 5y = 8(\sin 3x - 3 \cos 3x),$ $y(0) = 1,$ $y'(0) = -7$

27. $y'' + 2y' + 2y = 2 \sin 2x - 4 \cos 2x,$ $y(0) = 0,$ $y'(0) = 0$

28. $y'' - y = 2 - x^2,$ $y(0) = 2,$ $y'(0) = 0$

29. $y'' + 4y' + 3y = 4 \sin x + 8 \cos x,$ $y(0) = 3,$ $y'(0) = -1$

30. $y'' + y' - 2y = -6(\sin 2x + 3 \cos 2x),$ $y(0) = 2,$ $y'(0) = 2$

The method of undetermined coefficients is useful for certain first-order equations, too, and simpler than the usual method (Sec. 1.7). Using both methods, solve:

31. $y' - y = x^5$ **32.** $y' + 2y = \cos 2x$ **33.** $y' - 8y = 4 \sin 3x$

2.13   FORCED OSCILLATIONS RESONANCE

In Sec. 2.6 we considered free oscillations of a body on a spring as shown in Fig. 65. These motions are governed by the homogeneous equation

$$(1) \qquad\qquad m\ddot{y} + c\dot{y} + ky = 0$$

where m is the mass of the body, c is the damping constant, and k is the spring modulus. We shall now extend our consideration, assuming that a variable force $r(t)$ acts on the system. In this way we shall become familiar with further interesting facts which are fundamental in engineering mathematics.

We remember that the equation (1) was obtained by considering the forces acting on the body and using Newton's second law. From this it is immediately clear that the differential equation corresponding to the present situation is obtained from (1) by adding the force $r(t)$; this yields

$$m\ddot{y} + c\dot{y} + ky = r(t).$$

$r(t)$ is called the **input** or **driving force**, and a corresponding solution is called an **output** or a **response** *of the system to the driving force.* (Cf. also Sec. 1.7.) The resulting motion is called a **forced motion**, in contrast to the **free motion** corresponding to (1), which is a motion in the absence of an external force $r(t)$.

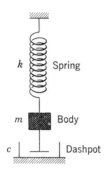

Fig. 65. Mass on a spring.

Of particular interest are periodic inputs. We shall consider a sinusoidal input, say,

$$r(t) = F_0 \cos \omega t \qquad (F_0 > 0, \omega > 0).$$

More complicated periodic inputs will be considered later in Sec. 8.7.

The differential equation now under consideration is

$$(2) \qquad m\ddot{y} + c\dot{y} + ky = F_0 \cos \omega t.$$

We want to determine and discuss its general solution, which represents the general output of our vibrating system. Since a general solution of the corresponding homogeneous equation (1) is known from Sec. 2.6 we must now determine a particular solution $y_p(t)$ of (2).

This can be done by the method of undetermined coefficients (Sec. 2.12), starting from

$$(3) \qquad y_p(t) = a \cos \omega t + b \sin \omega t.$$

By differentiating this function we have

$$\dot{y}_p = -\omega a \sin \omega t + \omega b \cos \omega t, \qquad \ddot{y}_p = -\omega^2 a \cos \omega t - \omega^2 b \sin \omega t.$$

By substituting these expressions into (2) and collecting the cosine and the sine terms we immediately obtain

$$[(k - m\omega^2)a + \omega cb] \cos \omega t + [-\omega ca + (k - m\omega^2)b] \sin \omega t = F_0 \cos \omega t.$$

By equating the coefficients of the cosine and sine terms on both sides we have

$$(4) \qquad \begin{aligned} (k - m\omega^2)a + \omega cb &= F_0 \\ -\omega ca + (k - m\omega^2)b &= 0. \end{aligned}$$

The solution of this system of equations in the unknowns a and b is (cf. Sec. 0.3)

$$a = F_0 \frac{k - m\omega^2}{(k - m\omega^2)^2 + \omega^2 c^2}, \qquad b = F_0 \frac{\omega c}{(k - m\omega^2)^2 + \omega^2 c^2}$$

provided the denominator is not zero. Setting $\sqrt{k/m} = \omega_0 \, (>0)$ as in Sec. 2.6, p. 119, this becomes

(5) $\quad a = F_0 \dfrac{m(\omega_0^2 - \omega^2)}{m^2(\omega_0^2 - \omega^2)^2 + \omega^2 c^2}, \qquad b = F_0 \dfrac{\omega c}{m^2(\omega_0^2 - \omega^2)^2 + \omega^2 c^2}.$

We thus obtain the general solution

(6) $$y(t) = y_h(t) + y_p(t)$$

where y_h is a general solution of (1) and y_p is given by (3) with coefficients (5).

We shall now discuss the behavior of the mechanical system, distinguishing between the two cases $c = 0$ (no damping) and $c > 0$, which will correspond to two different types of the output.

Case 1. Undamped forced oscillations. If there is no damping, then $c = 0$, and assuming that $\omega \neq \omega_0$, we obtain from (3) and (5)

(7) $\quad y_p(t) = \dfrac{F_0}{m(\omega_0^2 - \omega^2)} \cos \omega t = \dfrac{F_0}{k[1 - (\omega/\omega_0)^2]} \cos \omega t.$

From this and (6*) in Sec. 2.6 we have the general solution

(8) $$y(t) = C \cos (\omega_0 t - \delta) + \dfrac{F_0}{m(\omega_0^2 - \omega^2)} \cos \omega t.$$

This output represents a superposition of two harmonic oscillations; the frequencies are the "natural frequency" $\omega_0/2\pi\,[cycles/sec]$ of the system (that is, the frequency of the free undamped motion) and the frequency $\omega/2\pi$ of the input.

From (7) we see that the maximum amplitude of y_p is

(9) $\quad a_0 = \dfrac{F_0}{k} \rho \qquad$ where $\qquad \rho = \dfrac{1}{1 - (\omega/\omega_0)^2}.$

It depends on ω and ω_0. As $\omega \to \omega_0$, the quantities ρ and a_0 tend to infinity. This phenomenon of excitation of large oscillations by matching input and natural frequencies ($\omega = \omega_0$) is known as **resonance**, and is of basic importance in the study of vibrating systems (cf. below). The quantity ρ is called the *resonance factor* (Fig. 66). From (9) we see that ρ/k is the ratio of the amplitudes of the function y_p and the input.

In the case of resonance the equation (2) becomes

(10) $$\ddot{y} + \omega_0^2 y = \dfrac{F_0}{m} \cos \omega_0 t.$$

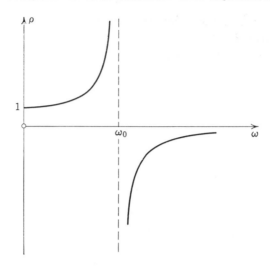

Fig. 66. Resonance factor $\rho(\omega)$.

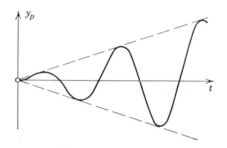

Fig. 67. Particular solution in the case of resonance.

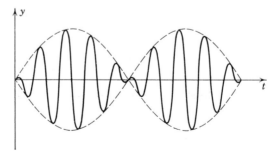

Fig. 68. Forced undamped oscillation when the difference of the input and natural frequencies is small ("**beats**").

From the modification rule in the preceding section we conclude that a particular solution of (10) has the form

$$y_p(t) = t(a \cos \omega_0 t + b \sin \omega_0 t).$$

By substituting this into (10) we find $a = 0$, $b = F_0/2m\omega_0$, and (Fig. 67)

(11) $$y_p(t) = \frac{F_0}{2m\omega_0} t \sin \omega_0 t.$$

Another interesting and highly important type of oscillations is obtained when ω is close to ω_0. Take, for example, the particular solution [cf. (8)]

(12) $$y(t) = \frac{F_0}{m(\omega_0^2 - \omega^2)} (\cos \omega t - \cos \omega_0 t) \qquad (\omega \neq \omega_0)$$

corresponding to the initial conditions $y(0) = 0$, $\dot{y}(0) = 0$. From $(11a)$ in Sec. 0.1 it follows that

$$y(t) = \frac{2F_0}{m(\omega_0^2 - \omega^2)} \sin \frac{\omega_0 + \omega}{2} t \sin \frac{\omega_0 - \omega}{2} t.$$

Since ω is close to ω_0 the difference $\omega_0 - \omega$ is small, so that the period of the last sine function is large, and we obtain an oscillation of the type shown in Fig. 68.

Case 2. Damped forced oscillations. If there is damping, then $c > 0$, and we know from Sec. 2.6 that the general solution y_h of (1) approaches zero as t approaches infinity (practically: after a sufficiently long time); that is, the general solution (6) of (2) now represents the **transient solution** and tends to the **steady-state solution** y_p. *Hence, after a sufficiently long time, the output corresponding to a purely sinusoidal input will approximate a harmonic oscillation whose frequency is that of the input. This characterizes the practical situation because no physical system is completely undamped.*

While in the undamped case the amplitude y_p approaches infinity as ω approaches ω_0, this will not happen in the present case. *The amplitude will always be finite*, but may have a maximum for some ω, depending on c. This may be called *practical resonance*. It is of great importance because it shows that some input may excite oscillations with such a large amplitude that the system may be destroyed. Such cases happened in practice, in particular in earlier times when less was known about resonance. Cars, ships, airplanes, and bridges are vibrating mechanical systems, and it is sometimes rather difficult to find constructions which are completely free of undesired resonance effects.

To investigate the amplitude of y_p as a function of ω, we write (3) in the form

(13) $$y_p(t) = C^* \cos (\omega t - \eta)$$

where, according to (5),

(14)
$$C^*(\omega) = \sqrt{a^2 + b^2} = \frac{F_0}{\sqrt{m^2(\omega_0^2 - \omega^2)^2 + \omega^2 c^2}},$$

$$\tan\eta = \frac{b}{a} = \frac{\omega c}{m(\omega_0^2 - \omega^2)}.$$

Let us determine the maximum of $C^*(\omega)$. By equating $dC^*/d\omega$ to zero we find

$$[-2m^2(\omega_0^2 - \omega^2) + c^2]\omega = 0.$$

The expression in brackets is zero for

(15)
$$c^2 = 2m^2(\omega_0^2 - \omega^2).$$

For sufficiently large damping ($c^2 > 2m^2\omega_0^2 = 2mk$) the equation (15) has no real solution, and C^* decreases in a monotone way as ω increases (Fig. 69). If $c^2 \leqq 2mk$, the equation (15) has a real solution $\omega = \omega_{max}$, which increases as c decreases and approaches ω_0 as c approaches zero. The amplitude $C^*(\omega)$ has a maximum at $\omega = \omega_{max}$, and by inserting $\omega = \omega_{max}$ into (14) we find that

(16)
$$C^*(\omega_{max}) = \frac{2mF_0}{c\sqrt{4m^2\omega_0^2 - c^2}}.$$

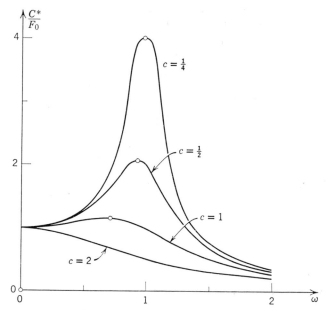

Fig. 69. Amplification C^*/F_0 as a function of ω for $m = 1$, $k = 1$, and various values of the damping constant c.

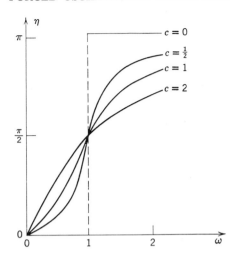

Fig. 70. Phase lag η as a function of ω for $m = 1$, $k = 1$, and various values of the damping constant c.

We see that $C^*(\omega_{max})$ is finite when $c > 0$. Since $dC^*(\omega_{max})/dc < 0$ when $c^2 < 2mk$, the value of $C^*(\omega_{max})$ increases as $c(\leq \sqrt{2mk})$ decreases and approaches infinity as c approaches zero, in agreement with our result in Case 1. Figure 69 shows the **amplification** C^*/F_0 (ratio of the amplitudes of output and input) as a function of ω for $m = 1$, $k = 1$, and various values of the damping constant c.

The angle η in (14) is called the **phase angle** or **phase lag** (Fig. 70) because it measures the lag of the output with respect to the input. If $\omega < \omega_0$, then $\eta < \pi/2$; if $\omega = \omega_0$, then $\eta = \pi/2$, and if $\omega > \omega_0$ then $\eta > \pi/2$.

PROBLEMS

Find the steady-state oscillations of the mechanical systems corresponding to the following equations.

1. $2\ddot{y} + \dot{y} + 4y = 10 \cos t$ 2. $4\ddot{y} + 6\dot{y} + y = 3.69 \cos 2t$
3. $3\ddot{y} + 10\dot{y} + 3y = 0.1 \cos 3t$ 4. $\ddot{y} + \dot{y} + y = 13 \cos 2t$
5. Find a particular solution of the equation

$$m\ddot{y} + c\dot{y} + ky = b \sin \omega t \qquad\qquad (c \neq 0).$$

Find the transient oscillations of the mechanical systems governed by the following equations.

6. $0.5\ddot{y} + \dot{y} + y = 4 \cos 2t - 2 \sin 2t$
7. $0.1\ddot{y} + \dot{y} + 2.9y = \cos t + 2.8 \sin t$
8. $\ddot{y} + 6\dot{y} + 18y = 2 \cos 2t - 26 \sin 2t$
9. $\ddot{y} + 4\dot{y} + 5y = 2(\cos 5t + \sin 5t)$
10. $0.1\ddot{y} + 0.8\dot{y} + 2.5y = 40 \cos 5t$

Solve the following initial value problems.

11. $\ddot{y} + y = -9 \sin 2t,$ $y(0) = 1,$ $\dot{y}(0) = 0$

12. $\ddot{y} + 9y = 8 \sin t,$ $y(0) = 1,$ $\dot{y}(0) = 1$

13. $\ddot{y} + 2\dot{y} + 2y = \sin 2t - 2 \cos 2t,$ $y(0) = 0,$ $\dot{y}(0) = 0$

14. $\ddot{y} + 4\dot{y} + 20y = 23 \sin t - 15 \cos t,$ $y(0) = 0,$ $\dot{y}(0) = -1$

15. $0.1\ddot{y} + 0.6\dot{y} + 1.3y = 2.1 \cos 4t + 16.8 \sin 4t,$ $y(0) = -3,$ $\dot{y}(0) = -2$

16. If y_1 and y_2 are, respectively, solutions of

$$m\ddot{y} + c\dot{y} + ky = a_1 \cos \omega_1 t \quad \text{and} \quad m\ddot{y} + c\dot{y} + ky = a_2 \cos \omega_2 t,$$

show that $y = y_1 + y_2$ is a solution of

$$m\ddot{y} + c\dot{y} + ky = a_1 \cos \omega_1 t + a_2 \cos \omega_2 t.$$

Find the steady-state solutions of the following equations.

17. $\ddot{y} + \dot{y} + y = \cos t + \cos 2t$ **18.** $2\ddot{y} + 4\dot{y} + y = \sin 3t + 3 \sin t$

19. $3\ddot{y} + \dot{y} + 2y = \cos t + 2 \sin 2t$ **20.** $2\ddot{y} + 2\dot{y} + 3y = 4 \cos 3t - \sin t$

21. Solve the initial value problem

$$\ddot{y} + y = \cos \omega t, \quad y(0) = 0, \quad \dot{y}(0) = 0.$$

Graph the amplitude as a function of ω.

22. Plot good graphs of the solution in Prob. 21, choosing $\omega = 0.5, 0.6, 0.7, 0.8, 0.9$.

23. Find the positions of the maxima and minima of the solution in Prob. 21 with $\omega = 0.5$. Does the result agree with the graph in Prob. 22?

24. In (12) let ω approach ω_0. Show that this leads to a solution of the form (11).

2.14   ELECTRIC CIRCUITS

The last section was devoted to the study of a mechanical system which is of great practical interest. We shall now consider a similarly important electrical system, which may be regarded as a basic building block in electrical networks. This consideration will also provide a striking example of the important fact that entirely different physical systems may correspond to the same differential equation, and thus illustrate the role which mathematics plays in unifying various phenomena of entirely different physical nature. We shall obtain a correspondence between mechanical and electrical systems which is not merely qualitative but strictly quantitative in the sense that to a given mechanical system we can construct an electric circuit whose current will give the exact values of the displacement in the mechanical system when suitable scale factors are introduced. The practical importance of such an analogy between mechanical and electrical systems is almost obvious. The analogy may be used for constructing an "electrical model" of a given mechanical system; in many cases this will be an essential simplification, because electric circuits are easy to assemble and currents and voltages are easy to measure, while the construction of a mechanical model may be complicated and expensive, and the measurement of displacements will be time-consuming and inaccurate.

We shall consider the "*RLC*-circuit" in Fig. 71. Simpler circuits were considered in Sec. 1.9, and it will be assumed that the student is familiar with those simpler cases, because they will immediately provide the starting point for obtaining the differential equation of our present circuit. We remember that the differential equations of those circuits were obtained by equating the sum of the voltage drops across the elements of the circuits to the impressed electromotive force. This was done by using Kirchhoff's second law, which therefore plays a role in circuits similar to that of Newton's second law (Sec. 2.6) in mechanical systems.

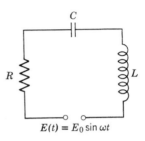

$$E(t) = E_0 \sin \omega t$$

Fig. 71. *RLC*-circuit.

To obtain the differential equation of the circuit in Fig. 71, we may use the equation of an *RC*-circuit [cf. (7), Sec. 1.9] and add to it the voltage drop $L\dot{I}$ across the inductor in our present circuit. This yields

$$L\dot{I} + RI + \frac{1}{C} \int I \, dt = E(t) = E_0 \sin \omega t.$$

Differentiating this equation with respect to t, we obtain the differential equation of our *RLC*-circuit in the form

(1) $$L\ddot{I} + R\dot{I} + \frac{1}{C} I = E_0 \omega \cos \omega t.$$

This equation and the equation (2) in Sec. 2.13 are essentially the same. This shows that our RLC-circuit is the electrical analogue of the mechanical system in Sec. 2.13, and we note the following correspondence between the electrical and mechanical quantities:

Inductance L	$\leftrightarrow$	*mass m*
Resistance R	$\leftrightarrow$	*damping constant c*
Reciprocal of capacitance 1/C	$\leftrightarrow$	*spring modulus k*
Derivative of electromotive force $E_0\omega \cos \omega t$	$\leftrightarrow$	*driving force $F_0 \cos \omega t$ (Input)*
Current I(t)	$\leftrightarrow$	*displacement y(t) (Output)*

To obtain a particular solution of (1) we may proceed as in Sec. 2.13. By substituting

(2) $$I_p(t) = a \cos \omega t + b \sin \omega t$$

into (1) we obtain

(3) $$a = \frac{-E_0 S}{R^2 + S^2}, \qquad b = \frac{E_0 R}{R^2 + S^2}$$

where S is the so-called **reactance**, given by the expression

(4) $$S = \omega L - \frac{1}{\omega C}.$$

In any practical case, $R = 0$ so that the denominator in (3) is not zero. The result is that (2), with a and b given by (3), is a particular solution of (1).

Using (3), we may write I_p in the form

(5) $$I_p(t) = I_0 \sin (\omega t - \theta)$$

where (cf. Sec. 0.1)

$$I_0 = \sqrt{a^2 + b^2} = \frac{E_0}{\sqrt{R^2 + S^2}}, \qquad \tan \theta = -\frac{a}{b} = \frac{S}{R}.$$

The quantity $\sqrt{R^2 + S^2}$ is called the **impedance**.

The characteristic equation

$$\lambda^2 + \frac{R}{L} \lambda + \frac{1}{LC} = 0$$

of the homogeneous differential equation corresponding to (1) has the roots $\lambda_1 = -\alpha + \beta$ and $\lambda_2 = -\alpha - \beta$ where

$$\alpha = \frac{R}{2L}, \qquad \beta = \frac{1}{2L} \sqrt{R^2 - \frac{4L}{C}}.$$

As in Sec. 2.13 we conclude that if $R > 0$ (which, of course, is true in any practical case) the general solution $I_h(t)$ of the homogeneous equation approaches zero as t approaches infinity (practically: after a sufficiently long time). Hence, the transient current $I = I_h + I_p$ tends to the steady-state current I_p, and *after a sufficiently long time the output will practically be a harmonic oscillation, which is given by (5) and whose frequency is that of the input.*

PROBLEMS

Find the steady-state current in the circuit in Fig. 72 where
  1. $R = 10$ ohms, $L = 5$ henrys, $C = 10^{-2}$ farads, $E = 87\frac{2}{9} \sin 3t$ volts
  2. $R = 4$ ohms, $L = 1$ henry, $C = 2.10^{-4}$ farads, $E = 220$ volts
  3. $R = 10$ ohms, $L = 2$ henrys, $C = \frac{1}{2}$ farad, $E = 10.9 \cos 2t$ volts
  4. $R = 20$ ohms, $L = 10$ henrys, $C = 10^{-3}$ farads, $E = 100 \cos t$ volts

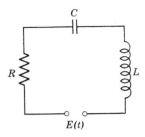

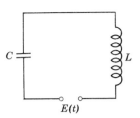

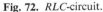

Fig. 72. *RLC*-circuit.   Fig. 73. *LC*-circuit.

5. Let $I(t)$ be the current in the *LC*-circuit in Fig. 73. If at $t = 0$ the charge in the capacitor is $q(0)$, show that

$$\dot{I}(0) = \frac{E(0)}{L} - \frac{q(0)}{LC}.$$

Find the current $I(t)$ in the *LC*-circuit in Fig. 73, assuming zero initial current and charge, and

6. $L = 1$ henry, $C = 1$ farad, $E = 100$ volts
7. $L = 1$ henry, $C = 0.25$ farads, $E = 30 \sin t$ volts
8. $L = 10$ henrys, $C = 1/90$ farads, $E = 10 \cos 2t$ volts
9. $L = 2$ henrys, $C = 0.03125$ farad, $E = 200 \sin 4t$ volts
10. $L = 1$ henry, $C = 1$ farad, $E = 10 \cos t$ volts
11. $L = 10$ henrys, $C = 0.1$ farads, $E = 10t$ volts
12. $L = 1$ henry, $C = 0.04$ farads, $E = t^2$ volts
13. Show that if $E(t)$ in Fig. 73 has a jump of magnitude J at $t = a$, then $\dot{I}(t)$ has a jump of magnitude J/L at $t = a$ while $I(t)$ is continuous at $t = a$.

Using the result of Prob 13, find the current $I(t)$ in the *LC*-circuit in Fig. 73, assuming $L = 1$ henry, $C = 1$ farad, zero initial current and charge, and

14. $E = \begin{cases} 1 & \text{when } 0 < t < a \\ 0 & \text{when } t > a \end{cases}$ **15.** $E = \begin{cases} t & \text{when } 0 < t < a \\ 0 & \text{when } t > a \end{cases}$

16. $E = \begin{cases} t & \text{when } 0 < t < a \\ a & \text{when } t > a \end{cases}$ **17.** $E = \begin{cases} 1 - e^{-t} & \text{when } 0 < t < \pi \\ 0 & \text{when } t > \pi \end{cases}$

18. Show that if the initial charge in the capacitor in Fig. 74 is $q(0)$, the initial current in the *RC*-circuit is

$$I(0) = \frac{E(0)}{R} - \frac{q(0)}{RC}.$$

19. Show that if $E(t)$ in Fig. 74 has a jump of magnitude J at $t = a$, then the current $I(t)$ in the circuit has a jump of magnitude J/R at $t = a$.

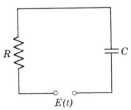

Fig. 74. *RC*-circuit.

Using the result of Prob. 19, find the current $I(t)$ in the RC-circuit in Fig. 74, assuming $R = 1$ ohm, $C = 1$ farad, zero initial charge on the capacitor, and

20. $E = \begin{cases} t & \text{when } 0 < t < a \\ 0 & \text{when } t > a \end{cases}$ **21.** $E = \begin{cases} t & \text{when } 0 < t < a \\ a & \text{when } t > a \end{cases}$

22. $E = \begin{cases} t + 1 & \text{when } 0 < t < a \\ a + 1 & \text{when } t > a \end{cases}$ **23.** $E = \begin{cases} t + 1 & \text{when } 0 < t < a \\ 0 & \text{when } t > a \end{cases}$

2.15 COMPLEX METHOD FOR OBTAINING PARTICULAR SOLUTIONS

Given an equation of the form (1) in Sec. 2.14, for example,

$$(1) \qquad \ddot{I} + \dot{I} + 2I = 6 \cos t,$$

we know that we can obtain a particular solution $I_p(t)$ by the method of undetermined coefficients, that is, by substituting

$$I_p(t) = a \cos t + b \sin t$$

into (1) and determining a and b. The result will be

$$I_p(t) = 3 \cos t + 3 \sin t.$$

Engineers often prefer a simple and elegant complex method for obtaining $I_p(t)$. This method proceeds as follows.

We start from the differential equation

$$(2) \qquad \ddot{I} + \dot{I} + 2I = 6e^{it}. \qquad (i = \sqrt{-1}).$$

This equation suggests to determine a complex particular solution of the form

$$(3) \qquad I_p^*(t) = Ke^{it}.$$

By substituting this function and its derivatives

$$\dot{I}_p^* = iKe^{it}, \qquad \ddot{I}_p^* = -Ke^{it}$$

into the equation (2), we have

$$(-1 + i + 2)Ke^{it} = 6e^{it}.$$

Solving for K, we obtain [cf. (4) in Sec. 0.4]

$$K = \frac{6}{1 + i} = \frac{6(1 - i)}{(1 + i)(1 - i)} = 3 - 3i.$$

Hence

$$I_p^*(t) = (3 - 3i)e^{it} = (3 - 3i)(\cos t + i \sin t)$$

is a solution of (2); here the last expression is obtained by means of the Euler formula (Sec. 2.4). The real part of I_p^* is

$$I_p(t) = 3 \cos t + 3 \sin t$$

and this function is a solution of the real part of the differential equation (2), that is, of the given differential equation (1). In fact, the function is identical with that obtained above. This illustrates the practical procedure of the complex method.

Our equation (1) is a particular case of the equation

$$(4) \qquad\qquad L\ddot{I} + R\dot{I} + \frac{1}{C}I = E_0\omega \cos \omega t \qquad [\text{cf. (1), Sec. 2.14}]$$

which we shall now consider, assuming that $R \neq 0$. The corresponding complex equation is

$$(5) \qquad\qquad L\ddot{I} + R\dot{I} + \frac{1}{C}I = E_0\omega e^{i\omega t}.$$

The function on the right suggests a particular solution of the form

$$(6) \qquad\qquad I_p^*(t) = Ke^{i\omega t}, \qquad\qquad (i = \sqrt{-1}).$$

By substituting this function and its derivatives

$$\dot{I}_p^* = i\omega K e^{i\omega t}, \qquad \ddot{I}_p^* = -\omega^2 K e^{i\omega t}$$

into (5) we immediately have

$$\left(-\omega^2 L + i\omega R + \frac{1}{C}\right)Ke^{i\omega t} = E_0\omega e^{i\omega t}.$$

Solving this equation for K, we obtain

$$(7) \qquad K = \frac{E_0\omega}{\dfrac{1}{C} - \omega^2 L + i\omega R} = \frac{E_0}{iZ}$$

where Z is the so-called **complex impedance**, given by

$$(8) \qquad Z = R + i\left(\omega L - \frac{1}{\omega C}\right).$$

It follows that (6) with K given by (7) is a solution of (5).

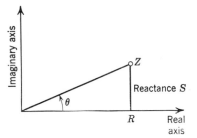

Fig. 75. Complex impedance Z.

We see that the imaginary part of Z is the reactance S defined by (4), Sec. 2.14, and $|Z|$ is the impedance defined in connection with (5), Sec. 2.14. Thus

$$Z = |Z|e^{i\theta} \quad \text{where} \quad \tan \theta = \frac{S}{R},$$

and (6) with K according to (7) can be written in the form

$$I_p^* (t) = \frac{E_0}{iZ} e^{i\omega t} = -i \frac{E_0}{|Z|} e^{i(\omega t - \theta)}.$$

The real part is

$$(9) \qquad I_p(t) = \frac{E_0}{|Z|} \sin (\omega t - \theta) = \frac{E_0}{\sqrt{R^2 + S^2}} \sin (\omega t - \theta),$$

and this is a solution of the real part of the differential equation (5), that is, $I_p(t)$ is a solution of (4). We see that this function is identical with (5) in the previous section. Since

$$\sin (\omega t - \theta) = \sin \omega t \cos \theta - \cos \omega t \sin \theta$$

and furthermore

$$\cos \theta = \frac{\operatorname{Re} Z}{|Z|} = \frac{R}{\sqrt{R^2 + S^2}}, \qquad \sin \theta = \frac{\operatorname{Im} Z}{|Z|} = \frac{S}{\sqrt{R^2 + S^2}}$$

the solution can be written in the form

$$(10) \qquad I_p(t) = \frac{E_0}{R^2 + S^2} [R \sin \omega t - S \cos \omega t].$$

This is identical with (2) in the previous section, where a and b are given by (3) in that section.

PROBLEMS

Determine the steady-state output of the following equations by means of the complex method.

1. $\ddot{y} + 2\dot{y} + 2y = \cos 2t$ **2.** $\ddot{y} + \dot{y} + 9y = -3 \sin 3t$
3. $\ddot{y} + 3\dot{y} + 16y = 2 \cos 4t$ **4.** $\ddot{y} + \dot{y} + 4y = 8 \sin 2t$
5. $\ddot{y} + 2\dot{y} + 4y = 6 \cos 3t$

Determine the steady-state current $I_p(t)$ in the RLC-circuit governed by (4), where

6. $L = 2, R = 1, C = 1, E_0 = 4, \omega = 2$
7. $L = 4, R = 20, C = 0.5, E_0 = 10, \omega = 10$
8. $L = 1, R = 1, C = 0.1, E_0 = 3, \omega = 4$
9. $L = 3, R = 5, C = 0.25, E_0 = 2, \omega = 4$
10. $L = 2, R = 4, C = 1/8, E_0 = 10, \omega = 5$

2.16 GENERAL METHOD FOR SOLVING NONHOMOGENEOUS EQUATIONS

The method of undetermined coefficients in Sec. 2.12 is a simple procedure for determining particular solutions of nonhomogeneous linear equations, and we have seen in Secs. 2.13–2.15 that it has important applications in connection with vibrations. However, it is limited to certain simpler types of differential equations. The method to be discussed in this section will be more general, but more complicated than that method.

We consider equations of the form

$$(1) \qquad y'' + f(x)y' + g(x)y = r(x)$$

assuming that f, g, and r are continuous functions on some interval I. We shall obtain a particular solution of (1) by using the method of **variation of parameters**[13] as follows.

We know that the corresponding homogeneous equation

$$(2) \qquad y'' + f(x)y' + g(x)y = 0$$

has a general solution $y_h(x)$ on I, which is of the form

$$y_h(x) = c_1 y_1(x) + c_2 y_2(x).$$

The method consists in replacing c_1 and c_2 by functions $u(x)$ and $v(x)$ to be determined such that the resulting function

$$(3) \qquad y_p(x) = u(x)y_1(x) + v(x)y_2(x)$$

is a particular solution of (1) on I. By differentiating (3) we obtain

$$y_p' = u'y_1 + uy_1' + v'y_2 + vy_2'.$$

We shall see that we can determine u and v such that

$$(4) \qquad u'y_1 + v'y_2 = 0.$$

This reduces the expression for y_p' to the form

$$(5) \qquad y_p' = uy_1' + vy_2'.$$

By differentiating this function we obtain

$$(6) \qquad y_p'' = u'y_1' + uy_1'' + v'y_2' + vy_2''.$$

---

[13] The student may wish to review the simpler application of the method in Sec. 1.8.

By substituting (3), (5), and (6) into (1) and collecting terms containing u and terms containing v we readily obtain

$$u(y_1'' + fy_1' + gy_1) + v(y_2'' + fy_2' + gy_2) + u'y_1' + v'y_2' = r.$$

Since y_1 and y_2 are solutions of the homogeneous equation (2), this reduces to

$$u'y_1' + v'y_2' = r.$$

Equation (4) is

$$u'y_1 + v'y_2 = 0.$$

This is a system of two linear algebraic equations for the unknown functions u' and v'. The solution is obtained by Cramer's rule (cf. Sec. 0.3). We find

(7) $$u' = -\frac{y_2 r}{W}, \qquad v' = \frac{y_1 r}{W},$$

where

$$W = y_1 y_2' - y_1' y_2$$

is the Wronskian of y_1 and y_2. Clearly, $W \neq 0$, because the functions y_1 and y_2 constitute a fundamental system. By integrating (7) we have

$$u = -\int \frac{y_2 r}{W}\, dx, \qquad v = \int \frac{y_1 r}{W}\, dx.$$

Since $r(x)$ is continuous, these integrals exist. By substituting these expressions for u and v into (3) we obtain the desired solution of (1),

(8) $$y_p(x) = -y_1 \int \frac{y_2 r}{W}\, dx + y_2 \int \frac{y_1 r}{W}\, dx.$$

Note that if the constants of integration in (8) are left arbitrary, then (8) represents a general solution of (1).

Example. Solve the differential equation

(9) $$y'' + y = \sec x.$$

The method of undetermined coefficients cannot be applied. The functions

$$y_1 = \cos x, \qquad y_2 = \sin x$$

constitute a fundamental system of the homogeneous equation, and their Wronskian is

$$W(y_1, y_2) = \cos x \cos x - (-\sin x) \sin x = 1.$$

From (8) we thus obtain the following solution of (9)

$$y_p = -\cos x \int \sin x \sec x\, dx + \sin x \int \cos x \sec x\, dx$$
$$= \cos x \ln (\cos x) + x \sin x.$$

Hence the general solution of the differential equation (9) is

$$y = y_h + y_p = [c_1 + \ln (\cos x)] \cos x + (c_2 + x) \sin x.$$

PROBLEMS

Find the general solution of the following equations.

1. $y'' + 4y = \sec 2x$

2. $y'' + 4y' + 4y = e^{-2x}/x^2$

3. $y'' - 2y' + y = 2e^x/x^3$

4. $y'' - 2y' + y = -e^x \sin x$

5. $y'' + 2y' + y = e^{-x} \ln x$

6. $y'' - 4y' + 4y = (3x^2 + 2)e^x$

7. $x^2y'' - 2xy' + 2y = 6x^4$

8. $x^2y'' + xy' - y = 8x^3$

9. $x^2y'' + xy' - y = (x^3 + 3x^2)e^x$

10. $x^2y'' - 2xy' + 2y = -x^3 \sin x$

11. $x^2y'' - 2xy' + 2y = -x^3 \cos x$

12. $xy'' - y' = (3 + x)x^2e^x$

13. $x^2y'' - 4xy' + 6y = -x^4 \sin x$

14. $x^2y'' - 2xy' + 2y = 6/x$

15. $x^2y'' - 4xy' + 6y = 42/x^4$

2.17 NUMERICAL METHODS FOR SECOND-ORDER DIFFERENTIAL EQUATIONS

We shall now consider two important numerical methods for solving initial value problems of the form

$$(1) \qquad y'' = f(x, y, y'), \qquad y(x_0) = y_0, \qquad y'(x_0) = y_0'$$

where f is assumed to be such that the problem has a unique solution on some interval containing x_0.

We shall obtain approximate values of the solution $y(x)$ of (1) at equidistant points $x_1 = x_0 + h, x_2 = x_0 + 2h, \cdots$; these values will be denoted by $y_1, y_2, \cdots$, respectively. Similarly, approximate values of the derivative $y'(x)$ at those points will be denoted by $y_1', y_2', \cdots$, respectively.

In Sec. 1.13 we have seen that numerical methods for solving first-order differential equations can be obtained by the use of the Taylor series

$$(2) \qquad y(x + h) = y(x) + hy'(x) + \frac{h^2}{2} y''(x) + \frac{h^3}{3!} y'''(x) + \cdots .$$

In the present consideration we shall use this series for the same purpose, and we shall also need the Taylor series for the derivative,

$$(3) \qquad y'(x + h) = y'(x) + hy''(x) + \frac{h^2}{2} y'''(x) + \cdots .$$

The roughest numerical method is obtained by neglecting the terms containing y''' and the further terms in (2) and (3); this yields the approximations

$$y(x + h) \approx y(x) + hy'(x) + \frac{h^2}{2} y''(x),$$

$$y'(x + h) \approx y'(x) + hy''(x).$$

In the first step of the method we compute

$$y_0'' = f(x_0, y_0, y_0')$$

from (1), then

$$y_1 = y_0 + hy_0' + \frac{h^2}{2} y_0'',$$

which approximates $y(x_1) = y(x_0 + h)$, and furthermore

$$y_1' = y_0' + hy_0''$$

which will be needed in the next step. In the second step we compute

$$y_1'' = f(x_1, y_1, y_1')$$

from (1), then

$$y_2 = y_1 + hy_1' + \frac{h^2}{2} y_1''$$

which approximates $y(x_2) = y(x_0 + 2h)$, and furthermore

$$y_2' = y_1' + hy_1''.$$

In the $(n + 1)$th step we compute

$$y_n'' = f(x_n, y_n, y_n')$$

from (1), then the new value

(4a) $$y_{n+1} = y_n + hy_n' + \frac{h^2}{2} y_n''$$

which is an approximation for $y(x_{n+1})$, and furthermore

(4b) $$y'_{n+1} = y_n' + hy_n''$$

which is an approximation for $y'(x_{n+1})$ needed in the next step.

Note that, geometrically speaking, this method is an approximation of the curve of $y(x)$ by portions of parabolas.

Example 1. Apply (4) to the initial value problem

(5) $\qquad y'' = \frac{1}{2}(x + y + y' + 2), \qquad y(0) = 0, \qquad y'(0) = 0,$

choosing $h = 0.2$. Here (4) becomes

$$y_{n+1} = y_n + 0.2y_n' + 0.02y_n''$$
$$y'_{n+1} = y_n' + 0.2y_n''$$

where $\qquad y_n'' = \frac{1}{2}(x_n + y_n + y_n' + 2).$

The computations are as follows:

n	x_n	y_n	$y_n{'}$	$0.2y_n{'}$	$\begin{array}{c}x_n + y_n \\ + y_n{'} + 2\end{array}$	$0.2y_n{''}$	$0.02y_n{''}$	$\begin{array}{c}0.2y_n{'} \\ + 0.02y_n{''}\end{array}$
0	0	0	0	0	2.0000	0.2000	0.0200	0.0200
1	0.2	0.0200	0.2000	0.0400	2.4200	0.2420	0.0242	0.0642
2	0.4	0.0842	0.4420	0.0884	2.9262	0.2926	0.0293	0.1177
3	0.6	0.2019	0.7346	0.1469	3.5365	0.3537	0.0354	0.1823
4	0.8	0.3842	1.0883	0.2177	4.2725	0.4273	0.0427	0.2604
5	1.0	0.6446						

The student may show that the exact solution of the problem is

$$y = e^x - x - 1.$$

The errors of our approximate values are shown in Table 13 at the end of this section.

A much more accurate method is the **Runge-Kutta-Nyström method**[14] which is a generalization of the Runge-Kutta method in Sec. 1.13. We mention without proof that this is a *fourth-order method*, which means that in the Taylor formulas for y and y' the first terms inclusive that containing h^4 are given exactly.

In the general step [the $(n + 1)$th step] of the method, we first compute the auxiliary quantities

$$A_n = \frac{h}{2} f(x_n, y_n, y_n{'})$$

(6a)
$$B_n = \frac{h}{2} f\left(x_n + \frac{h}{2}, y_n + \beta_n, y_n{'} + A_n\right)$$
$$C_n = \frac{h}{2} f\left(x_n + \frac{h}{2}, y_n + \beta_n, y_n{'} + B_n\right)$$
where $\beta_n = \frac{h}{2}\left(y_n{'} + \frac{A_n}{2}\right)$

$$D_n = \frac{h}{2} f(x_n + h, y_n + \delta_n, y_n{'} + 2C_n) \quad \text{where} \quad \delta_n = h(y_n{'} + C_n)$$

then the new value

(6b) $y_{n+1} = y_n + h(y_n{'} + K_n)$ where $K_n = \frac{1}{3}(A_n + B_n + C_n)$

---

[14] E. J. NYSTRÖM, Finnish mathematician. His paper on the method appeared in *Acta Soc. Sci. fennicae*, vol. 50 (1925).

which is an approximation for $y(x_{n+1})$, and furthermore,

(6c) $y'_{n+1} = y_n' + K_n^*$ where $K_n^* = \frac{1}{3}(A_n + 2B_n + 2C_n + D_n)$

which is an approximation for $y'(x_{n+1})$ needed in the next step.
Table 10 shows the arrangement of the computations of the first step.

TABLE 10. RUNGE-KUTTA-NYSTRÖM METHOD, FIRST STEP.

n	x	y	y'		
	x_0	y_0	y_0'	A_0	A_0
	$x_0 + h/2$	$y_0 + \beta_0$	$y_0' + A_0$	B_0	$2B_0$
0	$x_0 + h/2$	$y_0 + \beta_0$	$y_0' + B_0$	C_0	$2C_0$
	$x_0 + h$	$y_0 + \delta_0$	$y_0' + 2C_0$		D_0
				$3K_0$	$3K_0^*$
				K_0	
				$h(y_0' + K_0)$	K_0^*
	x_1	y_1	y_1'		

Example 2. Apply the Runge-Kutta-Nyström method to the initial value
problem (5), choosing $h = 0.2$. Here $f = (x + y + y' + 2)/2$, and (6a) becomes

$A_n = 0.05(x_n + y_n + y_n' + 2)$,
$B_n = 0.05(x_n + 0.1 + y_n + \beta_n + y_n' + A_n + 2)$,
$C_n = 0.05(x_n + 0.1 + y_n + \beta_n + y_n' + B_n + 2)$, $\beta_n = 0.1(y_n' + \frac{1}{2}A_n)$
$D_n = 0.05(x_n + 0.2 + y_n + \delta_n + y_n' + 2C_n + 2)$, $\delta_n = 0.2(y_n' + C_n)$

Table 11 shows the computations of the first step, arranged as in Table 10.

TABLE. 11. FIRST STEP OF THE RUNGE-KUTTA-NYSTRÖM METHOD
(WITH $h = 0.2$) APPLIED TO THE INITIAL VALUE PROBLEM (5).

n	x	y	y'		
	0	0	0	0.100 0000	0.100 0000
	0.1	0.005 0000	0.100 0000	0.110 2500	0.220 5000
0	0.1	0.005 0000	0.110 2500	0.110 7625	0.221 5250
	0.2	0.022 1525	0.221 5250		0.122 1839
				0.321 0125	0.664 2089
				0.107 0042	
				0.021 4008	0.221 4030
	0.2	0.021 4008	0.221 4030		

In the present case the differential equation is simple, and so are the expressions for A_n, B_n, C_n, and D_n. Hence we may insert A_n into B_n, then B_n into C_n, and, finally, C_n into D_n. The result of this elementary calculation is

$$B_n = 0.05[1.0525(x_n + y_n) + 1.152\,5y_n' + 2.205]$$

$$C_n = 0.05[1.055\,125(x_n + y_n) + 1.160\,125y_n' + 2.215\,25]$$

$$D_n = 0.05[1.116\,063\,75(x_n + y_n) + 1.327\,613\,75y_n' + 2.443\,677\,5]$$

From this we may now determine K_n and K_n^* and insert the resulting expressions into (6b) and (6c), finding

$$
\begin{aligned}
y_{n+1} &= y_n + a(x_n + y_n) + by_n' + c \\
y_{n+1}' &= y_n' + a^*(x_n + y_n) + b^*y_n' + c^*
\end{aligned}
$$
(7)

where

$$a = 0.010\,3588 \qquad b = 0.211\,0421 \qquad c = 0.021\,4008$$

$$a^* = 0.105\,5219 \qquad b^* = 0.115\,8811 \qquad c^* = 0.221\,4030$$

Table 12 shows the corresponding computations. The errors of the approximate values for $y(x)$ are much smaller than those in Ex. 1 (cf. Table 13).

TABLE 12. RUNGE-KUTTA-NYSTRÖM METHOD (WITH $h = 0.2$) APPLIED TO THE INITIAL VALUE PROBLEM (5); FIVE STEPS COMPUTED BY THE USE OF (7).

n	x_n	y_n	y_n'	$a(x_n + y_n)$ $+ by_n' + c$	$a^*(x_n + y_n)$ $+ b^*y_n' + c^*$
0	0	0	0	0.021 4008	0.221 4030
1	0.2	0.021 4008	0.221 4030	0.070 4196	0.270 4220
2	0.4	0.091 8204	0.491 8250	0.130 2913	0.330 2940
3	0.6	0.222 1117	0.822 1190	0.203 4186	0.403 4219
4	0.8	0.425 5303	1.225 5409	0.292 7365	0.492 7403
5	1.0	0.718 2668	1.718 2812		

TABLE 13. COMPARISON OF ACCURACY OF THE TWO METHODS UNDER CONSIDERATION IN THE CASE OF THE INITIAL VALUE PROBLEM (5), WITH $h = 0.2$.

x	$y = e^x - x - 1$	Absolute value of error	
		Ex. 1	Table 12
0.2	0.021 4028	0.0014	0.000 0020
0.4	0.091 8247	0.0076	0.000 0043
0.6	0.222 1188	0.0202	0.000 0071
0.8	0.425 5409	0.0413	0.000 0106
1.0	0.718 2818	0.0737	0.000 0150

PROBLEMS

1. Repeat the computation in Ex. 1, choosing $h = 0.1$, and compare the errors of the values thus obtained with those in Ex. 1 (listed in Table 13).

Apply (4) to the following initial value problems. (Carry out five steps.)

2. $y'' = -y$, $y(0) = 0$, $y'(0) = 1$, $h = 0.1$

3. $y'' = -y$, $y(0) = 1$, $y'(0) = 0$, $h = 0.1$

4. $y'' = -y$, $y(0) = 1$, $y'(0) = 0$, $h = 0.05$

5. $y'' = y$, $y(0) = 1$, $y'(0) = 1$, $h = 0.1$

6. $y'' = y$, $y(0) = 1$, $y'(0) = -1$, $h = 0.1$

7. Show that in the case of the initial value problem

$$(1 - x^2)y'' - 2xy' + 2y = 0, \qquad y(0) = 0, \qquad y'(0) = 1$$

the formulas (4) with $h = 0.1$ take the form

$$y_{n+1} = y_n + 0.1y_n' + 0.01 \frac{x_n y_n' - y_n}{1 - x_n^2}$$

$$y_{n+1}' = y_n' + 0.2 \frac{x_n y_n' - y_n}{1 - x_n^2}.$$

Carry out five steps. Verify by substitution that the exact solution of the problem is $y = x$.

8. Apply (4) with $h = 0.1$ to the initial value problem

$$(1 - x^2)y'' - 2xy' + 6y = 0, \qquad y(0) = -\tfrac{1}{2}, \qquad y'(0) = 0.$$

Carry out five steps. Verify by substitution that the exact solution is

$$y = \tfrac{1}{2}(3x^2 - 1).$$

9. Apply (4) with $h = 0.1$ to the initial value problem

$$y'' = xy' - 3y, \qquad y(0) = 0, \qquad y'(0) = -3.$$

Carry out five steps. Verify by substitution that the exact solution is $y = x^3 - 3x$.

10. Apply (4) with $h = 0.1$ to the initial value problem

$$y'' = xy' - 4y, \qquad y(0) = 3, \qquad y'(0) = 0.$$

Carry out five steps. Verify by substitution that the exact solution is

$$y = x^4 - 6x^2 + 3.$$

11. Apply the Runge-Kutta-Nyström method to the initial value problem in Prob. 2. Choose $h = 0.2$, carry out five steps, and compare the results with the exact values (cf. Table 1 in Sec. 0.1).

12. In Prob. 11, replace $h = 0.2$ by $h = 0.1$, carry out four steps, and compare the results with the corresponding values in Prob. 11 and with the exact values

0.099 833 417,   0.198 669 331,   0.295 520 207,   0.389 418 342.

POWER SERIES
SOLUTIONS OF
DIFFERENTIAL
EQUATIONS

In the preceding chapter we have seen that linear homogeneous differential equations with constant coefficients can be solved by algebraic methods, and the solutions are elementary functions known from calculus. In the case of equations with variable coefficients, the situation is more complicated and the solutions may be nonelementary functions. Bessel's equation, Legendre's equation, and the hypergeometric equation are of this type. Since these and other equations and their solutions play an important role in engineering mathematics, we shall now consider a method for solving such equations. The solutions will appear in the form of power series, and the method is, therefore, known as the power series method. We shall also consider some basic properties of the solutions, so that the student may get acquainted with these "higher transcendental functions" and with some standard procedures used in connection with special functions.

Prerequisite for this chapter: Chap. 2.

Sections which may be omitted in a shorter course: 3.2, 3.6, 3.7.

References: Appendix 1, Part B.

Answers to problems: Appendix 2.

3.1   THE POWER SERIES METHOD

We shall now consider solving differential equations by the so-called *power series method* which yields solutions in the form of power series. It is a very effective standard procedure in connection with linear differential equations whose coefficients are variable.

We first remember that a **power series**[1] (in powers of $x - a$) is an infinite series of the form

$$(1) \qquad \sum_{m=0}^{\infty} c_m(x - a)^m = c_0 + c_1(x - a) + c_2(x - a)^2 + \cdots$$

where $c_0, c_1, \cdots$ are constants, called the **coefficients** of the series, a is a constant, called the **center**, and x is a variable.

If in particular $a = 0$, we obtain a *power series in powers of x*

$$(2) \qquad \sum_{m=0}^{\infty} c_m x^m = c_0 + c_1 x + c_2 x^2 + c_3 x^3 + \cdots.$$

We shall assume in this section that all variables and constants are real.

Familiar examples of power series are the Maclaurin series

$$\frac{1}{1 - x} = \sum_{m=0}^{\infty} x^m = 1 + x + x^2 + \cdots \qquad (|x| < 1, geometric\ series)$$

$$e^x = \sum_{m=0}^{\infty} \frac{x^m}{m!} = 1 + x + \frac{x^2}{2!} + \frac{x^3}{3!} + \cdots$$

$$\cos x = \sum_{m=0}^{\infty} \frac{(-1)^m x^{2m}}{(2m)!} = 1 - \frac{x^2}{2!} + \frac{x^4}{4!} - + \cdots$$

$$\sin x = \sum_{m=0}^{\infty} \frac{(-1)^m x^{2m+1}}{(2m + 1)!} = x - \frac{x^3}{3!} + \frac{x^5}{5!} - + \cdots$$

The basic idea of the power series method for solving differential equations is very simple and natural. We shall describe the practical procedure and illustrate it by simple examples, postponing the mathematical justification of the method to the next section.

A differential equation being given, we first represent all given functions in the equation by power series in powers of x (or in powers of $x - a$, if

---

[1] The term "power series" alone usually refers to a series of the form (1), including the particular case (2), but does not include series of negative powers of x such as $c_0 + c_1 x^{-1} + c_2 x^{-2} + \cdots$ or series involving fractional powers of x. Note that in (1) we write, for convenience, $(x - a)^0 = 1$, even when $x = a$.

solutions in the form of power series in powers of $x - a$ are wanted). Then we assume a solution in the form of a power series, say,

$$(3) \qquad y = c_0 + c_1 x + c_2 x^2 + c_3 x^3 + \cdots = \sum_{m=0}^{\infty} c_m x^m$$

and insert this series and the series obtained by termwise differentiation,

$$(a) \quad y' = c_1 + 2c_2 x + 3c_3 x^2 + \cdots = \sum_{m=1}^{\infty} m c_m x^{m-1}$$

(4)

$$(b) \quad y'' = 2c_2 + 3 \cdot 2c_3 x + 4 \cdot 3c_4 x^2 + \cdots = \sum_{m=2}^{\infty} m(m-1) c_m x^{m-2}$$

etc., into the equation. Adding all the terms containing the same power of x, the resulting equation may then be written

$$(5) \qquad k_0 + k_1 x + k_2 x^2 + \cdots = 0$$

where the constants $k_0, k_1, \cdots$ are expressions containing the unknown coefficients $c_0, c_1, \cdots$ in (3). In order that (5) holds for all x in some interval, we must have

$$k_0 = 0, \qquad k_1 = 0, \qquad k_2 = 0, \cdots.$$

From these equations we may then determine the coefficients $c_0, c_1, \cdots$ successively.

Let us now illustrate the practical procedure for some simple equations which can also be solved by elementary methods.

Example 1. Solve

$$y' - y = 0.$$

In the first step, we insert (3) and (4a) into the equation:

$$(c_1 + 2c_2 x + 3c_3 x^2 + \cdots) - (c_0 + c_1 x + c_2 x^2 + \cdots) = 0.$$

Then we collect like powers of x, finding

$$(c_1 - c_0) + (2c_2 - c_1)x + (3c_3 - c_2)x^2 + \cdots = 0.$$

Equating the coefficient of each power of x to zero, we have

$$c_1 - c_0 = 0, \qquad 2c_2 - c_1 = 0, \qquad 3c_3 - c_2 = 0, \cdots.$$

Solving these equations, we may express $c_1, c_2, \cdots$ in terms of c_0 which remains arbitrary:

$$c_1 = c_0, \qquad c_2 = \frac{c_1}{2} = \frac{c_0}{2!}, \qquad c_3 = \frac{c_2}{3} = \frac{c_0}{3!}, \cdots.$$

With these values (3) becomes

$$y = c_0 + c_0 x + \frac{c_0}{2!} x^2 + \frac{c_0}{3!} x^3 + \cdots,$$

and we see that we have obtained the familiar general solution

$$y = c_0 \left(1 + x + \frac{x^2}{2!} + \frac{x^3}{3!} + \cdots \right) = c_0 e^x.$$

Example 2. Solve

$$y'' + y = 0.$$

By inserting (3) and (4b) into the equation we obtain

$$(2c_2 + 3 \cdot 2c_3 x + 4 \cdot 3c_4 x^2 + \cdots) + (c_0 + c_1 x + c_2 x^2 + \cdots) = 0.$$

Collecting like powers of x, we find

$$(2c_2 + c_0) + (3 \cdot 2c_3 + c_1)x + (4 \cdot 3c_4 + c_2)x^2 + \cdots = 0.$$

Equating the coefficient of each power of x to zero, we have

$$2c_2 + c_0 = 0, \qquad 3 \cdot 2c_3 + c_1 = 0, \qquad 4 \cdot 3c_4 + c_2 = 0, \cdots.$$

Solving these equations, we see that c_2, c_4, $\cdots$ may be expressed in terms of c_0, while $c_3, c_5, \cdots$ may be expressed in terms of c_1:

$$c_2 = -\frac{c_0}{2!}, \qquad c_3 = -\frac{c_1}{3!}, \qquad c_4 = -\frac{c_2}{4 \cdot 3} = \frac{c_0}{4!}, \cdots;$$

c_0 and c_1 are arbitrary. With these values (3) becomes

$$y = c_0 + c_1 x - \frac{c_0}{2!} x^2 - \frac{c_1}{3!} x^3 + \frac{c_0}{4!} x^4 + \frac{c_1}{5!} x^5 + \cdots.$$

This may be written

$$y = c_0 \left(1 - \frac{x^2}{2!} + \frac{x^4}{4!} - + \cdots \right) + c_1 \left(x - \frac{x^3}{3!} + \frac{x^5}{5!} - + \cdots \right)$$

and we recognize the familiar general solution

$$y = c_0 \cos x + c_1 \sin x.$$

Example 3. Solve

$$(x + 1)y' - (x + 2)y = 0.$$

By inserting (3) and (4a) into the equation we obtain

$$(x + 1)(c_1 + 2c_2 x + 3c_3 x^2 + \cdots) - (x + 2)(c_0 + c_1 x + c_2 x^2 + \cdots) = 0.$$

By performing the indicated multiplications we get

$$c_1 x + 2c_2 x^2 + 3c_3 x^3 + 4c_4 x^4 + 5c_5 x^5 + \cdots + sc_s x^s + \cdots$$
$$+ c_1 + 2c_2 x + 3c_3 x^2 + 4c_4 x^3 + 5c_5 x^4 + 6c_6 x^5 + \cdots + (s + 1)c_{s+1} x^s + \cdots$$
$$- c_0 x - c_1 x^2 - c_2 x^3 - c_3 x^4 - c_4 x^5 - \cdots - c_{s-1} x^s - \cdots$$
$$-2c_0 - 2c_1 x - 2c_2 x^2 - 2c_3 x^3 - 2c_4 x^4 - 2c_5 x^5 - \cdots - 2c_s x^s - \cdots = 0.$$

Since this must be an identity in x, the sum of the coefficients of each power of x must be zero; we thus obtain

(6)   (a) $c_1 - 2c_0 = 0$ (b) $2c_2 - c_1 - c_0 = 0$, etc.

and in general

(7) $sc_s + (s + 1)c_{s+1} - c_{s-1} - 2c_s = 0.$

By solving $(6a)$ for c_1 and (7) for c_{s+1} we have

(8) (a) $c_1 = 2c_0$, (b) $c_{s+1} = \dfrac{1}{s+1}[c_{s-1} + (2-s)c_s]$, $s = 1, 2, \cdots$.

Formula $(8b)$ is a **recursion formula**, from which we may now determine $c_2, c_3, \cdots$, successively; if we wish, we may arrange the calculation in tabular form:

s	c_{s-1}	$(2-s)c_s$	Sum	$s+1$	$c_{s+1} = \dfrac{\text{Sum}}{s+1}$	c_{s+1} in terms of c_0
						$c_1 = 2c_0$
1	c_0	c_1	$c_0 + c_1$	2	$\dfrac{c_0}{2} + \dfrac{c_1}{2}$	$c_2 = \dfrac{3}{2}c_0$
2	c_1	0	c_1	3	$\dfrac{c_1}{3}$	$c_3 = \dfrac{2}{3}c_0$
3	c_2	$-c_3$	$c_2 - c_3$	4	$\dfrac{c_2}{4} - \dfrac{c_3}{4}$	$c_4 = \dfrac{5}{24}c_0$
.	..	..	...	.	...	...

With these values (3) becomes

$$y = c_0\left(1 + 2x + \tfrac{3}{2}x^2 + \tfrac{2}{3}x^3 + \tfrac{5}{24}x^4 + \cdots\right),$$

and the reader may verify that the explicitly written terms are the first few terms of the Maclaurin series of

$$y = c_0(1 + x)e^x,$$

the general solution of the equation obtained by separating variables.

PROBLEMS

Apply the power series method to the following differential equations.
1. $y' + y = 0$ **2.** $y' - 2y = 0$ **3.** $y' - ky = 0$
4. $y' - 2xy = 0$ **5.** $y'' - y = 0$ **6.** $y'' + 4y = 0$
7. $y'' - 9y = 0$ **8.** $(x+1)y' - 2y = 0$ **9.** $(x-2)y' - 3y = 0$
10. $(x^2 + 1)y' + (x - 1)^2 y = 0$
(More problems of this type are included at the end of Sec. 3.2.)

3.2 THEORETICAL BASIS OF THE POWER SERIES METHOD

We have seen that the power series method yields solutions of differential equations in the form of power series. The solution y of a given equation is assumed in the form of a power series with undetermined coefficients, and the coefficients are determined successively by inserting that series and the series for the derivatives of y into the given equation.

The practical usefulness of the method becomes obvious if we remember that power series may be used for computing values of the solutions. Furthermore, many general properties of the solutions can be derived from their power series; this will be seen in our further consideration.

The power series method involves various operations on power series, for example, differentiation, addition, and multiplication of power series. Therefore, to justify the method we have to consider the theoretical basis of these operations. This will be done in the present section. The discussion will involve some concepts and facts which may be already known to the student from elementary calculus, as well as other concepts which are not considered in elementary classes. [Corresponding proofs and further details (which will not be used in this chapter) can be found in Secs. 10.4–10.9].

A **power series** is an infinite series of the form

(1) $$\sum_{m=1}^{\infty} c_m(x-a)^m = c_0 + c_1(x-a) + c_2(x-a)^2 + \cdots,$$

and we assume that the variable x, the *center a*, and the *coefficients* $c_0, c_1, \cdots$ are real, as in the previous section.

The expression

(2) $$s_n(x) = c_0 + c_1(x-a) + \cdots + c_n(x-a)^n$$

is called the nth **partial sum** of the series (1). Clearly if we omit the terms of s_n from (1) the remaining expression is

(3) $$R_n(x) = c_{n+1}(x-a)^{n+1} + c_{n+2}(x-a)^{n+2} + \cdots,$$

and this expression is called the **remainder** *of* (1) *after the term* $c_n(x-a)^n$.

For example, in the case of the geometric series

$$1 + x + x^2 + \cdots + x^n + \cdots$$

we have

$$s_1 = 1 + x, \qquad R_1 = x^2 + x^3 + x^4 + \cdots$$
$$s_2 = 1 + x + x^2, \qquad R_2 = x^3 + x^4 + x^5 + \cdots, \text{ etc.}$$

In this way we have now associated with (1) the sequence of the partial sums $s_1(x), s_2(x), \cdots$. It may happen that for some $x = x_0$ this sequence converges, say,

$$\lim_{n \to \infty} s_n(x_0) = s(x_0).$$

Then we say that the series (1) **converges**, or *is convergent, at* $x = x_0$; the number $s(x_0)$ is called the **value** or *sum* of (1) at x_0, and we write

$$s(x_0) = \sum_{m=0}^{\infty} c_m(x_0 - a)^m.$$

If that sequence is divergent at $x = x_0$, then the series (1) is said to **diverge**, or to *be divergent*, at $x = x_0$.

We remember that a *sequence* $s_1, s_2, \cdots$ is said to *converge* to a number s, or to be convergent with the limit s, if to each given positive number ϵ (no matter how small, but not zero) we can find a number N such that

(4) $$|s_n - s| < \epsilon \qquad \text{for each } n > N.$$

Geometrically speaking, (4) means that s_n with $n > N$ lies between $s - \epsilon$ and $s + \epsilon$ (Fig. 76). Of course, N will in general depend on the choice of ϵ.

Now in our case, $s = s_n + R_n$ or $R_n = s - s_n$. Hence

$$|s_n - s| = |R_n|$$

in (4), and convergence at $x = x_0$ means that we can make $|R_n(x_0)|$ as small as we please, by taking n large enough. In other words, in the case of convergence, $s_n(x_0)$ is an approximation of $s(x_0)$, and the error $|R_n(x_0)|$ of the approximation can be made smaller than any prescribed positive number ϵ by taking n sufficiently large.

If we choose $x = x_0 = a$ in (1), the series reduces to the single term c_0 because the other terms are zero. This shows that the series (1) converges at $x = a$. In some cases this may be the only value of x for which (1) converges. If there are other values of x for which the series converges, these values form an interval, the **convergence interval**, having the midpoint $x = a$. This interval may be finite, as in Fig. 77. Then the series converges for all x in the interior of the interval, that is, for all x for which

(5) $$|x - a| < R$$

and diverges when $|x - a| > R$. The interval may also be infinite, that is, the series may converge for all x.

Fig. 76. Convergence of a sequence.

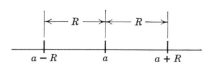

Fig. 77. Convergence interval (5) of a power series with center a.

The quantity R in Fig. 77 is called the **radius of convergence** of (1); it is the distance of each end point of the convergence interval from the center a. If the series converges for all x, then we set $R = \infty$ (and $1/R = 0$).

The radius of convergence can be determined from the coefficients of the series by means of each of the formulas

(6) $(a)\ \dfrac{1}{R} = \lim_{m \to \infty} \sqrt[m]{|c_m|}$ $(b)\ \dfrac{1}{R} = \lim_{m \to \infty} \left| \dfrac{c_{m+1}}{c_m} \right|$

provided the limits in (6) exist. (Proofs of these facts can be found in Sec. 10.8.)

For each x for which (1) converges, it has a certain value $s(x)$, depending on x; if the radius of convergence R of (1) is not zero, we write

$$s(x) = \sum_{m=0}^{\infty} c_m (x - a)^m \qquad (|x - a| < R)$$

and we say that the series (1) *represents* the function $s(x)$ in the interval of convergence.

Example 1. In the case of the **geometric series,**

$$\frac{1}{1 - x} = \sum_{m=0}^{\infty} x^m = 1 + x + x^2 + \cdots \qquad (|x| < 1).$$

In fact, $c_m = 1$ for all m, and from (6) we obtain $R = 1$, that is, the geometric series converges and represents $1/(1 - x)$ when $|x| < 1$.

Example 2. In the case of the series

$$e^x = \sum_{m=0}^{\infty} \frac{x^m}{m!} = 1 + x + \frac{x^2}{2!} + \cdots$$

we have $c_m = 1/m!$. Hence in (6b),

$$\frac{c_{m+1}}{c_m} = \frac{1/(m + 1)!}{1/m!} = \frac{1}{m + 1} \to 0 \qquad \text{as } m \to \infty$$

which means $R = \infty$; the series converges for all x.

Example 3. In the case of the series

$$\sum_{m=0}^{\infty} m!\, x^m = 1 + x + 2x^2 + 6x^3 + \cdots$$

we have $c_m = m!$, and in (6b),

$$\frac{c_{m+1}}{c_m} = \frac{(m + 1)!}{m!} = m + 1 \to \infty \qquad \text{as} \quad m \to \infty.$$

Thus $R = 0$, and the series converges only at the center $x = 0$.

We shall now consider the operations on power series which are used in connection with the power series method.

A power series may be differentiated term by term. More precisely: if

$$y(x) = \sum_{m=0}^{\infty} c_m(x-a)^m$$

converges for $|x-a| < R$ where $R > 0$, then the series obtained by differentiating term by term also converges for those x and represents the derivative y':

$$y'(x) = \sum_{m=1}^{\infty} mc_m(x-a)^{m-1}.$$

(Proof in Sec. 10.9, Theorems 3 and 5.)

Two power series may be added term by term. More precisely: if the series

(7) $$\sum_{m=0}^{\infty} b_m(x-a)^m \quad \text{and} \quad \sum_{m=0}^{\infty} c_m(x-a)^m$$

have positive radii of convergence and their sums are $f(x)$ and $g(x)$, then the series

$$\sum_{m=0}^{\infty} (b_m + c_m)(x-a)^m$$

converges and represents $f(x) + g(x)$ for each x which lies in the interior of the convergence interval of each of the given series. (Proof in Sec. 10.8.)

Two power series may be multiplied term by term. More precisely: Suppose that the series (7) have positive radii of convergence and let $f(x)$ and $g(x)$ be their sums. Then the series obtained by multiplying each term of the first series by each term of the second series and collecting like powers of $x - a$, that is,

$$b_0 c_0 + (b_0 c_1 + b_1 c_0)(x-a) + \cdots$$

$$= \sum_{n=0}^{\infty} (b_0 c_n + b_1 c_{n-1} + \cdots + b_n c_0)(x-a)^n$$

converges and represents $f(x)g(x)$ for each x in the interior of the convergence interval of each of the given series. (Proof in Sec. 10.8, Theorem 3.)

If a power series has a positive radius of convergence and a sum which is identically zero throughout its interval of convergence, then each coefficient of the series is zero. (Proof in Sec. 10.9, Theorem 2.)

These properties of power series form the theoretical basis of the power series method. The remaining question is whether a given differential equation has solutions representable by power series at all. We may answer this question by using the following concept.

A function $f(x)$ is said to be **analytic** *at a point* $x = a$, if it can be represented by a power series in powers of $x - a$ with radius of convergence $R > 0$.

Using this notion, a basic criterion of the desired type may be formulated as follows.

Theorem 1. *If the functions f, g, and r in the differential equation*

(8) $$y'' + f(x)y' + g(x)y = r(x)$$

are analytic at $x = a$, then every solution $y(x)$ of (8) is analytic at $x = a$ and can thus be represented by a power series in powers of $x - a$ with radius of convergence[2] $R > 0$.

The proof requires advanced methods of complex analysis and can be found in Ref. [B5] in Appendix 1. In applying this theorem it is important to write the linear equation in the form (8), with 1 as the coefficient of y''.

PROBLEMS

Find the radius of convergence of the following series.

1. $\displaystyle\sum_{m=0}^{\infty} \frac{x^m}{2^m}$
2. $\displaystyle\sum_{m=1}^{\infty} m\,\frac{x^m}{3^m}$
3. $\displaystyle\sum_{m=0}^{\infty} \frac{x^{2m}}{m!}$

4. $\displaystyle\sum_{m=0}^{\infty} \frac{(-1)^m x^{2m}}{(2m)!}$
5. $\displaystyle\sum_{m=0}^{\infty} \frac{(2m)!}{(m!)^2}\,x^m$
6. $\displaystyle\sum_{m=0}^{\infty} \frac{(3m)!}{(m!)^3}\,x^m$

7. $\displaystyle\sum_{m=0}^{\infty} \frac{(-1)^m x^{2m}}{2^{2m}(m!)^2}$
8. $\displaystyle\sum_{m=0}^{\infty} (-1)^m x^{2m}$
9. $\displaystyle\sum_{m=0}^{\infty} \frac{x^{m^2}}{2^m}$

10. $\displaystyle\sum_{m=1}^{\infty} \frac{x^m}{m^2 2^m}$
11. $\displaystyle\sum_{m=1}^{\infty} \frac{m+1}{3^m m}\,(x-2)^m$
12. $\displaystyle\sum_{m=0}^{\infty} \frac{(-1)^m}{5^{m+1}}\,(x-1)^{2m}$

Show that:

13. $\displaystyle\left(\sum_{m=0}^{\infty} \frac{(-1)^m}{(2m+1)!}\,x^{2m+1}\right)^2 = x^2 - \frac{1}{3}x^4 + \frac{2}{45}x^6 - + \cdots$

14. $\displaystyle\left(\sum_{m=0}^{\infty} x^m\right)^{p+1} = \sum_{m=0}^{\infty} \binom{m+p}{p}x^m,\qquad p = 0, 1, \cdots$ $\qquad(|x| < 1)$

15. $\displaystyle\sum_{k=0}^{\infty} \frac{x_1{}^k}{k!} \sum_{m=0}^{\infty} \frac{x_2{}^m}{m!} = \sum_{n=0}^{\infty} \frac{(x_1 + x_2)^n}{n!}$

Apply the power series method to the following differential equations.

16. $(x + 1)y' - (2x + 3)y = 0$ 17. $(x^4 - 1)y' + (x^4 - 4x^3 - 1)y = 0$
18. $(x - 3)y' - xy = 0$ 19. $y'' - 3y' + 2y = 0$
20. $y'' + 3y' + 2y = 0$ 21. $y'' + y = 2x^2 + x$

---

[2] R is at least equal to the distance between the point $x = a$ and that point (or those points) closest to $x = a$ at which one of the functions f, g, r, *as functions of a complex variable*, is not analytic. (Note that that point may not lie on the x-axis, but somewhere in the complex plane.)

22. $(x + 1)^2 y'' - 2(x + 1)y' + 2y = 0$

23. $(x^2 + 1)^2 y'' - 4x(x^2 + 1)y' + (6x^2 - 2)y = 0$

24. $y'' - 4xy' + (4x^2 - 2)y = 0$

25. $y'' + 2y' + y = e^{-x}$ [*Hint:* represent e^{-x} by its Maclaurin series.]

26. $(x + 1)^2 y'' - 2(x + 1)y' + (x^2 + 2x + 3)y = 0$

27. $(2x^2 - 3x + 1)y'' + 2xy' - 2y = 0$

28. Show that $y' = \dfrac{y}{x} + 1$ cannot be solved for y as a power series in x. Solve this equation for y as a power series in powers of $x - 1$. [*Hint:* introduce $t = x - 1$ as a new independent variable and solve the resulting equation for y as a power series in t.] Compare the result with that obtained by the appropriate elementary method.

Solve for y as a power series in powers of $x - 1$:

29. $y' = ky$ **30.** $y'' + y = 0$ **31.** $(x^2 + 1)y' + (x - 1)^2 y = 0$

32. Weber's[3] equation is $w'' + \left(p + \dfrac{1}{2} - \dfrac{x^2}{4} \right) w = 0$, where p is a given real number. Show that the substitution $w(x) = y(x)e^{-x^2/4}$ gives the equation $y'' - xy' + py = 0$. Show that the power series method yields the solution $y = c_0 y_1 + c_2 y_2$ where

$$y_1 = 1 - \frac{p}{2!} x^2 + \frac{p(p - 2)}{4!} x^4 - \frac{p(p - 2)(p - 4)}{6!} x^6 + - \cdots$$

$$y_2 = x - \frac{p - 1}{3!} x^3 + \frac{(p - 1)(p - 3)}{5!} x^5 - \frac{(p - 1)(p - 3)(p - 5)}{7!} x^7 + - \cdots.$$

Show that these series converge for all x.

33. Show that for $p = 0, 2, 4, \cdots$ the solution y_1 in Prob. 32 reduces to a polynomial, and for $p = 1, 3, 5, \cdots$ the same is true for y_2. These polynomials, each multiplied by a constant such that the coefficient of the highest power becomes 1, are called **Hermite[4] polynomials** and are denoted by $H_0(x), H_1(x), \cdots$. Show that

$$H_0(x) = 1 \ (p = 0), \qquad H_1(x) = x \ (p = 1), \qquad H_2(x) = x^2 - 1 \ (p = 2),$$
$$H_3(x) = x^3 - 3x \ (p = 3), \qquad H_4(x) = x^4 - 6x^2 + 3 \ (p = 4).$$

3.3 LEGENDRE'S EQUATION LEGENDRE POLYNOMIALS

Legendre's differential equation[5]

(1) $(1 - x^2)y'' - 2xy' + n(n + 1)y = 0$

arises in numerous physical problems, particularly in boundary value

---

[3] HEINRICH WEBER (1842–1913), German mathematician.

[4] CHARLES HERMITE (1822–1901), French mathematician, is known by his work in algebra and number theory.

[5] ADRIEN MARIE LEGENDRE (1752–1833), French mathematician, who made important contributions to the theory of numbers and elliptic functions.

problems for sphere. The parameter n in (1) is a given real number. Any solution of (1) is called a **Legendre function**. We note that (1) may be written

(1') $$[(1 - x^2)y']' + n(n + 1)y = 0.$$

Dividing (1) by $1 - x^2$, we obtain the standard form (8), Sec. 3.2, and we see that the coefficients of the resulting equation are analytic at $x = 0$, so that we may apply the power series method. Substituting

(2) $$y = \sum_{m=0}^{\infty} c_m x^m$$

and its derivatives into (1) and denoting the constant $n(n + 1)$ by k we obtain

$$(1 - x^2) \sum_{m=2}^{\infty} m(m - 1)c_m x^{m-2} - 2x \sum_{m=1}^{\infty} mc_m x^{m-1} + k \sum_{m=0}^{\infty} c_m x^m = 0$$

or by writing the first expression as two separate series

$$\sum_{m=2}^{\infty} m(m - 1)c_m x^{m-2} - \sum_{m=2}^{\infty} m(m - 1)c_m x^m - 2 \sum_{m=1}^{\infty} mc_m x^m + k \sum_{m=0}^{\infty} c_m x^m = 0.$$

Writing each series at length this becomes

$$
\begin{aligned}
2 \cdot 1c_2 + 3 \cdot 2c_3 x + 4 \cdot 3c_4 x^2 + \cdots &+ (s + 2)(s + 1)c_{s+2}x^s + \cdots \\
- 2 \cdot 1c_2 x^2 - \cdots &\quad - s(s - 1)c_s x^s - \cdots \\
- 2 \cdot 1c_1 x - 2 \cdot 2c_2 x^2 - \cdots &\quad - 2sc_s x^s - \cdots \\
+ kc_0 \quad + kc_1 x \quad + kc_2 x^2 + \cdots &\quad + kc_s x^s + \cdots = 0.
\end{aligned}
$$

Since this must be an identity in x if (2) is to be a solution of (1), the sum of the coefficients of each power of x must be zero; remembering that $k = n(n + 1)$ we thus have

(3a) $$2c_2 + n(n + 1)c_0 = 0, \qquad 6c_3 + [-2 + n(n + 1)]c_1 = 0$$

and in general

(3b) $$(s + 2)(s + 1)c_{s+2} + [-s(s - 1) - 2s + n(n + 1)]c_s = 0,$$
$$s = 2, 3, \cdots.$$

Since the expression in brackets $[\cdots]$ can be written $(n - s)(n + s + 1)$ we thus obtain from (3)

(4) $$c_{s+2} = - \frac{(n - s)(n + s + 1)}{(s + 2)(s + 1)} c_s, \qquad s = 0, 1, \cdots.$$

This is a recursion formula, giving each coefficient in terms of the second one preceding it, except for c_0 and c_1, which are left as arbitrary constants. We find successively

$$c_2 = -\frac{n(n+1)}{2!}c_0 \qquad\qquad c_3 = -\frac{(n-1)(n+2)}{3!}c_1$$

$$c_4 = -\frac{(n-2)(n+3)}{4\cdot 3}c_2 \qquad\qquad c_5 = -\frac{(n-3)(n+4)}{5\cdot 4}c_3$$

$$= \frac{(n-2)n(n+1)(n+3)}{4!}c_0 \qquad = \frac{(n-3)(n-1)(n+2)(n+4)}{5!}c_1$$

etc. By inserting these values for the coefficients into (2) we obtain

$$(5) \qquad\qquad y(x) = c_0 y_1(x) + c_1 y_2(x)$$

where

$$(6) \qquad y_1(x) = 1 - \frac{n(n+1)}{2!}x^2 + \frac{(n-2)n(n+1)(n+3)}{4!}x^4 - + \cdots$$

and

$$(7) \quad y_2(x) = x - \frac{(n-1)(n+2)}{3!}x^3 + \frac{(n-3)(n-1)(n+2)(n+4)}{5!}x^5 - + \cdots.$$

These series converge for $|x| < 1$. Since (6) contains even powers of x only, while (7) contains odd powers of x only, the ratio y_1/y_2 is not a constant, and y_1 and y_2 are linearly independent solutions. Hence (5) is a general solution of (1) on the interval $-1 < x < 1$.

In many applications the parameter n in Legendre's equation will be a nonnegative integer. Then the right hand side of (4) is zero when $s = n$, and, therefore, $c_{n+2} = 0$, $c_{n+4} = 0$, $c_{n+6} = 0, \cdots$. Hence, if n is even, $y_1(x)$ reduces to a polynomial of degree n. If n is odd, the same is true with respect to $y_2(x)$. These polynomials, multiplied by some constants, are called **Legendre polynomials**. Because they are of great practical importance, let us consider them in more detail. For this purpose we write (4) in the form

$$(8) \qquad\qquad c_s = -\frac{(s+2)(s+1)}{(n-s)(n+s+1)}c_{s+2} \qquad\qquad (s \leq n-2)$$

and may then express all the nonvanishing coefficients in terms of the coefficient c_n of the highest power of x of the polynomial. The coefficient c_n is then arbitrary. It is customary to choose $c_n = 1$ when $n = 0$ and

$$(9) \qquad\qquad c_n = \frac{(2n)!}{2^n(n!)^2} = \frac{1\cdot 3\cdot 5\cdots(2n-1)}{n!}, \qquad n = 1, 2, \cdots,$$

the reason being that for this choice of c_n all those polynomials will have the value 1 when $x = 1$ (cf. Prob. 21). We then obtain from (8) and (9)

$$c_{n-2} = -\frac{n(n-1)}{2(2n-1)}c_n = -\frac{n(n-1)(2n)!}{2(2n-1)2^n(n!)^2}$$

(9*)

$$= -\frac{n(n-1)2n(2n-1)(2n-2)!}{2(2n-1)2^n n(n-1)!\, n(n-1)(n-2)!},$$

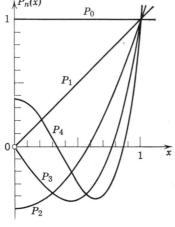

$P_n(x)$

P_0

P_1

P_4

P_3

P_2

Fig. 78. Legendre polynomials.

that is,

$$c_{n-2} = -\frac{(2n-2)!}{2^n(n-1)!\,(n-2)!}.$$

Similarly,

$$c_{n-4} = -\frac{(n-2)(n-3)}{4(2n-3)}c_{n-2}$$

$$= \frac{(2n-4)!}{2^n 2!\,(n-2)!\,(n-4)!}$$

etc., and in general, when $n - 2m \geqq 0$,

(10)

$$c_{n-2m} = (-1)^m \frac{(2n-2m)!}{2^n m!\,(n-m)!\,(n-2m)!}.$$

The resulting solution of Legendre's equation is called the **Legendre polynomial** *of degree n* and is denoted by $P_n(x)$; from (10) we obtain

$$P_n(x) = \sum_{m=0}^{M} (-1)^m \frac{(2n-2m)!}{2^n m!\,(n-m)!\,(n-2m)!}x^{n-2m}$$

(11)

$$= \frac{(2n)!}{2^n(n!)^2}x^n - \frac{(2n-2)!}{2^n 1!\,(n-1)!\,(n-2)!}x^{n-2} + - \cdots$$

where $M = n/2$ or $(n-1)/2$ whichever is an integer. In particular (Fig. 78)

$$P_0(x) = 1, \qquad\qquad\qquad P_1(x) = x,$$

(11′) $P_2(x) = \frac{1}{2}(3x^2 - 1)$, $\qquad\qquad P_3(x) = \frac{1}{2}(5x^3 - 3x)$,

$\qquad\quad P_4(x) = \frac{1}{8}(35x^4 - 30x^2 + 3)$, $\qquad P_5(x) = \frac{1}{8}(63x^5 - 70x^3 + 15x)$,

etc.

PROBLEMS

1. Show that Legendre's equation (1) may be written in the form (1′).

2. Derive (11′) from (11). Find and graph $P_6(x)$.

3. Verify by inserting that $P_n(x)$, $n = 0, 1, \cdots, 5$ [cf. (11')] is a solution of (1).

4. Show that $P_n(-x) = (-1)^n P_n(x)$.

5. Find a solution of $(a^2 - z^2)y'' - 2zy' + 12y = 0$, $a \neq 0$. *Hint:* set $z = ax$.

6. Show that

$$(12) \qquad P_n(x) = \frac{1}{2^n n!} \frac{d^n}{dx^n} [(x^2 - 1)^n] \qquad \textbf{(Rodrigues' formula).}$$

Hint: apply the binomial theorem to $(x^2 - 1)^n$, differentiate the result n times term by term, and compare with (11).

7. Using (12) and integrating n times by parts, show that

$$(13) \qquad \int_{-1}^{1} P_n^2(x)\, dx = \frac{2}{2n + 1} \qquad n = 0, 1, \cdots.$$

8. Verify (13) for $n = 0, 1, 2, 3$ by direct integration.

9. Start from the Legendre equations

$$[(1 - x^2)P_m']' = -m(m + 1)P_m, \qquad [(1 - x^2)P_n']' = -n(n + 1)P_n.$$

Multiply the first by P_n, the last by $-P_m$ and add. Integrate the resulting equation over x from -1 to 1. Integrate the integrals on the left by parts, finding

$$[(1 - x^2)(P_n P_m' - P_m P_n')]\Big|_{-1}^{1} - \int_{-1}^{1} (1 - x^2)(P_n' P_m' - P_m' P_n')\, dx$$

$$= (n - m)(m + n + 1) \int_{-1}^{1} P_m P_n\, dx.$$

Conclude that

$$(14) \qquad \int_{-1}^{1} P_m(x)P_n(x)\, dx = 0 \qquad (m \neq n).$$

(This so-called *orthogonality* of the Legendre polynomials on the interval $-1 \leq x \leq 1$ will be considered from a more general point of view in Sec. 8.12.)

10. Verify (14) for $m, n = 0, 1, 2$ by direct calculation.

11. Show that $f(x) = 3x^2 - 4x + 5$ can be represented in the form

$$f(x) = c_0 P_0 + c_1 P_1(x) + c_2 P_2(x).$$

12. Show that any polynomial $f(x)$ of degree n can be represented in the form

$$(15) \qquad f(x) = c_0 P_0 + c_1 P_1(x) + \cdots + c_n P_n(x).$$

Hint: proceed by induction.

13. Multiplying (15) by $P_m(x)$, integrating from -1 to 1, and using (13) and (14), show that in (15),

$$(16) \qquad c_m = \frac{2m + 1}{2} \int_{-1}^{1} f(x)P_m(x)\, dx, \qquad m = 0, 1, \cdots, n.$$

14. Determine c_0, c_1, c_2 in Prob. 11 by means of (16).

Represent the following polynomials in the form (15).

15. $10x^3 - 3x^2 - 5x - 1$ **16.** $35x^4 + 15x^3 - 30x^2 - 15x + 3$

17. Show that if $f(x)$ is an even polynomial,

$$\int_{-1}^{1} f(x) P_m(x)\, dx = 0 \qquad (m \text{ odd}).$$

18. Represent each of the functions 1, x, x^2, x^3 in terms of Legendre polynomials.

19. Using the idea in Prob. 9 and the fact that $y_n = \sin nx$ satisfies the differential equation $y'' + n^2 y = 0$, show that

$$\int_{-\pi}^{\pi} \sin mx \sin nx\, dx = 0 \qquad (m, n \text{ integral and positive, } m \neq n).$$

20. Show that

(17)
$$\frac{1}{\sqrt{1 - 2xu + u^2}} = P_0 + P_1(x)u + P_2(x)u^2 + P_3(x)u^3 + \cdots.$$

Hint: start from the binomial expansion of $1/\sqrt{1 - v}$, set $v = 2xu - u^2$, multiply the powers of $2xu - u^2$ out, collect all the terms involving u^n and verify that the sum of these terms is $P_n(x)u^n$.

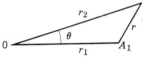

Fig. 79. Problem 22.

21. Using (17), show that
$$P_n(1) = 1, \; P_n(-1) = (-1)^n, \; P_{2n+1}(0) = 0,$$
$$P_{2n}(0) = (-1)^n \frac{1 \cdot 3 \cdots (2n - 1)}{2 \cdot 4 \cdots (2n)}.$$

22. Let A_1 and A_2 be two points in space (Fig. 79, $r_2 > 0$). Using (17), show that

$$\frac{1}{r} = \frac{1}{\sqrt{r_1^2 + r_2^2 - 2r_1 r_2 \cos \theta}} = \frac{1}{r_2}\left[P_0 + P_1(\cos \theta)\frac{r_1}{r_2} + P_2(\cos \theta)\left(\frac{r_1}{r_2}\right)^2 + \cdots \right].$$

23. Show that the series (6) and (7) converge for $|x| < 1$.
24. Obtain the formulas (11') by means of Rodrigues' formula (Prob. 6).

3.4 EXTENDED POWER SERIES METHOD. INDICIAL EQUATION

Several second-order differential equations, which are highly important in many applications, have coefficients which are not analytic at $x = 0$ (definition in Sec. 3.2), but are such that the following theorem can be applied.

Theorem 1. *Any differential equation of the form*

(1)
$$y'' + \frac{a(x)}{x} y' + \frac{b(x)}{x^2} y = 0,$$

where the functions $a(x)$ and $b(x)$ are analytic at $x = 0$, has at least one solution which can be represented in the form

(2)
$$y(x) = x^r \sum_{m=0}^{\infty} c_m x^m = x^r(c_0 + c_1 x + c_2 x^2 + \cdots) \qquad (c_0 \neq 0)$$

where the exponent r may be any (real or complex) number (and is chosen so that $c_0 \neq 0$).[6]

The *proof* requires advanced methods of complex analysis and can be found in Ref. [B5], Appendix 1. The following method for solving (1) is called the **Frobenius' method.**[7]

To solve (1), we write it in the somewhat more convenient form

(1')
$$x^2 y'' + x a(x) y' + b(x) y = 0.$$

We first expand $a(x)$ and $b(x)$ in power series,

$$a(x) = a_0 + a_1 x + a_2 x^2 + \cdots, \qquad b(x) = b_0 + b_1 x + b_2 x^2 + \cdots.$$

Then we differentiate (2) term by term, finding

$$y'(x) = \sum_{m=0}^{\infty} (m + r) c_m x^{m+r-1} = x^{r-1}[rc_0 + (r + 1)c_1 x + \cdots]$$

$$y''(x) = \sum_{m=0}^{\infty} (m + r)(m + r - 1) c_m x^{m+r-2}$$

$$= x^{r-2}[r(r - 1)c_0 + (r + 1) r c_1 x + \cdots].$$

By inserting all these series into (1') we readily obtain

$$x^r[r(r - 1)c_0 + \cdots] + (a_0 + a_1 x + \cdots)x^r(rc_0 + \cdots)$$
$$+ (b_0 + b_1 x + \cdots)x^r(c_0 + c_1 x + \cdots) = 0.$$

We now equate the sum of the coefficients of each power of x to zero, as before. This yields a system of equations involving the unknown coefficients c_m. The smallest power is x^r, and the corresponding equation is

$$[r(r - 1) + a_0 r + b_0]c_0 = 0.$$

Since by assumption $c_0 \neq 0$ we obtain

(3)
$$r^2 + (a_0 - 1)r + b_0 = 0.$$

This important quadratic equation is called the **indicial equation** of the differential equation (1). We shall see that our method will yield a fundamental system of solutions; one of the solutions will always be of the form

[6] In this theorem, the variable x may be replaced by $x - a$ where a is any number.
[7] GEORG FROBENIUS (1849–1917), German mathematician, who also made important contributions to the theory of matrices and groups.

(2), but for the form of the other solution there will be three different possibilities corresponding to the following cases.

Case 1. *The roots of the indicial equation are distinct and do not differ by an integer* $(1, 2, 3, \cdots)$.[8]

Case 2. *The indicial equation has a double root.*

Case 3. *The roots of the indicial equation differ by an integer.*

Let us discuss these cases separately.

Case 1 is the simplest case. Let r_1 and r_2 be the roots of (3). If we insert $r = r_1$ into the aforementioned system of equations and determine the coefficients $c_1, c_2, \cdots$ successively, as before, then we obtain a solution

$$y_1(x) = x^{r_1}(c_0 + c_1 x + c_2 x^2 + \cdots).$$

To obtain another solution of (1), we insert $r = r_2$ in that system and determine another set of coefficients, say, $c_1{}^*, c_2{}^*, \cdots$. Of course these coefficients will, in general, be different from those in y_1. In this way we obtain another solution

$$y_2(x) = x^{r_2}(c_0{}^* + c_1{}^* x + c_2{}^* x^2 + \cdots).$$

Since $r_1 - r_2$ is not an integer, y_1/y_2 is not constant, and y_1 and y_2 are linearly independent solutions. Hence they form a fundamental system of (1) on the interval of convergence of both series.

Case 2. The indicial equation (3) has a double root r if, and only if, $(a_0 - 1)^2 - 4b = 0$, and then $r = (1 - a_0)/2$. We may determine a first solution

$$(4) \qquad\qquad y_1(x) = x^r(c_0 + c_1 x + c_2 x^2 + \cdots) \qquad \left(r = \frac{1 - a_0}{2}\right)$$

as before. To find another solution we may apply the method of variation of parameters, that is, we replace the constant c in the solution cy_1 by a function $u(x)$ to be determined such that

$$(5) \qquad\qquad y_2(x) = u(x)y_1(x)$$

is a solution of (1). By inserting (5) and the derivatives

$$y_2{}' = u'y_1 + uy_1{}', \qquad y_2{}'' = u''y_1 + 2u'y_1{}' + uy_1{}''$$

into the differential equation (1') we obtain

$$x^2\,(u''y_1 + 2u'y_1{}' + uy_1{}'') + xa(u'y_1 + uy_1{}') + buy_1 = 0.$$

---

[8] Note that this case includes complex conjugate roots r_1 and $r_2 = \bar{r}_1$, because $r_1 - r_2 = r_1 - \bar{r}_1 = 2i\,\text{Im}\,r_1 \neq \pm 1, \pm 2, \cdots$.

Since y_1 is a solution of (1'), the sum of the terms involving u is zero, and the last equation reduces to

$$x^2 y_1 u'' + 2x^2 y_1' u' + x a y_1 u' = 0.$$

By dividing by $x^2 y_1$ and inserting the power series for a we obtain

$$u'' + \left(2 \frac{y_1'}{y_1} + \frac{a_0}{x} + \cdots \right) u' = 0.$$

Here and in the following the dots designate terms which are constant or involve positive powers of x. Now from (4) it follows that

$$\frac{y_1'}{y_1} = \frac{x^{r-1}[rc_0 + (r+1)c_1 x + \cdots]}{x^r[c_0 + c_1 x + \cdots]}$$

$$= \frac{1}{x} \left(\frac{rc_0 + (r+1)c_1 x + \cdots}{c_0 + c_1 x + \cdots} \right) = \frac{r}{x} + \cdots.$$

Hence the last equation can be written

$$(6) \qquad u'' + \left(\frac{2r + a_0}{x} + \cdots \right) u' = 0.$$

Since $r = (1 - a_0)/2$ the term $(2r + a_0)/x$ equals $1/x$, and by dividing by u' we thus have

$$\frac{u''}{u'} = -\frac{1}{x} + \cdots.$$

By integration we obtain

$$\ln u' = -\ln x + \cdots \qquad \text{or} \qquad u' = \frac{1}{x} e^{(\cdots)}.$$

Expanding the exponential function in powers of x and integrating once more, we see that the expression for u will be of the form

$$u = \ln x + k_1 x + k_2 x^2 + \cdots.$$

By inserting this into (5) we have the following result.

If the indicial equation has a double root r, then linearly independent solutions of (1) *are of the form* (4) *and*

$$(7) \qquad y_2(x) = y_1(x) \ln x + x^r \sum_{m=1}^{\infty} A_m x^m.$$

The simplest illustration of this result is given by the Cauchy equation (Sec. 2.7) in the critical case (cf. also Ex. 2, below).

Case 3. If the roots r_1 and r_2 of the indicial equation (3) differ by an integer, say, $r_1 = r$ and $r_2 = r - p$ where p is a positive integer, then we may always determine one solution as before, namely, the solution

$$y_1(x) = x^{r_1}(c_0 + c_1 x + c_2 x^2 + \cdots)$$

corresponding to the root r_1. However, for the root r_2 there may arise difficulties, and it may not be possible to determine a solution y_2 by the method used in Case 1. Let us illustrate this unexpected fact by an example.

Example 1. We consider the differential equation

$$(Ax^2 - 2)x^2 y'' - (Ax^2 + 2)xy' + (Ax^2 + 2)y = 0,$$

where A is a given constant. By substituting (2) and its derivatives into the equation we first have

$$(Ax^2 - 2) \sum_{m=0}^{\infty} (m + r)(m + r - 1)c_m x^{m+r}$$

$$- (Ax^2 + 2) \sum_{m=0}^{\infty} (m + r)c_m x^{m+r} + (Ax^2 + 2) \sum_{m=0}^{\infty} c_m x^{m+r} = 0.$$

Performing the indicated multiplications, we obtain

$$A \sum_{m=0}^{\infty} [(m + r)(m + r - 1) - (m + r) + 1]c_m x^{m+r+2}$$

$$-2 \sum_{m=0}^{\infty} [(m + r)(m + r - 1) + (m + r) - 1]c_m x^{m+r} = 0.$$

Simplifying the expressions in brackets, this becomes

$$(8) \quad A \sum_{m=0}^{\infty} (m + r - 1)^2 c_m x^{m+r+2} - 2 \sum_{m=0}^{\infty} (m + r + 1)(m + r - 1)c_m x^{m+r} = 0.$$

By equating the coefficient of x^r to zero we obtain the indicial equation

$$(r + 1)(r - 1) = 0.$$

The roots $r_1 = 1$ and $r_2 = -1$ differ by an integer.
By equating the coefficient of x^{r+1} in (8) to zero we find

$$[-2(r + 2)r]c_1 = 0.$$

For both r_1 and r_2 the expression in brackets is not zero and, therefore, $c_1 = 0$.
By equating the sum of the coefficients of x^{s+r+2} in (8) to zero we find

$$(9) \qquad A(s + r - 1)^2 c_s = 2(s + r + 3)(s + r + 1)c_{s+2}, \quad s = 0, 1, \cdots.$$

For the larger root $r_1 = 1$ this becomes

$$As^2 c_s = 2(s + 4)(s + 2)c_{s+2} \qquad \text{or} \qquad c_{s+2} = \frac{As^2}{2(s + 4)(s + 2)} c_s.$$

Since $c_1 = 0$, it follows that $c_3 = 0$, $c_5 = 0$, etc. For $s = 0$ we obtain $c_2 = 0$, and, taking $s = 2, 4, \cdots$, it follows from this that $c_4 = 0$, $c_6 = 0$, etc. Hence the solution corresponding to the root $r_1 = 1$ is

$$y_1 = c_0 x.$$

For the smaller root $r_2 = -1$ the formula (9) becomes

(10) $$A(s - 2)^2 c_s = 2(s + 2)s c_{s+2}, \qquad s = 0, 1, \cdots.$$

Hence, if $A = 0$, we obtain from this $c_2 = 0$, $c_3 = 0$, etc., and since $c_1 = 0$ (see before) a second solution is

$$y_2 = c_0 x^{-1} = \frac{c_0}{x} \qquad\qquad (A = 0).$$

In fact, for $A = 0$ our equation reduces to the Cauchy equation (cf. Sec. 2.7)

$$x^2 y'' + xy' - y = 0.$$

However, if $A \neq 0$, then (10) with $s = 0$ becomes

$$4Ac_0 = 0,$$

which requires $c_0 = 0$. This contradicts our initial assumption that $c_0 \neq 0$ and shows that in this case we do not obtain a solution of the form (2) corresponding to the smaller root r_2. We shall see in Ex. 4 (below) that when $A \neq 0$ the second solution is not of the form (2).

This example illustrates the situation in the present case. To determine a second solution corresponding to the smaller root, we may proceed as in Case 2. The first steps are literally the same and yield equation (6). We determine $2r + a_0$ in (6). From elementary algebra we know that the coefficient $a_0 - 1$ in (3) equals $-(r_1 + r_2)$. In our case, $r_1 = r$, $r_2 = r - p$, and, therefore, $a_0 - 1 = p - 2r$. Hence in (6), $2r + a_0 = p + 1$, and we obtain

$$\frac{u''}{u'} = - \left(\frac{p + 1}{x} + \cdots \right).$$

The further steps are as in Case 2. Integrating, we find

$$\ln u' = -(p + 1) \ln x + \cdots \qquad \text{or} \qquad u' = x^{-(p+1)} e^{(\cdots)}$$

where the dots stand for some series of nonnegative powers of x. By expanding the exponential function as before we obtain a series of the form

$$u' = \frac{1}{x^{p+1}} + \frac{k_1}{x^p} + \cdots + \frac{k_p}{x} + k_{p+1} + k_{p+2} x + \cdots.$$

By integrating once more we have

$$u = -\frac{1}{px^p} - \cdots + k_p \ln x + k_{p+1} x + \cdots.$$

Multiplying this expression by the series

$$y_1 = x^{r_1}(c_0 + c_1 x + \cdots)$$

and remembering that $r_1 - p = r_2$ we see that $y_2 = uy_1$ is of the form

(11) $$y_2(x) = k_p y_1(x) \ln x + x^{r_2} \sum_{m=0}^{\infty} C_m x^m.$$

We may sum up our result as follows.

If the roots of the indicial equation (3) differ by an integer, then to the root with the larger real part there corresponds a solution of (1) of the form (2), and to the other root (say, r_2) there corresponds a solution of the form (11). The solutions form a fundamental system of (1).

While in the case of a double root of (3) the second solution always contains a logarithmic term, the coefficient k_p in (11) may be zero and in the present case the logarithmic term may be missing (cf. Ex. 2).[9]

Example 2. In Sec. 2.7 we have seen that the **Cauchy equation**

(12) $$x^2 y'' + a_0 xy' + b_0 y = 0 \qquad (a_0, b_0 \text{ constant})$$

can be solved by substituting $y = x^r$ into (12). This yields the auxiliary equation

$$r^2 + (a_0 - 1)r + b_0 = 0.$$

Obviously, this is the indicial equation. If $r_1 \neq r_2$, then $y_1 = x^{r_1}$, $y_2 = x^{r_2}$ form a fundamental system; this corresponds to our present Cases 1 and 3. If $r_1 = r_2 = r$, then the solutions

$$y_1 = x^r, \qquad y_2 = y_1 \ln x = x^r \ln x$$

form a fundamental system, as follows by substituting (7) into (12), in agreement with the result in Sec. 2.7.

Example 3. Solve

(13) $$x(x - 1)y'' + (3x - 1)y' + y = 0.$$

Writing this equation in the standard form (1), we see that it satisfies the assumptions in Theorem 1. By inserting (2) and its derivatives into (13) we have

(14)
$$\sum_{m=0}^{\infty} (m + r)(m + r - 1)c_m x^{m+r} - \sum_{m=0}^{\infty} (m + r)(m + r - 1)c_m x^{m+r-1}$$
$$+ 3 \sum_{m=0}^{\infty} (m + r)c_m x^{m+r} - \sum_{m=0}^{\infty} (m + r)c_m x^{m+r-1} + \sum_{m=0}^{\infty} c_m x^{m+r} = 0.$$

The smallest power is x^{r-1}; by equating the sum of its coefficients to zero we have

$$[-r(r - 1) - r]c_0 = 0 \qquad \text{or} \qquad r^2 = 0.$$

Hence this indicial equation has the double root $r = 0$. We insert this value into (14) and equate the sum of the coefficients of the power x^s to zero, finding

$$s(s - 1)c_s - (s + 1)sc_{s+1} + 3sc_s - (s + 1)c_{s+1} + c_s = 0$$

[9] A general consideration about the convergence of those series will not be presented here, but in each individual case convergence may be tested in the usual way.

or $c_{s+1} = c_s$. Hence $c_0 = c_1 = c_2 = \cdots$, and by choosing $c_0 = 1$ we obtain

$$y_1(x) = \sum_{m=0}^{\infty} x^m = \frac{1}{1-x}.$$

To obtain a second solution we substitute $y_2 = uy_1$ into (13), finding

$$x(x - 1)(u''y_1 + 2u'y_1' + uy_1'') + (3x - 1)(u'y_1 + uy_1') + uy_1 = 0.$$

Since y_1 is a solution of (13), this reduces to

$$x(x - 1)(u''y_1 + 2u'y_1') + (3x - 1)u'y_1 = 0.$$

By inserting the expressions for y_1 and y_1' and simplifying we obtain

$$xu'' + u' = 0 \qquad \text{or} \qquad \frac{u''}{u'} = -\frac{1}{x}.$$

By integrating twice we finally obtain $u = \ln x$, and a second solution is

$$y_2 = uy_1 = \frac{\ln x}{1-x}.$$

In Cases 2 and 3, a second solution may be obtained by the method of variation of parameters (Ex. 3) or by substituting the appropriate general expression (7) or (11) into the equation and determining the unknown coefficients in these expressions successively. The latter method may be preferable if the integrations required in the other method are complicated. Let us illustrate this method by the following example.

Example 4. Find a second independent solution of the differential equation in Ex. 1 when $A \neq 0$. Since the roots of the indicial equation differ by an integer and the smaller root is $r_2 = -1$, we see from (11) that the desired solution must be of the form

$$y_2(x) = kx \ln x + \frac{1}{x} \sum_{m=0}^{\infty} C_m x^m.$$

Substituting this and the derivatives into the differential equation, we obtain

$$(Ax^2 - 2)x^2 \left[\frac{k}{x} + \sum_{m=0}^{\infty} (m - 1)(m - 2)C_m x^{m-3} \right]$$

$$-(Ax^2 + 2)x \left[k \ln x + k + \sum_{m=0}^{\infty} (m - 1)C_m x^{m-2} \right]$$

$$+(Ax^2 + 2) \left[kx \ln x + \sum_{m=0}^{\infty} C_m x^{m-1} \right] = 0.$$

The logarithmic terms cancel out, and simplification yields

$$-4kx + A \sum_{m=0}^{\infty} [(m - 1)(m - 2) - (m - 1) + 1]C_m x^{m+1}$$

$$- 2 \sum_{m=0}^{\infty} [(m - 1)(m - 2) + (m - 1) - 1]C_m x^{m-1} = 0.$$

Simplifying the expressions in brackets, this becomes

$$A \sum_{m=0}^{\infty} (m-2)^2 C_m x^{m+1} = 4kx + 2 \sum_{m=0}^{\infty} m(m-2)C_m x^{m-1}.$$

By equating the coefficients of each occurring power x^s on both sides we obtain

$$0 = C_1 \qquad\qquad\qquad (s = 0)$$

(15) $$\qquad 4AC_0 = 4k \qquad\qquad \text{or} \qquad k = AC_0 \qquad\qquad (s = 1)$$

$$A(s-3)^2 C_{s-1} = 2(s^2-1)C_{s+1} \qquad \text{or} \qquad C_{s+1} = \frac{A(s-3)^2}{2(s^2-1)} C_{s-1}$$

$$(s = 2, 3, \cdots)$$

For $s = 3$ we obtain $C_4 = 0$ and, therefore, by taking $s = 5, 7, \cdots$ we see that $C_6 = 0$, $C_8 = 0$, etc. Since $C_1 = 0$, taking $s = 2, 4, \cdots$, it follows that $C_3 = 0$, $C_5 = 0$, etc. Since $k = AC_0$ and C_2 remains arbitrary we have the result

$$y_2 = AC_0 x \ln x + \frac{1}{x}(C_0 + C_2 x^2).$$

We see that the last term is $C_2 y_1$, and we may choose $C_2 = 0$. Taking $C_0 = 1$, our second solution becomes

(16) $$\qquad\qquad y_2 = Ax \ln x + \frac{1}{x}.$$

PROBLEMS

Using the Frobenius method, find a fundamental system of solutions of the following equations. In each case try to identify the obtained series as expansions of known functions.

1. $x^2 y'' + 6xy' + (6 - x^2)y = 0$

2. $xy'' + 2y' + xy = 0$

3. $x(1-x)y'' + 2(1-2x)y' - 2y = 0$

4. $2x(x-1)y'' - (x+1)y' + y = 0$

5. $x^2 y'' + \dfrac{x}{2} y' - \frac{3}{2}y = 0$

6. $x^2 y'' + \frac{3}{16}y = 0$

7. $xy'' + y' - xy = 0$

8. $xy'' - y = 0$

9. $2x(x-1)y'' - (4x^2 - 3x + 1)y' + (2x^2 - x + 2)y = 0$

10. $x^2(x+1)^2 y'' - (5x^2 + 8x + 3)xy' + (9x^2 + 11x + 4)y = 0$

11. $4x^2 y'' + 8xy' + y = 0$

12. $x^2 y'' + 2xy' - 6y = 0$

13. $2x(1-2x)y'' + (4x^2 + 1)y' - (2x + 1)y = 0$

14. $(1+x)x^2 y'' - (1+2x)xy' + (1+2x)y = 0$

15. $x(x+1)^2 y'' + (1-x^2)y' + (x-1)y = 0$

16. $2x^2 y'' + (4x+5)xy' + (2x^2 + 5x - 2)y = 0$

17. $xy'' + (1-2x)y' + (x-1)y = 0$

18. $x^2 y'' + x^3 y' + (x^2 - 2)y = 0$
19. $2x(1 - 2x)y'' + (12x^2 - 4x + 1)y' - 2(4x^2 + 1)y = 0$
20. $2x^2(1 - 2x)y'' + (4x^2 - 8x + 5)xy' + (2x^2 - x + 1)y = 0$
21. The equation

(17) $x(1 - x)y'' + [c - (a + b + 1)x]y' - aby = 0$

$\hspace{6cm}$ (a, b, c constant)

is known as **Gauss's hypergeometric equation.** Show that the roots of the corresponding indicial equation are $r_1 = 0$ and $r_2 = 1 - c$.

22. Show that for $r_1 = 0$ in Prob. 21 the Frobenius method yields the solution

$$y_1(x) = 1 + \frac{ab}{1!\,c}\,x + \frac{a(a + 1)b(b + 1)}{2!\,c(c + 1)}\,x^2$$

(18)

$$+ \frac{a(a + 1)(a + 2)b(b + 1)(b + 2)}{3!\,c(c + 1)(c + 2)}\,x^3 + \cdots$$

$$(c \neq 0, -1, -2, \cdots).$$

This series is called the **hypergeometric series**; its sum $y_1(x)$ is usually denoted by $F(a, b, c; x)$ and is called the **hypergeometric function.** It satisfies numerous relations, and many elementary functions are special cases of $F(a, b, c; x)$; cf. the following problems.

Using (18), prove the following statements and relations.
23. The series (18) converges for $|x| < 1$.
24. $F(1, b, b; x) = 1 + x + x^2 + \cdots$, the geometric series.
25. If a or b is a negative integer, (18) reduces to a polynomial.
26. $\dfrac{dF(a, b, c; x)}{dx} = \dfrac{ab}{c}\,F(a + 1, b + 1, c + 1; x)$,

$\dfrac{d^2 F(a, b, c; x)}{dx^2} = \dfrac{a(a + 1)b(b + 1)}{c(c + 1)}\,F(a + 2, b + 2, c + 2; x)$, etc.

27. $(1 + x)^n = F(-n, b, b; -x)$, $\qquad \ln(1 + x) = xF(1, 1, 2; -x)$,

$\quad$ arc sin $x = xF(\tfrac{1}{2}, \tfrac{1}{2}, \tfrac{3}{2}; x^2)$, $\qquad \ln\dfrac{1 + x}{1 - x} = 2xF(\tfrac{1}{2}, 1, \tfrac{3}{2}; x^2)$.

28. Show that for $r_2 = 1 - c$ in Prob. 21 the Frobenius method yields the solution

$$y_2(x) = x^{1-c}\left[1 + \frac{(a - c + 1)(b - c + 1)}{1!\,(-c + 2)}\,x \right.$$

$$\left. + \frac{(a - c + 1)(a - c + 2)(b - c + 1)(b - c + 2)}{2!\,(-c + 2)(-c + 3)}\,x^2 + \cdots \right]$$

$$(c \neq 2, 3, 4, \cdots).$$

29. Show that in Prob. 28,

$$y_2(x) = x^{1-c}F(a - c + 1, b - c + 1, 2 - c; x).$$

30. Show that if $c \neq 0, \pm 1, \pm 2, \cdots$, the functions y_1 and y_2 (Probs. 22, 28) constitute a fundamental system of the hypergeometric equation (17).

Solve, in terms of the hypergeometric function, the following equations.

31. $4x(1 - x)y'' + 2(1 - 4x)y' - y = 0$

32. $2x(1 - x)y'' - (6x + 1)y' - 2y = 0$

33. $3x(1 - x)y'' + (1 - 5x)y' + y = 0$

34. $x(1 - x)y'' + (Cx + K)y' + My = 0$ (C, K, M are constants.)

35. Consider the equation

$$(t^2 + At + B)\frac{d^2y}{dt^2} + (Ct + D)\frac{dy}{dt} + Ky = 0$$

where A, B, C, D, and K are constants and $t^2 + At + B$ has the distinct real roots t_1 and t_2. Show that by introducing the new independent variable

$$x = \frac{t - t_1}{t_2 - t_1}.$$

the equation becomes the hypergeometric equation where

$$\frac{Ct_1 + D}{t_2 - t_1} = -c, \quad C = a + b + 1, \quad K = ab.$$

3.5   BESSEL'S EQUATION. BESSEL FUNCTIONS OF THE FIRST KIND

One of the most important differential equations in applied mathematics is **Bessel's differential equation**[10]

(1) $$x^2y'' + xy' + (x^2 - \nu^2)y = 0$$

where the parameter ν is a given number. We assume that ν is real and nonnegative. This equation is of the type characterized in Theorem 1, Sec. 3.4, and therefore has a solution of the form

(2) $$y(x) = \sum_{m=0}^{\infty} c_m x^{m+r} \qquad (c_0 \neq 0).$$

Substituting this expression and its first and second derivatives into Bessel's equation, we readily obtain

$$\sum_{m=0}^{\infty} (m + r)(m + r - 1)c_m x^{m+r} + \sum_{m=0}^{\infty} (m + r)c_m x^{m+r}$$
$$+ \sum_{m=0}^{\infty} c_m x^{m+r+2} - \nu^2 \sum_{m=0}^{\infty} c_m x^{m+r} = 0.$$

---

[10] FRIEDRICH WILHELM BESSEL (1784–1846), German astronomer and mathematician.

By equating the sum of the coefficients of x^{s+r} to zero we find

$$\text{(a)} \qquad\qquad r(r-1)c_0 + rc_0 - v^2c_0 = 0 \qquad\qquad (s=0)$$
$$\text{(3) (b)} \qquad\qquad (r+1)rc_1 + (r+1)c_1 - v^2c_1 = 0 \qquad\qquad (s=1)$$
$$\text{(c)} \quad (s+r)(s+r-1)c_s + (s+r)c_s + c_{s-2} - v^2c_s = 0 \quad (s=2,3,\cdots).$$

From (3a) we obtain the indicial equation

$$\text{(4)} \qquad\qquad (r+v)(r-v) = 0.$$

The roots are $r_1 = v\ (\geq 0)$ and $r_2 = -v$.

Let us first determine a solution corresponding to the root r_1. For this value of r, equation (3b) yields $c_1 = 0$. Equation (3c) may be written

$$(s+r+v)(s+r-v)c_s + c_{s-2} = 0,$$

and for $r = v$ this takes the form

$$\text{(5)} \qquad\qquad (s+2v)sc_s + c_{s-2} = 0.$$

Since $c_1 = 0$ and $v \geq 0$ it follows that $c_3 = 0$, $c_5 = 0, \cdots$, successively. If we set $s = 2m$ in (5), we obtain

$$\text{(6)} \qquad\qquad c_{2m} = -\frac{1}{2^2 m(v+m)}\, c_{2m-2}, \qquad m = 1, 2, \cdots$$

and may determine the coefficients c_2, c_4, $\cdots$ successively.

c_0 is arbitrary. It is customary to put

$$\text{(7)} \qquad\qquad c_0 = \frac{1}{2^v\Gamma(v+1)}$$

where $\Gamma(v+1)$ is the **Gamma function**. The properties of this important function will be considered in Sec. 14.1. For the present purpose it suffices to know that $\Gamma(\alpha)$ is defined by the integral

$$\text{(8)} \qquad\qquad \Gamma(\alpha) = \int_0^\infty e^{-t}t^{\alpha-1}\, dt \qquad\qquad (\alpha > 0).$$

By integration by parts we obtain

$$\Gamma(\alpha+1) = \int_0^\infty e^{-t}t^\alpha\, dt = -e^{-t}t^\alpha\Big|_0^\infty + \alpha\int_0^\infty e^{-t}t^{\alpha-1}\, dt.$$

The first expression on the right is zero, and the integral on the right is $\Gamma(\alpha)$. This yields the basic relation

$$\text{(9)} \qquad\qquad \Gamma(\alpha+1) = \alpha\Gamma(\alpha).$$

Since

$$\Gamma(1) = \int_0^\infty e^{-t}\, dt = 1$$

we conclude from (9) that

$$\Gamma(2) = \Gamma(1) = 1!, \qquad \Gamma(3) = 2\Gamma(2) = 2!, \cdots$$

and in general

(10) $$\Gamma(k + 1) = k! \qquad (k = 0, 1, \cdots).$$

This shows that the Gamma function may be regarded as a generalization of the factorial function known from elementary calculus.

Returning to our problem, we obtain from (6), (7), and (9)

$$c_2 = -\frac{c_0}{2^2(v + 1)} = -\frac{1}{2^{2+v}1! \, \Gamma(v + 2)}$$

$$c_4 = -\frac{c_2}{2^2 2(v + 2)} = \frac{1}{2^{4+v}2! \, \Gamma(v + 3)}$$

and so on; in general

(11) $$c_{2m} = \frac{(-1)^m}{2^{2m+v} m! \, \Gamma(v + m + 1)}.$$

By inserting these coefficients in (2) and remembering that $c_1 = 0, c_3 = 0, \cdots$ we obtain a particular solution of Bessel's equation which is denoted by $J_v(x)$:

(12) $$J_v(x) = x^v \sum_{m=0}^{\infty} \frac{(-1)^m x^{2m}}{2^{2m+v} m! \, \Gamma(v + m + 1)}.$$

This solution of (1) is known as the **Bessel function of the first kind** *of order v*. The ratio test shows that the series converges for all x. Furthermore, we see that (12) may also be written in the form

(12′) $$J_v(x) = \left(\frac{x}{2}\right)^v \sum_{m=0}^{\infty} \frac{(-1)^m}{m! \, \Gamma(v + m + 1)} \left(\frac{x}{2}\right)^{2m}.$$

Integer values of v are frequently denoted by n. Thus, for $n \geqq 0$,

(12″) $$J_n(x) = x^n \sum_{m=0}^{\infty} \frac{(-1)^m x^{2m}}{2^{2m+n} m! \, (n + m)!}.$$

For example the Bessel function of the first kind of order zero is

$$J_0(x) = 1 - \frac{x^2}{2^2(1!)^2} + \frac{x^4}{2^4(2!)^2} - \frac{x^6}{2^6(3!)^2} + - \cdots,$$

(cf. Fig. 80). The Bessel function of the first kind of first order is

$$J_1(x) = \frac{x}{2} - \frac{x^3}{2^3 1! \, 2!} + \frac{x^5}{2^5 2! \, 3!} - \frac{x^7}{2^7 3! \, 4!} + - \cdots.$$

It is interesting to note that for $v = \frac{1}{2}$ the series in (12) becomes a familiar Maclaurin expansion. Using the relation $\Gamma(\frac{1}{2}) = \sqrt{\pi}$ (which will be proved in Sec. 14.1), the reader may show that

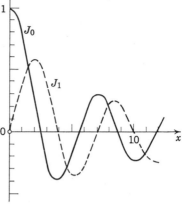

$$(13) \qquad J_{\frac{1}{2}}(x) = \sqrt{\frac{2}{\pi x}} \sin x.$$

Further cases ($v = \frac{3}{2}, \frac{5}{2}, \cdots$) in which $J_v(x)$ is an elementary function will be considered later.

We shall now determine a second independent solution of Bessel's equation, starting with the case when v is not an integer. From the indicial equation we see that this is Case 1 of our general terminology in Sec. 3.4. (A second solution for integer $v = n$ will be obtained later, in Sec. 3.7.) Replacing v by $-v$ in (12) we have

Fig. 80. Bessel functions of the first kind.

$$(14) \qquad J_{-v}(x) = x^{-v} \sum_{m=0}^{\infty} \frac{(-1)^m x^{2m}}{2^{2m-v} m! \, \Gamma(m - v + 1)}.$$

Since Bessel's equation involves v^2, the functions J_v and J_{-v} are solutions of the equation for the same v. They are linearly independent, because the first term in (12) and the first term in (14) are finite nonzero multiples of x^v and x^{-v}, respectively. Hence, *when v is not an integer, the general solution of Bessel's equation for all $x \neq 0$ is*

$$(15) \qquad y(x) = a_1 J_v(x) + a_2 J_{-v}(x).$$

We note that the second solution $J_{-v}(x)$ may also be obtained by replacing v by $-v$ in (5) and the subsequent formulas and determining the coefficients as before.

PROBLEMS

1. Show that the series in (12) converges for all x.

2. Show that (12) may be written in the form (12′).

3. Show that for small $|x|$, $J_0(x) \approx 1 - \frac{x^2}{4}$. Compute $J_0(x)$ for $x = 0.2, 0.4, 0.6$ by means of this formula and determine the relative error by comparison with the exact values.

TABLE 14. BESSEL FUNCTIONS $J_0(x)$ AND $J_1(x)$.
(Zeros of J_0 see in Sec. 9.10. For more
extensive tables see Ref. [A7] in Appendix 1.)

x	$J_0(x)$	$J_1(x)$	x	$J_0(x)$	$J_1(x)$	x	$J_0(x)$	$J_1(x)$
0.0	1.0000	0.0000	3.0	−0.2601	0.3391	6.0	0.1506	−0.2767
0.1	0.9975	0.0499	3.1	−0.2921	0.3009	6.1	0.1773	−0.2559
0.2	0.9900	0.0995	3.2	−0.3202	0.2613	6.2	0.2017	−0.2329
0.3	0.9776	0.1483	3.3	−0.3443	0.2207	6.3	0.2238	−0.2081
0.4	0.9604	0.1960	3.4	−0.3643	0.1792	6.4	0.2433	−0.1816
0.5	0.9385	0.2423	3.5	−0.3801	0.1374	6.5	0.2601	−0.1538
0.6	0.9120	0.2867	3.6	−0.3918	0.0955	6.6	0.2740	−0.1250
0.7	0.8812	0.3290	3.7	−0.3992	0.0538	6.7	0.2851	−0.0953
0.8	0.8463	0.3688	3.8	−0.4026	0.0128	6.8	0.2931	−0.0652
0.9	0.8075	0.4059	3.9	−0.4018	−0.0272	6.9	0.2981	−0.0349
1.0	0.7652	0.4401	4.0	−0.3971	−0.0660	7.0	0.3001	−0.0047
1.1	0.7196	0.4709	4.1	−0.3887	−0.1033	7.1	0.2991	0.0252
1.2	0.6711	0.4983	4.2	−0.3766	−0.1386	7.2	0.2951	0.0543
1.3	0.6201	0.5220	4.3	−0.3610	−0.1719	7.3	0.2882	0.0826
1.4	0.5669	0.5419	4.4	−0.3423	−0.2028	7.4	0.2786	0.1096
1.5	0.5118	0.5579	4.5	−0.3205	−0.2311	7.5	0.2663	0.1352
1.6	0.4554	0.5699	4.6	−0.2961	−0.2566	7.6	0.2516	0.1592
1.7	0.3980	0.5778	4.7	−0.2693	−0.2791	7.7	0.2346	0.1813
1.8	0.3400	0.5815	4.8	−0.2404	−0.2985	7.8	0.2154	0.2014
1.9	0.2818	0.5812	4.9	−0.2097	−0.3147	7.9	0.1944	0.2192
2.0	0.2239	0.5767	5.0	−0.1776	−0.3276	8.0	0.1717	0.2346
2.1	0.1666	0.5683	5.1	−0.1443	−0.3371	8.1	0.1475	0.2476
2.2	0.1104	0.5560	5.2	−0.1103	−0.3432	8.2	0.1222	0.2580
2.3	0.0555	0.5399	5.3	−0.0758	−0.3460	8.3	0.0960	0.2657
2.4	0.0025	0.5202	5.4	−0.0412	−0.3453	8.4	0.0692	0.2708
2.5	−0.0484	0.4971	5.5	−0.0068	−0.3414	8.5	0.0419	0.2731
2.6	−0.0968	0.4708	5.6	0.0270	−0.3343	8.6	0.0146	0.2728
2.7	−0.1424	0.4416	5.7	0.0599	−0.3241	8.7	−0.0125	0.2697
2.8	−0.1850	0.4097	5.8	0.0917	−0.3110	8.8	−0.0392	0.2641
2.9	−0.2243	0.3754	5.9	0.1220	−0.2951	8.9	−0.0653	0.2559

$J_1(x) = 0$ for $x = 0$, 3.832, 7.016, 10.173, 13.324, $\cdots$

4. How many terms of the Maclaurin series are needed to compute $J_0(1)$ with an error less than 1 unit of the fifth decimal place? How many terms are needed to compute ln 2 from the Maclaurin series of ln $(1 + x)$ with the same degree of accuracy?

5. Using the Maclaurin series of J_0, show that the smallest positive root of $J_0(x) = 0$ lies between 2 and $\sqrt{8}$ (≈ 2.83). (The root is $x = 2.404 \cdots$.)

6. Show that the smallest positive root of $J_1(x) = 0$ is greater than $\sqrt{8}$. (The actual value of the root is $3.831 \cdots$.)

7. Derive (13) from (12).

8. Show that $J_n(x)$ is even for even n and odd for odd n.

9. Show that $J_0'(x) = -J_1(x)$.

10. Show that under the transformation $y = u/\sqrt{x}$, Bessel's equation becomes

$$u'' + \left(1 + \frac{1 - 4\nu^2}{4x^2}\right)u = 0.$$

11. Using the result of Prob. 10, find the general solution of (1) with $\nu = \frac{1}{2}$.

12. Derive (14) directly by replacing ν by $-\nu$ in (5) and the subsequent formulas and determining the coefficients.

13. It can be shown that for large x,

$$J_0(x) \approx \sqrt{\frac{2}{\pi x}} \cos\left(x - \frac{\pi}{4}\right).$$

Using this formula, graph J_0 for large x, compute approximate values of the first four positive zeros of $J_0(x)$, and compare the results with the more accurate values 2.405, 5.520, 8.654, 11.792.

The following problems illustrate that various differential equations can be reduced to Bessel's equation. Using the indicated substitutions, solve, in terms of Bessel functions of the first kind, the following equations.

14. $x^2y'' + xy' + (x^2 - \frac{1}{4})y = 0$

15. $x^2y'' + xy' + (\lambda^2x^2 - \nu^2)y = 0$ $(x = z/\lambda)$

16. $xy'' + 2y' + xy = 0$ $(y = u/\sqrt{x})$

17. $xy'' + (1 + 2\nu)y' + xy = 0$ $(y = u/x^\nu)$

18. $x^2y'' + xy' + 4(x^4 - \nu^2)y = 0$ $(x^2 = z)$

19. $x^2y'' + xy' + \frac{1}{4}(x - \nu^2)y = 0$ $(\sqrt{x} = z)$

20. $y'' + xy = 0$ $(y = u\sqrt{x}, \frac{2}{3}x^{3/2} = z)$

21. $xy'' - y' + xy = 0$ $(y = xu)$

22. $x^2y'' - 3xy' + 4(x^4 - 3)y = 0$ $(y = x^2u, x^2 = z)$

23. $x^2y'' + (1 - 2\nu)xy' + \nu^2(x^{2\nu} + 1 - \nu^2)y = 0$ $(y = x^\nu u, x^\nu = z)$

24. $y'' + (e^{2x} - \frac{1}{9})y = 0$ $(e^x = z)$

3.6 FURTHER PROPERTIES OF BESSEL FUNCTIONS OF THE FIRST KIND

Bessel functions play an important role in various engineering problems. Some typical applications will be considered in connection with partial differential equations. In working with Bessel functions it is necessary to know that these functions satisfy various relations, and, in fact, the number of formulas for Bessel functions is incredibly large; the student may look into Ref. [B9], the standard book on Bessel functions, or Ref. [A5] in Appendix 1.

To show how to obtain properties of functions from their series representations we shall now consider some important relations for Bessel functions of the first kind.

From (12) in Sec. 3.5 we obtain

$$x^\nu J_\nu(x) = \sum_{m=0}^\infty \frac{(-1)^m x^{2m+2\nu}}{2^{2m+\nu} m! \, \Gamma(\nu+m+1)} \, .$$

By differentiating and then using (9), Sec. 3.5, we readily find

$$(x^\nu J_\nu)' = \sum_{m=0}^\infty \frac{(-1)^m 2(m+\nu) x^{2m+2\nu-1}}{2^{2m+\nu} m! \, \Gamma(\nu+m+1)} = x^\nu x^{\nu-1} \sum_{m=0}^\infty \frac{(-1)^m x^{2m}}{2^{2m+\nu-1} m! \, \Gamma(\nu+m)} \, .$$

From (12), Sec. 3.5, it follows that the last expression is $x^\nu J_{\nu-1}(x)$ and, therefore,

(1) $$\frac{d}{dx}[x^\nu J_\nu(x)] = x^\nu J_{\nu-1}(x).$$

Similarly, from (12) in Sec. 3.5 it follows that

$$(x^{-\nu} J_\nu)' = \sum_{m=1}^\infty \frac{(-1)^m x^{2m-1}}{2^{2m+\nu-1}(m-1)! \, \Gamma(\nu+m+1)} = \sum_{s=0}^\infty \frac{(-1)^{s+1} x^{2s+1}}{2^{2s+\nu+1} s! \, \Gamma(\nu+s+2)}$$

(where $m = s + 1$). Since the expression on the right is $-x^{-\nu} J_{\nu+1}(x)$ this proves

(2) $$\frac{d}{dx}[x^{-\nu} J_\nu(x)] = -x^{-\nu} J_{\nu+1}(x).$$

Writing these formulas at length and multiplying the last by $x^{2\nu}$, we get

(1') $$\nu x^{\nu-1} J_\nu + x^\nu J_\nu' = x^\nu J_{\nu-1}$$
(2') $$-\nu x^{\nu-1} J_\nu + x^\nu J_\nu' = -x^\nu J_{\nu+1}.$$

Subtracting (2') from (1') and dividing the result by x^ν, we find

(3) $$J_{\nu-1}(x) + J_{\nu+1}(x) = \frac{2\nu}{x} J_\nu(x).$$

Adding (1') and (2') and dividing the result by x^ν, we obtain

(4) $$J_{\nu-1}(x) - J_{\nu+1}(x) = 2 J_\nu'(x).$$

The **recurrence relations** (3) and (4) are of great practical importance. For example, (3) serves to express Bessel functions of high orders in terms of functions of low orders, and this is useful for computing tables.

Example 1.   Express $J_3(x)$ in terms of $J_0(x)$ and $J_1(x)$. From (3) we obtain

$$J_2(x) = \frac{2}{x} J_1(x) - J_0(x),$$

$$J_3(x) = \frac{4}{x} J_2(x) - J_1(x) = \left(\frac{8}{x^2} - 1 \right) J_1(x) - \frac{4}{x} J_0(x).$$

The formulas (1) and (2) are useful in connection with integrals involving Bessel functions, as the following examples illustrate.

Example 2.   Integrate $\int x^{-3} J_4(x)\, dx$. From (2) and Ex. 1 we obtain

$$\int \frac{J_4(x)}{x^3}\, dx = -\frac{J_3(x)}{x^3} = \left(\frac{1}{x^3} - \frac{8}{x^5} \right) J_1(x) + \frac{4}{x^4} J_0(x) + c.$$

Example 3.   Express $\int x^{-2} J_2(x)\, dx$ in terms of Bessel functions. Integrating by parts and using (1), we obtain

$$\int x^{-2} J_2\, dx = \int x^{-4}(x^2 J_2)\, dx = -\frac{x^{-3}}{3} x^2 J_2 + \int \frac{x^{-3}}{3} x^2 J_1 dx = -\frac{J_2}{3x} + \frac{1}{3} \int x^{-1} J_1 dx.$$

Similarly, $\int x^{-1} J_1\, dx = \int x^{-2}(x J_1)\, dx = -x^{-1} x J_1 + \int x^{-1} x J_0 dx.$

Therefore, $\int x^{-2} J_2(x)\, dx = -\frac{J_2(x)}{3x} - \frac{J_1(x)}{3} + \frac{1}{3} \int J_0(x)\, dx.$

The remaining integral, which cannot be evaluated in finite form, has been tabulated; cf. Ref. [B9] in Appendix 1.

We have already mentioned that [cf. (13), Sec. 3.5]

(5) $$J_{1/2}(x) = \sqrt{\frac{2}{\pi x}} \sin x.$$

In a similar fashion it follows directly from (14) in the last section that

(6) $$J_{-1/2}(x) = \sqrt{\frac{2}{\pi x}} \cos x.$$

By applying our recurrence relation (3) we thus obtain

$$J_{3/2}(x) = \frac{1}{x} J_{1/2}(x) - J_{-1/2}(x) = \sqrt{\frac{2}{\pi x}} \left(\frac{\sin x}{x} - \cos x \right),$$

$$J_{-3/2}(x) = -\frac{1}{x} J_{-1/2}(x) - J_{1/2}(x) = -\sqrt{\frac{2}{\pi x}} \left(\frac{\cos x}{x} + \sin x \right),$$

and so on. Continuing in this fashion we see that *for* $\nu = \pm\frac{1}{2}, \pm\frac{3}{2}, \pm\frac{5}{2}, \cdots$ *the Bessel functions $J_\nu(x)$ are elementary functions.*

Another important result follows from the representation (14), Sec. 3.5, for $J_{-\nu}(x)$, if we let ν approach a positive integer n. Then the Gamma functions in the coefficients of the first n terms become infinite (cf. Fig. 386 in Sec. 14.1), the coefficients become zero, and the summation starts with $m = n$; since in this case $\Gamma(m - n + 1) = (m - n)!$ [cf. (10), Sec. 3.5] we obtain

$$J_{-n}(x) = \sum_{m=n}^{\infty} \frac{(-1)^m x^{2m-n}}{2^{2m-n} m! \, (m - n)!}.$$

Changing the variable of summation by setting $m = n + s$, we have $m - n = s$, and the representation becomes

$$J_{-n}(x) = \sum_{s=0}^{\infty} \frac{(-1)^{n+s} x^{2s+n}}{2^{2s+n}(n + s)! \, s!}.$$

From (12″) in Sec. 3.5 we see that the right side is equal to $(-1)^n J_n(x)$. The result is, therefore,

(7) $$J_{-n}(x) = (-1)^n J_n(x) \qquad \text{when} \qquad n = 1, 2, \cdots.$$

Hence, for integer $\nu = n$, the Bessel functions $J_n(x)$ and $J_{-n}(x)$ are linearly dependent.

PROBLEMS

1. Carry out the details of the derivation of (3) and (4) from (1) and (2).

2. Express $J_{5/2}(x)$ and $J_{-5/2}(x)$ in terms of cosine and sine functions.

3. Solve Prob. 9 at the end of Sec. 3.5 by means of (2).

4. Using (1) and (2) and Rolle's theorem, show that between two consecutive zeros of $J_0(x)$ there is precisely one zero of $J_1(x)$.

5. Prove that between any two consecutive positive zeros of $J_n(x)$ there is one, and only one, zero of $J_{n+1}(x)$.

6. Derive Bessel's equation from (1) and (2). *Hint:* start from (2), with ν replaced by $\nu - 1$, and replace $J_{\nu-1}$ by the expression resulting from (1).

7. Using (4) and (2), show that $J_0''(x) = \frac{1}{2}[J_2(x) - J_0(x)]$.

8. Show that $J_2(x) = \frac{2}{x} J_1(x) - J_0(x)$, and compute $J_2(x)$ and $J_{-2}(x)$ for $x = 0$, 0.2, 0.4, 0.6, 0.8, 1.0 from the table in Sec. 3.5.

9. Express $J_4(x)$ in terms of $J_0(x)$ and $J_1(x)$.

10. Express $J_5(x)$ in terms of $J_2(x)$ and $J_3(x)$.

Show that:

11. $J_2'(x) = \frac{1}{2}[J_1(x) - J_3(x)]$ 　　　　　**12.** $J_3''(x) = \frac{1}{2}[J_2'(x) - J_4'(x)]$

13. $J_2'(x) = \left(1 - \dfrac{4}{x^2}\right) J_1(x) + \dfrac{2}{x} J_0(x)$ 　**14.** $J_3'(x) = \left(1 - \dfrac{12}{x^2}\right) J_2(x) + \dfrac{3}{x} J_1(x)$

15. Prove (7) by induction and by the use of (3).

16. Derive (6) from (5) and (1).

17. Using (5) and (2), express $J_{3/2}(x)$ in terms of sine and cosine.

18. Using (6) and (1), express $J_{-3/2}(x)$ in terms of sine and cosine.

Show that:

19. $J_n'' = \frac{1}{4}(J_{n-2} - 2J_n + J_{n+2})$

20. $J_n'''' = \frac{1}{16}(J_{n-4} - 4J_{n-2} + 6J_n - 4J_{n+2} + J_{n+4})$

21. $\int x^\nu J_{\nu-1}(x)\,dx = x^\nu J_\nu(x) + c, \quad \int x^{-\nu} J_{\nu+1}(x)\,dx = -x^{-\nu} J_\nu(x) + c$

Using the formulas in Prob. 21 (and, if necessary, integration by parts), show that:

22. $\int J_1(x)\,dx = -J_0(x) + c$ **23.** $\int x J_0(x)\,dx = x J_1(x) + c$

24. $\int x J_1(x)\,dx = -x J_0(x) + \int J_0(x)\,dx$

25. $\int J_2(x)\,dx = -2 J_1(x) + \int J_0(x)\,dx$

26. $\int J_3(x)\,dx = -J_0(x) - 2J_2(x) + c.$ *Hint:* use (4) with $\nu = 2$ and integrate.

27. $\int J_3(x)\,dx = -J_2(x) - \frac{2}{x} J_1(x) + c$

28. $\int x^2 J_0(x)\,dx = x^2 J_1(x) + x J_0(x) - \int J_0(x)\,dx$

29. $\int x^3 J_0(x)\,dx = x^3 J_1(x) - 2x^2 J_2(x) + c$

30. Obtain the formula in Prob. 26 from that in Prob. 27 by applying (3).

3.7 BESSEL FUNCTIONS OF THE SECOND KIND

For integer $\nu = n$, the Bessel functions $J_n(x)$ and $J_{-n}(x)$ are linearly dependent (Sec. 3.6) and do not form a fundamental system. We shall now obtain a second independent solution, starting with the case $n = 0$. In this case Bessel's equation may be written

$$(1) \qquad\qquad xy'' + y' + xy = 0,$$

the indicial equation has the double root $r = 0$, and we see from (7) in Sec. 3.4, that the desired solution must have the form

$$(2) \qquad\qquad y_2(x) = J_0(x) \ln x + \sum_{m=1}^{\infty} A_m x^m.$$

When we substitute y_2 and its derivatives

$$y_2' = J_0' \ln x + \frac{J_0}{x} + \sum_{m=1}^{\infty} mA_m x^{m-1}$$

$$y_2'' = J_0'' \ln x + \frac{2J_0'}{x} - \frac{J_0}{x^2} + \sum_{m=1}^{\infty} m(m-1)A_m x^{m-2}$$

into (1), the logarithmic terms disappear because J_0 is a solution of (1), the other two terms containing J_0 cancel, and we find

$$2J_0' + \sum_{m=1}^{\infty} m(m-1)A_m x^{m-1} + \sum_{m=1}^{\infty} mA_m x^{m-1} + \sum_{m=1}^{\infty} A_m x^{m+1} = 0.$$

From (12) in Sec. 3.5 we obtain the power series of J_0' in the form

$$J_0'(x) = \sum_{m=1}^{\infty} \frac{(-1)^m 2m x^{2m-1}}{2^{2m}(m!)^2} = \sum_{m=1}^{\infty} \frac{(-1)^m x^{2m-1}}{2^{2m-1} m! (m-1)!}.$$

By inserting this series we have

$$\sum_{m=1}^{\infty} \frac{(-1)^m x^{2m-1}}{2^{2m-2} m! (m-1)!} + \sum_{m=1}^{\infty} m^2 A_m x^{m-1} + \sum_{m=1}^{\infty} A_m x^{m+1} = 0.$$

We first show that the A_m with odd subscripts are all zero. The coefficient of the power x^0 is A_1, and so, $A_1 = 0$. By equating the sum of the coefficients of the power x^{2s} to zero we obtain

$$(2s + 1)^2 A_{2s+1} + A_{2s-1} = 0 \qquad s = 1, 2, \cdots.$$

Since $A_1 = 0$, we thus obtain $A_3 = 0$, $A_5 = 0$, $\cdots$, successively. Equating the sum of the coefficients of x^{2s+1} to zero, we have

$$-1 + 4A_2 = 0 \qquad\qquad (s = 0)$$

$$\frac{(-1)^{s+1}}{2^{2s}(s+1)! \, s!} + (2s + 2)^2 A_{2s+2} + A_{2s} = 0, \qquad (s = 1, 2, \cdots).$$

For $s = 0$ this yields $4A_2 = 1$ or $A_2 = \frac{1}{4}$. For $s = 1$ we find

$$\frac{1}{8} + 16A_4 + A_2 = 0 \qquad \text{or} \qquad A_4 = -\frac{3}{128},$$

and in general

$$(3) \qquad A_{2m} = \frac{(-1)^{m-1}}{2^{2m}(m!)^2}\left(1 + \frac{1}{2} + \frac{1}{3} + \cdots + \frac{1}{m}\right), \qquad m = 1, 2, \cdots.$$

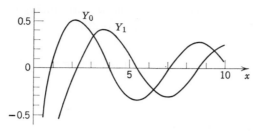

Fig. 81. Bessel functions of the second kind.

Using the short notation

(4) $$h_m = 1 + \frac{1}{2} + \cdots + \frac{1}{m}$$

and inserting (3) and $A_1 = A_3 = \cdots = 0$ into (2), we obtain the result

(5)
$$y_2(x) = J_0(x) \ln x + \sum_{m=1}^{\infty} \frac{(-1)^{m-1} h_m}{2^{2m}(m!)^2} x^{2m}$$

$$= J_0(x) \ln x + \frac{1}{4} x^2 - \frac{3}{128} x^4 + - \cdots .$$

Since J_0 and y_2 are linearly independent functions, they form a fundamental system of (1). Of course, another fundamental system is obtained by replacing y_2 by an independent particular solution of the form $a(y_2 + bJ_0)$ where $a (\neq 0)$ and b are constants. It is customary to choose $a = 2/\pi$ and $b = \gamma - \ln 2$ where $\gamma = 0.5772 \cdots$ is the so-called *Euler constant*, which is defined as the limit of $1 + \frac{1}{2} + \cdots + \frac{1}{s} - \ln s$ as s approaches infinity. The standard particular solution thus obtained is known as the **Bessel function of the second kind** *of order zero* (Fig. 81) or **Neumann's function** *of order zero* and is denoted by $Y_0(x)$. Thus

(6) $$Y_0(x) = \frac{2}{\pi} \left[J_0(x) \left(\ln \frac{x}{2} + \gamma \right) + \sum_{m=1}^{\infty} \frac{(-1)^{m-1} h_m}{2^{2m}(m!)^2} x^{2m} \right],$$

where h_m is defined by (4).

If $\nu = n = 1, 2, \cdots$, a second solution can be obtained by similar manipulations, starting from (11), Sec. 3.4. It turns out that also in these cases the solution contains a logarithmic term.

The situation is not yet completely satisfactory, because the second solution is defined differently, depending on whether the order ν is integral or not. To provide uniformity of formalism and numerical tabulation, it is desirable to adopt a form of the second solution which is valid for all values of the order. This is the reason for introducing a standard second solution $Y_\nu(x)$ defined for all ν by the formula

(7)
$$(a) \quad Y_\nu(x) = \frac{1}{\sin \nu\pi} [J_\nu(x) \cos \nu\pi - J_{-\nu}(x)]$$

$$(b) \qquad Y_n(x) = \lim_{\nu \to n} Y_\nu(x).$$

This function is known as the **Bessel function of the second kind** *of order* ν or **Neumann's function**[11] *of order* ν.

For nonintegral order ν, the function $Y_\nu(x)$ is evidently a solution of Bessel's equation because $J_\nu(x)$ and $J_{-\nu}(x)$ are solutions of that equation. Since for those ν the solutions J_ν and $J_{-\nu}$ are linearly independent and Y_ν involves $J_{-\nu}$, the functions J_ν and Y_ν are linearly independent. Furthermore, it can be shown that the limit in (7b) exists and Y_n is a solution of Bessel's equation for integral order; cf. Ref. [B9] in Appendix 1. We shall see that the series development of $Y_n(x)$ contains a logarithmic term. Hence $J_n(x)$ and $Y_n(x)$ are linearly independent solutions of Bessel's equation. The series development of $Y_n(x)$ can be obtained by inserting the series (12) and (14), Sec. 3.5, for $J_\nu(x)$ and $J_{-\nu}(x)$ into (7a) and then letting ν approach n; for details see Ref. [B9]; the result is

(8)
$$Y_n(x) = \frac{2}{\pi} J_n(x) \left(\ln \frac{x}{2} + \gamma \right) + \frac{x^n}{\pi} \sum_{m=0}^{\infty} \frac{(-1)^{m-1}(h_m + h_{m+n})}{2^{2m+n} m! (m+n)!} x^{2m}$$
$$- \frac{x^{-n}}{\pi} \sum_{m=0}^{n-1} \frac{(n-m-1)!}{2^{2m-n} m!} x^{2m} \qquad (x > 0, n = 0, 1, \cdots),$$

where

$$h_0 = 0, \qquad h_s = 1 + \frac{1}{2} + \frac{1}{3} + \cdots + \frac{1}{s} \qquad (s = 1, 2, \cdots)$$

and when $n = 0$ the last sum in (8) is to be replaced by 0. For $n = 0$ the representation (8) takes the form (6). Furthermore, it can be shown that

$$Y_{-n}(x) = (-1)^n Y_n(x).$$

Our result is that

(9)
$$y(x) = C_1 J_\nu(x) + C_2 Y_\nu(x)$$

is a general solution of Bessel's equation for all values of ν.

---

[11] CARL NEUMANN (1832–1925), German mathematician and physicist. The solutions $Y_\nu(x)$ are sometimes denoted by $N_\nu(x)$; in Ref. [B9] they are called Weber's functions. Euler's constant in (6) is often denoted by C or $\ln \gamma$ (instead of γ).

We finally mention that there is a practical need for solutions of Bessel's equation which are complex for real values of x. For this reason the solutions

(10)
$$H_\nu^{(1)}(x) = J_\nu(x) + iY_\nu(x)$$
$$H_\nu^{(2)}(x) = J_\nu(x) - iY_\nu(x)$$

are frequently used and have been tabulated (cf. Ref. [A6] in Appendix 1). These linearly independent functions are called **Bessel functions of the third kind** *of order* ν or *first and second* **Hankel functions**[12] *of order* ν.

TABLE 15. BESSEL FUNCTIONS $Y_0(x)$ AND $Y_1(x)$.
(For more extensive tables, see Ref. [A7].)

x	$Y_0(x)$	$Y_1(x)$	x	$Y_0(x)$	$Y_1(x)$	x	$Y_0(x)$	$Y_1(x)$
0.0	$(-\infty)$	$(-\infty)$	2.5	0.498	0.146	5.0	−0.309	0.148
0.5	−0.445	−1.471	3.0	0.377	0.325	5.5	−0.340	−0.024
1.0	0.088	−0.781	3.5	0.189	0.410	6.0	−0.288	−0.175
1.5	0.382	−0.412	4.0	−0.017	0.398	6.5	−0.173	−0.274
2.0	0.510	−0.107	4.5	−0.195	0.301	7.0	−0.026	−0.303

PROBLEMS

1. It can be shown that, for large x,

$$Y_n(x) \approx \sqrt{\frac{2}{\pi x}} \sin\left(x - \frac{n\pi}{2} - \frac{\pi}{4}\right).$$

Using this formula, graph $Y_0(x)$ and $Y_1(x)$ for $4 \leq x \leq 12$, find approximate values of the first three positive zeros of $Y_0(x)$, and determine the deviation from the more accurate values 0.89, 3.96, and 7.09.

2. Using (6), show that for small x, $Y_0(x) \approx \dfrac{2}{\pi}\left(\ln\dfrac{x}{2} + \gamma\right).$

Using the indicated substitutions, find the general solution of the following equations.

3. $xy'' + y' + xy = 0$

4. $x^2y'' + xy' + (x^2 - 4)y = 0$

5. $xy'' - y' + xy = 0 \quad (y = xu)$

6. $x^2y'' + xy' + 4(x^2 - 1)y = 0 \quad (x = z/2)$

7. $xy'' + 3y' + xy = 0 \quad (y = u/x)$

8. $x^2y'' + xy' + 4(x^4 - 4)y = 0 \quad (x^2 = z)$

9. $4xy'' + 4y' + y = 0 \quad (\sqrt{x} = z)$

10. $x^2y'' - xy' + (4x^2 + 1)y = 0 \quad (y = xu, z = 2x)$

11. $x^2y'' + (x^2 + \frac{1}{4})y = 0 \quad (y = u\sqrt{x})$

12. $x^2y'' + \frac{1}{4}(x + 1)y = 0 \quad (y = u\sqrt{x}, \sqrt{x} = z)$

[12] HERMANN HANKEL (1839–1873), German mathematician.

13. Show that $J_\nu(ix)$, $i = \sqrt{-1}$, is a solution of
$$x^2 y'' + xy' - (x^2 + \nu^2)y = 0.$$

14. Show that
$$J_\nu(ix) = i^\nu \sum_{m=0}^{\infty} \frac{x^{2m+\nu}}{2^{2m+\nu}\, m!\, \Gamma\,(m+\nu+1)}.$$

15. Show that the function
$$I_\nu(x) = i^{-\nu} J\,(ix)$$
is real for real x (and real ν). This function is called the **modified Bessel function**
of the first kind of order ν.

16. Show that for $\nu = n = 0, 1, 2, \cdots, I_{-n}(x) = I_n(x)$.

17. Show that $I_\nu(x) \neq 0$ for all real $x \neq 0$.

18. Show that for small $|x|$, $I_0(x) \approx 1 + \dfrac{x^2}{4} + \dfrac{x^4}{64}$.

19. The function
$$K_\nu(x) = \frac{\pi}{2}\left(\frac{I_{-\nu}(x) - I_\nu(x)}{\sin \nu\pi}\right)$$
is called the *modified Bessel function of the third kind.* Show that $K_\nu(x)$ is a
solution of the equation in Prob. 13.

Show that the given functions are solutions of the corresponding equations.

20. $y'' + k^2 xy = 0$, $\quad y = \sqrt{x}\, Y_{1/3}\left(\dfrac{2k}{3}\, x^{3/2}\right)$

21. $y'' + k^2 x^2 y = 0$, $\quad y = \sqrt{x}\, Y_{1/4}\left(\dfrac{k}{2}\, x^2\right)$

22. $y'' + k^2 x^4 y = 0$, $\quad y = \sqrt{x}\, Y_{1/6}\left(\dfrac{k}{3}\, x^3\right)$

chapter 4

LAPLACE
TRANSFORMATION

The Laplace transformation is a powerful method for solving linear differential equations arising in engineering mathematics. It consists essentially of three steps. In the first step the given differential equation is transformed into an algebraic equation (*subsidiary equation*). Then the latter is solved by purely algebraic manipulations. Finally, the solution of the subsidiary equation is transformed back in such a way that it becomes the required solution of the original differential equation.

In this way the Laplace transformation reduces the problem of solving a differential equation to an algebraic problem. Another advantage is that it takes care of initial conditions without the necessity of first determining the general solution and then obtaining from it a particular solution. Also, when applying the classical method to a nonhomogeneous equation, we must first solve the corresponding homogeneous equation, while the Laplace transformation immediately yields the solution of the nonhomogeneous equation.

In the present chapter we shall consider the Laplace transformation from a practical point of view and illustrate its use by important engineering applications.

Prerequisite for this chapter: Chap. 2.

References: Appendix 1, Part B.

Answers to problems: Appendix 2.

4.1 LAPLACE TRANSFORM.
INVERSE TRANSFORM. LINEARITY

Let $f(t)$ be a given function which is defined for all positive values of t. We multiply $f(t)$ by e^{-st} and integrate with respect to t from zero to infinity. Then, if the resulting integral exists, it is a function of s, say, $F(s)$:

$$F(s) = \int_0^\infty e^{-st} f(t)\, dt.$$

The function $F(s)$ is called the **Laplace transform**[1] of the original function $f(t)$, and will be denoted by $\mathscr{L}(f)$. Thus

(1) $$F(s) = \mathscr{L}(f) = \int_0^\infty e^{-st} f(t)\, dt.$$

The described operation on $f(t)$ is called the *Laplace transformation*.

Furthermore the original function $f(t)$ in (1) is called the *inverse transform* or **inverse** of $F(s)$ and will be denoted by $\mathscr{L}^{-1}(F)$; that is, we shall write

$$f(t) = \mathscr{L}^{-1}(F).$$

We shall denote the original function by a lower case letter and its transform by the same letter in capital.

Example 1. Let $f(t) = 1$ when $t > 0$. Then

$$\mathscr{L}(f) = \mathscr{L}(1) = \int_0^\infty e^{-st}\, dt = -\frac{1}{s} e^{-st} \Big|_0^\infty;$$

hence, when $s > 0$,

$$\mathscr{L}(1) = \frac{1}{s}.$$

Example 2. Let $f(t) = e^{at}$ when $t > 0$, where a is a constant Then

$$\mathscr{L}(e^{at}) = \int_0^\infty e^{-st} e^{at}\, dt = \frac{1}{a-s} e^{-(s-a)t} \Big|_0^\infty;$$

consequently, when $s - a > 0$,

$$\mathscr{L}(e^{at}) = \frac{1}{s-a}.$$

We shall see that the Laplace transformation possesses various general properties, in consequence of which transforms of many functions can be

---

[1] PIERRE SIMON DE LAPLACE (1749–1827), great French mathematician, who developed the foundation of potential theory and made important contributions to celestial mechanics and probability theory.

obtained in very simple ways. The most important property of the Laplace transformation is stated in the following theorem.

Theorem 1.   (Linearity property).   *The Laplace transformation is a linear operation, that is,*

$$\mathcal{L}\{af(t) + bg(t)\} = a\mathcal{L}(f) + b\mathcal{L}(g),$$

where a and b are constants.

Proof.   By definition,

$$\mathcal{L}\{af(t) + bg(t)\} = \int_0^\infty e^{-st}[af(t) + bg(t)]\, dt$$

$$= a \int_0^\infty e^{-st}f(t)\, dt + b \int_0^\infty e^{-st}g(t)\, dt = a\mathcal{L}(f) + b\mathcal{L}(g).$$

Example 3.   Let $f(t) = \cosh at = (e^{at} + e^{-at})/2$. Then, using Theorem 1 and the result of Ex. 2, we find

$$\mathcal{L}(\cosh at) = \frac{1}{2}\mathcal{L}(e^{at}) + \frac{1}{2}\mathcal{L}(e^{-at}) = \frac{1}{2}\left(\frac{1}{s-a} + \frac{1}{s+a}\right) ;$$

that is, when $s > a$,

$$\mathcal{L}(\cosh at) = \frac{s}{s^2 - a^2} .$$

A short list of some important elementary functions and their Laplace transforms is given in Table 16, and a more extensive list in Table 17, Sec. 4.12.   Cf. also the references in Appendix 1, Part B.

TABLE 16.   SOME ELEMENTARY FUNCTIONS $f(t)$
AND THEIR LAPLACE TRANSFORMS $\mathcal{L}(f)$.

	$f(t)$	$\mathcal{L}(f)$		$f(t)$	$\mathcal{L}(f)$
1	1	$1/s$	6	e^{at}	$\dfrac{1}{s-a}$
2	t	$1/s^2$	7	$\cos \omega t$	$\dfrac{s}{s^2 + \omega^2}$
3	t^2	$2!/s^3$	8	$\sin \omega t$	$\dfrac{\omega}{s^2 + \omega^2}$
4	t^n (n a positive integer)	$\dfrac{n!}{s^{n+1}}$	9	$\cosh at$	$\dfrac{s}{s^2 - a^2}$
5	t^a (a positive)	$\dfrac{\Gamma(a+1)}{s^{a+1}}$	10	$\sinh at$	$\dfrac{a}{s^2 - a^2}$

Once we know the transforms in Table 16, nearly all the transforms we shall need can be obtained through the use of some simple general theorems which we shall consider in the subsequent sections.

To prove formula (5) in Table 16, we have

$$\mathscr{L}(t^a) = \int_0^\infty e^{-st} t^a \, dt.$$

We set $st = x$. Then $dt = dx/s$. Using (8) in Sec. 3.5, we obtain

$$\mathscr{L}(t^a) = \int_0^\infty e^{-x}\left(\frac{x}{s}\right)^a \frac{dx}{s} = \frac{1}{s^{a+1}} \int_0^\infty e^{-x} x^a \, dx = \frac{\Gamma(a+1)}{s^{a+1}} \quad (s > 0).$$

Formula (4) follows from formula (5) and $\Gamma(n+1) = n!$, where n is a positive integer [cf. (10), Sec. 3.5]. The first three formulas in Table 16 are special cases of formula (4).

Formula (6) was proved in Ex. 2. To prove the formulas (7) and (8), we set $a = i\omega$ in formula (6). Then

$$\mathscr{L}(e^{i\omega t}) = \frac{1}{s - i\omega} = \frac{s + i\omega}{(s - i\omega)(s + i\omega)} = \frac{s + i\omega}{s^2 + \omega^2} = \frac{s}{s^2 + \omega^2} + i\frac{\omega}{s^2 + \omega^2}.$$

On the other hand, by Theorem 1,

$$\mathscr{L}(e^{i\omega t}) = \mathscr{L}(\cos \omega t + i \sin \omega t) = \mathscr{L}(\cos \omega t) + i\mathscr{L}(\sin \omega t).$$

Equating the real and imaginary parts of these two equations, we obtain the formulas (7) and (8).

Formula (9) was proved in Ex. 3, and formula (10) can be proved in a similar manner.

Further transforms can be obtained by the following important property of the Laplace transformation.

Theorem 2. (First shifting theorem). *If* $\mathscr{L}(f) = F(s)$ *when* $s > \alpha$, *then*

$$\mathscr{L}\{e^{at}f(t)\} = F(s - a) \qquad (s > \alpha + a);$$

that is, the substitution of $s - a$ *for* s *in the transform corresponds to the multiplication of the original function by* e^{at}.

Proof. By definition,

$$F(s) = \int_0^\infty e^{-st} f(t) \, dt$$

and, therefore,

$$F(s - a) = \int_0^\infty e^{-(s-a)t} f(t) \, dt = \int_0^\infty e^{-st}[e^{at}f(t)] \, dt = \mathscr{L}\{e^{at}f(t)\}.$$

Example 4. From $\mathscr{L}(1) = 1/s$ and Theorem 2,

$$\mathscr{L}(e^{at}) = \frac{1}{s - a}.$$

Similarly, from $\mathscr{L}(\cos \omega t) = s/(s^2 + \omega^2)$ and Theorem 2,

$$\mathscr{L}(e^{at} \cos \omega t) = \frac{s - a}{(s - a)^2 + \omega^2}.$$

Example 5. Let $\mathscr{L}(f) = \dfrac{s + 5}{s^2 + 2s + 5}$. Find $f(t)$. We have

$$f(t) = \mathscr{L}^{-1}\left\{\frac{s + 5}{s^2 + 2s + 5}\right\} = \mathscr{L}^{-1}\left\{\frac{s + 5}{(s + 1)^2 + 4}\right\}$$

$$= \mathscr{L}^{-1}\left\{\frac{s + 1}{(s + 1)^2 + 2^2}\right\} + 2\mathscr{L}^{-1}\left\{\frac{2}{(s + 1)^2 + 2^2}\right\}.$$

Now from Table 16 in this section,

$$\mathscr{L}^{-1}\left\{\frac{s}{s^2 + 2^2}\right\} = \cos 2t, \qquad \mathscr{L}^{-1}\left\{\frac{2}{s^2 + 2^2}\right\} = \sin 2t.$$

Therefore, by Theorem 2,

$$f(t) = e^{-t} \cos 2t + 2e^{-t} \sin 2t = e^{-t} (\cos 2t + 2 \sin 2t).$$

We shall now state simple sufficient conditions for the existence of the Laplace transform of a function. These conditions are that f is piecewise continuous and $|f|$ does not increase too rapidly as t approaches infinity. We first state the definition of piecewise continuity.

A function $f(t)$ is said to be **piecewise continuous** on a finite interval $a \leq t \leq b$, if it is defined on that interval and is such that the interval can be subdivided into finitely many intervals, in each of which $f(t)$ is continuous and has finite limits as t approaches either end point of the interval of subdivision from the interior.

It follows from the definition that finite jumps are the only discontinuities which a piecewise continuous function may have; these are known as *ordinary discontinuities*. Furthermore, it is clear that the class of piecewise continuous functions includes every continuous function.

Theorem 3.   (Existence theorem). *Let $f(t)$ be a function which is piecewise continuous on every finite interval in the range $t \geq 0$ and satisfies*

(2) $|f(t)| \leq Me^{\alpha t}$ *for all $t \geq 0$*

and for some constants α and M. Then the Laplace transform of $f(t)$ exists for all $s > \alpha$.

Proof.   Since $f(t)$ is piecewise continuous, $e^{-st}f(t)$ is integrable over any finite interval on the t-axis, and from (2),

$$|\mathcal{L}(f)| = \left| \int_0^\infty e^{-st}f(t)\, dt \right| \leq \int_0^\infty e^{-st}|f(t)|\, dt \leq \int_0^\infty e^{-st}Me^{\alpha t}\, dt$$

$$= M \int_0^\infty e^{-(s-\alpha)t}\, dt = \frac{M}{s-\alpha} \qquad\qquad (s > \alpha).$$

This completes the proof.

The conditions in Theorem 3 are practical for most applications, and it is simple to find whether a given function satisfies an inequality of the form (2). For example,

$$\cosh t \leq e^t, \qquad t^n < n!\, e^t\ (n = 0, 1, \cdots) \qquad \text{for all } t > 0,$$

and any function which is bounded in absolute value for all $t \geq 0$, such as the sine and cosine function of a real variable, satisfies that condition. An example of a function which does not satisfy a relation of the form (2), is the exponential function e^{t^2}, because, no matter how large we choose the numbers M and α in (2),

$$e^{t^2} > Me^{\alpha t} \qquad\qquad \text{for all } t > t_0$$

where t_0 is a sufficiently large number, depending on M and α.

It should be noted that the conditions in Theorem 3 are sufficient rather than necessary. For example, the function $1/\sqrt{t}$ is infinite at $t = 0$, but its transform exists; in fact, from the definition and $\Gamma(\tfrac{1}{2}) = \sqrt{\pi}$ [cf. (10) in Sec. 14.1] we obtain

$$\mathcal{L}(t^{-\frac{1}{2}}) = \int_0^\infty e^{-st}t^{-\frac{1}{2}}\, dt = \frac{1}{\sqrt{s}} \int_0^\infty e^{-x}x^{-\frac{1}{2}}\, dx = \frac{1}{\sqrt{s}}\, \Gamma(\tfrac{1}{2}) = \sqrt{\frac{\pi}{s}}.$$

If the Laplace transform of a given function exists, it is uniquely determined. Conversely, it can be shown that two functions having the same transform cannot differ over an interval of positive length, although they may differ at various isolated points (cf. Ref. [B10] in Appendix 1). Since this is of no importance in applications, we may say that the inverse of a given transform is essentially unique. In particular, if two *continuous* functions have the same transform, they are completely identical.

PROBLEMS

1. Show that Theorem 1 can be extended to linear combinations of three or more functions.

Find the Laplace transforms of the following functions, where a, b, etc. are constants.

2. $2t - 4$ **3.** $at + b$ **4.** $t^2 + at + b$ **5.** $2t^3 - 6t + 8$
6. $a_n t^n + a_{n-1} t^{n-1} + \cdots + a_1 t + a_0$ (n a positive integer)
7. $\sinh 3t$ **8.** $\cos^2 t \; [= (1 + \cos 2t)/2]$ **9.** $\sin^2 t$
10. e^{at+b} **11.** $\sqrt{t}$ **12.** $\cosh^2 2t$ **13.** $\sin t \cos t$
14. $b \sin(\omega t + \theta)$ **15.** $a \cos(\omega t + \theta)$ **16.** $\sin t \sin 2t$ **17.** $t^3 e^{-3t}$
18. $e^{-t} \sin \pi t$ **19.** $e^{-at} \cos \omega t$ **20.** $e^t \cos^2 t$ **21.** $e^t \sin^2 t$

22.   **23.**

   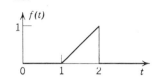

24. Derive the formulas 7 and 8 in Table 16 by integration by parts.
Find $f(t)$ if $\mathscr{L}(f)$ equals:

25. $1/s^n$ ($n = 1, 2, \cdots$)   **26.** $\dfrac{a_1}{s} + \dfrac{a_2}{s^2} + \cdots + \dfrac{a_n}{s^n}$ (n a positive integer)

27. $\dfrac{2}{s + 3}$ **28.** $\dfrac{1}{s^2 + 4}$ **29.** $\dfrac{s}{s^2 + \pi}$ **30.** $\dfrac{4 - 3s}{s^2}$

31. $\dfrac{1}{(s - a)^n}$ ($n = 1, 2, \cdots$)   **32.** $\dfrac{1}{(s - a)(s - b)}$, $a \neq b$

33. Show that $\cosh t \leq e^t$ and $t^n < n! \, e^t$ ($n = 0, 1, \cdots$) for all $t \geq 0$.
34. Derive the formulas 9 and 10 in Table 16 from the formulas 7 and 8 by the
use of the relations $\cosh x = \cos(ix)$, $\sinh x = -i \sin(ix)$ where $i = \sqrt{-1}$.
Representing the hyperbolic functions in terms of exponential functions and
applying Theorem 2, show that:

35. $\mathscr{L}(\cosh at \cos at) = \dfrac{s^3}{s^4 + 4a^4}$ **36.** $\mathscr{L}(\cosh at \sin at) = \dfrac{a(s^2 + 2a^2)}{s^4 + 4a^4}$

37. $\mathscr{L}(\sinh at \cos at) = \dfrac{a(s^2 - 2a^2)}{s^4 + 4a^4}$ **38.** $\mathscr{L}(\sinh at \sin at) = \dfrac{2a^2 s}{s^4 + 4a^4}$

4.2   LAPLACE TRANSFORMS OF DERIVATIVES AND INTEGRALS

We shall now see that, roughly speaking, differentiation and integration
of $f(t)$ corresponds to multiplication and division of the transform

$$F(s) = \mathscr{L}(f)$$

by s. The great importance of this property of the Laplace transformation
is obvious, because in this way operations of calculus may be replaced by
simple algebraic operations on the transforms. We start with the following
theorem.

Theorem 1.   [Differentiation of $f(t)$].   *Suppose that $f(t)$ is continuous for all $t \geq 0$, satisfies (2), p. 209, for some α and M, and has a derivative $f'(t)$ which is piecewise continuous on every finite interval in the range $t \geq 0$. Then the Laplace transform of the derivative $f'(t)$ exists when $s > \alpha$, and*

(1) $$\mathscr{L}(f') = s\mathscr{L}(f) - f(0).$$ $(s > \alpha).$

Proof.   We first consider the case when $f'(t)$ is continuous for all $t \geq 0$. Then, by definition and by integrating by parts,

$$\mathscr{L}(f') = \int_0^\infty e^{-st} f'(t)\, dt$$
$$= [e^{-st} f(t)]_0^\infty + s\int_0^\infty e^{-st} f(t)\, dt.$$

Since f satisfies (2), Sec. 4.1, the integrated portion on the right is zero at the upper limit when $s > \alpha$, and at the lower limit it is $-f(0)$. The last integral is $\mathscr{L}(f)$, the existence for $s > \alpha$ being a consequence of Theorem 3 in Sec. 4.1. This proves that the expression on the right exists when $s > \alpha$, and is equal to $-f(0) + s\mathscr{L}(f)$. Consequently, $\mathscr{L}(f')$ exists when $s > \alpha$, and (1) holds.

If $f'(t)$ is merely piecewise continuous, the proof is quite similar; in this case, the range of integration in the original integral must be broken up into parts such that f' is continuous in each such part.

This theorem may be extended to piecewise continuous functions $f(t)$, but in place of (1) we then obtain the formula (1*) in Prob. 2 at the end of the current section.

By applying (1) to the second-order derivative $f''(t)$ we obtain

$$\mathscr{L}(f'') = s\mathscr{L}(f') - f'(0)$$
$$= s[s\mathscr{L}(f) - f(0)] - f'(0);$$

that is,

(2) $$\mathscr{L}(f'') = s^2\mathscr{L}(f) - sf(0) - f'(0).$$

Similarly,

(3) $$\mathscr{L}(f''') = s^3\mathscr{L}(f) - s^2f(0) - sf'(0) - f''(0),$$

etc.   By induction we thus obtain the following extension of Theorem 1.

Theorem 2.   (Derivative of any order n).   *Let $f(t)$ and its derivatives $f'(t)$, $f''(t), \cdots, f^{(n-1)}(t)$ be continuous functions for all $t \geq 0$, satisfying (2), p. 209, for some α and M, and let the derivative $f^{(n)}(t)$ be piecewise continuous on every finite interval in the range $t \geq 0$. Then the Laplace transform of $f^{(n)}(t)$ exists when $s > \alpha$, and is given by the formula*

(4) $$\mathscr{L}(f^{(n)}) = s^n\mathscr{L}(f) - s^{n-1}f(0) - s^{n-2}f'(0) - \cdots - f^{(n-1)}(0).$$

An obvious application of Theorems 1 and 2 will be the transformation of derivatives in differential equations; this problem will be considered in the next section. However, these theorems may also be used for determining transforms; cf. the following examples.

Example 1. Let $f(t) = t^2/2$. Find $\mathscr{L}(f)$. We have $f(0) = 0$, $f'(0) = 0$, $f''(t) = 1$. Since $\mathscr{L}(1) = 1/s$, we obtain from (2)

$$\mathscr{L}(f'') = \mathscr{L}(1) = \frac{1}{s} = s^2\mathscr{L}(f) \quad \text{or} \quad \mathscr{L}\left(\frac{t^2}{2}\right) = \frac{1}{s^3}.$$

Example 2. Let $f(t) = \cos \omega t$. Find $\mathscr{L}(f)$. We have $f(0) = 1$, and furthermore

$$f'(t) = -\omega \sin \omega t, \quad f'(0) = 0, \quad f''(t) = -\omega^2 \cos \omega t = -\omega^2 f(t).$$

From this and (2), it follows that

$$-\omega^2\mathscr{L}(f) = \mathscr{L}(f'') = s^2\mathscr{L}(f) - s \quad \text{or} \quad \mathscr{L}(f)(s^2 + \omega^2) = s.$$

Hence we obtain the expected result

$$\mathscr{L}(\cos \omega t) = \frac{s}{s^2 + \omega^2}.$$

Example 3. Let $f(t) = t \sin \omega t$. Find $\mathscr{L}(f)$. We have $f(0) = 0$,

$$f'(t) = \sin \omega t + \omega t \cos \omega t, \quad f'(0) = 0,$$

and furthermore

$$f''(t) = 2\omega \cos \omega t - \omega^2 t \sin \omega t = 2\omega \cos \omega t - \omega^2 f(t).$$

From this and (2) it follows that

$$2\omega\mathscr{L}(\cos \omega t) - \omega^2\mathscr{L}(f) = \mathscr{L}(f'') = s^2\mathscr{L}(f).$$

Using the formula for the Laplace transform of $\cos \omega t$, we thus obtain

$$(s^2 + \omega^2)\mathscr{L}(f) = 2\omega\mathscr{L}(\cos \omega t) = \frac{2\omega s}{s^2 + \omega^2}.$$

Consequently, the result is

$$\mathscr{L}(t \sin \omega t) = \frac{2\omega s}{(s^2 + \omega^2)^2}.$$

We have seen that differentiation of $f(t)$ corresponds to multiplication of $\mathscr{L}(f)$ by s (and addition of a constant). We shall now prove that *integration of $f(t)$* corresponds to *division of $\mathscr{L}(f)$ by s*.

Theorem 3. **[Integration of $f(t)$].** *If $f(t)$ is piecewise continuous and satisfies an inequality of the form (2), p. 209, then*

(5)
$$\mathscr{L}\left\{\int_0^t f(\tau)\, d\tau\right\} = \frac{1}{s}\mathscr{L}\{f(t)\} \qquad (s > 0, s > \alpha).$$

Proof. Suppose that $f(t)$ is piecewise continuous and satisfies (2), p. 209, for some α and M. Clearly, if (2) holds for some negative α it also holds for positive α, and we may assume that α is positive. Then the integral

$$g(t) = \int_0^t f(\tau)\, d\tau$$

is continuous, and by using (2) we obtain

$$|g(t)| \le \int_0^t |f(\tau)|\, d\tau \le M \int_0^t e^{\alpha\tau}\, d\tau = \frac{M}{\alpha}(e^{\alpha t} - 1) \qquad (\alpha > 0).$$

Furthermore, $g'(t) = f(t)$, except for points at which $f(t)$ is discontinuous. Hence $g'(t)$ is piecewise continuous on each finite interval, and, according to Theorem 1,

$$\mathscr{L}\{f(t)\} = \mathscr{L}\{g'(t)\} = s\mathscr{L}\{g(t)\} - g(0) \qquad (s > \alpha).$$

Clearly, $g(0) = 0$, and, therefore,

$$\mathscr{L}(g) = \frac{1}{s}\mathscr{L}(f).$$

This completes the proof.

Example 4. Let $\mathscr{L}(f) = \dfrac{1}{s^2(s^2 + \omega^2)}$. Find $f(t)$. From Table 16 in Sec. 4.1 we have

$$\mathscr{L}^{-1}\left(\frac{1}{s^2 + \omega^2}\right) = \frac{1}{\omega}\sin \omega t.$$

From this and Theorem 3 it follows that

$$\mathscr{L}^{-1}\left\{\frac{1}{s}\left(\frac{1}{s^2 + \omega^2}\right)\right\} = \frac{1}{\omega}\int_0^t \sin \omega\tau\, d\tau = \frac{1}{\omega^2}(1 - \cos \omega t).$$

Applying Theorem 3 once more, we obtain the desired answer

$$\mathscr{L}^{-1}\left\{\frac{1}{s^2}\left(\frac{1}{s^2 + \omega^2}\right)\right\} = \frac{1}{\omega^2}\int_0^t (1 - \cos \omega\tau)\, d\tau = \frac{1}{\omega^2}\left(t - \frac{\sin \omega t}{\omega}\right).$$

PROBLEMS

1. Carry out the details of the proof of Theorem 1, assuming that $f'(t)$ has finite jumps at $t_1, t_2, \cdots t_m$, where $0 < t_1 < t_2 < \cdots < t_m$.

2. If $f(t)$ is continuous, except for an ordinary discontinuity at $t = a\ (> 0)$, the other conditions remaining the same as in Theorem 1, show that

(1*) $\mathscr{L}(f') = s\mathscr{L}(f) - f(0) - [f(a + 0) - f(a - 0)]\, e^{-as}$

where $f(a + 0)$ and $f(a - 0)$ are the limits of f at $t = a$ as t approaches a from the right and from the left, respectively, so that the quantity in brackets is the jump of f at $t = a$ (Fig. 82).

3. Derive (2) directly, without using (1).

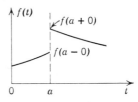

Using Theorem 2, show that:

4. $\mathscr{L}(t \cos \omega t) = \dfrac{s^2 - \omega^2}{(s^2 + \omega^2)^2}$

5. $\mathscr{L}(t \cosh at) = \dfrac{s^2 + a^2}{(s^2 - a^2)^2}$

6. $\mathscr{L}(t \sinh at) = \dfrac{2as}{(s^2 - a^2)^2}$

Fig. 82. Problem 2.

7. Derive the formula in Prob. 5 from that in Prob. 4 by using the relation between the cosine and the hyperbolic cosine.

8. Derive $\mathscr{L}(\cos t)$ from $\mathscr{L}(\sin t)$ by using (1).

9. Find $f(t)$ in Ex. 4 by noting that $\mathscr{L}(f) = \dfrac{1}{\omega^2}\left(\dfrac{1}{s^2} - \dfrac{1}{s^2 + \omega^2}\right)$.

10. Show that formula (5) in Table 16, Sec. 4.1, is valid **(a)** for real $a > -1$, **(b)** for complex a whose real part is greater than -1.

Find $f(t)$ by using Theorem 3, if $\mathscr{L}(f)$ equals:

11. $\dfrac{1}{s(s^2 + 4)}$ **12.** $\dfrac{1}{s(s^2 - 4)}$ **13.** $\dfrac{1}{s^2(s^2 - 4)}$

14. $\dfrac{a}{s(s + a)}$ **15.** $\dfrac{1}{s}\left(\dfrac{s - a}{s + a}\right)$ **16.** $\dfrac{1}{s^2}\left(\dfrac{s - a}{s + a}\right)$

17. $\dfrac{2s - \pi}{s(s - \pi)}$ **18.** $\dfrac{2s - \pi}{s^3(s - \pi)}$ **19.** $\dfrac{\pi^5}{s^4(s^2 + \pi^2)}$

20. $\dfrac{2}{s^3(s - 2)}$ **21.** $\dfrac{4}{s^2}\left(\dfrac{s - 2}{s^2 + 4}\right)$ **22.** $\dfrac{1}{s^2}\left(\dfrac{s + 1}{s^2 + 1}\right)$

4.3 TRANSFORMATION OF ORDINARY DIFFERENTIAL EQUATIONS

We shall now see that ordinary linear differential equations with constant coefficients can be reduced to algebraic equations of the transform. For example, consider the equation

(1) $$y''(t) + \omega^2 y(t) = r(t)$$

where $r(t)$ and ω are given. Applying the Laplace transformation and using (2), Sec. 4.2, we obtain

(2) $$s^2 Y(s) - sy(0) - y'(0) + \omega^2 Y(s) = R(s),$$

where $Y(s)$ is the Laplace transform of the (unknown) function $y(t)$, and

$R(s)$ is the Laplace transform of $r(t)$. This algebraic equation is called the **subsidiary equation** of the given differential equation. Its solution is clearly

$$(3) \qquad Y(s) = \frac{sy(0) + y'(0)}{s^2 + \omega^2} + \frac{R(s)}{s^2 + \omega^2}.$$

Note that the first term on the right is completely determined by means of given initial conditions, $y(0) = k_1$, $y'(0) = k_2$.

The last step of the procedure is to determine the inverse $\mathscr{L}^{-1}(Y) = y(t)$ which is then the desired solution of (1).

Note that (2) was obtained from (1) by means of Theorem 2, Sec. 4.2. Instead of justifying this step by showing that the final result $y(t)$ satisfies the conditions of that theorem, it is simpler and more natural to see by substitution whether $y(t)$ satisfies the given equation and the initial conditions.

Example 1. Find the solution of the differential equation

$$y'' + 9y = 0,$$

satisfying the initial conditions $y(0) = 0$, $y'(0) = 2$.

From (2) it follows that the subsidiary equation is

$$s^2 Y(s) - 2 + 9Y(s) = 0.$$

Solving for $Y(s)$, we obtain

$$Y(s) = \frac{2}{s^2 + 9} = \frac{2}{3}\left(\frac{3}{s^2 + 9}\right).$$

From this and Table 16 in Sec. 4.1 we find

$$y(t) = \mathscr{L}^{-1}(Y) = \tfrac{2}{3} \sin 3t.$$

By substitution we see that this function satisfies the given equation and the initial conditions.

Example 2. A small body of mass $m = 2$ is attached at the lower end of an elastic spring whose upper end is fixed, the spring modulus being $k = 10$. Let $y(t)$ be the displacement of the body from the position of static equilibrium. Determine the free vibrations of the body, starting from the initial position $y(0) = 2$ with the initial velocity $y'(0) = -4$, assuming that there is damping proportional to the velocity, the damping constant being $c = 4$.

The motion is described by the solution $y(t)$ of the initial value problem

$$y'' + 2y' + 5y = 0, \qquad y(0) = 2, \qquad y'(0) = -4,$$

cf. (7), Sec. 2.6. Using (1) and (2) in Sec. 4.2, we obtain the subsidiary equation

$$s^2 Y - 2s + 4 + 2(s Y - 2) + 5 Y = 0.$$

The solution is

$$Y(s) = \frac{2s}{(s + 1)^2 + 2^2} = 2\frac{s + 1}{(s + 1)^2 + 2^2} - \frac{2}{(s + 1)^2 + 2^2}.$$

Now

$$\mathscr{L}^{-1}\left(\frac{s}{s^2 + 2^2}\right) = \cos 2t, \qquad \mathscr{L}^{-1}\left(\frac{2}{s^2 + 2^2}\right) = \sin 2t.$$

From this and Theorem 2 in Sec. 4.1 we obtain the expected type of solution

$$y(t) = \mathscr{L}^{-1}(Y) = e^{-t}(2 \cos 2t - \sin 2t).$$

PROBLEMS

Solve the following initial value problems by means of the Laplace transformation.

1. $y'' + y = 0$, $y(0) = 1$, $y'(0) = -1$
2. $4y'' + y = 0$, $y(0) = 3$, $y'(0) = 0$
3. $y'' + 25y = 0$, $y(0) = -2$, $y'(0) = 20$
4. $y'' + 9y = 0$, $y(0) = 0$, $y'(0) = 1$
5. $y'' - 4y = 0$, $y(0) = 2$, $y'(0) = 0$
6. $y'' - y = 0$, $y(0) = 0$, $y'(0) = -1$
7. $y'' - 9y = 0$, $y(0) = 3$, $y'(0) = -9$
8. $y'' - \pi^2 y = 0$, $y(0) = -1$, $y'(0) = \pi$
9. $y'' + 2y' + 2y = 0$, $y(0) = 0$, $y'(0) = 1$
10. $y'' - 4y' + 5y = 0$, $y(0) = 1$, $y'(0) = 2$
11. $y'' + 4y' + 5y = 0$, $y(0) = 1$, $y'(0) = -4$
12. $y'' - 2y' + 10y = 0$, $y(0) = 3$, $y'(0) = 3$
13. $y'' + 2y' + 17y = 0$, $y(0) = 0$, $y'(0) = 12$
14. $4y'' - 8y' + 5y = 0$, $y(0) = 0$, $y'(0) = 1$
15. $4y'' + 4y' + 5y = 0$, $y(0) = 1$, $y'(0) = -\frac{1}{2}$
16. $16y'' - 8y' + 17y = 0$, $y(0) = 0$, $y'(0) = 1$

17. Using the Laplace transformation, show that the initial value problem

$$y'' + \omega^2 y = 0 \qquad\qquad (\omega \text{ real, not zero}),$$

$$y(0) = A, \qquad y'(0) = B$$

has the solution $y(t) = A \cos \omega t + \dfrac{B}{\omega} \sin \omega t$.

18. Using the Laplace transformation, show that the initial value problem

$$y'' - a^2 y = 0 \qquad\qquad (a \text{ real, not zero}),$$

$$y(0) = k_1, \qquad y'(0) = k_2$$

has the solution

$$y(t) = k_1 \cosh at + \frac{k_2}{a} \sinh at.$$

19. Show that the subsidiary equation of the differential equation

$$y'' + ay' + by = r(t) \qquad\qquad (a, b \text{ constant})$$

has the solution

$$Y(s) = \frac{(s + a)y(0) + y'(0)}{s^2 + as + b} + \frac{R(s)}{s^2 + as + b}$$

where $R(s)$ is the Laplace transform of $r(t)$.

20. Show that the subsidiary equation of the differential equation

$$y''' + ay'' + by' + cy = r(t) \qquad (a, b, c \text{ constant})$$

has the solution

$$Y(s) = \frac{(s^2 + as + b)y(0) + (s + a)y'(0) + y''(0)}{s^3 + as^2 + bs + c} + \frac{R(s)}{s^3 + as^2 + bs + c}$$

where $R(s)$ is the Laplace transform of $r(t)$.

4.4 PARTIAL FRACTIONS. UNREPEATED FACTORS

Our previous consideration shows that in many cases of practical importance the solution of the subsidiary equation of a given differential equation will be of the form

(1) $$Y(s) = \frac{G(s)}{H(s)}$$

where G and H are polynomials of s. We may assume that G and H have no factors in common and that the degree of G is lower than that of H. Then we can determine $y(t) = \mathscr{L}^{-1}(Y)$ by expressing $Y(s)$ in terms of partial fractions.

Let us first consider a simple example and then approach the present problem in a systematic way.

Example 1.   Find $\mathscr{L}^{-1}\left\{\dfrac{s + 1}{s^3 + s^2 - 6s}\right\}$. The numerator is of lower degree in s than the denominator. The latter has the three distinct linear factors s, $s - 2$, and $s + 3$. Hence we can determine constants A_1, A_2, and A_3 such that

$$\frac{s + 1}{s^3 + s^2 - 6s} = \frac{s + 1}{s(s - 2)(s + 3)} = \frac{A_1}{s} + \frac{A_2}{s - 2} + \frac{A_3}{s + 3}$$

for all values of s. Clearing fractions, we have

$$s + 1 = A_1(s - 2)(s + 3) + A_2 s(s + 3) + A_3 s(s - 2).$$

Equating coefficients of like powers of s, we obtain

$$A_1 + A_2 + A_3 = 0, \qquad A_1 + 3A_2 - 2A_3 = 1, \qquad -6A_1 = 1$$

and from this, $A_1 = -\frac{1}{6}$, $A_2 = \frac{3}{10}$, $A_3 = -\frac{2}{15}$. Therefore,

$$\frac{s + 1}{s^3 + s^2 - 6s} = -\frac{1}{6}\left(\frac{1}{s}\right) + \frac{3}{10}\left(\frac{1}{s - 2}\right) - \frac{2}{15}\left(\frac{1}{s + 3}\right).$$

Since we know the inverse transforms of the three functions on the right (cf. Table 16 in Sec. 4.1), we have the result

$$\mathcal{L}^{-1}\left\{\frac{s+1}{s^3+s^2-6s}\right\} = -\frac{1}{6}\mathcal{L}^{-1}\left(\frac{1}{s}\right) + \frac{3}{10}\mathcal{L}^{-1}\left(\frac{1}{s-2}\right) - \frac{2}{15}\mathcal{L}^{-1}\left(\frac{1}{s+3}\right)$$

$$= -\frac{1}{6} + \frac{3}{10}e^{2t} - \frac{2}{15}e^{-3t}.$$

There is a simpler way of determining those constants. To determine A_1, we multiply the first equation in the present example by s:

$$\frac{s+1}{(s-2)(s+3)} = A_1 + s\left(\frac{A_2}{s-2} + \frac{A_3}{s+3}\right).$$

Then we put $s = 0$, finding

$$\frac{1}{(-2)\cdot 3} = A_1 \quad \text{or} \quad A_1 = -\tfrac{1}{6}.$$

To determine A_2, we multiply that equation by $s - 2$ and then put $s = 2$, etc. This is the procedure which we shall now consider in the general case.

We shall now develop a more systematic and rapid method of determining the inverse of (1) where the polynomials $G(s)$ and $H(s)$ satisfy the above assumptions.

Suppose that $H(s)$ has a linear factor $s - a$, *not repeated*. Then in the representation of $G(s)/H(s)$ in terms of partial fractions this factor will have corresponding to it a fraction of the form $A/(s - a)$. Denoting the sum of the fractions corresponding to all the other (unrepeated and repeated) factors of $H(s)$ by $W(s)$, we may write

(2) $$\frac{G(s)}{H(s)} = \frac{A}{s-a} + W(s).$$

To determine A, we multiply this identity by $s - a$, finding

$$Q(s) = A + (s-a)W(s)$$

where

(3) $$Q(s) = \frac{(s-a)G(s)}{H(s)}.$$

If we let s approach a, the second member on the right vanishes, since none of the terms of $W(s)$ contains a factor $s - a$ in the denominator. Also, since $Q(s)$ is continuous at $s = a$, it approaches $Q(a)$ as s approaches a. Thus

(4) $$A = Q(a).$$

Another useful form of (4) is obtained by writing Q in the form

$$Q(s) = \frac{G(s)}{H(s)/(s-a)}.$$

The limit of the numerator, as s approaches a, is $G(a)$. The denominator appears as an indeterminate of the form $0/0$; evaluating it in the usual way, we obtain

$$\lim_{s \to a} \frac{H(s)}{s - a} = \lim_{s \to a} \frac{H'(s)}{(s - a)'} = H'(a).$$

Hence the desired formula is

(4*)
$$A = \frac{G(a)}{H'(a)}.$$

Since the inverse of $1/(s - a)$ is e^{at}, the inverse of the term $A/(s - a)$ in (2) is

$$\mathscr{L}^{-1}\left\{\frac{A}{s - a}\right\} = A\mathscr{L}^{-1}\left\{\frac{1}{s - a}\right\} = Ae^{at}$$

where A is given by (4) or (4*).

It follows that if *all* the linear factors $s - a_1, s - a_2, \cdots, s - a_n$ of $H(s)$ are unrepeated, then

(5)
$$\mathscr{L}^{-1}\left\{\frac{G(s)}{H(s)}\right\} = A_1 e^{a_1 t} + A_2 e^{a_2 t} + \cdots + A_n e^{a_n t}$$

where the constants $A_1, \cdots, A_n$ are given by the formula

(4')
$$A_k = Q(a_k) = \frac{G(a_k)}{H'(a_k)}, \qquad k = 1, 2, \cdots, n.$$

Repeated factors of $H(s)$ will be considered later.

Example 2. In Ex. 1 we have $a_1 = 0$, $a_2 = 2$, $a_3 = -3$, $G(s) = s + 1$, $H'(s) = 3s^2 + 2s - 6$, $G(0) = 1$, $H'(0) = -6$, etc., and by (4') and (5),

$$\mathscr{L}^{-1}\left\{\frac{s + 1}{s^3 + s^2 - 6s}\right\} = -\frac{1}{6} + \frac{3}{10} e^{2t} - \frac{2}{15} e^{-3t}.$$

PROBLEMS

Find $f(t)$, if $\mathscr{L}(f)$ equals

1. $\dfrac{s + 12}{s^2 + 4s}$

2. $\dfrac{2s - 6}{s^2 - 1}$

3. $\dfrac{6s}{s^2 + 2s - 8}$

4. $\dfrac{s - 3}{s^2 - 3s + 2.5}$

5. $\dfrac{6s^2 + 22s + 18}{s^3 + 6s^2 + 11s + 6}$

6. $\dfrac{s^2 - 6s + 4}{s^3 - 3s^2 + 2s}$

7. $\dfrac{s^2 - 10s - 25}{s^3 - 25s}$

8. $\dfrac{2s^2 + 5s - 1}{s^3 - s}$

9. $\dfrac{2s^4 + s^3 - 10s^2 + 8s + 8}{s(s^2 - 1)(s^2 - 4)}$

10. $\dfrac{s + 13}{s^2 + s - 6}$

11. $\dfrac{4 - s}{s(s^2 + s - 2)}$

12. $\dfrac{5s^2 + s - 2}{s^3 - s}$

13. $\dfrac{3s^2 - s - 18}{(s^2 - 9)(s - 1)}$

Solve the following initial value problems by means of the Laplace transformation.

14. $y'' - 4y' + 3y = 0$, $y(0) = 3$, $y'(0) = 7$
15. $y'' - 4y' + 3y = e^{2t}$, $y(0) = 0$, $y'(0) = 0$
16. $y'' - y' - 2y = 7 \sinh 3t - 3 \cosh 3t$, $y(0) = 2$, $y'(0) = 4$
17. $y'' - 2y' - 3y = 4$, $y(0) = 1$, $y'(0) = -1$
18. $y'' - y' - 12y = -24e^t - 12$, $y(0) = 5$, $y'(0) = 3$
19. $y'' + y' - 2y = 3 \cos 3t - 11 \sin 3t$, $y(0) = 0$, $y'(0) = 6$
20. $y''' - 2y'' - y' + 2y = 0$, $y(0) = 3$, $y'(0) = 2$, $y''(0) = 6$
21. $y''' - 3y'' - 4y' + 12y = 12e^{-t}$, $y(0) = 4$, $y'(0) = 2$, $y''(0) = 18$

4.5 SIMPLE COMPLEX ROOTS

The method described in the preceding section is valid in the case of any unrepeated factor $s - a$ of the product representation of $H(s)$, no matter whether a is real or complex. If a is complex, say,

$$a = \alpha + i\beta$$

and if $H(s)$ has real coefficients, it is known from algebra that $H(s)$ has also the unrepeated factor $s - \bar{a}$ where

$$\bar{a} = \alpha - i\beta$$

is the conjugate of a. Then $Y(s)$ may be written in the form

$$Y(s) = \frac{G(s)}{H(s)} = \frac{A_1}{s - a} + \frac{A_2}{s - \bar{a}} + W(s),$$

and from (4') and (5) in the last section we obtain the inverse

(1) $$y(t) = \mathscr{L}^{-1}(Y) = A_1 e^{at} + A_2 e^{\bar{a}t} + \mathscr{L}^{-1}(W)$$

where

(2) $$A_1 = Q(a) \quad \text{and} \quad A_2 = Q(\bar{a}).$$

It is of great practical importance to write the sum of the first two terms on the right-hand side of (1) in real form. Since

$$e^{at} = e^{(\alpha + i\beta)t} = e^{\alpha t}(\cos \beta t + i \sin \beta t),$$

$$e^{\bar{a}t} = e^{(\alpha - i\beta)t} = e^{\alpha t}(\cos \beta t - i \sin \beta t),$$

we see from (1) that $y(t)$ can be represented in the form

(3) $$y(t) = e^{\alpha t}[(A_1 + A_2) \cos \beta t + i(A_1 - A_2) \sin \beta t] + \mathscr{L}^{-1}(W).$$

We now assume that not only H(s) but also G(s) has real coefficients. Then, writing the complex number $Q(a)$ in the form

$$Q(a) = Q_1 + iQ_2 \qquad\qquad (Q_1, Q_2 \text{ real}),$$

it is not difficult to see that

$$Q(\bar{a}) = \overline{Q(a)} = Q_1 - iQ_2.$$

From this and (2) it follows that in (3),

$$A_1 + A_2 = 2Q_1,$$

$$i(A_1 - A_2) = -2Q_2.$$

By inserting this into (3) we have the simple final result

(4) $$y(t) = 2e^{\alpha t}(Q_1 \cos \beta t - Q_2 \sin \beta t) + \mathscr{L}^{-1}(W).$$

Another approach to the present problem is left to the student as an exercise (Prob. 25).

Example 1 (Free oscillations).   Determine the free damped oscillation corresponding to the initial value problem

$$y'' + 2y' + 5y = 0, \qquad y(0) = 2, y'(0) = -4.$$

The solution of the subsidiary equation is (cf. Ex. 2 in Sec. 4.3)

$$Y(s) = \frac{2s}{s^2 + 2s + 5} = \frac{2s}{(s - a)(s - \bar{a})}$$

where $a = \alpha + i\beta = -1 + 2i$, so that $\alpha = -1$ and $\beta = 2$. Furthermore,

$$Q(s) = \frac{2s}{s - \bar{a}}, \qquad Q(a) = Q_1 + iQ_2 = \frac{2a}{a - \bar{a}} = \frac{2(\alpha + i\beta)}{2i\beta} = 1 + \frac{i}{2},$$

that is, $Q_1 = 1$, $Q_2 = \frac{1}{2}$. Hence, from (4) we obtain the solution

$$y(t) = \mathscr{L}^{-1}(Y) = e^{-t}(2 \cos 2t - \sin 2t).$$

Example 2 (Forced oscillations).   Solve the initial value problem

$$my'' + ky = F_0 \sin pt, \qquad y(0) = 0, y'(0) = 0 \qquad \left(p^2 \neq \frac{k}{m}\right).$$

From Sec. 2.13 we know that this equation governs the forced oscillations of a body of mass m attached at the lower end of an elastic spring whose upper end is fixed (Fig. 83). k is the spring modulus, and $F_0 \sin pt$ is the driving force or input. Setting $\omega_0 = \sqrt{k/m}$, we may write the equation in the form

$$y'' + \omega_0^2 y = K \sin pt \qquad \left(K = \frac{F_0}{m}\right).$$

The subsidiary equation is

$$s^2 Y + \omega_0^2 Y = K \frac{p}{s^2 + p^2}.$$

Solving for Y and representing the solution in terms of partial fractions, we have

$$(5) \quad Y(s) = \frac{Kp}{(s^2 + \omega_0^2)(s^2 + p^2)}$$

$$= \frac{A_1}{s - i\omega_0} + \frac{A_2}{s + i\omega_0} + \frac{A_1{}^*}{s - ip} + \frac{A_2{}^*}{s + ip}.$$

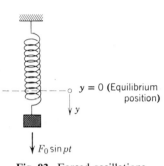

We determine the inverse of the first two terms. Here, $a = \alpha + i\beta = i\omega_0$; that is, $\alpha = 0$, $\beta = \omega_0$. Furthermore,

$$Q(s) = \frac{(s - i\omega_0)Kp}{(s^2 + \omega_0^2)(s^2 + p^2)}$$

$$= \frac{Kp}{(s + i\omega_0)(s^2 + p^2)}.$$

Fig. 83. Forced oscillations.

For $s = a$ this expression takes the form

$$Q(a) = Q_1 + iQ_2 = \frac{Kp}{(a + i\omega_0)(a^2 + p^2)} = \frac{Kp}{2i\omega_0(p^2 - \omega_0^2)} = -i\frac{Kp}{2\omega_0(p^2 - \omega_0^2)}.$$

We see that $Q(a)$ is a pure imaginary number; thus

$$Q_1 = 0, \qquad Q_2 = -\frac{Kp}{2\omega_0(p^2 - \omega_0^2)}.$$

Hence, from (4), it follows that the inverse transform of those two terms is

$$\frac{Kp}{\omega_0(p^2 - \omega_0^2)} \sin \omega_0 t.$$

Similarly, the inverse transform of the last two terms in (5) is

$$-\frac{K}{p^2 - \omega_0^2} \sin pt.$$

By adding these two transforms we obtain the desired solution

$$y(t) = \mathcal{L}^{-1}(Y) = \frac{K}{p^2 - \omega_0^2}\left(\frac{p}{\omega_0} \sin \omega_0 t - \sin pt\right).$$

The vibration is a superposition of two harmonic motions, one of which has the frequency of the driving force and the other has the frequency of the freely vibrating system.

PROBLEMS

Find $f(t)$, if $\mathscr{L}(f)$ equals

1. $\dfrac{6s - 2}{s^2 + 9}$ 2. $\dfrac{1 - s}{s^2 + 1}$ 3. $\dfrac{s^2 + 1}{s^3 + 4s}$ 4. $\dfrac{3s^2 - 2s - 1}{(s - 3)(s^2 + 1)}$

5. $\dfrac{4s}{s^2 - 2s + 2}$ 6. $\dfrac{3(s + 1)}{s^2 + 4s + 13}$ 7. $\dfrac{s - 3}{s^2 + 2s + 5}$

8. $\dfrac{s}{s^2 - 2\pi s + 2\pi^2}$ 9. $\dfrac{3s - 7}{s^2 - 6s + 10}$ 10. $\dfrac{s + \sqrt{3} - \sqrt{2}}{s^2 - 2\sqrt{2}s + 5}$

Show that

11. $\mathscr{L}^{-1}\left\{\dfrac{s^3}{s^4 + 4a^4}\right\} = \cosh at \cos at$

12. $\mathscr{L}^{-1}\left\{\dfrac{s^2}{s^4 + 4a^4}\right\} = \dfrac{1}{2a}(\cosh at \sin at + \sinh at \cos at)$

13. $\mathscr{L}^{-1}\left\{\dfrac{s}{s^4 + 4a^4}\right\} = \dfrac{1}{2a^2}\sinh at \sin at$

14. $\mathscr{L}^{-1}\left\{\dfrac{1}{s^4 + 4a^4}\right\} = \dfrac{1}{4a^3}(\cosh at \sin at - \sinh at \cos at)$

Find $f(t)$, if $\mathscr{L}(f)$ equals

15. $\dfrac{2s^2}{s^4 + 4}$ 16. $\dfrac{s^2 + 8}{s^4 + 64}$ 17. $\dfrac{s^3 + s^2 - 2}{s^4 + 4}$

18. $\dfrac{s^3 + 2s^2 - 2s}{s^4 + 4}$ 19. $\dfrac{s^3 - 2s^2 + s}{(s^2 - 4s + 5)(s^2 - 2s + 5)}$

Solve the following initial value problems by the use of the Laplace transformation.

20. $y'' + y' - 2y = \sin 3t$, $y(0) = 0$, $y'(0) = 0$
21. $y'' - 2y' + 2y = 0$, $y(0) = 0$, $y'(0) = 1$
22. $y'' - 2y' + 2y = 2\cos 2t - 4\sin 2t$, $y(0) = 0$, $y'(0) = 0$
23. $y'' - 2y' + 2y = 4\cos 2t + 2\sin 2t$, $y(0) = 1$, $y'(0) = 1$
24. $y'' + 4y' + 13y = 4\sin t - 12\cos t$, $y(0) = 0$, $y'(0) = -2$
25. Let the polynomials $G(s)$ and $H(s)$ have real coefficients, and let $H(s) = 0$ have simple complex conjugate roots $a = \alpha + i\beta$ and $\bar{a} = \alpha - i\beta$ ($\beta \neq 0$). Show that the inverse of the sum of the two partial fractions corresponding to these roots can be obtained directly in real form, without using the results of the preceding section. For this purpose, start from

$$Y(s) = \frac{G(s)}{H(s)} = \frac{As + B}{(s - a)(s - \bar{a})} + W(s) = \frac{As + B}{(s - \alpha)^2 + \beta^2} + W(s),$$

where A and B are real constants. Multiply both sides by $(s - a)(s - \bar{a})$. Let s approach a. Separating the real and the imaginary parts of the resulting equation, obtain $A = T_2/\beta$, $B = T_1 - \alpha T_2/\beta$ where

$$T_1 + iT_2 = T(a) = [(s - \alpha)^2 + \beta^2]\frac{G(s)}{H(s)}\bigg|_{s=a}.$$

Insert A and B in the above fraction and show that this leads to

$$y(t) = \mathscr{L}^{-1}(Y) = \frac{1}{\beta} e^{\alpha t}(T_2 \cos \beta t + T_1 \sin \beta t) + \mathscr{L}^{-1}(W).$$

26. Show that the final formula in Prob. 25 and the formula (4) are equivalent.

4.6 MULTIPLE ROOTS

We continue the consideration of the inverse transform of

$$(1) \qquad\qquad Y(s) = \frac{G(s)}{H(s)}$$

where G and H are polynomials in s without common factors, and the degree of G is lower than that of H. Suppose that $H(s)$ has a repeated factor $(s - a)^m$. From the elementary theory of partial fractions it follows that in this case the representation of $G(s)/H(s)$ in terms of partial fractions assumes the form

$$(2) \quad \frac{G(s)}{H(s)} = \frac{A_m}{(s - a)^m} + \frac{A_{m-1}}{(s - a)^{m-1}} + \cdots + \frac{A_2}{(s - a)^2} + \frac{A_1}{s - a} + W(s)$$

where $W(s)$ denotes the sum of the fractions corresponding to all the other (repeated and unrepeated) factors of $H(s)$.

To determine the constant A_m, we multiply (2) by $(s - a)^m$. This gives

$$(3) \quad Q(s) = A_m + (s - a)A_{m-1} + (s - a)^2 A_{m-2} + \cdots + (s - a)^m W(s),$$

where

$$(4) \qquad\qquad Q(s) = \frac{(s - a)^m G(s)}{H(s)}.$$

If we let s approach a in (3), we obtain our first result

$$A_m = Q(a).$$

To determine A_{m-1}, we differentiate (3) with respect to s and then let s approach a. We find

$$Q'(s) = A_{m-1} + 2(s - a)A_{m-2} + 3(s - a)^2 A_{m-3} + \cdots$$
$$+ m(s - a)^{m-1} W(s) + (s - a)^m W'(s),$$

and from this we immediately have our next result

$$A_{m-1} = Q'(a).$$

Continuing in this fashion and noting that the first $m - 1$ derivatives of the function $(s - a)^m W(s)$ in (3) are zero at $s = a$, we obtain successively

$$Q''(a) = 2! A_{m-2}, \ Q'''(a) = 3! A_{m-3}, \cdots, Q^{(m-1)}(a) = (m - 1)! A_1.$$

We thus have the result that the constants $A_1, \cdots, A_m$ in (2) are

(5) $A_m = Q(a), \qquad A_k = \dfrac{1}{(m-k)!} \dfrac{d^{m-k}Q(a)}{ds^{m-k}}, \qquad k = 1, 2, \cdots, m-1,$

where $Q(s)$ is given by (4).

Recalling that the inverse of $1/s^k$ is $t^{k-1}/(k-1)!$ (Table 16 in Sec. 4.1) and applying Theorem 2 in Sec. 4.1 we have

$$\mathscr{L}^{-1}\left\{\frac{1}{(s-a)^k}\right\} = \frac{e^{at}t^{k-1}}{(k-1)!}, \qquad k = 1, 2, \cdots, m.$$

From this we obtain the desired formula

(6)
$$y(t) = \mathscr{L}^{-1}(Y) = \mathscr{L}^{-1}\left\{\frac{G(s)}{H(s)}\right\}$$
$$= \left[A_m \frac{t^{m-1}}{(m-1)!} + A_{m-1}\frac{t^{m-2}}{(m-2)!} + \cdots + A_2\frac{t}{1!} + A_1\right]e^{at}$$
$$+ \mathscr{L}^{-1}(W),$$

where the constants $A_1, \cdots, A_m$ are given by (5).

Example 1. Find $\mathscr{L}^{-1}\left\{\dfrac{s+2}{s^5 - 2s^4 + s^3}\right\}$. We have

$$\frac{s+2}{s^5 - 2s^4 + s^3} = \frac{s+2}{s^3(s-1)^2} = \frac{A_3}{s^3} + \frac{A_2}{s^2} + \frac{A_1}{s} + \frac{B_2}{(s-1)^2} + \frac{B_1}{s-1}.$$

We first determine A_1, A_2, A_3. From (4) and (5) we obtain

$$Q(s) = \frac{s+2}{(s-1)^2}, \qquad A_3 = Q(0) = 2, \qquad A_2 = Q'(0) = 5, \qquad A_1 = \frac{Q''(0)}{2} = 8.$$

Then we determine B_1 and B_2. From (4) and (5) we now obtain

$$Q^*(s) = \frac{s+2}{s^3}, \qquad B_2 = Q^*(1) = 3, \qquad B_1 = Q^{*\prime}(1) = -8.$$

From this and (6), it follows that

$$\mathscr{L}^{-1}\left\{\frac{s+2}{s^5 - 2s^4 + s^3}\right\} = t^2 + 5t + 8 + (3t - 8)e^t.$$

Example 2. Solve the initial value problem

$$y''' - 3y'' + 3y' - y = 0, \qquad y(0) = 1, \; y'(0) = -1, \; y''(0) = -1.$$

Using (1), (2), and (3) in Sec. 4.2, we obtain the subsidiary equation

$$s^3 Y - s^2 + s + 1 - 3(s^2 Y - s + 1) + 3(sY - 1) - Y = 0.$$

Collecting the terms containing Y, this becomes

$$(s-1)^3 Y - s^2 + 4s - 5 = 0.$$

Solving for Y and writing the solution in terms of partial fractions, we have

$$Y(s) = \frac{s^2 - 4s + 5}{(s-1)^3} = \frac{A_3}{(s-1)^3} + \frac{A_2}{(s-1)^2} + \frac{A_1}{s-1}.$$

From (4) and (5) we see that in the present case

$$Q(s) = s^2 - 4s + 5, \qquad A_3 = Q(1) = 2, \ A_2 = Q'(1) = -2, \ A_1 = \tfrac{1}{2}Q''(1) = 1.$$

From (6) we thus obtain the result

$$y(t) = \mathscr{L}^{-1}(Y) = \left(2\frac{t^2}{2} - 2t + 1\right)e^t = (t-1)^2 e^t.$$

By substitution we can easily verify that $y(t)$ satisfies the given differential equation and the initial conditions.

Example 3. Solve the initial value problem

$$y'' - 3y' + 2y = 4t + e^{3t}, \qquad y(0) = 1, \ y'(0) = -1.$$

The subsidiary equation is

$$s^2 Y - s + 1 - 3(sY - 1) + 2Y = \frac{4}{s^2} + \frac{1}{s-3}.$$

Solving and representing Y in terms of partial fractions, we have

$$Y(s) = \frac{G(s)}{H(s)} = \frac{s^4 - 7s^3 + 13s^2 + 4s - 12}{s^2(s-3)(s^2 - 3s + 2)}$$

$$= \frac{A_2}{s^2} + \frac{A_1}{s} + \frac{B}{s-3} + \frac{C}{s-2} + \frac{D}{s-1}.$$

We first determine A_1 and A_2. We have

$$Q(s) = \frac{G(s)}{(s-3)(s^2 - 3s + 2)}, \qquad A_2 = Q(0) = 2, \qquad A_1 = Q'(0) = 3.$$

For the other three coefficients we obtain

$$B = \frac{G(s)}{s^2(s^2 - 3s + 2)}\bigg|_{s=3} = \tfrac{1}{2}, \qquad C = \frac{G(s)}{s^2(s-3)(s-1)}\bigg|_{s=2} = -2,$$

$$D = \frac{G(s)}{s^2(s-3)(s-2)}\bigg|_{s=1} = -\tfrac{1}{2}.$$

Hence, by using (5) in Sec. 4.4 and (6) in the current section it follows that

$$y(t) = \mathscr{L}^{-1}(Y) = 2t + 3 + \tfrac{1}{2}e^{3t} - 2e^{2t} - \tfrac{1}{2}e^t.$$

The student may solve the problem by the classical method and convince himself that the present approach is much simpler and much more rapid.

PROBLEMS

1. Solve Ex. 1 by applying Theorem 3 in Sec. 4.2.

Find $f(t)$, if $\mathcal{L}(f)$ equals

2. $\dfrac{3s - 2}{(s - 1)^2}$

3. $\dfrac{10 - 4s}{(s - 2)^2}$

4. $\dfrac{s^2 + 4s + 5}{(s + 1)^3}$

5. $\dfrac{2 - s - s^2}{(s + 1)^3}$

6. $\dfrac{4 - \pi^2 - 2\pi s - s^2}{(s + \pi)^3}$

7. $\dfrac{2s^3 + 5s^2 + 6s + 1}{s(s + 1)^3}$

8. $\dfrac{s^3 + s^2 - 2s + 1}{s^2(s - 1)^2}$

9. $\dfrac{9 - 6s + 5s^2 - s^3}{s^2(s - 3)^2}$

10. $\dfrac{2(s^3 - 7s^2 + 14s - 9)}{(s - 1)^2(s - 2)^3}$

11. $\dfrac{4s^3 + 18s^2 + 30s + 17}{(s + 2)^4}$

12. $\dfrac{s^4 + 3(s + 1)^3}{s^4(s + 1)^3}$

13. $\dfrac{5 - 7s + 4s^2 - s^3}{(s - 1)^3(s - 2)^2}$

Solve the following initial value problems by means of the Laplace transformation.

14. $y'' - 2y' + y = 0$, $\quad y(0) = 1$, $\quad y'(0) = 3$

15. $y'' + 8y' + 16y = 0$, $\quad y(0) = 3$, $\quad y'(0) = -14$

16. $y'' - 4y' + 4y = 9e^{-t}$, $\quad y(0) = 1$, $\quad y'(0) = 0$

17. $y'' + 2y' + y = e^{-2t}$, $\quad y(0) = 0$, $\quad y'(0) = 0$

18. $y''' - 4y'' + 5y' - 2y = 0$, $\quad y(0) = 2$, $\quad y'(0) = 4$, $\quad y''(0) = 7$

19. $y''' + 6y'' + 12y' + 8y = 0$, $\quad y(0) = 4$, $\quad y'(0) = -12$, $\quad y''(0) = 34$

20. $y''' + y'' - y' - y = 9e^{2t}$, $\quad y(0) = 2$, $\quad y'(0) = 4$, $\quad y''(0) = 3$

4.7 MULTIPLE COMPLEX ROOTS

In the case of a complex multiple root of $H(s) = 0$, the formula (6) in the last section gives the result in complex form, and it is of practical importance to convert it to the real form. The consideration will be similar to that in Sec. 4.5.

We assume that $G(s)$ and $H(s)$ have real coefficients. Let $(s - a)^m$ be a factor of $H(s)$, where $a = \alpha + i\beta$ and $\beta \neq 0$. Then $(s - \bar{a})^m$, $\bar{a} = \alpha - i\beta$, is also a factor of $H(s)$, and we may write the representation of $G(s)/H(s)$ in terms of partial fractions in the form

$$Y(s) = \frac{G(s)}{H(s)} = \frac{A_m}{(s - a)^m} + \frac{A_{m-1}}{(s - a)^{m-1}} + \cdots + \frac{A_1}{s - a}$$

(1)

$$+ \frac{B_m}{(s - \bar{a})^m} + \frac{B_{m-1}}{(s - \bar{a})^{m-1}} + \cdots + \frac{B_1}{s - \bar{a}} + W(s).$$

Now from formula (6) in the last section we obtain

$$\mathscr{L}^{-1}\left\{\frac{A_k}{(s-a)^k} + \frac{B_k}{(s-\bar{a})^k}\right\} = \frac{t^{k-1}}{(k-1)!}(A_k e^{at} + B_k e^{\bar{a}t})$$

(2)
$$= \frac{t^{k-1}}{(k-1)!}\, e^{\alpha t}[(A_k + B_k)\cos\beta t + i(A_k - B_k)\sin\beta t],$$

$$k = 1, 2, \cdots, m,$$

and, by (5) in that section,

$$A_k = \frac{1}{(m-k)!}\, Q(a)^{(m-k)}$$

where
$$Q(s) = \frac{(s-a)^m G(s)}{H(s)};$$

here the superscript $(m-k)$ denotes the $(m-k)$th derivative. Similarly,

$$B_k = \frac{1}{(m-k)!}\, Q^*(\bar{a})^{(m-k)}$$

where
$$Q^*(s) = \frac{(s-\bar{a})^m G(s)}{H(s)}.$$

The expression for A_k is a complex number, and we write it in the form

$$\frac{1}{(m-k)!}\, Q(a)^{(m-k)} = Q_{k1} + iQ_{k2} \qquad (Q_{k1}, Q_{k2}\text{ real}).$$

Then, since G and H have real coefficients, it follows that

$$\frac{1}{(m-k)!}\, Q^*(\bar{a})^{(m-k)} = Q_{k1} - iQ_{k2}.$$

From these expressions for A_k and B_k we now readily obtain

$$A_k + B_k = 2Q_{k1}, \qquad i(A_k - B_k) = -2Q_{k2}.$$

By inserting this into (2) we obtain the desired result

(3) $$\mathscr{L}^{-1}\left\{\frac{A_k}{(s-a)^k} + \frac{B_k}{(s-\bar{a})^k}\right\} = 2\frac{t^{k-1}}{(k-1)!}\, e^{\alpha t}(Q_{k1}\cos\beta t - Q_{k2}\sin\beta t).$$

Hence the inverse of $Y(s)$ equals the sum over k from 1 to m of the expressions (3), plus the inverse of $W(s)$.

In particular, if $m = 2$ and $W(s) = 0$, then from (1) and (3),

(4) $$y(t) = \mathscr{L}^{-1}(Y) = 2e^{\alpha t}[(Q_{21}t + Q_{11})\cos\beta t - (Q_{22}t + Q_{12})\sin\beta t].$$

Example 1. Find the inverse of

$$Y(s) = \frac{G(s)}{H(s)} = \frac{s^3 + 7s^2 + 16s + 12}{(s^2 + 2s + 2)^2}.$$

The roots of the denominator are $a = -1 + i$ and $\bar{a} = -1 - i$, so that $\alpha = -1$ and $\beta = 1$. Furthermore,

$$Q(s) = (s - a)^2 Y(s) = \frac{G(s)}{(s - \bar{a})^2},$$

$$Q(a) = Q_{21} + iQ_{22} = \frac{G(a)}{(a - \bar{a})^2} = \frac{-2 + 4i}{-4} = \frac{1}{2} - i,$$

$$Q'(s) = \frac{G'(s)}{(s - \bar{a})^2} - 2\frac{G(s)}{(s - \bar{a})^3},$$

$$Q'(a) = Q_{11} + iQ_{12} = \frac{2 + 8i}{-4} - 2\frac{-2 + 4i}{-8i} = \frac{1}{2} - \frac{3}{2}i.$$

Hence, $Q_{11} = \frac{1}{2}$, $Q_{12} = -\frac{3}{2}$, $Q_{21} = \frac{1}{2}$, $Q_{22} = -1$ and from (4) we obtain the answer

$$y(t) = \mathcal{L}^{-1}(Y) = e^{-t}[(t + 1) \cos t + (2t + 3) \sin t].$$

Example 2 (Resonance). In Ex. 2, Sec. 4.5, we found that the subsidiary equation corresponding to the initial value problem

$$y'' + \omega^2 y = K \sin pt, \qquad y(0) = 0, \, y'(0) = 0$$

has the solution

$$Y(s) = \frac{Kp}{(s^2 + \omega^2)(s^2 + p^2)},$$

and we solved the initial value problem, assuming that $p^2 \neq \omega^2$.

If $p = \omega$ then we have resonance (cf. Sec. 2.13), and in this case,

$$Y(s) = \frac{K\omega}{(s^2 + \omega^2)^2}.$$

The denominator has the double roots $a = \alpha + i\beta = i\omega$ and $\bar{a} = -i\omega$; that is, $\alpha = 0$, $\beta = \omega$. Furthermore,

$$Q(s) = (s - a)^2 Y(s) = \frac{K\omega}{(s - \bar{a})^2},$$

$$Q(a) = \frac{K\omega}{(a - \bar{a})^2} = \frac{K\omega}{(2i\omega)^2} = -\frac{K}{4\omega} = Q_{21}, \qquad Q_{22} = 0,$$

$$Q'(s) = -2\frac{K\omega}{(s - \bar{a})^3},$$

$$Q'(a) = -2\frac{K\omega}{(a - \bar{a})^3} = -i\frac{K}{4\omega^2} = iQ_{12}, \qquad Q_{11} = 0.$$

From this and (4) we obtain the solution

(5) $$\qquad\qquad y(t) = \frac{K}{2\omega^2}(\sin \omega t - \omega t \cos \omega t).$$

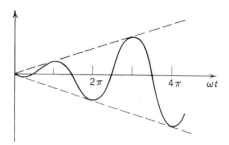

Fig. 84. Last term in (5).

In view of the last term, the amplitude of the oscillations of the mass increases indefinitely (Fig. 84).

PROBLEMS

Find $f(t)$, if $\mathscr{L}(f)$ equals

1. $\dfrac{s^2 + 2s}{(s^2 + 2s + 2)^2}$

2. $\dfrac{1 - s}{(s^2 - 2s + 2)^2}$

3. $\dfrac{s^2 - 6s + 7}{(s^2 - 4s + 5)^2}$

4. $\dfrac{3s^2 - 6s + 7}{(s^2 - 2s + 5)^2}$

5. $\dfrac{s^3 + 8s^2 + 22(s + 1)}{(s^2 + 6s + 10)^2}$

6. $\dfrac{s^3 - 3s^2 + 6s - 4}{(s^2 - 2s + 2)^2}$

7. $\dfrac{s^3 + 3s^2 - s - 3}{(s^2 + 2s + 5)^2}$

8. $\dfrac{s^3 - 6s^2 + 27s - 38}{(s^2 - 4s + 13)^2}$

9. $\dfrac{2(s^3 + 2s^2 - s - 47)}{(s^2 + 4s + 13)^2}$

10. Find

$$\mathscr{L}^{-1}\left\{ \frac{G(s)}{(s - a)^2(s - \bar{a})^2} \right\},$$

$a = \alpha + i\beta$, by using a representation in terms of partial fractions of the form

$$\frac{G(s)}{[(s - \alpha)^2 + \beta^2]^2} = \frac{A(s - \alpha) + B}{[(s - \alpha)^2 + \beta^2]^2} + \frac{C(s - \alpha) + D}{(s - \alpha)^2 + \beta^2}.$$

Hint: express A, B, C, D in terms of the real and imaginary parts of $G(a)$ and $G'(a)$ and use

$$\mathscr{L}^{-1}\left\{ \frac{1}{(s^2 + k^2)^2} \right\} = \frac{1}{2k^3}(\sin kt - kt \cos kt),$$

$$\mathscr{L}^{-1}\left\{ \frac{s}{(s^2 + k^2)^2} \right\} = \frac{1}{2k} t \sin kt.$$

11. Apply the result of Prob. 10 to Probs. 1 and 3.

Solve the following initial value problems by means of the Laplace transformation.

12. $y'' + y = -2 \sin t$, $y(0) = 0$, $y'(0) = 1$

13. $y'' + y = 2 \cos t$, $y(0) = 0$, $y'(0) = 0$

14. $y'' + y = 2 \cos t$, $y(0) = 1$, $y'(0) = 0$

15. $y'' + y = 2(\cos t + \sin t)$, $y(0) = 0$, $y'(0) = -1$

16. $y'' + 4y = -4 \sin 2t$, $y(0) = 0$, $y'(0) = 3$

17. $y'' + 9y = 6 \cos 3t$, $y(0) = 2$, $y'(0) = 0$
18. $y'' + 4y = 4(\cos 2t - \sin 2t)$, $y(0) = 1$, $y'(0) = 3$
19. $y'' + 25y = 10(\cos 5t - 2 \sin 5t)$, $y(0) = 1$, $y'(0) = 2$
20. $y'' + 16y = 16 \cos 4t$, $y(0) = 2$, $y'(0) = 12$

4.8 DIFFERENTIATION AND INTEGRATION OF TRANSFORMS

It can be shown that if $f(t)$ satisfies the conditions of the existence theorem in Sec. 4.1, then the derivative of the corresponding transform

$$F(s) = \mathscr{L}(f) = \int_0^\infty e^{-st} f(t)\, dt$$

with respect to s can be obtained by differentiating under the integral sign with respect to s (proof in Ref. [B2]); thus

$$F'(s) = -\int_0^\infty e^{-st}[tf(t)]\, dt.$$

Consequently, if $\mathscr{L}(f) = F(s)$, then

(1) $$\mathscr{L}\{tf(t)\} = -F'(s);$$

differentiation of the transform of a function corresponds to the multiplication of the function by $-t$.

This property of the Laplace transformation enables us to obtain new transforms from given ones.

Example 1. We know that

$$\mathscr{L}(\sin \omega t) = \frac{\omega}{s^2 + \omega^2},$$

and from (1), it follows that

$$\mathscr{L}(t \sin \omega t) = \frac{2\omega s}{(s^2 + \omega^2)^2}.$$

It is clear that this result may also be written in the following form:

(2) $$\mathscr{L}^{-1}\left\{\frac{s}{(s^2 + \omega^2)^2}\right\} = \frac{t}{2\omega} \sin \omega t.$$

Similarly, from the known formula

$$\mathscr{L}(\cos \omega t) = \frac{s}{s^2 + \omega^2}$$

and (1) we obtain

(3) $$\mathscr{L}(t \cos \omega t) = -\frac{1(s^2 + \omega^2) - 2s^2}{(s^2 + \omega^2)^2} = \frac{s^2 - \omega^2}{(s^2 + \omega^2)^2}.$$

Furthermore, since

$$\frac{s^2 - \omega^2}{(s^2 + \omega^2)^2} = \frac{1}{s^2 + \omega^2} - \frac{2\omega^2}{(s^2 + \omega^2)^2},$$

as we may readily verify, and

$$\mathscr{L}^{-1}\left\{\frac{1}{s^2 + \omega^2}\right\} = \frac{1}{\omega}\sin \omega t$$

we obtain from (3) the intermediate result

$$t \cos \omega t = \mathscr{L}^{-1}\left\{\frac{s^2 - \omega^2}{(s^2 + \omega^2)^2}\right\} = \frac{1}{\omega}\sin \omega t - 2\omega^2 \mathscr{L}^{-1}\left\{\frac{1}{(s^2 + \omega^2)^2}\right\}.$$

It follows that

(4)
$$\mathscr{L}^{-1}\left\{\frac{1}{(s^2 + \omega^2)^2}\right\} = \frac{1}{2\omega^3}(\sin \omega t - \omega t \cos \omega t).$$

From this and (3) we obtain

$$\mathscr{L}^{-1}\left\{\frac{s^2}{(s^2 + \omega^2)^2}\right\} = \mathscr{L}^{-1}\left\{\frac{s^2 - \omega^2}{(s^2 + \omega^2)^2} + \frac{\omega^2}{(s^2 + \omega^2)^2}\right\}$$

$$= t \cos \omega t + \frac{1}{2\omega}(\sin \omega t - \omega t \cos \omega t).$$

This yields another useful formula, namely,

(5)
$$\mathscr{L}^{-1}\left\{\frac{s^2}{(s^2 + \omega^2)^2}\right\} = \frac{1}{2\omega}(\sin \omega t + \omega t \cos \omega t).$$

Similarly, if $f(t)$ satisfies the conditions of the existence theorem in Sec. 4.1 and the limit of $f(t)/t$, as t approaches 0 from the right, exists, then

(6)
$$\mathscr{L}\left\{\frac{f(t)}{t}\right\} = \int_s^\infty F(\tilde{s})\, d\tilde{s} \qquad\qquad (s > \alpha);$$

in this manner, *integration of the transform of a function $f(t)$ corresponds to the division of $f(t)$ by t.*

In fact, from the definition it follows that

$$\int_s^\infty F(\tilde{s})\, d\tilde{s} = \int_s^\infty \left[\int_0^\infty e^{-\tilde{s}t} f(t)\, dt\right] d\tilde{s},$$

and it can be shown (cf. Ref. [B2]) that under the above assumptions the order of integration can be reversed, giving

$$\int_s^\infty F(\tilde{s})\, d\tilde{s} = \int_0^\infty \left[\int_s^\infty e^{-\tilde{s}t} f(t)\, d\tilde{s}\right] dt$$

$$= \int_0^\infty f(t)\left[\int_s^\infty e^{-\tilde{s}t}\, d\tilde{s}\right] dt.$$

The integral over $\tilde{s}$ on the right equals e^{-st}/t when $s > \alpha$, and, therefore,

$$\int_s^\infty F(\tilde{s})\, d\tilde{s} = \int_0^\infty e^{-st}\frac{f(t)}{t}\, dt = \mathscr{L}\left\{\frac{f(t)}{t}\right\} \qquad (s > \alpha).$$

This completes the proof.

Example 2. Find the inverse transform of $\ln\dfrac{s+b}{s+a}$.

We may write

$$\ln\frac{s+b}{s+a} = \ln(s+b) - \ln(s+a) = \int_s^\infty\left(\frac{1}{\tilde{s}+a} - \frac{1}{\tilde{s}+b}\right) d\tilde{s}$$

when $s > -a$ and $s > -b$. From Table 16 in Sec. 4.1 we find

$$F(s) = \frac{1}{s+a} - \frac{1}{s+b} = \mathscr{L}(e^{-at} - e^{-bt}).$$

Therefore, since $e^{-at} - e^{-bt}$ satisfies the assumptions under which (6) is valid,

$$\ln\frac{s+b}{s+a} = \int_s^\infty F(\tilde{s})\, d\tilde{s} = \mathscr{L}\left(\frac{e^{-at} - e^{-bt}}{t}\right).$$

This result may be written

(7) $$\mathscr{L}^{-1}\left(\ln\frac{s+b}{s+a}\right) = \frac{e^{-at} - e^{-bt}}{t} \qquad (s > -a, s > -b).$$

Example 3. Find the transform of $(\sin \omega t)/t$.

Let $f(t) = \sin \omega t$. Then

$$\mathscr{L}(f) = \frac{\omega}{s^2 + \omega^2}.$$

The limit of $(\sin \omega t)/t$, as t approaches 0, exists (and equals ω), and $f(t)$ satisfies the assumptions of the existence theorem in Sec. 4.1. Hence, according to (6),

$$\mathscr{L}\left\{\frac{f(t)}{t}\right\} = \int_s^\infty \frac{\omega}{\tilde{s}^2 + \omega^2}\, d\tilde{s} = \arctan\frac{\tilde{s}}{\omega}\Big|_s^\infty = \frac{\pi}{2} - \arctan\frac{s}{\omega}$$

or

(8) $$\mathscr{L}\left\{\frac{\sin \omega t}{t}\right\} = \operatorname{arc\,cot}\frac{s}{\omega}.$$

Example 4. Find the inverse of $\ln\left(1 + \dfrac{\omega^2}{s^2}\right)$.

By differentiation we first have

$$-\frac{d}{ds}\ln\left(1 + \frac{\omega^2}{s^2}\right) = \frac{2\omega^2}{s(s^2 + \omega^2)} \equiv F(s).$$

Writing $F(s)$ in terms of partial fractions, we obtain

$$f(t) = \mathscr{L}^{-1}(F) = \mathscr{L}^{-1}\left\{\frac{2}{s} - 2\frac{s}{s^2 + \omega^2}\right\} = 2 - 2\cos \omega t.$$

This function satisfies the conditions under which (6) holds. Therefore,

$$\mathscr{L}^{-1}\left\{\ln\left(1 + \frac{\omega^2}{s^2}\right)\right\} = \int_s^\infty F(\tilde{s})\, d\tilde{s} = \frac{f(t)}{t}.$$

Our result is

(9)
$$\mathscr{L}^{-1}\left\{\ln\left(1 + \frac{\omega^2}{s^2}\right)\right\} = \frac{2}{t}(1 - \cos \omega t).$$

PROBLEMS

1. Verify (1) for $f(t) = t^2$.
Using (1), find the Laplace transform of

2. $t \sin 3t$ **3.** te^t **4.** $t \cosh t$
5. $t \sinh 2t$ **6.** $t^2 e^{2t}$ **7.** $t^2 e^{-t}$
8. $t^2 \sin t$ **9.** $t^2 \cos \omega t$ **10.** $t^2 \sinh 2t$
11. $te^{-t} \cos t$ **12.** $te^{-2t} \sin \omega t$ **13.** $te^{-t} \cosh 2t$

14. Find $\mathscr{L}(t^n e^{at})$ by the use of Theorem 2, Sec. 4.1, and by repeated application of (1).

Using (6), find $f(t)$, if $\mathscr{L}(f)$ equals

15. $\dfrac{s}{(s^2 + 1)^2}$ **16.** $\dfrac{1}{(s - a)^2}$ **17.** $\dfrac{1}{(s - a)^3}$

Proceeding as in Ex. 2 or 4, find the inverse of the following Laplace transforms.

18. $\dfrac{1}{2}\ln\dfrac{s^2}{s^2 + 1}$ **19.** $\ln\dfrac{s}{s - 1}$ **20.** $\dfrac{1}{2}\ln\dfrac{s + 1}{s - 1}$

21. arc cot $(s + 1)$ **22.** $\dfrac{1}{2}\ln\dfrac{s^2 + 1}{(s - 1)^2}$ **23.** $\dfrac{1}{2}\ln\dfrac{s^2 - 1}{s^2}$

4.9 UNIT STEP FUNCTION

The unit step function $u_a(t)$ is defined as follows (Fig. 85):

(1)
$$u_a(t) = \begin{cases} 0 & \text{when } t < a \\ 1 & \text{when } t > a \end{cases} \qquad (a \geq 0).$$

In particular when $a = 0$ (Fig. 86),

(2)
$$u_0(t) = \begin{cases} 0 & \text{when } t < 0 \\ 1 & \text{when } t > 0. \end{cases}$$

The transform of $u_a(t)$ is

$$\mathscr{L}\{u_a(t)\} = \int_0^\infty e^{-st} u_a(t)\, dt = \int_0^a e^{-st} 0\, dt + \int_a^\infty e^{-st} 1\, dt = -\frac{1}{s} e^{-st}\Big|_a^\infty,$$

that is, assuming $s > 0$,

(3)
$$\mathscr{L}\{u_a(t)\} = \frac{e^{-as}}{s}.$$

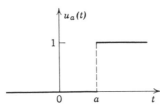

Fig. 85. Unit step function $u_a(t)$.

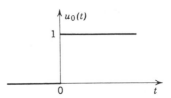

Fig. 86. Unit step function $u_0(t)$.

The unit step function is very important. It can be considered the basic building block of certain functions whose knowledge greatly increases the use of the Laplace transformation.

Example 1. Find the transform of the function $f(t)$ shown in Fig. 87. Obviously

$$f(t) = k[u_a(t) - u_b(t)],$$

and from (3) we obtain the result

$$\mathscr{L}(f) = \frac{k}{s}(e^{-as} - e^{-bs}).$$

Example 2. (Periodic square wave). Represent the square wave function $f(t)$, shown in Fig. 88, in terms of unit step functions and find its transform. Obviously,

$$f(t) = k[u_0(t) - 2u_a(t) + 2u_{2a}(t) - 2u_{3a}(t) + - \cdots].$$

From this and (3) we obtain

$$\mathscr{L}(f) = k\left[\frac{1}{s} - 2\frac{e^{-as}}{s} + 2\frac{e^{-2as}}{s} - + \cdots\right]$$

$$= \frac{k}{s}[1 - 2e^{-as}(1 - e^{-as} + e^{-2as} - + \cdots)].$$

The expression in parentheses $(\cdots)$ is a geometric series; using the well-known formula

$$\sum_{n=0}^{\infty} x^n = 1 + x + x^2 + \cdots = \frac{1}{1-x} \qquad |x| < 1$$

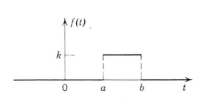

Fig. 87. $f(t)$ in Example 1.

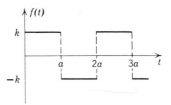

Fig. 88. Example 2.

and setting $x = -e^{-as}$ it follows that

$$\mathcal{L}(f) = \frac{k}{s}\left(1 - \frac{2e^{-as}}{1 + e^{-as}}\right) = \frac{k}{s}\left(\frac{1 - e^{-as}}{1 + e^{-as}}\right)$$

$$= \frac{k}{s}\frac{e^{-as/2}(e^{as/2} - e^{-as/2})}{e^{-as/2}(e^{as/2} + e^{-as/2})} = \frac{k}{s}\tanh\frac{as}{2}\qquad (a > 0, s > 0).$$

Example 3. Find the transform of the function $g(t)$ shown in Fig. 89. We see that $g(t)$ is the integral of the function $f(t)$ considered in Ex. 2, where $k = 1$. Hence, by Theorem 3 in Sec. 4.2,

$$\mathcal{L}(g) = \frac{1}{s}\mathcal{L}(f) = \frac{1}{s^2}\tanh\frac{as}{2}.$$

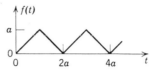

Fig. 89. Example 3.

PROBLEMS

Represent the following functions in terms of unit step functions and find their Laplace transforms.

1.

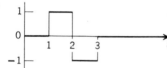

2.

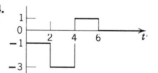

3.

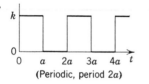

4.

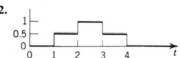

5.

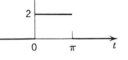

(Periodic, period $2a$)

6.

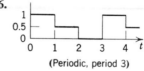

(Periodic, period 3)

7.

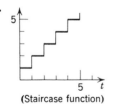

(Staircase function)

8.

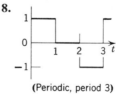

(Periodic, period 3)

9.

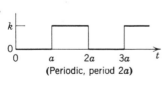

(Periodic, period $2a$)

Find the Laplace transforms of the following functions.

10.   *Hint:* apply Theorem 3, Sec. 4.2, to Prob. 1.

11.

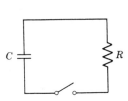

12.

13. $f(t) = \begin{cases} 2t \text{ if } 0 < t < \pi \\ 0 \text{ if } t > \pi \end{cases}$ *Hint:* apply (1), Sec. 4.8 to Prob. 1.

14. $f(t) = \begin{cases} 2e^t \text{ if } 0 < t < \pi \\ 0 \text{ if } t > \pi \end{cases}$ *Hint:* apply Theorem 2, Sec. 4.1 to Prob. 1.

15. $f(t) = \begin{cases} e^{-t} \text{ if } 0 < t < \pi \\ 0 \text{ if } t > \pi \end{cases}$

16. Solve Prob. 14 by using the definition of the Laplace transform and integration.

17. A capacitor of capacitance C is charged so that its potential is V_0. At $t = 0$ the switch in Fig. 90 is closed and the capacitor starts to discharge through the resistor of resistance R. Using the Laplace transform find the charge $q(t)$ on the capacitor.

18. Solve Prob. 11 by using the definition of the Laplace transform and integration.

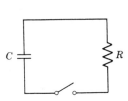

Fig. 90. Problem 17.   **Fig. 91.** Problem 19.

19. Find the current $i(t)$ in the circuit in Fig. 91, assuming that no current flows when $t \leq 0$, and the switch is closed at $t = 0$.

Find $f(t)$, if $\mathscr{L}(f)$ equals
20. e^{-s}/s **21.** $(e^{-2s} - e^{-4s})/s$ **22.** $3(1 - e^{-3s})/s$
23. e^{-as}/s^2 **24.** $(e^{-s} - e^{-2s} - e^{-3s} + e^{-4s})/s^2$
25. $(e^{-s} + e^{-2s} - 3e^{-3s} + e^{-6s})/s^2$

4.10   SHIFTING ON THE t-AXIS

In Sec. 4.1 it was shown that

if $F(s) = \mathcal{L}\{f(t)\}$,   then $F(s - a) = \mathcal{L}\{e^{at}f(t)\}$.

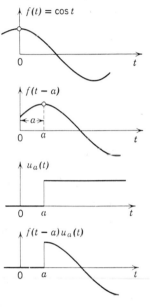

This theorem answers the question how the function changes when the argument s of the *transform* is replaced by $s - a$ (*shifting on the s-axis*). Conversely, we may ask how the *transform* of a function $f(t)$ changes when the argument t of the *function* is replaced by $t - a$ (*shifting on the t-axis*).

The latter question is of importance in connection with systems which are acted upon by a disturbance beginning not at $t = 0$ but at some later time $t = a$.

Suppose that the transform

$$F(s) = \mathcal{L}\{f(\tau)\} = \int_0^\infty e^{-s\tau}f(\tau)\,d\tau$$

of a given function $f(\tau)$ exists. Multiplying by e^{-as}, where a is some positive constant, we have

$$e^{-as}F(s) = \int_0^\infty e^{-s(\tau+a)}f(\tau)\,d\tau.$$

Substituting $\tau + a = t$ in the integral, we obtain

$$e^{-as}F(s) = \int_a^\infty e^{-st}f(t - a)\,dt.$$

Fig. 92. $f(t - a)u_a(t)$ where $f(t) = \cos t$.

We want to write this integral as an integral from 0 to ∞. For this purpose we may replace $f(t - a)$ by the function which is zero on the interval $0 \le t < a$ and is equal to $f(t - a)$ when $t > a$. From the definition of the unit step function it follows that the function

$$f(t - a)u_a(t) = \begin{cases} 0 & (t < a) \\ f(t - a) & (t > a) \end{cases}$$

has the desired property. (Fig. 92 shows an illustrative example.) Therefore,

$$e^{-as}F(s) = \int_0^\infty e^{-st}f(t - a)u_a(t)\,dt = \mathcal{L}\{f(t - a)u_a(t)\}.$$

We may sum up our result as follows.

Theorem 1 (Second shifting theorem).   *If*

$$F(s) = \mathscr{L}\{f(t)\},$$

then for any positive constant a,

(1) $e^{-as}F(s) = \mathscr{L}\{f(t - a)u_a(t)\}$

where the unit step function $u_a(t)$ is defined by (1), *Sec.* 4.9.

Example 1. Find the inverse of e^{-3s}/s^3.
Since $\mathscr{L}^{-1}(1/s^3) = t^2/2$ (cf. Table 16 in Sec. 4.1), Theorem 1 gives

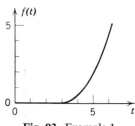

$$\mathscr{L}^{-1}(e^{-3s}/s^3) = \tfrac{1}{2}(t - 3)^2 u_3(t) \qquad \text{(cf. Fig. 93).}$$

Fig. 93. Example 1.

Example 2. (Response of an RC-circuit to a single square wave). Find the current $i(t)$ flowing in the circuit in Fig. 94, if a single square wave with voltage of height V_0 is applied. The circuit is assumed to be quiescent before the square wave is applied. The equation of the circuit is (cf. Sec. 1.9)

$$Ri(t) + \frac{q(t)}{C} = Ri(t) + \frac{1}{C}\int_0^t i(\tau)\, d\tau = v(t)$$

where $v(t)$ can be represented in terms of two unit step functions:

$$v(t) = V_0[u_a(t) - u_b(t)].$$

Using Theorem 3 in Sec. 4.2 and formula (3) in Sec. 4.9, we obtain the subsidiary equation

$$RI(s) + \frac{I(s)}{sC} = \frac{V_0}{s}[e^{-as} - e^{-bs}].$$

The solution of this equation may be written

$$I(s) = F(s)(e^{-as} - e^{-bs}) \qquad \text{where} \qquad F(s) = \frac{V_0/R}{s + 1/RC}.$$

From Table 16 in Sec. 4.1 we have

$$\mathscr{L}^{-1}(F) = \frac{V_0}{R} e^{-t/RC}.$$

Hence, by the use of Theorem 1, we obtain the solution (Fig. 95)

$$i(t) = \mathscr{L}^{-1}(I) = \mathscr{L}^{-1}\{e^{-as}F(s)\} - \mathscr{L}^{-1}\{e^{-bs}F(s)\}$$

$$= \frac{V_0}{R}[e^{-(t-a)/RC}u_a(t) - e^{-(t-b)/RC}u_b(t)];$$

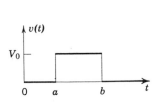

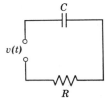

Fig. 94. Example 2.

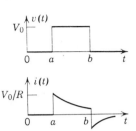

Fig. 95. Voltage and current in Example 2.   **Fig. 96.** Example 3.

that is, $i = 0$ when $t < a$, and

$$i(t) = \begin{cases} K_1 e^{-t/RC} & \text{when } a < t < b \\ \\ (K_1 - K_2)e^{-t/RC} & \text{when } t > b \end{cases} \qquad \text{where} \qquad \begin{aligned} K_1 &= \frac{V_0}{R} e^{a/RC} \\ \\ K_2 &= \frac{V_0}{R} e^{b/RC}. \end{aligned}$$

Example 3. (Response of a damped vibrating system to a single square wave). Determine the response of the damped vibrating system corresponding to the equation

$$y'' + 3y' + 2y = r(t)$$

where $r(t) = 1$ when $0 < t < 1$ and 0 otherwise (Fig. 96); assume that $y(0) = 0$ and $y'(0) = 0$.

We have
$$r(t) = u_0(t) - u_1(t).$$

The subsidiary equation is

$$s^2 Y + 3s Y + 2Y = \frac{1}{s}(1 - e^{-s}).$$

Solving for Y, we obtain

$$Y(s) = F(s)(1 - e^{-s}) \qquad \text{where} \qquad F(s) = \frac{1}{s(s+1)(s+2)}.$$

Using the method of partial fractions [cf. (5) in Sec. 4.4] it follows that

$$f(t) = \mathscr{L}^{-1}(F) = \tfrac{1}{2} - e^{-t} + \tfrac{1}{2} e^{-2t}.$$

Therefore, by Theorem 1, we have

$$\mathscr{L}^{-1}\{e^{-s}F(s)\} = f(t - 1)u_1(t) = \begin{cases} 0 & (t < 1) \\ \tfrac{1}{2} - e^{-(t-1)} + \tfrac{1}{2}e^{-2(t-1)} & (t > 1) \end{cases}$$

This yields the solution (cf. Fig. 97)

$$y(t) = \mathscr{L}^{-1}(Y) = f(t) - f(t - 1)u_1(t) = \begin{cases} \tfrac{1}{2} - e^{-t} + \tfrac{1}{2}e^{-2t} & (0 \le t < 1) \\ K_1 e^{-t} - K_2 e^{-2t} & (t \ge 1) \end{cases}$$

where $K_1 = e - 1$ and $K_2 = (e^2 - 1)/2$.

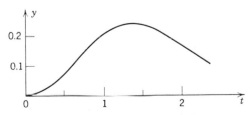

Fig. 97. Output in Example 3.

PROBLEMS

Show the following functions graphically and find their Laplace transforms.

1. $(t - 2)u_2(t)$ **2.** $(1 - t)u_1(t)$ **3.** $(t - 1)^2 u_1(t)$
4. $u_{2\pi}(t) \sin t$ **5.** $u_\pi(t) \cos t$ **6.** $e^t u_1(t)$
7. $e^{-2t} u_1(t)$ **8.** $t u_2(t)$ **9.** $t^2 u_1(t)$

Find the inverse transforms of the following functions and show the result graphically.
10. e^{-s}/s **11.** e^{-2s}/s^2 **12.** e^{-s}/s^4
13. $e^{-2s}/(s - 2)$ **14.** $se^{-\pi s}/(s^2 + 4)$ **15.** $e^{-s}/(s^2 + \pi^2)$

16. Solve Prob. 9, Sec. 4.9, by applying Theorem 1, this section, to the solution of Prob. 5, Sec. 4.9.

17. If $\mathscr{L}\{f(t)\} = F(s)$ show that $\mathscr{L}\{f(at)\} = \dfrac{1}{a} F\left(\dfrac{s}{a}\right)$ $(a > 0)$.

18. Using the result of Prob. 17, derive the transform of $\cos \omega t$ from that of $\cos t$.

19. If $F(s) = \mathscr{L}\{f(t)\}$, show that $F(as - b) = \mathscr{L}\left\{\dfrac{1}{a} e^{bt/a} f\left(\dfrac{t}{a}\right)\right\}$ $(a > 0)$.

Find the inverse of the following transforms.

20. $\dfrac{1}{(2s - 4)^4}$ **21.** $\dfrac{\pi^2 s + 3\pi}{(\pi s + 3)^2 + \pi^2}$ **22.** $\dfrac{1}{(4s + 3)^2 - 9}$

Find the transforms of the following functions.

23. $f(t) = \begin{cases} K \sin \omega t & \text{if } 0 < t < \pi/\omega \\ 0 & \text{if } t > \pi/\omega \end{cases}$

24. $f(t) = \begin{cases} V_0 \cos \omega t & \text{if } 0 < t < \pi/\omega \\ 0 & \text{if } t > \pi/\omega \end{cases}$

25. $f(t) = \begin{cases} t & \text{if } 0 < t < a \\ 0 & \text{if } t > a \end{cases}$ **26.** $f(t) = \begin{cases} 0 & \text{if } 0 < t < a \\ t & \text{if } t > a \end{cases}$

Find the current $i(t)$ in the LC-circuit in Fig. 98, assuming $L = 1$ henry, $C = 1$ farad, zero initial current and charge on the capacitor and $v(t)$ as follows.

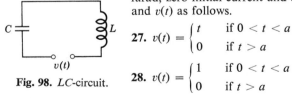

Fig. 98. LC-circuit.

27. $v(t) = \begin{cases} t & \text{if } 0 < t < a \\ 0 & \text{if } t > a \end{cases}$

28. $v(t) = \begin{cases} 1 & \text{if } 0 < t < a \\ 0 & \text{if } t > a \end{cases}$

29. $v(t) = \begin{cases} 1 - e^{-t} & \text{if } 0 < t < \pi \\ 0 & \text{if } t > \pi \end{cases}$ **30.** $v(t) = \begin{cases} t & \text{if } 0 < t < a \\ a & \text{if } t > a \end{cases}$

4.11 PERIODIC FUNCTIONS

The Laplace transforms of some special periodic functions were already considered in Sec. 4.9, and we shall now approach the problem of determining such transforms in a systematic way.

Let $f(t)$ be a function which is defined for all positive t and has the period p (>0), that is,

$$f(t + p) = f(t) \qquad \text{for all } t > 0.$$

If $f(t)$ is piecewise continuous over an interval of length p, then its Laplace transform exists, and we can write the integral from zero to infinity as the series of integrals over successive periods:

$$\mathscr{L}(f) = \int_0^\infty e^{-st} f(t) \, dt = \int_0^p e^{-st} f \, dt + \int_p^{2p} e^{-st} f \, dt + \int_{2p}^{3p} e^{-st} f \, dt + \cdots.$$

If we substitute $t = \tau + p$ in the second integral, $t = \tau + 2p$ in the third integral, $\cdots$, $t = \tau + (n - 1)p$ in the nth integral, $\cdots$, then the new limits are 0 and p. Since

$$f(\tau + p) = f(\tau), \qquad f(\tau + 2p) = f(\tau),$$

etc., we thus obtain

$$\mathscr{L}(f) = \int_0^p e^{-s\tau} f(\tau) \, d\tau + \int_0^p e^{-s(\tau + p)} f(\tau) \, d\tau + \int_0^p e^{-s(\tau + 2p)} f(\tau) \, d\tau + \cdots.$$

Taking the factors which do not depend on τ out from under the integral signs, this becomes

$$\mathscr{L}(f) = [1 + e^{-sp} + e^{-2sp} + \cdots] \int_0^p e^{-s\tau} f(\tau) \, d\tau.$$

The series in brackets $[\cdots]$ is a geometric series whose sum is $1/(1 - e^{-ps})$ (cf. also Ex. 2 in Sec. 4.9). The following result is therefore established.

Theorem 1 (Transform of periodic functions). *The Laplace transform of a piecewise continuous periodic function $f(t)$ with period p is*

$$(1) \qquad \mathscr{L}(f) = \frac{1}{1 - e^{-ps}} \int_0^p e^{-st} f(t) \, dt \qquad (s > 0).$$

Example 1 (Half-wave rectifier). Find the Laplace transform of the following function $f(t)$ with period $p = 2\pi/\omega$:

$$f(t) = \begin{cases} \sin \omega t & \text{when } \quad 0 < t < \pi/\omega, \\ 0 & \text{when } \pi/\omega < t < 2\pi/\omega. \end{cases}$$

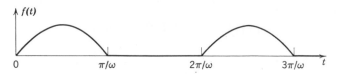

Fig. 99. Half-wave rectification of sin ωt.

Note that this function is the half-wave rectification of sin ωt (Fig. 99). From (1) we obtain

$$\mathscr{L}(f) = \frac{1}{1 - e^{-2\pi s/\omega}} \int_0^{\pi/\omega} e^{-st} \sin \omega t \, dt.$$

Integrating by parts or noting that the integral is the imaginary part of the integral

$$\int_0^{\pi/\omega} e^{(-s+i\omega)t} \, dt = \frac{1}{-s + i\omega} e^{(-s+i\omega)t} \Big|_0^{\pi/\omega} = \frac{-s - i\omega}{s^2 + \omega^2}(-e^{-s\pi/\omega} - 1)$$

we obtain the result

$$\mathscr{L}(f) = \frac{\omega(1 + e^{-\pi s/\omega})}{(s^2 + \omega^2)(1 - e^{-2\pi s/\omega})} = \frac{\omega}{(s^2 + \omega^2)(1 - e^{-\pi s/\omega})}.$$

Example 2 (Saw-tooth wave). Find the Laplace transform of the function (Fig. 100)

$$f(t) = \frac{k}{p} t \quad \text{when } 0 < t < p, \quad f(t + p) = f(t).$$

Since, by integration by parts,

$$\int_0^p e^{-st} t \, dt = -\frac{t}{s} e^{-st} \Big|_0^p + \frac{1}{s} \int_0^p e^{-st} \, dt$$

$$= -\frac{p}{s} e^{-sp} - \frac{1}{s^2}(e^{-sp} - 1)$$

we obtain from (1) the result

$$\mathscr{L}(f) = \frac{k}{ps^2} - \frac{ke^{-ps}}{s(1 - e^{-ps})} \qquad (s > 0).$$

Example 3 (Staircase function). Find the Laplace transform of the staircase function (Fig. 101)

$$g(t) = kn \qquad [np < t < (n + 1)p, \quad n = 0, 1, 2, \cdots].$$

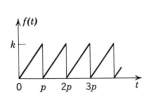

Fig. 100. Saw-tooth wave.

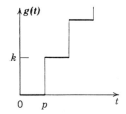

Fig. 101. Staircase function.

Since $g(t)$ is the difference of the functions $h(t) = kt/p$ (whose transform is k/ps^2) and $f(t)$ in Ex. 2, we obtain

$$\mathscr{L}(g) = \mathscr{L}(h) - \mathscr{L}(f) = \frac{ke^{-ps}}{s(1 - e^{-ps})} \qquad (s > 0).$$

The next example illustrates the application of the Laplace transformation to a linear nonhomogeneous differential equation which has a periodic function on the right-hand side.

Example 4 (Forced oscillations). Solve the differential equation

(2) $y'' + 2y' + 10y = r(t)$

where (Fig. 102)

$$r(t) = \begin{cases} 1 & (0 < t < \pi) \\ -1 & (\pi < t < 2\pi) \end{cases}, \quad r(t + 2\pi) = r(t).$$

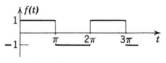

Fig. 102. Input $r(t)$ in Example 4.

We have (cf. Ex. 2 in Sec. 4.9)

$$R(s) = \mathscr{L}(r) = \frac{1}{s}[1 - 2e^{-\pi s} + 2e^{-2\pi s} - 2e^{-3\pi s} + - \cdots].$$

The subsidiary equation of (2) is

$$s^2 Y - sy(0) - y'(0) + 2[s Y - y(0)] + 10 Y = R(s).$$

By solving for Y we obtain

(3) $$Y(s) = \frac{(s + 2)y(0) + y'(0)}{s^2 + 2s + 10} + \frac{R(s)}{s^2 + 2s + 10}.$$

The roots of the denominator are

$$a = -1 + 3i \qquad \text{and} \qquad \bar{a} = -1 - 3i.$$

The inverse transform of the first term in (3) is

(4) $$\mathscr{L}^{-1}\left\{\frac{(s + 2)y(0) + y'(0)}{s^2 + 2s + 10}\right\} = \mathscr{L}^{-1}\left\{\frac{(s + 1)y(0)}{(s + 1)^2 + 9} + \frac{y(0) + y'(0)}{(s + 1)^2 + 9}\right\}$$

$$= e^{-t}\left(y(0) \cos 3t + \frac{y(0) + y'(0)}{3} \sin 3t\right).$$

This is the solution of the homogeneous equation corresponding to (2). The last term in (3) is

$$\frac{R(s)}{s^2 + 2s + 10} = \frac{1}{s[(s + 1)^2 + 9]} \{1 - 2e^{-\pi s} + - \cdots\}.$$

Now we know that

$$\mathscr{L}^{-1}\left\{\frac{1}{(s + 1)^2 + 9}\right\} = \frac{1}{3} e^{-t} \sin 3t.$$

Therefore, according to Theorem 3 in Sec. 4.2,

(5) $$\mathscr{L}^{-1}\left\{\frac{1}{s}\left(\frac{1}{(s + 1)^2 + 9}\right)\right\} = \frac{1}{3}\int_0^t e^{-\tau} \sin 3\tau \, d\tau = \frac{1}{10}[1 - h(t)]$$

where

(6) $$h(t) = e^{-t}(\cos 3t + \tfrac{1}{3} \sin 3t).$$

Denoting the function on the right-hand side of (5) by $f(t)$, that is,

$$f(t) = \frac{1}{10} - \frac{h(t)}{10},$$

and applying Theorem 1, Sec. 4.10, we thus obtain

(7) $\quad \mathscr{L}^{-1}\left\{\dfrac{R(s)}{s^2 + 2s + 10}\right\} = f(t) - 2f(t - \pi)u_\pi(t) + 2f(t - 2\pi)u_{2\pi}(t) - + \cdots.$

Now in the terms on the right,

$$h(t - \pi) = e^{-(t-\pi)}[\cos 3(t - \pi) + \tfrac{1}{3}\sin 3(t - \pi)] = -h(t)\,e^\pi$$

and similarly,

$$h(t - 2\pi) = h(t)\,e^{2\pi}, \qquad h(t - 3\pi) = -h(t)\,e^{3\pi},$$

etc. It follows that in (7),

$$f(t - \pi) = \frac{1}{10} - \frac{h(t - \pi)}{10} = \frac{1}{10} + \frac{h(t)}{10}\,e^\pi$$

$$f(t - 2\pi) = \frac{1}{10} - \frac{h(t - 2\pi)}{10} = \frac{1}{10} - \frac{h(t)}{10}\,e^{2\pi}$$

etc., and the right-hand side of (7) equals

$$\frac{1}{10} - \frac{h(t)}{10} \qquad\qquad\qquad\qquad \text{when } 0 < t < \pi,$$

$$-\frac{1}{10} - \frac{h(t)}{10} - \frac{h(t)}{5}\,e^\pi \qquad\qquad \text{when } \pi < t < 2\pi,$$

$$\frac{1}{10} - \frac{h(t)}{10} - \frac{h(t)}{5}(e^\pi + e^{2\pi}) \qquad \text{when } 2\pi < t < 3\pi,$$

$$\frac{(-1)^n}{10} + \frac{h(t)}{10} - \frac{h(t)}{5}(1 + e^\pi + \cdots + e^{n\pi}) \qquad \text{when } n\pi < t < (n + 1)\pi.$$

Summing the finite geometric progression in parentheses, we see that the expression in the last line may be written

$$\frac{(-1)^n}{10} + \frac{h(t)}{10} - \frac{h(t)}{5}\left(\frac{e^{(n+1)\pi} - 1}{e^\pi - 1}\right).$$

Writing $h(t)$ at length, this becomes

(8)
$$\left[\frac{1}{10} + \frac{1}{5(e^\pi - 1)}\right]e^{-t}\left(\cos 3t + \frac{1}{3}\sin 3t\right)$$

$$+ \frac{(-1)^n}{10} - \frac{1}{5(e^\pi - 1)}\,e^{-[t-(n+1)\pi]}\left(\cos 3t + \frac{1}{3}\sin 3t\right),$$

and the solution of (2) on the interval $n\pi < t < (n + 1)\pi$ is the sum of (8) and the right-hand side of (4).

Clearly the function in (4) and the function in the first line of (8) approach zero as t approaches infinity. The function in the last line of (8) will be denoted

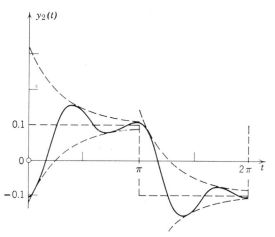

Fig. 103. Steady-state output (9) in Example 4.

by $y_2(t)$. It is a periodic function of t with period 2π and thus represents the *steady-state solution* of our problem. To see this more distinctly we may set $t - n\pi = \tau$. Then $t = \tau + n\pi$, and τ ranges from 0 to π as t ranges from $n\pi$ to $(n + 1)\pi$. Also

$$\cos 3t = \cos (3\tau + 3n\pi) = \cos 3\tau \cos 3n\pi = (-1)^n \cos 3\tau,$$
$$\sin 3t = \sin (3\tau + 3n\pi) = \sin 3\tau \cos 3n\pi = (-1)^n \sin 3\tau,$$

and the function y_2 becomes

(9) $$y_2 = (-1)^n \left[\frac{1}{10} - \frac{e^{-\tau+\pi}}{5(e^{\pi} - 1)} \left(\cos 3\tau + \frac{1}{3} \sin 3\tau \right) \right]$$
$$\approx (-1)^n [0.1 - 0.22 \, e^{-\tau} \cos (3\tau - 0.32)]$$

where $0 < \tau < \pi$, and $t = \tau + n\pi$, $n = 0, 1, \cdots$. Figure 103 shows this function; the graph for $0 < t < \pi$ is obtained from (9) with $n = 0$ and $t = \tau$, and for $\pi < t < 2\pi$ it is obtained from (9) with $n = 1$ and $t = \tau + \pi$.

We have the surprising result that the output y_2 tends to oscillate more rapidly than the input $r(t)$. The reason for this unexpected behavior of our system will become obvious from our later consideration of Fourier series in Sec. 8.7.

PROBLEMS

1. Find the Laplace transform of the half-wave rectification of $-\sin \omega t$ (Fig. 104), (*i*) by direct calculation, (*ii*) by applying Theorem 1, Sec. 4.10, to the result of Ex. 1.

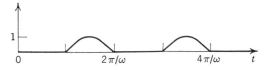

Fig. 104. Problem 1.

2. Evaluate the integral in Ex. 1 by integration by parts.

3. Find the Laplace transform of $|\sin \omega t|$ (the full-wave rectification of the function $\sin \omega t$, cf. Fig. 105), (*i*) by direct calculation, (*ii*) by using the results of Ex. 1 and Prob. 1.

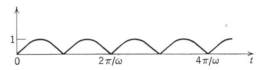

Fig. 105. Problem 3.

4. Find the Laplace transform of $|\cos \omega t|$.

5. Apply Theorem 1 to the function $f(t) = 1$ which is periodic with any period p.

6. Show that the solution y_2 in Ex. 4 is continuous at 0 and π.

Find the transforms of the following functions $f(t)$ which are assumed to have the period 2π; show $f(t)$ graphically.

7. $f(t) = 2\pi - t \qquad (0 < t < 2\pi)$ **8.** $f(t) = t^2 \qquad (0 < t < 2\pi)$

9. $f(t) = e^t \qquad (0 < t < 2\pi)$ **10.** $f(t) = \sin \dfrac{t}{2} \qquad (0 < t < 2\pi)$

11. $f(t) = \begin{cases} t & \text{if } 0 < t < \pi \\ \pi - t & \text{if } \pi < t < 2\pi \end{cases}$ **12.** $f(t) = \begin{cases} 1 & \text{if } 0 < t < \pi \\ -1 & \text{if } \pi < t < 2\pi \end{cases}$

13. $f(t) = \begin{cases} t & \text{if } 0 < t < \pi \\ 0 & \text{if } \pi < t < 2\pi \end{cases}$ **14.** $f(t) = \begin{cases} 0 & \text{if } 0 < t < \pi \\ t - \pi & \text{if } \pi < t < 2\pi \end{cases}$

15. Solve Prob. 14 by applying Theorem 1, Sec. 4.10, to the result of Prob. 13.

16. Solve Prob. 11 by subtracting the result of Prob. 14 from that of Prob. 13.

17. Find the steady-state current in the circuit in Fig. 106.

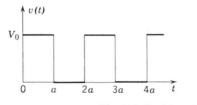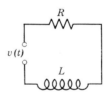

Fig. 106. Problem 17.

18. Solve Prob. 17 without the use of the Laplace transformation.

19. Find the ramp-wave response of the RC-circuit in Fig. 107 assuming that the circuit is quiescent at $t = 0$.

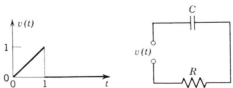

Fig. 107. Problem 19.

20. Solve Prob. 19 without the use of the Laplace transformation. Explain the reason for the jump of $i(t)$ at $t = 1$.

21. Solve Prob. 19 by means of the Laplace transformation, starting from the equation of the form $Ri' + (1/C)i = v'$.

22. Using the Laplace transformation, show that the current $i(t)$ in the RLC-circuit in Fig. 108 (constant electromotive force V_0, zero initial current and charge) is

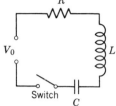

$$i(t) = \begin{cases} (K/\omega^*)e^{-\alpha t}\sin \omega^* t & \text{if } \omega^{*2} > 0 \\ Kte^{-\alpha t} & \text{if } \omega^{*2} = 0 \\ (K/\beta)e^{-\alpha t}\sinh \beta t & \text{if } \omega^{*2} = -\beta^2 < 0; \end{cases}$$

here $K = V_0/L$, $\alpha = R/2L$, $\omega^{*2} = (1/LC) - \alpha^2$.

23. Find the current $i(t)$ in the RC-circuit in Fig. 107 when $v(t) = \sin \omega t \ (0 < t < \pi/\omega)$, $v(t) = 0 \ (t > \pi/\omega)$, and $i(0) = 0$.

Fig. 108. Problem 22.

24. Find the current in the circuit in Prob. 22, assuming that the electromotive force applied at $t = 0$ is $V_0 \sin pt$, and the current and charge at $t = 0$ are zero.

25. Find the current $i(t)$ in the circuit in Fig. 109, assuming that $i(0) = 0$.

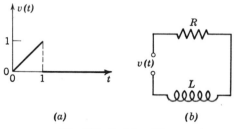

(a)   (b)

Fig. 109. Problem 25.

26. Find the current in Prob. 22, assuming that at $t = 0$ the charge on the capacitor is zero, and $i(0) = i_0$.

27. Find the current in the RLC-circuit in Fig. 108, if a battery of electromotive force V_0 is connected to the circuit at $t = 0$ and short-circuited at $t = a$. Assume that the initial current and charge are zero, and ω^{*2}, as defined in Prob. 22, is positive.

28. A capacitor ($C = 1$ farad) is charged to the potential $V_0 = 100$ volts and discharged starting at $t = 0$ by closing the switch in Fig. 110. Find the current in the circuit and the charge in the capacitor.

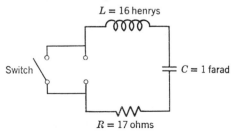

$L = 16$ henrys

Switch

$C = 1$ farad

$R = 17$ ohms

Fig. 110. Problem 28.

29. Steady current is flowing in the circuit in Fig. 111 with the switch closed. At $t = 0$ the switch is opened. Find the current $i(t)$.

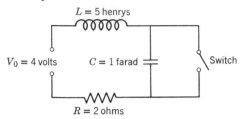

$L = 5$ henrys

$V_0 = 4$ volts $C = 1$ farad   Switch

$R = 2$ ohms

Fig. 111. Problem 29.

30. Find the steady-state current in the circuit in Fig. 109b, if $v(t) = t$ when $0 < t < 1$ and $v(t + 1) = v(t)$ as shown in Fig. 112.

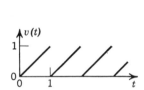

$v(t)$

Fig. 112. Problem 30.

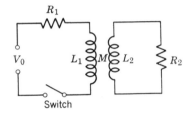

R_1

V_0 L_1 M L_2 R_2

Switch

Fig. 113. Problem 31.

31. The circuits in Fig. 113 are coupled by mutual inductance M, and at $t = 0$ the currents $i_1(t)$ and $i_2(t)$ are zero. Applying Kirchhoff's second law (Sec. 1.9), show that the differential equations for the currents are

$$L_1 i_1' + R_1 i_1 = M i_2' + V_0 u_0(t)$$
$$L_2 i_2' + R_2 i_2 = M i_1'$$

where $u_0(t)$ is the unit step function. Setting $\mathscr{L}(i_1) = I_1(s)$ and $\mathscr{L}(i_2) = I_2(s)$ show that the subsidiary equations are

$$L_1 s I_1 + R_1 I_1 = M s I_2 + \frac{V_0}{s}$$
$$L_2 s I_2 + R_2 I_2 = M s I_1.$$

Assuming that $A \equiv L_1 L_2 - M^2 > 0$, show that the expression for I_2, obtained by solving these algebraic equations, may be written

$$I_2 = \frac{K}{(s + \alpha)^2 + \omega^{*2}}$$

where $K = A^{-1} V_0 M$, $\alpha = (2A)^{-1}(R_1 L_2 + R_2 L_1)$, $\omega^{*2} = A^{-1} R_1 R_2 - \alpha^2$. Show that $i_2(t) = \mathscr{L}^{-1}(I_2)$ is of the same form as $i(t)$ in Prob. 22, where the constants K, α, and ω^* are now those defined in the present problem.

32. Find $i_1(t)$ in Prob. 31.

33. Show that when $A = 0$ in Prob. 31, then

$$i_2(t) = K_0 e^{-at}$$

where

$$K_0 = BV_0 M, \qquad a = BR_1 R_2, \qquad B = 1/(R_1 L_2 + R_2 L_1).$$

34. Suppose that in the first circuit in Fig. 113 the switch is closed and a steady current V_0/R_1 is flowing in it. At $t = 0$ the switch is opened. Find the secondary current $i_2(t)$. *Hint:* note that $i_1(0) = V_0/R_1$, $i_1 = 0$ when $t > 0$, and $i_2(0) = 0$.

35. Two flywheels (moments of inertia M_1 and M_2) are connected by an elastic shaft (moment of inertia negligible), and are rotating with constant angular velocity ω. At $t = 0$ a constant retarding couple P is applied to the first wheel. Find the subsequent angular velocity $v(t)$ of the other wheel.

36. Same conditions as in Prob. 35, but the retarding couple is applied during the interval $0 < t < 1$ only. Find $v(t)$.

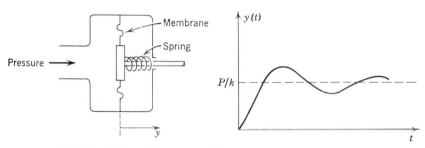

Fig. 114. Problem 37.   **Fig. 115.** Displacement $y(t)$ in Problem 37.

37. Figure 114 shows a system for automatic control of pressure. $y(t)$ is the displacement where $y = 0$ corresponds to the equilibrium position due to a given constant pressure. We make the following assumptions. The damping of the system is proportional to the velocity y'. For $t < 0$, the system is at rest. At $t = 0$ the pressure is suddenly increased in the form of a unit step function. Show that the corresponding differential equation is

$$my'' + cy' + ky = Pu_0(t)$$

(m = effective mass of the moving parts, c = damping constant, k = spring modulus, P = force due to the increase of pressure at $t = 0$). Using the Laplace transformation, show that if $c^2 < 4mk$, then (Fig. 115)

$$y(t) = \frac{P}{k} [1 - e^{-\alpha t} \sqrt{1 + (\alpha/\omega^*)^2} \cos (\omega^* t + \theta)]$$

where $\alpha = c/2m$, $\omega^* = \sqrt{(k/m) - \alpha^2}$ (> 0), $\tan \theta = -\alpha/\omega^*$.

38. Solve Prob. 37 when $c^2 > 4mk$ and when $c^2 = 4mk$.

4.12   TABLE 17.   SOME LAPLACE TRANSFORMS

Remark. For a more extensive list of Laplace transforms and their inverse transforms, see Ref. [B11] in Appendix 1.

	$F(s) = \mathscr{L}\{f(t)\}$	$f(t)$
1	$1/s$	1
2	$1/s^2$	t
3	$1/s^n$, $\quad (n = 1,2,\cdots)$	$t^{n-1}/(n-1)!$
4	$1/\sqrt{s}$	$1/\sqrt{\pi t}$
5	$1/s^{3/2}$	$2\sqrt{t/\pi}$
6	$1/s^a \quad (a > 0)$	$t^{a-1}/\Gamma(a)$
7	$\dfrac{1}{s-a}$	e^{at}
8	$\dfrac{1}{(s-a)^2}$	te^{at}
9	$\dfrac{1}{(s-a)^n} \quad (n = 1,2,\cdots)$	$\dfrac{1}{(n-1)!}\,t^{n-1}e^{at}$
10	$\dfrac{1}{(s-a)^k} \quad (k > 0)$	$\dfrac{1}{\Gamma(k)}\,t^{k-1}e^{at}$
11	$\dfrac{1}{(s-a)(s-b)} \quad (a \neq b)$	$\dfrac{1}{(a-b)}\,(e^{at} - e^{bt})$
12	$\dfrac{s}{(s-a)(s-b)} \quad (a \neq b)$	$\dfrac{1}{(a-b)}\,(ae^{at} - be^{bt})$
13	$\dfrac{1}{s^2 + \omega^2}$	$\dfrac{1}{\omega}\sin \omega t$
14	$\dfrac{s}{s^2 + \omega^2}$	$\cos \omega t$
15	$\dfrac{1}{s^2 - a^2}$	$\dfrac{1}{a}\sinh at$
16	$\dfrac{s}{s^2 - a^2}$	$\cosh at$
17	$\dfrac{1}{(s-a)^2 + \omega^2}$	$\dfrac{1}{\omega}e^{at}\sin \omega t$
18	$\dfrac{s-a}{(s-a)^2 + \omega^2}$	$e^{at}\cos \omega t$

$F(s) = \mathscr{L}\{f(t)\}$	$f(t)$
19 $\dfrac{1}{s(s^2 + \omega^2)}$	$\dfrac{1}{\omega^2}(1 - \cos \omega t)$
20 $\dfrac{1}{s^2(s^2 + \omega^2)}$	$\dfrac{1}{\omega^3}(\omega t - \sin \omega t)$
21 $\dfrac{1}{(s^2 + \omega^2)^2}$	$\dfrac{1}{2\omega^3}(\sin \omega t - \omega t \cos \omega t)$
22 $\dfrac{s}{(s^2 + \omega^2)^2}$	$\dfrac{t}{2\omega} \sin \omega t$
23 $\dfrac{s^2}{(s^2 + \omega^2)^2}$	$\dfrac{1}{2\omega}(\sin \omega t + \omega t \cos \omega t)$
24 $\dfrac{s}{(s^2 + a^2)(s^2 + b^2)}$ $(a^2 \neq b^2)$	$\dfrac{1}{b^2 - a^2}(\cos at - \cos bt)$
25 $\dfrac{1}{s^4 + 4a^4}$	$\dfrac{1}{4a^3}(\sin at \cosh at - \cos at \sinh at)$
26 $\dfrac{s}{s^4 + 4a^4}$	$\dfrac{1}{2a^2} \sin at \sinh at$
27 $\dfrac{1}{s^4 - a^4}$	$\dfrac{1}{2a^3}(\sinh at - \sin at)$
28 $\dfrac{s}{s^4 - a^4}$	$\dfrac{1}{2a^2}(\cosh at - \cos at)$
29 $\sqrt{s - a} - \sqrt{s - b}$	$\dfrac{1}{2\sqrt{\pi t^3}}(e^{bt} - e^{at})$
30 $\dfrac{1}{\sqrt{s + a}\,\sqrt{s + b}}$	$e^{-(a+b)t/2}I_0\left(\dfrac{a - b}{2}t\right)$ (cf. Sec. 3.7)
31 $\dfrac{1}{\sqrt{s^2 + a^2}}$	$J_0(at)$ (cf. Sec. 3.5)
32 $\dfrac{s}{(s - a)^{3/2}}$	$\dfrac{1}{\sqrt{\pi t}}\, e^{at}(1 + 2at)$
33 $\dfrac{1}{(s^2 - a^2)^k}$ $(k > 0)$	$\dfrac{\sqrt{\pi}}{\Gamma(k)}\left(\dfrac{t}{2a}\right)^{k-1/2} I_{k-1/2}(at)$ (cf. Sec. 3.7)

	$F(s) = \mathscr{L}\{f(t)\}$	$f(t)$	
34	$\dfrac{1}{s}\,e^{-k/s}$	$J_0(2\sqrt{kt})$	(cf. Sec. 3.5)
35	$\dfrac{1}{\sqrt{s}}\,e^{-k/s}$	$\dfrac{1}{\sqrt{\pi t}}\cos 2\sqrt{kt}$	
36	$\dfrac{1}{s^{3/2}}\,e^{k/s}$	$\dfrac{1}{\sqrt{\pi k}}\sinh 2\sqrt{kt}$	
37	$\dfrac{1}{s}\ln s$	$-\ln t - \gamma\ \ (\gamma \approx 0.5772;\ \text{cf. Sec. 3.7})$	
38	$\ln\dfrac{s-a}{s-b}$	$\dfrac{1}{t}\,(e^{bt} - e^{at})$	
39	$\ln\dfrac{s^2 + \omega^2}{s^2}$	$\dfrac{2}{t}\,(1 - \cos \omega t)$	
40	$\ln\dfrac{s^2 - a^2}{s^2}$	$\dfrac{2}{t}\,(1 - \cosh at)$	
41	$\arctan\dfrac{\omega}{s}$	$\dfrac{1}{t}\sin \omega t$	
42	$\dfrac{1}{s}\operatorname{arc\,cot} s$	$Si(t)$	(cf. Sec. 14.2)

chapter 5

VECTOR
ANALYSIS

Vectors are useful tools in engineering mathematics, because many phys-ical quantities—for example, forces and velocities—may be represented by vectors, and in several respects the rules of vector calculation are as simple as the rules governing the system of real numbers. In this chapter we shall consider the basic concepts and methods of vector analysis and their appli-cations to various physical and geometrical problems. It is true that any problem which can be solved by the use of vectors, can also be treated by nonvectorial methods, but vector analysis is a shorthand which simplifies many calculations considerably. Furthermore, it is a way of visualizing physical and geometrical quantities and relations between them. For all those reasons extensive use is made of vector notation in modern technical literature.

Prerequisite for this chapter: determinants of the third order (Sec. 0.3), elementary differential calculus.

Sections which may be omitted in a shorter course: 5.8, 5.11–5.14, 5.17.

References: Appendix 1, Part C.

Answers to problems: Appendix 2.

5.1 SCALARS AND VECTORS

In physics and geometry there are quantities each of which is completely specified when its magnitude—that is, its size or number of units according

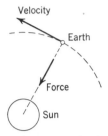

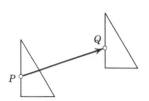

Fig. 116. Force and velocity.   Fig. 117. Translation.

to some scale—is given. Examples are the mass of a body, the charge of an electron, the specific heat of water, the resistance of a resistor, the diameter of a circle, the area of a triangle, and the volume of a cube. Each of these quantities is described by a single number (after a suitable choice of units of measure). Such a quantity is called a **scalar**.[1]

However, there are other physical and geometrical quantities which cannot be described by a single number, because they require for their complete characterization the specification of the direction as well as the magnitude.

For example, forces in mechanics are quantities of this type. We know that we may represent a force graphically by an arrow, or *directed line segment*, which indicates the direction of the force and whose length is equal to the magnitude of the force according to some suitable scale. Figure 116 shows the force of attraction for the earth's motion around the sun. The instantaneous velocity of the earth may also be represented by an arrow of suitable length and direction, and this illustrates that a velocity is also a quantity which is characterized by a magnitude and a direction.

Figure 117 shows the translation (displacement without rotation) of a triangle in the plane. This motion can be characterized by its magnitude (distance travelled by each point of the triangle) and its direction. The translation may be indicated graphically by a directed line segment whose *initial point* is the original position P of a point of the triangle and whose *terminal point* is the new position Q of that point after the translation. If we do this for each point of the triangle, we obtain a family of directed line segments which have the *same length* and the *same direction* (that is, are parallel and are directed in the same sense). We may say that each of these directed line segments "carries" a point of the triangle from its original position to its new position.

This situation suggests the following definition.

Definition. *A directed line segment is called a* **vector**. *Its length is called the* **length** *or* **magnitude** *of the vector, and its direction is called the* **direction**

---

[1] It is essential that the number which characterizes the scalar is independent of the choice of coordinates, but we shall discuss this point later (in Sec. 5.9).

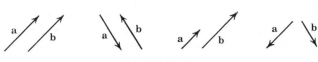

Fig. 118. Vectors.

of the vector. Two vectors are equal if, and only if, they have the same length and the same direction.

Hence a vector may be arbitrarily translated (that is, displaced without rotation) or, what amounts to the same thing, its initial point may be chosen arbitrarily. Clearly, if we choose a certain point as the initial point of a given vector, its terminal point is uniquely determined.

We shall denote vectors by lower-case boldfaced letters,[2] such as **a, b, u, v,** etc. The length of a vector **v** will be denoted by |**v**|.

If two vectors **a** and **b** are equal we write

$$\mathbf{a} = \mathbf{b},$$

and if they are different, we may write

$$\mathbf{a} \neq \mathbf{b}.$$

Any vector may be represented graphically as an arrow of suitable length and direction, as is illustrated in Fig. 118.

A vector of length 1 is called a **unit vector.**

For the sake of completeness, we mention that in physics and geometry there are situations where we want to impose restrictions on the position of the initial point of a vector. For example, as is known from mechanics, a force acting on a rigid body may be equally well applied to any point of the body on its line of action. This suggests the concept of a **sliding vector,** that is, a vector whose initial point can be any point on a straight line which is parallel to the vector. A force acting on an elastic body is a vector whose initial point cannot be changed at all. In fact, if we choose another point of application of the force, its effect will in general be different. This suggests the notion of a **bound vector** that is, a vector having a certain fixed initial point (*point of application*). Since these concepts occur in the literature, the student should know about them, but they will not be of particular importance in our further considerations.

5.2 COMPONENTS OF A VECTOR

We introduce a coordinate system in space whose axes are three mutually perpendicular straight lines. On all three axes we choose the same scale.

---

[2] This is customary in printed work; in hand-written work one may characterize vectors by arrows, for example $\vec{a}$ (in place of **a**), $\vec{b}$, etc.

Then the three *unit points* on the axes, whose coordinates are $(1, 0, 0)$, $(0, 1, 0)$, and $(0, 0, 1)$, have the same distance from the *origin*, the point of intersection of the axes. The rectangular coordinate system thus obtained is called a **Cartesian coordinate system** in space (cf. Fig. 119).

We consider now a vector **a** obtained by directing a line segment PQ such that P is the initial point and Q is the terminal point (Fig. 120). Let (x_1, y_1, z_1) and (x_2, y_2, z_2) be the coordinates of P and Q, respectively. Then the numbers

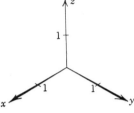

$$\text{(1)} \qquad \begin{aligned} a_1 &= x_2 - x_1, \\ a_2 &= y_2 - y_1, \\ a_3 &= z_2 - z_1 \end{aligned}$$

are called the **components** of the vector **a** with respect to that Cartesian coordinate system.

Fig. 119. Cartesian coordinate system.

By definition, the length $|\mathbf{a}|$ of the vector **a** is the distance $\overline{PQ}$, and from (1) and the theorem of Pythagoras it follows that

$$\text{(2)} \qquad |\mathbf{a}| = \sqrt{a_1^2 + a_2^2 + a_3^2}.$$

Example 1. The vector **a** with initial point P: $(3, 1, 4)$ and terminal point Q: $(1, -2, 4)$ has the components

$$a_1 = 1 - 3 = -2, \qquad a_2 = -2 - 1 = -3, \qquad a_3 = 4 - 4 = 0$$

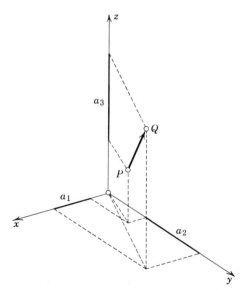

Fig. 120. Components of a vector.

and the length

$$|\mathbf{a}| = \sqrt{(-2)^2 + (-3)^2 + 0^2} = \sqrt{13}.$$

If we choose $(-1, 5, 8)$ as the initial point of $\mathbf{a}$, then the corresponding terminal point is $(-3, 2, 8)$.

From (1) we see immediately that *the components a_1, a_2, a_3 of the vector $\mathbf{a}$ are independent of the choice of the initial point of $\mathbf{a}$*, because if we translate $\mathbf{a}$ then corresponding coordinates of P and Q are altered by the same amount. *Hence, a fixed Cartesian coordinate system being given, each vector is uniquely determined by the ordered triple of its components with respect to that coordinate system.*

If we introduce the *null vector* or **zero vector 0** defined as the vector with components 0, 0, 0, then any ordered triple of real numbers, including the triple 0, 0, 0, can be chosen as the components of a vector. The coordinate system being fixed, the correspondence between the ordered triples of real numbers and the vectors in space is one-to-one, that is, to each such triple there corresponds a vector in space that has those three numbers as its components with respect to that coordinate system, and conversely.

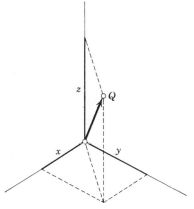

Fig. 121. Position vector.

It follows that two vectors $\mathbf{a}$ and $\mathbf{b}$ are equal if, and only if, corresponding components of these vectors are equal. Consequently a vector equation

$$\mathbf{a} = \mathbf{b}$$

is equivalent to the three equations

$$a_1 = b_1, \qquad a_2 = b_2, \qquad a_3 = b_3$$

for the components a_1, a_2, a_3 and b_1, b_2, b_3 of the vectors with respect to a given Cartesian coordinate system.

A fixed Cartesian coordinate system being given, any point Q in space is uniquely determined by its coordinates x, y, z. Now x, y, z may be regarded as the components of a vector $\mathbf{r}$ whose initial point is the origin of that coordinate system. Then Q is the terminal point of $\mathbf{r}$, and $\mathbf{r}$ is called the **position vector** of Q with respect to that coordinate system (Fig. 121).

PROBLEMS

In each case, find the components and the length of the vector **v** with given initial point P: (x_1, y_1, z_1) and terminal point Q: (x_2, y_2, z_2), and represent **v** graphically.

1. P: $(1, 0, 0)$, Q: $(3, 2, 0)$ **2.** P: $(3, 2, 0)$, Q: $(1, 0, 0)$

3. P: $(-1, -1, 0)$, Q: $(0, 0, 0)$ **4.** P: $(-3, 2, 0)$, Q: $(1, 2, 0)$

5. P: $(2, -3, 0)$, Q: $(1, 2, 0)$ **6.** P: $(1, 1, 1)$, Q: $(0, -2, 4)$

7. P: $(0, 1, 0)$, Q: $(2, 0, 2)$ **8.** P: $(2, 4, 6)$, Q: $(1, 2, 3)$

9. P: $(-1, -2, -2)$, Q: $(0, 3, -3)$ **10.** P: $(0, 0, 1)$, Q: $(-1, 2, -3)$

In each case, the components of a vector **v** and a particular initial point P are given. Find the corresponding terminal point.

11. $v_1 = 2$, $v_2 = 4$, $v_3 = -1$, P: $(0, 2, 4)$

12. $v_1 = 2$, $v_2 = 1$, $v_3 = 0$, P: $(2, 1, 0)$

13. $v_1 = -2$, $v_2 = 0.5$, $v_3 = -1$, P: $(1.5, 4, -1.5)$

14. $v_1 = 1$, $v_2 = 0$, $v_3 = -1$, P: $(0, 0, 0)$

15. $v_1 = 0$, $v_2 = 0$, $v_3 = 1$, P: $(-3, -3, 0)$

16. $v_1 = 1$, $v_2 = -2$, $v_3 = 4$, P: $(-1, 2, -4)$

5.3 VECTOR ADDITION. MULTIPLICATION BY SCALARS

Experiments show that the resultant of two forces can be determined by the familiar parallelogram law (Fig. 122). This suggests the following definition of vector addition.

Given two vectors **a** *and* **b**, *put the initial point of* **b** *at the terminal point*

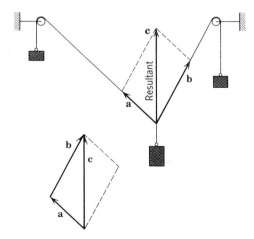

Fig. 122. Resultant of two forces (parallelogram law).

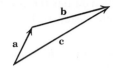

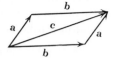

Fig. 123. Vector addition. Fig. 124. Commutativity of vector addition.

of **a**; *then the* **sum** *of* **a** *and* **b** *is defined as the vector* **c** *drawn from the initial point of* **a** *to the terminal point of* **b** (Fig. 123), and we write

$$\mathbf{c} = \mathbf{a} + \mathbf{b}.$$

If in some fixed coordinate system **a** has the components a_1, a_2, a_3 and **b** has the components b_1, b_2, b_3, then *the components* c_1, c_2, c_3 *of the sum vector* $\mathbf{c} = \mathbf{a} + \mathbf{b}$ *are obtained by adding corresponding components of* **a** *and* **b**; thus

(1) $$c_1 = a_1 + b_1, \qquad c_2 = a_2 + b_2, \qquad c_3 = a_3 + b_3.$$

From the definition or from (1) it follows that (Figs. 124, 125)

$$\mathbf{a} + \mathbf{b} = \mathbf{b} + \mathbf{a}, \qquad (\mathbf{u} + \mathbf{v}) + \mathbf{w} = \mathbf{u} + (\mathbf{v} + \mathbf{w}),$$

that is, vector addition is commutative and associative. Furthermore, for any vector **a**,

$$\mathbf{a} + \mathbf{0} = \mathbf{0} + \mathbf{a} = \mathbf{a}.$$

Instead of $\mathbf{a} + \mathbf{a}$ we also write $2\mathbf{a}$ and so on. By $-\mathbf{a}$ we mean the vector whose direction is opposite to **a** and whose length is $|\mathbf{a}|$. This suggests the following definition of multiplication of vectors by real numbers.

Let **a** *be any vector and* q *any real number. Then the vector* $q\mathbf{a}$ *is defined as follows.*
The length of $q\mathbf{a}$ *is* $|q|\,|\mathbf{a}|$.
If $\mathbf{a} \neq \mathbf{0}$ *and* $q > 0$ *then* $q\mathbf{a}$ *has the direction of* **a**.
If $\mathbf{a} \neq \mathbf{0}$ *and* $q < 0$ *then* $q\mathbf{a}$ *has the direction opposite to* **a**.
If $\mathbf{a} = \mathbf{0}$ *or* $q = 0$ (*or both*) *then* $q\mathbf{a} = \mathbf{0}$.

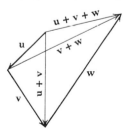

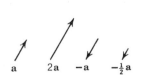

Fig. 125. Associativity of vector addition. Fig. 126. Multiplication of vectors by numbers.

Clearly, if **a** has the components a_1, a_2, a_3, then q**a** has the components qa_1, qa_2, qa_3 (with respect to the same coordinate system). Furthermore, from the definition it follows that

$$(c + k)\mathbf{a} = c\mathbf{a} + k\mathbf{a}, \quad c(k\mathbf{a}) = (ck)\mathbf{a} = ck\mathbf{a}, \quad q(\mathbf{a} + \mathbf{b}) = q\mathbf{a} + q\mathbf{b},$$

$$1\mathbf{a} = \mathbf{a}, \quad (-1)\mathbf{a} = -\mathbf{a}, \quad \mathbf{a} + (-\mathbf{a}) = \mathbf{0}.$$

Instead of $\mathbf{b} + (-\mathbf{a})$ we simply write $\mathbf{b} - \mathbf{a}$ (Fig. 127).

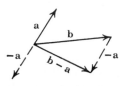

Fig. 127. Difference of vectors.

A Cartesian coordinate system being given, we may now represent a vector **a** with components a_1, a_2, a_3 as the sum of three vectors parallel to the coordinate axes. For this purpose we associate with that coordinate system three unit vectors **i**, **j**, **k** which have the positive directions of the three coordinate axes. Then (Fig. 128)

$$(2) \qquad \mathbf{a} = a_1\mathbf{i} + a_2\mathbf{j} + a_3\mathbf{k}.$$

Figure 128 shows the vectors **i**, **j**, **k** when the origin is chosen as their common initial point. These vectors are mutually perpendicular. Instead of *perpendicular* the term **orthogonal** is also used, and we say that **i**, **j**, **k** form a *triple of orthogonal unit vectors*. This triple is also known as the *fundamental orthogonal triad* associated with that coordinate system.

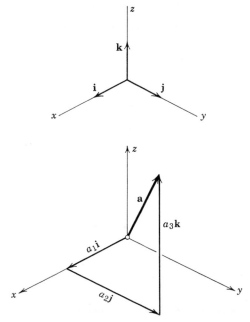

Fig. 128. The unit vectors **i**, **j**, **k** and the representation (2).

Example. With respect to a given coordinate system, let

$$a = 4i + k \quad \text{and} \quad b = 2i - 4j + 3k.$$

Then

$$2b = 4i - 8j + 6k, \quad -b = -2i + 4j - 3k, \quad \tfrac{3}{2}a - b = 4i + 4j - \tfrac{3}{2}k.$$

PROBLEMS

Let $a = 2i + j - k$, $b = -i + 4k$, $c = i + 2j + 3k$, and $d = 3j - 2k$. Find

1. $a + b$ 2. $a - b$ 3. $|c - a|$ 4. $|a + b + c + d|$
5. $b - c - d$ 6. $2a + 3b$ 7. $4c - a$ 8. $b + 0.5d$
9. $|3c - 4d|$ 10. $a/|a|$ 11. $4b - c$ 12. $|a| + |b|$

In each case, find the resultant of the given forces.

13. $p = i + 2j + k$, $q = -i + 3j$
14. $p = -i - 3k$, $q = -j + 3k$, $u = i - k$, $v = 4i + 4j - k$
15. $p = 2i + j - k$, $q = i - j + 4k$, $u = -3i - 3k$

16. Let a, b, c be vectors which have the same initial point and do not lie in a plane. What is the vector $a + b + c$ in relation to the parallelepiped of which a, b, c are edges?

Using vectors, prove the following statements.

17. The diagonals of a parallelogram bisect each other.
18. The medians of a triangle meet at a point P which divides each median in the ratio 1 : 2.
19. The line which joins one vertex of a parallelogram to the midpoint of an opposite side divides the diagonal in the ratio 1 : 2.
20. The sum of the vectors drawn from the center of a regular polygon to its vertices is the null vector.

5.4 SCALAR PRODUCT

The **scalar product** (*or* **dot product**) *of two vectors* a *and* b is written $a \cdot b$ and is defined as

$$a \cdot b = |a|\,|b|\cos\gamma \qquad \text{(when } a \neq 0, b \neq 0\text{)}$$

(1)

$$a \cdot b = 0 \qquad \text{(when } a = 0 \text{ or } b = 0\text{)};$$

here γ $(0 \leq \gamma \leq \pi)$ *is the angle between* a *and* b (*computed when the vectors have their initial point coinciding*). (Cf. Fig. 129.)

The value of the scalar product is a scalar, a real number which is independent of the choice of Cartesian coordinate systems in space. Because

Fig. 129. Angle between vectors.

the cosine in (1) may be negative or positive, the same is true for the scalar product. Since that cosine is zero if, and only if, $\gamma = \pi/2$, we obtain the following important result.

Theorem 1. *Two nonzero vectors are orthogonal if, and only if, their scalar product is zero.*

Furthermore, $\mathbf{a} \cdot \mathbf{a} = |\mathbf{a}|^2$ or

$$(2) \qquad\qquad |\mathbf{a}| = \sqrt{\mathbf{a} \cdot \mathbf{a}} \qquad (\geq 0).$$

From this and (1) we obtain the useful formula

$$(3) \qquad\qquad \cos \gamma = \frac{\mathbf{a} \cdot \mathbf{b}}{|\mathbf{a}|\,|\mathbf{b}|} = \frac{\mathbf{a} \cdot \mathbf{b}}{\sqrt{\mathbf{a} \cdot \mathbf{a}}\sqrt{\mathbf{b} \cdot \mathbf{b}}},$$

where γ is defined as before.

From the definition it follows readily that *scalar multiplication of vectors is commutative and is distributive with respect to vector addition:*

$$(4) \qquad (a)\ \mathbf{a} \cdot \mathbf{b} = \mathbf{b} \cdot \mathbf{a}, \qquad (b)\ \mathbf{a} \cdot (\mathbf{b} + \mathbf{c}) = \mathbf{a} \cdot \mathbf{b} + \mathbf{a} \cdot \mathbf{c}.$$

Let $\mathbf{a}$ and $\mathbf{b}$ $(\neq \mathbf{0})$ be given vectors and let γ denote the angle between them. Then the real number

$$p = |\mathbf{a}|\cos\gamma$$

is called the **component** *of* $\mathbf{a}$ *in the direction of* $\mathbf{b}$. If $\mathbf{a} = \mathbf{0}$ then γ is undefined, and we set $p = 0$.

It follows that $|p|$ is the length of the orthogonal projection of $\mathbf{a}$ on a straight line l in the direction of $\mathbf{b}$. p may be positive, zero, or negative (Fig. 130).

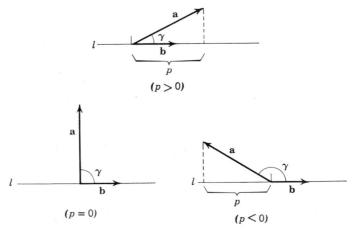

Fig. 130. Component of a vector $\mathbf{a}$ in the direction of a vector $\mathbf{b}$.

From this definition we see that in particular the components of a vector **a** in the directions of the unit vectors **i, j, k** of the fundamental triad associated with a Cartesian coordinate system are the components a_1, a_2, a_3 of **a** as defined in Sec. 5.2. This shows that our present use of the term "component" is merely a slight generalization of the previous one.

From (3) we obtain

$$(5) \qquad\qquad p = |\mathbf{a}| \cos \gamma = \frac{\mathbf{a} \cdot \mathbf{b}}{|\mathbf{b}|} \qquad\qquad (\mathbf{b} \neq 0)$$

and if in particular **b** is a unit vector, then we simply have

$$(6) \qquad\qquad p = \mathbf{a} \cdot \mathbf{b}.$$

Given a fixed Cartesian coordinate system, we may easily express the scalar product **a · b** of two vectors

$$(7) \qquad \mathbf{a} = a_1\mathbf{i} + a_2\mathbf{j} + a_3\mathbf{k} \qquad \text{and} \qquad \mathbf{b} = b_1\mathbf{i} + b_2\mathbf{j} + b_3\mathbf{k}$$

in terms of the components of these vectors. Since **i, j**, and **k** are unit vectors we have

$$\mathbf{i} \cdot \mathbf{i} = 1, \qquad \mathbf{j} \cdot \mathbf{j} = 1, \qquad \mathbf{k} \cdot \mathbf{k} = 1,$$

and since they are orthogonal, it follows from Theorem 1 that

$$\mathbf{i} \cdot \mathbf{j} = 0, \qquad \mathbf{j} \cdot \mathbf{k} = 0, \qquad \mathbf{k} \cdot \mathbf{i} = 0.$$

Hence, if we substitute (7) into **a · b** and use the distributive law (4b), we first have a sum of nine scalar products,

$$\mathbf{a} \cdot \mathbf{b} = a_1 b_1 \mathbf{i} \cdot \mathbf{i} + a_1 b_2 \mathbf{i} \cdot \mathbf{j} + \cdots + a_3 b_3 \mathbf{k} \cdot \mathbf{k}.$$

Since six of these products are zero, we obtain the simple basic formula

$$(8) \qquad\qquad \mathbf{a} \cdot \mathbf{b} = a_1 b_1 + a_2 b_2 + a_3 b_3.$$

The following examples may illustrate the usefulness of scalar products. Various other applications will be considered later.

Example 1 (Work done by a force).   Consider a particle on which a constant force **a** acts. Let the particle be given a displacement **d**. Then the work W done by **a** in the displacement is defined as the product of $|\mathbf{d}|$ and the component of **a** in the direction of **d**, that is,

$$(9) \qquad W = |\mathbf{a}||\mathbf{d}| \cos \alpha = \mathbf{a} \cdot \mathbf{d}$$

where α is the angle between **d** and **a** (Fig. 131).

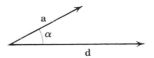

Example 2 (Orthogonal straight lines in a plane). Find a representation of the straight line L_1 through the point P: (1, 3) in the xy-plane and perpendicular to the line L_2 represented by $x - 2y + 2 = 0$.

Fig. 131. Work done by a force.

Any straight line L_1 in the xy-plane can be represented in the form $a_1x + a_2y = c$. If $c = 0$, then L_1 passes through the origin. If $c \neq 0$, then $a_1x + a_2y = 0$ represents a line $L_1{}^*$ through the origin and parallel to L_1. The position vector of a point on $L_1{}^*$ is $\mathbf{r} = x\mathbf{i} + y\mathbf{j}$. Introducing the vector $\mathbf{a} = a_1\mathbf{i} + a_2\mathbf{j}$, it follows from (8) that the representation of $L_1{}^*$ may be written

$$\mathbf{a} \cdot \mathbf{r} = 0.$$

Certainly $\mathbf{a} \neq \mathbf{0}$ and, by Theorem 1, the vector $\mathbf{a}$ is perpendicular to $\mathbf{r}$ and, therefore, perpendicular to the line $L_1{}^*$. It is called a **normal vector** to $L_1{}^*$. Since L_1 and $L_1{}^*$ are parallel, $\mathbf{a}$ is also a normal vector to L_1. Hence two lines L_1 and L_2: $b_1x + b_2y = d$ are perpendicular or orthogonal if, and only if, their normal vectors $\mathbf{a}$ and $\mathbf{b} = b_1\mathbf{i} + b_2\mathbf{j}$ are orthogonal, that is, $\mathbf{a} \cdot \mathbf{b} = 0$. Note that this implies that the slopes of the lines are negative reciprocals.

In our case, $\mathbf{b} = \mathbf{i} - 2\mathbf{j}$, and a vector perpendicular to $\mathbf{b}$ is $\mathbf{a} = 2\mathbf{i} + \mathbf{j}$. Hence the representation of L_1 must be of the form $2x + y = c$, and by substituting the coordinates of P we obtain $c = 5$. This yields the solution

$$y = -2x + 5.$$

Example 3 (Normal vector to a plane). Find a unit vector perpendicular to the plane $4x + 2y + 4z = -7$.

Any plane in space can be represented in the form

(10) $$a_1x + a_2y + a_3z = c.$$

The position vector of a point in the plane is $\mathbf{r} = x\mathbf{i} + y\mathbf{j} + z\mathbf{k}$. Introducing the vector $\mathbf{a} = a_1\mathbf{i} + a_2\mathbf{j} + a_3\mathbf{k}$ and using (8), we may write (10) in the form

(11) $$\mathbf{a} \cdot \mathbf{r} = c.$$

Certainly $\mathbf{a} \neq \mathbf{0}$, and the unit vector in the direction of $\mathbf{a}$ is

$$\mathbf{n} = \frac{\mathbf{a}}{|\mathbf{a}|}.$$

Dividing by $|\mathbf{a}|$, we obtain from (11)

(12) $$\mathbf{n} \cdot \mathbf{r} = p \qquad \text{where} \qquad p = \frac{c}{|\mathbf{a}|}.$$

From (6) we see that p is the projection of $\mathbf{r}$ in the direction of $\mathbf{n}$, and this projection has the same constant value $c/|\mathbf{a}|$ for the position vector $\mathbf{r}$ of any point in the plane. Clearly this holds if, and only if, $\mathbf{n}$ is perpendicular to the plane. $\mathbf{n}$ is

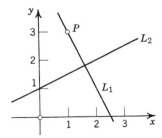

Fig. 132. Example 2.

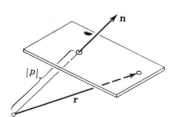

Fig. 133. Normal vector to a plane.

called a **unit normal vector** to the plane (the other being $-\mathbf{n}$). Furthermore from this and the definition of projection it follows that $|p|$ is the distance of the plane from the origin. Representation (12) is called **Hesse's**[3] **normal form** of a plane.

In our case, $\mathbf{a} = 4\mathbf{i} + 2\mathbf{j} + 4\mathbf{k}$, $c = -7$, $|\mathbf{a}| = 6$,

$$\mathbf{n} = \tfrac{1}{6}\mathbf{a} = \tfrac{2}{3}\mathbf{i} + \tfrac{1}{3}\mathbf{j} + \tfrac{2}{3}\mathbf{k},$$

and the plane has the distance $7/6$ from the origin.

PROBLEMS

Let $\mathbf{a} = \mathbf{i} + 5\mathbf{k}$, $\mathbf{b} = 3\mathbf{i} + \mathbf{j} + 4\mathbf{k}$, and $\mathbf{c} = \mathbf{i} - \mathbf{j} + 2\mathbf{k}$. Find
1. $\mathbf{a} \cdot \mathbf{b}, \mathbf{b} \cdot \mathbf{c}, \mathbf{c} \cdot \mathbf{a}$ 2. $|\mathbf{a}|, |\mathbf{b}|, |\mathbf{c}|$ 3. $\mathbf{a} \cdot (\mathbf{b} + \mathbf{c}), \mathbf{a} \cdot (\mathbf{b} - \mathbf{c})$
4. $2\mathbf{b} \cdot (3\mathbf{a} - 4\mathbf{c})$ 5. $|\mathbf{a} + \mathbf{b}|, |\mathbf{b} + \mathbf{c}|$ 6. $|\mathbf{a} + \mathbf{c}|, |\mathbf{a}| + |\mathbf{c}|$

Let $\mathbf{a}$, $\mathbf{b}$, and $\mathbf{c}$ be as before. Find the cosine of the angle between the following vectors.
7. $\mathbf{a}, \mathbf{b}$ 8. $\mathbf{a}, -\mathbf{b}$ 9. $\mathbf{a}, \mathbf{c} - \mathbf{b}$ 10. $\mathbf{a} - \mathbf{b}, \mathbf{b} - \mathbf{c}$

11. Determine λ such that $\mathbf{u} = 3\mathbf{i} - 2\mathbf{j}$ and $\mathbf{v} = 4\mathbf{i} + \lambda\mathbf{j}$ are orthogonal vectors.

12. Prove that scalar multiplication of vectors is commutative and distributive with respect to vector addition.

Find the work done by a force $\mathbf{p}$ acting on a particle if the particle is displaced from a point A to a point B along the straight segment AB, where
13. A: $(0, 0, 0)$, B: $(2, 0, 0)$, $\mathbf{p} = 3\mathbf{i} + 3\mathbf{j} + \mathbf{k}$
14. A: $(0, 1, 0)$, B: $(4, 1, 0)$, $\mathbf{p} = -\mathbf{i} + 2\mathbf{j} - \mathbf{k}$
15. A: $(1, 1, 1)$, B: $(3, 3, 3)$, $\mathbf{p} = 2\mathbf{i} - 2\mathbf{k}$
16. A: $(2, 2, 0)$, B: $(6, 6, 0)$, $\mathbf{p} = 3\mathbf{i} - 3\mathbf{j}$
17. A: $(0, 0, 0)$, B: $(-4, 6, -1)$, $\mathbf{p} = 3\mathbf{i} - \mathbf{j} + \mathbf{k}$

18. Find the angle between the planes $x + 2y + z = 2$ and $2x - y + 3z = -4$.

Determine the angles of the triangle whose vertices are
19. A: $(1, 1, 0)$, B: $(3, 1, 0)$, C: $(1, 3, 0)$
20. A: $(0, 0, 0)$, B: $(4, -1, 3)$, C: $(1, 2, 3)$
21. A: $(-1, 2, 3)$, B: $(2, 1, 2)$, C: $(0, 3, 0)$

22. Let $\mathbf{a} = \cos \alpha \, \mathbf{i} + \sin \alpha \, \mathbf{j}$, and $\mathbf{b} = \cos \beta \, \mathbf{i} + \sin \beta \, \mathbf{j}$ where $0 \leq \alpha \leq \beta \leq 2\pi$. Show that $\mathbf{a}$ and $\mathbf{b}$ are unit vectors. Use (8) to obtain the trigonometric identity for $\cos (\beta - \alpha)$.

23. In Fig. 134, $\mathbf{c} = \mathbf{a} - \mathbf{b}$. Hence, $|\mathbf{c}|^2 = (\mathbf{a} - \mathbf{b}) \cdot (\mathbf{a} - \mathbf{b})$. Deduce the law of cosines from this relation.

24. Show that the sum of the squares of the diagonals of a parallelogram is equal to the sum of the squares of its sides.

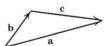

Fig. 134. Problem 23.

5.5 VECTOR PRODUCT

Various applications suggest the introduction of another kind of vector multiplication in which the product of two vectors is again a vector. This

---

[3] LUDWIG OTTO HESSE (1811–1874), German mathematician, who contributed to the theory of curves and surfaces.

so-called **vector product** or **cross product** of two vectors **a** and **b** is written

$$\mathbf{a} \times \mathbf{b}$$

and is a vector **v** which is defined as follows.

If **a** *and* **b** *have the same or opposite direction or one of these vectors is the zero vector, then* **v** = **0**.

In any other case, **v** *is the vector whose length is equal to the area of the parallelogram with* **a** *and* **b** *as adjacent sides and whose direction is perpendicular to both* **a** *and* **b** *and is such that* **a**, **b**, **v**, *in this order, form a right-handed triple or right-handed triad, as shown in Fig. 135.*

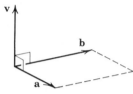
Fig. 135. Vector product.

The term **right-handed** comes from the fact that the vectors **a**, **b**, **v**, in this order, assume the same sort of orientation as the thumb, index finger, and middle finger of the right hand when these are held as shown in Fig. 136. We may also say that if **a** is rotated into the direction of **b** through the angle $\alpha(<\pi)$, then **v** advances in the same direction as a right-handed screw would if turned in the same way (cf. Fig. 137).

Since the parallelogram with **a** and **b** as adjacent sides has the area $|\mathbf{a}|\ |\mathbf{b}|\ \sin \gamma$ (cf. Fig. 135), we obtain

(1) $$|\mathbf{v}| = |\mathbf{a}|\ |\mathbf{b}|\ \sin \gamma.$$

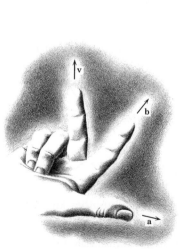

Fig. 136. Right-handed triple of vectors **a, b, v**.   **Fig. 137.** Right-handed screw.

Let $\mathbf{a} \times \mathbf{b} = \mathbf{v}$ and let $\mathbf{b} \times \mathbf{a} = \mathbf{w}$. Then, by definition, $|\mathbf{v}| = |\mathbf{w}|$, and in order that $\mathbf{b}$, $\mathbf{a}$, $\mathbf{w}$ form a right-handed triple we must have $\mathbf{w} = -\mathbf{v}$ (Fig. 138). Hence,

$$(2) \qquad\qquad \mathbf{b} \times \mathbf{a} = -(\mathbf{a} \times \mathbf{b});$$

that is, *cross multiplication of vectors is* **not commutative** *but anticommutative.* The order of the factors in a vector product is, therefore, of great importance and must be carefully observed.

From the definition it follows that for any constant k,

$$(3) \qquad (k\mathbf{a}) \times \mathbf{b} = k(\mathbf{a} \times \mathbf{b}) = \mathbf{a} \times (k\mathbf{b}).$$

Furthermore, cross multiplication is distributive with respect to vector addition,

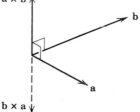

$$(4) \qquad \begin{aligned} \mathbf{a} \times (\mathbf{b} + \mathbf{c}) &= (\mathbf{a} \times \mathbf{b}) + (\mathbf{a} \times \mathbf{c}), \\ (\mathbf{a} + \mathbf{b}) \times \mathbf{c} &= (\mathbf{a} \times \mathbf{c}) + (\mathbf{b} \times \mathbf{c}). \end{aligned}$$

Fig. 138. Anticommutativity of cross multiplication.

The proof will be given in the next section. More complicated cross products will be considered later, but we want to mention now that

$$\mathbf{a} \times (\mathbf{b} \times \mathbf{c}) \neq (\mathbf{a} \times \mathbf{b}) \times \mathbf{c},$$

ordinarily.

From (1) in this section and (1) in the last section it follows that

$$|\mathbf{v}|^2 = |\mathbf{a}|^2 |\mathbf{b}|^2 \sin^2 \gamma = |\mathbf{a}|^2 |\mathbf{b}|^2 (1 - \cos^2 \gamma) = (\mathbf{a} \cdot \mathbf{a})(\mathbf{b} \cdot \mathbf{b}) - (\mathbf{a} \cdot \mathbf{b})^2.$$

Hence we obtain the formula

$$(5) \qquad\qquad |\mathbf{a} \times \mathbf{b}| = \sqrt{(\mathbf{a} \cdot \mathbf{a})(\mathbf{b} \cdot \mathbf{b}) - (\mathbf{a} \cdot \mathbf{b})^2},$$

which is convenient for computing the magnitude of a vector product.

5.6   VECTOR PRODUCTS IN TERMS OF COMPONENTS

We shall now represent a vector product in terms of the components of its factors with respect to a Cartesian coordinate system. In this connection it is important to note that there are two types of such systems, depending on the orientation of the axes, namely, right-handed and left-handed. The definitions are as follows.

A Cartesian coordinate system is called **right-handed**, if the corresponding unit vectors **i, j, k** in the positive directions of the axes form a right-handed triple (Fig. 139*a*); it is called **left-handed**, if these vectors form a *left-handed triple*, that is, assume the same sort of orientation as the thumb, index finger, and middle finger of the left hand (Fig. 139*b*).

In applications we use preferably right-handed systems.

With respect to a given right-handed or left-handed Cartesian coordinate system, let a_1, a_2, a_3 and b_1, b_2, b_3 be the components of two vectors **a** and **b**, respectively. We want to express the components v_1, v_2, v_3 of the product vector

$$\mathbf{v} = \mathbf{a} \times \mathbf{b}$$

in terms of the components of **a** and **b**. We need only consider the case when $\mathbf{v} \neq \mathbf{0}$. Since **v** is perpendicular to both **a** and **b** it follows from Theorem 1, Sec. 5.4, that $\mathbf{a} \cdot \mathbf{v} = 0$ and $\mathbf{b} \cdot \mathbf{v} = 0$ or, by (8) in Sec. 5.4,

(1)
$$a_1 v_1 + a_2 v_2 + a_3 v_3 = 0$$
$$b_1 v_1 + b_2 v_2 + b_3 v_3 = 0.$$

Multiplying the first equation by b_3, the last by a_3, and subtracting, we obtain

$$(a_3 b_1 - a_1 b_3) v_1 = (a_2 b_3 - a_3 b_2) v_2.$$

Multiplying the first equation of (1) by b_1, the last by a_1, and subtracting, we obtain

$$(a_1 b_2 - a_2 b_1) v_2 = (a_3 b_1 - a_1 b_3) v_3.$$

We readily see that these two equations are satisfied by

(2) $\quad v_1 = c(a_2 b_3 - a_3 b_2), \quad v_2 = c(a_3 b_1 - a_1 b_3), \quad v_3 = c(a_1 b_2 - a_2 b_1),$

where c is a constant. The reader may verify by inserting that (2) also satisfies (1). Now each of the equations in (1) represents a plane through

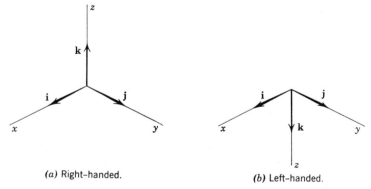

(a) Right-handed.   (b) Left-handed.

Fig. 139. The two types of Cartesian coordinate systems.

the origin in $v_1v_2v_3$-space. The vectors **a** and **b** are normal vectors of these planes (cf. Ex. 3 in Sec. 5.4). Since $\mathbf{v} \neq \mathbf{0}$ these vectors are not parallel and the two planes do not coincide. Hence their intersection is a straight line L through the origin. Since (2) is a solution of (1) and, for varying c, represents a straight line, we conclude that (2) represents L, and every solution of (1) must be of the form (2). In particular, the components of **v** must be of this form, where c is to be determined. From (2) we obtain

$$|\mathbf{v}|^2 = v_1{}^2 + v_2{}^2 + v_3{}^2 = c^2[(a_2b_3 - a_3b_2)^2 + (a_3b_1 - a_1b_3)^2 + (a_1b_2 - a_2b_1)^2],$$

and we may readily verify that this may be written

$$|\mathbf{v}|^2 = c^2[(a_1{}^2 + a_2{}^2 + a_3{}^2)(b_1{}^2 + b_2{}^2 + b_3{}^2) - (a_1b_1 + a_2b_2 + a_3b_3)^2].$$

Using (8), Sec. 5.4, we thus have

$$|\mathbf{v}|^2 = c^2[(\mathbf{a} \cdot \mathbf{a})(\mathbf{b} \cdot \mathbf{b}) - (\mathbf{a} \cdot \mathbf{b})^2].$$

By comparing this with (5) in the last section we conclude that $c = \pm 1$.

From now on it will matter whether the coordinate system is right-handed or left-handed. We first consider the case of a right-handed system, and we want to show that then $c = +1$. This can be done as follows.

If we change the lengths and directions of **a** and **b** continuously and such that at the end $\mathbf{a} = \mathbf{i}$ and $\mathbf{b} = \mathbf{j}$ (Fig. 139a), then **v** will change its length and direction continuously, and at the end, $\mathbf{v} = \mathbf{i} \times \mathbf{j} = \mathbf{k}$. Obviously we may effect the change so that both **a** and **b** remain different from the zero vector and are not parallel at any instant. Then **v** is never equal to the zero vector, and since the change is continuous and c can only assume the values $+1$ or -1, it follows that at the end c must have the same value as before. Now at the end $\mathbf{a} = \mathbf{i}$, $\mathbf{b} = \mathbf{j}$, $\mathbf{v} = \mathbf{k}$ and, therefore, $a_1 = 1, b_2 = 1, v_3 = 1$, and the other components in (2) are zero. Hence, from (2), $v_3 = c = +1$. Noting that the expressions in parentheses in (2) may be written in the form of second-order determinants, we may sum up our result as follows.

With respect to a right-handed Cartesian coordinate system,

$$(3) \qquad \mathbf{a} \times \mathbf{b} = \mathbf{i} \begin{vmatrix} a_2 & a_3 \\ b_2 & b_3 \end{vmatrix} + \mathbf{j} \begin{vmatrix} a_3 & a_1 \\ b_3 & b_1 \end{vmatrix} + \mathbf{k} \begin{vmatrix} a_1 & a_2 \\ b_1 & b_2 \end{vmatrix},$$

where a_1, a_2, a_3 and b_1, b_2, b_3 are the components of **a** *and* **b**, *respectively.*

For memorizing, it is useful to note that (3) can be interpreted as the expansion of the determinant

$$(4) \qquad \mathbf{a} \times \mathbf{b} = \begin{vmatrix} \mathbf{i} & \mathbf{j} & \mathbf{k} \\ a_1 & a_2 & a_3 \\ b_1 & b_2 & b_3 \end{vmatrix}$$

by the first row, but we should keep in mind that this is not an ordinary determinant because the elements of the first row are vectors.

In a *left-handed* Cartesian coordinate system, $\mathbf{i} \times \mathbf{j} = -\mathbf{k}$ (Fig. 139b), and the above reasoning leads to $c = -1$ in (2). Hence *with respect to a left-handed Cartesian coordinate system,*

$$(5) \qquad\qquad \mathbf{a} \times \mathbf{b} = - \begin{vmatrix} \mathbf{i} & \mathbf{j} & \mathbf{k} \\ a_1 & a_2 & a_3 \\ b_1 & b_2 & b_3 \end{vmatrix}.$$

Example 1. With respect to a right-handed Cartesian coordinate system, let $\mathbf{a} = 4\mathbf{i} - \mathbf{k}$ and $\mathbf{b} = -2\mathbf{i} + \mathbf{j} + 3\mathbf{k}$. Then

$$\mathbf{a} \times \mathbf{b} = \begin{vmatrix} \mathbf{i} & \mathbf{j} & \mathbf{k} \\ 4 & 0 & -1 \\ -2 & 1 & 3 \end{vmatrix} = \mathbf{i} - 10\mathbf{j} + 4\mathbf{k}.$$

We may now prove the distributive law (4) in the previous section. From (3) it follows that the first component of $\mathbf{a} \times (\mathbf{b} + \mathbf{c})$ is

$$\begin{vmatrix} a_2 & a_3 \\ b_2 + c_2 & b_3 + c_3 \end{vmatrix} = a_2(b_3 + c_3) - a_3(b_2 + c_2)$$

$$= (a_2 b_3 - a_3 b_2) + (a_2 c_3 - a_3 c_2)$$

$$= \begin{vmatrix} a_2 & a_3 \\ b_2 & b_3 \end{vmatrix} + \begin{vmatrix} a_2 & a_3 \\ c_2 & c_3 \end{vmatrix}.$$

The expression on the right is the first component of $\mathbf{a} \times \mathbf{b} + \mathbf{a} \times \mathbf{c}$. For the other two components of that vector the consideration is similar. This proves the first of the relations (4) in the previous section, and the last one can be proved by the same argument.

The definition of cross-multiplication is suggested by many applications, two of which may be illustrated by the following examples. Further physical and geometrical applications will be considered later.

Example 2 (Moment of a force). In mechanics the moment m of a force $\mathbf{p}$ about a point Q is defined as the product $m = |\mathbf{p}| \, d$ where d is the (perpendicular) distance between Q and the line of action L of $\mathbf{p}$ (Fig. 140). If $\mathbf{r}$ is the vector from Q to any point A on L, then $d = |\mathbf{r}| \sin \gamma$ (Fig. 140) and

$$m = |\mathbf{r}| \, |\mathbf{p}| \sin \gamma.$$

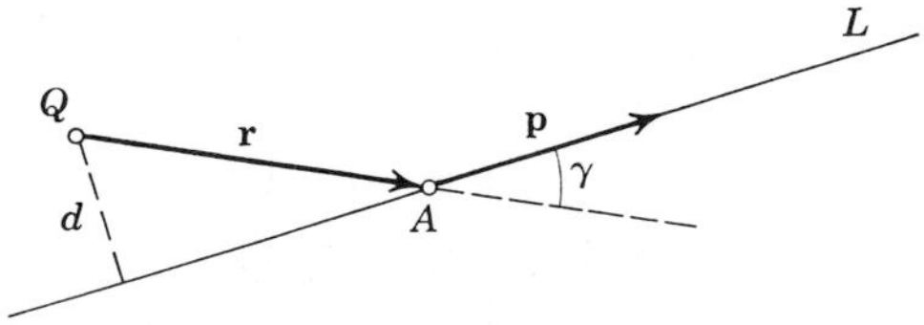

Fig. 140. Moment of a force.

Since γ is the angle between **r** and **p**,

$$m = |\mathbf{r} \times \mathbf{p}|,$$

as follows from (1) in the last section. The vector

(6) $$\mathbf{m} = \mathbf{r} \times \mathbf{p}$$

is called the **moment vector** or **vector moment** of **p** about Q. Its magnitude is m, and its direction is that of the axis of the rotation about Q which **p** has the tendency to produce.

Example 3 (Velocity of a rotating body). A rotation of a rigid body B in space can be simply and uniquely described by a vector **w** as follows. The direction of **w** is that of the axis of rotation and such that the rotation appears clockwise, if one looks from the initial point of **w** to its terminal point. The length of **w** is equal to the *angular speed* ω (>0) of the rotation, that is the linear (or tangential) speed of a point of B divided by its distance from the axis of rotation.

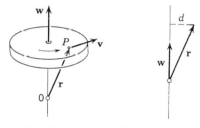

Let P be any point of B and d its distance from the axis. Then P has the speed ωd. Let **r** be the position vector of P referred to a coordinate system with origin 0 on the axis of rotation. Then $d = |\mathbf{r}| \sin \gamma$ where γ is the angle between **w** and **r**. Therefore,

Fig. 141. Rotation of a rigid body.

$$\omega d = |\mathbf{w}| \, |\mathbf{r}| \sin \gamma = |\mathbf{w} \times \mathbf{r}|.$$

From this and the definition of vector product, we see that the velocity vector **v** of P can be represented in the form (Fig. 141)

(7) $$\mathbf{v} = \mathbf{w} \times \mathbf{r}.$$

This simple formula is useful for determining **v** at any point of B.

PROBLEMS

With respect to a right-handed Cartesian coordinate system, let $\mathbf{a} = \mathbf{i} + \mathbf{j}$, $\mathbf{b} = -\mathbf{i} + 2\mathbf{j}$, $\mathbf{c} = 2\mathbf{i} + 3\mathbf{j} + \mathbf{k}$. Find

1. $\mathbf{a} \times \mathbf{b}$, $\mathbf{b} \times \mathbf{a}$
2. $\mathbf{a} \times \mathbf{c}$, $|\mathbf{a} \times \mathbf{c}|$
3. $\mathbf{b} \times \mathbf{c}$, $|\mathbf{b} \times \mathbf{c}|$, $\mathbf{b} \cdot \mathbf{c}$
4. $2\mathbf{a} \times 3\mathbf{b}$
5. $(\mathbf{a} + \mathbf{b}) \times \mathbf{c}$
6. $\mathbf{a} \times (\mathbf{b} + \mathbf{c})$
7. $(\mathbf{a} - \mathbf{b}) \times (\mathbf{c} - \mathbf{a})$
8. $(\mathbf{a} + 3\mathbf{c}) \times \mathbf{b}$
9. $(\mathbf{a} + 4\mathbf{b}) \times \mathbf{b}$
10. $(\mathbf{b} - \mathbf{c}) \times 2\mathbf{a}$
11. $(\mathbf{a} - 2\mathbf{c}) \times 3\mathbf{b}$
12. $(\mathbf{b} - \mathbf{a}) \times 0.5\mathbf{c}$

Find two unit vectors perpendicular to both vectors

13. $\mathbf{i}$, $\mathbf{j}$
14. $3\mathbf{i} + 2\mathbf{j}$, $-\mathbf{i} - \mathbf{j}$
15. $3\mathbf{k}$, $2\mathbf{j} + \mathbf{k}$
16. $\mathbf{i} + \mathbf{j} + \mathbf{k}$, $\mathbf{i}$
17. $2\mathbf{i} - 2\mathbf{j}$, $2\mathbf{j} + \mathbf{k}$
18. $3\mathbf{i} + 2\mathbf{j} + 5\mathbf{k}$, $3\mathbf{j} - \mathbf{k}$
19. $2\mathbf{j} - 3\mathbf{k}$, $2\mathbf{i}$
20. $\mathbf{i} + \mathbf{j}$, $\mathbf{i} - \mathbf{j}$
21. $\mathbf{i} + \mathbf{j} - \mathbf{k}$, $\mathbf{j} + 2\mathbf{k}$

Are the following vectors parallel? Perpendicular?

22. $-\mathbf{i} + 2\mathbf{j}$, $3\mathbf{k}$
23. $4\mathbf{j} + 3\mathbf{k}$, $8\mathbf{j} + 6\mathbf{k}$
24. $-\mathbf{i} + \mathbf{j} - 3\mathbf{k}$, $4\mathbf{i} - 4\mathbf{j} + 12\mathbf{k}$
25. $\mathbf{i} + \mathbf{j}$, $\mathbf{j} + 2\mathbf{k}$
26. $\mathbf{i} - 2\mathbf{j} + 3\mathbf{k}$, $3\mathbf{i} + 5\mathbf{j}$
27. $3\mathbf{i} + 2\mathbf{j} + \mathbf{k}$, $6\mathbf{i} + 4\mathbf{j} + 2\mathbf{k}$

Find the area of the parallelogram of which the given vectors are adjacent sides.

28. $i + 2j$, $-2i + 3j$ **29.** $3i + 2j + k$, $3i + k$ **30.** i, $2j$
31. $j - k$, $i - k$ **32.** $i + j + k$, $3k$ **33.** $-i + 2j$, $2j - 3k$

Find the area of the parallelogram that has the following vertices in the xy-plane.

34. $(1, 1)$, $(4, 1)$, $(2, 2)$, $(5, 2)$ **35.** $(-4, 2)$, $(-6, 5)$, $(-3, 6)$, $(-5, 9)$
36. $(8, -3)$, $(10, 1)$, $(9, 0)$, $(11, 4)$ **37.** $(1, 2)$, $(0, 0)$, $(2, 6)$, $(1, 4)$

Find the area of the triangle that has the following vertices.

38. $(0, 0, 0)$, $(1, 2, 0)$, $(3, -1, 0)$ **39.** $(4, -2, 6)$, $(6, -1, 7)$, $(5, 0, 5)$
40. $(4, 4, 2)$, $(2, 4, 2)$, $(3, 3, 6)$ **41.** $(0, 4, 0)$, $(1, 1, 1)$, $(-2, 1, -3)$

42. If $v = a \times b$, show that $a \cdot v = 0$ and $b \cdot v = 0$.

43. If $c = a \times b$ and $b = a \times c$, show that $b = 0$ and $c = 0$.

Using (5), Sec. 5.5, find $|a \times b|$ where:

44. $a = i + j - k$, $b = 2i + k$ **45.** $a = 3i + 4j$, $b = -j + 2k$
46. $a = 3i + 2j + k$, $b = -i + 4k$ **47.** $a = -i + 3k$, $b = i + j + 2k$

A force p acts on a line through a point R. Find the moment m of p about a point S, where:

48. $p = i$, R: $(0, -2, 0)$, S: $(0, 0, 0)$
49. $p = k$, R: $(0, 0, 0)$, S: $(0, 0, 5)$
50. $p = i - 2j$, R: $(1, 1, 1)$, S: $(2, -1, 3)$
51. $p = 4i + 4k$, R: $(0, 2, 0)$, S: $(4, 0, 4)$
52. $p = 2i + 4j + k$, R: $(4, 2, -1)$, S: $(0, 1, 2)$

53. A sphere of radius 4 cm with center at the origin rotates about the z-axis with angular velocity $\omega = 2$ radians per second such that the rotation appears counterclockwise if we look in the positive z-direction. Find the corresponding rotation vector w. Find the velocity vector v of a point P on the "equator" of the sphere at the instant when P has the position $\sqrt{8}i - \sqrt{8}j$ in space. The coordinates are right-handed.

54. Let a and b be adjacent sides of any triangle, and $c = b - a$. Show that $c \times a = c \times b$ and derive the sine law of trigonometry.

Find a unit normal vector to the plane through the following points.

55. $(1, 0, 0)$, $(0, 1, 0)$, $(0, 0, 1)$ **56.** $(1, 0, -7)$, $(2, 0, 1)$, $(-2, 0, 6)$
57. $(1, 3, 5)$, $(-2, 0, 6)$, $(3, 3, 0)$ **58.** $(1, 1, 1)$, $(0, 0, 0)$, $(4, -1, 0)$

59. Find a vector v parallel to the line of intersection of the planes

$$2x + 3y + 4z = 0 \quad \text{and} \quad x - y + z = 2.$$

60. Find a vector v parallel to the plane $x + y + z = 1$ and perpendicular to the line $y = x$, $z = 0$.

5.7 SCALAR TRIPLE PRODUCT LINEAR DEPENDENCE OF VECTORS

Repeated products of vectors that have three or more factors occur frequently in applications. The most important of these products is the **scalar triple product** or *mixed triple product* $a \cdot (b \times c)$ of three vectors. With respect to any right-handed Cartesian coordinate system, let

$$a = a_1 i + a_2 j + a_3 k, \qquad b = b_1 i + b_2 j + b_3 k, \qquad c = c_1 i + c_2 j + c_3 k.$$

Then from (4), Sec. 5.6, it follows that

$$\mathbf{a} \cdot (\mathbf{b} \times \mathbf{c}) = (a_1\mathbf{i} + a_2\mathbf{j} + a_3\mathbf{k}) \cdot \begin{vmatrix} \mathbf{i} & \mathbf{j} & \mathbf{k} \\ b_1 & b_2 & b_3 \\ c_1 & c_2 & c_3 \end{vmatrix}.$$

From this and (8), Sec. 5.4, we see that the scalar triple product takes the form

$$(1) \qquad\qquad \mathbf{a} \cdot (\mathbf{b} \times \mathbf{c}) = \begin{vmatrix} a_1 & a_2 & a_3 \\ b_1 & b_2 & b_3 \\ c_1 & c_2 & c_3 \end{vmatrix}.$$

The scalar triple product $\mathbf{a} \cdot (\mathbf{b} \times \mathbf{c})$ will be denoted by $(\mathbf{a}\ \mathbf{b}\ \mathbf{c})$.

Since interchanging of two rows reverses the sign of the determinant (cf. Sec. 0.3), we have

$$(2) \qquad\qquad (\mathbf{a}\ \mathbf{b}\ \mathbf{c}) = -(\mathbf{b}\ \mathbf{a}\ \mathbf{c}), \qquad \text{etc.}$$

Interchanging twice, it follows that

$$(3) \qquad\qquad (\mathbf{a}\ \mathbf{b}\ \mathbf{c}) = (\mathbf{b}\ \mathbf{c}\ \mathbf{a}) = (\mathbf{c}\ \mathbf{a}\ \mathbf{b}).$$

Now, by definition,

$$(\mathbf{a}\ \mathbf{b}\ \mathbf{c}) = \mathbf{a} \cdot (\mathbf{b} \times \mathbf{c}), \qquad (\mathbf{c}\ \mathbf{a}\ \mathbf{b}) = \mathbf{c} \cdot (\mathbf{a} \times \mathbf{b}),$$

and since scalar multiplication is commutative, the last expression is equal to $(\mathbf{a} \times \mathbf{b}) \cdot \mathbf{c}$. Therefore,

$$(4) \qquad\qquad \mathbf{a} \cdot (\mathbf{b} \times \mathbf{c}) = (\mathbf{a} \times \mathbf{b}) \cdot \mathbf{c}.$$

Furthermore, for any constant k,

$$(5) \qquad\qquad (k\mathbf{a}\ \mathbf{b}\ \mathbf{c}) = k(\mathbf{a}\ \mathbf{b}\ \mathbf{c}).$$

The absolute value of the scalar triple product $(\mathbf{a}\ \mathbf{b}\ \mathbf{c})$ *has a simple geometrical interpretation. It is equal to the volume of the parallelepiped P with* $\mathbf{a}$, $\mathbf{b}$, $\mathbf{c}$ *as adjacent edges.*

Indeed, from (1) in Sec. 5.4 we obtain

$$(\mathbf{a}\ \mathbf{b}\ \mathbf{c}) = \mathbf{a} \cdot (\mathbf{b} \times \mathbf{c}) = |\mathbf{a}|\ |\mathbf{b} \times \mathbf{c}|\ \cos \beta$$

where β is the angle between $\mathbf{a}$ and the product vector $\mathbf{b} \times \mathbf{c}$. Now $|\mathbf{b} \times \mathbf{c}|$ is the area of the base of P, and the altitude h of P is equal to the absolute value of $|\mathbf{a}| \cos \beta$ (Fig. 142). This proves our statement.

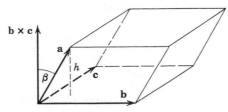

Fig. 142. Geometrical interpretation of a scalar triple product.

From this geometrical consideration it follows that the value of the scalar triple product is a real number which is independent of the choice of right-handed Cartesian coordinates in space. But we should keep in mind that for left-handed Cartesian coordinate systems we have to use (5) instead of (4), Sec. 5.6, and this leads to a minus sign in front of the determinant in (1). We may also say that the value of the determinant is invariant under transformations of right-handed into right-handed, or left-handed into left-handed, Cartesian coordinate systems, but is multiplied by -1 under a transition from a right-handed to a left-handed system (or conversely).

Example 1. Find the volume of the tetrahedron with **a**, **b**, **c** as adjacent edges where, with respect to right-handed Cartesian coordinates,

$$\mathbf{a} = \mathbf{i} + 2\mathbf{k}, \qquad \mathbf{b} = 4\mathbf{i} + 6\mathbf{j} + 2\mathbf{k}, \qquad \mathbf{c} = 3\mathbf{i} + 3\mathbf{j} - 6\mathbf{k}.$$

The volume V of the parallelepiped having **a**, **b**, **c** as adjacent edges is obtained from the scalar triple product

$$(\mathbf{a}\ \mathbf{b}\ \mathbf{c}) = \begin{vmatrix} 1 & 0 & 2 \\ 4 & 6 & 2 \\ 3 & 3 & -6 \end{vmatrix} = -54$$

and $V = 54$; the minus sign indicates that the vectors **a**, **b**, **c**, in this order, form a left-handed triple. The volume of the tetrahedron is $\frac{1}{6}$ of that of the parallelepiped, namely, 9.

We shall now introduce the basic notions of linear dependence and independence of vectors.

n given vectors $\mathbf{a}_{(1)}, \cdots, \mathbf{a}_{(n)}$ are said to be **linearly dependent**, if at least one of them can be represented as a **"linear combination"** of the other $n - 1$ vectors, that is, as the sum of those vectors, each multiplied by a constant (which may be zero or not). If none of the vectors can be represented in this fashion, they are said to be **linearly independent**.

Consider the vector equation

(6) $$k_1\mathbf{a}_{(1)} + k_2\mathbf{a}_{(2)} + \cdots + k_n\mathbf{a}_{(n)} = \mathbf{0},$$

where $k_1, \cdots, k_n$ are real numbers. This equation certainly holds for $k_1 = k_2 = \cdots = k_n = 0$. If we can find numbers $k_1, \cdots, k_n$, not all zero,

Fig. 143. Tetrahedron.

Fig. 144. Collinear vectors.

such that (6) holds, then we can divide by a number $k_i \neq 0$ and represent the corresponding vector $\mathbf{a}_{(i)}$ as a linear combination of the others. $\left[\vphantom{\int}\right.$ For example, if $k_1 \neq 0$, we obtain from (6)

$$\mathbf{a}_{(1)} = -\frac{k_2}{k_1}\mathbf{a}_{(2)} - \cdots - \frac{k_n}{k_1}\mathbf{a}_{(n)}.\left.\vphantom{\int}\right]$$

Hence, in this case the vectors are linearly dependent. However, if $k_1 = k_2 = \cdots = k_n = 0$ is the only set of numbers for which (6) holds, we cannot solve (6) for any of the vectors, and the vectors are linearly independent. This proves the following criterion.

n vectors $\mathbf{a}_{(1)}, \cdots, \mathbf{a}_{(n)}$ *are linearly dependent if, and only if,* (6) *holds for a set of constants* $k_1, \cdots, k_n$, *not all zero.*

Example 2. The vectors

$\mathbf{a} = \mathbf{i} + 2\mathbf{j} + \mathbf{k}$, $\mathbf{b} = 3\mathbf{k}$, $\mathbf{c} = 2\mathbf{i} + 4\mathbf{j}$

are linearly dependent because $6\mathbf{a} - 2\mathbf{b} - 3\mathbf{c} = \mathbf{0}$; we have $\mathbf{a} = \frac{1}{3}\mathbf{b} + \frac{1}{2}\mathbf{c}$. The vectors $\mathbf{i}$, $\mathbf{j}$, $\mathbf{k}$ are linearly independent.

If one of those vectors is the zero vector, then the vectors are linearly dependent, because if, say, $\mathbf{a}_{(1)} = \mathbf{0}$, then (6) holds for any number k_1 and $k_2 = \cdots = k_n = 0$.

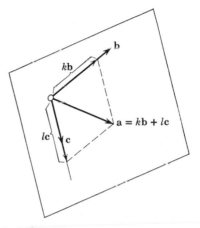

Fig. 145. Coplanar vectors.

Two linearly dependent nonzero vectors $\mathbf{a}$ and $\mathbf{b}$ are **collinear**, that is, if we let their initial points coincide, then they lie in the same line (Fig. 144). In this case, $\mathbf{a} \times \mathbf{b} = \mathbf{0}$. Conversely, if $\mathbf{a} \times \mathbf{b} = \mathbf{0}$, then

$$|\mathbf{a} \times \mathbf{b}| = |\mathbf{a}|\,|\mathbf{b}|\,\sin\gamma = 0,$$

and when $\mathbf{a} \neq \mathbf{0}$ and $\mathbf{b} \neq \mathbf{0}$ then $\gamma = 0$ or $\gamma = \pi$. This yields the following result.

Theorem 1. *Two vectors are linearly dependent if, and only if, their vector product is the zero vector.*

Three linearly dependent nonzero vectors $\mathbf{a}$, $\mathbf{b}$, and $\mathbf{c}$ are **coplanar**, that is, if we let their initial points coincide, then they lie in the same plane (Fig. 145). In fact, linear dependence implies that one of the vectors is a linear combination of the other two vectors, for example, $\mathbf{a} = k\mathbf{b} + l\mathbf{c}$, and thus lies in the plane[4] determined by $\mathbf{b}$ and $\mathbf{c}$. Remembering the

---

[4] Or in the straight line, if $\mathbf{b}$ and $\mathbf{c}$ are collinear.

geometrical interpretation of the scalar triple product we obtain the following useful criterion.

Theorem 2. *Three vectors are linearly dependent if, and only if, their scalar triple product is zero.*

Example 3. Theorem 2 confirms our results in Ex. 2, because

$$(\mathbf{a}\ \mathbf{b}\ \mathbf{c}) = \begin{vmatrix} 1 & 2 & 1 \\ 0 & 0 & 3 \\ 2 & 4 & 0 \end{vmatrix} = 0, \qquad (\mathbf{i}\ \mathbf{j}\ \mathbf{k}) = \begin{vmatrix} 1 & 0 & 0 \\ 0 & 1 & 0 \\ 0 & 0 & 1 \end{vmatrix} = 1.$$

Finally we have

Theorem 3. *Four or more vectors in three-dimensional space are always linearly dependent.*

Proof. Equation (6) is equivalent to a system of three equations for the three components of the vectors. Since the number of unknowns n (≥ 4) is greater than the number of equations, the system has a solution $k_1, \cdots, k_n$, where not all k_i are zero (Theorem 2, Sec. 7.6), and this means linear dependence of the n vectors.

PROBLEMS

Find the value of (**a b c**) where, with respect to right-handed Cartesian coordinates,

1. $\mathbf{a} = \mathbf{i}$, $\mathbf{b} = \mathbf{j}$, $\mathbf{c} = \mathbf{k}$ **2.** $\mathbf{a} = \mathbf{j}$, $\mathbf{b} = \mathbf{k}$, $\mathbf{c} = \mathbf{i}$
3. $\mathbf{a} = \mathbf{j}$, $\mathbf{b} = \mathbf{i}$, $\mathbf{c} = \mathbf{k}$ **4.** $\mathbf{a} = \mathbf{k}$, $\mathbf{b} = \mathbf{j}$, $\mathbf{c} = \mathbf{i}$
5. $\mathbf{a} = 5\mathbf{i} + 3\mathbf{j} - \mathbf{k}$, $\mathbf{b} = \mathbf{k}$, $\mathbf{c} = 3\mathbf{i} - \mathbf{j} + 2\mathbf{k}$
6. $\mathbf{a} = 0$, $\mathbf{b} = 3\mathbf{i} + \mathbf{k}$, $\mathbf{c} = 8\mathbf{i} + 4\mathbf{j} + 2\mathbf{k}$
7. $\mathbf{a} = 28\mathbf{i} - \mathbf{j} + 4\mathbf{k}$, $\mathbf{b} = -14\mathbf{i} + \mathbf{j} + \mathbf{k}$, $\mathbf{c} = 35\mathbf{i} + 3\mathbf{k}$
8. $\mathbf{a} = -4\mathbf{i} - 2\mathbf{j} + 4\mathbf{k}$, $\mathbf{b} = 5\mathbf{i} + 10\mathbf{j} - 15\mathbf{k}$, $\mathbf{c} = 8\mathbf{i} + 24\mathbf{j} - 32\mathbf{k}$
9. $\mathbf{a} = \mathbf{i} + \mathbf{j}$, $\mathbf{b} = \mathbf{j} + \mathbf{k}$, $\mathbf{c} = \mathbf{i} + \mathbf{k}$
10. $\mathbf{a} = 0.5\mathbf{i} + 1.5\mathbf{j} - 2\mathbf{k}$, $\mathbf{b} = 0.2\mathbf{j}$, $\mathbf{c} = 5\mathbf{i} - 5\mathbf{j} + 10\mathbf{k}$

Find the volume of the parallelepiped that has the following vectors as adjacent edges.

11. $\mathbf{i}$, $\mathbf{j}$, $5\mathbf{k}$ **12.** $\mathbf{i} - \mathbf{j}$, $\mathbf{i} + \mathbf{j}$, $\mathbf{i} + 2\mathbf{j} + 4\mathbf{k}$
13. $-\mathbf{i} + \mathbf{j} + 3\mathbf{k}$, $\mathbf{i} - \mathbf{j} - \mathbf{k}$, $3\mathbf{i} + 5\mathbf{j} - 2\mathbf{k}$
14. $3\mathbf{i} - 2\mathbf{j}$, $\mathbf{i} + \mathbf{j} - \mathbf{k}$, $3\mathbf{i} - \mathbf{j} + 2\mathbf{k}$
15. $2\mathbf{j} - 4\mathbf{k}$, $6\mathbf{i} + 3\mathbf{j} - 9\mathbf{k}$, $\mathbf{i} + \mathbf{j} + \mathbf{k}$

Find the volume of the tetrahedron that has the following vertices.

16. $(0, 0, 0)$, $(1, 0, 0)$, $(0, 1, 0)$, $(0, 0, 1)$
17. $(2, 0, 0)$, $(2, 1, 0)$, $(0, 1, 0)$, $(0, 0, 5)$
18. $(1, 1, 1)$, $(0, 4, 7)$, $(3, 6, 0)$, $(4, 1, 8)$
19. $(3, 0, -1)$, $(1, 4, 2)$, $(0, 0, 5)$, $(0, -2, 6)$
20. $(1, 4, 2)$, $(-6, -1, 0)$, $(0, 4, -3)$, $(2, 2, -2)$

Are the following vectors linearly dependent or independent?

21. $2\mathbf{i}$, $-\mathbf{j}$ **22.** $\mathbf{i}$, $\mathbf{j}$, 0 **23.** $\mathbf{i}$, $\mathbf{j}$, $-\mathbf{k}$
24. $\mathbf{i}$, $\mathbf{j}$, $\mathbf{k}$, $3\mathbf{i} - 4\mathbf{j} + 2\mathbf{k}$ **25.** $\mathbf{i}$, $-\mathbf{j}$, $\mathbf{k}$, 0
26. $2\mathbf{i} + 3\mathbf{j}$, $-6\mathbf{i} - 9\mathbf{j}$ **27.** $4\mathbf{i} + 5\mathbf{j}$, $\mathbf{i} + 2\mathbf{j}$, $-\mathbf{i} + 3\mathbf{j}$

28. $i + k,$ $3i - 5k,$ $8k$ **29.** $j + k,$ $-3j + 4k,$ $j - k$
30. $i + j,$ $j + k,$ $k + i$ **31.** $4i + 3k,$ $6j,$ $8i - 4j$
32. $3i + 6j + 9k,$ $-i + 5j + k,$ $2i - 8j + 4k$
33. $i - 6j + 2k,$ $2j + 7k,$ $-2i + 12j - 4k$
34. A system of three homogeneous linear equations in three unknowns has a nontrivial solution if, and only if, the determinant of the coefficients of the system is zero. Using this familiar theorem, prove Theorem 2.

5.8   OTHER REPEATED PRODUCTS

Other types of repeated products that occur frequently in applications may be expressed in terms of scalar, vector, and scalar triple products.

We first show that

$$(1) \qquad \mathbf{b} \times (\mathbf{c} \times \mathbf{d}) = (\mathbf{b} \cdot \mathbf{d})\mathbf{c} - (\mathbf{b} \cdot \mathbf{c})\mathbf{d}.$$

Proof. We choose a right-handed Cartesian coordinate system such that the x-axis has the direction of $\mathbf{d}$ and the xy-plane contains $\mathbf{c}$. Then the vectors in (1) are of the form

$$\mathbf{b} = b_1\mathbf{i} + b_2\mathbf{j} + b_3\mathbf{k}, \qquad \mathbf{c} = c_1\mathbf{i} + c_2\mathbf{j} \qquad \mathbf{d} = d_1\mathbf{i}.$$

Hence, $\mathbf{c} \times \mathbf{d} = -c_2 d_1 \mathbf{k}$ and, furthermore,

$$\mathbf{b} \times (\mathbf{c} \times \mathbf{d}) = \begin{vmatrix} \mathbf{i} & \mathbf{j} & \mathbf{k} \\ b_1 & b_2 & b_3 \\ 0 & 0 & -c_2 d_1 \end{vmatrix} = -b_2 c_2 d_1 \mathbf{i} + b_1 c_2 d_1 \mathbf{j}.$$

On the other hand, we obtain

$$(\mathbf{b} \cdot \mathbf{d})\mathbf{c} - (\mathbf{b} \cdot \mathbf{c})\mathbf{d} = b_1 d_1(c_1\mathbf{i} + c_2\mathbf{j}) - (b_1 c_1 + b_2 c_2)d_1\mathbf{i} = b_1 c_2 d_1\mathbf{j} - b_2 c_2 d_1\mathbf{i}.$$

This proves (1) for our special coordinate system. Now the magnitude and direction of a vector and a vector product, and the value of a scalar product, are independent of the choice of the coordinates. Furthermore, the representation of $\mathbf{b} \times (\mathbf{c} \times \mathbf{d})$ in terms of $\mathbf{i}, \mathbf{j}, \mathbf{k}$ will be the same for right-handed and left-handed systems, because of the double cross-multiplication. Hence, (1) holds in any Cartesian coordinate system, and the proof is complete.

From (1) we obtain

$$(\mathbf{b} \times \mathbf{c}) \times \mathbf{d} = -\mathbf{d} \times (\mathbf{b} \times \mathbf{c}) = (\mathbf{d} \cdot \mathbf{b})\mathbf{c} - (\mathbf{d} \cdot \mathbf{c})\mathbf{b}.$$

This shows that in general $\mathbf{b} \times (\mathbf{c} \times \mathbf{d})$ and $(\mathbf{b} \times \mathbf{c}) \times \mathbf{d}$ are different vectors, that is, *cross-multiplication is not associative*, and the parentheses in (1) are important and cannot be omitted.

Example 1. With respect to a right-handed Cartesian coordinate system we have

$$(\mathbf{i} \times \mathbf{j}) \times \mathbf{j} = \mathbf{k} \times \mathbf{j} = -\mathbf{i}, \quad \text{but} \quad \mathbf{i} \times (\mathbf{j} \times \mathbf{j}) = 0.$$

Taking the scalar product of both sides of (1) and any vector $\mathbf{a}$, we find

$$\mathbf{a} \cdot [\mathbf{b} \times (\mathbf{c} \times \mathbf{d})] = (\mathbf{a} \cdot \mathbf{c})(\mathbf{b} \cdot \mathbf{d}) - (\mathbf{a} \cdot \mathbf{d})(\mathbf{b} \cdot \mathbf{c}).$$

On the other hand, by using scalar triple products, we have [cf. (4) in the last section]

$$\mathbf{a} \cdot [\mathbf{b} \times (\mathbf{c} \times \mathbf{d})] = (\mathbf{a} \quad \mathbf{b} \quad [\mathbf{c} \times \mathbf{d}]) = (\mathbf{a} \times \mathbf{b}) \cdot (\mathbf{c} \times \mathbf{d}).$$

By comparing these two results we obtain the important **identity of Lagrange**

(2) $$(\mathbf{a} \times \mathbf{b}) \cdot (\mathbf{c} \times \mathbf{d}) = (\mathbf{a} \cdot \mathbf{c})(\mathbf{b} \cdot \mathbf{d}) - (\mathbf{a} \cdot \mathbf{d})(\mathbf{b} \cdot \mathbf{c}).$$

If we replace $\mathbf{b}$ by $\mathbf{a} \times \mathbf{b}$ in (1), then we obtain

$$(\mathbf{a} \times \mathbf{b}) \times (\mathbf{c} \times \mathbf{d}) = [(\mathbf{a} \times \mathbf{b}) \cdot \mathbf{d}]\mathbf{c} - [(\mathbf{a} \times \mathbf{b}) \cdot \mathbf{c}]\mathbf{d}$$

and, therefore,

(3) $$(\mathbf{a} \times \mathbf{b}) \times (\mathbf{c} \times \mathbf{d}) = (\mathbf{a} \, \mathbf{b} \, \mathbf{d})\mathbf{c} - (\mathbf{a} \, \mathbf{b} \, \mathbf{c})\mathbf{d}.$$

PROBLEMS

With respect to a right-handed Cartesian coordinate system, let $\mathbf{a} = 3\mathbf{i} + 2\mathbf{k}$, $\mathbf{b} = 4\mathbf{i} + 4\mathbf{j} - 2\mathbf{k}$, $\mathbf{c} = \mathbf{i} - 2\mathbf{j} + 3\mathbf{k}$, $\mathbf{d} = 2\mathbf{i} - \mathbf{j} + 5\mathbf{k}$. Find

1. $\mathbf{a} \times (\mathbf{b} \times \mathbf{c})$, $(\mathbf{a} \times \mathbf{b}) \times \mathbf{c}$
2. $\mathbf{b} \times (\mathbf{c} \times \mathbf{d})$, $(\mathbf{b} \times \mathbf{c}) \times \mathbf{d}$
3. $4\mathbf{c} \times (3\mathbf{a} \times \mathbf{b})$
4. $(\mathbf{a} + \mathbf{b}) \times (\mathbf{c} \times \mathbf{d})$
5. $(\mathbf{c} - 2\mathbf{d}) \times (\mathbf{a} \times \mathbf{b})$
6. $(\mathbf{a} - \mathbf{b}) \times (2\mathbf{c} \times 3\mathbf{d})$
7. $\mathbf{a} \cdot (\mathbf{b} \times \mathbf{c})$, $(\mathbf{a} \times \mathbf{b}) \cdot \mathbf{c}$
8. $(\mathbf{d} \times \mathbf{c}) \cdot (\mathbf{a} - \mathbf{b})$
9. $(\mathbf{a} \times \mathbf{b}) \cdot (\mathbf{c} \times \mathbf{d})$, $(\mathbf{b} \times \mathbf{a}) \cdot (\mathbf{d} \times \mathbf{c})$
10. $(\mathbf{b} \times \mathbf{c}) \cdot (\mathbf{a} \times \mathbf{d})$
11. $(\mathbf{b} \times \mathbf{c}) \cdot (\mathbf{b} \times \mathbf{d})$
12. $(\mathbf{a} \times \mathbf{b}) \times (\mathbf{c} \times \mathbf{d})$
13. $(\mathbf{a} \times \mathbf{c}) \times (\mathbf{b} \times \mathbf{d})$
14. $(\mathbf{a} \times \mathbf{b}) \times (\mathbf{a} \times \mathbf{d})$
15. $(\mathbf{a} \times \mathbf{d}) \times (\mathbf{c} \times \mathbf{b})$

16. Show that if the vector $\mathbf{v} = (\mathbf{a} \times \mathbf{b}) \times (\mathbf{c} \times \mathbf{d})$ is not the null vector, it is directed along the line of intersection of the plane of $\mathbf{a}$ and $\mathbf{b}$ and the plane of $\mathbf{c}$ and $\mathbf{d}$.

17. Let the pairs $\mathbf{a}$, $\mathbf{b}$ and $\mathbf{c}$, $\mathbf{d}$ each determine a plane. Show that these planes are parallel if, and only if, $(\mathbf{a} \times \mathbf{b}) \times (\mathbf{c} \times \mathbf{d}) = 0$.

18. What does it mean geometrically if in Prob. 17, $(\mathbf{a} \times \mathbf{b}) \cdot (\mathbf{c} \times \mathbf{d}) = 0$?

19. Let the vectors $\mathbf{a}$ and $\mathbf{b}$ determine a plane P, and let $\mathbf{c}$ be directed along a line L. What does it mean geometrically if $(\mathbf{a} \times \mathbf{b}) \cdot \mathbf{c} = 0$?

20. What does it mean geometrically if in Prob. 19, $(\mathbf{a} \times \mathbf{b}) \times \mathbf{c} = 0$?

5.9 SCALAR FIELDS AND VECTOR FIELDS

A **scalar function** is a single-valued function which is defined at certain points in space and whose values are real numbers depending only on the points in space but not on the particular choice of the coordinate system. In most applications the domain of definition D of a scalar function f will be a curve, a surface, or a three-dimensional region in space. The function f associates with each point in D a scalar, a real number, and we say that a **scalar field** is given in D.

If we introduce coordinates x, y, z then f may be represented in terms of the coordinates, and we write $f(x, y, z)$, but we should keep in mind that the value of f at any point P is independent of the particular choice of coordinates. In order to indicate this fact it is also customary to write $f(P)$ instead of $f(x, y, z)$. The function f may also depend on parameters such as time.

Example 1. The distance $f(P)$ of any point P from a fixed point P_0 in space is a scalar function whose domain of definition D is the whole space. $f(P)$ defines a scalar field in space. If we introduce a Cartesian coordinate system and P_0 has the coordinates x_0, y_0, z_0, then f is given by the well-known formula

$$f(P) = f(x, y, z) = \sqrt{(x - x_0)^2 + (y - y_0)^2 + (z - z_0)^2}$$

where x, y, z are the coordinates of P. If we replace the given Cartesian coordinate system by another such system, then the values of the coordinates of P and P_0 will in general change, but $f(P)$ will have the same value as before. Hence, $f(P)$ is a scalar function. The direction cosines of the line through P and P_0 are not scalars because their values will depend on the choice of the coordinate system.

Example 2. The temperature T within a body B is a scalar function. It defines a scalar field, namely, the temperature field in B. The function T may depend on the time or other parameters. Other examples of scalar fields are the pressure within a region through which a compressible fluid is flowing, and the density of the air of the earth's atmosphere.

If to each point P of a certain set of points in space (for example, the points of a curve, a surface, or a three-dimensional region) a vector $v(P)$ is assigned, then a **vector field** is said to be given at those points, and $v(P)$ is called a **vector function**.

If we introduce Cartesian coordinates x, y, z, then we may write

$$v(P) = v(x, y, z) = v_1(x, y, z)\mathbf{i} + v_2(x, y, z)\mathbf{j} + v_3(x, y, z)\mathbf{k},$$

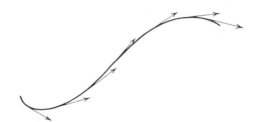

Fig. 146. Field of tangent vectors of a curve.

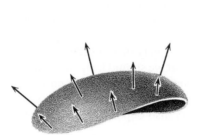

Fig. 147. Field of normal vectors of a surface.

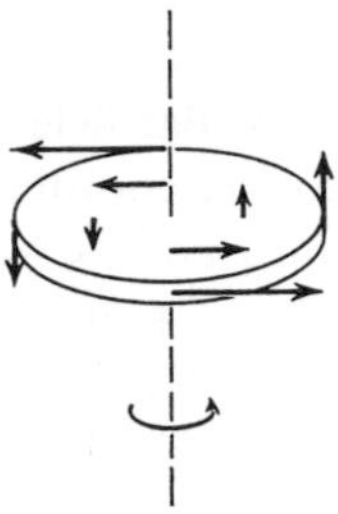

Fig. 148. Velocity field of a rotating body.

but we should keep in mind that $\mathbf{v}$ depends only on the points of its domain of definition, and at any such point defines the same vector for every choice of the coordinate system.

Example 3 (Velocity field). At any instant the velocity vectors $\mathbf{v}(P)$ of a rotating body B constitute a vector field, the so-called *velocity field* of the rotation. If we introduce a Cartesian coordinate system having the origin on the axis of rotation, then (cf. Ex. 3 in Sec. 5.6)

$$(1) \qquad \mathbf{v}(P) = \mathbf{v}(x, y, z) = \mathbf{w} \times (x\mathbf{i} + y\mathbf{j} + z\mathbf{k})$$

where x, y, z are the coordinates of any point P of B at the instant under consideration. If the coordinates are such that the z-axis is the axis of rotation and $\mathbf{w}$ points in the positive z-direction, then $\mathbf{w} = \omega\mathbf{k}$ and

$$\mathbf{v} = \begin{vmatrix} \mathbf{i} & \mathbf{j} & \mathbf{k} \\ 0 & 0 & \omega \\ x & y & z \end{vmatrix} = \omega(-y\mathbf{i} + x\mathbf{j}).$$

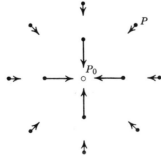

Fig. 149. Gravitational field.

Example 4 (Field of force). Let a particle A of mass M be fixed at a point P_0 and let a particle B of mass m be free to take up various positions P in space. Then A attracts B. According to **Newton's law of gravitation** the corresponding gravitational force **p** is directed from P to P_0, and its magnitude is proportional to $1/r^2$ where r is the distance between P and P_0, say,

$$(2) \qquad\qquad |\mathbf{p}| = \frac{c}{r^2}, \qquad\qquad c = GMm$$

where $G\,(= 6.67 \cdot 10^{-8}\ \text{cm}^3/\text{gm} \cdot \text{sec}^2)$ is the gravitational constant. Hence **p** defines a vector field in space. If we introduce Cartesian coordinates such that P_0 has the coordinates x_0, y_0, z_0 and P has the coordinates x, y, z, then

$$r = \sqrt{(x - x_0)^2 + (y - y_0)^2 + (z - z_0)^2} \qquad\qquad (\geqq 0).$$

Assuming that $r > 0$ and introducing the vector

$$\mathbf{r} = (x - x_0)\mathbf{i} + (y - y_0)\mathbf{j} + (z - z_0)\mathbf{k},$$

we have $|\mathbf{r}| = r$, and $-\mathbf{r}/r$ is a unit vector in the direction of **p**, the minus sign indicating that **p** is directed from P to P_0 (Fig. 149). From this and (2) we obtain

$$(3) \qquad \mathbf{p} = |\mathbf{p}|\left(-\frac{\mathbf{r}}{r}\right) = -c\frac{\mathbf{r}}{r^3} = -c\frac{x - x_0}{r^3}\mathbf{i} - c\frac{y - y_0}{r^3}\mathbf{j} - c\frac{z - z_0}{r^3}\mathbf{k}.$$

This vector function describes the gravitational force acting on B.

PROBLEMS

Determine and plot several of the isotherms (lines of constant temperature T) of the temperature field in the xy-plane given by the function:

  1. $T = x$ **2.** $T = x^2 - y^2$ **3.** $T = xy$

  4. $T = x^3 - 3xy^2$ **5.** $T = x^2 y - y^3$ **6.** $T = \ln(x^2 + y^2)$

  7. $T = \dfrac{x}{x^2 + y^2}$ **8.** $T = \arctan\dfrac{y}{x}$ **9.** $T = \sin x \cosh y$

10. Find the temperature in Prob. 4 at the points $(0, 0)$, $(2, 3)$, $(-1, 2)$, and $(-3, -2)$.

11. Draw figures of the scalar functions in Probs. 3 and 6 as surfaces in space.

12. Find analytic expressions for the temperature in Prob. 4 on the x-axis, on the line $y = x$, on the line $y = -x$, and on the parabola $y = x^2$.

Find the level surfaces (surfaces $f = const$) of the scalar fields in space given by the following functions.

13. $f = \dfrac{1}{x^2 + y^2 + z^2}$ **14.** $f = \dfrac{1}{(x - 1)^2 + (y + 2)^2 + (z - 2)^2}$

15. $f = x + y + z$ **16.** $f = x^2 + y^2 + 4z^2$

Draw figures (similar to Fig. 149) of the vector fields given by the following vector functions.

17. $\mathbf{v} = \mathbf{i}$ **18.** $\mathbf{v} = 2\mathbf{i} + 3\mathbf{j}$ **19.** $\mathbf{v} = 2x\mathbf{i} - 2y\mathbf{j}$

20. $\mathbf{v} = y\mathbf{i} + x\mathbf{j}$ **21.** $\mathbf{v} = (x^2 - y^2)\mathbf{i} - 2xy\mathbf{j}$

22. $\mathbf{v} = \dfrac{x}{x^2 + y^2}\mathbf{i} + \dfrac{y}{x^2 + y^2}\mathbf{j}$ **23.** $\mathbf{v} = -\dfrac{y}{x^2 + y^2}\mathbf{i} + \dfrac{x}{x^2 + y^2}\mathbf{j}$

24. In Prob. 21 find **v** at the points $(0, 0)$, $(1, -1)$, and $(-3, 4)$.

25. Plot the parabola $y = x^2$ and the vectors given by **v** in Prob. 19 at the points of this parabola.

Plot the curves on which $\mathbf{v}$ has constant length and the curves on which $\mathbf{v}$ has constant direction, where

26. $\mathbf{v} = y\mathbf{i} + x\mathbf{j}$ **27.** $\mathbf{v} = (x^2 - y^2)\mathbf{i} - 2xy\mathbf{j}$
28. $\mathbf{v} = y\mathbf{i} + x^2\mathbf{j}$ **29.** $\mathbf{v} = y\mathbf{i} + 4x\mathbf{j}$
30. Find the surfaces on which $\mathbf{v} = y\mathbf{i} + z\mathbf{j} + x\mathbf{k}$ has constant length.

5.10   VECTOR CALCULUS

The basic concepts of calculus, such as convergence, continuity, and differentiability, can be introduced to vector analysis in a simple and natural way as follows.

An infinite sequence of vectors $\mathbf{a}_{(n)}$, $n = 1, 2, \cdots$, is said to **converge** to a limit vector $\mathbf{a}$ if

$$(1) \qquad\qquad \lim_{n \to \infty} |\mathbf{a}_{(n)} - \mathbf{a}| = 0,$$

and then we write

$$(2) \qquad\qquad \lim_{n \to \infty} \mathbf{a}_{(n)} = \mathbf{a}.$$

Clearly, if a Cartesian coordinate system has been introduced, then that sequence of vectors converges to $\mathbf{a}$ if, and only if, the three sequences of the components of the vectors converge to the corresponding components of $\mathbf{a}$. The simple proof is left to the reader.

Similarly, a vector function $\mathbf{u}(t)$ of a real variable t is said to have the **limit** $\mathbf{l}$ as t approaches t_0, if $\mathbf{u}(t)$ is defined in some *neighborhood*[5] of t_0 (possibly except at t_0) and

$$(3) \qquad\qquad \lim_{t \to t_0} |\mathbf{u}(t) - \mathbf{l}| = 0.$$

Then we write

$$(4) \qquad\qquad \lim_{t \to t_0} \mathbf{u}(t) = \mathbf{l}.$$

A vector function $\mathbf{u}(t)$ is said to be **continuous** at $t = t_0$ if it is defined in some neighborhood of t_0 and

$$(5) \qquad\qquad \lim_{t \to t_0} \mathbf{u}(t) = \mathbf{u}(t_0).$$

If a Cartesian coordinate system has been introduced, then $\mathbf{u}(t)$ is continuous at t_0 if, and only if, its three components are continuous at t_0.

[5] That is, in some interval on the t-axis containing t_0 as an interior point.

A vector function $\mathbf{u}(t)$ is said to be *differentiable* at a point t if the limit

(6)
$$\mathbf{u}'(t) = \lim_{\Delta t \to 0} \frac{\mathbf{u}(t + \Delta t) - \mathbf{u}(t)}{\Delta t}$$

exists. The vector $\mathbf{u}'(t)$ is called the **derivative** of $\mathbf{u}(t)$. Cf. Fig. 150.
With respect to any Cartesian coordinate system, let

$$\mathbf{u}(t) = u_1(t)\mathbf{i} + u_2(t)\mathbf{j} + u_3(t)\mathbf{k}.$$

Then $\mathbf{u}'(t)$ exists if, and only if, the derivatives of the three components

$$u_m'(t) = \lim_{\Delta t \to 0} \frac{u_m(t + \Delta t) - u_m(t)}{\Delta t},$$

where $m = 1, 2, 3$, exist, and

(7) $\mathbf{u}'(t) = u_1'(t)\mathbf{i} + u_2'(t)\mathbf{j} + u_3'(t)\mathbf{k};$

that is, *to differentiate a vector function one differentiates each component separately.*

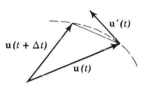

Fig. 150. Derivative of a vector function.

The familiar rules of differentiation yield corresponding rules for differentiating vector functions, for example,

$$(c\mathbf{u})' = c\mathbf{u}' \ (c \text{ constant}), \qquad (\mathbf{u} + \mathbf{v})' - \mathbf{u}' + \mathbf{v}'$$

and in particular

(8) $(\mathbf{u} \cdot \mathbf{v})' = \mathbf{u}' \cdot \mathbf{v} + \mathbf{u} \cdot \mathbf{v}'$

(9) $(\mathbf{u} \times \mathbf{v})' = \mathbf{u}' \times \mathbf{v} + \mathbf{u} \times \mathbf{v}'$

(10) $(\mathbf{u}\,\mathbf{v}\,\mathbf{w})' = (\mathbf{u}'\,\mathbf{v}\,\mathbf{w}) + (\mathbf{u}\,\mathbf{v}'\,\mathbf{w}) + (\mathbf{u}\,\mathbf{v}\,\mathbf{w}').$

In (9), the order of the vectors must be carefully observed because cross-multiplication is not commutative.

To prove (8), let

$$\mathbf{u} = u_1\mathbf{i} + u_2\mathbf{j} + u_3\mathbf{k} \qquad \text{and} \qquad \mathbf{v} = v_1\mathbf{i} + v_2\mathbf{j} + v_3\mathbf{k}.$$

Then from (8), Sec. 5.4, it follows that

$$(\mathbf{u} \cdot \mathbf{v})' = (u_1v_1 + u_2v_2 + u_3v_3)'$$
$$= u_1'v_1 + u_2'v_2 + u_3'v_3 + u_1v_1' + u_2v_2' + u_3v_3'$$
$$= \mathbf{u}' \cdot \mathbf{v} + \mathbf{u} \cdot \mathbf{v}'.$$

The rules (9) and (10) may be proved in a similar fashion.

Example 1. Let $\mathbf{u}(t)$ be a vector function whose magnitude is constant, say, $|\mathbf{u}(t)| = c$. Then $|\mathbf{u}|^2 = \mathbf{u} \cdot \mathbf{u} = c^2$, and $(\mathbf{u} \cdot \mathbf{u})' = 2\mathbf{u} \cdot \mathbf{u}' = 0$, by differentiation [cf. (8)]. This yields the following result. *The derivative of a vector function* $\mathbf{u}(t)$ *of constant magnitude is either the zero vector or is orthogonal to* $\mathbf{u}(t)$.

Example 2 (Tangent).   The vector function $\mathbf{r}(t) = t\mathbf{i} + t^2\mathbf{j}$ may be interpreted as the position vector of the points of the parabola $y = x^2$ in the xy-plane. Then $\mathbf{r}(t + \Delta t) - \mathbf{r}(t)$ is the vector from P to Q in Fig. 151, and the vector

$$\frac{\mathbf{r}(t + \Delta t) - \mathbf{r}(t)}{\Delta t}$$

is parallel to that vector and approaches $\mathbf{r}'(t)$ as Δt approaches zero. Also, Q approaches P, and the straight line through P and Q approaches the tangent of the parabola at P. Hence $\mathbf{r}'(t) = \mathbf{i} + 2t\mathbf{j}$ is a tangent vector to the parabola at P.

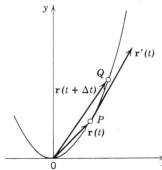

Fig. 151. Tangent vector.

Further important applications of derivatives will be considered in the following sections.

From our considerations the way of introducing partial differentiation to vector analysis is obvious. Let the components of a vector function

$$\mathbf{u} = u_1\mathbf{i} + u_2\mathbf{j} + u_3\mathbf{k}$$

be differentiable functions of n variables $t_1, \cdots, t_n$. Then the partial derivative of $\mathbf{u}$ with respect to t_l is denoted by $\partial\mathbf{u}/\partial t_l$ and is defined as the vector function

$$\frac{\partial\mathbf{u}}{\partial t_l} = \frac{\partial u_1}{\partial t_l}\mathbf{i} + \frac{\partial u_2}{\partial t_l}\mathbf{j} + \frac{\partial u_3}{\partial t_l}\mathbf{k}.$$

Similarly,

$$\frac{\partial^2\mathbf{u}}{\partial t_l\,\partial t_m} = \frac{\partial^2 u_1}{\partial t_l\,\partial t_m}\mathbf{i} + \frac{\partial^2 u_2}{\partial t_l\,\partial t_m}\mathbf{j} + \frac{\partial^2 u_3}{\partial t_l\,\partial t_m}\mathbf{k},$$

and so on.

Example 3.   Let $\mathbf{r}(t_1, t_2) = a\cos t_1\,\mathbf{i} + a\sin t_1\,\mathbf{j} + t_2\mathbf{k}$. Then

$$\frac{\partial\mathbf{r}}{\partial t_1} = -a\sin t_1\,\mathbf{i} + a\cos t_1\,\mathbf{j}, \qquad \frac{\partial\mathbf{r}}{\partial t_2} = \mathbf{k}.$$

Note that if $\mathbf{r}(t_1, t_2)$ is interpreted as a position vector it represents a cylinder of revolution of radius a, having the z-axis as axis of rotation. (Representations of surfaces will be considered in Sec. 6.5.)

PROBLEMS

Find $\mathbf{u}'$, $\mathbf{u}''$, $|\mathbf{u}'|$, and $|\mathbf{u}''|$ where
1. $\mathbf{u}(t) = \mathbf{a} + \mathbf{b}t$ (**a** and **b** are constant vectors)   2. $\mathbf{u} = \mathbf{a} + \mathbf{b}t^2$
3. $\mathbf{u} = 4\cos t\,\mathbf{i} + 4\sin t\,\mathbf{j}$ 4. $\mathbf{u} = 4\cos t\,\mathbf{i} - 4\sin t\,\mathbf{j}$
5. $\mathbf{u} = 3\cos t^2\,\mathbf{i} + 3\sin t^2\,\mathbf{j}$ 6. $\mathbf{u} = \cos t\,\mathbf{i} + \sin t\,\mathbf{j} - 2\mathbf{k}$
7. $\mathbf{u} = 2\cos 2t\,\mathbf{i} + 2\sin 2t\,\mathbf{j} + 4t\mathbf{k}$ 8. $\mathbf{u} = \cos t\,\mathbf{i} + \sin 2t\,\mathbf{j}$
9. $\mathbf{u} = 3\cos t\,\mathbf{i} + 2\sin t\,\mathbf{j}$ 10. $\mathbf{u} = 10\sin 3t\,(\mathbf{i} + \mathbf{j})$
11. $\mathbf{u} = t\mathbf{i} + t^2\mathbf{j} + t^3\mathbf{k}$ 12. $\mathbf{u} = e^{-t}\cos t\,\mathbf{i} + e^{-t}\sin t\,\mathbf{j}$

13. If $\mathbf{u}(t)$ is a unit vector and $\mathbf{u}'(t) \neq \mathbf{0}$, show that $\mathbf{u}$ and $\mathbf{u}'$ are perpendicular.

14. Prove (9).

15. Since $\mathbf{u} \times \mathbf{u} = \mathbf{0}$, also $(\mathbf{u} \times \mathbf{u})' = \mathbf{0}$. How does this follow from (9)?

16. Derive (10) from (8) and (9).

Let $\mathbf{u} = t^2\mathbf{i} - 3t\mathbf{k}$, $\mathbf{v} = -4t^3\mathbf{j} + (t+1)\mathbf{k}$, $\mathbf{w} = 3t^2\mathbf{i} + t\mathbf{j} - t^3\mathbf{k}$. Find

17. $(\mathbf{u} \cdot \mathbf{v})'$, $|\mathbf{u}|'$, $[(\mathbf{u} - \mathbf{v}) \cdot \mathbf{w}]'$ 18. $(\mathbf{u} \times \mathbf{v})'$, $(\mathbf{v} \times \mathbf{u})'$, $(\mathbf{u} \times \mathbf{u}')'$

19. $(\mathbf{u}\ 3\mathbf{v}\ 2\mathbf{w})'$ 20. $[\mathbf{u} \times (\mathbf{v} \times \mathbf{w})]'$

21. Show that $(\mathbf{u}\,\mathbf{u}'\mathbf{u}'')' = (\mathbf{u}\,\mathbf{u}'\mathbf{u}''')$, $(\mathbf{u} \times \mathbf{u}')' = \mathbf{u} \times \mathbf{u}''$.

22. Find formulas similar to (8) – (10) for $(\mathbf{u} \cdot \mathbf{v})''$, $(\mathbf{u} \times \mathbf{v})''$, $(\mathbf{u}\,\mathbf{v}\,\mathbf{w})''$, and $[\mathbf{u} \times (\mathbf{v} \times \mathbf{w})]'$.

23. Show that the equation $\mathbf{u}'(t) = \mathbf{c}$ has the solution $\mathbf{u}(t) = \mathbf{c}t + \mathbf{b}$ where $\mathbf{c}$ and $\mathbf{b}$ are constant vectors.

24. Show that $\mathbf{u}(t) = \mathbf{b}e^{\lambda t} + \mathbf{c}e^{-\lambda t}$ satisfies the equation $\mathbf{u}'' - \lambda^2\mathbf{u} = \mathbf{0}$. ($\mathbf{b}$ and $\mathbf{c}$ are constant vectors.)

25. Show that $\left[\dfrac{\mathbf{u}(t)}{|\mathbf{u}(t)|}\right]' = \dfrac{\mathbf{u}'(\mathbf{u} \cdot \mathbf{u}) - \mathbf{u}(\mathbf{u} \cdot \mathbf{u}')}{(\mathbf{u} \cdot \mathbf{u})^{3/2}}$.

Differentiate

26. $\dfrac{\mathbf{i} + t\mathbf{j} + t^2\mathbf{k}}{|\mathbf{i} + t\mathbf{j} + t^2\mathbf{k}|}$ 27. $\dfrac{t\mathbf{i} + t^2\mathbf{j}}{|t\mathbf{i} + t^2\mathbf{j}|}$

Find the first partial derivatives of the following vector functions.

28. $\mathbf{v}(x, y) = y\mathbf{i} + x\mathbf{j}$ 29. $\mathbf{v}(x, y) = (x^2 - y^2)\mathbf{i} - 2xy\mathbf{j}$

30. $\mathbf{v}(t_1, t_2) = 4\cos 2t_1\,\mathbf{i} + \sin 2t_1\,\mathbf{j} + t_2\mathbf{k}$

5.11 CURVES

As an important application of vector calculus, let us now consider some basic facts about curves in space. The student will know that curves occur in many considerations in calculus as well as in physics, for example, as paths of moving particles.

A Cartesian coordinate system being given, we may represent a curve C by a vector function (Fig. 152)

(1) $$\mathbf{r}(t) = x(t)\mathbf{i} + y(t)\mathbf{j} + z(t)\mathbf{k};$$

to each value t_0 of the real variable t there corresponds a point of C having the position vector $\mathbf{r}(t_0)$, that is, the coordinates $x(t_0)$, $y(t_0)$, $z(t_0)$.

A representation of the form (1) is called a **parametric representation** of the curve C, and t is called the *parameter* of this representation. This type of representation is useful in many applications, for example, in mechanics where the variable t may be the time.

Other types of representations of curves in space are

(2) $$y = f(x), \qquad z = g(x)$$

and

(3) $$F(x, y, z) = 0, \qquad G(x, y, z) = 0.$$

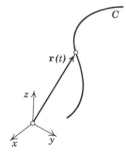

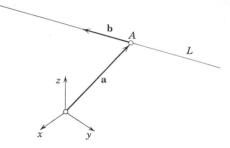

Fig. 152. Parametric representation of a curve.

Fig. 153. Parametric representation of a straight line.

By setting $x = t$ we may write (2) in the form (1), namely

$$r(t) = ti + f(t)j + g(t)k.$$

In (3), each equation represents a surface, and the curve is the intersection of the two surfaces.

A **plane curve** is a curve which lies in a plane in space. A curve which is not a plane curve is called a **twisted curve**.

Example 1. Any **straight line** L can be represented in the form

(4) $\qquad r(t) = a + tb = (a_1 + tb_1)i + (a_2 + tb_2)j + (a_3 + tb_3)k$

where a and b are constant vectors. L passes through the point A with position vector $r = a$ and has the direction of b (Fig. 153). If b is a unit vector, its components are the *direction cosines* of L, and in this case, $|t|$ measures the distance of the points of L from A.

Example 2. The twisted curve C represented by the vector function

(5) $\qquad r(t) = a \cos t \, i + a \sin t \, j + ct k \qquad (c \neq 0)$

is called a **circular helix**. It lies on the cylinder $x^2 + y^2 = a^2$ (Fig. 154). If $c > 0$, the helix is shaped like a right-handed screw. If $c < 0$, it looks like a left-handed screw.

Example 3. The vector function

(6) $\qquad r(t) = a \cos t \, i + b \sin t \, j$

represents an **ellipse** in the xy-plane with center at the origin and principal axes in the directions of the x and y axes. Since $\cos^2 t + \sin^2 t = 1$ we obtain from (6)

$$\frac{x^2}{a^2} + \frac{y^2}{b^2} = 1, \qquad z = 0.$$

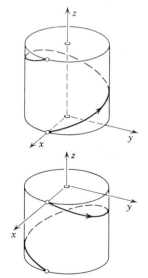

Fig. 154. Circular helix.

If $b = a$, then (6) represents a *circle* of radius a.

Fig. 155. Curves having double points.

The portion between any two points of a curve is often called an **arc** *of a curve*. For the sake of simplicity we shall use the single term "curve" to denote an entire curve as well as an arc of a curve.

A curve may have self-intersections; the points of intersection are called *multiple points* of the curve. A curve having no multiple points is called a **simple curve**.

Example 4. Ellipses and helices are simple curves. The curve represented by

$$\mathbf{r}(t) = (t^2 - 1)\mathbf{i} + (t^3 - t)\mathbf{j}$$

is not simple since it has a double point at the origin; this point corresponds to the two values $t = 1$ and $t = -1$.

We finally mention that a given curve C may be represented by various vector functions. For example, if C is represented by (1) and we set $t = h(t^*)$, then we obtain a new vector function $\mathbf{r}(t^*)$ representing C, provided $h(t^*)$ takes on all the values of t occurring in (1).

Example 5. The parabola $y = x^2$ in the xy-plane may be represented by the vector function

$$\mathbf{r}(t) = t\mathbf{i} + t^2\mathbf{j} \qquad\qquad (-\infty < t < \infty).$$

If we set $t = -2t^*$, we obtain another representation of the parabola:

$$\mathbf{r}(t^*) = -2t^*\mathbf{i} + 4t^{*2}\mathbf{j}.$$

If we set $t = t^{*2}$, we obtain

$$\mathbf{r}(t^*) = t^{*2}\mathbf{i} + t^{*4}\mathbf{j},$$

but this function represents only the portion of the parabola in the first quadrant, because $t^{*2} \geq 0$ for all t^*.

PROBLEMS

Find a parametric representation of the straight line through a point A in the direction of a vector $\mathbf{b}$, where
1. A: $(1, 4, 1)$, $\mathbf{b} = \mathbf{i} + \mathbf{j} + 2\mathbf{k}$
2. A: $(-3, 1, -2)$, $\mathbf{b} = 3\mathbf{i} - \mathbf{k}$
3. A: $(0, 0, 0)$, $\mathbf{b} = -\mathbf{i} + 2\mathbf{j}$

Find a parametric representation of the straight line through the points A and B, where
4. A: $(1, 0, 1)$, B: $(0, 1, 0)$ 5. A: $(1, 2, -3)$, B: $(2, 2, 2)$
6. A: $(0, 0, 0)$, B: $(4, 2, 1)$ 7. A: $(-2, 0, 1)$, B: $(1, -2, 4)$

Find a parametric representation of the straight line represented by
8. $x + y + z = 1, y - z = 0$ **9.** $7x - 3y + z = 14, 4x - 3y - 2z = -1$
10. Find the direction cosines of the straight lines in Probs. 2, 4, and 9.
11. Determine the point of intersection of the line

$$\mathbf{r}(t) = (9 + 3t)\mathbf{i} - (10 + 4t)\mathbf{j} + (7 + 2t)\mathbf{k}$$

and the yz-plane.

Find a parametric representation of the following curves.
12. $x^2 + y^2 = 9, z = 0$ **13.** $x^2 + y^2 - 6x - 4y + 12 = 0, z = 0$
14. $y = 3x^3, z = 0$ **15.** $(x - 1)^2 + 4(y - 2)^2 = 4, z = 0$

Sketch figures of the following curves.
16. $\mathbf{r}(t) = 2 \cos t\, \mathbf{i} + 2 \sin t\, \mathbf{j} + 3t\mathbf{k}$
17. $\mathbf{r}(t) = 2 \cos t\, \mathbf{i} + 2 \sin t\, \mathbf{j} - t\mathbf{k}$
18. $\mathbf{r}(t) = 2 \cos t\, \mathbf{i} + \sin t\, \mathbf{j} + t\mathbf{k}$
19. $\mathbf{r}(t) = t\mathbf{i} + t^2\mathbf{j} + t^3\mathbf{k}$
20. $\mathbf{r}(t) = \dfrac{3t}{1 + t^3}\mathbf{i} + \dfrac{3t^2}{1 + t^3}\mathbf{j}$ ("folium of Descartes")

5.12   ARC LENGTH

To define the length of a curve C we may proceed as follows. We inscribe in C a broken line of n chords joining the two end points of C as

shown in Fig. 156. This we do for each positive integer n in an arbitrary way but such that the maximum chord-length approaches zero as n approaches infinity. The lengths of these lines of chords can be obtained from the theorem of Pythagoras. If the sequence of these lengths $l_1, l_2, \cdots$ is convergent with the limit l, then C is said to be **rectifiable**, and l is called the **length** of C.

Fig. 156. Length of a curve.

If C can be represented by a continuously differentiable[6] vector function

$$\mathbf{r} = \mathbf{r}(t) \qquad\qquad (a \leq t \leq b),$$

then it can be shown that C is rectifiable, and its length l is given by the integral

(1)
$$l = \int_a^b \sqrt{\dot{\mathbf{r}} \cdot \dot{\mathbf{r}}}\, dt \qquad\qquad \left(\dot{\mathbf{r}} = \frac{d\mathbf{r}}{dt}\right)$$

whose value is independent of the choice of the parametric representation. The proof is quite similar to that for plane curves usually considered in elementary integral calculus (cf. Ref. [A13]) and can be found in Ref. [C4] in Appendix 1.

---

[6] "*Continuously differentiable*" means that the derivative exists and is continuous.

If we replace the fixed upper limit b in (1) with a variable upper limit t, the integral becomes a function of t, say, $s(t)$; denoting the variable of integration by t^*, we have

$$(2) \qquad s(t) = \int_a^t \sqrt{\dot{\mathbf{r}} \cdot \dot{\mathbf{r}}} \, dt^*. \qquad \left(\dot{\mathbf{r}} = \frac{d\mathbf{r}}{dt^*} \right)$$

This function $s(t)$ is called the **arc length** of C.

The arc length s may serve as a parameter in parametric representations of curves, and we shall see that this will lead to a simplification of various formulas.

The constant a in (2) may be replaced by another constant; that is, the point of the curve corresponding to $s = 0$ may be chosen in an arbitrary manner. The sense corresponding to increasing values of s is called the **positive sense** on C; in this fashion any representation $\mathbf{r}(s)$ or $\mathbf{r}(t)$ of C defines a certain **orientation** of C. Obviously, there are two ways of *orienting C*, and it is not difficult to see that the transition from one orientation to the opposite orientation can be effected by a transformation of the parameter whose derivative is negative.

From (2) we obtain

$$(3) \qquad \left(\frac{ds}{dt} \right)^2 = \frac{d\mathbf{r}}{dt} \cdot \frac{d\mathbf{r}}{dt} = \left(\frac{dx}{dt} \right)^2 + \left(\frac{dy}{dt} \right)^2 + \left(\frac{dz}{dt} \right)^2.$$

It is customary to write

$$d\mathbf{r} = dx\,\mathbf{i} + dy\,\mathbf{j} + dz\,\mathbf{k}$$

and

$$(4) \qquad ds^2 = d\mathbf{r} \cdot d\mathbf{r} = dx^2 + dy^2 + dz^2.$$

ds is called the **linear element** of C.

Example 1. In the case of the circle

$$\mathbf{r}(t) = a \cos t\, \mathbf{i} + a \sin t\, \mathbf{j}$$

we have $\dot{\mathbf{r}} = -a \sin t\, \mathbf{i} + a \cos t\, \mathbf{j}$, $\dot{\mathbf{r}} \cdot \dot{\mathbf{r}} = a^2$, and therefore,

$$s(t) = \int_0^t a \, dt^* = at.$$

Hence a representation of the circle with the arc length as parameter is

$$\mathbf{r}(s) = a \cos \frac{s}{a}\, \mathbf{i} + a \sin \frac{s}{a}\, \mathbf{j}.$$

The circle is oriented in the counterclockwise sense, which corresponds to increasing values of s. Setting $s = -\bar{s}$, we obtain

$$\mathbf{r}(\bar{s}) = a \cos \frac{\bar{s}}{a}\, \mathbf{i} - a \sin \frac{\bar{s}}{a}\, \mathbf{j};$$

we have $ds/d\bar{s} = -1 < 0$, and the circle is now oriented in the clockwise sense.

PROBLEMS

Find the lengths of the following curves. Graph the curves.

1. *Circular helix* $\mathbf{r}(t) = a \cos t\, \mathbf{i} + a \sin t\, \mathbf{j} + ct\mathbf{k}$ from $(a, 0, 0)$ to $(a, 0, 2\pi c)$

2. *Catenary* $y = \cosh x$, $z = 0$, from $x = 0$ to $x = 1$

3. Four-cusped *hypocycloid* $\mathbf{r}(t) = a \cos^3 t\, \mathbf{i} + a \sin^3 t\, \mathbf{j}$, total length

4. $y = \frac{1}{3}(x^2 + 2)^{3/2}$, $z = 0$, from $x = 0$ to $x = 2$

5. *Semi-cubical parabola* $y = x^{3/2}$, $z = 0$, from $(0, 0, 0)$ to $(4, 8, 0)$

6. If a plane curve is represented in the form $y = f(x)$, $z = 0$ show that its length between $x = a$ and $x = b$ is

$$l = \int_a^b \sqrt{1 + y'^2}\, dx.$$

7. Find the arc length s of the ellipse $\dfrac{x^2}{a^2} + \dfrac{y^2}{b^2} = 1$. The integral occurring cannot be evaluated in terms of elementary functions. Develop this integral in a series of powers of the numerical eccentricity $\epsilon = \sqrt{a^2 - b^2}/a$.

8. If a curve is represented by a parametric representation, show that a transformation of the parameter whose derivative is negative reverses the orientation.

9. If a plane curve is represented in polar coordinates $\rho = \sqrt{x^2 + y^2}\,(\geq 0)$ and $\theta = \arctan \dfrac{y}{x}$, show that

$$ds^2 = \rho^2\, d\theta^2 + d\rho^2.$$

10. Graph the *cardioid* $\rho = a(1 - \cos \theta)$ and find its length.

5.13   TANGENT. CURVATURE AND TORSION

The *tangent* to a curve C at a point P of C is defined as the limiting position of the straight line L through P and another point Q of C as Q approaches P along the curve (Fig. 157).

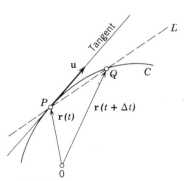

Let $\mathbf{r}(t)$ represent C where t is any parameter, and let P and Q correspond to t and $t + \Delta t$, respectively. Then L has the direction of the vector

$$[\mathbf{r}(t + \Delta t) - \mathbf{r}(t)]/\Delta t.$$

Hence, if the vector

$$(1) \qquad \dot{\mathbf{r}} = \lim_{\Delta t \to 0} \frac{\mathbf{r}(t + \Delta t) - \mathbf{r}(t)}{\Delta t}$$

is not the zero vector it has the direction of the tangent to C at P. It

Fig. 157. Tangent to a curve.

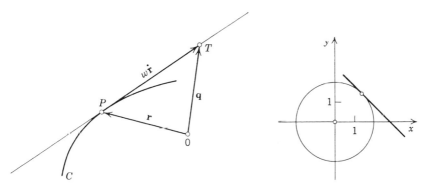

Fig. 158. Representation of the tangent to a curve.   **Fig. 159.** Tangent in Example 1.

points in the direction of increasing values of t, and its sense, therefore, depends on the orientation of the curve. $\dot{\mathbf{r}}$ is called a *tangent vector* of C at P, and the corresponding unit vector

$$(2) \qquad\qquad \mathbf{u} = \frac{\dot{\mathbf{r}}}{|\dot{\mathbf{r}}|}$$

is called the **unit tangent vector** to C at P.

If in particular C is represented by $\mathbf{r}(s)$, where s is the arc length, it follows from (3), Sec. 5.12, that the derivative $d\mathbf{r}/ds$ is a unit vector, and (2) becomes

$$(3) \qquad\qquad \mathbf{u} = \mathbf{r}' = \frac{d\mathbf{r}}{ds}.$$

Clearly the position vector of a point T on the tangent is the sum of the position vector $\mathbf{r}$ of P and a vector in the direction of the tangent. Hence a parametric representation of the tangent is (Fig. 158)

$$(4) \qquad\qquad \mathbf{q}(w) = \mathbf{r} + w\dot{\mathbf{r}}$$

where both $\mathbf{r}$ and $\dot{\mathbf{r}}$ depend on P and the parameter w is a real variable.

Example 1. In the case of the circle

$$\mathbf{r}(t) = a \cos t \, \mathbf{i} + a \sin t \, \mathbf{j}$$

we have

$$\dot{\mathbf{r}} = -a \sin t \, \mathbf{i} + a \cos t \, \mathbf{j}$$

and therefore

$$\mathbf{u} = -\sin t \, \mathbf{i} + \cos t \, \mathbf{j}.$$

By (4) the tangent to the circle at a point corresponding to $t = t_0$ is

$$\mathbf{q}(w) = a(\cos t_0 - w \sin t_0)\mathbf{i} + a(\sin t_0 + w \cos t_0)\mathbf{j}.$$

For example, if $a = 2$ and $t_0 = \pi/4$, then $\cos t_0 = \sin t_0 = 1/\sqrt{2}$ and (Fig. 159)

$$\mathbf{q}(w) = \sqrt{2}(1 - w)\mathbf{i} + \sqrt{2}(1 + w)\mathbf{j}.$$

PROBLEMS

Find a parametric representation of the tangent to the following curves at the given point P.

1. $\mathbf{r}(t) = 4 \cos t \, \mathbf{i} + 4 \sin t \, \mathbf{j}$, P: $(2\sqrt{2}, -2\sqrt{2}, 0)$

2. $\mathbf{r}(t) = \cos t \, \mathbf{i} + \sin t \, \mathbf{j} + 2t\mathbf{k}$, P: $(1, 0, 4\pi)$

3. $\mathbf{r}(t) = 2 \cos t \, \mathbf{i} + \sin t \, \mathbf{j}$, P: $(\sqrt{2}, 1/\sqrt{2}, 0)$

4. $\mathbf{r}(t) = t\mathbf{i} + 2t^4\mathbf{k}$, P: $(1, 0, 2)$

5. $\mathbf{r}(t) = t\mathbf{i} + t^2\mathbf{j} + t^3\mathbf{k}$, P: $(1, 1, 1)$

6. $\mathbf{r}(t) = t^2\mathbf{i} + t^3\mathbf{j}$, P: $(1, 1, 0)$ and P: $(0, 0, 0)$

7. Show that straight lines are the only curves whose unit tangent vector is constant.

8. Show that the angle between the unit tangent vector of the circular helix in Ex. 2, Sec. 5.11, and the z-axis is constant.

9. The **curvature** $\kappa(s)$ of a curve C represented by $\mathbf{r}(s)$, where s is the arc length, is defined by the formula

(5) $$\kappa(s) = |\mathbf{u}'| = |\mathbf{r}''|$$

where primes denote derivatives with respect to s. Show that for a straight line, $\kappa \equiv 0$.

10. Show that if $\kappa > 0$, then $\mathbf{u}$ and $\mathbf{u}'$ are orthogonal vectors. *Hint:* cf. Ex. 1, Sec. 5.10.

11. Show that the unit vector $\mathbf{p}$ in the direction of $\mathbf{u}'$ is

(6) $$\mathbf{p} = \frac{\mathbf{u}'}{\kappa} \qquad (\kappa > 0).$$

This vector is called the **unit principal normal vector** of C.

12. Show that if the curve C is represented by $\mathbf{r}(t)$ where t is any parameter, then the curvature is

(5') $$\kappa = \frac{\sqrt{(\dot{\mathbf{r}} \cdot \dot{\mathbf{r}})(\ddot{\mathbf{r}} \cdot \ddot{\mathbf{r}}) - (\dot{\mathbf{r}} \cdot \ddot{\mathbf{r}})^2}}{(\dot{\mathbf{r}} \cdot \dot{\mathbf{r}})^{3/2}}.$$

13. Using (5'), show that the curvature of the ellipse in Ex. 3, Sec. 5.11, is

$$\kappa = \frac{ab}{(a^2 \sin^2 t + b^2 \cos^2 t)^{3/2}}.$$

At which points of the ellipse is κ maximum and minimum?

14. Using (5'), show that the curvature of the circular helix in Ex. 2, Sec. 5.11, is constant, $\kappa = a/(a^2 + c^2)$.

15. Show that the usual representation $y = y(x)$ of a curve in the xy-plane can be written $\mathbf{r}(t) = t\mathbf{i} + y(t)\mathbf{j}$ where $t = x$, and for this representation, (5') becomes the familiar formula

$$\kappa = \frac{|y''|}{(1 + y'^2)^{3/2}}$$

where primes denote derivatives with respect to x.

16. Show that the so-called **unit binormal vector**

(7)
$$\mathbf{b} = \mathbf{u} \times \mathbf{p}$$
$$(\kappa > 0)$$

of C is a unit vector such that the vectors $\mathbf{u}$, $\mathbf{p}$, $\mathbf{b}$ constitute a right-handed triple of orthogonal unit vectors (Sec. 5.3). This triple is called the **trihedron** of C at the point under consideration (Fig. 160).

17. If C is a plane curve (and $\kappa > 0$), show that $\mathbf{u}$ and $\mathbf{p}$ lie in the plane of the curve while $\mathbf{b}$ is a normal vector to that plane.

18. Using (7), show that

(8)
$$\mathbf{b}' = \mathbf{u} \times \mathbf{p}'.$$

19. Show that if $\mathbf{b}' \neq \mathbf{0}$, then $\mathbf{b}$ and $\mathbf{b}'$ are orthogonal. Using this and (8), show that $\mathbf{b}'$ must be of the form

$$\mathbf{b}' = \alpha\mathbf{p}$$

where α is a scalar function.

20. Setting $\alpha = -\tau$ in the previous formula show that

(9)
$$\tau = -\mathbf{p} \cdot \mathbf{b}'.$$

τ is called the **torsion** of the curve under consideration.

21. Show that the torsion of a plane curve (with $\kappa > 0$) is identically zero.

22. Using (8) and (9), show that

$$\tau = (\mathbf{u} \; \mathbf{p} \; \mathbf{p}').$$

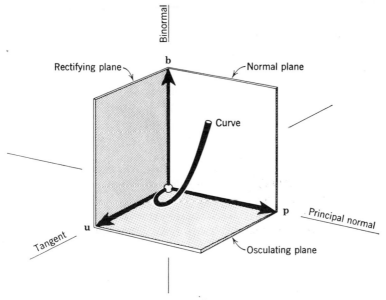

Fig. 160. Trihedron.

23. Using (6), show that the formula in Prob. 22 can be written

(10)
$$\tau = \frac{(\mathbf{r'}\ \mathbf{r''}\ \mathbf{r'''})}{\kappa^2} \qquad (\kappa > 0).$$

24. Using (5′), show that if the curve C is represented by $\mathbf{r}(t)$, where t is any parameter, then (10) becomes

(10′)
$$\tau = \frac{(\dot{\mathbf{r}}\ \ddot{\mathbf{r}}\ \dddot{\mathbf{r}})}{(\dot{\mathbf{r}} \cdot \dot{\mathbf{r}})(\ddot{\mathbf{r}} \cdot \ddot{\mathbf{r}}) - (\dot{\mathbf{r}} \cdot \ddot{\mathbf{r}})^2} \qquad (\kappa > 0).$$

Hint: use $\mathbf{r'} = \dot{\mathbf{r}}/\dot{s}$, $\mathbf{r''} = \ddot{\mathbf{r}}/\dot{s}^2 + \cdots$, $\mathbf{r'''} = \dddot{\mathbf{r}}/\dot{s}^3 + \cdots$ where the dots denote terms which can be made to vanish when the determinant is simplified according to Rule F in Sec. 0.3.

25. Show that the torsion of the circular helix in Ex. 2, Sec. 5.11, is constant, $\tau = c/(a^2 + c^2)$. Note that $\tau > 0$ when the helix looks like a right-handed screw ($c > 0$).

26. Prove the so-called **Frenet formulas**

(11)
$$\begin{aligned}
(a)\ \ &\mathbf{u'} = \kappa\mathbf{p} \\
(b)\ \ &\mathbf{p'} = -\kappa\mathbf{u} + \tau\mathbf{b} \\
(c)\ \ &\mathbf{b'} = -\tau\mathbf{p}
\end{aligned}$$

Hint: note that (11a) follows from (6), and (11c) follows from (9). For deriving (11b), start from $\mathbf{p} = \mathbf{b} \times \mathbf{u}$, differentiate, and use (11a) and (11c).

5.14   VELOCITY AND ACCELERATION

Let $\mathbf{r}(t)$ be the position vector of a moving particle P in space, where t is the time. Then $\mathbf{r}(t)$ represents the path C of P. From the previous section we know that the vector

(1)
$$\mathbf{v} = \dot{\mathbf{r}} = \frac{d\mathbf{r}}{dt}$$

is tangent to C and, therefore, points in the instantaneous direction of motion of P. From (3) in Sec. 5.12 we see that

$$|\mathbf{v}| = \sqrt{\dot{\mathbf{r}} \cdot \dot{\mathbf{r}}} = \frac{ds}{dt}$$

where s is the arc length, which measures the distance of P from a fixed point ($s = 0$) on C along the curve. Hence ds/dt is the **speed** of P. The vector $\mathbf{v}$ is, therefore, called the **velocity vector**[7] of the motion.

The derivative of the velocity vector is called the **acceleration vector** and will be denoted by $\mathbf{a}$; thus

(2)
$$\mathbf{a}(t) = \dot{\mathbf{v}}(t) = \ddot{\mathbf{r}}(t).$$

---

[7] When no confusion is likely to arise, the word "*velocity*" is often used to denote the speed, the magnitude of $\mathbf{v}$.

Example 1. Consider the motion of a car of mass m corresponding to

$$\mathbf{r}(t) = (2t - t^2)\mathbf{i}$$

during the interval of time $0 \leq t \leq 1$; here $\mathbf{i}$ is the unit vector in the positive x-direction. The velocity vector is

$$\mathbf{v} = \dot{\mathbf{r}} = (2 - 2t)\mathbf{i},$$

and the acceleration vector is

$$\mathbf{a} = \dot{\mathbf{v}} = -2\mathbf{i}.$$

Since $\mathbf{r}(0) = 0$ and $\mathbf{r}(1) = \mathbf{i}$, the motion starts at the origin $x = 0$ and ends at the point $x = 1$. The speed $|\mathbf{v}| = 2 - 2t$ of the car decreases, and the acceleration vector is directed opposite to the direction of motion. The corresponding force is $m\mathbf{a} = -2m\mathbf{i}$, a constant braking force. Note that the driver (mass m_0) feels the force $-m_0\mathbf{a} = +2m_0\mathbf{i}$ directed *in* the direction of motion and tending to retain the instantaneous speed of the driver with respect to the street.

Example 2 (Centripetal acceleration). The vector function

$$\mathbf{r}(t) = R \cos \omega t\, \mathbf{i} + R \sin \omega t\, \mathbf{j} \qquad (\omega > 0)$$

represents a circle C of radius R with center at the origin of the xy-plane and describes a motion of a particle P in the counter-clockwise sense. The velocity vector

$$\mathbf{v} = \dot{\mathbf{r}} = -R\omega \sin \omega t\, \mathbf{i} + R\omega \cos \omega t\, \mathbf{j}$$

is tangent to C, and its magnitude, the speed

$$|\mathbf{v}| = \sqrt{\dot{\mathbf{r}} \cdot \dot{\mathbf{r}}} = R\omega$$

is constant. The **angular speed** (speed divided by the distance R from the center) is equal to ω. The acceleration vector is

(3) $$\mathbf{a} = \dot{\mathbf{v}} = -R\omega^2 \cos \omega t\, \mathbf{i} - R\omega^2 \sin \omega t\, \mathbf{j} = -\omega^2 \mathbf{r}.$$

We see that there is an acceleration of constant magnitude $|\mathbf{a}| = \omega^2 R$ toward the origin, the so-called *centripetal acceleration*, which results from the fact that the velocity vector is changing direction at a constant rate. The centripetal force is $m\mathbf{a}$, where m is the mass of P. The opposite vector $-m\mathbf{a}$ is called the *centrifugal force*, and the two forces are in equilibrium at each instant of the motion.

It is clear that $\mathbf{a}$ is the rate of change of $\mathbf{v}$. In Ex. 2, $|\mathbf{v}| = const$, but $|\mathbf{a}| \neq 0$, which illustrates that the magnitude of $\mathbf{a}$ is not in general the rate of change of $|\mathbf{v}|$. The reason is that in general $\mathbf{a}$ is not tangent to the path C. In fact, by applying the chain rule of differentiation to (1), and denoting derivatives with respect to s by primes, we have

$$\mathbf{v} = \frac{d\mathbf{r}}{dt} = \frac{d\mathbf{r}}{ds}\frac{ds}{dt} = \mathbf{r}' \frac{ds}{dt}$$

and by differentiating this again,

(4) $$\mathbf{a} = \frac{d\mathbf{v}}{dt} = \frac{d}{dt}\left(\mathbf{r}' \frac{ds}{dt}\right) = \mathbf{r}'' \left(\frac{ds}{dt}\right)^2 + \mathbf{r}' \frac{d^2s}{dt^2}.$$

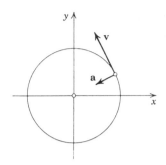

Fig. 161. Centripetal acceleration.   **Fig. 162.** Motion in Example 3.

Since $\mathbf{r}'$ is the unit tangent vector $\mathbf{u}$ to C (Sec. 5.13) and its derivative $\mathbf{u}' = \mathbf{r}''$ is perpendicular to $\mathbf{u}$ (Prob. 10, Sec. 5.13) the formula (4) is a decomposition of the acceleration vector into its normal component $\mathbf{r}''\dot{s}^2$ and its tangential component $\mathbf{r}'\ddot{s}$. From this we see that if, and only if, the normal component is zero, $|\mathbf{a}|$ equals the time rate of change of $|\mathbf{v}| = \dot{s}$ (except for the sign), because then $|\mathbf{a}| = |\mathbf{r}'|\,|\ddot{s}| = |\ddot{s}|$.

Example 3 (Coriolis[8] acceleration). A particle P moves on a straight line from the center of a disk towards the edge, the position vector being

(5) $$\mathbf{r}(t) = t\mathbf{b}$$

where $\mathbf{b}$ is a unit vector, rotating together with the disk with constant angular speed ω in the counterclockwise sense (Fig. 162). Find the acceleration $\mathbf{a}$ of P.

Because of the rotation, $\mathbf{b}$ is of the form

(6) $$\mathbf{b}(t) = \cos \omega t\,\mathbf{i} + \sin \omega t\,\mathbf{j}.$$

Differentiating (5), we obtain the velocity

(7) $$\mathbf{v} = \dot{\mathbf{r}} = \mathbf{b} + t\dot{\mathbf{b}}.$$

Obviously $\mathbf{b}$ is the velocity of P relative to the disk, and $t\dot{\mathbf{b}}$ is the additional velocity due to the rotation. Differentiating once more, we obtain the acceleration

(8) $$\mathbf{a} = \dot{\mathbf{v}} = 2\dot{\mathbf{b}} + t\ddot{\mathbf{b}}.$$

In the last term of (8) we have $\ddot{\mathbf{b}} = -\omega^2\mathbf{b}$, as follows by differentiating (6). Hence this acceleration $t\ddot{\mathbf{b}}$ is directed toward the center of the disk, and from Ex. 2 we see that this is the centripetal acceleration due to the rotation. In fact, the distance of P from the center is equal to t which, therefore, plays the role of R in Ex. 2.

The most interesting and probably unexpected term in (8) is $2\dot{\mathbf{b}}$, the so-called *Coriolis acceleration*, which results from the interaction of the rotation of the disk and the motion of P on the disk. It has the direction of $\dot{\mathbf{b}}$, that is, it is tangential to the edge of the disk and, referred to the fixed xy-coordinate system, it points in the direction of the rotation. If P is a person of mass m_0 walking on the disk according to (5), he will feel a force $-2m_0\dot{\mathbf{b}}$ in the opposite direction,

[8] GUSTAVE GASPARD CORIOLIS (1792–1843), French physicist.

that is, against the sense of rotation; this is quite similar as in Ex. 1 where the driver feels a force opposite to that acting on the car.

Example 4 (Superposition of two rotations). Find the acceleration of a particle P moving on a "meridian" M of a rotating sphere with constant speed relative to the sphere.

The motion of P on M can be described analytically in the form

(9) $\mathbf{r}(t) = R \cos \gamma t\ \mathbf{b} + R \sin \gamma t\ \mathbf{k}$

where R is the radius of the sphere, γ (>0) the angular speed of P on M, $\mathbf{b}$ a horizontal unit vector in the plane of M (Fig. 163), and $\mathbf{k}$ the unit vector in the positive z-direction. Since $\mathbf{b}$ rotates to-gether with the sphere, it is of the form

(10) $\mathbf{b} = \cos \omega t\ \mathbf{i} + \sin \omega t\ \mathbf{j}$

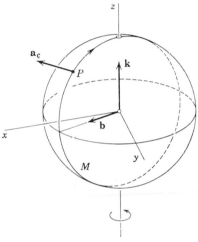

where ω (>0) is the angular speed of the sphere and $\mathbf{i}$ and $\mathbf{j}$ are the unit vectors in the positive x and y directions, which are fixed in space. By differentiating (9) we obtain the velocity

(11) $\mathbf{v} = \dot{\mathbf{r}} = R \cos \gamma t\ \dot{\mathbf{b}} - \gamma R \sin \gamma t\ \mathbf{b}$
$+ \gamma R \cos \gamma t\ \mathbf{k}.$

By differentiating this again we obtain the acceleration

(12) $\mathbf{a} = \dot{\mathbf{v}} = R \cos \gamma t\ \ddot{\mathbf{b}} - 2\gamma R \sin \gamma t\ \dot{\mathbf{b}}$
$- \gamma^2 R \cos \gamma t\ \mathbf{b} - \gamma^2 R \sin \gamma t\ \mathbf{k},$

where, by (10),

$\dot{\mathbf{b}} = -\omega \sin \omega t\ \mathbf{i} + \omega \cos \omega t\ \mathbf{j},$

$\ddot{\mathbf{b}} = -\omega^2 \cos \omega t\ \mathbf{i} - \omega^2 \sin \omega t\ \mathbf{j} = -\omega^2 \mathbf{b}.$

Fig. 163. Superposition of two rotations.

From (9) we see that the sum of the last two terms in (12) is equal to $-\gamma^2 \mathbf{r}$, and (12) becomes

(13) $\mathbf{a} = \omega^2 R \cos \gamma t\ \mathbf{b} - 2\gamma R \sin \gamma t\ \dot{\mathbf{b}} - \gamma^2 \mathbf{r}.$

The first term on the right is the centripetal acceleration caused by the rotation of the sphere, and the last term is the centripetal acceleration resulting from the rotation of P on M. The second term is the *Coriolis acceleration*

(14) $\mathbf{a}_c = -2\gamma R \sin \gamma t\ \dot{\mathbf{b}}.$

On the "Northern hemisphere," $\sin \gamma t > 0$ [cf. (9)] and because of the minus sign, $\mathbf{a}_c$ is directed opposite to $\dot{\mathbf{b}}$, that is, tangential to the surface of the sphere, perpendicular to M, and opposite to the rotation of the sphere. Its magnitude $2\gamma R |\sin \gamma t| \omega$ is maximum at the "North pole" and zero at the equator. If P is a fly of mass m_0 walking according to (9), it will feel a force $-m_0 \mathbf{a}_c$, opposite to $m_0 \mathbf{a}_c$; this is quite similar to the forces felt in Exs. 1 and 3. This force tends to let the fly deviate from the path M to the right. On the "Southern hemisphere," $\sin \gamma t < 0$ and that force acts in the opposite direction, tending to let the fly deviate from M to the left. This effect can be observed in connection with missiles and other projectiles. The flow of the air towards an area of low pressure also shows these deviations.

PROBLEMS

Let $r(t)$ be the position vector of a moving particle where $t(\geq 0)$ is the time. Describe the geometric shape of the path and find the velocity vector, the speed, and the acceleration vector.

1. $r = 3t\mathbf{i}$ 2. $r = 4t\mathbf{i} - 4t\mathbf{j} + 2t\mathbf{k}$
3. $r = 4t^2\mathbf{k}$ 4. $r = (1 + t^3)\mathbf{i} + 2t^3\mathbf{j} + (2 - t^3)\mathbf{k}$
5. $r = \sin t\,\mathbf{j}$ 6. $r = 10e^{-t}\mathbf{i} + 5e^{-t}\mathbf{j}$
7. $r = (2 + 3\cos 2t)\mathbf{i} + (4 + 3\sin 2t)\mathbf{j}$
8. $r = (2 + 3\cos 2t)\mathbf{i} + (4 - 3\sin 2t)\mathbf{j}$
9. $r = \cos t^2\,\mathbf{i} + \sin t^2\,\mathbf{j}$ 10. $r = 3\cos 2t\,\mathbf{i} + 2\sin 3t\,\mathbf{j}$
11. Obtain (3) by differentiating (7), Sec. 5.6.
12. Find the Coriolis acceleration in Ex. 3 with (5) replaced by $r = t^2\mathbf{b}$.

5.15 CHAIN RULE AND MEAN VALUE THEOREM FOR FUNCTIONS OF SEVERAL VARIABLES

We shall now consider some facts about functions of several variables which will be needed in the following sections. For the sake of simplicity we shall formulate everything for functions of two variables; the generalization to functions of three or more variables will be obvious. Familiarity of the student with the content of Sec. 0.2 on partial derivatives will be assumed.

A function $f(x, y)$ is said to be **continuous** *at a point* (x_0, y_0), if f is defined in a *neighborhood*[9] of that point and if for any positive number ϵ (no matter how small, but not zero) we can find a positive number δ such that

$$|f(x, y) - f(x_0, y_0)| < \epsilon$$

for all (x, y) for which

$$(x - x_0)^2 + (y - y_0)^2 < \delta^2.$$

Geometrically speaking, continuity of $f(x, y)$ at (x_0, y_0) means that to each interval of length 2ϵ with midpoint $f(x_0, y_0)$ we can find a circular disk with nonzero radius δ and center (x_0, y_0) in the xy-plane such that for every point (x, y) in the disk the corresponding function value $f(x, y)$ lies in that interval (Fig. 164).

---

[9] That is, in some circular disk $(x - x_0)^2 + (y - y_0)^2 < r^2$, $(r > 0)$.

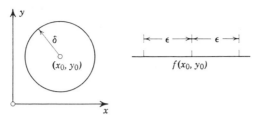

Fig. 164. Continuity of a function of two variables.

From elementary calculus we know that if w is a differentiable function of x, and x is a differentiable function of t, then

$$\frac{dw}{dt} = \frac{dw}{dx}\frac{dx}{dt}.$$

This so-called chain rule of differentiation can be generalized as follows.

Theorem 1 (Chain rule). *Let $w = f(x, y)$ be continuous and have continuous first partial derivatives at every point of a domain[10] D in the xy-plane. Let $x = x(t)$ and $y = y(t)$ be differentiable functions of a variable t in some interval T such that, for each t in T, the point $[x(t), y(t)]$ lies in D. Then $w = f[x(t), y(t)]$ is a differentiable function for all t in T, and*

(1) $$\frac{dw}{dt} = \frac{\partial w}{\partial x}\frac{dx}{dt} + \frac{\partial w}{\partial y}\frac{dy}{dt}.$$

Proof. We choose a t in T and Δt so small that $t + \Delta t$ is also in T, and set

(2) $$\Delta x = x(t + \Delta t) - x(t), \qquad \Delta y = y(t + \Delta t) - y(t),$$

and furthermore

$$\Delta w = f(x + \Delta x, y + \Delta y) - f(x, y).$$

By adding and subtracting a term this may be written

$$\Delta w = [f(x + \Delta x, y + \Delta y) - f(x, y + \Delta y)] + [f(x, y + \Delta y) - f(x, y)].$$

If we apply the mean value theorem for a function of a single variable (cf. Ref. [A13]) to each of the two expressions in brackets, we obtain

(3) $$\Delta w = \Delta x \left.\frac{\partial f}{\partial x}\right|_{x_1,\, y + \Delta y} + \Delta y \left.\frac{\partial f}{\partial y}\right|_{x,\, y_1}.$$

[10] A **domain** D is an open connected point set, where "connected" means that any two points of D can be joined by a broken line of finitely many linear segments all of whose points belong to D, and "open" means that every point of D has a neighborhood all of whose points belong to D. For example, the interior of a rectangle or a circle is a domain.

where x_1 lies between x and $x + \Delta x$, and y_1 lies between y and $y + \Delta y$. On the other hand, by applying the mean value theorem to (2) we have

$$\Delta x = \frac{dx}{dt} \Delta t, \qquad \Delta y = \frac{dy}{dt} \Delta t,$$

the derivatives being evaluated at suitable points between t and $t + \Delta t$. If we insert this into (3) and divide the resulting equation by Δt, we find

$$\frac{\Delta w}{\Delta t} = \frac{\partial f}{\partial x} \frac{dx}{dt} + \frac{\partial f}{\partial y} \frac{dy}{dt},$$

the derivatives being evaluated as indicated before. By letting Δt approach zero the chain rule (1) follows, and the proof is complete.

This theorem may now immediately be extended as follows.

Theorem 2. *Let $w = f(x, y)$ be continuous and have continuous first partial derivatives in a domain D of the xy-plane. Let $x = x(u, v)$ and $y = y(u, v)$ be functions which have first partial derivatives in a domain B of the uv-plane, which is such that, for any point (u, v) in B, the corresponding point $[x(u, v), y(u, v)]$ lies in D. Then the function $w = f(x(u, v), y(u, v))$ is defined and has first partial derivatives in B, and*

(4)
$$\frac{\partial w}{\partial u} = \frac{\partial w}{\partial x} \frac{\partial x}{\partial u} + \frac{\partial w}{\partial y} \frac{\partial y}{\partial u},$$

$$\frac{\partial w}{\partial v} = \frac{\partial w}{\partial x} \frac{\partial x}{\partial v} + \frac{\partial w}{\partial y} \frac{\partial y}{\partial v}.$$

The proof follows immediately from Theorem 1 by keeping one of the two variables u and v constant.

From elementary calculus we know that if a function $f(x)$ is differentiable, then

$$f(x_0 + h) - f(x_0) = h \frac{df}{dx},$$

the derivative being evaluated at a suitable point between x_0 and $x_0 + h$ (cf. Ref. [A13]). This so-called mean-value theorem of differential calculus can be extended to functions of two variables as follows.

Theorem 3 (Mean-value theorem). *Let $f(x, y)$ be continuous and have continuous first partial derivatives in a domain D. Furthermore, let (x_0, y_0) and $(x_0 + h, y_0 + k)$ be points in D such that the line segment joining these points lies in D (Fig. 165). Then*

(5) $$f(x_0 + h, y_0 + k) - f(x_0, y_0) = h \frac{\partial f}{\partial x} + k \frac{\partial f}{\partial y},$$

the partial derivatives being evaluated at a suitable point of that segment.

Proof. Let

$$x = x_0 + th, \qquad y = y_0 + tk \qquad\qquad (0 \le t \le 1)$$

and, furthermore,

$$F(t) = f(x_0 + th, y_0 + tk).$$

Then

$$f(x_0 + h, y_0 + k) = F(1), \qquad f(x_0, y_0) = F(0)$$

and, by the mean-value theorem for a function of a single variable,

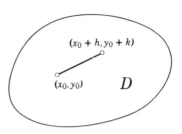

Fig. 165. Mean value theorem.

$$(6) \qquad f(x_0 + h, y_0 + k) - f(x_0, y_0)$$
$$= F(1) - F(0) = F'(t_1)$$

where t_1 is a value between 0 and 1. Since $dx/dt = h$ and $dy/dt = k$, we obtain from Theorem 1

$$(7) \qquad F'(t_1) = \frac{\partial f}{\partial x} h + \frac{\partial f}{\partial y} k,$$

the derivatives on the right being evaluated at the point $(x_0 + t_1 h, y_0 + t_1 k)$, which lies on the line segment with end points (x_0, y_0) and $(x_0 + h, y_0 + k)$. By inserting (7) into (6) we obtain (5), and the proof is complete.

For a function $f(x, y, z)$ of three variables, satisfying conditions analogous to those in Theorem 3, the consideration is quite similar and leads to the formula

$$(8) \qquad f(x_0 + h, y_0 + k, z_0 + l) - f(x_0, y_0, z_0) = h \frac{\partial f}{\partial x} + k \frac{\partial f}{\partial y} + l \frac{\partial f}{\partial z},$$

the partial derivatives being evaluated at a suitable point of the segment with end points (x_0, y_0, z_0) and $(x_0 + h, y_0 + k, z_0 + l)$.

PROBLEMS

1. Prove Theorem 2.   **2.** Derive (8).

Find dw/dt by means of (1), where

3. $w = \sqrt{x^2 + y^2}$, $x = e^t$, $y = \sin t$ **4.** $w = x + y$, $x = 4(t^2 - 1)$, $y = \ln t$
5. $w = x^y$, $x = t$, $y = t$ **6.** $w = (x^2 + y^2)^3$, $x = \cos t, y = \sin t$
7. $w = x^y$, $x = \cos t$, $y = \sin t$ **8.** $w = x/y$, $x = g(t)$, $y = h(t)$
9. Let $w = f(x, y, z)$ where x, y, z are functions of t. Show that under conditions similar to those in Theorem 1,

$$\frac{dw}{dt} = \frac{\partial w}{\partial x} \frac{dx}{dt} + \frac{\partial w}{\partial y} \frac{dy}{dt} + \frac{\partial w}{\partial z} \frac{dz}{dt}.$$

Find dw/dt by using the chain rule, where

10. $w = x^2 + y^2 + z^2$, $x = e^t \cos t$, $y = e^t \sin t$, $z = e^t$

11. $w = (x^2 + y^2 + z^2)^{-\frac{1}{2}}$, $x = t$, $y = \cos t$, $z = \sin t$

Find $\partial w/\partial u$ and $\partial w/\partial v$, where

12. $w = x^2 + y^2$, $x = u + v$, $y = u - v$

13. $w = xy$, $x = e^u \cos v$, $y = e^u \sin v$

14. $w = x^2 - y^2$, $x = u^2 - v^2$, $y = 2uv$

15. $w = \ln (x^2 + y^2)$, $x = e^u \cos v$, $y = e^u \sin v$

16. Let $w = f(x, y)$ and $x = r \cos \theta$, $y = r \sin \theta$. Show that

$$\left(\frac{\partial w}{\partial r}\right)^2 + \frac{1}{r^2} \left(\frac{\partial w}{d\theta}\right)^2 = \left(\frac{\partial w}{\partial x}\right)^2 + \left(\frac{\partial w}{\partial y}\right)^2.$$

17. Let $w = f(x, y)$, $x = u + v$, $y = u - v$. Show that

$$\frac{\partial w}{\partial u} \frac{\partial w}{\partial v} = \left(\frac{\partial w}{\partial x}\right)^2 - \left(\frac{\partial w}{\partial y}\right)^2.$$

18. Let $w = f(x, y)$ and $x = x(u, v)$, $y = y(u, v)$. Using (4) twice, show that, granted sufficient differentiability,

$$w_{uu} = w_{xx}x_u^2 + 2w_{xy}x_u y_u + w_{yy}y_u^2 + w_x x_{uu} + w_y y_{uu}$$

where subscripts denote partial derivatives.

19. Let $w = f(v, z)$ and $v = x + ct$, $z = x - ct$ where c is a constant. Show that, granted sufficient differentiability,

$$c^2 w_{xx} - w_{tt} = 4c^2 w_{vz}.$$

20. Let $w = f(x, y)$ and $x = r \cos \theta$, $y = r \sin \theta$. Show that

$$w_{xx} = \frac{x^2}{r^2} w_{rr} - 2 \frac{xy}{r^3} w_{r\theta} + \frac{y^2}{r^4} w_{\theta\theta} + \frac{y^2}{r^3} w_r + 2 \frac{xy}{r^4} w_\theta.$$

Find a similar expression for w_{yy} and add both expressions, finding

$$w_{xx} + w_{yy} = w_{rr} + \frac{1}{r} w_r + \frac{1}{r^2} w_{\theta\theta}.$$

Hint: note that $r = \sqrt{x^2 + y^2}$, $\theta = \arctan \dfrac{y}{x}$, $r_x = x/r$, $\theta_x = -y/r^2$, $r_{xx} = y^2/r^3$, etc.

5.16   DIRECTIONAL DERIVATIVE. GRADIENT OF A SCALAR FIELD

We consider a scalar field in space (Sec. 5.9) given by a scalar function $f(P) = f(x, y, z)$. We know that the first partial derivatives of f are the rates of change of f in the directions of the coordinate axes. It seems unnatural to restrict attention to these three directions, and we may ask for the rate of change of f in any direction. This simple idea leads to the notion of a directional derivative.

To define that derivative we choose a point P in space and a direction at P, given by a unit vector $\mathbf{b}$. Let C be the ray from P in the direction of $\mathbf{b}$, and let Q be a point on C, whose distance from P is s (Fig. 166). Then if the limit

(1) $$\frac{\partial f}{\partial s} = \lim_{s \to 0} \frac{f(Q) - f(P)}{s} \qquad (s = \text{distance between } P \text{ and } Q)$$

exists, it is called the **directional derivative** of f at P *in the direction of* $\mathbf{b}$. Obviously, $\partial f / \partial s$ is the rate of change of f at P in the direction of $\mathbf{b}$.

In this way there are now infinitely many directional derivatives of f at P, each corresponding to a certain direction. But, a Cartesian coordinate system being given, we may represent any such derivative in terms of the first partial derivatives of f at P as follows.

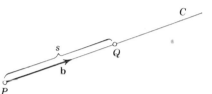

Fig. 166. Directional derivative.

If P has the position vector $\mathbf{a}$, then the ray C can be represented in the form

(2) $$\mathbf{r}(s) = x(s)\mathbf{i} + y(s)\mathbf{j} + z(s)\mathbf{k} = \mathbf{a} + s\mathbf{b} \qquad (s \geqq 0),$$

and $\partial f / \partial s$ is the derivative of the function $f[x(s), y(s), z(s)]$ with respect to the arc length s of C. Hence, assuming that f has continuous first partial derivatives and applying the chain rule (Theorem 1 in the last section) we obtain

(3) $$\frac{\partial f}{\partial s} = \frac{\partial f}{\partial x} x' + \frac{\partial f}{\partial y} y' + \frac{\partial f}{\partial z} z'$$

where primes denote derivatives with respect to s. Now from (2),

$$\mathbf{r}' = x'\mathbf{i} + y'\mathbf{j} + z'\mathbf{k} = \mathbf{b}.$$

This suggests that we introduce the vector

(4) $$\operatorname{grad} f = \frac{\partial f}{\partial x}\mathbf{i} + \frac{\partial f}{\partial y}\mathbf{j} + \frac{\partial f}{\partial z}\mathbf{k}$$

and write (3) in the form of a scalar product:

(5) $$\frac{\partial f}{\partial s} = \mathbf{b} \cdot \operatorname{grad} f \qquad (|\mathbf{b}| = 1).$$

The vector $\operatorname{grad} f$ is called the **gradient** of the scalar function f.

By introducing the *differential operator*

$$\nabla = \frac{\partial}{\partial x}\mathbf{i} + \frac{\partial}{\partial y}\mathbf{j} + \frac{\partial}{\partial z}\mathbf{k}$$

(read **nabla** or "del") we may write

$$\operatorname{grad} f = \nabla f = \frac{\partial f}{\partial x}\mathbf{i} + \frac{\partial f}{\partial y}\mathbf{j} + \frac{\partial f}{\partial z}\mathbf{k}.$$

The notation ∇f for the gradient is frequently used in the engineering literature.

We note that if in particular $\mathbf{b}$ has the direction of the positive x-axis, then $\mathbf{b} = \mathbf{i}$, and

$$\frac{\partial f}{\partial s} = \mathbf{b} \cdot \operatorname{grad} f = \frac{\partial f}{\partial x} \mathbf{i} \cdot \mathbf{i} = \frac{\partial f}{\partial x}.$$

Similarly, the directional derivative in the positive y-direction is $\partial f / \partial y$, etc.

We want to show that *grad f is a vector, that is, has a magnitude and direction which is independent of the choice of coordinates in space.*

This is, of course, not obvious; the definition (4) merely shows that grad f looks like a vector, but since (4) involves partial derivatives, which depend on the choice of the coordinates, we don't know yet whether the corresponding expression

$$\frac{\partial f}{\partial x^*} \mathbf{i} + \frac{\partial f}{\partial y^*} \mathbf{j} + \frac{\partial f}{\partial z^*} \mathbf{k}$$

with respect to other Cartesian coordinates x^*, y^*, z^* will have the same magnitude and direction as (4). For comparison, the expression

$$\frac{\partial f}{\partial x} \mathbf{i} + 2 \frac{\partial f}{\partial y} \mathbf{j} + \frac{\partial f}{\partial z} \mathbf{k}$$

looks like a vector, too, but the corresponding expression in another coordinate system will generally have another magnitude and direction, and the expression, therefore, is not a vector.

To show that grad f is a vector, we may reason as follows. By definition of a scalar function, the value of f at a point P depends on P but is independent of the coordinates, and s, the arc length of that ray C, has the same property. Hence $\partial f / \partial s$ is independent of the particular choice of coordinates. From (5) we obtain

$$\frac{\partial f}{\partial s} = |\mathbf{b}| \, |\operatorname{grad} f| \cos \gamma = |\operatorname{grad} f| \cos \gamma$$

where γ is the angle between $\mathbf{b}$ and grad f. We see that $\partial f / \partial s$ is maximum when $\cos \gamma = 1$, $\gamma = 0$, and then $\partial f / \partial s = |\operatorname{grad} f|$. This shows that the magnitude and direction of grad f are independent of the coordinates, and we have the following result.

Theorem 1. *Let $f(P) = f(x, y, z)$ be a scalar function having continuous first partial derivatives. Then grad f exists and is a vector. If at a point P the gradient of f is not the zero vector, it has the direction of maximum increase of f at P.*

Another important geometrical characterization of the gradient can be obtained as follows. Consider a scalar function $f(x, y, z)$ and suppose that for each constant c the equation

(6) $$f(x, y, z) = c = const$$

represents a surface S in space. Then, by letting c assume all values, we obtain a family of surfaces, which are called the **level surfaces** of the function f. We shall assume that f is such that through each point in space there passes one, and only one, level surface of f. We remember that a curve C in space may be represented in the form (cf. Sec. 5.11)

(7) $$r(t) = x(t)\mathbf{i} + y(t)\mathbf{j} + z(t)\mathbf{k}.$$

If we now require that C lies on S, then the functions $x(t), y(t)$, and $z(t)$ in (7) must be such that

$$f[x(t), y(t), z(t)] = c;$$

cf. (6). By differentiating this with respect to t and using the chain rule (Sec. 5.15), we obtain

(8) $$\frac{\partial f}{\partial x}\dot{x} + \frac{\partial f}{\partial y}\dot{y} + \frac{\partial f}{\partial z}\dot{z} = (\text{grad } f) \cdot \dot{\mathbf{r}} = 0,$$

where the vector

$$\dot{\mathbf{r}} = \dot{x}\mathbf{i} + \dot{y}\mathbf{j} + \dot{z}\mathbf{k}$$

is tangent to C (cf. Sec. 5.13). If we consider curves on S passing through a point P of S in various directions, their tangents at P will, in general, lie in the same plane which touches S at P. This plane is called the **tangent plane** of S at P. The straight line through P and perpendicular to the tangent plane is called the **normal** of S at P (Fig. 167). From (8) and Theorem 1, Sec. 5.4, we thus obtain the following result.

Theorem 2. *If f is a scalar function such that through a point P in space there passes precisely one level surface S of f, and grad $f \neq 0$ at P, then grad f is perpendicular to S at P, that is, has the direction of the normal of S at P.*

Example 1. Find the directional derivative $\partial f/\partial s$ of $f(x, y, z) = 2x^2 + 3y^2 + z^2$ at the point $P: (2, 1, 3)$ in the direction of the vector $\mathbf{a} = \mathbf{i} - 2\mathbf{k}$. We obtain

$$\text{grad } f = 4x\mathbf{i} + 6y\mathbf{j} + 2z\mathbf{k}, \quad \text{and at } P, \quad \text{grad } f = 8\mathbf{i} + 6\mathbf{j} + 6\mathbf{k}.$$

Since $|\mathbf{a}| = \sqrt{5}$, the unit vector in the direction of $\mathbf{a}$ is

$$\mathbf{b} = \frac{\mathbf{a}}{|\mathbf{a}|} = \frac{1}{\sqrt{5}}\mathbf{i} - \frac{2}{\sqrt{5}}\mathbf{k}.$$

Therefore,

$$\frac{\partial f}{\partial s} = (8\mathbf{i} + 6\mathbf{j} + 6\mathbf{k}) \cdot \left(\frac{1}{\sqrt{5}}\mathbf{i} - \frac{2}{\sqrt{5}}\mathbf{k}\right) = -\frac{4}{\sqrt{5}}.$$

The minus sign indicates that f decreases in the direction under consideration.

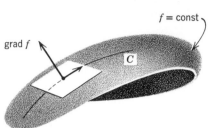

Fig. 167. Level surface and gradient.　　**Fig. 168.** Intersection of the xz-plane and the cone in Example 2.

Example 2 (Normal to a surface). Find a unit normal vector $\mathbf{n}$ of the cone of revolution $z^2 = 4(x^2 + y^2)$ at the point P: $(1, 0, 2)$. We may regard the cone as the level surface $f = 0$ of the function $f(x, y, z) = 4(x^2 + y^2) - z^2$. Then

$$\operatorname{grad} f = 8x\mathbf{i} + 8y\mathbf{j} - 2z\mathbf{k} \quad \text{and at } P, \quad \operatorname{grad} f = 8\mathbf{i} - 4\mathbf{k}.$$

Hence, by Theorem 2,

$$\mathbf{n} = \frac{\operatorname{grad} f}{|\operatorname{grad} f|} = \frac{2}{\sqrt{5}}\mathbf{i} - \frac{1}{\sqrt{5}}\mathbf{k}$$

is a unit normal vector of the cone at P, and $-\mathbf{n}$ is the other one (Fig. 168).

Example 3 (Normal to a plane curve). The level curves $f = const$ of the function $f(x, y) = \ln(x^2 + y^2)$ are concentric circles about the origin. The gradient

$$\operatorname{grad} f = \frac{\partial f}{\partial x}\mathbf{i} + \frac{\partial f}{\partial y}\mathbf{j} = \frac{2x}{x^2 + y^2}\mathbf{i} + \frac{2y}{x^2 + y^2}\mathbf{j}$$

has the direction of the normals to the circles, and its direction corresponds to that of the maximum increase of f. For example, at the point P: $(2, 1)$, we have (cf. Fig. 169)

$$\operatorname{grad} f = \frac{4}{5}\mathbf{i} + \frac{2}{5}\mathbf{j}.$$

Some of the vector fields occurring in physics are given by vector functions which can be obtained as the gradients of suitable scalar functions. Such a scalar function is then called the *potential function* or **potential** of the corresponding vector field. The use of potentials simplifies the investigation of those vector fields considerably. To obtain a first impression of this approach to vector fields, let us consider an important example.

Example 4 (Gravitational field. Laplace's equation). In Ex. 4, Sec. 5.9, we have seen that, according to Newton's law of gravitation, the force of attraction between two particles is

$$(9) \qquad \mathbf{p} = -c\frac{\mathbf{r}}{r^3} = -c\left(\frac{x - x_0}{r^3}\mathbf{i} + \frac{y - y_0}{r^3}\mathbf{j} + \frac{z - z_0}{r^3}\mathbf{k}\right)$$

where

$$r = \sqrt{(x - x_0)^2 + (y - y_0)^2 + (z - z_0)^2}$$

is the distance between the two particles and c is a constant. Observing that

(10a) $$\frac{\partial}{\partial x}\left(\frac{1}{r}\right) = -\frac{2(x - x_0)}{2[(x - x_0)^2 + (y - y_0)^2 + (z - z_0)^2]^{3/2}} = -\frac{x - x_0}{r^3}$$

and similarly

(10b) $$\frac{\partial}{\partial y}\left(\frac{1}{r}\right) = -\frac{y - y_0}{r^3}, \qquad \frac{\partial}{\partial z}\left(\frac{1}{r}\right) = -\frac{z - z_0}{r^3}$$

we see that $\mathbf{p}$ is the gradient of the scalar function

$$f(x, y, z) = \frac{c}{r} \qquad\qquad (r > 0);$$

that is, f is the potential of that gravitational field.

By differentiating (10) we find

$$\frac{\partial^2}{\partial x^2}\left(\frac{1}{r}\right) = -\frac{1}{r^3} + \frac{3(x - x_0)^2}{r^5}, \qquad \frac{\partial^2}{\partial y^2}\left(\frac{1}{r}\right) = -\frac{1}{r^3} + \frac{3(y - y_0)^2}{r^5},$$

$$\frac{\partial^2}{\partial z^2}\left(\frac{1}{r}\right) = -\frac{1}{r^3} + \frac{3(z - z_0)^2}{r^5}.$$

Since the sum of the three expressions on the right is zero, we see that the potential $f = c/r$ satisfies the equation

(11) $$\frac{\partial^2 f}{\partial x^2} + \frac{\partial^2 f}{\partial y^2} + \frac{\partial^2 f}{\partial z^2} = 0.$$

This important partial differential equation is called **Laplace's equation**; it will

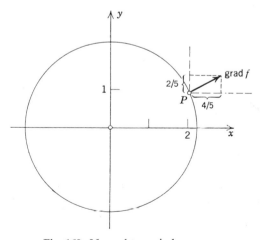

Fig. 169. Normal to a circle.

be considered in detail in Chaps. 9 and 13. The expression on the left is called the **Laplacian** of f and is denoted by $\nabla^2 f$ or Δf. The differential operator

$$\nabla^2 = \Delta = \frac{\partial^2}{\partial x^2} + \frac{\partial^2}{\partial y^2} + \frac{\partial^2}{\partial z^2}$$

(read "nabla squared" or "delta") is called the **Laplace operator**. Using this operator, we may write (11) in the form

$$\nabla^2 f = 0.$$

It can be shown that the field of force produced by any distribution of masses is given by a vector function which is the gradient of a scalar function f, and f satisfies (11) in any region of space which is free of matter.

There are other laws in physics which are of the same form as Newton's law of gravitation. For example, in electrostatics the force of attraction (or repulsion) between two particles of opposite (or like) charges Q_1 and Q_2 is

$$\mathbf{p} = k\,\frac{\mathbf{r}}{r^3} \qquad \text{(Coulomb's law)}$$

where $k = Q_1 Q_2/4\pi\epsilon$, and ϵ is the dielectric constant. Hence $\mathbf{p}$ is the gradient of the potential $f = -k/r$, and f satisfies (11).

If the vector function defining a vector field is the gradient of a scalar function, the field is said to be **conservative**, because, as we shall see in Sec. 6.12, in such a field the work done in displacing a particle from a point P_1 to a point P_2 in the field depends only on P_1 and P_2 but not on the path along which the particle is displaced from P_1 to P_2. We shall see that not every field is conservative.

PROBLEMS

Find ∇f. Plot some level curves $f = const$ and indicate ∇f by arrows at some points of these curves.

1. $f = xy$ **2.** $f = x^2 - y^2$ **3.** $f = x^3 - 3xy^2$

4. $f = 3x^2 y - y^3$ **5.** $f = \dfrac{x}{x^2 + y^2}$ **6.** $f = \arctan \dfrac{y}{x}$

Find ∇f, where

7. $f = e^x \cos y$ **8.** $f = \sin x \cosh y$ **9.** $f = 1/\sqrt{x^2 + y^2 + z^2}$

10. $f = 2xy - 4yz$ **11.** $f = (x^2 - y^2)z$ **12.** $f = \sin(x^2 + y^2 + z^2)$

13. $f = x^2 + 4y^2 + z^2$ **14.** $f = (x^2 + y^2 + z^2)^2$ **15.** $f = xyz$

Find a normal vector $\mathbf{n}$ to the given plane curve at the point $A: (x, y)$. Plot the result.

16. $y = 3x - 4$, $A: (1, -1)$ **17.** $y = 2x^2$, $A: (2, 8)$

18. $y = x^2 - 2x$, $A: (1, -1)$ **19.** $x^2 + y^2 = 25$, $A: (4, 3)$

20. $3x^2 - 2y^2 = 1$, $A: (1, 1)$ **21.** $y^2 = x^3$, $A: (4, -8)$

Find a normal vector $\mathbf{n}$ to the given surface at the indicated point $P: (x, y, z)$.

22. $x + y + z = 1$, $P: (4, 2, -5)$ **23.** $z = x^2 + y^2$, $P: (1, 1, 2)$

24. $z = y^4$, $P: (2, 1, 1)$ **25.** $x^2 + y^2 + z^2 = 9$, $P: (1, 2, 2)$

26. $x^2 + y^2 + z^2 = 25$, $P: (5, 0, 0)$ **27.** $z = xy$, $P: (2, 3, 6)$

Show that

28. $\nabla(fg) = f\nabla g + g\nabla f$

29. $\nabla^2(fg) = g\nabla^2 f + 2\nabla f \cdot \nabla g + f\nabla^2 g$

30. Show that the functions f in Probs. 1-8 are solutions of Laplace's equation.

31. Let r be the distance from a fixed point P to a point Q: (x, y, z). What are the level surfaces of r? Show that ∇r is a unit vector in the direction from P to Q.

Find a scalar function f such that $\mathbf{v} = \nabla f$ where

32. $\mathbf{v} = \mathbf{i} + \mathbf{j} + \mathbf{k}$ **33.** $\mathbf{v} = 2x\mathbf{i} + 2y\mathbf{j} + 2z\mathbf{k}$

34. $\mathbf{v} = 8x\mathbf{i} + 18y\mathbf{j} - 2z\mathbf{k}$ **35.** $\mathbf{v} = e^x \sin y\, \mathbf{i} + e^x \cos y\, \mathbf{j}$

36. $\mathbf{v} = (x\mathbf{i} + y\mathbf{j})/\sqrt{x^2 + y^2}$ **37.** $\mathbf{v} = (-y\mathbf{i} + x\mathbf{j})/(x^2 + y^2)$

38. What are the directional derivatives of a function $f(x, y, z)$ in the negative x, y, and z directions?

39. Find the directional derivative of $f = x^2 + y^2$ at the point P: $(2, 2)$ in the directions of the vectors $\mathbf{i}$, $\mathbf{i} + \mathbf{j}$, $\mathbf{j}$, $-\mathbf{i} + \mathbf{j}$, $-\mathbf{i}$, $-\mathbf{i} - \mathbf{j}$, $-\mathbf{j}$, and $\mathbf{i} - \mathbf{j}$.

Find the directional derivative of f at P in the direction of $\mathbf{a}$, where

40. $f = 4x^2 - 9y^2 + z^2$, P: $(0, -1, 2)$, $\mathbf{a} = \mathbf{i} + \mathbf{j} + \mathbf{k}$

41. $f = x/z$, P: $(1, -1, 3)$, $\mathbf{a} = -\mathbf{i} - \mathbf{k}$

42. $f = 1/(x^2 + y^2 + z^2)$, P: $(1, 2, -3)$, $\mathbf{a} = 2\mathbf{i} - 3\mathbf{j} + \mathbf{k}$

43. $f = e^{x+y+z}$, P: $(0, 0, 0)$, $\mathbf{a} = \mathbf{i} + 2\mathbf{j} - 2\mathbf{k}$

44. $f = x^3 - 3xy^2$, P: $(0, 2, 0)$, $\mathbf{a} = \mathbf{i} + \mathbf{j} + 2\mathbf{k}$

45. $f = x^2 + y^2 + z^2$, P: $(2, 2, 2)$, $\mathbf{a} = \mathbf{i} + 2\mathbf{j} - 3\mathbf{k}$

5.17   TRANSFORMATION OF COORDINATE SYSTEMS AND VECTOR COMPONENTS

We shall now characterize the transformations which carry Cartesian co-ordinate systems into Cartesian coordinate systems and investigate the change of vector components under such a transformation. This problem is basic for theoretical as well as practical reasons.

Let x, y, z and x^*, y^*, z^* be any two systems of Cartesian coordinates. Let

$$(1) \quad (a) \ \mathbf{v} = v_1\mathbf{i} + v_2\mathbf{j} + v_3\mathbf{k} \quad \text{and} \quad (b) \ \mathbf{v} = v_1^*\mathbf{i}^* + v_2^*\mathbf{j}^* + v_3^*\mathbf{k}^*$$

be the representations of a given vector $\mathbf{v}$ in these two coordinate systems; here $\mathbf{i}, \mathbf{j}, \mathbf{k}$ and $\mathbf{i}^*, \mathbf{j}^*, \mathbf{k}^*$ are unit vectors in the positive x, y, z and x^*, y^*, z^* directions, respectively. We want to express the components v_1^*, v_2^*, v_3^* in terms of the components v_1, v_2, v_3, and conversely.

From (1a) it follows that

$$(2) \qquad\qquad \mathbf{i}^* \cdot \mathbf{v} = v_1\mathbf{i}^* \cdot \mathbf{i} + v_2\mathbf{i}^* \cdot \mathbf{j} + v_3\mathbf{i}^* \cdot \mathbf{k}.$$

Similarly, by taking the scalar product of (1b) and $\mathbf{i}^*$, we have

$$\mathbf{i}^* \cdot \mathbf{v} = v_1^*\mathbf{i}^* \cdot \mathbf{i}^* + v_2^*\mathbf{i}^* \cdot \mathbf{j}^* + v_3^*\mathbf{i}^* \cdot \mathbf{k}^*.$$

Since the first scalar product on the right is 1 and the others are zero,

$$\mathbf{i}^* \cdot \mathbf{v} = v_1{}^*.$$

From this and (2) it follows that

$$v_1{}^* = \mathbf{i}^* \cdot \mathbf{i} v_1 + \mathbf{i}^* \cdot \mathbf{j} v_2 + \mathbf{i}^* \cdot \mathbf{k} v_3.$$

Similarly,
$$v_2{}^* = \mathbf{j}^* \cdot \mathbf{i} v_1 + \mathbf{j}^* \cdot \mathbf{j} v_2 + \mathbf{j}^* \cdot \mathbf{k} v_3,$$

$$v_3{}^* = \mathbf{k}^* \cdot \mathbf{i} v_1 + \mathbf{k}^* \cdot \mathbf{j} v_2 + \mathbf{k}^* \cdot \mathbf{k} v_3.$$

Hence the components of a vector $\mathbf{v}$ in a Cartesian coordinate system can be expressed as linear functions of the components of $\mathbf{v}$ with respect to another Cartesian coordinate system.

To write our transformation formulas in a simpler form we adopt the notation

(3)
$$
\begin{array}{ccc}
\mathbf{i}^* \cdot \mathbf{i} = a_{11} & \mathbf{i}^* \cdot \mathbf{j} = a_{12} & \mathbf{i}^* \cdot \mathbf{k} = a_{13} \\
\mathbf{j}^* \cdot \mathbf{i} = a_{21} & \mathbf{j}^* \cdot \mathbf{j} = a_{22} & \mathbf{j}^* \cdot \mathbf{k} = a_{23} \\
\mathbf{k}^* \cdot \mathbf{i} = a_{31} & \mathbf{k}^* \cdot \mathbf{j} = a_{32} & \mathbf{k}^* \cdot \mathbf{k} = a_{33}.
\end{array}
$$

Then we have

(4)
$$
\begin{aligned}
v_1{}^* &= a_{11} v_1 + a_{12} v_2 + a_{13} v_3 \\
v_2{}^* &= a_{21} v_1 + a_{22} v_2 + a_{23} v_3 \\
v_3{}^* &= a_{31} v_1 + a_{32} v_2 + a_{33} v_3.
\end{aligned}
$$

Using summation signs, we may write this more briefly

(4')
$$v_k{}^* = \sum_{l=1}^{3} a_{kl} v_l, \qquad k = 1, 2, 3.$$

A similar consideration leads to the inverse formulas

(5)
$$
\begin{aligned}
v_1 &= a_{11} v_1{}^* + a_{21} v_2{}^* + a_{31} v_3{}^* \\
v_2 &= a_{12} v_1{}^* + a_{22} v_2{}^* + a_{32} v_3{}^* \\
v_3 &= a_{13} v_1{}^* + a_{23} v_2{}^* + a_{33} v_3{}^*
\end{aligned}
$$

or, more briefly,

(5')
$$v_l = \sum_{m=1}^{3} a_{ml} v_m{}^*, \qquad l = 1, 2, 3.$$

Note that (4) and (5) contain the same coefficients a_{kl}, but these coefficients (except for a_{11}, a_{22}, a_{33}) occupy different positions in (4) and (5).

The geometrical interpretation of those nine coefficients a_{kl} is very simple. Since $\mathbf{i}$ and $\mathbf{i}^*$ are unit vectors, it follows from (1) in Sec. 5.4 that $a_{11} = \mathbf{i}^* \cdot \mathbf{i}$ is the cosine of the angle between the positive x^* and x axes. Similarly, $a_{12} = \mathbf{i}^* \cdot \mathbf{j}$ is the cosine of the angle between the positive x^* and y axes, and so on.

The coefficients a_{kl} satisfy certain important relations which we shall now derive. By inserting (5′) into (4′) we find

$$(6) \qquad v_k{}^* = \sum_{l=1}^{3} a_{kl} v_l = \sum_{l=1}^{3} a_{kl} \sum_{m=1}^{3} a_{ml} v_m{}^* = \sum_{m=1}^{3} v_m{}^* \left(\sum_{l=1}^{3} a_{kl} a_{ml} \right),$$

where $k = 1, 2, 3$. For example, if $k = 1$, this becomes

$$v_1{}^* = v_1{}^* \left(\sum_{l=1}^{3} a_{1l} a_{1l} \right) + v_2{}^* \left(\sum_{l=1}^{3} a_{1l} a_{2l} \right) + v_3{}^* \left(\sum_{l=1}^{3} a_{1l} a_{3l} \right).$$

In order that this relation hold for any vector $\mathbf{v} = v_1{}^* \mathbf{i}^* + v_2{}^* \mathbf{j}^* + v_3{}^* \mathbf{k}^*$, the first sum must be 1 and the other two sums must be zero. For $k = 2$ and $k = 3$ the situation is similar. Consequently, (6) holds for any vector if, and only if,

$$(7) \qquad \sum_{l=1}^{3} a_{kl} a_{ml} = \begin{cases} 0 & (k \neq m) \\ 1 & (k = m) \end{cases}.$$

Using the so-called *Kronecker*[11] *symbol* or **Kronecker delta**

$$\delta_{km} = \begin{cases} 0 & (k \neq m) \\ 1 & (k = m), \end{cases}$$

we may write (7) in the form

$$(7') \qquad \sum_{l=1}^{3} a_{kl} a_{ml} = \delta_{km} \qquad\qquad (k, m = 1, 2, 3).$$

Forming three vectors with components

$$a_{11}, a_{12}, a_{13} \qquad a_{21}, a_{22}, a_{23} \qquad a_{31}, a_{32}, a_{33}$$

we see that the left side of (7′) is the scalar product of two of these vectors, and (7′) implies that these vectors are orthogonal unit vectors. Hence their scalar triple product has the value $+1$ or -1; that is,

$$(8) \qquad \begin{vmatrix} a_{11} & a_{12} & a_{13} \\ a_{21} & a_{22} & a_{23} \\ a_{31} & a_{32} & a_{33} \end{vmatrix} = \pm 1.$$

We mention, without proof, that if both coordinate systems under consideration are right-handed (or both left-handed), then the determinant has the value $+1$, whereas if one system is right-handed and the other left-handed, the determinant has the value -1. We may now sum up our result as follows.

[11] LEOPOLD KRONECKER (1823–1891), German mathematician, who made important contributions to algebra and the theory of numbers.

Theorem 1. *The components* v_1, v_2, v_3 *and* $v_1{}^*, v_2{}^*, v_3{}^*$ *of any vector* **v** *with respect to any two Cartesian coordinate systems can be obtained from each other by means of* (4) *and* (5), *where the coefficients* a_{kl} *are given by* (3) *and satisfy* (7) *and* (8).

From our consideration of vector components we may now immediately obtain the formulas for the transformation of a Cartesian coordinate system into any other such system as follows.

If the xyz and $x^*y^*z^*$ coordinate systems have the same origin, then **v** may be bound at the origin and regarded as the position vector of its terminal point Q. If (x, y, z) and (x^*, y^*, z^*) are the coordinates of Q with respect to the two coordinate systems, then in (4) and (5)

$$v_1 = x,\ v_2 = y,\ v_3 = z \quad \text{and} \quad v_1{}^* = x^*,\ v_2{}^* = y^*,\ v_3{}^* = z^*.$$

Consequently, (4) and (5), written in terms of x, y, z and x^*, y^*, z^* instead of v_1, v_2, v_3 and $v_1{}^*, v_2{}^*, v_3{}^*$, represent the transformations between those two coordinate systems with common origin.

The most general transformation of a Cartesian coordinate system into another such system may be decomposed into a transformation of the type just considered and a translation. Under a translation, corresponding coordinates differ merely by a constant. We thus obtain

Theorem 2. *The transformation of any Cartesian xyz-coordinate system into any other Cartesian $x^*y^*z^*$-coordinate system is of the form*

(9)
$$x^* = a_{11}x + a_{12}y + a_{13}z + b_1$$
$$y^* = a_{21}x + a_{22}y + a_{23}z + b_2$$
$$z^* = a_{31}x + a_{32}y + a_{33}z + b_3$$

and conversely

(10)
$$x = a_{11}x^* + a_{21}y^* + a_{31}z^* + c_1$$
$$y = a_{12}x^* + a_{22}y^* + a_{32}z^* + c_2$$
$$z = a_{13}x^* + a_{23}y^* + a_{33}z^* + c_3$$

where the coefficients a_{kl} *are given by* (3) *and satisfy* (7) *and* (8), *and* b_1, b_2, b_3, c_1, c_2, c_3 *are constants.*

Important applications of our results will be considered in the following two sections.

PROBLEMS

1. Derive (5).

2. Interpret all coefficients a_{kl} in (4′) geometrically.

Determine the constants a_{kl} and b_k such that (9) represents:

3. A translation which carries the origin into the point $(1, 3, -4)$

4. A translation which carries the point $(1, -1, 2)$ into the point $(0, -3, 5)$

5. A rotation about the x-axis through an angle ϕ

6. A rotation about the z-axis through an angle γ

7. A rotation such that the positive x^*, y^*, z^* axes coincide with the positive y, z, x axes, respectively

8. A reflection in the yz-plane.

9. What are the values of the determinant (8) in Probs. 3–8?

10. From (1), Sec. 5.4, it follows that the value of a scalar product is independent of the particular choice of Cartesian coordinates. Using (4) or (5) in this section, show that this follows also from (8), Sec. 5.4.

5.18 DIVERGENCE OF A VECTOR FIELD

Let $\mathbf{v}(x, y, z)$ be a differentiable vector function, where x, y, z are Cartesian coordinates in space, and let v_1, v_2, v_3 be the components of $\mathbf{v}$. Then the function

$$
\textbf{(1)} \qquad \operatorname{div} \mathbf{v} = \frac{\partial v_1}{\partial x} + \frac{\partial v_2}{\partial y} + \frac{\partial v_3}{\partial z}
$$

is called the **divergence** *of* $\mathbf{v}$ or the *divergence of the vector field defined by* $\mathbf{v}$. Another common notation for the divergence of $\mathbf{v}$ is $\nabla \cdot \mathbf{v}$,

$$
\operatorname{div} \mathbf{v} = \nabla \cdot \mathbf{v} = \left(\frac{\partial}{\partial x} \mathbf{i} + \frac{\partial}{\partial y} \mathbf{j} + \frac{\partial}{\partial z} \mathbf{k} \right) \cdot (v_1 \mathbf{i} + v_2 \mathbf{j} + v_3 \mathbf{k})
$$

$$
= \frac{\partial v_1}{\partial x} + \frac{\partial v_2}{\partial y} + \frac{\partial v_3}{\partial z},
$$

with the understanding that the "product" $\dfrac{\partial}{\partial x} v_1$ in the scalar product means the partial derivative $\partial v_1 / \partial x$, etc. This is a convenient notation, but nothing more. Note that $\nabla \cdot \mathbf{v}$ means the scalar div $\mathbf{v}$ while ∇f means the vector grad f defined in Sec. 5.16.

We shall see later that the divergence has an important physical meaning. Clearly the values of a function which characterizes a physical or geometrical property must be independent of the particular choice of coordinates; that is, those values must be invariant with respect to coordinate transformations.

Theorem 1. *The divergence is a scalar function; that is, the values of* div $\mathbf{v}$ *depend only on the points in space (and, of course, on* $\mathbf{v}$) *but not on the particular choice of the coordinates in* (1), *so that with respect to other*

Cartesian coordinates x^*, y^*, z^* *and corresponding components* v_1^*, v_2^*, v_3^* *of* **v** *the function* div **v** *is given by*

(2) $$\text{div } \mathbf{v} = \frac{\partial v_1^*}{\partial x^*} + \frac{\partial v_2^*}{\partial y^*} + \frac{\partial v_3^*}{\partial z^*}.$$

Proof. We shall derive (2) from (1). To simplify our formulas in this proof, we adopt the notation

$$x_1 = x, \quad x_2 = y, \quad x_3 = z \quad \text{and} \quad x_1^* = x^*, \quad x_2^* = y^*, \quad x_3^* = z^*.$$

Using this notation, formula (9) in Sec. 5.17 may be written in the short form

(3) $$x_k^* = \sum_{l=1}^{3} a_{kl} x_l + b_k \qquad (k = 1, 2, 3).$$

By applying the chain rule for functions of several variables (cf. Sec. 5.15) we obtain

(4) $$\frac{\partial v_l}{\partial x_l} = \sum_{k=1}^{3} \frac{\partial v_l}{\partial x_k^*} \frac{\partial x_k^*}{\partial x_l}.$$

In this sum, $\partial x_k^*/\partial x_l = a_{kl}$, as follows from (3). Furthermore, by (5′) in Sec. 5.17,

$$v_l = \sum_{m=1}^{3} a_{ml} v_m^*.$$

By differentiating this we have

$$\frac{\partial v_l}{\partial x_k^*} = \sum_{m=1}^{3} a_{ml} \frac{\partial v_m^*}{\partial x_k^*}.$$

If we substitute these expressions into (4) we obtain

$$\frac{\partial v_l}{\partial x_l} = \sum_{k=1}^{3} \sum_{m=0}^{3} a_{ml} \frac{\partial v_m^*}{\partial x_k^*} a_{kl} \qquad l = 1, 2, 3.$$

By adding these three formulas it follows that

$$\text{div } \mathbf{v} = \sum_{l=1}^{3} \frac{\partial v_l}{\partial x_l} = \sum_{k=1}^{3} \sum_{m=1}^{3} \sum_{l=1}^{3} a_{kl} a_{ml} \frac{\partial v_m^*}{\partial x_k^*}.$$

Because of (7′) in Sec. 5.17, this reduces to

$$\text{div } \mathbf{v} = \sum_{k=1}^{3} \sum_{m=1}^{3} \delta_{km} \frac{\partial v_m^*}{\partial x_k^*} = \frac{\partial v_1^*}{\partial x_1^*} + \frac{\partial v_2^*}{\partial x_2^*} + \frac{\partial v_3^*}{\partial x_3^*}.$$

We see that the expression on the right is identical with that in (2), and the proof is complete.

If $f(x, y, z)$ is a twice differentiable scalar function, then

$$\operatorname{grad} f = \frac{\partial f}{\partial x}\,\mathbf{i} + \frac{\partial f}{\partial y}\,\mathbf{j} + \frac{\partial f}{\partial z}\,\mathbf{k}$$

and by (1),

$$\operatorname{div}(\operatorname{grad} f) = \frac{\partial^2 f}{\partial x^2} + \frac{\partial^2 f}{\partial y^2} + \frac{\partial^2 f}{\partial z^2}.$$

The expression on the right is the Laplacian of f (cf. Sec. 5.16). Thus

(5) $\operatorname{div}(\operatorname{grad} f) = \nabla^2 f.$

Example 1. The gravitational force **p** in Ex. 4, Sec. 5.16, is the gradient of the scalar function $f(x, y, z) = c/r$, which satisfies Laplace's equation $\nabla^2 f = 0$. According to (5), this means that div $\mathbf{p} = 0$ $(r > 0)$.

The following example, taken from hydrodynamics, may serve as an introductory illustration of the physical significance of the divergence of a vector field. A more detailed physical interpretation of the divergence will be given later (in Sec. 6.9).

Example 2 (Motion of a compressible fluid). We consider the motion of a fluid in a region R having no *sources* or *sinks* in R, that is, no points at which fluid is produced or disappears. The concept of *fluid state* is meant to cover also gases and vapors. Fluids in the restricted sense, or *liquids*, have small compressibility which can be neglected in many problems, while gases and vapors have consider-able compressibility; that is, their density

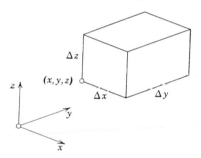

Fig. 170. Physical interpretation of the divergence.

ρ ($=$ mass per unit volume) depends on the coordinates x, y, z in space (and may depend on the time t). We assume that our fluid is compressible.

We consider the flow through a small rectangular parallelepiped W of dimensions[12] Δx, Δy, Δz with edges parallel to the coordinate axes (Fig. 170). W has the volume $\Delta V = \Delta x \Delta y \Delta z$. Let

$$\mathbf{v} = v_1\mathbf{i} + v_2\mathbf{j} + v_3\mathbf{k}$$

be the velocity vector of the motion. We set

(6) $\mathbf{u} = \rho\mathbf{v} = u_1\mathbf{i} + u_2\mathbf{j} + u_3\mathbf{k}$

and assume that **u** and **v** are continuously differentiable vector functions of x, y, z, and t. Let us calculate the change in the mass included in W by con-sidering the **flux** across the boundary, that is, the total loss of mass leaving W per unit time. Consider the flow through the left-hand face of W, whose area is $\Delta x \Delta z$. The components v_1 and v_3 of **v** are parallel to that face and contribute

---

[12] It is a standard usage to indicate small quantities by Δ; this has, of course, nothing to do with the Laplacian.

nothing to that flow. Hence the mass of fluid entering through that face during a short time interval Δt is given approximately by

$$(\rho v_2)_y \Delta x \Delta z \Delta t = u_2(y) \Delta x \Delta z \Delta t$$

where the subscript y indicates that this expression refers to the left-hand face. The mass of fluid leaving W through the opposite face during the same time interval is approximately $u_2(y + \Delta y) \Delta x \Delta z \Delta t$. The difference

$$\Delta u_2 \Delta x \Delta z \Delta t = \frac{\Delta u_2}{\Delta y} \Delta V \Delta t \qquad [\Delta u_2 = u_2(y + \Delta y) - u_2(y)]$$

is the approximate loss of mass. Two similar expressions are obtained by considering the other two pairs of parallel faces of W. If we add these three expressions, we find that the total loss of mass in W during the time interval Δt is approximately

$$\left(\frac{\Delta u_1}{\Delta x} + \frac{\Delta u_2}{\Delta y} + \frac{\Delta u_3}{\Delta z} \right) \Delta V \Delta t$$

where

$$\Delta u_1 = u_1(x + \Delta x) - u_1(x) \qquad \text{and} \qquad \Delta u_3 = u_3(z + \Delta z) - u_3(z).$$

This loss of mass in W is caused by the time rate of change of the density and is thus equal to

$$-\frac{\partial \rho}{\partial t} \Delta V \Delta t.$$

If we equate both expressions, divide the resulting equation by $\Delta V \Delta t$, and let Δx, Δy, Δz, and Δt approach zero, then we obtain

$$\text{div } \mathbf{u} = \text{div } (\rho \mathbf{v}) = -\frac{\partial \rho}{\partial t}$$

or

(7) $$\frac{\partial \rho}{\partial t} + \text{div } (\rho \mathbf{v}) = 0.$$

This important relation is called the *condition for the conservation of mass* or the **continuity equation** *of a compressible fluid flow.*

If the flow is *steady,* that is, independent of time t, then $\partial \rho / \partial t = 0$, and the continuity equation is

(8) $$\text{div } (\rho \mathbf{v}) = 0.$$

If the fluid is incompressible, then the density ρ is constant, and (8) becomes

(9) $$\text{div } \mathbf{v} = 0.$$

This relation is known as the **condition of incompressibility.** It expresses the fact that the balance of outflow and inflow for a given volume element is zero at any time. Clearly the assumption that the flow has no sources or sinks in R is essential to our argument.

PROBLEMS

1. Is it obvious from (1) that div $\mathbf{v}$ is a scalar?

Find the divergence of the following vector functions.

2. $x\mathbf{i} + 2y\mathbf{j} + z\mathbf{k}$ **3.** $xyz(\mathbf{i} + \mathbf{j} + \mathbf{k})$

4. $(x - y)^2\mathbf{i} + z^2\mathbf{j} + xz\mathbf{k}$ **5.** $(x\mathbf{i} + y\mathbf{j})/(x^2 + y^2)$

6. $x^2\mathbf{i} + y^2\mathbf{j} + z^2\mathbf{k}$ **7.** $(x\mathbf{i} + y\mathbf{j} + z\mathbf{k})/(x^2 + y^2 + z^2)^{3/2}$

8. $\cos x \cosh y\, \mathbf{i} + \sin x \sinh y\, \mathbf{j}$ **9.** $(3x^2 + 6xz + 3z^2)\mathbf{i}$

10. Show that div (grad f) $= \nabla^2 f$.

11. Show that div $(f\mathbf{v}) = f$ div $\mathbf{v} + \mathbf{v} \cdot \nabla f$.

Using the result of Prob. 11, find the divergence of

12. $(x\mathbf{i} + y\mathbf{j} + z\mathbf{k})/(x^2 + y^2 + z^2)^{3/2}$ **13.** $e^x(\sin y\, \mathbf{i} + \cos y\, \mathbf{j})$

14. Show that div $(f\nabla g) = f\nabla^2 g + \nabla f \cdot \nabla g$.

15. Find div $(f\nabla g) -$ div $(g\nabla f)$.

16. Let $f = a_1 x^2 + a_2 y^2 + a_3 z^2 + b_1 yz + b_2 xz + b_3 xy$, where $a_1, \cdots, b_3$ are constants. Show that div $(\nabla f) = 0$ if, and only if, $a_1 + a_2 + a_3 = 0$.

17. Verify the result in Ex. 1 by direct calculation.

18. Show that the continuity equation (7) may be written

$$\frac{\partial \rho}{\partial t} + \rho \text{ div } \mathbf{v} + \mathbf{v} \cdot \nabla \rho = 0.$$

Find the directional derivative of div $\mathbf{u}$ at the point P:(2, 2, 1) in the direction of the outer normal to the sphere $x^2 + y^2 + z^2 = 9$ where

19. $\mathbf{u} = x^5\mathbf{i} + y^5\mathbf{j} + z^5\mathbf{k}$ **20.** $\mathbf{u} = x^2 z\mathbf{i} + xy^2\mathbf{j} + yz^2\mathbf{k}$

21. Consider a steady flow whose velocity vector is $\mathbf{v} = y\mathbf{i}$. Show that it has the following properties. The flow is incompressible. The particles which at time $t = 0$ are in the cube bounded by the planes $x = 0$, $x = 1$, $y = 0$, $y = 1$, $z = 0$, $z = 1$ occupy at $t = 1$ the volume 1.

22. Consider a steady flow having the velocity $\mathbf{v} = x\mathbf{i}$. Show that the individual particles have the position vectors $\mathbf{r}(t) = c_1 e^t\mathbf{i} + c_2\mathbf{j} + c_3\mathbf{k}$ where c_1, c_2, c_3 are constants, the flow is compressible, and e is the volume occupied by the particles which at $t = 0$ fill the cube in Prob. 21.

5.19   CURL OF A VECTOR FIELD

Let x, y, z be right-handed Cartesian coordinates in space, and let

$$\mathbf{v}(x, y, z) = v_1\mathbf{i} + v_2\mathbf{j} + v_3\mathbf{k}$$

be a differentiable vector function. Then the function

(1)
$$\text{curl } \mathbf{v} = \nabla \times \mathbf{v} = \begin{vmatrix} \mathbf{i} & \mathbf{j} & \mathbf{k} \\ \dfrac{\partial}{\partial x} & \dfrac{\partial}{\partial y} & \dfrac{\partial}{\partial z} \\ v_1 & v_2 & v_3 \end{vmatrix}$$

$$= \left(\frac{\partial v_3}{\partial y} - \frac{\partial v_2}{\partial z}\right)\mathbf{i} + \left(\frac{\partial v_1}{\partial z} - \frac{\partial v_3}{\partial x}\right)\mathbf{j} + \left(\frac{\partial v_2}{\partial x} - \frac{\partial v_1}{\partial y}\right)\mathbf{k}$$

is called the **curl** *of the vector function* $\mathbf{v}$ or the *curl of the vector field defined by* $\mathbf{v}$. In the case of a left-handed Cartesian coordinate system, the symbolic determinant in (1) is preceded by a minus sign, in agreement with (5) in Sec. 5.6.

Instead of curl $\mathbf{v}$ the notation rot $\mathbf{v}$ is also used in the literature.

Theorem 1. Curl $\mathbf{v}$ *is a vector.*

Proof. The definition (1) of the curl involves coordinates. We have to show that curl $\mathbf{v}$, having the appearance of a vector, has a magnitude and direction which is independent of the particular choice of Cartesian coordinates in space, or, what amounts to the same thing, we have to prove that the components of the curl, as defined by (1), with respect to different Cartesian coordinate systems are related by formulas of the form (4) or (5), Sec. 5.17, which are characteristic for vector components.

Let x, y, z and x^*, y^*, z^* be any two systems of right-handed Cartesian coordinates in space and let v_1, v_2, v_3 and v_1^*, v_2^*, v_3^*, respectively, be the components of $\mathbf{v}$ with respect to these coordinate systems. For the sake of simplicity we adopt the notation

$$x_1 = x, \quad x_2 = y, \quad x_3 = z \quad \text{and} \quad x_1^* = x^*, \quad x_2^* = y^*, \quad x_3^* = z^*.$$

Then the components of curl $\mathbf{v}$ in the $x_1 x_2 x_3$-system are

$$(2) \qquad c_1 = \frac{\partial v_3}{\partial x_2} - \frac{\partial v_2}{\partial x_3}, \quad c_2 = \frac{\partial v_1}{\partial x_3} - \frac{\partial v_3}{\partial x_1}, \quad c_3 = \frac{\partial v_2}{\partial x_1} - \frac{\partial v_1}{\partial x_2},$$

and with respect to the other coordinate system curl $\mathbf{v}$ has the components

$$(3) \quad c_1^* = \frac{\partial v_3^*}{\partial x_2^*} - \frac{\partial v_2^*}{\partial x_3^*}, \quad c_2^* = \frac{\partial v_1^*}{\partial x_3^*} - \frac{\partial v_3^*}{\partial x_1^*}, \quad c_3^* = \frac{\partial v_2^*}{\partial x_1^*} - \frac{\partial v_1^*}{\partial x_2^*}.$$

We have to show that these components are related by formulas of the form (5') Sec. 5.17, that is,

$$(4) \qquad\qquad c_l = \sum_{m=1}^{3} a_{ml} c_m^* \qquad\qquad l = 1, 2, 3.$$

We consider c_1. Since $\mathbf{v}$ is a vector we may apply (5'), Sec. 5.17, and have

$$v_2 = \sum_{m=1}^{3} a_{m2} v_m^*, \qquad v_3 = \sum_{m=1}^{3} a_{m3} v_m^*.$$

From this we obtain by differentiation

$$(5) \qquad c_1 = \frac{\partial v_3}{\partial x_2} - \frac{\partial v_2}{\partial x_3} = \sum_{m=1}^{3} \left(a_{m3} \frac{\partial v_m^*}{\partial x_2} - a_{m2} \frac{\partial v_m^*}{\partial x_3} \right).$$

The chain rule for functions of several variables yields

$$(6) \qquad \frac{\partial v_m^*}{\partial x_k} = \sum_{l=1}^{3} \frac{\partial v_m^*}{\partial x_l^*} \frac{\partial x_l^*}{\partial x_k} = \sum_{l=1}^{3} \frac{\partial v_m^*}{\partial x_l^*} a_{lk}$$

where the expression on the right follows from

$$x_l^* = \sum_{k=1}^{3} a_{lk} x_k + b_l$$

corresponding to (9), Sec. 5.17 (written in our present notation for the co-ordinates). By inserting (6) into (5) we find

$$c_1 = \sum_{m=1}^{3} \sum_{l=1}^{3} (a_{m3} a_{l2} - a_{m2} a_{l3}) \frac{\partial v_m^*}{\partial x_l^*}.$$

This double sum has nine terms. The three terms for which $m = l$ are equal to zero. Writing the remaining six terms at length, we have

$$c_1 = (a_{33} a_{22} - a_{32} a_{23})\left(\frac{\partial v_3^*}{\partial x_2^*} - \frac{\partial v_2^*}{\partial x_3^*}\right) + (a_{13} a_{32} - a_{12} a_{33})\left(\frac{\partial v_1^*}{\partial x_3^*} - \frac{\partial v_3^*}{\partial x_1^*}\right)$$

$$+ (a_{23} a_{12} - a_{22} a_{13})\left(\frac{\partial v_2^*}{\partial x_1^*} - \frac{\partial v_1^*}{\partial x_2^*}\right).$$

From (3) we see that this may be written

(7) $\quad c_1 = (a_{33} a_{22} - a_{32} a_{23}) c_1^* + (a_{13} a_{32} - a_{12} a_{33}) c_2^* + (a_{23} a_{12} - a_{22} a_{13}) c_3^*.$

Using (3) in Sec. 5.17 and Lagrange's identity in Sec. 5.8 we find

$$a_{33} a_{22} - a_{32} a_{23} = (\mathbf{k}^* \cdot \mathbf{k})(\mathbf{j}^* \cdot \mathbf{j}) - (\mathbf{k}^* \cdot \mathbf{j})(\mathbf{j}^* \cdot \mathbf{k}) = (\mathbf{k}^* \times \mathbf{j}^*) \cdot (\mathbf{k} \times \mathbf{j}).$$

Since both coordinate systems are right-handed, it follows that

(8) $\qquad\qquad \mathbf{k}^* \times \mathbf{j}^* = -\mathbf{i}^* \qquad$ and $\qquad \mathbf{k} \times \mathbf{j} = -\mathbf{i}.$

Therefore,

$$a_{33} a_{22} - a_{32} a_{23} = \mathbf{i}^* \cdot \mathbf{i} = a_{11}.$$

In a similar fashion we obtain the corresponding formulas

$$a_{13} a_{32} - a_{12} a_{33} = a_{21} \qquad \text{and} \qquad a_{23} a_{12} - a_{22} a_{13} = a_{31}.$$

Equation (7) thus takes the form

$$c_1 = a_{11} c_1^* + a_{21} c_2^* + a_{31} c_3^*$$

which is (4) with $l = 1$. The other two formulas (4) can be proved by the same argument.

If the $x_1 x_2 x_3$-coordinate system is left-handed, then, instead of (8),

$$\mathbf{k} \times \mathbf{j} = \mathbf{i},$$

etc., but in (1) there is then a minus sign in front of the determinant. This proves that curl $\mathbf{v}$ is a vector also in this case.

The curl plays an important role in many applications. Its significance will be explained in more detail in Sec. 6.11. Now we confine ourselves to some simple examples and remarks.

Example 1 (Rotation of a rigid body). We have seen in Ex. 3, Sec. 5.6, that a rotation of a right body B about a fixed axis in space can be described by a vector **w** of magnitude ω in the direction of the axis of rotation, where ω (> 0) is the angular speed of the rotation, and **w** is directed so that the rotation appears clockwise if we look in the direction of **w**. According to (7), Sec. 5.6, the velocity field of the rotation can be represented in the form

$$\mathbf{v} = \mathbf{w} \times \mathbf{r}$$

where **r** is the position vector of a moving point with respect to a Cartesian coordinate system having the origin on the axis of rotation. Let us choose right-handed Cartesian coordinates such that $\mathbf{w} = \omega\mathbf{k}$; that is, the axis of rotation is the z-axis. Then (cf. Ex. 3 in Sec. 5.9)

$$\mathbf{v} = \mathbf{w} \times \mathbf{r} = -\omega y\mathbf{i} + \omega x\mathbf{j},$$

and, therefore,

$$\operatorname{curl} \mathbf{v} = \begin{vmatrix} \mathbf{i} & \mathbf{j} & \mathbf{k} \\ \dfrac{\partial}{\partial x} & \dfrac{\partial}{\partial y} & \dfrac{\partial}{\partial z} \\ -\omega y & \omega x & 0 \end{vmatrix} = 2\omega\mathbf{k},$$

that is,

(9) $$\operatorname{curl} \mathbf{v} = 2\mathbf{w}.$$

Hence, in the case of a rotation of a rigid body, the curl of the velocity field has the direction of the axis of rotation, and its magnitude equals twice the angular speed ω of the rotation.

Note that our result does not depend on the particular choice of the Cartesian coordinate system, since we are dealing with vectors.

For any twice continuously differentiable scalar function f,

(10) $$\operatorname{curl} (\operatorname{grad} f) = \mathbf{0},$$

as can easily be verified by direct calculation. In words: *if a vector function is the gradient of a scalar function, its curl is the zero vector.* Since the curl characterizes the rotation in a field, we also say more briefly that *gradient fields describing a motion are irrotational.* (If such a field occurs in some other connection, not as a velocity field, it is usually called *conservative*; cf. at the end of Sec. 5.16.)

Example 2. The gravitational field in Ex. 4, Sec. 5.16, has curl $\mathbf{p} = \mathbf{0}$. The field in Ex. 1, this section, is not irrotational. A similar velocity field is obtained by stirring coffee in a cup.

For any twice continuously differentiable vector function **v**,

(11) $$\operatorname{div} (\operatorname{curl} \mathbf{v}) = 0,$$

as can readily be verified by direct calculation; that is, *if a vector function is the curl of another vector function, its divergence is identically zero.*

We finally mention two further useful relations. Granted sufficient differentiability, we have

$$\text{(12)} \qquad \text{curl}\,(f\mathbf{v}) = \text{grad}\,f \times \mathbf{v} + f\,\text{curl}\,\mathbf{v}$$

and

$$\text{(13)} \qquad \text{div}\,(\mathbf{u} \times \mathbf{v}) = \mathbf{v} \cdot \text{curl}\,\mathbf{u} - \mathbf{u} \cdot \text{curl}\,\mathbf{v}.$$

PROBLEMS

Find curl $\mathbf{v}$ where, with respect to right-handed Cartesian coordinates,

1. $\mathbf{v} = x\mathbf{i} + 3xy\mathbf{j}$
2. $\mathbf{v} = xyz\mathbf{i} - z\mathbf{j} + (x + y + z)\mathbf{k}$
3. $v = x\mathbf{i} + yz\mathbf{j} - (x^2 + z^2)\mathbf{k}$
4. $\mathbf{v} = z\mathbf{i} + x\mathbf{j} + y\mathbf{k}$
5. $\mathbf{v} = y^2\mathbf{i} + z^2\mathbf{j} + x^2\mathbf{k}$
6. $\mathbf{v} = yz\mathbf{i} + zx\mathbf{j} + xy\mathbf{k}$
7. $\mathbf{v} = e^x \sin y\,\mathbf{i} + e^x \cos y\,\mathbf{j}$
8. $\mathbf{v} = (x\mathbf{i} + y\mathbf{j} + z\mathbf{k})/(x^2 + y^2 + z^2)^{3/2}$

9. Consider the proof of Theorem 1 and prove (4) for $l = 2$ and $l = 3$.

10. With respect to right-handed Cartesian coordinates, let $\mathbf{u} = z\mathbf{i} + x\mathbf{j} + y\mathbf{k}$, $\mathbf{v} = (x - y)^2\mathbf{i} + (y - z)^2\mathbf{j} + (z - x)^2\mathbf{k}$, and $\mathbf{w} = 2xy\mathbf{i} + 4yz\mathbf{j} - xz\mathbf{k}$. Find curl $\mathbf{u}$, curl $\mathbf{v}$, curl $\mathbf{w}$, curl $(\mathbf{u} - \mathbf{v})$, curl $(\mathbf{u} \times \mathbf{w})$, grad $(\mathbf{u} \cdot \mathbf{v})$, and div $(\mathbf{u} \times \mathbf{v})$.

11. Verify by direct calculation that, in Ex. 2, curl $\mathbf{p} = \mathbf{0}$.

12. Show that curl $(\mathbf{u} + \mathbf{v}) = $ curl $\mathbf{u} + $ curl $\mathbf{v}$.

13. Verify (10) for $f = 1/\sqrt{x^2 + y^2 + z^2}$. Prove (10) by direct calculation.

14. Verify (11) for $\mathbf{v} = xyz^3\mathbf{i} + x^3yz\mathbf{j} + xy^3z\mathbf{k}$. Prove (11).

15. Verify (12) for $f = (x^2 + y^2 + z^2)^{-3/2}$, $\mathbf{v} = x\mathbf{i} + y\mathbf{j} + z\mathbf{k}$. Prove (12).

16. Verify (13) for $\mathbf{u} = xyz^2\mathbf{i} + x^2yz\mathbf{j} + xy^2z\mathbf{k}$, $\mathbf{v} = z\mathbf{i}$. Prove (13).

17. Using (12) and (13) show that div $(g\nabla f \times f\nabla g) = 0$.

18. A steady fluid motion has velocity $\mathbf{v} = x\mathbf{i} + y\mathbf{j}$. Find curl $\mathbf{v}$. Is the motion incompressible? Find the paths of the particles.

19. Same situation and questions as in Prob. 18 when $\mathbf{v} = -2y\mathbf{i} + 2x\mathbf{j}$.

20. Same situation and questions as in Prob. 18 when $\mathbf{v} = y^2\mathbf{i}$.

chapter 6

LINE AND SURFACE INTEGRALS. INTEGRAL THEOREMS

In this chapter we shall define line integrals and surface integrals, and consider some important applications of such integrals which occur frequently in connection with physical and engineering problems. We shall see that a line integral is a natural generalization of a definite integral, and a surface integral is a generalization of a double integral.

Line integrals can be transformed into double integrals (Sec. 6.4) or into surface integrals (Sec. 6.10), and conversely. Triple integrals can be transformed into surface integrals (Sec. 6.8). These transformations are of great practical importance. The corresponding formulas of Gauss, Green, and Stokes serve as powerful tools in many applications as well as in theoretical problems. We shall see that they also lead to a better understanding of the physical meaning of the divergence and the curl of a vector function.

Prerequisites for this chapter: elementary integral calculus, vector analysis (Chap. 5).

Sections which may be omitted in a shorter course: 6.6, 6.9, 6.11.

References: Appendix 1, Part C.

Answers to problems: Appendix 2.

6.1 LINE INTEGRAL

The concept of a line integral is a simple and natural generalization of the concept of a definite integral

(1) $$\int_a^b f(x)\,dx.$$

In (1) we integrate along the x-axis, and the integrand $f(x)$ is a (single-valued) function defined at each point between a and b. We shall see that, in the case of a line integral, we integrate along a curve in space (or in the plane), and the integrand is a single-valued function defined at the points of that curve.

The way of defining a line integral is quite similar to the familiar way of defining a definite integral known from calculus. We may proceed as follows.

We consider a curve C in space and orient C by choosing one of the two directions along C as the *positive direction*; the opposite direction along C is then called the *negative direction*. Let A be the initial point and B the terminal point of C under the chosen orientation. (These points may coincide as in Fig. 171b; then C is closed.)

We may now represent C by a parametric representation

(2) $\mathbf{r}(s) = x(s)\mathbf{i} + y(s)\mathbf{j} + z(s)\mathbf{k}$ $(a \leq s \leq b)$

where s is the arc length of C (cf. Sec. 5.12) and A and B correspond to $s = a$ and $s = b$, respectively.

We assume that $\mathbf{r}(s)$ is continuous and has a continuous first derivative which is different from the zero vector for all s under consideration. Then C has a unique tangent at each of its points. A curve satisfying these assumptions will be called a **smooth curve**.

Let $f(x, y, z)$ be a given function which is defined (at least) at each point of C, and is a continuous function of s. Instead of $f\,[x(s), y(s), z(s)]$, we simply write $f(P)$ where P is the point on C with coordinates $x(s), y(s), z(s)$.

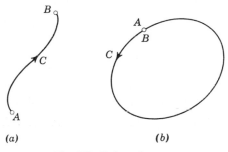

(a)   (b)

Fig. 171. Oriented curve.

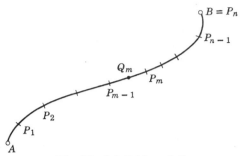

Fig. 172. Subdivision of C.

We subdivide C into n portions in an arbitrary manner (Fig. 172); let $P_0(=A)$, P_1, $\cdots$, P_{n-1}, $P_n(=B)$ be the end points of these portions, and let

$$s_0(=a) < s_1 < s_2 < \cdots < s_n(=b)$$

be the corresponding values of s. Then we choose an arbitrary point on each portion, say, a point Q_1 between P_0 and P_1, a point Q_2 between P_1 and P_2, etc., and form the sum

$$J_n = \sum_{m=1}^{n} f(Q_m) \Delta s_m$$

where

$$\Delta s_m = s_m - s_{m-1}.$$

This we do for each $n = 2, 3, \cdots$ in a completely independent manner, but such that the greatest Δs_m approaches zero as n approaches infinity. In this way we obtain a sequence of real numbers $J_2, J_3, \cdots$. The limit of this sequence is called the **line integral** *of f along C from A to B*, and is denoted by

$$\int_C f(P)\, ds \qquad \text{or} \qquad \int_C f(x, y, z)\, ds.$$

The curve C is called the *path of integration*.

Since, by assumption, f is continuous and C is smooth, that limit exists and is independent of the choice of those subdivisions and points Q_m. In fact, the position of a point P on C is determined by the corresponding value of the arc length s; since A and B correspond to $s = a$ and $s = b$, respectively, we thus have

$$\int_C f(P)\, ds = \int_a^b f(s)\, ds.$$

Hence the line integral is equal to the definite integral on the right, for which the statement holds, as is known from calculus.

Throughout this book all paths of integration for line integrals will be assumed to be **piecewise smooth**, *that is, will consist of finitely many smooth curves.*

From the definition it follows that familiar properties of ordinary definite integrals are equally valid for line integrals:

(3)

$$(a) \quad \int_C kf \, ds = k \int_C f \, ds \qquad (k \text{ constant})$$

$$(b) \quad \int_C (f + g) \, ds = \int_C f \, ds + \int_C g \, ds$$

$$(c) \quad \int_C f \, ds = \int_{C_1} f \, ds + \int_{C_2} f \, ds$$

where in (3c) the path C is subdivided into two arcs C_1 and C_2 which have the same orientation as C (Fig. 173). In (3b) the orientation of C is the same in all three integrals. If the sense of integration along C is reversed, the value of the integral is multiplied by -1.

Examples will be considered in the following sections.

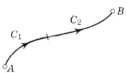

Fig. 173. Formula (3c).

6.2 EVALUATION OF LINE INTEGRALS

To evaluate a line integral we first have to write it as an ordinary definite integral. This is quite simple and can be done by using the given representation of the path of integration C.

If C is represented in the form

$$\mathbf{r}(s) = x(s)\mathbf{i} + y(s)\mathbf{j} + z(s)\mathbf{k} \qquad (a \leq s \leq b),$$

[cf. (2) in Sec. 6.1], then we immediately have

$$\int_C f(x, y, z) \, ds = \int_a^b f[x(s), y(s), z(s)] \, ds,$$

the integral on the right being a definite integral.

In most cases the representation of C will be of the form

(1)
$$\mathbf{r}(t) = x(t)\mathbf{i} + y(t)\mathbf{j} + z(t)\mathbf{k} \qquad (t_0 \leq t \leq t_1)$$

or may easily be converted to this form; here, t denotes any parameter, and $\mathbf{r}(t)$ is continuous and has a continuous derivative. Then, using the familiar substitution formula for definite integrals, we obtain

$$\int_a^b f[x(s), y(s), z(s)] \, ds = \int_{t_0}^{t_1} f[x(t), y(t), z(t)] \frac{ds}{dt} \, dt.$$

Therefore, if C is represented in the form (1), then

(2) $$\int_C f(x, y, z)\, ds = \int_{t_0}^{t_1} f[x(t),\, y(t),\, z(t)]\, \frac{ds}{dt}\, dt$$

where, according to (3) in Sec. 5.12,

$$\frac{ds}{dt} = \sqrt{\dot{\mathbf{r}} \cdot \dot{\mathbf{r}}} = \sqrt{\dot{x}^2 + \dot{y}^2 + \dot{z}^2}.$$

Example 1. Evaluate $\displaystyle\int_C xy^3\, ds$, where C is the segment of the line $y = 2x$ in the xy-plane from A: $(-1, -2, 0)$ to B: $(1, 2, 0)$.

Representing C in the form[1]

$$\mathbf{r}(t) = t\mathbf{i} + 2t\mathbf{j} \qquad\qquad (-1 \leq t \leq 1)$$

we have

$$\dot{\mathbf{r}} = \mathbf{i} + 2\mathbf{j} \quad \text{and} \quad \frac{ds}{dt} = \sqrt{\dot{\mathbf{r}} \cdot \dot{\mathbf{r}}} = \sqrt{5}.$$

On C, $xy^3 = t(2t)^3 = 8t^4$, and therefore

$$\int_C xy^3\, ds = 8\sqrt{5} \int_{-1}^{1} t^4\, dt = \frac{16}{\sqrt{5}} \approx 7.16.$$

Example 2. Evaluate $\displaystyle\int_C x^{-1}(y + z)\, ds$, where C is the arc of the circle $x^2 + y^2 = 4$ in the xy-plane from A: $(2, 0, 0)$ to B: $(\sqrt{2},\, \sqrt{2}, 0)$, cf. Fig. 174.

Representing C in the form

(3) $$\mathbf{r}(t) = 2\cos t\, \mathbf{i} + 2\sin t\, \mathbf{j} \qquad\qquad (0 \leq t \leq \pi/4),$$

we obtain $ds/dt = 2$. On C, we have $x^{-1}(y + z) = \dfrac{2\sin t}{2\cos t} = \tan t$. Therefore, by (2),

$$\int_C \frac{y + z}{x}\, ds = 2 \int_0^{\pi/4} \tan t\, dt = -2\ln(\cos t)\Big|_0^{\pi/4} = \ln 2.$$

Example 3. Evaluate $\displaystyle\int_C (x^2 + y^2 + z^2)^2\, ds$ where C is the arc of the circular helix (Sec. 5.11)

$$\mathbf{r}(t) = \cos t\, \mathbf{i} + \sin t\, \mathbf{j} + 3t\mathbf{k}$$

from A: $(1, 0, 0)$ to B: $(1, 0, 6\pi)$. We find $ds/dt = \sqrt{10}$. On C,

$$(x^2 + y^2 + z^2)^2 = [\cos^2 t + \sin^2 t + (3t)^2]^2 = (1 + 9t^2)^2.$$

Since C corresponds to $0 \leq t \leq 2\pi$, we thus have

$$\int_C (x^2 + y^2 + z^2)^2\, ds = \sqrt{10} \int_0^{2\pi} (1 + 9t^2)^2\, dt$$

$$= \sqrt{10}\, [2\pi + 6(2\pi)^3 + \tfrac{81}{5}(2\pi)^5] \approx 506\,400.$$

Line integrals which involve empirically given functions or lead to complicated definite integrals may be evaluated by using numerical or graphical methods of integration.

---

[1] Of course, since $x = t$ we may write x in place of t.

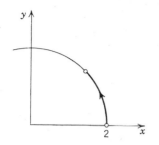

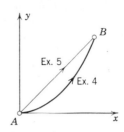

Fig. 174. Example 2.   **Fig. 175.** Paths in Examples 4 and 5.

In many applications the integrands of line integrals are of the form

$$g(x, y, z)\frac{dx}{ds}, \qquad g(x, y, z)\frac{dy}{ds}, \qquad \text{or} \qquad g(x, y, z)\frac{dz}{ds}$$

where dx/ds, dy/ds, and dz/ds are the derivatives of the functions occurring in the parametric representation of the path of integration. Then we simply write

(4) $$\int_C g(x, y, z)\frac{dx}{ds}\, ds = \int_C g(x, y, z)\, dx,$$

and similarly in the other two cases. For sums of these types of integrals along the same path C, we adopt the simplified notation

(5) $$\int_C f\, dx + \int_C g\, dy + \int_C h\, dz = \int_C (f\, dx + g\, dy + h\, dz).$$

Using the representation of C, we may eliminate two of the three independent variables in the integrand and then evaluate the resulting definite integral in which the remaining independent variable is the variable of integration.

Example 4. Evaluate the line integral $I = \int_C [x^2 y\, dx + (x - z)\, dy + xyz\, dz]$ where C is the arc of the parabola $y = x^2$ in the plane $z = 2$ from $A: (0, 0, 2)$ to $B: (1, 1, 2)$. Since $y = x^2$, we have $dy/dx = 2x$ or $dy = 2x\, dx$. Since $z = 2$ is constant, it follows that the integral of the last term in the integrand is zero. Thus

$$I = \int_0^1 [x^2 x^2\, dx + (x - 2)2x\, dx] = \int_0^1 (x^4 + 2x^2 - 4x)\, dx = -\tfrac{17}{15}.$$

Example 5. Evaluate the line integral I in Ex. 4 where C is the segment of the straight line $y = x$, $z = 2$ from $A: (0, 0, 2)$ to $B: (1, 1, 2)$. Now $dy = dx$, and

$$I = \int_0^1 (x^3 + x - 2)\, dx = -\tfrac{5}{4}.$$

In Ex. 4 and Ex. 5 the integrands and the end points of the paths are the same, but the values of I are different. This illustrates the important fact that, *in general, the value of a line integral of a given function depends not only on the end points but also on the geometric shape of the path of integration.* We shall consider this basic fact in Sec. 6.12.

In many cases the functions f, g, and h in (5) are the components v_1, v_2, and v_3, respectively, of a vector function

$$\mathbf{v} = v_1\mathbf{i} + v_2\mathbf{j} + v_3\mathbf{k}.$$

Then

$$v_1\,dx + v_2\,dy + v_3\,dz = \left(v_1\frac{dx}{ds} + v_2\frac{dy}{ds} + v_3\frac{dz}{ds}\right)ds,$$

the expression in parentheses being the scalar product of the vector $\mathbf{v}$ and the unit tangent vector

$$\frac{d\mathbf{r}}{ds} = \frac{dx}{ds}\mathbf{i} + \frac{dy}{ds}\mathbf{j} + \frac{dz}{ds}\mathbf{k} \qquad \text{(cf. Sec. 5.13)}$$

where $\mathbf{r}(s)$ represents the path of integration C. Therefore,

$$(6) \qquad \int_C (v_1\,dx + v_2\,dy + v_3\,dz) = \int_C \mathbf{v}\cdot\frac{d\mathbf{r}}{ds}\,ds.$$

This is sometimes written

$$\int_C \mathbf{v}\cdot\frac{d\mathbf{r}}{ds}\,ds = \int_C \mathbf{v}\cdot d\mathbf{r}$$

where

$$d\mathbf{r} = dx\mathbf{i} + dy\mathbf{j} + dz\mathbf{k},$$

but we should note that this is merely a convenient notation.

Example 6 (Work done by a force). Consider a particle on which a variable force $\mathbf{p}$ acts. Let the particle be displaced along a given path C in space. Then the work W done by $\mathbf{p}$ in this displacement is given by the line integral

$$(7) \qquad W = \int_C \mathbf{p}\cdot d\mathbf{r},$$

the integration being taken in the sense of the displacement. This definition of work is suggested by that in Ex. 1, Sec. 5.4, together with the definition of a line integral as the limit of a sum.

We may introduce the time t as the variable of integration. Then

$$d\mathbf{r} = \frac{d\mathbf{r}}{dt}\,dt = \mathbf{v}\,dt$$

where $\mathbf{v}$ is the velocity vector (cf. Sec. 5.14). Hence the line integral (7) becomes

$$(7') \qquad W = \int_{t_0}^{t_1} \mathbf{p}\cdot\mathbf{v}\,dt$$

where t_0 and t_1 are the initial and final values of t.

By Newton's second law (Sec. 2.6),

$$\mathbf{p} = m\ddot{\mathbf{r}} = m\dot{\mathbf{v}}$$

where m is the mass of the particle. By inserting this into (7') we obtain

$$W = \int_{t_0}^{t_1} m\dot{\mathbf{v}} \cdot \mathbf{v} \, dt = \int_{t_0}^{t_1} \frac{d}{dt}\left(\frac{m}{2}\mathbf{v} \cdot \mathbf{v}\right) dt = \int_{t_0}^{t_1} \frac{d}{dt}\left(\frac{m}{2}|\mathbf{v}|^2\right) dt = \frac{m}{2}|\mathbf{v}|^2 \Big|_{t_0}^{t_1};$$

that is, *the work done equals the gain in kinetic energy.* This is a basic law in mechanics.

We finally mention that for a line integral over a *closed* path C the symbol

$$\oint_C \qquad \left(\text{instead of } \int_C\right)$$

is sometimes used in the literature.

Example 7. Find the work done by the force $\mathbf{p} = x\mathbf{i} - z\mathbf{j} + 2y\mathbf{k}$ in the displacement along the closed path C consisting of the segments C_1, C_2, and C_3 shown in Fig. 176. We see that

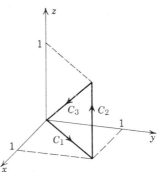

Fig. 176. Example 7.

$$\text{on } C_1, \ 0 \le x \le 1, \ y = x, \ z = 0, \ dy = dx, dz = 0,$$
$$\text{on } C_2, \ 0 \le z \le 1, \ x = 1, \ y = 1, \ dx = 0, dy = 0,$$
$$\text{on } C_3, \ 1 \ge x \ge 0, \ y = z = x, \ dy = dz = dx.$$

Therefore,

$$W = \oint (x \, dx - z \, dy + 2y \, dz) = \int_0^1 x \, dx + 2\int_0^1 dz + 2\int_1^0 x \, dx = \frac{3}{2}.$$

PROBLEMS

Evaluate $\int_C (x^2 + y^2) \, ds$ (orienting C so that the sense of integration becomes the positive sense on C):

1. Over the path $y = x$ from $(0, 0)$ to $(1, 1)$
2. Over the path $y = 3x$ from $(0, 0)$ to $(2, 6)$
3. Over the x-axis from $(0, 0)$ to $(1, 0)$ and then parallel to the y-axis from $(1, 0)$ to $(1, 1)$
4. Over the y-axis from $(0, 0)$ to $(0, 1)$ and then parallel to the x-axis from $(0, 1)$ to $(1, 1)$
5. Counterclockwise along the circle $x^2 + y^2 = 1$ from $(1, 0)$ to $(0, 1)$
6. Clockwise along the circle $x^2 + y^2 = 1$ from $(0, 1)$ to $(1, 0)$
7. Counterclockwise around the circle $x^2 + y^2 = 4$ from $(0, 2)$ to $(0, 2)$.

8. Show that $\int_C [xyz \, dx + (y - z)^2 \, dy + 2zx \, dz] = \dfrac{85}{84}$ where C is the curve $\mathbf{r}(t) = t\mathbf{i} + t^2\mathbf{j} + t^3\mathbf{k}$ from $(0, 0, 0)$ to $(1, 1, 1)$.

Evaluate $\int_C (y^2\, dx - x^2\, dy)$:

9. Along the straight line from $(0, 1)$ to $(1, 0)$

10. Counterclockwise along the circle $x^2 + y^2 = 1$ from $(0, 1)$ to $(1, 0)$

11. Counterclockwise along the circle $x^2 + y^2 = 1$ from $(1, 0)$ to $(0, 1)$

12. Counterclockwise around the circle $x^2 + y^2 = 1$ from $(0, 1)$ to $(0, 1)$

Find the work done by the force $\mathbf{p} = y^2\mathbf{i} - x^2\mathbf{j} + xyz\mathbf{k}$ in the displacement:

13. Along the x-axis from -1 to 1

14. Along the parabola $y = x^2$, $z = 1$, from $(0, 0, 1)$ to $(1, 1, 1)$

15. Along the cubical parabola $z = x^3$, $y = 2$, from $(0, 2, 0)$ to $(1, 2, 1)$

Find the work done by the force $\mathbf{p} = 2xy\mathbf{i} - 4y\mathbf{j} + \mathbf{k}$ in the displacement along a curve C from A to B, where

16. $C: y = 2x$, $z = 0$, $A:(0, 0, 0)$, $B:(3, 6, 0)$

17. $C: y = 2x$, $z = 0$, $A:(3, 6, 0)$, $B:(0, 0, 0)$

18. $C: y = 2x$, $z = 2$, $A:(0, 0, 2)$, $B:(3, 6, 2)$

19. $C: y = 2x$, $z = 2x$, $A:(0, 0, 0)$, $B:(3, 6, 6)$

20. $C: y = 2x^2/3$, $z = 0$, $A:(0, 0, 0)$, $B:(3, 6, 0)$

21. $C: x^2 + y^2 = 4$, $z = 0$, $A:(2, 0, 0)$, $B:(2, 0, 0)$

22. Let $f(x, y)$ be given by the values

(x, y)	$(0, 0)$	$(0.25, 0.25)$	$(0.5, 0.5)$	$(0.75, 0.75)$	$(1, 1)$
$f(x, y)$	1.0	1.5	1.7	1.5	1.0

and let C be the segment of the straight line $y = x$ from $(0, 0)$ to $(1, 1)$. Using the trapezoidal rule (Sec. 0.8), show that

$$\int_C f(x, y)\, ds \approx \frac{\sqrt{2}}{4}(0.5 + 1.5 + 1.7 + 1.5 + 0.5) = 2.015.$$

23. Let $\mathbf{p}$ be a vector function defined at all points of a curve C, and suppose that $|\mathbf{p}|$ is bounded, say, $|\mathbf{p}| < M$ on C, where M is some positive number. Show that

$$(8) \qquad\qquad \left| \int_C \mathbf{p} \cdot d\mathbf{r} \right| < Ml$$

where l is the length of C.

24. Using (8), find an upper bound for the absolute value of the work W done by the force $\mathbf{p} = x\mathbf{i} + y^2\mathbf{j}$ in the displacement along the straight line from $(0, 0, 0)$ to $(1, 1, 0)$. Find W by integration and compare the results.

6.3 DOUBLE INTEGRALS

In our further consideration we shall need the concept of a double integral. Although the reader will be familiar with double integrals from calculus, we shall now present a brief review.

In the case of a definite integral

$$\int_a^b f(x)\,dx$$

the integrand is a function $f(x)$ which exists for all x in an interval $a \leq x \leq b$ of the x-axis. In the case of a double integral the integrand will be a function $f(x, y)$ which is given for all (x, y) in a closed bounded[2] region R of the xy-plane.

The definition of the double integral is quite similar to that of the definite integral. We subdivide the region R by drawing parallels to the x and y axes (Fig. 177). We number those rectangles which are within R from 1 to n. In each such rectangle we choose a point, say, (x_k, y_k) in the kth rectangle, and then we form the sum

$$J_n = \sum_{k=1}^n f(x_k, y_k)\,\Delta A_k$$

where ΔA_k is the area of the kth rectangle. This we do for each positive integer n in a completely independent manner but so that the length of the maximum diagonal of the rectangles approaches zero as n approaches infinity. In this fashion we obtain a sequence of real numbers $J_1, J_2, \cdots$. Assuming that $f(x, y)$ is continuous in R and R is bounded by finitely many smooth curves (cf. Sec. 6.1) it can be shown[3] that the sequence converges and its limit is independent of the choice of subdivisions and corresponding points (x_k, y_k). This limit is called the **double integral** *of $f(x, y)$ over the region* R, and is denoted by the symbol

$$\iint_R f(x, y)\,dx\,dy.$$

From the definition it follows that double integrals enjoy properties which are quite similar to those of the definite integral. Let f and g be functions

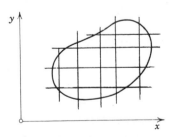

Fig. 177. Subdivision of R.

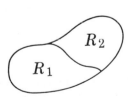

Fig. 178. Formula (1).

[2] "Closed" means that the boundary is part of the region, and "bounded" means that the region can be enclosed in a circle of sufficiently large radius.

[3] Cf. Ref. [A1] in Appendix 1.

of x and y, defined and continuous in a region R, then

$$\iint_R kf \, dx \, dy = k \iint_R f \, dx \, dy \qquad (k \text{ constant})$$

(1)
$$\iint_R (f + g) \, dx \, dy = \iint_R f \, dx \, dy + \iint_R g \, dx \, dy$$

$$\iint_R f \, dx \, dy = \iint_{R_1} f \, dx \, dy + \iint_{R_2} f \, dx \, dy \qquad (\text{cf. Fig. 178}).$$

Furthermore, there exists at least one point (x_0, y_0) in R such that

(2)
$$\iint_R f(x, y) \, dx \, dy = f(x_0, y_0)A,$$

where A is the area of R; this is called the **mean value theorem** *for double integrals.*

Double integrals over a region R may be evaluated by two successive integrations as follows.

Suppose that R can be described by inequalities of the form

$$a \leq x \leq b, \qquad g(x) \leq y \leq h(x)$$

(Fig. 179) so that $y = g(x)$ and $y = h(x)$ represent the boundary of R. Then

(3)
$$\iint_R f(x, y) \, dx \, dy = \int_a^b \left[\int_{g(x)}^{h(x)} f(x, y) \, dy \right] dx.$$

We first integrate the inner integral

$$\int_{g(x)}^{h(x)} f(x, y) \, dy.$$

In this definite integral, x plays the role of a parameter, and the result of the integration will be a function of x, say, $F(x)$. By integrating $F(x)$ over x from a to b we then obtain the value of the double integral in (3).

Similarly, if R can be described by inequalities of the form

$$c \leq y \leq d, \qquad p(y) \leq x \leq q(y)$$

(Fig. 180), then we obtain

(4)
$$\iint_R f(x, y) \, dx \, dy = \int_c^d \left[\int_{p(y)}^{q(y)} f(x, y) \, dx \right] dy;$$

we now integrate first over x and then the resulting function of y over y from c to d.

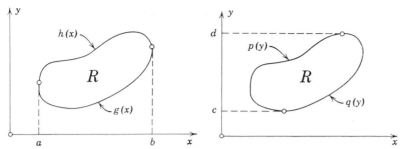

Fig. 179. Evaluation of a double integral. **Fig. 180.** Evaluation of a double integral.

If R cannot be represented by those inequalities, then we first subdivide R into suitable portions which have that property, integrate $f(x, y)$ over each portion separately, and finally add the results; this will give us the value of the double integral of $f(x, y)$ over that region R.

Double integrals have various geometrical and physical applications. For example, the **area** A of R is

$$A = \iint_R dx \, dy.$$

The **volume** V beneath the surface $z = f(x, y)$ (> 0) and above the region R in the xy-plane is (Fig. 181)

$$V = \iint_R f(x, y) \, dx \, dy,$$

because the term $f(x_k, y_k)\Delta A_k$ in J_n on p. 333 represents the volume of a rectangular parallelepiped with base ΔA_k and altitude $f(x_k, y_k)$.

Let $f(x, y)$ be the density ($=$ mass per unit area) of a distribution of mass in the xy-plane. Then the total mass M in R is

$$M = \iint_R f(x, y) \, dx \, dy,$$

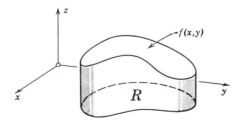

Fig. 181. Double integral as volume.

the **center of gravity** of the mass in R has the coordinates

$$\bar{x} = \frac{1}{M} \iint\limits_R xf(x, y) \, dx \, dy \quad \text{and} \quad \bar{y} = \frac{1}{M} \iint\limits_R yf(x, y) \, dx \, dy,$$

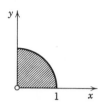

the **moments of inertia** I_x and I_y of the mass in R about the x and y axes, respectively, are

$$I_x = \iint\limits_R y^2 f(x, y) \, dx \, dy, \qquad I_y = \iint\limits_R x^2 f(x, y) \, dx \, dy,$$

and the *polar moment of inertia* about the origin is

Fig. 182. Example 1.

$$I_0 = I_x + I_y = \iint\limits_R (x^2 + y^2) f(x, y) \, dx \, dy.$$

Example 1. Let $f(x, y) = 1$ be the density of mass in the quarter-circle $R: 0 \leq y \leq \sqrt{1 - x^2}, \, 0 \leq x \leq 1$ (Fig. 182). Find the center of gravity and the moments of inertia I_x, I_y, and I_0. The total mass in R is

$$M = \iint\limits_R dx \, dy = \int_0^1 \left[\int_0^{\sqrt{1-x^2}} dy \right] dx = \int_0^1 \sqrt{1 - x^2} \, dx = \int_0^{\pi/2} \cos^2 \theta \, d\theta = \frac{\pi}{4}$$

$$(x = \sin \theta),$$

which is the area of R. The coordinates of the center of gravity are

$$\bar{x} = \frac{4}{\pi} \iint\limits_R x \, dx \, dy = \frac{4}{\pi} \int_0^1 \left[\int_0^{\sqrt{1-x^2}} x \, dy \right] dx = \frac{4}{\pi} \int_0^1 x \sqrt{1 - x^2} \, dx$$

$$= -\frac{4}{\pi} \int_1^0 z^2 \, dz = \frac{4}{3\pi} \qquad (\sqrt{1 - x^2} = z),$$

and $\bar{y} = \bar{x}$, for reasons of symmetry. Furthermore,

$$I_x = \iint\limits_R y^2 \, dx \, dy = \int_0^1 \left[\int_0^{\sqrt{1-x^2}} y^2 \, dy \right] dx = \frac{1}{3} \int_0^1 (\sqrt{1 - x^2})^3 \, dx$$

$$= \frac{1}{3} \int_0^{\pi/2} \cos^4 \theta \, d\theta = \frac{\pi}{16}, \qquad I_y = \frac{\pi}{16}, \qquad I_0 = I_x + I_y = \frac{\pi}{8} \approx 0.3927.$$

It will often be necessary to change the variables of integration in double integrals. We know from calculus that in the case of a definite integral

$$\int_a^b f(x) \, dx$$

a new variable of integration u can be introduced by setting

$$x = x(u)$$

where the function $x(u)$ is continuous and has a continuous derivative in some interval $\alpha \leq u \leq \beta$ such that $x(\alpha) = a$, $x(\beta) = b$ [or $x(\alpha) = b, x(\beta) = a$] and $x(u)$ varies between a and b when u varies between α and β. Then

$$(5) \qquad \int_a^b f(x)\,dx = \int_\alpha^\beta f(x(u))\,\frac{dx}{du}\,du.$$

For example, let $f(x) = \sqrt{1 - x^2}$, $a = 0$, $b = 1$, and set $x = \sin u$. Then

$$f[x(u)] = \sqrt{1 - \sin^2 u} = \cos u, \qquad \frac{dx}{du} = \cos u, \qquad \alpha = 0, \qquad \beta = \frac{\pi}{2},$$

and

$$\int_0^1 \sqrt{1 - x^2}\,dx = \int_0^{\pi/2} \cos^2 u\,du = \frac{\pi}{4}.$$

In the case of a double integral

$$\iint_R f(x, y)\,dx\,dy$$

new variables of integration u, v can be introduced by setting

$$x = x(u, v), \qquad y = y(u, v)$$

where the functions $x(u, v)$ and $y(u, v)$ are continuous and have continuous first partial derivatives in some region R^* in the uv-plane so that each point (u_0, v_0) in R^* corresponds to a point $[x(u_0, v_0), y(u_0, v_0)]$ in R and conversely, and furthermore the **Jacobian**[4]

$$J = \frac{\partial(x, y)}{\partial(u, v)} = \begin{vmatrix} \dfrac{\partial x}{\partial u} & \dfrac{\partial x}{\partial v} \\ \dfrac{\partial y}{\partial u} & \dfrac{\partial y}{\partial v} \end{vmatrix}$$

is either positive throughout R^* or negative throughout R^*. Then

$$(6) \qquad \iint_R f(x, y)\,dx\,dy = \iint_{R^*} f[x(u, v), y(u, v)] \left| \frac{\partial(x, y)}{\partial(u, v)} \right| du\,dv;$$

that is, the integrand is expressed in terms of u and v, and $dx\,dy$ is replaced by the absolute value of the Jacobian J times $du\,dv$. For the proof cf. Ref. [A12] in Appendix 1.

For example, polar coordinates r and θ can be introduced by setting

$$x = r \cos \theta, \qquad y = r \sin \theta.$$

[4] Named after the German mathematician CARL GUSTAV JACOB JACOBI (1804–1851), who became particularly known by his investigations on elliptic functions.

Then

$$J = \frac{\partial(x, y)}{\partial(r, \theta)} = \begin{vmatrix} \cos\theta & -r\sin\theta \\ \sin\theta & r\cos\theta \end{vmatrix} = r,$$

and

(7) $$\iint_R f(x, y)\, dx\, dy = \iint_{R^*} f(r\cos\theta, r\sin\theta) r\, dr\, d\theta,$$

where R^* is the region in the $r\theta$-plane corresponding to R in the xy-plane.

Example 2. Using (7), we obtain for I_x in Ex. 1

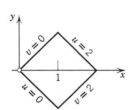

$$I_x = \iint_R y^2\, dx\, dy = \int_0^{\pi/2}\int_0^1 r^2\sin^2\theta\, r\, dr\, d\theta$$

$$= \int_0^{\pi/2} \sin^2\theta\, d\theta \int_0^1 r^3\, dr = \frac{\pi}{4}\cdot\frac{1}{4} = \frac{\pi}{16}.$$

Example 3. Evaluate the double integral

Fig. 183. Region in Example 4.

$$\iint_R e^{-x^2-y^2}\, dx\, dy$$

where R is the annulus bounded by the concentric circles $x^2 + y^2 = 1$ and $x^2 + y^2 = 4$. The shape of R suggests the use of polar coordinates. From (7),

$$\iint_R e^{-x^2-y^2}\, dx\, dy = \int_0^{2\pi}\int_1^2 e^{-r^2}r\, dr\, d\theta = 2\pi\int_1^2 e^{-r^2}r\, dr = \pi\left(\frac{1}{e} - \frac{1}{e^4}\right) \approx 1.098.$$

Example 4. Evaluate the double integral

$$\iint_R (x^2 + y^2)\, dx\, dy$$

where R is the square in Fig. 183. The shape of R suggests the transformation $x + y = u$, $x - y = v$. Then $x = \frac{1}{2}(u + v)$, $y = \frac{1}{2}(u - v)$, the Jacobian is

$$J = \frac{\partial(x, y)}{\partial(u, v)} = \begin{vmatrix} \frac{1}{2} & \frac{1}{2} \\ \frac{1}{2} & -\frac{1}{2} \end{vmatrix} = -\frac{1}{2},$$

R corresponds to the square $0 \leq u \leq 2$, $0 \leq v \leq 2$, and, therefore,

$$\iint_R (x^2 + y^2)\, dx\, dy = \int_0^2\int_0^2 \frac{1}{2}(u^2 + v^2)\frac{1}{2}\, du\, dv = \frac{8}{3}.$$

PROBLEMS

Find the area of the following regions in the xy-plane.

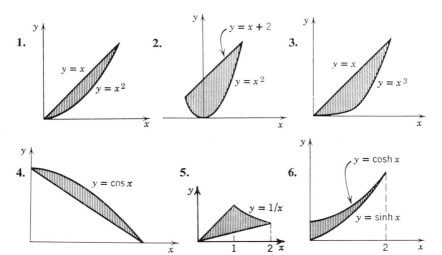

Evaluate and describe the regions of integration:

7. $\displaystyle\int_0^1 \int_x^{2x} (1 + x^2 + y^2)\, dy\, dx$ 8. $\displaystyle\int_0^\pi \int_{-1}^1 xy\, dx\, dy$

9. $\displaystyle\int_0^\pi \int_0^{1-\cos\theta} r\, dr\, d\theta$ 10. $\displaystyle\int_0^1 \int_0^{\sqrt{1-x^2}} (x^2 + y^2)\, dy\, dx$

Find the volume of the following regions in space.

11. The first octant section cut from the region inside the cylinder $x^2 + z^2 = a^2$ by the planes $y = 0$, $z = 0$, $x = y$.

12. The tetrahedron cut from the first octant by the plane $3x + 4y + 2z = 12$.

13. The region between the paraboloid $z = 1 - x^2 - y^2$ and the xy-plane.

14. The first octant region bounded by the coordinate planes and the surfaces $y = 1 - x^2$, $z = 1 - x^2$.

15. The region bounded by the surfaces $y = x^2$, $x = y^2$ and the planes $z = 0$, $z = 3$.

16. The region bounded by the cylinders $x^2 + y^2 = 1$ and $y^2 + z^2 = 1$.

Find the coordinates $\bar{x}$, $\bar{y}$ of the center of gravity of a mass of density $f(x, y)$ in a region R, where:

17. $f(x, y) = 1$, R the rectangle $0 \leq x \leq 4$, $0 \leq y \leq 2$

18. $f(x, y) = xy$, R as in Prob. 17

19. $f(x, y) = 1$, R the region $x^2 + y^2 \leq a^2$ in the first quadrant

20. $f(x, y) = x^2 + y^2$, R as in Prob. 19

Find the moments of inertia I_x, I_y, I_0 (p. 336) of a mass of density $f(x, y) = 1$ in a region R shown in the following figures.

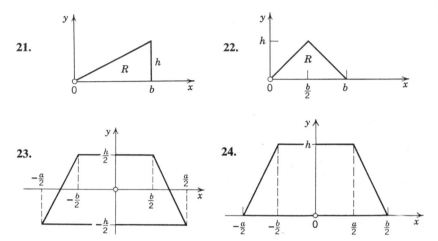

21.   22.

23.   24.

6.4   TRANSFORMATION OF DOUBLE INTEGRALS INTO LINE INTEGRALS

Double integrals over a plane region may be transformed into line integrals over the boundary of the region and conversely. This transformation is of practical as well as theoretical interest and can be done by means of the following basic theorem.

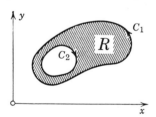

Fig. 184. Region R whose boundary C consists of two parts; C_1 is traversed in the counterclockwise sense, while C_2 is traversed in the clockwise sense.

Green's[5] theorem in the plane.   *Let R be a closed bounded region in the xy-plane whose boundary C consists of finitely many smooth curves. Let $f(x, y)$ and $g(x, y)$ be functions which are continuous and have continuous partial derivatives $\partial f/\partial y$ and $\partial g/\partial x$ everywhere in some domain containing R. Then*

(1) $$\iint\limits_{R} \left(\frac{\partial g}{\partial x} - \frac{\partial f}{\partial y} \right) dx\, dy = \int_{C} (f\, dx + g\, dy),$$

the integration being taken along the entire boundary C of R such that R is on the left as one advances in the direction of integration (cf. Fig. 184).

[5] GEORGE GREEN (1793–1841), English mathematician.

Proof. We first prove the theorem for a *special region* R which can be represented in both of the forms

$$a \leq x \leq b, \qquad u(x) \leq y \leq v(x),$$
and
$$c \leq y \leq d, \qquad p(y) \leq x \leq q(y)$$

(Fig. 185). Using (3) in Sec. 6.3, we obtain

(2)
$$\iint\limits_{R} \frac{\partial f}{\partial y} \, dx \, dy = \int_{a}^{b} \left[\int_{u(x)}^{v(x)} \frac{\partial f}{\partial y} \, dy \right] dx.$$

We integrate the inner integral:

$$\int_{u(x)}^{v(x)} \frac{\partial f}{\partial y} \, dy = f(x, y) \Big|_{y \,=\, u(x)}^{y \,=\, v(x)} = f[x, v(x)] - f[x, u(x)].$$

By inserting this into (2) we find

$$\iint\limits_{R} \frac{\partial f}{\partial y} \, dx \, dy = \int_{a}^{b} f[x, v(x)] \, dx - \int_{a}^{b} f[x, u(x)] \, dx$$

$$= - \int_{a}^{b} f[x, u(x)] \, dx - \int_{b}^{a} f[x, v(x)] \, dx.$$

Since $y = u(x)$ represents the oriented curve C^* (Fig. 185a), and $y = v(x)$ represents C^{**}, the integrals on the right may be written as line integrals over C^* and C^{**}, and, therefore,

(3)
$$\iint\limits_{R} \frac{\partial f}{\partial y} \, dx \, dy = - \int_{C^*} f(x, y) \, dx - \int_{C^{**}} f(x, y) \, dx$$

$$= - \int_{C} f(x, y) \, dx.$$

If portions of C are segments parallel to the y-axis (such as $\tilde{C}$ and $\tilde{\tilde{C}}$ in Fig. 186), then the result is the same as before, because the integrals over

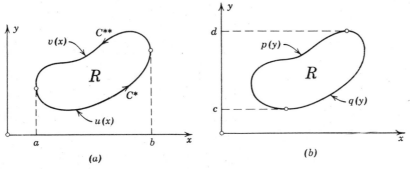

Fig. 185. Example of a special region for Green's theorem.

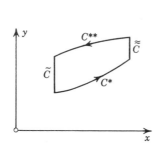

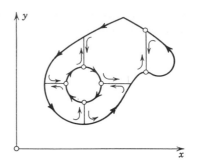

Fig. 186. Proof of Green's theorem.   **Fig. 187.** Proof of Green's theorem.

these portions are zero and may be added to the integrals over C^* and C^{**} to obtain the integral over the whole boundary C in (3). Similarly, using (4), Sec. 6.3, we obtain

$$\iint\limits_{R} \frac{\partial g}{\partial x}\,dx\,dy = \int_c^d \left[\int_{p(y)}^{q(y)} \frac{\partial g}{\partial x}\,dx \right] dy = \int_C g(x,\,y)\,dy.$$

From this and (3), the formula (1) follows, and the theorem is proved for special regions.

We now prove the theorem for a region R which itself is not a special region but can be subdivided into finitely many special regions (Fig. 187). In this case we apply the theorem to each such subregion and then add the results; the left-hand members add up to the integral over R while the right-hand members add up to the line integral over C plus integrals over the curves introduced for subdividing R. Each of the latter integrals occurs twice, taken once in each direction. Hence these two integrals cancel each other, and we are left with the line integral over C.

The proof thus far covers all regions which are of interest in engineering problems. To prove the theorem for the most general region R satisfying the conditions in the theorem, we must approximate R by a region of the type just considered and then use a limiting process. For details see Ref. [A12] in Appendix 1.

Green's theorem will be of basic importance in our further consideration. For the time being we consider a few simple illustrative examples.

Example 1 (Area of a plane region as a line integral over the boundary). In (1), let $f = 0$ and $g = x$. Then

$$\iint\limits_{R} dx\,dy = \int_C x\,dy.$$

The integral on the left is the area A of R. Similarly, let $f = -y$ and $g = 0$; then from (1),

$$A = \iint_R dx \, dy = -\int_C y \, dx.$$

By adding both formulas we obtain

(4)
$$A = \frac{1}{2} \int_C (x \, dy - y \, dx),$$

the integration being taken as indicated in Green's theorem. This interesting formula expresses the area of R in terms of a line integral over the boundary. It has various applications; for example, the theory of certain planimeters (cf. Sec. 0.8) is based upon this formula.

In the case of the ellipse

$$\frac{x^2}{a^2} + \frac{y^2}{b^2} = 1 \qquad \text{or} \qquad x = a \cos t, \qquad y = b \sin t$$

we have

$$x \, dy - y \, dx = a \cos t \, (b \cos t) \, dt - b \sin t \, (-a \sin t) \, dt = ab \, dt$$

and, therefore,

$$A = \frac{1}{2} \int_0^{2\pi} ab \, dt = \pi ab.$$

Example 2 (Area of a plane region in polar coordinates). Let r and θ be polar coordinates defined by $x = r \cos \theta$, $y = r \sin \theta$. Then

$$dx = \cos \theta \, dr - r \sin \theta \, d\theta, \qquad dy = \sin \theta \, dr + r \cos \theta \, d\theta,$$

and (4) assumes the form

(5)
$$A = \frac{1}{2} \int_C r^2 \, d\theta.$$

This formula is well known from calculus.

As an application of (5), consider the cardioid $r = a(1 - \cos \theta)$ where $0 \le \theta \le 2\pi$ (Fig. 188 on the next page). We find

$$A = \frac{a^2}{2} \int_0^{2\pi} (1 - \cos \theta)^2 \, d\theta = \frac{3\pi}{2} a^2.$$

Example 3 (Transformation of a double integral of the Laplacian of a function into a line integral of its normal derivative). Let $w(x, y)$ be a function which is continuous and has continuous first and second derivatives in some region R of the xy-plane where R is of the type indicated in Green's theorem. We set $f = -\partial w / \partial y$ and $g = \partial w / \partial x$. Then $\partial f / \partial y$ and $\partial g / \partial x$ are continuous in R, and

(6)
$$\frac{\partial g}{\partial x} - \frac{\partial f}{\partial y} = \frac{\partial^2 w}{\partial x^2} + \frac{\partial^2 w}{\partial y^2} = \nabla^2 w,$$

the Laplacian of w (cf. Sec. 5.16). Furthermore,

(7)
$$\int_C (f \, dx + g \, dy) = \int_C \left(f \frac{dx}{ds} + g \frac{dy}{ds} \right) ds = \int_C \left(-\frac{\partial w}{\partial y} \frac{dx}{ds} + \frac{\partial w}{\partial x} \frac{dy}{ds} \right) ds$$

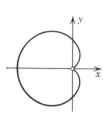

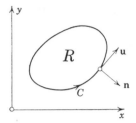

Fig. 188. Cardioid.   Fig. 189. Example 3.

where s is the arc length of C, and C is oriented as shown in Fig. 189. The integrand of the last integral may be written as the scalar product of the vectors

$$\text{grad } w = \frac{\partial w}{\partial x} \mathbf{i} + \frac{\partial w}{\partial y} \mathbf{j} \quad \text{and} \quad \mathbf{n} = \frac{dy}{ds} \mathbf{i} - \frac{dx}{ds} \mathbf{j};$$

that is,

(8) $$-\frac{\partial w}{\partial y}\frac{dx}{ds} + \frac{\partial w}{\partial x}\frac{dy}{ds} = (\text{grad } w) \cdot \mathbf{n}.$$

The vector $\mathbf{n}$ is a unit normal vector to C, because the vector

$$\mathbf{u} = \frac{d\mathbf{r}}{ds} = \frac{dx}{ds} \mathbf{i} + \frac{dy}{ds} \mathbf{j} \qquad \text{(cf. Sec. 5.13)}$$

is the unit tangent vector to C, and $\mathbf{u} \cdot \mathbf{n} = 0$. Furthermore, it is not difficult to see that $\mathbf{n}$ is directed to the exterior of C. From this and (5) in Sec. 5.16 it follows that the expression on the right-hand side of (8) is the derivative of w in the direction of the outward normal to C. Denoting this directional derivative by $\partial w/\partial n$ and taking (6), (7), and (8) into account, we obtain from Green's theorem the following useful integral formula:

(9) $$\iint\limits_{R} \nabla^2 w \, dx \, dy = \int_C \frac{\partial w}{\partial n} \, ds.$$

Further important applications and consequences of Green's theorem in the plane will be considered in the following sections.

PROBLEMS

1. Evaluate $\int_C (y \, dx - x \, dy)$ by direct calculation and by using Green's theorem; C is the boundary of the square $0 \leq x \leq 1$, $0 \leq y \leq 1$ (counterclockwise). Using Green's theorem, evaluate:

2. $\int_C (xy \, dx - 2xy \, dy)$ clockwise around the boundary of the rectangle $1 \leq x \leq 2$, $0 \leq y \leq 4$

3. $\int_C [(\frac{6}{5}xy^5 - 2y + \ln x) \, dx + (3x^2y^4 - 6 \sin y) \, dy]$ counterclockwise around the boundary of the rectangle $1 \leq x \leq 3$, $1 \leq y \leq 2$

4. $\int_C (x^2 + y^2)\, dy$ clockwise around the boundary of the square $2 \leq x \leq 4$, $2 \leq y \leq 4$

5. $\int_C \left[\left(3x^2 e^y - x^2 y - \frac{y^3}{3} \right) dx + (x^3 e^y + \cos y)\, dy \right]$ counterclockwise around the circle $x^2 + y^2 = 1$

6. $\int_C (e^x \sin y\, dx + e^x \cos y\, dy)$ around the boundary of any region satisfying the conditions in Green's theorem

7. $\int_C [(4y + e^x \cos y)\, dx - (y^2 + e^x \sin y)\, dy]$ counterclockwise around the parallelogram with vertices at $(0, 0)$, $(2, 0)$, $(3, 1)$, and $(1, 1)$

8. $\int_C (2xy^3\, dx + 3x^2 y^2\, dy)$ counterclockwise around the circle $x^2 + y^2 = 1$

9. $\int_C [(\sinh x - 1) \sin y\, dx + \cosh x \cos y\, dy]$ counterclockwise around the boundary of the rectangle $0 \leq x \leq 2$, $0 \leq y \leq \pi/2$

10. $\int_C [(2x - y)\, dx + (x + 3y)\, dy]$ counterclockwise around the ellipse $x^2 + 4y^2 = 4$

11. $\int_C \left[2 \arctan \frac{y}{x}\, dx + \ln (x^2 + y^2)\, dy \right]$ clockwise around the circle $(x - 2)^2 + y^2 = 1$

12. $\int_C \left[\left(\frac{2}{3} xy^3 - x^2 y \right) dx + x^2 y^2\, dy \right]$ counterclockwise around the boundary of the triangle with vertices $(0, 0)$, $(0, 1)$, $(1, 1)$

13. $\int_C [(\cos x \sin y - xy)\, dx + \sin x \cos y\, dy]$ clockwise around the boundary of the region bounded by $y = x^2$ and $y = 1$

14. $\int_C [(y^3 e^x - y)\, dx + 3y^2 e^x\, dy]$ counterclockwise around the boundary of the region in the first quadrant bounded by $x^2 + y^2 = 1$ and $x^2 + y^2 = 4$

Using one of the formulas in Ex. 1, find the area of the following regions in the xy-plane.

15. The region in the first quadrant bounded by $y = x$ and $y = x^3$
16. The region bounded by $y = x^2$ and $y = x + 2$
17. The region in the first quadrant bounded by $y = x$, $y = 1/x$, and $y = x/4$

18. Show that the formula in Green's theorem may be written in the form

(10) $$\iint_R \operatorname{div} \mathbf{v}\, dx\, dy = \int_C \mathbf{v} \cdot \mathbf{n}\, ds$$

where $\mathbf{n}$ is the outward unit normal vector to C (Fig. 189) and s is the arc length of C. *Hint:* introduce $\mathbf{v} = g\mathbf{i} - f\mathbf{j}$.

19. Show that the formula in Green's theorem may be written

$$(11) \qquad \iint_R (\text{curl } \mathbf{v}) \cdot \mathbf{k} \, dx \, dy = \int_C \mathbf{v} \cdot \mathbf{u} \, ds$$

where $\mathbf{k}$ is a unit vector perpendicular to the xy-plane, $\mathbf{u}$ is the unit tangent vector to C, and s is the arc length of C.

20. If $w(x, y)$ satisfies Laplace's equation $\nabla^2 w = 0$ in a region R, show that

$$\iint_R \left[\left(\frac{\partial w}{\partial x} \right)^2 + \left(\frac{\partial w}{\partial y} \right)^2 \right] dx \, dy = \int_C w \frac{\partial w}{\partial n} \, ds$$

where $\partial w / \partial n$ is defined as in Ex. 3. *Hint:* model your work somewhat after that of Ex. 3.

21. Evaluate $\displaystyle\int_C w \frac{\partial w}{\partial n} \, ds$ counterclockwise around the boundary of the square $0 \leqq x \leqq 1$, $0 \leqq y \leqq 1$, where $w = e^x \cos y$. (*a*) Use the result of Prob. 20. (*b*) Calculate directly.

22. Evaluate $\displaystyle\int_C \frac{\partial w}{\partial n} \, ds$, $w = x$, C as in Prob. 21. (*a*) Use (9). (*b*) Calculate directly.

6.5   SURFACES

In Sec. 6.7 we shall consider surface integrals. This consideration will require knowledge of some basic facts about surfaces which we shall now explain and illustrate by simple examples.

A surface S may be represented in the form

$$(1) \qquad\qquad f(x, y, z) = 0$$

where x, y, z are Cartesian coordinates in space. Then the gradient of f is normal to S (cf. Theorem 2 in Sec. 5.16), provided $\text{grad} f \neq \mathbf{0}$. Consequently, for S to have a unique normal at each point whose direction depends continuously on the points of S, we must require that f *has continuous first partial derivatives, and at each point, at least one of these three derivatives is not zero.* Then the vector

$$(2) \qquad\qquad \mathbf{n} = \frac{\text{grad} f}{|\text{grad} f|}$$

is a unit normal vector of S (and $-\mathbf{n}$ is the other).

Example 1. The sphere $x^2 + y^2 + z^2 - a^2 = 0$ has the unit normal vector

$$\mathbf{n}(x,y,z) = \frac{x}{a} \mathbf{i} + \frac{y}{a} \mathbf{j} + \frac{z}{a} \mathbf{k}.$$

Sometimes it is convenient to use an *explicit representation*

(3) $$z = g(x, y)$$

of a given surface. Clearly, by writing $z - g(x, y) = 0$ we immediately obtain an *implicit representation* of the form (1).

In Sec. 5.11 the usefulness of parametric representations of curves was demonstrated. We shall now see that surfaces may also be represented in parametric form. Suppose that

(4) $$\mathbf{r}(u, v) = x(u, v)\mathbf{i} + y(u, v)\mathbf{j} + z(u, v)\mathbf{k}$$

is a vector function of two independent real variables u and v which is single-valued and continuous in a simply-connected bounded region R of the uv-plane and is at least once continuously differentiable in R. Then to any point (u_0, v_0) in R there corresponds a point with position vector $\mathbf{r}(u_0, v_0)$ in space. Furthermore, we assume that

(5) $$\mathbf{r}_u \times \mathbf{r}_v \neq \mathbf{0}$$

everywhere in R; *here, and in the following, subscripts u and v denote partial derivatives.* We shall see that a vector function $\mathbf{r}(u, v)$ satisfying these conditions represents a surface S in space which has a unique normal whose direction depends continuously on the points of S. The representation (4) is called a **parametric representation** of S, and the variables u and v are called the *parameters* of this representation or the *coordinates on S*. The curves $u = const$ and $v = const$ form a net on S; they are called *coordinate curves on S*.

If a surface S has a unique normal whose direction depends continuously on the points of S, then S is called a **smooth surface**.

If S is not smooth but can be subdivided into finitely many smooth portions, then it is called a **piecewise smooth surface**.

For example, the surface of a sphere is smooth, while the surface of a cube is piecewise smooth.

Example 2. The sphere in Ex. 1 may be represented in the form

(6) $\mathbf{r}(u, v) = a \cos v \cos u \, \mathbf{i}$
        $+ a \cos v \sin u \, \mathbf{j} + a \sin v \, \mathbf{k}$

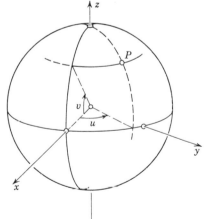

Fig. 190. Parametric representation of the sphere.

where $0 \leq u \leq 2\pi$, $-\pi/2 \leq v \leq \pi/2$; that is,

$$x = a \cos v \cos u, \qquad y = a \cos v \sin u, \qquad z = a \sin v.$$

The curves $u = const$ and $v = const$ are the "meridians" and "parallels" on S (cf. Fig. 190). The relation (5) is satisfied everywhere except at the "poles" $v = -\pi/2$ and $v = \pi/2$. *The representation* (6) *is used in geography for measuring the latitude and longitude of points on the globe.*

PROBLEMS

What surfaces are represented by the following parametric representations? What are the coordinate curves?

1. $r = u\mathbf{i} + v\mathbf{j}$ **2.** $r = (u + v)\mathbf{i} + (u - v)\mathbf{j}$

3. $r = u \cos v\, \mathbf{i} + u \sin v\, \mathbf{j}$ **4.** $r = a \cos u\, \mathbf{i} + a \sin u\, \mathbf{j} + v\mathbf{k}$

5. $r = u \cos v\, \mathbf{i} + u \sin v\, \mathbf{j} + u\mathbf{k}$ **6.** $r = u\mathbf{i} + u^3\mathbf{j} + v\mathbf{k}$

Represent the following surfaces in the form (1).

7. The ellipsoid $r = a \cos v \cos u\, \mathbf{i} + b \cos v \sin u\, \mathbf{j} + c \sin v\, \mathbf{k}$

8. The elliptic paraboloid $r = au \cos v\, \mathbf{i} + bu \sin v\, \mathbf{j} + u^2\mathbf{k}$

9. The hyperbolic paraboloid $r = au \cosh v\, \mathbf{i} + bu \sinh v\, \mathbf{j} + u^2\mathbf{k}$

10. The hyperboloid of two sheets

$$r = a \sinh u \cos v\, \mathbf{i} + b \sinh u \sin v\, \mathbf{j} + c \cosh u\, \mathbf{k}$$

11. Sketch figures of the surfaces in Probs. 6–10. (Choose $a = 1$, $b = 2$, $c = 3$.)

Find a parametric representation of each of the following surfaces.

12. The yz-plane   **13.** The plane $y = x$

14. The parabolic cylinder $z = y^2$ **15.** The elliptic cylinder $x^2 + 4y^2 = 4$

16. The surface generated by the tangents of the circular helix in Ex. 2, Sec. 5.11. (Draw a figure of this surface.)

17. The cylinder of revolution of radius 2 whose axis is the y-axis

18. Find a representation of the unit normal vector $\mathbf{n}$ of a surface S which is represented in the form $z = g(x, y)$.

19. Show that the torus in Fig. 191 may be represented in the form

$$r = (a + b \cos v) \cos u\, \mathbf{i} + (a + b \cos v) \sin u\, \mathbf{j} + b \sin v\, \mathbf{k}$$

and draw the coordinate curves on the torus.

20. Find $\mathbf{r}_u \times \mathbf{r}_v$ in Ex. 2, Prob. 3, and Prob. 5, and determine the points at which (5) is not satisfied.

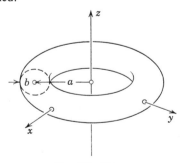

Fig. 191. Torus.

6.6   TANGENT PLANE.
FIRST FUNDAMENTAL FORM. AREA

If a surface S is represented in the form $\mathbf{r} = \mathbf{r}(u, v)$, then a curve on S can be represented by a pair of continuous functions

(1) $u = g(t), \qquad v = h(t)$

of a real parameter t.

Example 1. The vector function $\mathbf{r}(u, v) = a \cos u\, \mathbf{i} + a \sin u\, \mathbf{j} + v\mathbf{k}$ represents a cylinder of revolution S of radius a. The equations $u = t$, $v = ct$ represent a circular helix on S. In fact, by substituting these equations into the representation of S we obtain (cf. Ex. 2 in Sec. 5.11)

$$\mathbf{r}[u(t), v(t)] = a \cos t\, \mathbf{i} + a \sin t\, \mathbf{j} + ct\mathbf{k}.$$

Let S be a smooth surface represented by a vector function $\mathbf{r}(u, v)$, and let C be a curve on S represented in the form (1). Then C, considered as a curve in space, is represented by the vector function

(2) $\mathbf{r}(t) = \mathbf{r}[u(t), v(t)].$

Suppose that both functions in (1) have continuous first derivatives such that for each t at least one of these derivatives is not zero. Then C has a tangent at each of its points whose direction depends continuously on the points, and a tangent vector to C is

$$\dot{\mathbf{r}}(t) \equiv \frac{d\mathbf{r}}{dt} = \mathbf{r}_u \dot{u} + \mathbf{r}_v \dot{v}.$$

From (5) in the last section it follows that the vectors $\mathbf{r}_u \equiv \partial \mathbf{r}/\partial u$ and $\mathbf{r}_v \equiv \partial \mathbf{r}/\partial v$ are linearly independent. Hence they determine a plane. This plane is called the **tangent plane** of S at the corresponding point P of S and will be denoted by $T(P)$. It touches S at P. From (2) it follows that $T(P)$ *contains the tangent to any curve on S through P, at that point P* (see also Sec. 5.16).

The straight line through P and perpendicular to $T(P)$ is called the **normal** to S at P. Since the vectors $\mathbf{r}_u$ and $\mathbf{r}_v$ lie in $T(P)$, the unit vector

(3) $$\mathbf{n} = \frac{\mathbf{r}_u \times \mathbf{r}_v}{|\mathbf{r}_u \times \mathbf{r}_v|}$$

(Fig. 192) is perpendicular to $T(P)$. This vector is called the **unit normal vector** of S at P. Its sense depends on the choice of the coordinates u and v; the transformation $u = -\bar{u}$, $v = \bar{v}$ or any other transformation whose Jacobian (cf. Sec. 6.3) has a negative value, reverses the sense of $\mathbf{n}$.

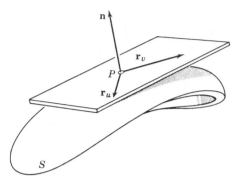

Fig. 192. Tangent plane and normal vector.

We shall now determine the *linear element* of a curve C, represented in the form (1), on a surface S, represented by $\mathbf{r}(u, v)$. We have

$$d\mathbf{r} = \mathbf{r}_u \, du + \mathbf{r}_v \, dv,$$

and, by (4) in Sec. 5.12,

$$ds^2 = d\mathbf{r} \cdot d\mathbf{r} = (\mathbf{r}_u \, du + \mathbf{r}_v \, dv) \cdot (\mathbf{r}_u \, du + \mathbf{r}_v \, dv)$$
$$= \mathbf{r}_u \cdot \mathbf{r}_u \, du^2 + 2\mathbf{r}_u \cdot \mathbf{r}_v \, du \, dv + \mathbf{r}_v \cdot \mathbf{r}_v \, dv^2.$$

Using the standard notation

(4) $$E = \mathbf{r}_u \cdot \mathbf{r}_u, \qquad F = \mathbf{r}_u \cdot \mathbf{r}_v, \qquad G = \mathbf{r}_v \cdot \mathbf{r}_v,$$

the last expression assumes the form

(5) $$ds^2 = E \, du^2 + 2F \, du \, dv + G \, dv^2.$$

This quadratic differential form is called the **first fundamental form** of S.

Example 2. The vector function

$$\mathbf{r}(u, v) = u \cos v \, \mathbf{i} + u \sin v \, \mathbf{j}$$

represents the xy-plane, and u and v are polar coordinates. We find

$$\mathbf{r}_u = \cos v \, \mathbf{i} + \sin v \, \mathbf{j}, \qquad \mathbf{r}_v = -u \sin v \, \mathbf{i} + u \cos v \, \mathbf{j}.$$

Hence $E = 1$, $F = 0$, $G = u^2$, and the first fundamental form corresponding to polar coordinates $u = \rho$ and $v = \theta$ is

(6) $$ds^2 = d\rho^2 + \rho^2 \, d\theta^2.$$

We shall now see that *the first fundamental form is of basic importance because it enables us to measure lengths, angles between curves, and areas on the corresponding surface S.*

From (1) and (4) in Sec. 5.12 and the above formula (5) it follows that a curve

$$C: \quad u(t), v(t), \qquad a \leq t \leq b,$$

on a surface S: $\mathbf{r}(u, v)$ has the length

(7) $$l = \int_a^b \sqrt{\dot{\mathbf{r}} \cdot \dot{\mathbf{r}}} \, dt = \int_a^b \frac{ds}{dt} \, dt = \int_a^b \sqrt{E\dot{u}^2 + 2F\dot{u}\dot{v} + G\dot{v}^2} \, dt.$$

We now consider two curves

$$C_1: \quad u = g(t), v = h(t) \qquad \text{and} \qquad C_2: \quad u = p(t), v = q(t)$$

on a surface S: $\mathbf{r}(u, v)$ which intersect at a point P of S. The vectors

$$\mathbf{a} = \frac{d}{dt} \mathbf{r}[g(t), h(t)] = \mathbf{r}_u \dot{g} + \mathbf{r}_v \dot{h}$$

and

$$\mathbf{b} = \frac{d}{dt} \mathbf{r}[p(t), q(t)] = \mathbf{r}_u \dot{p} + \mathbf{r}_v \dot{q}$$

at P are tangent to C_1 and C_2, respectively. The angle of intersection between C_1 and C_2 at P is defined as the angle γ between $\mathbf{a}$ and $\mathbf{b}$, and from (3) in Sec. 5.4 we have

(8) $$\cos \gamma = \frac{\mathbf{a} \cdot \mathbf{b}}{|\mathbf{a}| \, |\mathbf{b}|}$$

where

$$\mathbf{a} \cdot \mathbf{b} = (\mathbf{r}_u \dot{g} + \mathbf{r}_v \dot{h}) \cdot (\mathbf{r}_u \dot{p} + \mathbf{r}_v \dot{q}) = E\dot{g}\dot{p} + F(\dot{g}\dot{q} + \dot{h}\dot{p}) + G\dot{h}\dot{q}$$

and similarly

$$|\mathbf{a}| = \sqrt{\mathbf{a} \cdot \mathbf{a}} = \sqrt{E\dot{g}^2 + 2F\dot{g}\dot{h} + G\dot{h}^2},$$

$$|\mathbf{b}| = \sqrt{\mathbf{b} \cdot \mathbf{b}} = \sqrt{E\dot{p}^2 + 2F\dot{p}\dot{q} + G\dot{q}^2}.$$

This important result shows that the angle between two intersecting curves on a surface can be expressed in terms of E, F, G and the derivatives of the functions representing the curves, evaluated at the point of intersection.

We have shown that the coefficients E, F, and G of the first fundamental form permit the measurement of lengths and angles on a surface. We shall now demonstrate that they also permit the measurement of areas on a surface.

The **area** A of a surface S: $\mathbf{r}(u, v)$ is defined by the double integral

(9) $$A = \iint_R \sqrt{EG - F^2} \, du \, dv$$

over the region R in the uv-plane corresponding to that surface; here the positive sign of the square root is taken. The expression

(10) $$dA = \sqrt{EG - F^2} \, du \, dv$$

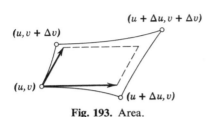

(u + Δu, v + Δv)

(u, v + Δv)

(u, v)

(u + Δu, v)

Fig. 193. Area.

is called the *element of area* of S. The formula (10) can be made plausible by noting that

$$\Delta A = \sqrt{EG - F^2} \, \Delta u \Delta v$$

is the area of a small parallelogram whose sides are the vectors

$$\mathbf{r}_u \Delta u \quad \text{and} \quad \mathbf{r}_v \Delta v$$

(Fig. 193). Indeed, from the definition of a vector product it follows that

$$\Delta A = |\mathbf{r}_u \Delta u \times \mathbf{r}_v \Delta v| = |\mathbf{r}_u \times \mathbf{r}_v| \, \Delta u \Delta v,$$

and from (5) in Sec. 5.5 and (4) in the current section we obtain

$$|\mathbf{r}_u \times \mathbf{r}_v|^2 = (\mathbf{r}_u \cdot \mathbf{r}_u)(\mathbf{r}_v \cdot \mathbf{r}_v) - (\mathbf{r}_u \cdot \mathbf{r}_v)^2;$$

that is,

(11) $$|\mathbf{r}_u \times \mathbf{r}_v|^2 = EG - F^2.$$

The integral (9) is obtained by subdividing S into parts $S_1, \cdots, S_n$, approximating each part S_k by a portion of the tangent plane of S at a point in S_k, and forming the sum of all the approximating areas. This is done for each $n = 1, 2, \cdots$ such that the dimensions of the largest S_k approach zero as n approaches infinity. The limit of those sums is the integral (9). For details see Ref. [C4] in Appendix 1.

Example 3 (Torus). The vector function

$$\mathbf{r}(u, v) = (a + b \cos v) \cos u \, \mathbf{i} + (a + b \cos v) \sin u \, \mathbf{j} + b \sin v \, \mathbf{k} \quad (a > b > 0)$$

represents a torus (Fig. 194) which is obtained by rotating a circle C about a fixed straight line A so that the plane of C always passes through A, and C does not intersect A. (Cf. also Fig. 191.) Using (4), we find

$$E = (a + b \cos v)^2, \quad F = 0, \quad G = b^2,$$
$$EG - F^2 = b^2(a + b \cos v)^2,$$

and the total area is

$$A = \int_0^{2\pi} \int_0^{2\pi} b(a + b \cos v) \, du \, dv = 4\pi^2 ab.$$

If S is represented in the form

$$z = g(x, y),$$

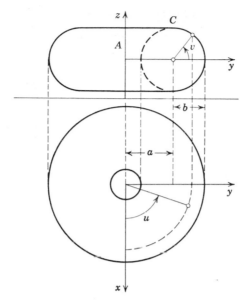

Fig. 194. Torus.

we may set $x = u$ and $y = v$ and write the representation in parametric form:

$$\mathbf{r}(u, v) = u\mathbf{i} + v\mathbf{j} + g(u, v)\mathbf{k}.$$

Then the partial derivatives of $\mathbf{r}$ with respect to u and v are

(12) $\mathbf{r}_u = \mathbf{i} + g_u\mathbf{k}, \qquad \mathbf{r}_v = \mathbf{j} + g_v\mathbf{k}.$

It follows that the coefficients of the first fundamental form are

$$E = 1 + g_u^{\,2}, \qquad F = g_u g_v, \qquad G = 1 + g_v^{\,2}.$$

From this we obtain

$$EG - F^2 = 1 + g_u^{\,2} + g_v^{\,2}.$$

Since $u = x$ and $v = y$, the integral (9) now assumes the form

(9′) $$A = \iint_{\bar{S}} \sqrt{1 + \left(\frac{\partial g}{\partial x}\right)^2 + \left(\frac{\partial g}{\partial y}\right)^2}\, dx\, dy$$

where $\bar{S}$ is the orthogonal projection of S into the xy-plane. Clearly,

(10′) $$dA = \sqrt{1 + \left(\frac{\partial g}{\partial x}\right)^2 + \left(\frac{\partial g}{\partial y}\right)^2}\, dx\, dy.$$

We want to show that this may be written

$$(10'') \qquad\qquad dA = \sec \gamma \, dx \, dy$$

where γ is the *acute* angle between the z-axis and the undirected normal to S.
In fact, the vector product of the vectors in (12) is perpendicular to S; denoting it by $\mathbf{a}$ and observing that $u = x$, $v = y$, we have

$$\mathbf{a} = \frac{\partial \mathbf{r}}{\partial x} \times \frac{\partial \mathbf{r}}{\partial y} = -\frac{\partial g}{\partial x}\mathbf{i} - \frac{\partial g}{\partial y}\mathbf{j} + \mathbf{k}, \qquad |\mathbf{a}| = \sqrt{1 + \left(\frac{\partial g}{\partial x}\right)^2 + \left(\frac{\partial g}{\partial y}\right)^2}.$$

Furthermore $\mathbf{a} \cdot \mathbf{k} = |\mathbf{a}| \cos \gamma^* = 1$ where γ^* is the angle between $\mathbf{a}$ and the positive z-axis. Clearly $\cos \gamma^* > 0$ and therefore $\gamma^* < \pi/2$, that is, γ^* is acute and thus equal to γ. Hence

$$|\mathbf{a}| \cos \gamma = 1 \qquad \text{or} \qquad \sec \gamma = |\mathbf{a}| \qquad \left(\gamma < \frac{\pi}{2}\right)$$

and $(10'')$ is established.

PROBLEMS

Find a representation of the tangent plane T of a surface S at a point P, if S is represented in the form
1. $\mathbf{r} = \mathbf{r}(u, v)$ **2.** $z = g(x, y)$ **3.** $f(x, y, z) = 0$
4. Show that another form of the solution of Prob. 1 is

$$(\mathbf{r}^* - \mathbf{r} \qquad \mathbf{r}_u \qquad \mathbf{r}_v) = 0$$

where $\mathbf{r}^*$ is the position vector of a running point in T.

5. Under what condition do the coordinate curves $p = const$ and $q = const$ in the solution of Prob. 1 intersect at right angles?
Find a representation of the tangent plane of the surface $f(x, y, z) = 0$ at a point $P_0 : (x_0, y_0, z_0)$, where

6. $f = x^2 + y^2 - z^2$, $P_0 : (1, 0, 1)$ **7.** $f = x^2 + y^2 + z^2 - 1$, $P_0 : \left(\dfrac{1}{\sqrt{2}}, \dfrac{1}{\sqrt{2}}, 0\right)$

8. $f = z - x^2$, $P_0 : (1, 0, 1)$ **9.** $f = y^2 + z^2 - 4$, $P_0 : (3, -\sqrt{2}, \sqrt{2})$
Find the first fundamental form of the following surfaces.
10. $\mathbf{r} = u\mathbf{i} + v\mathbf{j}$ **11.** $\mathbf{r} = u\mathbf{i} + u^2\mathbf{j} + v\mathbf{k}$
12. $\mathbf{r} = u\mathbf{i} + v\mathbf{j} + u^3\mathbf{k}$ **13.** The sphere in Ex. 2, Sec. 6.5
14. $\mathbf{r} = 2\cos u\,\mathbf{i} + 2\sin u\,\mathbf{j} + v\mathbf{k}$ **15.** $\mathbf{r} = v\cos u\,\mathbf{i} + v\sin u\,\mathbf{j} + v^2\mathbf{k}$

16. Show that the coordinate curves $u = const$ and $v = const$ on a surface $\mathbf{r} = \mathbf{r}(u, v)$ intersect at right angles if, and only if, $F = \mathbf{r}_u \cdot \mathbf{r}_v = 0$. Give examples.
17. Determine the first fundamental form of a surface represented in the form $z = z(x, y)$.
Using (9), find the area of the following surfaces.
18. The sphere (6), Sec. 6.5   **19.** $x^2 + y^2 = 4$, $-1 \leq z \leq 1$
20. $z^2 = x^2 + y^2$, $-1 \leq z \leq i$ **21.** $z = x^2 + y^2$, $0 \leq z \leq 1$

22. Show that the area A in Ex. 3 can be obtained by the **Theorem of Pappus**, which states that the area of a surface of revolution equals the product of the length of a meridian C and the length of the path of the center of gravity of C when C is rotated through the angle 2π.

23. Solve Prob. 21 by the Theorem of Pappus.

24. In (6), Sec. 6.5, let $u = -\bar{u}$, $v = \bar{v}$. Show that the unit normal vector (3) corresponding to the resulting representation is opposite to that corresponding to the original representation (6).

6.7 SURFACE INTEGRALS

The concept of a surface integral is a natural generalization of the concept of a double integral considered in Sec. 6.3. Surface integrals occur in many applications, for example, in connection with the center of gravity of a curved lamina, the potential due to charges distributed on surfaces, etc.

The definition of a surface integral parallels that of a double integral. Let S be a portion of a surface of finite area, and let $f(P) = f(x, y, z)$ be a single-valued function which is defined and continuous on S. We subdivide S into n parts $S_1, \cdots, S_n$ of areas $\Delta A_1, \cdots, \Delta A_n$. In each part S_k we choose an arbitrary point P_k and form the sum

(1) $$J_n = \sum_{k=1}^{n} f(P_k)\, \Delta A_k.$$

This we do for each $n = 1, 2, \cdots$ in an arbitrary manner, but so that the largest part S_k shrinks to a point as n approaches infinity. The infinite sequence $J_1, J_2, \cdots$ has a limit which is independent of the choice of subdivisions and points P_k; the proof is similar to that in the case of a double integral. This limit is called the **surface integral** *of $f(x, y, z)$ over S* and is denoted by

(2) $$\iint_{S} f(x, y, z)\, dA.$$

To evaluate the surface integral (2), *we may reduce it to a double integral as follows.* If S is represented in parametric form by a vector function $\mathbf{r}(u, v)$, then $dA = \sqrt{EG - F^2}\, du\, dv$, cf. (10) in the previous section, and

(3) $$\iint_{S} f(x, y, z)\, dA = \iint_{R} f[x(u, v), y(u, v), z(u, v)]\sqrt{EG - F^2}\, du\, dv$$

where R is the region corresponding to S in the uv-plane.

Similarly, if S is represented in the form $z = g(x, y)$, then from $(10')$ and $(10'')$ in the last section it follows that

$$
\iint_S f(x, y, z)\, dA = \iint_{\bar{S}} f[x, y, g(x, y)]\sqrt{1 + \left(\frac{\partial g}{\partial x}\right)^2 + \left(\frac{\partial g}{\partial y}\right)^2}\, dx\, dy
$$

(4)

$$
= \iint_{\bar{S}} f[x, y, g(x, y)] \sec \gamma\, dx\, dy \qquad (\gamma < \pi/2)
$$

where γ is the acute angle between the normal to S and the z-axis, and $\bar{S}$ is the orthogonal projection of S in the xy-plane. Of course, here we must assume that $g(x, y)$ is single-valued. Geometrically, this means that different points of S are projected onto different points of $\bar{S}$. The condition $\gamma < \pi/2$ means that the normal of S is nowhere perpendicular to the z-axis.

Example 1 (Moment of inertia). Find the moment of inertia I of a homogeneous spherical lamina S: $x^2 + y^2 + z^2 = a^2$ of mass M about the z-axis.

If a mass is distributed over a surface S and $\mu(x, y, z)$ is the density of the mass (= mass per unit area), then the moment of inertia I of the mass with respect to a given axis L is defined by the surface integral

$$
(5) \qquad I = \iint_S \mu D^2\, dA
$$

where $D(x, y, z)$ is the distance of the point (x, y, z) from L.

Since, in the present example, μ is constant and S has the area $A = 4\pi a^2$ we have

$$
\mu = \frac{M}{A} = \frac{M}{4\pi a^2}.
$$

Representing S by (6), Sec. 6.5, we obtain from (4) in the previous section

$$
E = a^2 \cos^2 v, \qquad F = 0, \qquad G = a^2,
$$

$$
dA = \sqrt{EG - F^2}\, du\, dv = a^2 \cos v\, du\, dv.
$$

Furthermore, the square of the distance of a point (x, y, z) from the z-axis becomes

$$
D^2 = x^2 + y^2 = a^2 \cos^2 v.
$$

Hence we obtain the result

$$
I = \iint_S \mu D^2\, dA = \frac{M}{4\pi a^2}\int_{-\pi/2}^{\pi/2}\int_0^{2\pi} a^4 \cos^3 v\, du\, dv
$$

$$
= \frac{Ma^2}{2}\int_{-\pi/2}^{\pi/2} \cos^3 v\, dv = \frac{2Ma^2}{3}.
$$

In various applications there occur surface integrals for which the concept of orientation of a surface is essential. Therefore we shall now consider this concept, starting with the case of a smooth surface (cf. Sec. 6.5).

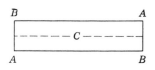

Fig. 195. Möbius strip.

Let S be a smooth surface, and let P be any point of S. Then we may choose a unit normal vector $\mathbf{n}$ of S at P. The direction of $\mathbf{n}$ is then called the *positive normal direction* of S at P. Obviously there are two possibilities in choosing $\mathbf{n}$.

A smooth surface S is said to be **orientable** if the positive normal direction, when given at an arbitrary point P_0 of S, can be continued in a unique and continuous way to the entire surface.

Hence the surface S is orientable provided there does not exist a closed curve C on S through P_0 such that the positive normal direction reverses when it is displaced continuously from P_0 along C and back to P_0.

A sufficiently small portion of a smooth surface is always orientable. However, this may not hold in the large. There are nonorientable surfaces. A well-known example of such a surface is the **Möbius**[6] **strip** shown in Fig. 195. When a normal vector, which is given at P_0, is displaced continuously along the curve C in Fig. 195, the resulting normal vector upon returning to P_0 is opposite to the original vector at P_0. A model of a Möbius strip can be made by taking a long rectangular piece of paper and sticking the shorter sides together so that the two points A and the two points B in Fig. 195 coincide.

If a smooth surface S is orientable then we may *orient* S by choosing one of the two possible directions of the normal vector $\mathbf{n}$.

If the boundary of S is a simple closed curve C then we may associate with each of the two possible orientations of S an orientation of C, as shown in Fig. 196a. Using this simple idea, we may now readily extend the concept of orientation to piecewise smooth surfaces as follows.

A piecewise smooth surface S is said to be **orientable** if we can orient each smooth piece of S in such a manner that along each curve C^* which is a common boundary of two pieces S_1 and S_2 the positive direction of C^* relative to S_1 is opposite to the positive direction of C^* relative to S_2.

Fig. 196b illustrates the situation for a surface consisting of two smooth pieces.

Let S be a given orientable surface. We orient S by choosing a unit

---

[6] AUGUST FERDINAND MÖBIUS (1790–1868), German mathematician, who made important contributions in the theory of surfaces and projective geometry.

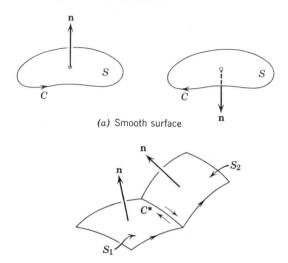

(a) Smooth surface

(b) Piecewise smooth surface

Fig. 196. Orientation of a surface.

normal vector $\mathbf{n}$. Denoting the angles between $\mathbf{n}$ and the positive x, y, and z axes by α, β, and γ, respectively, we have

(6) $$\mathbf{n} = \cos \alpha \, \mathbf{i} + \cos \beta \, \mathbf{j} + \cos \gamma \, \mathbf{k}.$$

Let $u_1(x, y, z)$, $u_2(x, y, z)$, and $u_3(x, y, z)$ be given functions which are defined and continuous at every point of S. Then the integrals to be considered are usually written in the form

$$\iint_S u_1 \, dy \, dz, \qquad \iint_S u_2 \, dz \, dx, \qquad \iint_S u_3 \, dx \, dy,$$

and *by definition* this means

(7)
$$\iint_S u_1 \, dy \, dz = \iint_S u_1 \cos \alpha \, dA,$$
$$\iint_S u_2 \, dz \, dx = \iint_S u_2 \cos \beta \, dA,$$
$$\iint_S u_3 \, dx \, dy = \iint_S u_3 \cos \gamma \, dA.$$

It is clear that the value of such an integral depends on the choice of $\mathbf{n}$, that is, on the orientation of S. The transition to the opposite orientation corresponds to the multiplication of the integral by -1, because then the components $\cos \alpha$, $\cos \beta$, and $\cos \gamma$ of $\mathbf{n}$ are multiplied by -1.

Sums of three such integrals may be written in a simple form by using vector notation. In fact, if we introduce the vector

$$\mathbf{u} = u_1 \mathbf{i} + u_2 \mathbf{j} + u_3 \mathbf{k}$$

then we obtain from the definition (7) the formula

(8) $$\iint_S (u_1 \, dy \, dz + u_2 \, dz \, dx + u_3 \, dx \, dy)$$

$$= \iint_S (u_1 \cos \alpha + u_2 \cos \beta + u_3 \cos \gamma) \, dA = \iint_S \mathbf{u} \cdot \mathbf{n} \, dA.$$

To evaluate the integrals (7) we may reduce them to double integrals over a plane region, as follows.

If S can be represented in the form $z = h(x, y)$ and is oriented such that $\mathbf{n}$ points upward then γ is acute. Hence from $(10'')$ in the last section and the above definition (7) we immediately have

(9a) $$\iint_S u_3(x, y, z) \, dx \, dy = + \iint_{\bar{R}} u_3[x, y, h(x, y)] \, dx \, dy$$

where $\bar{R}$ is the orthogonal projection of S in the xy-plane. If $\mathbf{n}$ points downward then γ is obtuse and we obtain

(9b) $$\iint_S u_3(x, y, z) \, dx \, dy = - \iint_{\bar{R}} u_3[x, y, h(x, y)] \, dx \, dy.$$

For the other two integrals in (7) the situation is quite similar.

If S is represented in parametric form

$$\mathbf{r}(u, v) = x(u, v)\mathbf{i} + y(u, v)\mathbf{j} + z(u, v)\mathbf{k}$$

then the normal vector is [cf. (3) in the last section]

(10)   (a) $$\mathbf{n} = + \frac{\mathbf{r}_u \times \mathbf{r}_v}{|\mathbf{r}_u \times \mathbf{r}_v|} \quad \text{or} \quad \text{(b)} \quad \mathbf{n} = - \frac{\mathbf{r}_u \times \mathbf{r}_v}{|\mathbf{r}_u \times \mathbf{r}_v|},$$

depending on the orientation. Now from (10) and (11) in the last section it follows that

$$dA = \sqrt{EG - F^2} \, du \, dv = |\mathbf{r}_u \times \mathbf{r}_v| \, du \, dv.$$

Since $\cos \gamma = \mathbf{k} \cdot \mathbf{n}$ we thus obtain

$$\cos \gamma \, dA = \mathbf{k} \cdot \mathbf{n} \, dA = \pm \mathbf{k} \cdot (\mathbf{r}_u \times \mathbf{r}_v) \, du \, dv = \pm \begin{vmatrix} 0 & 0 & 1 \\ x_u & y_u & z_u \\ x_v & y_v & z_v \end{vmatrix} du \, dv$$

$$= \pm \frac{\partial(x, y)}{\partial(u, v)} \, du \, dv,$$

where the last expression involves the Jacobian (cf. Sec. 6.3). Hence in (7),

$$(11) \quad \iint_S u_3(x, y, z) \, dx \, dy = \pm \iint_R u_3[x(u, v), y(u, v), z(u, v)] \frac{\partial(x, y)}{\partial(u, v)} \, du \, dv$$

with the plus sign when S is oriented such that (10a) holds and the minus sign in the case of the opposite orientation. Here R is the region corresponding to S in the uv-plane.

PROBLEMS

1. Construct a paper model of a Möbius strip. What happens if you cut it along the curve C in Fig. 195?

Representing S in parametric form and using (3), evaluate $\iint_S f(x, y, z) \, dA$ where

2. $f = x + 2$, $S: x^2 + y^2 = 1, 0 \leq z \leq 1$
3. $f = x + y + z$, $S: x^2 + y^2 = 1, 0 \leq z \leq 2$
4. $f = xy$, $S: x^2 + y^2 = 4, -1 \leq z \leq 1$
5. $f = 6x + z - y^2$, $S: z = y^2, 0 \leq x \leq 1, -1 \leq y \leq 1$
6. $f = \cos x + \sin y$, S: the portion of $x + y + z = 1$ in the first octant.
7. Using (4), solve Prob. 5.
8. The electrostatic potential at $(0, 0, -a)$ of a charge of constant density σ on the hemisphere $S: x^2 + y^2 + z^2 = a^2, z \geq 0$ is

$$U = \iint_S \frac{\sigma}{\sqrt{x^2 + y^2 + (z + a)^2}} \, dA.$$

Show that $U = 2\pi \sigma a(2 - \sqrt{2})$. *Hint:* represent S in the form

$$\mathbf{r} = a \sin u \cos v \, \mathbf{i} + a \sin u \sin v \, \mathbf{j} + a \cos u \, \mathbf{k}.$$

9. Consider a lamina S of density (mass per unit area) $\sigma(x, y, z)$ in space. Justify the following formulas: the total mass M is

$$M = \iint_S \sigma \, dA,$$

the center of gravity is at $(\bar{x}, \bar{y}, \bar{z})$ where

$$\bar{x} = \frac{1}{M} \iint_S x\sigma \, dA, \qquad \bar{y} = \frac{1}{M} \iint_S y\sigma \, dA, \qquad \bar{z} = \frac{1}{M} \iint_S z\sigma \, dA,$$

the moment of inertia about the z-axis is

$$I_z = \iint\limits_S (x^2 + y^2)\sigma \, dA.$$

10. In Prob. 9 find the formulas for the moment of inertia about the x-axis, the y-axis, and the line $y = x$, $z = 0$.

Find the moment of inertia of a lamina S of density $\sigma = 1$ about an axis A where

11. $S: x^2 + y^2 = a^2$, $0 \leq z \leq h$, A: the line $z = h/2$ in the xz-plane
12. S as in Prob. 11, A: the z-axis
13. S as in Prob. 11, A: the line $x = a$ in the xz-plane
14. S as in Prob. 11, A: the x-axis
15. $S: z^2 = x^2 + y^2$, $0 \leq z \leq h$, A: the z-axis
16. S as in Prob. 15, A: the x-axis
17. $S: z^2 = x^2 + y^2$, $h_1 \leq z \leq h_2$, where $h_1 > 0$, A: the z-axis
18. S: the torus in Ex. 3, Sec. 6.6, A: the z-axis
19. S as in Prob. 18, A: the line $x = a$ in the xz-plane
20. S as in Prob. 18, A: the line $x = a + b$ in the xz-plane
21. (Steiner's[7] theorem). If J_A is the moment of inertia of a mass distribution of total mass M with respect to an axis A through the center of gravity, show that its moment of inertia I_B with respect to an axis B, which is parallel to A and has the distance k from it, is

$$J_B = J_A + k^2 M.$$

22. Using Steiner's theorem and the solution of Prob. 18, solve Probs. 19 and 20.

6.8 TRIPLE INTEGRALS. DIVERGENCE THEOREM OF GAUSS

The triple integral is a generalization of the double integral introduced in Sec. 6.3. For defining this integral we consider a function $f(x, y, z)$ defined in a bounded closed[8] region T of space. We subdivide T by planes parallel to the three coordinate planes. Then we number the parallelepipeds inside T from 1 to n. In each such parallelepiped we choose an arbitrary point, say, (x_k, y_k, z_k) in the kth parallelepiped, and form the sum

$$J_n = \sum_{k=1}^{n} f(x_k, y_k, z_k) \, \Delta V_k$$

where ΔV_k is the volume of the kth parallelepiped. This we do for each positive integer n in an arbitrary manner, but so that the lengths of the edges of the largest parallelepiped of subdivision approach zero as n

[7] JACOB STEINER (1796–1863), Swiss geometer.
[8] Explained in footnote 2, p. 333 (with "sphere" instead of "circle").

approaches infinity. In this way we obtain a sequence of real numbers $J_1, J_2, \cdots$. Assuming that $f(x, y, z)$ is continuous in T, and T is bounded by finitely many *smooth surfaces*,[9] it can be shown (cf. Ref. [A1]) that the sequence converges to a limit which is independent of the choice of subdivisions and corresponding points (x_k, y_k, z_k). This limit is called the **triple integral** *of* $f(x, y, z)$ *over the region* T, and is denoted by

$$\iiint_T f(x, y, z) \, dx \, dy \, dz \quad \text{or} \quad \iiint_T f(x, y, z) \, dV.$$

We shall now show that the triple integral of the divergence of a continuously differentiable vector function $\mathbf{u}$ over a region T in space can be transformed into a surface integral of the normal component of $\mathbf{u}$ over the boundary surface S of T. This can be done by means of *the divergence theorem which is the three-dimensional analogue of Green's theorem in the plane* considered in Sec. 6.4. The divergence theorem is of basic importance in various theoretical and practical considerations.

Divergence theorem of Gauss. *Let T be a closed bounded region in space whose boundary is a piecewise smooth[10] orientable surface S. Let $\mathbf{u}(x, y, z)$ be a vector function which is continuous and has continuous first partial derivatives in some domain containing T. Then*

(1)
$$\iiint_T \operatorname{div} \mathbf{u} \, dV = \iint_S u_n \, dA$$

where

(2)
$$u_n = \mathbf{u} \cdot \mathbf{n}$$

is the component of $\mathbf{u}$ *in the direction of the outer normal of S with respect to T, and* $\mathbf{n}$ *is the outer unit normal vector of S.*

Remark. Writing $\mathbf{u}$ and $\mathbf{n}$ in terms of components, say

$$\mathbf{u} = u_1 \mathbf{i} + u_2 \mathbf{j} + u_3 \mathbf{k} \quad \text{and} \quad \mathbf{n} = \cos \alpha \, \mathbf{i} + \cos \beta \, \mathbf{j} + \cos \gamma \, \mathbf{k},$$

so that α, β, and γ are the angles between $\mathbf{n}$ and the positive x, y, and z axes, respectively, the formula (1) takes the form

$$\iiint_T \left(\frac{\partial u_1}{\partial x} + \frac{\partial u_2}{\partial y} + \frac{\partial u_3}{\partial z} \right) dx \, dy \, dz$$

(3*)
$$= \iint_S (u_1 \cos \alpha + u_2 \cos \beta + u_3 \cos \gamma) \, dA.$$

[9] Cf. Sec. 6.5.
[10] That is, a surface composed of finitely many smooth portions, so that S may have at most finitely many edges and cusps. Example: the surface of a parallelepiped.

Because of (8) in the last section this may be written

(3) $$\iiint\limits_{T} \left(\frac{\partial u_1}{\partial x} + \frac{\partial u_2}{\partial y} + \frac{\partial u_3}{\partial z}\right) dx\, dy\, dz$$

$$= \iint\limits_{S} (u_1\, dy\, dz + u_2\, dz\, dx + u_3\, dx\, dy).$$

Proof of the divergence theorem. Clearly, (3*) is true, if the following three relations hold simultaneously:

(4) $$\iiint\limits_{T} \frac{\partial u_1}{\partial x} dx\, dy\, dz = \iint\limits_{S} u_1 \cos \alpha\, dA,$$

(5) $$\iiint\limits_{T} \frac{\partial u_2}{\partial y} dx\, dy\, dz = \iint\limits_{S} u_2 \cos \beta\, dA,$$

(6) $$\iiint\limits_{T} \frac{\partial u_3}{\partial z} dx\, dy\, dz = \iint\limits_{S} u_3 \cos \gamma\, dA.$$

We first prove (6) for a *special region* T which is bounded by a piecewise smooth orientable surface S and has the property that any straight line parallel to any one of the coordinate axes and intersecting T has only *one* segment (or a single point) in common with T. This implies that T can be represented in the form

(7) $$g(x, y) \leqq z \leqq h(x, y)$$

where (x, y) varies in the orthogonal projection $\bar{R}$ of T in the xy-plane. Clearly, $z = g(x, y)$ represents the "bottom" S_2 of S (Fig. 197) while

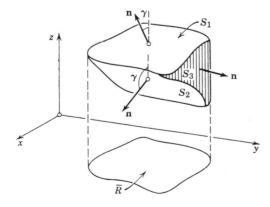

Fig. 197. Example of a special region.

$z = h(x, y)$ represents the "top" S_1 of S, and there may be a remaining vertical portion S_3 of S. (The portion S_3 may degenerate into a curve, as for a sphere.)

To prove (6), we use (7). Since $\mathbf{u}$ is continuously differentiable in some domain containing T, we have

$$\iiint_T \frac{\partial u_3}{\partial z} \, dx \, dy \, dz = \iint_{\bar{R}} \left[\int_{g(x,y)}^{h(x,y)} \frac{\partial u_3}{\partial z} \, dz \right] dx \, dy.$$

We integrate the inner integral:

$$\int_g^h \frac{\partial u_3}{\partial z} \, dz = u_3(x, y, h) - u_3(x, y, g).$$

Hence

(8)
$$\iiint_T \frac{\partial u_3}{\partial z} \, dx \, dy \, dz$$
$$= \iint_{\bar{R}} u_3[x, y, h(x, y)] \, dx \, dy - \iint_{\bar{R}} u_3[x, y, g(x, y)] \, dx \, dy.$$

We now show that the right-hand sides of (6) and (8) are equal. On the lateral portion S_3 of S (Fig. 197), we have $\gamma = \pi/2$ and $\cos \gamma = 0$. Hence this portion does not contribute to the surface integral in (6), and

$$\iint_S u_3 \cos \gamma \, dA = \iint_{S_1} u_3 \cos \gamma \, dA + \iint_{S_2} u_3 \cos \gamma \, dA,$$

cf. Fig. 197. On S_1 in Fig. 197, the angle γ is acute. Hence, by (10″) at the end of Sec. 6.6 we have $dA = \sec \gamma \, dx \, dy$. Since $\cos \gamma \sec \gamma = 1$, we thus obtain

$$\iint_{S_1} u_3 \cos \gamma \, dA = \iint_{\bar{R}} u_3[x, y, h(x, y)] \, dx \, dy$$

which is identical with the first double integral on the right-hand side of (8). On S_2, the angle γ is obtuse (Fig. 197) so that $\pi - \gamma$ corresponds to the acute angle in (10″), Sec. 6.6, and, therefore,

$$dA = \sec(\pi - \gamma) \, dx \, dy = -\sec \gamma \, dx \, dy.$$

Hence

$$\iint_{S_2} u_3 \cos \gamma \, dA = -\iint_{\bar{R}} u_3[x, y, g(x, y)] \, dx \, dy,$$

and this integral is identical with the last integral in (8). This proves (6).

The relations (4) and (5) then follow by merely relabeling the variables and using the fact that, by assumption, T has representations similar to (7), namely,

$$\tilde{g}(y, z) \leq x \leq \tilde{h}(y, z) \qquad \text{and} \qquad g^*(z, x) \leq y \leq h^*(z, x).$$

This establishes the divergence theorem for special regions.

For any region T which can be subdivided into *finitely many* special regions by means of auxiliary surfaces, the theorem follows by adding the result for each part separately; this procedure is analogous to that in the proof of Green's theorem in Sec. 6.4. The surface integrals over the auxiliary surfaces cancel in pairs, and the sum of the remaining surface integrals is the surface integral over the whole boundary S of T; the volume integrals over the parts of T add up to that over T.

The divergence theorem is now proved for any bounded region which is of interest in practical problems. The extension to the most general region T of the type characterized in the theorem would require a certain limit process; this is similar to the situation in the case of Green's theorem in Sec. 6.4.

Green's theorem in the plane (Sec. 6.4) can be used for evaluating line integrals. Similarly, the divergence theorem is suitable for evaluating surface integrals, as may be illustrated by the following example.

Example 1. By transforming to a triple integral evaluate

$$I = \iint\limits_{S} (x^3 \, dy \, dz + x^2 y \, dz \, dx + x^2 z \, dx \, dy)$$

where S is the closed surface consisting of the cylinder $x^2 + y^2 = a^2$ ($0 \leq z \leq b$) and the circular disks $z = 0$ and $z = b$ ($x^2 + y^2 \leq a^2$).

In (3) we now have

$$u_1 = x^3, \qquad u_2 = x^2 y, \qquad u_3 = x^2 z.$$

Hence, making use of the symmetry of the region T bounded by S, the triple integral in (3) assumes the form

$$\iiint\limits_{T} (3x^2 + x^2 + x^2) \, dx \, dy \, dz = 4 \cdot 5 \int_0^b \int_0^a \int_0^{\sqrt{a^2 - y^2}} x^2 \, dx \, dy \, dz.$$

The integral over x equals $\frac{1}{3}(a^2 - y^2)^{3/2}$. Setting $y = a \cos t$, we have

$$dy = -a \sin t \, dt, \qquad (a^2 - y^2)^{3/2} = a^3 \sin^3 t,$$

and the integral over y becomes

$$\frac{1}{3} \int_0^a (a^2 - y^2)^{3/2} \, dy = -\frac{1}{3} a^4 \int_{\pi/2}^0 \sin^4 t \, dt = \frac{\pi}{16} a^4.$$

The integral over z contributes the factor b, and therefore

$$I = 4 \cdot 5 \frac{\pi}{16} ba^4 = \frac{5\pi}{4} a^4 b.$$

6.9 CONSEQUENCES AND APPLICATIONS OF THE DIVERGENCE THEOREM

The divergence theorem has various applications and important consequences, some of which may be illustrated by the subsequent examples. In these examples the regions and functions are assumed to satisfy the conditions under which the divergence theorem holds, and in each case, $\mathbf{n}$ is the *outward* unit normal vector of the boundary surface of the region, as before.

Example 1 (Representation of the divergence independent of the coordinates). Dividing both sides of (1) in Sec. 6.8 by the volume $V(T)$ of the region T, we obtain

$$(1) \qquad \frac{1}{V(T)} \iiint_T \operatorname{div} \mathbf{u} \, dV = \frac{1}{V(T)} \iint_{S(T)} u_n \, dA$$

where $S(T)$ is the boundary surface of T. The basic properties of the triple integral are essentially the same as those of the double integral considered in Sec. 6.3. In particular the **mean value theorem** *for triple integrals* asserts that for any continuous function $f(x, y, z)$ in the region T under consideration,

$$\iiint_T f(x, y, z) \, dV = f(x_0, y_0, z_0) V(T)$$

where $Q: (x_0, y_0, z_0)$ is a (suitable) point in T. From this it follows that

$$(2) \qquad \frac{1}{V(T)} \iiint_T \operatorname{div} \mathbf{u} \, dV = \operatorname{div} \mathbf{u}(x_0, y_0, z_0).$$

Let $P: (x_1, y_1, z_1)$ be any fixed point in T, and let T shrink down onto P, so that the maximum distance $d(T)$ of the points of T from P approaches zero. Then Q must approach P, and from (1) and (2) it follows that the divergence of $\mathbf{u}$ at P is

$$(3) \qquad \operatorname{div} \mathbf{u}(x_1, y_1, z_1) = \lim_{d(T) \to 0} \frac{1}{V(T)} \iint_{S(T)} u_n \, dA.$$

This formula is sometimes used as a definition of the divergence. While the definition of the divergence in Sec. 5.18 involves coordinates, the formula (3) is independent of the coordinate system. Hence *from (3) it follows immediately that the divergence is a scalar function.*

Example 2 (Physical interpretation of the divergence). By means of the divergence theorem we may obtain an intuitive interpretation of the divergence of a vector. For this purpose it is convenient to consider the flow of an incompressible fluid (cf. p. 318) of constant density $\rho = 1$ which is *stationary* or *steady*, that is, does not vary with time. Such a flow is determined by the field of its velocity vector $v(P)$ at any point P.

Let S be the boundary surface of a region T in space, and let n be the outward unit normal vector of S. The mass of fluid which flows through a small portion ΔS of S of area ΔA per unit time from the interior of S to the exterior is equal to $v_n \Delta A$ where[11] $v_n = v \cdot n$ is the normal component of v in the direction of n, taken at a suitable point of ΔS. Consequently, the total mass of fluid which flows across S from T to the outside per unit of time is given by the surface integral

$$\iint_S v_n \, dA.$$

Hence this integral represents the total flow out of T, and the integral

(4)
$$\frac{1}{V} \iint_S v_n \, dA,$$

where V is the volume of T, represents the average flow out of T. Since the flow is steady and the fluid is incompressible, the amount of fluid flowing outward must be continuously supplied. Hence, if the value of the integral (4) is different from zero, there must be *sources (positive sources and negative sources, called sinks)* in T, that is, points where fluid is produced or disappears.

If we let T shrink down to a fixed point P in T we obtain from (4) the *source intensity* at P represented by the right-hand side of (3) (with u_n replaced by v_n). From this and (3) it follows that *the divergence of the velocity vector v of a steady incompressible flow is the source intensity of the flow at the corresponding point.* There are no sources in T if, and only if, $\text{div } v \equiv 0$; in this case,

$$\iint_{S*} v_n \, dA = 0$$

for any closed surface $S*$ in T.

Example 3 (Heat flow). We know that in a body heat will flow in the direction of decreasing temperature. Physical experiments show that the rate of flow is proportional to the gradient of the temperature. This means that the velocity v of the heat flow in a body is of the form

(5)
$$v = -K \text{ grad } U$$

where $U(x, y, z, t)$ is the temperature, t is the time, and K is a positive constant, called the *thermal conductivity* of the body.

Let R be a region in the body and let S be its boundary surface. Then the amount of heat leaving R per unit of time is

$$\iint_S v_n \, dA$$

---

[11] Note that v_n may be negative at a certain point, which means that fluid enters the interior of S at such a point.

where $v_n = \mathbf{v} \cdot \mathbf{n}$ is the component of $\mathbf{v}$ in the direction of the outer unit normal vector $\mathbf{n}$ of S. This expression is obtained in a fashion similar to that in the preceding example. From (5) and the divergence theorem we obtain

$$(6) \qquad \iint_S v_n \, dA = -K \iiint_R \text{div (grad } U) \, dx \, dy \, dz = -K \iiint_R \nabla^2 U \, dx \, dy \, dz;$$

cf. (5) in Sec. 5.18.

On the other hand, the total amount of heat H in R is

$$H = \iiint_R \sigma \rho U \, dx \, dy \, dz$$

where the constant σ is the specific heat of the material of the body and ρ is its density ($=$ mass per unit volume). Hence the time rate of decrease of H is

$$-\frac{\partial H}{\partial t} = -\iiint_R \sigma \rho \, \frac{\partial U}{\partial t} \, dx \, dy \, dz,$$

and this must be equal to the above amount of heat leaving R; from (6) we thus have

$$-\iiint_R \sigma \rho \, \frac{\partial U}{\partial t} \, dx \, dy \, dz = -K \iiint_R \nabla^2 U \, dx \, dy \, dz$$

or

$$\iiint_R \left(\sigma \rho \, \frac{\partial U}{\partial t} - K \nabla^2 U \right) dx \, dy \, dz = 0.$$

Since this holds for any region R in the body, the integrand (if continuous) must be zero everywhere; that is,

$$(7) \qquad \frac{\partial U}{\partial t} = c^2 \nabla^2 U \qquad\qquad c^2 = \frac{K}{\sigma \rho}.$$

This partial differential equation is called the **heat equation**; it is fundamental for heat conduction. Methods for solving problems in heat conduction will be considered in Chap. 9.

Example 4 (A basic property of solutions of Laplace's equation). Consider the formula in the divergence theorem:

$$(8^*) \qquad \iiint_T \text{div } \mathbf{u} \, dV = \iint_S u_n \, dA.$$

Assume that $\mathbf{u}$ is the gradient of a scalar function, say, $\mathbf{u} = \text{grad } f$. Then [cf. (5) in Sec. 5.18]

$$\text{div } \mathbf{u} = \text{div (grad } f) = \nabla^2 f.$$

Furthermore,

$$u_n = \mathbf{u} \cdot \mathbf{n} = \mathbf{n} \cdot \text{grad } f,$$

and from (5) in Sec. 5.16 we see that the right side is the directional derivative of f in the outward normal direction of S. Denoting this derivative by $\partial f/\partial n$, our formula (8*) becomes

(8)
$$\iiint_T \nabla^2 f \, dV = \iint_S \frac{\partial f}{\partial n} \, dA.$$

Obviously this is the three-dimensional analogue of the formula (9) in Sec. 6.4.

Taking into account the assumptions under which the divergence theorem holds, we immediately obtain from (8) the following result.

Theorem 1. *Let $f(x, y, z)$ be a solution of Laplace's equation*

$$\nabla^2 f = \frac{\partial^2 f}{\partial x^2} + \frac{\partial^2 f}{\partial y^2} + \frac{\partial^2 f}{\partial z^2} = 0$$

in some domain D, and suppose that the second partial derivatives of f are continuous in D. Then the integral of the normal derivative of f over any piecewise smooth[12] closed orientable surface in D is zero.

Example 5 (Green's theorem). Let f and g be scalar functions such that $\mathbf{u} = f \operatorname{grad} g$ satisfies the assumptions of the divergence theorem in some region T. Then
$$\operatorname{div} \mathbf{u} = \operatorname{div} (f \operatorname{grad} g) = f\nabla^2 g + \operatorname{grad} f \cdot \operatorname{grad} g$$

(cf. Prob. 14 at the end of Sec. 5.18). Furthermore

$$\mathbf{u} \cdot \mathbf{n} = \mathbf{n} \cdot (f \operatorname{grad} g) = f(\mathbf{n} \cdot \operatorname{grad} g).$$

The expression $\mathbf{n} \cdot \operatorname{grad} g$ is the directional derivative of g in the direction of the outward normal vector $\mathbf{n}$ of the surface S in the divergence theorem. Denoting this derivative by $\partial g/\partial n$ the formula in the divergence theorem becomes

(9)
$$\iiint_T (f\nabla^2 g + \operatorname{grad} f \cdot \operatorname{grad} g) \, dV = \iint_S f\frac{\partial g}{\partial n} \, dA.$$

This formula is called the **first Green's formula** or (together with the assumptions) the *first form of Green's theorem*.

By interchanging f and g we obtain a similar formula. On subtracting this formula from (9), we find

(10)
$$\iiint_T (f\nabla^2 g - g\nabla^2 f) \, dV = \iint_S \left(f\frac{\partial g}{\partial n} - g\frac{\partial f}{\partial n} \right) dA.$$

This formula is called the **second Green's formula** or (together with the assumptions) the *second form of Green's theorem*.

Example 6 (Uniqueness of solutions of Laplace's equation). From (9) we may easily derive the following result.

Theorem 2. *Let $f(x, y, z)$ satisfy the assumptions of Theorem 1, and let f be zero at all points of S. Then it vanishes identically in the region T bounded by S.*

---

[12] Cf. Sec. 6.5.

Proof. In (9), let $g = f$. Then since $\nabla^2 g = 0$, and f is zero on S,

$$\iiint\limits_{T} \operatorname{grad} f \cdot \operatorname{grad} f \, dV = \iiint\limits_{T} |\operatorname{grad} f|^2 \, dV = 0.$$

Since by assumption $|\operatorname{grad} f|$ is continuous in the closed region T and never negative, it must vanish at all points of T. Hence

$$\frac{\partial f}{\partial x} = \frac{\partial f}{\partial y} = \frac{\partial f}{\partial z} = 0,$$

and f is constant in T. But $f = 0$ on S, and as it is continuous in the closed region T, we have $f = 0$ throughout T, and the theorem is proved.

This theorem has an important consequence. Let f_1 and f_2 be functions which satisfy the assumptions of Theorem 1 and take on the same values on S. Then their difference $f_1 - f_2$ satisfies those assumptions and has the value 0 on S. Hence from Theorem 2 it follows that $f_1 - f_2 = 0$ throughout T, and we have the following result.

Theorem 3 (Uniqueness Theorem). *A solution of Laplace's equation which has continuous second partial derivatives in some region T, satisfying the assumptions of the divergence theorem, is uniquely determined by its values on the boundary surface S of T.*

PROBLEMS

Find the volume of the following regions by triple integration.
1. The region in the first octant bounded by the coordinate planes and the plane $x + y + z = 1$.
2. The cube $-1 \leq x \leq 1$, $-1 \leq y \leq 1$, $-1 \leq z \leq 1$.
3. The region in the first octant bounded by the coordinate planes and the plane $x/a + y/b + z/c = 1$ (a, b, c positive).
4. The region in the first octant bounded by $y = x$, $y = x^2$, $z = 1 - x$, and $z = -x^2$.

Find the total mass of a mass distribution of density $\sigma(x, y, z)$ in a region T where
5. $\sigma = x^2 y^2 z^2$, T: the cube in Prob. 2
6. $\sigma = x + y + 2z$, T: the region in Prob. 1
7. $\sigma = z$, T: the region in the first octant bounded by $y = 1 - x^2$ and $z = x$
8. $\sigma = xy$, T: the region in Prob. 1.

Find the moment of inertia $I_x = \iiint\limits_{T} (y^2 + z^2) \, dx \, dy \, dz$ of a mass of density 1 in

a region T about the x-axis, where T is:
9. The rectangular parallelepiped $0 \leq x \leq a$, $-b/2 \leq y \leq b/2$, $-c/2 \leq z \leq c/2$
10. The cube $0 \leq x \leq a$, $0 \leq y \leq a$, $0 \leq z \leq a$
11. The cylinder $y^2 + z^2 \leq a^2$, $0 \leq x \leq h$

12. The cone $y^2 + z^2 \leq x^2$, $0 \leq x \leq h$
13. The sphere $x^2 + y^2 + z^2 \leq a^2$

Evaluate the following surface integrals by the divergence theorem, assuming that S is oriented as in that theorem.

14. $\iint\limits_{S} (x\ dy\ dz + y\ dz\ dx + z\ dx\ dy)$, S: $x^2 + y^2 + z^2 = 1$

15. $\iint\limits_{S} (x^2\ dy\ dz + y^2\ dz\ dx + 2z(xy - x - y)\ dx\ dy)$, S: the surface of the cube

$0 \leq x \leq 1, 0 \leq y \leq 1, 0 \leq z \leq 1$

16. $\iint\limits_{S} (yz\ dy\ dz + zx\ dz\ dx + xy\ dx\ dy)$, S as in Prob. 15

17. $\iint\limits_{S} [3dy\ dz + (y^2 - x^2)\ dz\ dx + 2z(2 - y)\ dx\ dy]$, S: the surface of the

cylinder $x^2 + y^2 \leq a^2$, $0 \leq z \leq h$

Let T be a region in space and S its boundary surface. Using the divergence theorem, prove the following statements.
18. The volume of T is

$$V = \iint\limits_{S} x\ dy\ dz = \iint\limits_{S} y\ dz\ dx = \iint\limits_{S} z\ dx\ dy$$

$$= \frac{1}{3} \iint\limits_{S} (x\ dy\ dz + y\ dz\ dx + z\ dx\ dy).$$

19. If g is harmonic[13] in T, then $\iint\limits_{S} \dfrac{\partial g}{\partial n}\ dA = 0$.

20. If g is harmonic in T, then $\iint\limits_{S} g\ \dfrac{\partial g}{\partial n}\ dA = \iiint\limits_{T} |\mathrm{grad}\ g|^2\ dV$.

21. If g is harmonic in T and $\partial g/\partial n = 0$ on S, then g is constant in T.
22. If f and g are harmonic in T and $\partial f/\partial n = \partial g/\partial n$ on S, then $f = g + c$ in T, where c is a constant.

23. If f and g are harmonic in T, then $\iint\limits_{S} \left(f\ \dfrac{\partial g}{\partial n} - g\ \dfrac{\partial f}{\partial n} \right)\ dA = 0$.

24. Find the volume of the cylinder $x^2 + y^2 \leq a^2$, $0 \leq z \leq h$ by the use of one of the formulas in Prob. 18.
25. Verify the formula in Prob. 19 for the cube T: $0 \leq x \leq 1$, $0 \leq y \leq 1$, $0 \leq z \leq 1$ and $g = e^x \cos y$.
26. Verify the formula in Prob. 20 for T and g as in Prob. 25.

[13] This means that g is a solution of Laplace's equation, and its second partial derivatives are continuous in T.

27. Verify the formula in Prob. 23 for T and g as in Prob. 25 and $f = e^x \sin y$.

28. Using the divergence theorem, show that the volume V of a region T with boundary surface S is

$$V = \frac{1}{3} \iint_S r \cos \theta \, dA$$

where r is the distance of a variable point $P: (x, y, z)$ on S from the origin O, and θ is the angle between the directed line OP and the outer normal to S at P. *Hint:* put $\mathbf{u} = x\mathbf{i} + y\mathbf{j} + z\mathbf{k}$ in (1), Sec. 6.8.

29. Find the volume of a sphere of radius a by means of the formula in Prob. 28.

30. Show that the Laplacian can be represented independently of all coordinate systems in the form

$$\nabla^2 f = \lim_{d(T) \to 0} \frac{1}{V(T)} \iint_{S(T)} \frac{\partial f}{\partial n} \, dA$$

where $d(T)$ is the maximum distance of the points of a region T bounded by $S(T)$ from the point at which the Laplacian is evaluated and $V(T)$ is the volume of T. *Hint:* put $\mathbf{u} = \text{grad } f$ in (3) and use (5), Sec. 5.16, with $\mathbf{b} = \mathbf{n}$, the outer unit normal vector to S.

6.10 STOKES'S THEOREM

In Sec. 6.4 it was shown that double integrals over a plane region can be transformed into line integrals over the boundary curve of the region. Generalizing this result, we shall now consider the corresponding problem in the case of a surface integral.

Stokes's theorem.[14] *Let S be a piecewise smooth[15] oriented surface in space and let the boundary of S be a piecewise smooth simple closed curve C. Let $\mathbf{v}(x, y, z)$ be a continuous vector function which has continuous first partial derivatives in a region of space which contains S in its interior. Then*

(1)
$$\iint_S (\text{curl } \mathbf{v})_n \, dA = \int_C v_t \, ds;$$

here $(\text{curl } \mathbf{v})_n = (\text{curl } \mathbf{v}) \cdot \mathbf{n}$ *is the component of* curl $\mathbf{v}$ *in the direction of a unit normal vector* $\mathbf{n}$ *of S; the integration around C is taken in the sense shown in Fig. 198, and v_t is the component of* $\mathbf{v}$ *in the direction of the tangent vector of C in Fig. 198.*

[14] GEORGE GABRIEL STOKES (1819–1903), Irish mathematician and physicist, who made important contributions to the theory of infinite series and several branches of theoretical physics.

[15] Cf. Secs. 6.1 and 6.5.

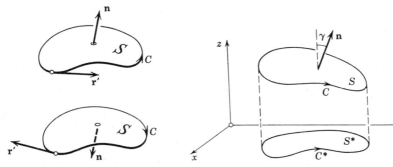

Fig. 198. Stokes's theorem.   **Fig. 199.** Proof of Stokes's theorem.

Proof. We first prove Stokes's theorem for a surface S which can be represented simultaneously in the forms

(2) (a) $z = f(x, y)$,   (b) $y = g(x, z)$,   and   (c) $x = h(y, z)$

where f, g, and h are continuous functions of the respective variables and have continuous first partial derivatives. Let

(3*) $n = \cos \alpha\, i + \cos \beta\, j + \cos \gamma\, k$

be the "upper" unit normal vector of S (Fig. 199), and let

$$v = v_1 i + v_2 j + v_3 k.$$

Representing C in the form $r = r(s)$ where the arc length s increases in the direction of integration, the unit tangent vector is

$$\frac{dr}{ds} = \frac{dx}{ds} i + \frac{dy}{ds} j + \frac{dz}{ds} k,$$

and, therefore,

$$v_t = v \cdot \frac{dr}{ds} = v_1 \frac{dx}{ds} + v_2 \frac{dy}{ds} + v_3 \frac{dz}{ds}.$$

From this we obtain

$$v_t\, ds = v \cdot \frac{dr}{ds}\, ds = v_1\, dx + v_2\, dy + v_3\, dz.$$

Consequently, using the representation of the curl in terms of right-handed Cartesian coordinates [cf. (1), Sec. 5.19], the formula in Stokes's theorem may be written

(3)
$$\iint_S \left[\left(\frac{\partial v_3}{\partial y} - \frac{\partial v_2}{\partial z} \right) \cos \alpha + \left(\frac{\partial v_1}{\partial z} - \frac{\partial v_3}{\partial x} \right) \cos \beta + \left(\frac{\partial v_2}{\partial x} - \frac{\partial v_1}{\partial y} \right) \cos \gamma \right] dA$$
$$= \int_C (v_1\, dx + v_2\, dy + v_3\, dz),$$

where α, β, and γ are defined in connection with (3*).

We prove that in (3) the integrals over the terms involving v_1 are equal; that is,

$$(4) \qquad \iint_S \left(\frac{\partial v_1}{\partial z} \cos \beta - \frac{\partial v_1}{\partial y} \cos \gamma \right) dA = \int_C v_1 \, dx.$$

Let S^* be the orthogonal projection of S in the xy-plane and let C^* be its boundary which is oriented as shown in Fig. 199. Using the representation (2a) of S, we may write the line integral over C as a line integral over C^*:

$$\int_C v_1(x, y, z) \, dx = \int_{C^*} v_1[x, y, f(x, y)] \, dx.$$

We now apply Green's theorem in the plane (Sec. 6.4) to the functions $v_1[x, y, f(x, y)]$ and 0 [instead of f and g in Sec. 6.4]. Then

$$\int_{C^*} v_1[x, y, f(x, y)] \, dx = - \iint_{S^*} \frac{\partial v_1}{\partial y} \, dx \, dy.$$

In the integral on the right,

$$\frac{\partial v_1[x, y, f(x, y)]}{\partial y} = \frac{\partial v_1(x, y, z)}{\partial y} + \frac{\partial v_1(x, y, z)}{\partial z} \frac{\partial f}{\partial y} \qquad [z = f(x, y)]$$

and, therefore,

$$(5) \qquad \int_C v_1(x, y, z) \, dx = - \iint_{S^*} \left(\frac{\partial v_1}{\partial y} + \frac{\partial v_1}{\partial z} \frac{\partial f}{\partial y} \right) dx \, dy.$$

We prove that the integral on the right-hand side of (5) equals the integral on the left-hand side of (4). In the latter integral, we introduce x and y as variables of integration. Writing (2a) in the form

$$F(x, y, z) = z - f(x, y) = 0,$$

we obtain

$$\text{grad } F = - \frac{\partial f}{\partial x} \mathbf{i} - \frac{\partial f}{\partial y} \mathbf{j} + \mathbf{k}.$$

Denoting the length of grad F by a, we have

$$a = |\text{grad } F| = \sqrt{1 + \left(\frac{\partial f}{\partial x} \right)^2 + \left(\frac{\partial f}{\partial y} \right)^2}.$$

Since grad F is normal to S we obtain

$$\mathbf{n} = \pm \frac{\text{grad } F}{a}$$

where $\mathbf{n}$ is defined as before. But the components of both $\mathbf{n}$ and grad F in the positive z-direction are positive, and, therefore,

$$\mathbf{n} = + \frac{\text{grad } F}{a}.$$

Hence from the above representations of $\mathbf{n}$ and grad F in terms of components with respect to the xyz-coordinate system we see that

$$\cos \alpha = -\frac{1}{a}\frac{\partial f}{\partial x}, \qquad \cos \beta = -\frac{1}{a}\frac{\partial f}{\partial y}, \qquad \cos \gamma = \frac{1}{a}.$$

Furthermore, from $(10'')$ at the end of Sec. 6.6 it follows that in (4), $dA = a\,dx\,dy$. Hence

$$\iint_S \left(\frac{\partial v_1}{\partial z}\cos\beta - \frac{\partial v_1}{\partial y}\cos\gamma\right) dA = \iint_{S^*} \left(\frac{\partial v_1}{\partial z}\left(-\frac{1}{a}\frac{\partial f}{\partial y}\right) - \frac{\partial v_1}{\partial y}\frac{1}{a}\right) a\,dx\,dy.$$

The integral on the right equals the right-hand side of (5), and (4) is proved.

If $-\mathbf{n}$ were chosen for the positive normal direction, then by assumption the sense of integration along C would be reversed, and the result would be the same as before. This shows that (4) holds for both choices of the positive normal of S.

Using the representations $(2b)$ and $(2c)$ of S and reasoning exactly as before, we obtain

$$(6) \qquad \iint_S \left(\frac{\partial v_2}{\partial x}\cos\gamma - \frac{\partial v_2}{\partial z}\cos\alpha\right) dA = \int_C v_2\,dy$$

and

$$(7) \qquad \iint_S \left(\frac{\partial v_3}{\partial y}\cos\alpha - \frac{\partial v_3}{\partial x}\cos\beta\right) dA = \int_C v_3\,dz.$$

By adding (4), (6), and (7) we obtain (1). This proves Stokes's theorem for a surface S which can be represented simultaneously in the forms $(2a)$, $(2b)$, and $(2c)$.

As in the proof of the divergence theorem, our result may be immediately extended to a surface S which can be decomposed into finitely many pieces, each of which is of the type considered before. This covers most of the cases which are of practical interest. The proof in the case of a most general surface S satisfying the assumptions of the theorem would require a limit process; this is similar to the situation in the case of Green's theorem in Sec. 6.4.

6.11 CONSEQUENCES AND APPLICATIONS OF STOKES'S THEOREM

Example 1 (Green's theorem in the plane as a special case of Stokes's theorem).
Let $\mathbf{v} = v_1\mathbf{i} + v_2\mathbf{j}$ be a vector function which is continuously differentiable in a simply-connected bounded closed region S in the xy-plane whose boundary C is a piecewise smooth simple closed curve. Then, according to (1) in Sec. 5.19,

$$(\text{curl } \mathbf{v})_n = \frac{\partial v_2}{\partial x} - \frac{\partial v_1}{\partial y}.$$

Furthermore, $v_t\, ds = v_1\, dx + v_2\, dy$, and (1) in the last section takes the form

$$\iint_S \left(\frac{\partial v_2}{\partial x} - \frac{\partial v_1}{\partial y} \right) dA = \int_C (v_1\, dx + v_2\, dy).$$

This shows that Green's theorem in the plane (Sec. 6.4) is a special case of Stokes's theorem.

Example 2 (Physical interpretation of the curl). Let S_r be a circular disk of radius r and center P bounded by the circle C_r (Fig. 200), and let $\mathbf{v}(Q) \equiv \mathbf{v}(x, y, z)$ be a continuously differentiable vector function in S_r. Then by Stokes's theorem and the law of the mean for integrals,

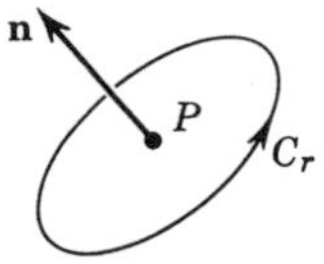

Fig. 200.
Example 2.

$$\int_{C_r} v_t\, ds = \iint_{S_r} (\text{curl } \mathbf{v})_n\, dA = [\text{curl } \mathbf{v}(P^*)]_n A_r$$

where A_r is the area of S_r and P^* is a suitable point of S_r. This may be written

$$[\text{curl } \mathbf{v}(P^*)]_n = \frac{1}{A_r} \int_{C_r} v_t\, ds.$$

In the case of a fluid motion with velocity $\mathbf{v}$, the integral

$$\int_{C_r} v_t\, ds$$

is called the **circulation** of the flow around C_r; it measures the extent to which the corresponding fluid motion is a rotation around the circle C_r. If we now let r approach zero, we find

(1) $$[\text{curl } \mathbf{v}(P)]_n = \lim_{r \to 0} \frac{1}{A_r} \int_{C_r} v_t\, ds;$$

that is, the component of the curl in the positive normal direction can be regarded as the *specific circulation* (circulation per unit area) of the flow in the surface at the corresponding point.

PROBLEMS

Evaluate $\displaystyle\iint\limits_{S} (\text{curl } \mathbf{v})_n \, dA$, where

1. $\mathbf{v} = z\mathbf{i} + x\mathbf{j} + y\mathbf{k}$, S: the square with vertices at $(0, 0, 0)$, $(1, 0, 0)$, $(1, 1, 0)$, $(0, 1, 0)$
2. $\mathbf{v} = z^2\mathbf{i} + x^2\mathbf{j} + y^2\mathbf{k}$, S: the square with vertices at $(0, 0, 1)$, $(1, 0, 1)$, $(1, 1, 1)$, $(0, 1, 1)$
3. $\mathbf{v} = -y^3\mathbf{i} + x^3\mathbf{j}$, S: the circular disk $x^2 + y^2 \leq 1$, $z = 0$

Verify Stokes's theorem for
4. $\mathbf{v}$ and S in Prob. 1   **5.** $\mathbf{v}$ and S in Prob. 2
6. $\mathbf{v}$ in Prob. 2, S: the rectangle with vertices at $(0, 0, 0)$, $(1, 1, 0)$, $(1, 1, 1)$ $(0, 0, 1)$
7. $\mathbf{v}$ and S in Prob. 3. (*Hint*: use a parametric representation of C.)

Evaluate $\displaystyle\int_{C} v_t \, ds$ by Stokes's theorem, where, with respect to right-handed Cartesian coordinates:

8. $\mathbf{v} = -3y\mathbf{i} + 3x\mathbf{j} + z\mathbf{k}$, C: the circle $x = \cos \alpha, y = \sin \alpha, z = 1$ $(0 \leq \alpha \leq 2\pi)$
9. $\mathbf{v} = y^2\mathbf{i} + x^2\mathbf{j} - (x + z)\mathbf{k}$, C: the boundary of the triangle with vertices at $(0, 0, 0)$, $(1, 0, 0)$, $(1, 1, 0)$, (counterclockwise)
10. $\mathbf{v} = 4z\mathbf{i} - 2x\mathbf{j} + 2x\mathbf{k}$, C: the intersection of $x^2 + y^2 = 1$ and $z = y + 1$, oriented clockwise as viewed from the origin
11. $\mathbf{v} = 2y\mathbf{i} + z\mathbf{j} + 3y\mathbf{k}$, C: the intersection of $x^2 + y^2 + z^2 = 6z$ and $z = x + 3$, oriented clockwise as viewed from the origin
12. $\mathbf{v} = y\mathbf{i} + xz^3\mathbf{j} - zy^3\mathbf{k}$, C: the circle $x^2 + y^2 = a^2$, $z = b$ (< 0), oriented counterclockwise as viewed from the origin
13. $\mathbf{v} = x^2\mathbf{i} + y^2\mathbf{j} + z^2\mathbf{k}$, C: the intersection of $x^2 + y^2 + z^2 = a^2$ and $z = y^2$

14. Evaluate $\displaystyle\int_{C} v_t \, ds$, $\mathbf{v} = (-y\mathbf{i} + x\mathbf{j})/(x^2 + y^2)$, C: $x^2 + y^2 = 1$ $(z = 0)$, oriented counterclockwise. Note that Stokes's theorem cannot be applied. Why?
15. If $\mathbf{v}$ and S satisfy the assumptions of Stokes's theorem and $\mathbf{v} = \text{grad } f$, show that $\displaystyle\int_{C} v_t \, ds = 0$ where C is the boundary of S.

Evaluate by Stokes's theorem [cf. (3) in the last section; the coordinates are right-handed]:

16. $\displaystyle\int_{C} (z \, dx + x \, dy + y \, dz)$ where C is the boundary of the triangle with vertices $(1, 0, 0)$, $(0, 1, 0)$, $(0, 0, 1)$, oriented clockwise as viewed from the origin
17. $\displaystyle\int_{C} [(x + y) \, dx + (2x - z) \, dy + (y + z) \, dz]$ where C is the boundary of the triangle with vertices $(2, 0, 0)$, $(0, 3, 0)$, $(0, 0, 6)$, oriented clockwise as viewed from the origin
18. $\displaystyle\int_{C} (\sin z \, dx - \cos x \, dy + \sin y \, dz)$ where C is the boundary of the rectangle $0 \leq x \leq \pi$, $0 \leq y \leq 1$, $z = 3$, oriented clockwise as viewed from the origin

19. $\int_C (yz\,dx + xz\,dy + xy\,dz)$ where C is the intersection of $x^2 + y^2 = 1$ and $z = y^2$

20. $\int_C (e^x\,dx + 2y\,dy - dz)$ where C is the intersection of $x^2 + y^2 + z^2 = 4$ and the coordinate planes

6.12 LINE INTEGRALS INDEPENDENT OF THE PATH

In Sec. 6.2 we saw that the value of a line integral

$$(1) \qquad\qquad \int_C (f\,dx + g\,dy + h\,dz)$$

will in general depend not only on the end points P and Q of the path C but also on C; that is, if we integrate from P to Q along different paths we shall, in general, obtain different values of the integral. We shall now see under what conditions that value depends only on P and Q but does not depend on the path C from P to Q. This problem is of great importance. We first state the following definition.

Let $f(x, y, z)$, $g(x, y, z)$, and $h(x, y, z)$ be functions which are defined and continuous in a domain D of space. Then a line integral of the form (1) is said to be **independent of path** *in* D, if for every pair of end points P and Q in D the value of the integral is the same for all paths C in D starting from P and ending at Q. This value will then, in general, depend on the choice of P and Q but not on the choice of the path joining them.

For formulating our results it will be convenient to use the following concepts.

An expression of the form

$$(2) \qquad\qquad f\,dx + g\,dy + h\,dz,$$

where f, g, h are functions defined in a domain D in space, is called a *first order differential form* in three variables. This form is said to be **exact** or *an exact differential in* D, if it is the differential

$$(3) \qquad\qquad du = \frac{\partial u}{\partial x}\,dx + \frac{\partial u}{\partial y}\,dy + \frac{\partial u}{\partial z}\,dz$$

of a *single-valued* differentiable function $u(x, y, z)$ everywhere in D; that is,

$$(4) \qquad\qquad f\,dx + g\,dy + h\,dz = du.$$

By comparing (3) and (4) we see that *the form* (2) *is exact in D if, and only if, there is a single-valued differentiable function* $u(x, y, z)$ *such that*

(5)
$$f = \frac{\partial u}{\partial x}, \qquad g = \frac{\partial u}{\partial y}, \qquad h = \frac{\partial u}{\partial z}$$

everywhere in D.

In vector language this means that *the form* (2) *is exact in D if, and only if, the vector function*

$$\mathbf{v} = f\mathbf{i} + g\mathbf{j} + h\mathbf{k}$$

is the gradient of a single-valued function $u(x, y, z)$ *in D:*

(5′)
$$\mathbf{v} = \operatorname{grad} u = \frac{\partial u}{\partial x}\mathbf{i} + \frac{\partial u}{\partial y}\mathbf{j} + \frac{\partial u}{\partial z}\mathbf{k}.$$

Theorem 1.   *Let* $f(x, y, z)$, $g(x, y, z)$, *and* $h(x, y, z)$ *be continuous in a domain D in space. Then the line integral*

(6)
$$\int (f\,dx + g\,dy + h\,dz)$$

is independent of path in D if and only if the differential form under the integral sign is exact in D.

Proof.   (a) Suppose that the integral under consideration is independent of path in D. We choose any fixed point P: (x_0, y_0, z_0) and a point Q: (x, y, z) in D. Then we define a function $u(x, y, z)$ as follows:

(7)
$$u(x, y, z) = u_0 + \int_P^Q (f\,dx + g\,dy + h\,dz)$$

where u_0 is a constant and we integrate along an arbitrary path in D from P to Q. Since the integral is independent of path and P is fixed, it does indeed depend only on the coordinates x, y, z of the end point Q and defines a function $u(x, y, z)$ in D. It remains to show that from (7) the relations (5) follow, which means that $f\,dx + g\,dy + h\,dz$ is exact in D. We prove the first of these three relations. Since the integral is independent of path, we may integrate from P to a point Q_1: (x_1, y, z) and then parallel to the x-axis along the line segment from Q_1 to Q (Fig. 201); here Q_1 is chosen so that the whole segment Q_1Q lies in D. Then

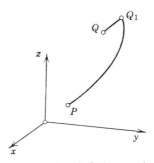

Fig. 201.   Proof of Theorem 1.

$$u(x, y, z) = u_0 + \int_P^{Q_1} (f\,dx + g\,dy + h\,dz) + \int_{Q_1}^Q (f\,dx + g\,dy + h\,dz).$$

We take the partial derivative with respect to x. Because P and Q_1 do not depend on x, that derivative of the first integral is zero. Since on the segment Q_1Q, y and z are constant, the last integral may be written as the definite integral

$$\int_{x_1}^{x} f(x, y, z) \, dx.$$

Hence the partial derivative of that integral with respect to x is $f(x, y, z)$, and the first of the relations (5) is proved. The other two relations can be proved by the same argument.

(b) Conversely, suppose that $f \, dx + g \, dy + h \, dz$ is exact in D. Then (5) holds in D for some single-valued function u. Let C be any path from P to Q in D, and let

$$\mathbf{r}(t) = x(t)\mathbf{i} + y(t)\mathbf{j} + z(t)\mathbf{k} \qquad (t_0 \leq t \leq t_1)$$

be a parametric representation of C so that P corresponds to $t = t_0$ and Q corresponds to $t = t_1$. Then

$$\int_P^Q (f \, dx + g \, dy + h \, dz) = \int_P^Q \left(\frac{\partial u}{\partial x} \, dx + \frac{\partial u}{\partial y} \, dy + \frac{\partial u}{\partial z} \, dz \right)$$

$$= \int_{t_0}^{t_1} \frac{du}{dt} \, dt = u[x(t), y(t), z(t)]_{t=t_0}^{t=t_1} = u(Q) - u(P).$$

This shows that the value of the integral is simply the difference of the values of u at the two end points of C and is, therefore, independent of the path C. Theorem 1 is proved.

The last formula in the proof,

(8) $$\int_P^Q (f \, dx + g \, dy + h \, dz) = u(Q) - u(P),$$

is the analogue of the usual formula

$$\int_a^b f(x) \, dx = F(x) \Big|_a^b = F(b) - F(a) \qquad [\text{where } F'(x) = f(x)]$$

for evaluating definite integrals which is known from elementary calculus. Formula (8) should be used whenever a line integral is independent of path. The practical use of this formula will be explained at the end of this section.

We remember that the work W done by a (variable) force

$$\mathbf{p} = f\mathbf{i} + g\mathbf{j} + h\mathbf{k}$$

in the displacement of a particle along a given path C in space is given by the line integral (7) in Sec. 6.2,

$$W = \int_C \mathbf{p} \cdot d\mathbf{r} = \int_C (f \, dx + g \, dy + h \, dz),$$

the integration being taken in the sense of the displacement. From Theorem 1 we conclude that W depends only on the end points P and Q of the path C if, and only if, the differential form under the integral sign is exact; and this form is exact if, and only if, $\mathbf{p}$ is the gradient of a scalar function u. In this case the field of force given by $\mathbf{p}$ is said to be **conservative** (cf. also at the end of Sec. 5.16).

Example 1. Find the work W done by the force $\mathbf{p} = yz\mathbf{i} + xz\mathbf{j} + xy\mathbf{k}$ in the displacement of a particle along the straight segment C from P: $(1, 1, 1)$ to Q: $(3, 3, 2)$. The work is given by the integral

$$W = \int_C (yz\,dx + xz\,dy + xy\,dz).$$

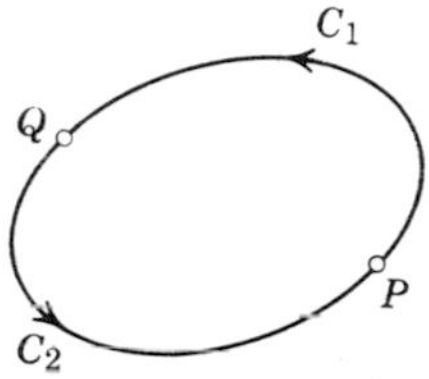

This integral is of the form (1) where

$$f = yz, \qquad g = xz, \qquad h = xy,$$

and (5) holds for $u = xyz$. Hence W is independent of path and we may use (8), finding

$$W = u(Q) - u(P) = u(3, 3, 2) - u(1, 1, 1) = 18 - 1 = 17.$$

Fig. 202. Proof of Theorem 2.

From Theorem 1 we may immediately derive the following important result.

Theorem 2.   *Let f, g, h be continuous in a domain D of space. Then the line integral*

$$\int_C (f\,dx + g\,dy + h\,dz)$$

is independent of path in D if, and only if, it is zero on every simple closed path in D.

Proof.   **(a)** Let C be a simple closed path in D and suppose that the integral is independent of path in D. We subdivide C into two arcs C_1 and C_2 (Fig. 202). Then

$$(9) \quad \oint_C (f\,dx + g\,dy + h\,dz)$$
$$= \int_{C_1} (f\,dx + g\,dy + h\,dz) + \int_{C_2} (f\,dx + g\,dy + h\,dz).$$

Because of independence of path,

$$\int_{C_2} (f\,dx + g\,dy + h\,dz)$$
$$= \int_{C_1{}^*} (f\,dx + g\,dy + h\,dz) = -\int_{C_1} (f\,dx + g\,dy + h\,dz)$$

where $C_1{}^*$ denotes C_1 traced in the reverse direction. From this it follows that the integral on the left-hand side of (9) is zero.

(b) Conversely, suppose that the integral under consideration is zero on every simple closed path in D. Let P and Q be any two points of D, and let C_1 and C_2 be two paths in D which join P and Q and do not cross (Fig. 202). C_1 and C_2 together form a simple closed path C. Therefore,

$$\int_{C_1} (f\,dx + g\,dy + h\,dz) + \int_{C_2} (f\,dx + g\,dy + h\,dz)$$
$$= \oint_C (f\,dx + g\,dy + h\,dz) = 0.$$

From this we obtain

$$\int_{C_2} (f\,dx + g\,dy + h\,dz)$$
$$= -\int_{C_1} (f\,dx + g\,dy + h\,dz) = \int_{C_1^*} (f\,dx + g\,dy + h\,dz).$$

This completes the proof of Theorem 2.

The extension of this theorem to the case of closed paths crossing a finite number of times is immediate.

To make effective practical use of the simple Theorem 1 we need a criterion by which we can decide whether the differential form under the integral sign is exact. Such a criterion will be given in Theorem 3, below. For formulating this theorem we shall need the following concept.

A domain D is called **simply connected** if every closed curve in D can be continuously shrunk to any point in D without leaving D.

For example, the interior of a sphere or a cube, the interior of a sphere with finitely many points removed, and the domain between two concentric spheres are simply connected, while the interior of a torus (cf. Sec. 6.6) and the interior of a cube with one space diagonal removed are not simply connected.

Theorem 3. *Let $f(x, y, z)$, $g(x, y, z)$, and $h(x, y, z)$ be continuous functions having continuous first partial derivatives in a domain D in space. If the line integral*

(10) $$\int (f\,dx + g\,dy + h\,dz)$$

is independent of path in D (and, consequently, $f\,dx + g\,dy + h\,dz$ is exact in D) then

(11) $$\frac{\partial h}{\partial y} = \frac{\partial g}{\partial z}, \qquad \frac{\partial f}{\partial z} = \frac{\partial h}{\partial x}, \qquad \frac{\partial g}{\partial x} = \frac{\partial f}{\partial y}$$

or, in vector language,

(11′) $$\text{curl } \mathbf{v} = \mathbf{0} \qquad\qquad (\mathbf{v} = f\mathbf{i} + g\mathbf{j} + h\mathbf{k})$$

everywhere in D. Conversely, if D is simply connected and (11) *holds everywhere in D, then the integral* (10) *is independent of path in D* (*and, consequently, f dx + g dy + h dz is exact in D*).

Proof. **(a)** Suppose that (10) is independent of path in D. Then, by Theorem 1, the form $f\,dx + g\,dy + h\,dz$ is exact in D and, by (5′),

$$\mathbf{v} = f\mathbf{i} + g\mathbf{j} + h\mathbf{k} = \text{grad } u.$$

From this and (10) in Sec. 5.19 we obtain

$$\text{curl } \mathbf{v} = \text{curl (grad } u) = \mathbf{0}.$$

(b) Conversely, suppose that D is simply connected and (11′) holds everywhere in D. Let C be any simple closed path in D. Since D is simply connected we can find a surface S in D bounded by C. Stokes's theorem (Sec. 6.10) is applicable, and we obtain

$$\int_C (f\,dx + g\,dy + h\,dz) = \int_C v_t\,ds = \iint_S (\text{curl } \mathbf{v})_n\,dA = 0$$

for proper direction on C and normal $\mathbf{n}$ on S. From this and Theorem 2 it follows that the integral (10) is independent of path in D. This completes the proof.

We see that in the case of a line integral

$$\int (f\,dx + g\,dy)$$

in the xy-plane, (11) reduces to the one equality

(11*) $$\dfrac{\partial g}{\partial x} = \dfrac{\partial f}{\partial y}.$$

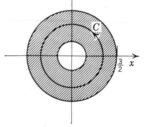

Fig. 203. Example 2.

The assumption that D be simply connected is essential and cannot be omitted. This can be seen from the following example.

Example 2. Let

$$f = -\frac{y}{x^2 + y^2}, \qquad g = \frac{x}{x^2 + y^2}, \qquad h = 0.$$

Differentiation shows that (11*) is satisfied in any domain of the xy-plane not containing the origin, for example, in the domain D: $\frac{1}{2} < \sqrt{x^2 + y^2} < \frac{3}{2}$ shown in Fig. 203. Clearly, D is not simply connected. If the integral

$$I = \int (f\,dx + g\,dy) = \int \frac{-y\,dx + x\,dy}{x^2 + y^2}$$

were independent of path in D, then $I = 0$ on any closed curve in D—for example, on the circle $x^2 + y^2 = 1$. But setting $x = r \cos \theta$, $y = r \sin \theta$, and noting that the circle is represented by $r = 1$, we easily obtain

$$I = \int_0^{2\pi} d\theta = 2\pi,$$

the integration being taken once around the circle in the counterclockwise sense. In fact, since D is not simply connected, we cannot apply Theorem 3 and conclude that I is independent of path in D. Furthermore, we see that

$$f \, dx + g \, dy = du \qquad \text{where} \qquad u = \arctan \frac{y}{x} = \theta,$$

but u is not single-valued in D. On the other hand, if we take the so-called "principal value" of u, defined by $-\pi < u \leq \pi$, then u is not differentiable (not even continuous) at the points of the negative x-axis in D; this was required in connection with the exactness of a differential form.

If a line integral is independent of path, it can be evaluated by means of the formula (8), and the corresponding function $u(x, y, z)$ can be found by a single integration as follows.

Let P: (x_0, y_0, z_0) and Q: (x, y, z), as before. Then we obtain from (8)

$$u(Q) = u(x, y, z) = u(x_0, y_0, z_0) + \int_{(x_0, y_0, z_0)}^{(x, y, z)} (f \, dx + g \, dy + h \, dz);$$

integrating from P to Q along the line segment

$$(12) \quad x = x_0 + (x - x_0)t, \qquad y = y_0 + (y - y_0)t, \qquad z = z_0 + (z - z_0)t$$
$$(0 \leq t \leq 1),$$

we obtain $dx = (x - x_0) \, dt$, etc. Therefore,

$$(13) \quad u(x, y, z) = u(x_0, y_0, z_0) + \int_0^1 [(x - x_0)f + (y - y_0)g + (z - z_0)h] \, dt$$

where $f = f(x, y, z)$, etc., and x, y, z are given by (12).

Another way of determining $u(x, y, z)$ is to integrate one of the relations (5), for example, $\partial u/\partial x = f$, finding

$$u = \int f \, dx + a(y, z),$$

and then to determine the function $a(y, z)$ by differentiating this result with respect to y and z and using the other two relations (5); cf. the following example.

Example 3. Evaluate

$$I = \int_C [2xyz^2 \, dx + (x^2z^2 + z \cos yz) \, dy + (2x^2yz + y \cos yz) \, dz]$$

on any path C from P: $(0, 0, 1)$ to Q: $(1, \pi/4, 2)$.

From Theorem 3 it follows that the integral is independent of path in space. Since $f = 2xyz^2$ we obtain from the first relation (5)

(14)
$$u = \int f \, dx = x^2yz^2 + a(y, z).$$

From this and the second relation (5) it follows that

$$\frac{\partial u}{\partial y} = x^2z^2 + \frac{\partial a}{\partial y} = g = x^2z^2 + z \cos yz.$$

Hence we must have

$$\frac{\partial a}{\partial y} = z \cos yz, \qquad a = \sin yz + c(z).$$

From this, the third relation (5), and (14) we obtain

$$\frac{\partial u}{\partial z} = 2x^2yz + y \cos yz + \frac{dc}{dz} = h = 2x^2yz + y \cos yz$$

Hence $dc/dz = 0$, $c = const$ and, therefore,

$$u(x, y, z) = x^2yz^2 + a = x^2yz^2 + \sin yz + c.$$

This yields the result

$$I = [x^2yz^2 + \sin yz + c]\Big|_P^Q = \pi + \sin\frac{\pi}{2} = \pi + 1.$$

PROBLEMS

Are the following differential forms exact?

1. $x \, dx + y \, dy + z \, dz$
2. $yz \, dx + xz \, dy + xy \, dz$
3. $y \cos xy \, dx + x \cos xy \, dy + \sin z \, dz$
4. $y \, dx + z \, dy + x \, dz$
5. $x^2 \, dx + z^2 \, dy + y^2 \, dz$
6. $dx - 2y \, dy + 3z^2 \, dz$
7. $6xy^3 \, dx + 9x^2y^2 \, dy$
8. $(x + y) \, dx + (x + y) \, dy + z \, dz$
9. $(x - y) \, dx + (y - x) \, dy + xy \, dz$
10. $e^{yz} \, dx + \sin xy \, dy - dz$

In each case show that the given differential form is exact and find a function u such that the form equals du.

11. $dx + dy + dz$
12. $2dx - 4dy + 6dz$
13. $x \, dx + y \, dy$
14. $yz \, dx + xz \, dy + xy \, dz$
15. $yze^{xyz} \, dx + xze^{xyz} \, dy + xye^{xyz} \, dz$
16. $\cos x \, dx + \sin y \, dy + dz$
17. $(y + z) \, dx + (x + z) \, dy + (y + x) \, dz$
18. $2xy \, dx + (x^2 + z^2) \, dy + 2yz \, dz$

Show that the form under the integral sign is exact and evaluate:

19. $\displaystyle\int_{(0,0,0)}^{(1,1,1)} (dx + dy + dz)$
20. $\displaystyle\int_{(2,0,0)}^{(1,2,3)} (x \, dx + y \, dy + z \, dz)$

21. $\displaystyle\int_{(0,0,1)}^{(1,0,-2)} [(1 + 3z) \, dx - dy + 3x \, dz]$
22. $\displaystyle\int_{(1,1,2)}^{(3,-2,-1)} (yz \, dx + xz \, dy + xy \, dz)$

23. $\displaystyle\int_{(0,0,0)}^{(a,b,c)} (2x \, dx + z \, dy + y \, dz)$
24. $\displaystyle\int_{(0,1,\pi/2)}^{(\pi,0,-\pi/2)} (\cos x \, dx + \sin z \, dz)$

25. Prove Theorem 2 for closed paths crossing a finite number of times.

chapter 7

MATRICES AND DETERMINANTS. SYSTEMS OF LINEAR EQUATIONS

Matrix calculus is an elegant and powerful mathematical language in connection with linear equations, linear transformations, systems of differential equations, etc. For this reason matrices have become more and more important in physics, engineering, statistics, and other fields. The development in this direction started about thirty years ago and will continue even more rapidly in the future.

The present chapter will be devoted to matrices (including matrix eigenvalue problems), determinants, and linear equations. In Secs. 7.1 and 7.2 we shall present the basic concepts and rules of matrix algebra. Then we shall consider determinants and systems of linear equations (Secs. 7.3–7.10), and finally matrix eigenvalue problems.

The chapter includes numerical methods for solving systems of linear equations and matrix eigenvalue problems.

Prerequisite for this chapter: vector algebra (Secs. 5.1–5.7).

Sections which may be omitted in a shorter course: 7.9, 7.13–7.15.

References: Appendix 1, Part D.

Answers to problems: Appendix 2.

7.1 BASIC CONCEPTS. ADDITION OF MATRICES

The concept of a matrix arises in connection with linear relations such as linear transformations and systems of linear equations. For example, consider the linear transformation

$$y_1 = a_{11}x_1 + a_{12}x_2$$
$$y_2 = a_{21}x_1 + a_{22}x_2$$

where the coefficients a_{11}, a_{12}, a_{21}, and a_{22} are given numbers while x_1, x_2 and also y_1, y_2 are variable quantities (for instance, the coordinates of two different coordinate systems in the plane). Arranging the coefficients in the way they occur in the transformation and enclosing them in parentheses, we obtain an array of the form

$$\begin{pmatrix} a_{11} & a_{12} \\ a_{21} & a_{22} \end{pmatrix}.$$

This array is an example of a matrix.

Let us now define the concept of a matrix and some related basic notions.

A rectangular array of (real or complex) numbers of the form

$$\begin{pmatrix} a_{11} & a_{12} & \cdots & a_{1n} \\ a_{21} & a_{22} & \cdots & a_{2n} \\ \cdot & \cdot & \cdots & \cdot \\ a_{m1} & a_{m2} & \cdots & a_{mn} \end{pmatrix}$$

is called a **matrix**. The numbers $a_{11}, \cdots, a_{mn}$ are called the **elements** of the matrix. The horizontal lines are called **rows** or *row vectors*, and the vertical lines are called **columns** or *column vectors* of the matrix. A matrix with m rows and n columns is called an $(m \times n)$ matrix (read "m by n matrix").

Matrices will be denoted by capital (upper case) bold-faced letters **A**, **B**, etc., or by (a_{jk}), (b_{jk}), etc., that is, by writing the general element of the matrix, enclosed in parentheses.

In the **double-subscript notation** *for the elements, the first subscript always denotes the row and the second subscript the column containing the given element.*

A matrix

$$(a_1, \cdots, a_n)$$

having only one row is called a **row matrix** or *row vector*. A matrix

$$\begin{pmatrix} b_1 \\ \cdot \\ \cdot \\ \cdot \\ b_m \end{pmatrix}$$

having only one column is called a **column matrix** or *column vector*. Row and column matrices will be denoted by small (lower case) bold-faced letters, in agreement with the notation used in vector calculus.

Two $(m \times n)$ matrices $A = (a_{jk})$ and $B = (b_{jk})$ are said to be **equal** if, and only if, corresponding elements are equal, that is,

$$a_{jk} = b_{jk} \quad \text{for all} \quad j = 1, \cdots, m, \quad k = 1, \cdots, n.$$

Then we write

$$A = B.$$

Note that this definition of equality refers only to matrices which have the *same* number of rows and the *same* number of columns.

We shall now consider the addition of matrices.

The **sum** of two $(m \times n)$ matrices $A = (a_{jk})$ and $B = (b_{jk})$ is defined as the $(m \times n)$ matrix $C = (c_{jk})$ whose elements are

$$(1) \qquad\qquad c_{jk} = a_{jk} + b_{jk}, \qquad \begin{aligned} j &= 1, \cdots, m, \\ k &= 1, \cdots, n, \end{aligned}$$

and we write

$$C = A + B.$$

Similarly, the matrix

$$D = A - B = (a_{jk} - b_{jk})$$

is called the *difference* of A and B.

Note that addition and subtraction are defined only for matrices having the same number of rows and the same number of columns.

Example 1. Let

$$A = \begin{pmatrix} -4 & 6 & 3 \\ 0 & 1 & 2 \end{pmatrix}, \qquad B = \begin{pmatrix} 5 & -1 & 0 \\ 3 & 1 & 0 \end{pmatrix}.$$

Then

$$A + B = \begin{pmatrix} 1 & 5 & 3 \\ 3 & 2 & 2 \end{pmatrix}, \qquad A - B = \begin{pmatrix} -9 & 7 & 3 \\ -3 & 0 & 2 \end{pmatrix}.$$

The **product** *of a matrix* $A = (a_{jk})$ *by a number* c is defined as the matrix (ca_{jk}) and is denoted by cA or Ac; thus

$$cA = Ac = \begin{pmatrix} ca_{11} & ca_{12} & \cdots & ca_{1n} \\ ca_{21} & ca_{22} & \cdots & ca_{2n} \\ \cdot & \cdot & \cdots & \cdot \\ ca_{m1} & ca_{m2} & \cdots & ca_{mn} \end{pmatrix}.$$

Instead of $(-1)\mathbf{A}$ we simply write $-\mathbf{A}$, and $\mathbf{A} + (-\mathbf{B})$ will be written $\mathbf{A} - \mathbf{B}$, in agreement with our definition of subtraction.

Example 2. Let

$$A = \begin{pmatrix} 2.7 & -1.8 \\ 0.9 & 3.6 \end{pmatrix}.$$

Then

$$\mathbf{A} + \mathbf{A} = 2\mathbf{A} = \begin{pmatrix} 5.4 & -3.6 \\ 1.8 & 7.2 \end{pmatrix}, \qquad \frac{10}{9}\mathbf{A} = \begin{pmatrix} 3 & -2 \\ 1 & 4 \end{pmatrix}.$$

The reader may prove that for any $(m \times n)$ matrices $\mathbf{A}$, $\mathbf{B}$, $\mathbf{C}$ and any constants a, b, c the following laws hold:

$$\mathbf{A} + \mathbf{B} = \mathbf{B} + \mathbf{A}$$
$$\mathbf{A} + (\mathbf{B} + \mathbf{C}) = (\mathbf{A} + \mathbf{B}) + \mathbf{C}$$
(2)
$$c(\mathbf{A} + \mathbf{B}) = c\mathbf{A} + c\mathbf{B}$$
$$(a + b)\mathbf{A} = a\mathbf{A} + b\mathbf{A}$$
$$a(b\mathbf{A}) = (ab)\mathbf{A}.$$

Another frequently used operation is the *transposition of a matrix*. The **transpose** of an $(m \times n)$ matrix $\mathbf{A} = (a_{jk})$ is defined as the $(n \times m)$ matrix (a_{kj}) and is denoted by $\mathbf{A}^{\mathsf{T}}$. Thus

$$\mathbf{A}^{\mathsf{T}} = (a_{kj}) = \begin{pmatrix} a_{11} & a_{21} & \cdots & a_{m1} \\ a_{12} & a_{22} & \cdots & a_{m2} \\ \cdot & \cdot & \cdots & \cdot \\ a_{1n} & a_{2n} & \cdots & a_{mn} \end{pmatrix},$$

and we see that the row vectors of $\mathbf{A}$ become the column vectors of $\mathbf{A}^{\mathsf{T}}$ and vice versa.

Example 3. If

$$A = \begin{pmatrix} 5 & -8 & 1 \\ 4 & 0 & 0 \end{pmatrix}, \qquad \text{then} \qquad A^{\mathsf{T}} = \begin{pmatrix} 5 & 4 \\ -8 & 0 \\ 1 & 0 \end{pmatrix}.$$

Example 4. If

$$\mathbf{b} = (7 \quad 5 \quad -2), \qquad \text{then} \qquad \mathbf{b}^{\mathsf{T}} = \begin{pmatrix} 7 \\ 5 \\ -2 \end{pmatrix}.$$

The reader may prove that

(3)
$$(\mathbf{A} + \mathbf{B})^{\mathsf{T}} = \mathbf{A}^{\mathsf{T}} + \mathbf{B}^{\mathsf{T}}.$$

The elements of a matrix may be real or complex numbers. If all the elements of a matrix are real, the matrix is called a **real matrix**.

A matrix having the same number of rows and columns is called a **square matrix**, and the number of rows is called its **order**. The diagonal containing the elements $a_{11}, a_{22}, \cdots, a_{nn}$ of the square matrix is called the **principal diagonal**. Square matrices are of particular importance.

A real square matrix $\mathbf{A} = (a_{jk})$ is said to be **symmetric** if it is equal to its transpose, that is, if

(4) $$\mathbf{A}^\mathsf{T} = \mathbf{A} \quad \text{or} \quad a_{kj} = a_{jk} \quad (j, k = 1, \cdots, n)$$

A real square matrix $\mathbf{A} = (a_{jk})$ is said to be **skew-symmetric** if

(5) $$\mathbf{A}^\mathsf{T} = -\mathbf{A}, \quad \text{that is,} \quad a_{kj} = -a_{jk} \quad (j, k = 1, \cdots, n).$$

Note that for $k = j$ in (5) we have $a_{jj} = -a_{jj}$ which implies that the elements in the principal diagonal of a skew-symmetric matrix are all zero.

Any real square matrix $\mathbf{A}$ may be written as the sum of the symmetric matrix $\mathbf{R}$ and a skew-symmetric matrix $\mathbf{S}$, where

$$\mathbf{R} = \tfrac{1}{2}(\mathbf{A} + \mathbf{A}^\mathsf{T})$$

and

$$\mathbf{S} = \tfrac{1}{2}(\mathbf{A} - \mathbf{A}^\mathsf{T}).$$

Example 5. The matrices

$$\mathbf{A} = \begin{pmatrix} -3 & 1 & 5 \\ 1 & 0 & -2 \\ 5 & -2 & 4 \end{pmatrix} \quad \text{and} \quad \mathbf{B} = \begin{pmatrix} 0 & -4 & 1 \\ 4 & 0 & -5 \\ -1 & 5 & 0 \end{pmatrix}$$

are symmetric and skew-symmetric, respectively. The matrix

$$\mathbf{A} = \begin{pmatrix} 2 & 3 \\ 5 & -1 \end{pmatrix}$$

may be written in the form $\mathbf{A} = \mathbf{R} + \mathbf{S}$ where

$$\mathbf{R} = \tfrac{1}{2}(\mathbf{A} + \mathbf{A}^\mathsf{T}) = \begin{pmatrix} 2 & 4 \\ 4 & -1 \end{pmatrix} \quad \text{and} \quad \mathbf{S} = \tfrac{1}{2}(\mathbf{A} - \mathbf{A}^\mathsf{T}) = \begin{pmatrix} 0 & -1 \\ 1 & 0 \end{pmatrix}$$

are symmetric and skew-symmetric, respectively.

A square matrix $\mathbf{A} = (a_{jk})$ whose elements above the principal diagonal (or below the principal diagonal) are all zero is called a **triangular matrix**.

For example,

$$\mathbf{T}_1 = \begin{pmatrix} 1 & 0 & 0 \\ -2 & 3 & 0 \\ 5 & 0 & 2 \end{pmatrix} \quad \text{and} \quad \mathbf{T}_2 = \begin{pmatrix} 1 & 6 & -1 \\ 0 & 2 & 3 \\ 0 & 0 & 4 \end{pmatrix}$$

are triangular matrices.

A square matrix $\mathbf{A} = (a_{jk})$ whose elements above and below the principal diagonal are all zero, that is, $a_{jk} = 0$ for all $j \neq k$, is called a **diagonal matrix**. For example,

$$\begin{pmatrix} 2 & 0 & 0 \\ 0 & 1 & 0 \\ 0 & 0 & -4 \end{pmatrix} \quad \text{and} \quad \begin{pmatrix} 2 & 0 & 0 \\ 0 & 2 & 0 \\ 0 & 0 & 2 \end{pmatrix}$$

are diagonal matrices.

A diagonal matrix whose elements in the principal diagonal are all 1 is called a **unit matrix** and will be denoted by $\mathbf{I}$. For example, the three-rowed unit matrix is

$$\mathbf{I} = \begin{pmatrix} 1 & 0 & 0 \\ 0 & 1 & 0 \\ 0 & 0 & 1 \end{pmatrix}.$$

A matrix whose elements are all zero is called a **zero matrix**, or **null matrix**, and is denoted by $\mathbf{0}$. Clearly, for any $(m \times n)$ matrix $\mathbf{A}$,

$$\mathbf{A} + \mathbf{0} = \mathbf{0} + \mathbf{A} = \mathbf{A},$$

where $\mathbf{0}$ is the $(m \times n)$ null matrix.

PROBLEMS

Let $\mathbf{A} = \begin{pmatrix} 2 & -4 & 1 \\ 0 & 3 & 5 \end{pmatrix}$, $\quad \mathbf{B} = \begin{pmatrix} -1 & 3 & 1 \\ 2 & 0 & 5 \end{pmatrix}$, $\quad \mathbf{C} = \begin{pmatrix} 0 & 1 & 2 \\ 0 & -1 & 3 \end{pmatrix}$. Find

1. $\mathbf{A} + \mathbf{B}$ 2. $\mathbf{B} - \mathbf{C}$ 3. $3\mathbf{A} - 2\mathbf{C}$ 4. $\mathbf{A}^\mathsf{T}, \mathbf{B}^\mathsf{T}, \mathbf{C}^\mathsf{T}$
5. $(\mathbf{B} + \mathbf{C})^\mathsf{T}$ 6. $(3\mathbf{B} - \mathbf{A})^\mathsf{T}$ 7. $(\mathbf{A}^\mathsf{T})^\mathsf{T}$ 8. $(\mathbf{A} + \mathbf{B} + \mathbf{C})^\mathsf{T}$
9. Is $\mathbf{A} + \mathbf{B}^\mathsf{T}$ defined?

Let $\mathbf{H} = \begin{pmatrix} 1 & 3 & 5 \\ 0 & 2 & 4 \\ 0 & 0 & 6 \end{pmatrix}$, $\mathbf{K} = \begin{pmatrix} 0 & -1 & 2 \\ 1 & 0 & 3 \\ -2 & -3 & 0 \end{pmatrix}$, $\mathbf{L} = \begin{pmatrix} 1 & 2 & 6 \\ 3 & 4 & 7 \\ 5 & 8 & 9 \end{pmatrix}$. Find

10. $\mathbf{H}^\mathsf{T}$ 11. $\mathbf{K}^\mathsf{T}$ 12. $\mathbf{H} - \mathbf{L}$ 13. $\mathbf{K} + \mathbf{K}^\mathsf{T}$
14. Represent $\mathbf{H}$ as the sum of a symmetric and a skew-symmetric matrix.
15. Same for $\mathbf{L}$.
16. Represent $\mathbf{L}$ as a sum of two triangular matrices. Is this representation unique?

Prove the following statements and formulas.

17. The formulas (2)   18. $(\mathbf{A} + \mathbf{B})^\mathsf{T} = \mathbf{A}^\mathsf{T} + \mathbf{B}^\mathsf{T}$
19. $(a\mathbf{A})^\mathsf{T} = a\mathbf{A}^\mathsf{T}, (\mathbf{A}^\mathsf{T})^\mathsf{T} = \mathbf{A}$
20. The transpose of a triangular matrix is triangular.

7.2   MATRIX MULTIPLICATION

We shall now define the multiplication of a matrix by a matrix. This definition will be suggested by the use of matrices in connection with linear transformations. To illustrate this, let us start with a very simple case.

We consider three coordinate systems in the plane which we denote as the x_1x_2-system, the y_1y_2-system, and the z_1z_2-system, and we assume that these systems are related by the linear transformations

(1)
$$x_1 = a_{11}y_1 + a_{12}y_2$$
$$x_2 = a_{21}y_1 + a_{22}y_2$$

and

(2)
$$y_1 = b_{11}z_1 + b_{12}z_2$$
$$y_2 = b_{21}z_1 + b_{22}z_2 .$$

Then it is clear that the x_1x_2-coordinates can be obtained directly from the z_1z_2-coordinates by a single linear transformation of the form

(3)
$$x_1 = c_{11}z_1 + c_{12}z_2$$
$$x_2 = c_{21}z_1 + c_{22}z_2$$

whose coefficients can be found by inserting (2) into (1),

$$x_1 = a_{11}(b_{11}z_1 + b_{12}z_2) + a_{12}(b_{21}z_1 + b_{22}z_2)$$
$$x_2 = a_{21}(b_{11}z_1 + b_{12}z_2) + a_{22}(b_{21}z_1 + b_{22}z_2)$$

and comparing this and (3); the result is

$$c_{11} = a_{11}b_{11} + a_{12}b_{21} \qquad c_{12} = a_{11}b_{12} + a_{12}b_{22}$$
$$c_{21} = a_{21}b_{11} + a_{22}b_{21} \qquad c_{22} = a_{21}b_{12} + a_{22}b_{22}$$

or briefly

(4)
$$c_{jk} = a_{j1}b_{1k} + a_{j2}b_{2k} = \sum_{i=1}^{2} a_{ji}b_{ik} \qquad j, k = 1, 2.$$

Now the coefficient matrices of the transformations (1) and (2) are

$$\mathbf{A} = \begin{pmatrix} a_{11} & a_{12} \\ a_{21} & a_{22} \end{pmatrix} \quad \text{and} \quad \mathbf{B} = \begin{pmatrix} b_{11} & b_{12} \\ b_{21} & b_{22} \end{pmatrix},$$

and we define the product $\mathbf{AB}$ (in this order) of $\mathbf{A}$ and $\mathbf{B}$ to be the coefficient matrix

$$\mathbf{C} = \begin{pmatrix} c_{11} & c_{12} \\ c_{21} & c_{22} \end{pmatrix}$$

of the "composed transformation" (3), that is,

$$C = AB$$

where the elements of C are given by (4).

If we write A in terms of row vectors, say,

$$A = \begin{pmatrix} \mathbf{a}_1 \\ \mathbf{a}_2 \end{pmatrix} \quad \text{where} \quad \begin{aligned} \mathbf{a}_1 &= (a_{11} \quad a_{12}) \\ \mathbf{a}_2 &= (a_{21} \quad a_{22}) \end{aligned}$$

and B in terms of column vectors, say,

$$B = (\mathbf{b}_1 \quad \mathbf{b}_2) \quad \text{where} \quad \mathbf{b}_1 = \begin{pmatrix} b_{11} \\ b_{21} \end{pmatrix}, \quad \mathbf{b}_2 = \begin{pmatrix} b_{12} \\ b_{22} \end{pmatrix},$$

then the elements of C may simply be written as scalar products:

$$c_{11} = \mathbf{a}_1 \cdot \mathbf{b}_1, \qquad c_{12} = \mathbf{a}_1 \cdot \mathbf{b}_2,$$
$$c_{21} = \mathbf{a}_2 \cdot \mathbf{b}_1, \qquad c_{22} = \mathbf{a}_2 \cdot \mathbf{b}_2.$$

Example 1. Let

$$A = \begin{pmatrix} 2 & 1 \\ 3 & 4 \end{pmatrix} \quad \text{and} \quad B = \begin{pmatrix} 1 & -2 \\ 5 & 3 \end{pmatrix}.$$

Then, by (4),

$$AB = \begin{pmatrix} 2 & 1 \\ 3 & 4 \end{pmatrix}\begin{pmatrix} 1 & -2 \\ 5 & 3 \end{pmatrix} = \begin{pmatrix} 2 \cdot 1 + 1 \cdot 5 & 2 \cdot (-2) + 1 \cdot 3 \\ 3 \cdot 1 + 4 \cdot 5 & 3 \cdot (-2) + 4 \cdot 3 \end{pmatrix} = \begin{pmatrix} 7 & -1 \\ 23 & 6 \end{pmatrix}.$$

To arrive at the definition of the multiplication of two matrices in the general case, we now extend the preceding consideration to two general linear transformations, say, the transformation

$$(5) \qquad \begin{aligned} x_1 &= a_{11}y_1 + \cdots + a_{1n}y_n \\ x_2 &= a_{21}y_1 + \cdots + a_{2n}y_n \\ &\cdots\cdots\cdots\cdots\cdots\cdots \\ x_m &= a_{m1}y_1 + \cdots + a_{mn}y_n \end{aligned}$$

and the transformation

$$(6) \qquad \begin{aligned} y_1 &= b_{11}z_1 + \cdots + b_{1p}z_p \\ y_2 &= b_{21}z_1 + \cdots + b_{2p}z_p \\ &\cdots\cdots\cdots\cdots\cdots\cdots \\ y_n &= b_{n1}z_1 + \cdots + b_{np}z_p. \end{aligned}$$

By inserting (6) into (5) we find that $x_1, \cdots, x_m$ can be expressed in terms of $z_1, \cdots, z_p$ in the form

$$(7) \qquad \begin{aligned} x_1 &= c_{11}z_1 + \cdots + c_{1p}z_p \\ x_2 &= c_{21}z_1 + \cdots + c_{2p}z_p \\ &\cdots\cdots\cdots\cdots\cdots\cdots \\ x_m &= c_{m1}z_1 + \cdots + c_{mp}z_p \end{aligned}$$

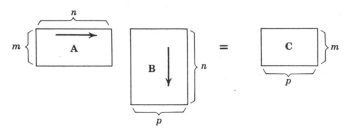

Fig. 204. Matrix multiplication. $\mathbf{AB} = \mathbf{C}$.

where the coefficients are given by the formula

$$c_{jk} = a_{j1}b_{1k} + a_{j2}b_{2k} + \cdots + a_{jn}b_{nk}.$$

The requirement that the product $\mathbf{AB}$ (in this order) of the coefficient matrices $\mathbf{A} = (a_{jk})$ and $\mathbf{B} = (b_{jk})$ of the transformations (5) and (6) be the coefficient matrix $\mathbf{C} = (c_{jk})$ of the "composed transformation" (7) leads to the following definition.

Definition. *Let* $\mathbf{A} = (a_{jk})$ *be an* $(m \times n)$ *matrix and* $\mathbf{B} = (b_{jk})$ *an* $(r \times p)$ *matrix, then the product* $\mathbf{AB}$ *(in this order) is defined only when* $r = n$ *and is the* $(m \times p)$ *matrix* $\mathbf{C} = (c_{jk})$ *whose elements are*

(8) $$c_{jk} = a_{j1}b_{1k} + a_{j2}b_{2k} + \cdots + a_{jn}b_{nk} = \sum_{i=1}^{n} a_{ji}b_{ik}.$$

Instead of $\mathbf{AA}$ we simply write $\mathbf{A}^2$, etc.

We see that c_{jk} *is the scalar product of the j-th row vector of the first matrix,* $\mathbf{A}$, *and the k-th column vector of the second matrix,* $\mathbf{B}$; *that is, if we write*

$$\mathbf{A} = \begin{pmatrix} \mathbf{a}_1 \\ \mathbf{a}_2 \\ \cdot \\ \cdot \\ \cdot \\ \mathbf{a}_m \end{pmatrix} \quad \text{and} \quad \mathbf{B} = (\mathbf{b}_1 \quad \mathbf{b}_2 \quad \cdots \quad \mathbf{b}_p)$$

where $\mathbf{a}_1, \cdots, \mathbf{a}_m$ *are the row vectors of* $\mathbf{A}$ *and* $\mathbf{b}_1, \cdots, \mathbf{b}_p$ *are the column vectors of* $\mathbf{B}$, *then*

(9) $$\mathbf{C} = \begin{pmatrix} \mathbf{a}_1 \cdot \mathbf{b}_1 & \mathbf{a}_1 \cdot \mathbf{b}_2 & \cdots & \mathbf{a}_1 \cdot \mathbf{b}_p \\ \mathbf{a}_2 \cdot \mathbf{b}_1 & \mathbf{a}_2 \cdot \mathbf{b}_2 & \cdots & \mathbf{a}_2 \cdot \mathbf{b}_p \\ \cdot & \cdot & \cdots & \cdot \\ \mathbf{a}_m \cdot \mathbf{b}_1 & \mathbf{a}_m \cdot \mathbf{b}_2 & \cdots & \mathbf{a}_m \cdot \mathbf{b}_p \end{pmatrix}.$$

The process of matrix multiplication is, therefore, conveniently referred to as the **multiplication of rows into columns**.

Example 2. Let

$$A = \begin{pmatrix} 3 & 2 & -1 \\ 0 & 4 & 6 \end{pmatrix} \qquad \text{and} \qquad B = \begin{pmatrix} 1 & 0 & 2 \\ 5 & 3 & 1 \\ 6 & 4 & 2 \end{pmatrix}.$$

Then, by (8), the product **AB** is

$$AB = \begin{pmatrix} 3 & 2 & -1 \\ 0 & 4 & 6 \end{pmatrix} \begin{pmatrix} 1 & 0 & 2 \\ 5 & 3 & 1 \\ 6 & 4 & 2 \end{pmatrix} = \begin{pmatrix} 7 & 2 & 6 \\ 56 & 36 & 16 \end{pmatrix},$$

while the product **BA** is not defined.

The multiplication of matrices by vectors and the matrix multiplication of vectors by vectors may be illustrated by the following examples.

Example 3.

$$\begin{pmatrix} 3 & 4 & 2 \\ 6 & 0 & -1 \\ -5 & -2 & 1 \end{pmatrix} \begin{pmatrix} 1 \\ 3 \\ 2 \end{pmatrix} = \begin{pmatrix} 19 \\ 4 \\ -9 \end{pmatrix}$$

Example 4.

$$(3\ 6\ 1) \begin{pmatrix} 1 \\ 2 \\ 4 \end{pmatrix} = (19), \qquad \begin{pmatrix} 1 \\ 2 \\ 4 \end{pmatrix} (3\ 6\ 1) = \begin{pmatrix} 3 & 6 & 1 \\ 6 & 12 & 2 \\ 12 & 24 & 4 \end{pmatrix}$$

Note that the first of these products corresponds to the scalar product as defined in vector calculus.

Numerical work can be checked by the use of the sums of the elements of the columns. In Ex. 2,

$$\begin{pmatrix} 3 & 2 & -1 \\ 0 & 4 & 6 \end{pmatrix} \begin{pmatrix} 1 & 0 & 2 \\ 5 & 3 & 1 \\ 6 & 4 & 2 \end{pmatrix} = \begin{pmatrix} 7 & 2 & 6 \\ 56 & 36 & 16 \end{pmatrix}$$

Sum   3   6   5   63   38   22

Check: $3 \cdot 1 + 6 \cdot 5 + 5 \cdot 6 = 63$

$3 \cdot 0 + 6 \cdot 3 + 5 \cdot 4 = 38$

$3 \cdot 2 + 6 \cdot 1 + 5 \cdot 2 = 22$

Figure 205 shows an arrangement of the matrices **A** and **B** in Ex. 2 and their product **AB**, which is very convenient for numerical work. The point is that each element c_{jk} of the product matrix occupies the intersection of that row of the first matrix and that column of the last matrix which are used for computing c_{jk}. The extension of the arrangement to computations of products of three and more matrices is obvious (Fig. 206).

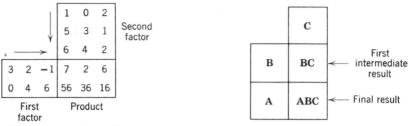

Fig. 205. Matrix multiplication.   **Fig. 206.** Matrix product ABC.

By using the definition of matrix multiplication we may now write the linear transformation (5) in the simple form

(5') $\mathbf{x} = \mathbf{A}\mathbf{y}$

where $\mathbf{A} = (a_{jk})$ and

$$\mathbf{x} = \begin{pmatrix} x_1 \\ x_2 \\ \cdot \\ \cdot \\ \cdot \\ x_m \end{pmatrix}, \qquad \mathbf{y} = \begin{pmatrix} y_1 \\ y_2 \\ \cdot \\ \cdot \\ \cdot \\ y_n \end{pmatrix}.$$

Similarly, (6) may be written

(6') $\mathbf{y} = \mathbf{B}\mathbf{z}$,

where $\mathbf{z}$ is the column matrix with elements $z_1, \cdots, z_p$. By inserting (6') into (5') and using the associative law of matrix multiplication (see right below), we obtain

(7') $\mathbf{x} = \mathbf{A}(\mathbf{B}\mathbf{z}) = \mathbf{A}\mathbf{B}\mathbf{z} = \mathbf{C}\mathbf{z}$,

in agreement with (7).

Matrix multiplication is associative and distributive; that is,

$$(\mathbf{A}\mathbf{B})\mathbf{C} = \mathbf{A}(\mathbf{B}\mathbf{C}) = \mathbf{A}\mathbf{B}\mathbf{C},$$
(10) $$(\mathbf{A} + \mathbf{B})\mathbf{C} = \mathbf{A}\mathbf{C} + \mathbf{B}\mathbf{C}$$
$$\mathbf{C}(\mathbf{A} + \mathbf{B}) = \mathbf{C}\mathbf{A} + \mathbf{C}\mathbf{B},$$

provided $\mathbf{A}$, $\mathbf{B}$, and $\mathbf{C}$ are such that the expressions on the left are defined. The proofs are left as an exercise.

The following two properties of matrix multiplication have no counterparts in the usual multiplication of numbers and should, therefore, be carefully observed.

Matrix multiplication is **not commutative**; that is, if **A** and **B** are matrices such that both **AB** and **BA** are defined, then

$$\mathbf{AB} \neq \mathbf{BA} \quad \text{in general.}$$

For example,

$$\begin{pmatrix} 1 & 0 \\ 0 & 0 \end{pmatrix}\begin{pmatrix} 0 & 1 \\ 1 & 0 \end{pmatrix} = \begin{pmatrix} 0 & 1 \\ 0 & 0 \end{pmatrix} \quad \text{but} \quad \begin{pmatrix} 0 & 1 \\ 1 & 0 \end{pmatrix}\begin{pmatrix} 1 & 0 \\ 0 & 0 \end{pmatrix} = \begin{pmatrix} 0 & 0 \\ 1 & 0 \end{pmatrix}.$$

Cf. also Ex. 4, above.

It is clear that *the order of the factors in a matrix product must be carefully observed*, and only in certain cases the equation **AB** = **BA** will hold. To be precise we say that, in the product **AB**, the matrix **B** is **premultiplied** by the matrix **A**, or, alternatively, that **A** is **postmultiplied** by **B**.

The other unusual property of matrix multiplication can be seen from the example

$$\begin{pmatrix} 1 & 1 \\ 2 & 2 \end{pmatrix}\begin{pmatrix} -1 & 1 \\ 1 & -1 \end{pmatrix} = \begin{pmatrix} 0 & 0 \\ 0 & 0 \end{pmatrix},$$

which illustrates that

$$\mathbf{AB} = 0 \quad does \text{ not } imply \quad \mathbf{A} = 0 \text{ or } \mathbf{B} = 0.$$

We shall consider this surprising fact in more detail in Sec. 7.4.

A diagonal matrix whose diagonal elements are all equal is called a **scalar matrix**. If

$$\mathbf{S} = \begin{pmatrix} k & 0 & \cdots & 0 \\ 0 & k & \cdots & \cdot \\ \cdot & \cdot & \cdots & \cdot \\ 0 & 0 & \cdots & k \end{pmatrix}$$

is an n-rowed scalar matrix and $\dot{\mathbf{A}}$ is any n-rowed square matrix,

(11) $$\mathbf{AS} = \mathbf{SA} = k\mathbf{A};$$

that is, the multiplication of an n-rowed square matrix **A** by an n-rowed scalar matrix has the same effect as the multiplication of **A** by a number, and **S** commutes with any n-rowed square matrix. The simple proof is left to the reader.

The transpose of a product equals the product of the transposed factors, taken in reverse order,

(12) $$(\mathbf{AB})^\mathsf{T} = \mathbf{B}^\mathsf{T}\mathbf{A}^\mathsf{T}.$$

The proof follows from the definition of matrix multiplication and is left to the reader.

If $\mathbf{b}_1, \cdots, \mathbf{b}_p$ are the column vectors of a matrix $\mathbf{B}$ and the product $\mathbf{AB}$ is defined, then from the definition of matrix multiplication it follows immediately that the product matrix $\mathbf{AB}$ has the column vectors $\mathbf{Ab}_1, \cdots, \mathbf{Ab}_p$,

$$(13) \qquad \mathbf{AB} = (\mathbf{Ab}_1 \quad \mathbf{Ab}_2 \quad \cdots \quad \mathbf{Ab}_p).$$

PROBLEMS

Let $\mathbf{A} = \begin{pmatrix} 4 & 6 & -1 \\ 3 & 0 & 2 \\ 1 & -2 & 5 \end{pmatrix}$, $\mathbf{B} = \begin{pmatrix} 2 & 4 \\ 0 & 1 \\ -1 & 2 \end{pmatrix}$, $\mathbf{C} = (3\ 1\ 2)$. Find those of the following expressions which are defined.

1. $\mathbf{AB}, \mathbf{BA}$ 2. $\mathbf{B}^2, \mathbf{A}^2$ 3. $\mathbf{AA}^\mathsf{T}, \mathbf{A}^\mathsf{T}\mathbf{A}$ 4. $\mathbf{BB}^\mathsf{T}, \mathbf{B}^\mathsf{T}\mathbf{B}$
5. $(\mathbf{AB})^\mathsf{T}, \mathbf{B}^\mathsf{T}\mathbf{A}^\mathsf{T}$ 6. $\mathbf{AC}, \mathbf{AC}^\mathsf{T}, \mathbf{CA}$ 7. $\mathbf{CC}^\mathsf{T}, \mathbf{C}^\mathsf{T}\mathbf{C}$ 8. $\mathbf{CAB}, (\mathbf{AB})^\mathsf{T}\mathbf{C}^\mathsf{T}$

9. Prove that $(\mathbf{A} + \mathbf{B})\mathbf{C} = \mathbf{AC} + \mathbf{BC}$, $\mathbf{C}(\mathbf{A} + \mathbf{B}) = \mathbf{CA} + \mathbf{CB}$.
10. Verify $(\mathbf{CA})\mathbf{B} = \mathbf{C}(\mathbf{AB})$ for the above matrices $\mathbf{A}, \mathbf{B}, \mathbf{C}$.
11. Prove that $(\mathbf{AB})\mathbf{C} = \mathbf{A}(\mathbf{BC})$.
12. Prove (11).
13. Show that $(\mathbf{AB})^\mathsf{T} = \mathbf{B}^\mathsf{T}\mathbf{A}^\mathsf{T}$.
14. Verify (13) for the above matrices $\mathbf{A}$ and $\mathbf{B}$.

15. Find $\mathbf{AB}$ and $\mathbf{BA}$ where $\mathbf{A} = \begin{pmatrix} 1 & -2 & 4 \\ 3 & 1 & 5 \\ 2 & 4 & 0 \end{pmatrix}$ and $\mathbf{B} = \begin{pmatrix} 2 & 4 & -2 \\ -1 & -2 & 1 \\ -1 & -2 & 1 \end{pmatrix}$.

16. Let $\mathbf{x} = \begin{pmatrix} x_1 \\ x_2 \end{pmatrix}$, $\mathbf{y} = \begin{pmatrix} y_1 \\ y_2 \end{pmatrix}$, $\mathbf{A} = \begin{pmatrix} \cos\theta & -\sin\theta \\ \sin\theta & \cos\theta \end{pmatrix}$. Show that the linear transformation $\mathbf{y} = \mathbf{Ax}$ represents a rotation of the Cartesian x_1x_2-coordinate system in the plane about the origin.

17. Interpret the transformation $\mathbf{x} = \mathbf{Bz}$ geometrically, where

$$\mathbf{x} = \begin{pmatrix} x_1 \\ x_2 \end{pmatrix}, \qquad \mathbf{z} = \begin{pmatrix} z_1 \\ z_2 \end{pmatrix}, \qquad \mathbf{B} = \begin{pmatrix} 1 & 0 \\ 0 & 2 \end{pmatrix}.$$

18. Consider the transformations $\mathbf{y} = \mathbf{Ax}$ and $\mathbf{x} = \mathbf{Bz}$ in Probs. 16 and 17. Find the composite transformation which expresses $\mathbf{y}$ in terms of $\mathbf{z}$. What does it mean geometrically that $\mathbf{AB} \neq \mathbf{BA}$?

19. Represent each of the transformations

$$\begin{aligned} x_1 &= 2y_1 - y_2 \\ x_2 &= -y_1 + 2y_2 \end{aligned} \qquad \text{and} \qquad \begin{aligned} y_1 &= z_1 + z_2 \\ y_2 &= z_1 - z_2 \end{aligned}$$

by the use of matrices and find the composite transformation which expresses x_1, x_2 in terms of z_1, z_2.

20. Find $\mathbf{AB}$ and $\mathbf{BA}$ where

$$\mathbf{A} = \begin{pmatrix} 2 & -1 & 0 \\ 0 & -2 & 1 \\ 1 & 0 & 1 \end{pmatrix} \qquad \text{and} \qquad \mathbf{B} = \begin{pmatrix} -2 & 1 & -1 \\ 1 & 2 & -2 \\ 2 & -1 & -4 \end{pmatrix}.$$

21. The so-called Pauli spin matrices are

$$\mathbf{S}_x = \begin{pmatrix} 0 & 1 \\ 1 & 0 \end{pmatrix}, \quad \mathbf{S}_y = \begin{pmatrix} 0 & -i \\ i & 0 \end{pmatrix}, \quad \mathbf{S}_z = \begin{pmatrix} 1 & 0 \\ 0 & -1 \end{pmatrix} \qquad (i = \sqrt{-1}).$$

Show that $\mathbf{S}_x \mathbf{S}_y = i\mathbf{S}_z$, $\mathbf{S}_y \mathbf{S}_x = -i\mathbf{S}_z$, $\mathbf{S}_x^2 = \mathbf{S}_y^2 = \mathbf{S}_z^2 = \mathbf{I}$.

7.3 DETERMINANTS

Determinants arise in connection with simultaneous linear algebraic equations. The solutions of the equations, while rather unmanageable when written at length, become simple-looking expressions by using determinants.

For example, the system

$$a_{11}x_1 + a_{12}x_2 = k_1$$
$$a_{21}x_1 + a_{22}x_2 = k_2$$

has the solution

$$x_1 = \frac{k_1 a_{22} - k_2 a_{12}}{a_{11}a_{22} - a_{12}a_{21}}, \qquad x_2 = \frac{a_{11}k_2 - a_{21}k_1}{a_{11}a_{22} - a_{12}a_{21}},$$

provided $a_{11}a_{22} - a_{12}a_{21}$ is not zero (cf. Sec. 0.3). This expression in the denominator is written in the form

$$\begin{vmatrix} a_{11} & a_{12} \\ a_{21} & a_{22} \end{vmatrix}$$

and is called a **determinant of second order**; thus

(1)
$$\begin{vmatrix} a_{11} & a_{12} \\ a_{21} & a_{22} \end{vmatrix} = a_{11}a_{22} - a_{12}a_{21}.$$

The solution may then be written

$$x_1 = \frac{D_1}{D}, \qquad x_2 = \frac{D_2}{D}$$

where

$$D = \begin{vmatrix} a_{11} & a_{12} \\ a_{21} & a_{22} \end{vmatrix}, \qquad D_1 = \begin{vmatrix} k_1 & a_{12} \\ k_2 & a_{22} \end{vmatrix}, \qquad D_2 = \begin{vmatrix} a_{11} & k_1 \\ a_{21} & k_2 \end{vmatrix}.$$

Systems of equations in three unknowns suggest the introduction of "third order determinants," and so on. We shall now define determinants of order n and consider their most important properties. The use of determinants in connection with systems of linear equations will be explained in Sec. 7.5.

A determinant of order n is a square array of n^2 quantities enclosed between vertical bars,

$$(2) \qquad D = \begin{vmatrix} a_{11} & a_{12} & \cdots & a_{1n} \\ a_{21} & a_{22} & \cdots & a_{2n} \\ \cdot & \cdot & \cdots & \cdot \\ \cdot & \cdot & \cdots & \cdot \\ a_{n1} & a_{n2} & \cdots & a_{nn} \end{vmatrix},$$

which has a certain value defined below. The quantities $a_{11}, \cdots, a_{nn}$, which are numbers (or sometimes functions), are called the **elements** of the determinant. The horizontal lines of elements are called **rows**; the vertical lines are called **columns**. The sloping line of elements extending from a_{11} to a_{nn} is called the *principal diagonal* of the determinant.

By deleting the ith row and the kth column from the determinant D we obtain an $(n-1)$th order determinant (a square array of $n-1$ rows and $n-1$ columns between vertical bars), which is called the **minor** of the element a_{ik} (which belongs to the deleted row and column) and is denoted by M_{ik}.

The minor M_{ik} multiplied by $(-1)^{i+k}$ is called the **cofactor** of a_{ik} and will be denoted by C_{ik}; thus

$$(3) \qquad C_{ik} = (-1)^{i+k} M_{ik}.$$

For example, in the third order determinant

$$\begin{vmatrix} a_{11} & a_{12} & a_{13} \\ a_{21} & a_{22} & a_{23} \\ a_{31} & a_{32} & a_{33} \end{vmatrix},$$

we have

$$C_{11} = M_{11} = \begin{vmatrix} a_{22} & a_{23} \\ a_{32} & a_{33} \end{vmatrix}, \quad C_{32} = -M_{32} = -\begin{vmatrix} a_{11} & a_{13} \\ a_{21} & a_{23} \end{vmatrix}, \text{ etc.}$$

We are now in a position to define an nth order determinant in a way which is most convenient for practical purposes.

Definition. *The symbol*

$$D = \begin{vmatrix} a_{11} & a_{12} & \cdots & a_{1n} \\ a_{21} & a_{22} & \cdots & a_{2n} \\ \cdot & \cdot & \cdots & \cdot \\ \cdot & \cdot & \cdots & \cdot \\ a_{n1} & a_{n2} & \cdots & a_{nn} \end{vmatrix},$$

called a **determinant of order** n, means the sum of the products of the elements of any row or column and their respective cofactors; that is,

(4a) $D = a_{i1}C_{i1} + a_{i2}C_{i2} + \cdots + a_{in}C_{in}$ $(i = 1, 2, \cdots, \text{or } n)$

or

(4b) $D = a_{1k}C_{1k} + a_{2k}C_{2k} + \cdots + a_{nk}C_{nk}$ $(k = 1, 2, \cdots, \text{or } n)$.

In this way, D is defined in terms of n determinants of order $n - 1$, each of which is, in turn, defined in terms of $n - 1$ determinants of order $n - 2$, and so on; we finally arrive at second order determinants, in which the cofactors of the elements are single elements of D. We see that *if the elements of D are numbers, the value of D will be a number.*

Furthermore, it follows from the definition that we may **develop** D *by any row or column,* that is, choose in (4) the elements of any row or column, similarly when developing the cofactors in (4), and so on. Consequently, before we accept this definition we have to show that *it is unambiguous, that is, yields the same value of D no matter which columns or rows we choose.*

For a second order determinant

$$D = \begin{vmatrix} a_{11} & a_{12} \\ a_{21} & a_{22} \end{vmatrix}$$

this is immediately clear, because then we have only four possible forms of (4), namely, the development by

the first row: $D = a_{11}a_{22} + a_{12}(-a_{21})$,
the last row: $D = a_{21}(-a_{12}) + a_{22}a_{11}$,
the first column: $D = a_{11}a_{22} + a_{21}(-a_{12})$,
and the last column: $D = a_{12}(-a_{21}) + a_{22}a_{11}$.

We see that we always obtain the same value of D, which value agrees with (1).

We shall now prove that *our definition of a determinant D of arbitrary order n yields the same value of D no matter which row or column is chosen.*

We shall prove first that *the same result is obtained no matter which row is chosen.*

The proof proceeds by induction. The statement is true for a second order determinant (see before). Assuming that it is true for a determinant of order $n - 1$, we prove that it is true for a determinant D of order n.

For this purpose we expand D, given in the definition, in terms of each of two arbitrary rows, say the ith and the jth, and compare the results. Without loss of generality let us assume $i < j$.

First expansion. We expand D by the ith row. A typical term in this expansion is

$$(5) \qquad a_{ik}C_{ik} = a_{ik} \cdot (-1)^{i+k}M_{ik}.$$

The minor M_{ik} of a_{ik} in D is an $(n-1)$th order determinant. By the induction hypothesis we may expand it by any row. We expand it by the row corresponding to the jth row of D. This row contains the elements $a_{jl}(l \neq k)$. It is the $(j-1)$th row of M_{ik}, because M_{ik} does not contain elements of the ith row of D, and $i < j$. We have to distinguish between two cases as follows.

Case I. If $l < k$, then the element a_{jl} belongs to the lth column of M_{ik} (cf. Fig. 207). Consequently, the term involving a_{jl} in this expansion is

$$(6) \qquad a_{jl} \cdot (\text{cofactor of } a_{jl} \text{ in } M_{ik}) = a_{jl} \cdot (-1)^{(j-1)+l}M_{ikjl}$$

where M_{ikjl} is the minor of a_{jl} in M_{ik}. Since this minor is obtained from M_{ik} by deleting the row and column of a_{jl}, it is obtained from D by deleting the ith and jth rows and the kth and lth columns of D. We insert the expansions of the M_{ik} into that of D. Then it follows from (5) and (6) that the terms of the resulting representation of D are of the form

$$(7\text{I}) \qquad a_{ik}a_{jl} \cdot (-1)^b M_{ikjl} \qquad\qquad (l < k)$$

where

$$b = i + k + j + l - 1.$$

Case II. If $l > k$, the only difference is that then a_{jl} belongs to the $(l-1)$th column of M_{ik}, because M_{ik} does not contain elements of the kth column of D, and $k < l$. This causes an additional minus sign in (6), and, instead of (7I), we therefore obtain

$$(7\text{II}) \qquad -a_{ik}a_{jl} \cdot (-1)^b M_{ikjl} \qquad\qquad (l > k)$$

where b is the same as before.

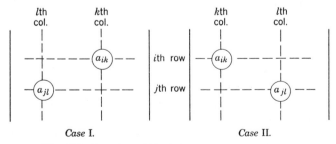

Case I.   *Case II.*

Fig. 207. Cases I and II of the two expansions of D.

Second expansion.   We now expand D at first by the jth row. A typical term in this expansion is

$$(8) \qquad a_{jl}C_{jl} = a_{jl} \cdot (-1)^{j+l}M_{jl}.$$

By induction hypothesis we may expand the minor M_{jl} of a_{jl} in D by its ith row, which corresponds to the ith row of D, since $j > i$.

Case I. If $k > l$, the element a_{ik} in that row belongs to the $(k-1)$th column of M_{jl} because M_{jl} does not contain elements of the lth column of D, and $l < k$ (cf. Fig. 207).   Hence the term involving a_{ik} in this expansion is

$$(9) \qquad a_{ik} \cdot (\text{cofactor of } a_{ik} \text{ in } M_{jl}) = a_{ik} \cdot (-1)^{i+(k-1)}M_{ikjl}$$

where the minor M_{ikjl} of a_{ik} in M_{jl} is obtained by deleting the ith and jth rows and the kth and lth columns of D [and is, therefore, identical with M_{ikjl} in (6), so that our notation is consistent].   We insert the expansions of the M_{jl} into that of D. It follows from (8) and (9) that this yields a representation whose terms are identical with those given by (7I) when $l < k$.

Case II. If $k < l$, then a_{ik} belongs to the kth column of M_{jl}, we obtain an additional minus sign, and the result agrees with that characterized by (7II).

We have shown that the two expansions of D consist of the same terms, and this proves our statement concerning rows.

The proof of the statement concerning *columns* is quite similar; if we expand D in terms of two arbitrary columns, say, the kth and the lth, we find that the general term involving $a_{jl}a_{ik}$ is exactly the same as before. This proves that not only all column expansions of D yield the same value, but also that their common value is equal to the common value of the row expansions of D.

This completes the proof and shows that *our definition of an nth order determinant is unambiguous.*

Example 1.   Let

$$D = \begin{vmatrix} 1 & 3 & 0 \\ 2 & 6 & 4 \\ -1 & 0 & 2 \end{vmatrix}.$$

The development by the first row is

$$D = 1\begin{vmatrix} 6 & 4 \\ 0 & 2 \end{vmatrix} - 3\begin{vmatrix} 2 & 4 \\ -1 & 2 \end{vmatrix} = 1(12 - 0) - 3(4 + 4) = -12.$$

The development by the first column is

$$D = 1\begin{vmatrix} 6 & 4 \\ 0 & 2 \end{vmatrix} - 2\begin{vmatrix} 3 & 0 \\ 0 & 2 \end{vmatrix} - 1\begin{vmatrix} 3 & 0 \\ 6 & 4 \end{vmatrix} = 12 - 12 - 12 = -12,$$

etc.

From our definition we may now readily obtain the most important properties of determinants, as follows.

Since the same value is obtained whether we expand a determinant by any row or any column we have

Theorem 1. *The value of a determinant is not altered if its rows are written as columns, in the same order.*

Example 2.

$$\begin{vmatrix} 1 & 3 & 0 \\ 2 & 6 & 4 \\ -1 & 0 & 2 \end{vmatrix} = \begin{vmatrix} 1 & 2 & -1 \\ 3 & 6 & 0 \\ 0 & 4 & 2 \end{vmatrix} = -12$$

Theorem 2. *If all the elements of one row (or one column) of a determinant are multiplied by the same factor k, the value of the new determinant is k times the value of the given determinant.*

Proof. Expand the determinant by that row (or column) whose elements are multiplied by k.

Note that kD equals a determinant obtained by multiplying the elements of *just one row* (or column) of D by k, while in the case of a matrix, $k\mathbf{A}$ equals the matrix obtained by multiplying *all the elements* of $\mathbf{A}$ by k.

Theorem 2 can be used for simplifying a given determinant; cf. the following example.

Example 3.

$$\begin{vmatrix} 1 & 3 & 0 \\ 2 & 6 & 4 \\ -1 & 0 & 2 \end{vmatrix} = 2\begin{vmatrix} 1 & 3 & 0 \\ 1 & 3 & 2 \\ -1 & 0 & 2 \end{vmatrix} = 6\begin{vmatrix} 1 & 1 & 0 \\ 1 & 1 & 2 \\ -1 & 0 & 2 \end{vmatrix} = 12\begin{vmatrix} 1 & 1 & 0 \\ 1 & 1 & 1 \\ -1 & 0 & 1 \end{vmatrix} = -12$$

From Theorem 2, with $k = 0$ or directly, by expanding, we obtain

Theorem 3. *If all the elements of a row (or a column) of a determinant are zero, the value of the determinant is zero.*

Theorem 4. *If each element of a row (or a column) of a determinant is expressed as a binomial, the determinant can be written as the sum of two determinants,* for example,

$$\begin{vmatrix} a_1 + d_1 & b_1 & c_1 \\ a_2 + d_2 & b_2 & c_2 \\ a_3 + d_3 & b_3 & c_3 \end{vmatrix} = \begin{vmatrix} a_1 & b_1 & c_1 \\ a_2 & b_2 & c_2 \\ a_3 & b_3 & c_3 \end{vmatrix} + \begin{vmatrix} d_1 & b_1 & c_1 \\ d_2 & b_2 & c_2 \\ d_3 & b_3 & c_3 \end{vmatrix}.$$

Proof. Expand the determinant by the row (or column) whose terms are binomials.

The generalization of Theorem 4 to the case of elements which are sums of more than two terms is obvious.

Example 4.

$$\begin{vmatrix} 4x+3 & 2 & 1 \\ x & 3 & 4 \\ 2x-1 & 1 & -1 \end{vmatrix} = \begin{vmatrix} 4x & 2 & 1 \\ x & 3 & 4 \\ 2x & 1 & -1 \end{vmatrix} + \begin{vmatrix} 3 & 2 & 1 \\ 0 & 3 & 4 \\ -1 & 1 & -1 \end{vmatrix}$$

Theorem 5. *If any two rows (or two columns) of a determinant are interchanged, the value of the determinant is multiplied by -1.*

Proof. Consider the determinant D in the definition. Carry out the development of D whose terms are of the form (7I) and (7II) ("First expansion," p. 402). Let D^* denote the determinant obtained from D by interchanging the ith and jth rows of D. Then the ith row of D^* consists of the elements $a_{jl}, l = 1, \cdots, n$, and the jth row consists of the elements $a_{ik}, k = 1, \cdots, n$. Develop D^* by its ith row and then each occurring $(n-1)$th order determinant by its row corresponding to the jth row of D^*. The terms of the resulting representation of D^* will be quite similar to those of D, given by (7I) and (7II). However, there is one essential difference. The element a_{jl} now appears already in the first step of the development. Hence, if $k > l$, the element a_{ik} appearing when developing the minor of a_{jl} in D^*, will belong to the $(k-1)$th column of that minor, because the minor does not contain elements of the lth column of D^*, and $k > l$. This causes an additional minus sign in the formula for D^*, corresponding to the formula (6) for D, and this minus sign will appear in the formula corresponding to (7I). Otherwise there will be no difference between these two formulas, because they will both contain $a_{ik}a_{jl}$, and M_{ikjl} will be as before, since it does not contain elements from the ith and jth rows of D and D^*, the only two rows by which these determinants differ from each other. Similarly, if $l > k$, an additional minus sign will appear in the formula corresponding to (7II). This completes the proof.

Example 5.

$$\begin{vmatrix} 2 & 6 & 4 \\ 1 & 3 & 0 \\ -1 & 0 & 2 \end{vmatrix} = - \begin{vmatrix} 1 & 3 & 0 \\ 2 & 6 & 4 \\ -1 & 0 & 2 \end{vmatrix} = 12$$

Theorem 6. *If corresponding elements of two rows (or two columns) of a determinant are proportional, the value of the determinant is zero.*

Proof. Let the elements of the ith and jth rows of D be proportional, say, $a_{ik} = ca_{jk}, k = 1, \cdots, n$. If $c = 0$, then $D = 0$. Let $c \neq 0$. By Theorem 2,

$$D = cB$$

where the ith and jth rows of B are identical. Interchange these rows. Then, by Theorem 5, B goes over into $-B$. On the other hand, since the rows are identical, the new determinant is still B. Thus $B = -B, B = 0$, and $D = 0$.

Example 6.

$$\begin{vmatrix} 3 & 6 & -4 \\ 1 & -1 & 3 \\ -6 & -12 & 8 \end{vmatrix} = 0$$

Before evaluating a determinant it is advisable to simplify it. This may be done by Theorem 2 and

Theorem 7. *The value of a determinant is left unchanged, if the elements of a row (or column) are altered by adding to them any constant multiple of the corresponding elements in any other row (or column).*

Proof. Apply Theorem 4 to the determinant that results from the given addition. This yields a sum of two determinants; one is the original determinant and the other contains two proportional rows. According to Theorem 6, the second determinant is zero and the proof is complete.

Example 7. Evaluate

$$D = \begin{vmatrix} 1 & 24 & 21 & 93 \\ 2 & -37 & -1 & 194 \\ -2 & 35 & 0 & -171 \\ -3 & 177 & 63 & 234 \end{vmatrix}.$$

Add the second row to the third, add three times the first row to the last, subtract two times the first row from the second, and develop the resulting determinant by the first column:

$$D = \begin{vmatrix} 1 & 24 & 21 & 93 \\ 0 & -85 & -43 & 8 \\ 0 & -2 & -1 & 23 \\ 0 & 249 & 126 & 513 \end{vmatrix} = \begin{vmatrix} -85 & -43 & 8 \\ -2 & -1 & 23 \\ 249 & 126 & 513 \end{vmatrix}.$$

Add three times the first row to the last row:

$$D = \begin{vmatrix} -85 & -43 & 8 \\ -2 & -1 & 23 \\ -6 & -3 & 537 \end{vmatrix}.$$

Subtract two times the second column from the first, and then develop the resulting determinant by the first column:

$$D = \begin{vmatrix} 1 & -43 & 8 \\ 0 & -1 & 23 \\ 0 & -3 & 537 \end{vmatrix} = \begin{vmatrix} -1 & 23 \\ -3 & 537 \end{vmatrix} = -537 + 69 = -468.$$

We shall now consider the multiplication of determinants. Of course we may obtain the product of any two determinants by evaluating the determinants and multiplying the results. However, if the determinants are of the same order n, it is often desirable to write their product again as an nth order determinant. This can be done by means of

Theorem 8.

$$
(10) \qquad
\begin{vmatrix} a_{11} & \cdots & a_{1n} \\ \cdot & \cdots & \cdot \\ \cdot & \cdots & \cdot \\ \cdot & \cdots & \cdot \\ a_{n1} & \cdots & a_{nn} \end{vmatrix}
\begin{vmatrix} b_{11} & \cdots & b_{1n} \\ \cdot & \cdots & \cdot \\ \cdot & \cdots & \cdot \\ \cdot & \cdots & \cdot \\ b_{n1} & \cdots & b_{nn} \end{vmatrix}
=
\begin{vmatrix} c_{11} & \cdots & c_{1n} \\ \cdot & \cdots & \cdot \\ \cdot & \cdots & \cdot \\ \cdot & \cdots & \cdot \\ c_{n1} & \cdots & c_{nn} \end{vmatrix},
$$

where the element c_{ik} in the ith row and kth column is

$$
(10') \qquad c_{ik} = a_{i1}b_{1k} + a_{i2}b_{2k} + \cdots + a_{in}b_{nk},
$$

the scalar product of the ith row vector of the first determinant and the kth column vector of the second determinant.

Remark. Note that this multiplication is performed in the same way as the multiplication of matrices (Sec. 7.2).

Proof of Theorem 8 for $n = 2$. Let

$$
D_1 = \begin{vmatrix} a_{11} & a_{12} \\ a_{21} & a_{22} \end{vmatrix}, \qquad
D_2 = \begin{vmatrix} b_{11} & b_{12} \\ b_{21} & b_{22} \end{vmatrix}, \qquad \text{and } D = D_1 D_2.
$$

We first show that

$$
(11) \qquad D = D_1 D_2 =
\begin{vmatrix}
a_{11} & a_{12} & 0 & 0 \\
a_{21} & a_{22} & 0 & 0 \\
-1 & 0 & b_{11} & b_{12} \\
0 & -1 & b_{21} & b_{22}
\end{vmatrix}.
$$

To prove (11), develop the determinant on the right by the first row and then the resulting two determinants again by their first rows:

$$
D = a_{11}
\begin{vmatrix} a_{22} & 0 & 0 \\ 0 & b_{11} & b_{12} \\ -1 & b_{21} & b_{22} \end{vmatrix}
- a_{12}
\begin{vmatrix} a_{21} & 0 & 0 \\ -1 & b_{11} & b_{12} \\ 0 & b_{21} & b_{22} \end{vmatrix}
$$

$$
= a_{11}a_{22}
\begin{vmatrix} b_{11} & b_{12} \\ b_{21} & b_{22} \end{vmatrix}
- a_{12}a_{21}
\begin{vmatrix} b_{11} & b_{12} \\ b_{21} & b_{22} \end{vmatrix}
= (a_{11}a_{22} - a_{12}a_{21})D_2 = D_1 D_2.
$$

We now transform the determinant in (11) as follows. We add the third row, multiplied by a_{11}, and the fourth row, multiplied by a_{12}, to the first row; then the first row takes the form

$$
0 \quad 0 \quad a_{11}b_{11} + a_{12}b_{21} \quad a_{11}b_{12} + a_{12}b_{22}.
$$

We now add the third row, multiplied by a_{21}, and the fourth row, multiplied by a_{22}, to the second row; then the second row becomes

$$
0 \quad 0 \quad a_{21}b_{11} + a_{22}b_{21} \quad a_{21}b_{12} + a_{22}b_{22}.
$$

Altogether,

$$D = \begin{vmatrix} 0 & 0 & a_{11}b_{11} + a_{12}b_{21} & a_{11}b_{12} + a_{12}b_{22} \\ 0 & 0 & a_{21}b_{11} + a_{22}b_{21} & a_{21}b_{12} + a_{22}b_{22} \\ -1 & 0 & b_{11} & b_{12} \\ 0 & -1 & b_{21} & b_{22} \end{vmatrix}.$$

Developing this determinant by the first column, and then the resulting third order determinant again by its first column, we obtain

$$D = D_1 D_2 = \begin{vmatrix} a_{11}b_{11} + a_{12}b_{21} & a_{11}b_{12} + a_{12}b_{22} \\ a_{21}b_{11} + a_{22}b_{21} & a_{21}b_{12} + a_{22}b_{22} \end{vmatrix}$$

which is (10) with $n = 2$.

Proof of Theorem 8 for arbitrary n. The steps are quite similar to those in the case $n = 2$. We first show that the product of the given determinants can be written as the $2n$th order determinant

$$D = \begin{vmatrix} a_{11} & \cdot & \cdots & a_{1n} & 0 & \cdots & 0 \\ \cdot & \cdot & \cdots & \cdot & \cdot & \cdots & \cdot \\ \cdot & \cdot & \cdots & \cdot & \cdot & \cdots & \cdot \\ a_{n1} & \cdot & \cdots & a_{nn} & 0 & \cdots & 0 \\ -1 & 0 & \cdots & 0 & b_{11} & \cdots & b_{1n} \\ 0 & -1 & \cdots & 0 & \cdot & \cdots & \cdot \\ \cdot & \cdot & \cdots & \cdot & \cdot & \cdots & \cdot \\ 0 & 0 & \cdots & -1 & b_{n1} & \cdots & b_{nn} \end{vmatrix}$$

To prove this, develop the determinant by the first row, the resulting determinants of order $2n - 1$ again by their first rows, etc. After n steps, the result will be of the form

$$(\cdots) \begin{vmatrix} b_{11} & \cdots & b_{1n} \\ \cdot & \cdots & \cdot \\ b_{n1} & \cdots & b_{nn} \end{vmatrix}$$

where $(\cdots)$ is the representation of the first of the given determinants in terms of products of its elements. Then D is transformed as follows. Add to the first row

the $(n + 1)$th row multiplied by a_{11},
the $(n + 2)$th row multiplied by a_{12},
....

the $2n$th row multiplied by a_{1n}.

The first row will then become

$$0 \cdots 0 \quad\quad a_{11}b_{11} + a_{12}b_{21} + \cdots + a_{1n}b_{n1} \quad\quad \cdots \quad\quad a_{11}b_{1n} + \cdots + a_{1n}b_{nn}$$

first n elements $(n + 1)$th element $= c_{11}$ last element $= c_{1n}$

Transforming the second, third, $\cdots$, nth row in a similar fashion, we altogether obtain

$$
D = \begin{vmatrix}
0 & \cdots & 0 & c_{11} & \cdots & c_{1n} \\
\cdot & \cdots & \cdot & \cdot & \cdots & \cdot \\
0 & \cdots & 0 & c_{n1} & \cdots & c_{nn} \\
-1 & \cdots & 0 & b_{11} & \cdots & b_{1n} \\
\cdot & \cdots & \cdot & \cdot & \cdots & \cdot \\
0 & \cdots & -1 & b_{n1} & \cdots & b_{nn}
\end{vmatrix}
$$

where c_{ik} is given by $(10')$. Developing this determinant by the first column, the resulting $(2n - 1)$th order determinant again by its first column, etc., the result will be the determinant on the right side of (10) multiplied by $(-1)^n$ and, if n is odd, by another -1 because then the cofactor of the element -1 in the first column is equal to minus one times the minor of this element. Hence, if n is odd, that determinant is multiplied by the factor $(-1)^{n+1} = +1$, and, if n is even, by $(-1)^n = +1$. This completes the proof.

Example 8.

$$
\begin{vmatrix}
2 & 4 & 3 \\
6 & 10 & 14 \\
4 & 7 & 9
\end{vmatrix}
\begin{vmatrix}
4 & 0 & 5 \\
-2 & 1 & -1 \\
3 & 0 & 4
\end{vmatrix}
=
\begin{vmatrix}
9 & 4 & 18 \\
46 & 10 & 76 \\
29 & 7 & 49
\end{vmatrix}
$$

The determinant of the elements of an n-rowed square matrix $\mathbf{A} = (a_{jk})$ is called the **determinant of the matrix** $\mathbf{A}$ and will be denoted by det $\mathbf{A}$; thus

$$
\det \mathbf{A} = \begin{vmatrix}
a_{11} & \cdots & a_{1n} \\
\cdot & \cdots & \cdot \\
\cdot & \cdots & \cdot \\
a_{n1} & \cdots & a_{nn}
\end{vmatrix}.
$$

Since the multiplication of determinants is performed in the same way as the multiplication of matrices, it follows that for any n-rowed square matrices $\mathbf{A}$ and $\mathbf{B}$,

(12) $\det (\mathbf{AB}) = \det \mathbf{A} \det \mathbf{B}.$

PROBLEMS

Evaluate the following determinants.

1. $\begin{vmatrix} 5 & 1 & 8 \\ 15 & 3 & 6 \\ 10 & 4 & 2 \end{vmatrix}$
2. $\begin{vmatrix} 4 & 96 & 85 \\ 0 & 1 & -7 \\ 0 & 0 & 6 \end{vmatrix}$
3. $\begin{vmatrix} 16 & 22 & 4 \\ 4 & -3 & 2 \\ 12 & 25 & 2 \end{vmatrix}$
4. $\begin{vmatrix} 1 & a & a^2 \\ 1 & b & b^2 \\ 1 & c & c^2 \end{vmatrix}$

5. $\begin{vmatrix} x & y & z \\ -x & y & k \\ -x & -y & z \end{vmatrix}$

6. $\begin{vmatrix} a^2 + 1 & ab & ac \\ ab & b^2 + 1 & bc \\ ac & bc & c^2 + 1 \end{vmatrix}$

7. $\begin{vmatrix} b^2 + c^2 & ab & ca \\ ab & c^2 + a^2 & bc \\ ca & bc & a^2 + b^2 \end{vmatrix}$

8. $\begin{vmatrix} b^2 + c^2 & a^2 & a^2 \\ b^2 & c^2 + a^2 & b^2 \\ c^2 & c^2 & a^2 + b^2 \end{vmatrix}$

9. $\begin{vmatrix} 28 & 18 & 24 \\ 12 & 27 & 12 \\ 70 & 15 & 40 \end{vmatrix}$

10. $\begin{vmatrix} 28 & 33 & 8 \\ 13 & 17 & 4 \\ 40 & 54 & 13 \end{vmatrix}$

11. $\begin{vmatrix} a - b & m - n & x - y \\ b - c & n - p & y - z \\ c - a & p - m & z - x \end{vmatrix}$

12. $\begin{vmatrix} 4 & 3 & 4 \\ 7 & -1 & 3 \\ 2 & 8 & 6 \end{vmatrix} + \begin{vmatrix} 4 & 3 & 4 \\ 5 & 1 & -3 \\ 2 & 8 & 6 \end{vmatrix} + \begin{vmatrix} 5 & 3 & 4 \\ -12 & 0 & 0 \\ 9 & 8 & 6 \end{vmatrix}$

13. $\begin{vmatrix} 1 & 2 & -1 & 2 \\ 3 & 0 & 1 & 5 \\ 1 & -2 & 0 & 3 \\ -2 & -4 & 1 & 6 \end{vmatrix}$

14. $\begin{vmatrix} -2 & 8 & -3 & 7 \\ -4 & 1 & 4 & -2 \\ -5 & -8 & 4 & -2 \\ 8 & 16 & -6 & 15 \end{vmatrix}$

Write the following products as determinants.

15. The determinant in Prob. 1 times that in Prob. 2.

16. The determinant in Prob. 13 times that in Prob. 14.

17. Prove that the definition of a determinant D of order n yields the same value of D no matter which column is chosen [cf. (4b)]. *Hint:* model your work somewhat after that for rows given in the text.

18. Carry out the proof of Theorem 2 in detail.

19. Carry out the proof of Theorem 4 in detail.

20. Verify (12) for $\mathbf{A} = \begin{pmatrix} 2 & 3 & 0 \\ 1 & 8 & -1 \\ 4 & 0 & 5 \end{pmatrix}$, $\mathbf{B} = \begin{pmatrix} -1 & 1 & 2 \\ 2 & 1 & -3 \\ 0 & 4 & 5 \end{pmatrix}$.

7.4 SUBMATRICES. RANK

Any matrix obtained by omitting some rows and columns from a given ($m \times n$) matrix $\mathbf{A}$ is called a **submatrix** of $\mathbf{A}$.

As a matter of convention and convenience the notion "submatrix" includes $\mathbf{A}$ itself (as the matrix obtained from $\mathbf{A}$ by omitting no rows or columns).

Example 1. The matrix

$$\begin{pmatrix} a_{11} & a_{12} & a_{13} \\ a_{21} & a_{22} & a_{23} \end{pmatrix}$$

contains three (2 × 2) submatrices, namely,

$$\begin{pmatrix} a_{11} & a_{12} \\ a_{21} & a_{22} \end{pmatrix}, \qquad \begin{pmatrix} a_{11} & a_{13} \\ a_{21} & a_{23} \end{pmatrix}, \qquad \begin{pmatrix} a_{12} & a_{13} \\ a_{22} & a_{23} \end{pmatrix},$$

two (1 × 3) submatrices (the two row vectors), three (2 × 1) submatrices (the column vectors), six (1 × 2) submatrices, namely,

$$(a_{11} \ a_{12}), \qquad (a_{11} \ a_{13}), \qquad (a_{12} \ a_{13}),$$
$$(a_{21} \ a_{22}), \qquad (a_{21} \ a_{23}), \qquad (a_{22} \ a_{23}),$$

and six (1 × 1) submatrices, (a_{11}), (a_{12}), $\cdots$, (a_{23}).

A matrix **A** *is said to be of* **rank** *r if it contains at least one r-rowed square submatrix with nonvanishing determinant, while the determinant of any square submatrix having r + 1 or more rows, possibly contained in* **A**, *is zero.*

It is clear that the rank r of an ($m \times n$) matrix can at most be equal to the smaller of the numbers m and n, but it may be less.

An ($n \times n$) matrix **A** has rank $r < n$ if, and only if, det **A** = 0; in this case **A** is called **singular**. The matrix has rank $r = n$ if, and only if, det **A** $\neq$ 0 and is then said to be **nonsingular**.

Rank **A** = 0 means that **A** is a null matrix.

The importance of the notion of rank will become obvious from our consideration of systems of linear equations in Secs. 7.6–7.8.

Example 1. The matrix

$$\mathbf{A} = \begin{pmatrix} 1 & -2 & -1 \\ -3 & 3 & 0 \\ 2 & 2 & 4 \end{pmatrix}$$

is singular because det **A** = 0. Its rank is 2 because, for example, a two-rowed square submatrix with nonzero determinant is

$$\begin{pmatrix} 1 & -2 \\ -3 & 3 \end{pmatrix}.$$

Example 2. The matrix

$$\mathbf{A} = \begin{pmatrix} 4 & 2 & 1 & 3 \\ 6 & 3 & 4 & 7 \\ 2 & 1 & 0 & 1 \end{pmatrix}$$

contains the four (3 × 3) submatrices

$$\begin{pmatrix} 4 & 2 & 1 \\ 6 & 3 & 4 \\ 2 & 1 & 0 \end{pmatrix}, \quad \begin{pmatrix} 4 & 2 & 3 \\ 6 & 3 & 7 \\ 2 & 1 & 1 \end{pmatrix}, \quad \begin{pmatrix} 4 & 1 & 3 \\ 6 & 4 & 7 \\ 2 & 0 & 1 \end{pmatrix}, \quad \begin{pmatrix} 2 & 1 & 3 \\ 3 & 4 & 7 \\ 1 & 0 & 1 \end{pmatrix},$$

whose determinants are zero. Hence rank $\mathbf{A} < 3$. In fact, rank $\mathbf{A} = 2$ because a (2×2) submatrix with nonzero determinant is

$$\begin{pmatrix} 4 & 1 \\ 6 & 4 \end{pmatrix}.$$

Theorem 1. *The rank of the transpose of a matrix is the same as that of the original matrix.*

Proof. Let rank $\mathbf{A} = r$, and let $\mathbf{R}$ be an r-rowed square submatrix of $\mathbf{A}$ with det $\mathbf{R} \neq 0$. Clearly $\mathbf{R}^\mathsf{T}$ is a submatrix of $\mathbf{A}^\mathsf{T}$. By Theorem 1 in the last section, det $\mathbf{R}^\mathsf{T} =$ det $\mathbf{R}$. Thus rank $\mathbf{A}^\mathsf{T} \geqq r$. On the other hand, if $\mathbf{A}$ contains an $(r + 1)$-rowed square submatrix $\mathbf{S}$, then, by definition of rank, det $\mathbf{S} = 0$. Since $\mathbf{S}$ corresponds to $\mathbf{S}^\mathsf{T}$ in $\mathbf{A}^\mathsf{T}$, and det $\mathbf{S}^\mathsf{T} = 0$, it follows that $\mathbf{A}^\mathsf{T}$ cannot contain an $(r + 1)$-rowed square submatrix with nonzero determinant. Hence rank $\mathbf{A}^\mathsf{T} \leqq r$. Altogether rank $\mathbf{A}^\mathsf{T} = r$, and the proof is complete.

Theorem 2. *The rank of a matrix equals the maximum number of linearly independent row vectors or column vectors.*

This will be proved in Sec. 7.8. (For linear dependence of vectors see Sec. 5.7.)

PROBLEMS

Find all submatrices of the following matrices.

$$\textbf{1.} \begin{pmatrix} -2 & 0 & 1 & 2 \\ 3 & 0 & 8 & 1 \\ -1 & 0 & 5 & 0 \end{pmatrix} \qquad \textbf{2.} \begin{pmatrix} 3 & 1 \\ 5 & 2 \\ 6 & 0 \end{pmatrix} \qquad \textbf{3.} \begin{pmatrix} 2 & 4 & 6 & 8 \\ 1 & 3 & 5 & 7 \end{pmatrix}$$

Determine the rank of the following matrices.

$$\textbf{4.} \begin{pmatrix} 2 & 3 & -1 \\ -4 & -6 & 2 \end{pmatrix} \qquad \textbf{5.} \begin{pmatrix} 1 & 7 & -1 \\ 3 & 0 & 4 \end{pmatrix} \qquad \textbf{6.} \begin{pmatrix} 3 & 8 \\ 2 & 5 \end{pmatrix}$$

$$\textbf{7.} \begin{pmatrix} 3 & 1 & 4 \\ 0 & 5 & 8 \\ -3 & 4 & 4 \end{pmatrix} \qquad \textbf{8.} \begin{pmatrix} 4 & 2 \\ 1 & 0 \\ -3 & 10 \end{pmatrix} \qquad \textbf{9.} \begin{pmatrix} 8 & 1 & 3 & 6 \\ 0 & 3 & 2 & 2 \\ -8 & -1 & -3 & 4 \end{pmatrix}$$

7.5 SYSTEMS OF n LINEAR EQUATIONS IN n UNKNOWNS. CRAMER'S RULE

This and subsequent sections will be devoted to systems of linear algebraic equations. In this section we consider a system in which the number of equations equals the number of the unknowns. We shall see later that other cases may be reduced to this case which, therefore, is basic in this connection.

The system now under consideration will consist of n equations in n unknowns $x_1, \cdots, x_n$:

$$
\begin{aligned}
a_{11}x_1 + a_{12}x_2 + \cdots + a_{1n}x_n &= b_1 \\
a_{21}x_1 + a_{22}x_2 + \cdots + a_{2n}x_n &= b_2 \\
&\cdots\cdots\cdots\cdots\cdots\cdots\cdots\cdots \\
a_{n1}x_1 + a_{n2}x_2 + \cdots + a_{nn}x_n &= b_n
\end{aligned}
$$

(1)

Here the a_{ik} and b_i are given numbers, called the **coefficients** of the system. The determinant

$$
(2) \qquad D = \begin{vmatrix} a_{11} & \cdots & a_{1n} \\ \cdot & \cdots & \cdot \\ \cdot & \cdots & \cdot \\ a_{n1} & \cdots & a_{nn} \end{vmatrix}
$$

is called the **determinant of the system**.

If the b_i are all zero, the system is said to be **homogeneous**. If at least one of the coefficients $b_1, \cdots, b_n$ is not zero, the system is said to be **nonhomogeneous**.

A set of numbers $x_1, \cdots, x_n$ which satisfy all the n equations (1) is called a **solution** of (1).

In the present section we shall derive a basic formula for the solutions of the system (1). This needs some preparation, as follows.

By developing D by the kth column we obtain

$$
(3) \qquad D = a_{1k}C_{1k} + a_{2k}C_{2k} + \cdots + a_{nk}C_{nk},
$$

where C_{ik} is the cofactor of the element a_{ik} in D. If we replace the elements of the kth column of D by any other numbers, we obtain a new determinant, say, $\tilde{D}$. Clearly, its development by the kth column will be of the form (3), with $a_{1k}, \cdots, a_{nk}$ replaced by those new elements and the cofactors C_{ik} as before. In particular, if we choose as new elements the elements $a_{1l}, \cdots, a_{nl}$ of the lth column of D (where $l \neq k$), then the development of the resulting determinant $\tilde{D}$ becomes

$$
(4) \qquad a_{1l}C_{1k} + a_{2l}C_{2k} + \cdots + a_{nl}C_{nk} = 0 \qquad (l \neq k),
$$

because $\tilde{D}$ has two identical columns and is zero (cf. Theorem 6 in Sec. 7.3).

Developing D by the ith row, we have

$$
(5) \qquad D = a_{i1}C_{i1} + a_{i2}C_{i2} + \cdots + a_{in}C_{in}.
$$

If we replace the ith row of D by the jth row, without changing the other rows (including the jth), the resulting determinant $\tilde{D}$ is zero, and by developing $\tilde{D}$ by the row which has been changed we obtain

$$
(6) \qquad a_{j1}C_{i1} + a_{j2}C_{i2} + \cdots + a_{jn}C_{in} = 0 \qquad (j \neq i).
$$

We now return to our system (1) and shall derive a formula for the solutions of the system when $D \neq 0$.

If we multiply the first equation (1) by C_{1k}, the second by $C_{2k}, \cdots,$ the last by C_{nk} and add the resulting equations, we first obtain

$$C_{1k}(a_{11}x_1 + \cdots + a_{1n}x_n) + \cdots + C_{nk}(a_{n1}x_1 + \cdots + a_{nn}x_n)$$
$$= b_1 C_{1k} + \cdots + b_n C_{nk}.$$

The expression on the left may be written

$$x_1(a_{11}C_{1k} + \cdots + a_{n1}C_{nk}) + \cdots + x_n(a_{1n}C_{1k} + \cdots + a_{nn}C_{nk}).$$

From (3) we conclude that the factor of x_k in this representation is equal to D, and from (4) it follows that the factor of x_l ($l \neq k$) is zero. Thus

$$x_k D = b_1 C_{1k} + b_2 C_{2k} + \cdots + b_n C_{nk}.$$

If $D \neq 0$ we may divide:

(7) $$x_k = \frac{1}{D}(b_1 C_{1k} + b_2 C_{2k} + \cdots + b_n C_{nk}), \qquad k = 1, \cdots, n.$$

Hence, if (1) has a solution $x_1, \cdots, x_n$, it must be given by (7).

Conversely, let us show that (7) actually is a solution of (1). By inserting (7) into the ith equation we obtain

$$a_{i1}x_1 + \cdots + a_{in}x_n$$

$$= \frac{1}{D}[a_{i1}(b_1 C_{11} + \cdots + b_n C_{n1}) + \cdots + a_{in}(b_1 C_{1n} + \cdots + b_n C_{nn})]$$

$$= \frac{1}{D}[b_1(a_{i1}C_{11} + \cdots + a_{in}C_{1n}) + \cdots + b_n(a_{i1}C_{n1} + \cdots + a_{in}C_{nn})].$$

From (5) we see that in this representation, b_i is multiplied by D, and from (6) it follows that b_j ($j \neq i$) is multiplied by zero. Hence the expression on the right reduces to

$$\frac{1}{D} b_i D = b_i,$$

which means that (7) satisfies (1).

Noting that the expression in parentheses in (7) is the development of the determinant obtained by replacing the kth column of D by the column with elements $b_1, \cdots, b_n$, we may sum up our result as follows.

Cramer's theorem. *If the determinant D of the system (1) of n linear equations in the same number of unknowns is not zero, the system has precisely one solution $x_1, \cdots, x_n$, given by the formulas*

(8) $$x_1 = \frac{D_1}{D}, \qquad x_2 = \frac{D_2}{D}, \cdots, \qquad x_n = \frac{D_n}{D} \qquad \text{(Cramer's rule)}$$

where D_k is the determinant obtained from D by replacing in D the kth column by the column with the elements $b_1, \cdots, b_n$.

Consequently, if the system is homogeneous ($b_1 = 0, \cdots, b_n = 0$), then $D_1 = 0, \cdots, D_n = 0$, and we obtain

Theorem 2. *A homogeneous system of n linear equations in n unknowns with nonvanishing determinant has only the* **trivial solution**

$$x_1 = 0, \ x_2 = 0, \cdots, x_n = 0.$$

On the other hand, we have

Theorem 3. *A nonhomogeneous system whose determinant is zero but $D_i \neq 0$ for at least one $i = 1, 2, \cdots, n$, has no solution.*

Example 1. Solve

$$\begin{aligned} 2x_1 - \ x_2 + 2x_3 &= \ 2 \\ x_1 + 10x_2 - 3x_3 &= \ 5 \\ -x_1 + \ x_2 + \ x_3 &= -3. \end{aligned}$$

The determinant of the system is

$$D = \begin{vmatrix} 2 & -1 & 2 \\ 1 & 10 & -3 \\ -1 & 1 & 1 \end{vmatrix} = 46.$$

The determinants in the numerators in (8) are

$$D_1 = \begin{vmatrix} 2 & -1 & 2 \\ 5 & 10 & -3 \\ -3 & 1 & 1 \end{vmatrix} = 92, \qquad D_2 = \begin{vmatrix} 2 & 2 & 2 \\ 1 & 5 & -3 \\ -1 & -3 & 1 \end{vmatrix} = 0,$$

$$D_3 = \begin{vmatrix} 2 & -1 & 2 \\ 1 & 10 & 5 \\ -1 & 1 & -3 \end{vmatrix} = -46.$$

Therefore, $x_1 = 2$, $x_2 = 0$, and $x_3 = -1$.

Example 2. In the case of the system

$$\begin{aligned} x + y &= 0 \\ x - y &= 0, \end{aligned}$$

the determinants occurring in (8) are $D = -2$, $D_1 = D_2 = 0$. Hence the only solution is $x = y = 0$, and our example illustrates Theorem 2.

Example 3. The nonhomogeneous system

$$\begin{aligned} x + y &= 1 \\ x + y &= 0 \end{aligned}$$

has no solution, because $D = 0$, $D_1 = 1$, $D_2 = -1$, in agreement with Theorem 3.

PROBLEMS

Solve the following systems of linear equations.

1. $3x - 4y = \quad 20$
          $-5x + 8y = -36$

2. $10x - 15y = 0$
       $3x - \quad 4y = 1$

3. $x - 2y = -5$
          $2x - \quad y = -1$

4. $x + \ y + \ z = \ 0$
        $2x - 5y - 3z = 10$
        $4x + 8y + 2z = \ 4$

5. $3x + 2y - 2z = \ 1$
        $-x + \ y + 4z = 13$
        $2x - 3y + 4z = \ 8$

6. $8x - 4y + \ z = 8$
       $4x + 2y - 2z = 0$
       $2x + 7y - 4z = 0$

7. $w + \ x + \ y - \ z = \quad 0$
          $3w + 3x - \ y + 2z = \quad 7$
          $-w + \ x + 2y - 2z = -1$
          $w \qquad\qquad + 3z = \quad 9$

8. $2w \qquad + 2y - \ z = \quad 7$
       $w - x + \ y \qquad = \quad 6$
       $3w \qquad + \ y - 2z = \quad 0$
       $4w + x - \ y - \ z = -1$

9. Consider the network in Fig. 208. Show that Kirchhoff's laws (Sec. 1.9) yield the following system of equations for the unknown currents:

$$I_1 \quad - I_2 \quad - I_3 = 0$$

$$R_2 I_2 - R_3 I_3 = 0$$

$$(R_1 + R_4)I_1 + R_2 I_2 \qquad = E_0$$

Determine the currents I_1, I_2, I_3.

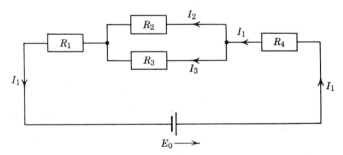

Fig. 208. Network in Problem 9.

Using Kirchhoff's laws, find the currents in the following networks.

10.

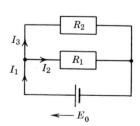

11. 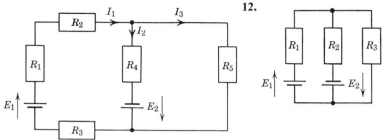 **12.**

13. Show that if $R_x/R_3 = R_1/R_2$ in Fig. 209, then $I = 0$. (R_0 is the resistance of the instrument by which I is measured.)

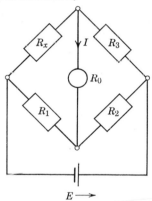

Fig. 209. Wheatstone bridge.

7.6 ARBITRARY HOMOGENEOUS SYSTEMS OF LINEAR EQUATIONS

We shall now consider homogeneous systems of linear equations where the number of equations may be different from the number of unknowns. Such a system is of the form

(1)
$$a_{11}x_1 + a_{12}x_2 + \cdots + a_{1n}x_n = 0$$
$$a_{21}x_1 + a_{22}x_2 + \cdots + a_{2n}x_n = 0$$
$$\cdot \cdot \cdot \cdot \cdot \cdot \cdot \cdot \cdot \cdot \cdot \cdot \cdot \cdot \cdot \cdot \cdot \cdot \cdot$$
$$a_{m1}x_1 + a_{m2}x_2 + \cdots + a_{mn}x_n = 0.$$

Any set of numbers $x_1, \cdots, x_n$ that satisfies all the equations (1) is called a **solution** of (1).

By substitution we see that the system has the **trivial solution**

$$x_1 = 0, x_2 = 0, \cdots, x_n = 0.$$

Any other solution, if it exists, is called a **nontrivial solution** of (1).

We shall obtain conditions under which the system (1) has nontrivial solutions and develop a method for determining all solutions of the system.

Suppose that the coefficient matrix of the system

$$
\mathbf{A} = \begin{pmatrix} a_{11} & \cdots & a_{1n} \\ \cdot & \cdots & \cdot \\ \cdot & \cdots & \cdot \\ a_{m1} & \cdots & a_{mn} \end{pmatrix}
$$

has rank r. We may assume $r > 0$, because $r = 0$ would mean that all the coefficients of the system are zero. Clearly, r is at most equal to the smaller of the numbers m and n. By definition of rank the matrix $\mathbf{A}$ contains an r-rowed square matrix $\mathbf{R}$ with nonvanishing determinant. Without specialization we may assume that the order of the equations and the order of the unknowns in each equation is chosen such that $\mathbf{R}$ is the submatrix

$$
\mathbf{R} = \begin{pmatrix} a_{11} & \cdots & a_{1r} \\ \cdot & \cdots & \cdot \\ \cdot & \cdots & \cdot \\ a_{r1} & \cdots & a_{rr} \end{pmatrix}, \qquad (\det \mathbf{R} \neq 0)
$$

which occupies the left upper corner of the matrix $\mathbf{A}$. The determinant of any larger square submatrix possibly contained in $\mathbf{A}$ is zero, by definition of rank.

Under our assumption about the order of equations and unknowns we can now prove the following statement, which will simplify our problem.

If $x_1, \cdots, x_n$ are solutions of the first r equations of the system (1), *they also satisfy the other $m - r$ equations of the system.*

Proof. If $r = m$, the statement is trivial and we may assume $r < m$. Let $y_1, \cdots, y_n$ be independent variables and let

$$
\begin{aligned}
f_1 &= a_{11}y_1 + a_{12}y_2 + \cdots + a_{1n}y_n \\
f_2 &= a_{21}y_1 + a_{22}y_2 + \cdots + a_{2n}y_n \\
&\cdot\cdot\cdot\cdot\cdot\cdot\cdot\cdot\cdot\cdot\cdot\cdot\cdot\cdot\cdot\cdot \\
f_m &= a_{m1}y_1 + a_{m2}y_2 + \cdots + a_{mn}y_n.
\end{aligned}
$$

We now consider the determinant

$$
\begin{vmatrix} a_{11} & \cdots & a_{1r} & f_1 \\ \cdot & \cdots & \cdot & \cdot \\ \cdot & \cdots & \cdot & \cdot \\ a_{r1} & \cdots & a_{rr} & f_r \\ a_{s1} & \cdots & a_{sr} & f_s \end{vmatrix} = \sum_{\nu=1}^{n} y_\nu \begin{vmatrix} a_{11} & \cdots & a_{1r} & a_{1\nu} \\ \cdot & \cdots & \cdot & \cdot \\ \cdot & \cdots & \cdot & \cdot \\ a_{r1} & \cdots & a_{rr} & a_{r\nu} \\ a_{s1} & \cdots & a_{sr} & a_{s\nu} \end{vmatrix}
$$

where s is a positive integer, $r < s \leq m$, and the sum of determinants on the right is obtained by applying Theorem 4 in Sec. 7.3 to the last column of the determinant on the left. The determinants on the right are of order $r + 1$. For $\nu \leq r$ they have two identical columns and are, therefore, zero. For $\nu > r$ they are the determinants of $(r + 1)$-rowed square submatrices of $\mathbf{A}$ and are zero, because rank $\mathbf{A} = r$, by assumption. Hence the determinant on the left is zero. Developing it by the last column, we have

$$f_1 D_{s1} + f_2 D_{s2} + \cdots + f_r D_{sr} + f_s \det \mathbf{R} = 0$$

where $D_{s1}, \cdots, D_{sr}$ are determinants of certain $(r \times r)$ submatrices of $\mathbf{A}$ (except for the sign). Since $\det \mathbf{R} \neq 0$, we may solve for f_s, finding

$$f_s = - \frac{1}{\det \mathbf{R}} (f_1 D_{s1} + \cdots + f_r D_{sr}).$$

By writing $f_1, \cdots, f_r, f_s$ at length this becomes

$$(2) \quad a_{s1} y_1 + \cdots + a_{sn} y_n = - \frac{1}{\det \mathbf{R}} [D_{s1}(a_{11} y_1 + \cdots + a_{1n} y_n)$$
$$+ \cdots + D_{sr}(a_{r1} y_1 + \cdots + a_{rn} y_n)].$$

Choosing for $y_1, \cdots, y_n$ a solution $x_1, \cdots, x_n$ of the first r equations of our system, we clearly have

$$a_{11} x_1 + \cdots + a_{1n} x_n = 0, \quad \cdots, \quad a_{r1} x_1 + \cdots + a_{rn} x_n = 0,$$

the right side of (2) is zero, and, therefore, also

$$a_{s1} x_1 + \cdots + a_{sn} x_n = 0, \quad (s = r + 1, r + 2, \cdots, m).$$

This proves our statement.

According to the statement just proved we need only consider the first r equations of our system. We may write these equations in the form

$$(3) \quad \begin{aligned} a_{11} x_1 + \cdots + a_{1r} x_r &= -(a_{1,r+1} x_{r+1} + \cdots + a_{1n} x_n) \\ a_{21} x_1 + \cdots + a_{2r} x_r &= -(a_{2,r+1} x_{r+1} + \cdots + a_{2n} x_n) \\ &\cdots\cdots\cdots\cdots\cdots\cdots\cdots\cdots\cdots\cdots \\ a_{r1} x_1 + \cdots + a_{rr} x_r &= -(a_{r,r+1} x_{r+1} + \cdots + a_{rn} x_n) \end{aligned}$$

(where if $r = n$, the expressions on the right are to be replaced by zeros).

If $r = n$, the system (3) is homogeneous, and since $\det \mathbf{R} \neq 0$, it follows from Theorem 2, Sec. 7.5, that the system has only the trivial solution

$$x_1 = 0, x_2 = 0, \cdots, x_n = 0.$$

If $r < n$, then we may assign arbitrary values to the unknowns $x_{r+1}, \cdots, x_n$ on the right side and then determine the unique corresponding values $x_1, \cdots, x_r$ by Cramer's rule.

We may sum up our result as follows.

Theorem 1. *If the coefficient matrix of a homogeneous system of linear equations in n unknowns has rank r, then the values of n — r unknowns (which must be such that the coefficients of the other r unknowns form a matrix of rank r) remain arbitrary, and the values of the other unknowns are then uniquely determined and can be obtained by means of Cramer's rule. If r = n the system has only the trivial solution $x_1 = 0, \cdots, x_n = 0$.*

The steps of solving our homogeneous system (1) are now as follows.

I. Determine the rank r of the coefficient matrix **A**.

II. If $r < m$, omit $m - r$ equations such that the coefficient matrix of the remaining equations still has rank r.

III. Write these equations in the form (3) such that the square matrix of the coefficients on the left has rank r.

IV. Solve (3) by Cramer's rule.

Example 1. Solve

$$4w + 2x + y + 3z = 0$$
$$6w + 3x + 4y + 7z = 0$$
$$2w + x \quad + z = 0.$$

I. The coefficient matrix **A** is the matrix considered in Ex. 2, Sec. 7.4. It is of rank 2, and a (2×2) submatrix **R** with nonzero determinant is obtained from **A** by omitting the second row and the first and third columns.

II. The second equation may be omitted.

III. The remaining system may be written

$$2x + 3z = -4w - y$$
$$x + z = -2w.$$

IV. In Cramer's rule,

$$D = \begin{vmatrix} 2 & 3 \\ 1 & 1 \end{vmatrix} = -1, \qquad D_1 = \begin{vmatrix} -4w - y & 3 \\ -2w & 1 \end{vmatrix} = 2w - y,$$

$$D_2 = \begin{vmatrix} 2 & -4w - y \\ 1 & -2w \end{vmatrix} = y.$$

Hence

$$x = \frac{D_1}{D} = y - 2w, \qquad z = \frac{D_2}{D} = -y.$$

For example, if we choose $w = 1$ and $y = -1$, then $x = -3$ and $z = 1$, etc.

Example 2. The coefficient matrix of the system

$$x + y + z = 0$$
$$3x + 2y + 2z = 0$$

has rank 2. Hence one of the unknowns is arbitrary. Choosing z arbitrarily, we find $x = 0$, $y = -z$. Choosing y arbitrarily, we find $x = 0$, $z = -y$. But x cannot be chosen arbitrarily because $x = 0$; in fact, the matrix of the coefficients of the variables y and z is

$$\begin{pmatrix} 1 & 1 \\ 2 & 2 \end{pmatrix}$$

and has only rank 1 but not rank 2.

According to Theorem 1, nontrivial solutions of (1) exist, if the rank r of A is less than the number of unknowns. This certainly happens if $m < n$, because then $r \leq m$. We thus obtain

Theorem 2. *If the number of equations of a homogeneous system of linear equations is less than the number of unknowns it has nontrivial solutions.*

Another immediate consequence of Theorem 1 is

Theorem 3. *A homogeneous system of n equations in the same number of unknowns has nontrivial solutions if, and only if, its coefficient determinant is zero.*

Let us use Theorem 3 to obtain some more information about the strange fact that

$$AB = 0 \quad \text{does not imply} \quad A = 0 \text{ or } B = 0$$

which was illustrated in Sec. 7.2 by the example

$$\begin{pmatrix} 1 & 1 \\ 2 & 2 \end{pmatrix} \begin{pmatrix} -1 & 1 \\ 1 & -1 \end{pmatrix} = \begin{pmatrix} 0 & 0 \\ 0 & 0 \end{pmatrix}.$$

We see that both matrices on the left are singular. In fact, the following theorem holds.

Theorem 4. *If A and B are n-rowed square matrices, not null matrices, such that $AB = 0$, then both A and B are singular.*

Proof. Let $\mathbf{b}_1, \cdots, \mathbf{b}_n$ be the column vectors of B. Then we may write $B = (\mathbf{b}_1 \, \mathbf{b}_2 \cdots \mathbf{b}_n)$. From (13) in Sec. 7.2 and $AB = 0$ we have

$$AB = (A\mathbf{b}_1 \cdots A\mathbf{b}_n) = (0 \cdots 0),$$

that is

(4) $$A\mathbf{b}_k = 0, \qquad k = 1, \cdots, n$$

where 0 designates a column vector of the $(n \times n)$ null matrix. Since B is not a null matrix, $\mathbf{b}_k \neq 0$ for at least one k. Regarding the corresponding vector equation (4) as a system of n linear equations in the "unknowns" $b_{1k}, \cdots, b_{nk}$, the components of $\mathbf{b}_k$, we conclude that A must be singular, because this is a necessary and sufficient condition for the existence of a nontrivial solution (Theorem 3). The proof that B must be singular follows by applying the same argument to the transposed equation

$$B^T A^T = 0$$

obtained from $AB = 0$ by the use of (12) in Sec. 7.2.

By interchanging the factors in the above example we obtain

$$\begin{pmatrix} -1 & 1 \\ 1 & -1 \end{pmatrix}\begin{pmatrix} 1 & 1 \\ 2 & 2 \end{pmatrix} = \begin{pmatrix} 1 & 1 \\ -1 & -1 \end{pmatrix}.$$

Hence, if both **A** and **B** are singular and **AB** = 0, it does *not* follow that **BA** = 0.

From the proof of Theorem 4 we immediately have

Theorem 5. *If* **AB** = 0 *and* **A** *is nonsingular, then* **B** = 0.

Furthermore, if **AB** = 0 and we set **B** = **S** − **T**, then

$$\textbf{AB} = \textbf{A}(\textbf{S} - \textbf{T}) = 0 \qquad or \qquad \textbf{AS} = \textbf{AT}.$$

From this and Theorem 5 we obtain

Theorem 6. *The matrix equation*

$$\textbf{AS} = \textbf{AT} \qquad implies \qquad \textbf{S} = \textbf{T}$$

only if **A** *is nonsingular.*

PROBLEMS

Find all solutions of the following systems of linear equations.

1.
$$x + 5y + 13z = 0$$
$$-x + y + 5z = 0$$

2.
$$4x - y = 0$$
$$-8x + 2y = 0$$

3.
$$6x - 4y = 0$$
$$x + 5y = 0$$

4.
$$4x - y + z = 0$$
$$x + 2y - z = 0$$
$$3x + y + 5z = 0$$

5.
$$3x + 4y + z = 0$$
$$-x + y + 2z = 0$$
$$2x + 5y + 3z = 0$$

6.
$$3x - 3y - 6z = 0$$
$$-x + y + 2z = 0$$
$$2x - 2y - 4z = 0$$

7.
$$2w + 3x - y - z = 0$$
$$4w - 6x - 2y + 2z = 0$$
$$-6w + 12x + 3y - 4z = 0$$

8.
$$4w + y - 2z = 0$$
$$w + x + 2y - 2z = 0$$
$$5x - y - z = 0$$

9.
$$7w - 3x + y - 7z = 0$$
$$w + 2x - y - z = 0$$
$$3w + 3x + 5y - 3z = 0$$

10. Prove Theorem 3.

11. Show that the straight line through two given points P_1: (x_1, y_1) and P_2: (x_2, y_2) in the xy-plane is

$$\begin{vmatrix} x & y & 1 \\ x_1 & y_1 & 1 \\ x_2 & y_2 & 1 \end{vmatrix} = 0.$$

12. Find the straight line through the points $(3, 5)$ and $(-4, 8)$.

13. Derive from the formula in Prob. 11 the familiar formula

$$\frac{x - x_1}{x_1 - x_2} = \frac{y - y_1}{y_1 - y_2}.$$

14. Show that three points (x_1, y_1), (x_2, y_2), and (x_3, y_3) lie on a line if, and only if,

$$\begin{vmatrix} x_1 & y_1 & 1 \\ x_2 & y_2 & 1 \\ x_3 & y_3 & 1 \end{vmatrix} = 0.$$

15. Show that the equation of the circle through three given points (x_1, y_1), (x_2, y_2), and (x_3, y_3) in the xy-plane is

$$\begin{vmatrix} x^2 + y^2 & x & y & 1 \\ x_1{}^2 + y_1{}^2 & x_1 & y_1 & 1 \\ x_2{}^2 + y_2{}^2 & x_2 & y_2 & 1 \\ x_3{}^2 + y_3{}^2 & x_3 & y_3 & 1 \end{vmatrix} = 0.$$

16. Find the center and the radius of the circle through the points (1, 1), (3, 1), and (2, 4).

7.7   ARBITRARY NONHOMOGENEOUS SYSTEMS OF LINEAR EQUATIONS

The last remaining type of systems are nonhomogeneous systems of linear equations where the number of unknowns may be different from the number of equations. Such a system may be written in the form

$$\begin{aligned} a_{11}x_1 + a_{12}x_2 + \cdots + a_{1n}x_n &= b_1 \\ a_{21}x_1 + a_{22}x_2 + \cdots + a_{2n}x_n &= b_2 \end{aligned}$$

(1)

$$\cdots \cdots \cdots \cdots \cdots \cdots \cdots$$

$$a_{m1}x_1 + a_{m2}x_2 + \cdots + a_{mn}x_n = b_m.$$

It is clear that the solutions of this system are identical with those solutions (if they exist) of the corresponding homogeneous system

$$\begin{aligned} a_{11}x_1 + \cdots + a_{1n}x_n + b_1 x_{n+1} &= 0 \\ a_{21}x_1 + \cdots + a_{2n}x_n + b_2 x_{n+1} &= 0 \end{aligned}$$

(2)

$$\cdots \cdots \cdots \cdots \cdots \cdots \cdots$$

$$a_{m1}x_1 + \cdots + a_{mn}x_n + b_m x_{n+1} = 0$$

for which $x_{n+1} = -1$. Since we know how to solve a homogeneous system, we may solve (2), set $x_{n+1} = -1$, and obtain the solutions of (1).

It may happen that (2) has only solutions for which $x_{n+1} = 0$. Then our system (1) has no solution at all.

If (2) has a solution with $x_{n+1} \neq 0$, we may multiply it by a suitable factor and obtain a solution with $x_{n+1} = -1$, which is then a solution of (1).

Necessary and sufficient conditions for the existence of a solution of (1) are as follows.

Theorem 1. *The system* (1) *has solutions if, and only if, the coefficient matrix* **A** *and the* **augmented matrix B**, *that is,*

$$A = \begin{pmatrix} a_{11} & \cdots & a_{1n} \\ \cdot & \cdots & \cdot \\ \cdot & \cdots & \cdot \\ a_{m1} & \cdots & a_{mn} \end{pmatrix} \quad and \quad B = \begin{pmatrix} a_{11} & \cdots & a_{1n} & b_1 \\ \cdot & \cdots & \cdot & \cdot \\ \cdot & \cdots & \cdot & \cdot \\ a_{m1} & \cdots & a_{mn} & b_m \end{pmatrix}$$

have the same rank.

Proof. If **A** has rank r, it contains an $(r \times r)$ submatrix **R** with nonzero determinant. Since **R** is also a submatrix of **B**, the rank of **B** is at least r. Assume that (1) has a solution $x_1^0, \cdots, x_n^0$. Then

$$b_1 = a_{11}x_1^0 + a_{12}x_2^0 + \cdots + a_{1n}x_n^0, \qquad \text{etc.,}$$

and we may write **B** in the form

$$B = \begin{pmatrix} a_{11} & \cdots & a_{1n} & a_{11}x_1^0 + \cdots + a_{1n}x_n^0 \\ \cdot & \cdots & \cdot & \cdot \\ \cdot & \cdots & \cdot & \cdot \\ a_{m1} & \cdots & a_{mn} & a_{m1}x_1^0 + \cdots + a_{mn}x_n^0 \end{pmatrix}.$$

Consequently, if **B** contains $(r + 1)$-rowed square submatrices, these are either submatrices of **A**, or their determinants can be written as sums of $(r + 1)$th order determinants of submatrices of **A** and $(r + 1)$th order determinants with two identical columns. The latter determinants are certainly zero, and the former are zero because **A** has rank r. Hence **B** does not contain $(r + 1)$-rowed square submatrices with nonvanishing determinants. Therefore, its rank is less than $r + 1$, that is, it is r.

Conversely, assume rank $\mathbf{A} = \text{rank } \mathbf{B} = r$. Then certainly $r \leq m$. As in Sec. 7.6, we may assume that the equations of (1) and the unknowns $x_1, \cdots, x_n$ are arranged so that the submatrix

$$(3) \qquad\qquad R = \begin{pmatrix} a_{11} & \cdots & a_{1r} \\ \cdot & \cdots & \cdot \\ \cdot & \cdots & \cdot \\ a_{r1} & \cdots & a_{rr} \end{pmatrix}$$

has a nonvanishing determinant. Then, by Theorem 1 in Sec. 7.6, the homogeneous system (2) has a solution for which $x_{r+1}, \cdots, x_n, x_{n+1}$ remain arbitrary. Hence we may choose $x_{n+1} = -1$ and obtain a solution of (1). This completes the proof.

The steps of solving our nonhomogeneous system (1) are quite similar to those in the homogeneous case (Sec. 7.6):

I.   Determine the ranks of $\mathbf{A}$ and $\mathbf{B}$. If rank $\mathbf{B} \neq$ rank $\mathbf{A}$, the system has no solution. If rank $\mathbf{B} =$ rank $\mathbf{A} = r$, the further steps are:

II. If rank $r < m$, omit $m - r$ equations such that the coefficient matrix of the remaining r equations still has rank r.

III. Write the remaining equations in a form similar to (3) in Sec. 7.6, that is, assuming that the equations and variables are arranged so that the matrix $\mathbf{R}$, given by (3), this section, has a nonvanishing determinant, write

$$
\begin{aligned}
a_{11}x_1 + \cdots + a_{1r}x_r &= b_1 - (a_{1,r+1}x_{r+1} + \cdots + a_{1n}x_n) \\
a_{21}x_1 + \cdots + a_{2r}x_r &= b_2 - (a_{2,r+1}x_{r+1} + \cdots + a_{2n}x_n) \\
&\cdots\cdots\cdots\cdots\cdots\cdots\cdots\cdots\cdots\cdots\cdots \\
a_{r1}x_1 + \cdots + a_{rr}x_r &= b_r - (a_{r,r+1}x_{r+1} + \cdots + a_{rn}x_n)
\end{aligned}
$$

(4)

(where, if $r = n$, the expressions on the right are $b_1, \cdots, b_r$).

IV. Solve (4) by Cramer's rule.

Example 1.   Solve

$$
\begin{aligned}
x_1 - x_2 + x_3 - x_4 &= -2 \\
2x_1 + x_2 - x_3 + 3x_4 &= 9 \\
x_1 + 2x_2 - 2x_3 + 4x_4 &= 11
\end{aligned}
$$

I. The four (3×3) submatrices in the coefficient matrix $\mathbf{A}$ have vanishing determinants, while the submatrix obtained by omitting from $\mathbf{A}$ the last row and the last two columns is

$$
\mathbf{R} = \begin{pmatrix} 1 & -1 \\ 2 & 1 \end{pmatrix}, \qquad \text{and} \qquad \det \mathbf{R} = 3
$$

so that rank $\mathbf{A} = 2$. Similarly, the augmented matrix has rank 2. Hence the system has solutions.

II. Omit the last equation, since this corresponds to the last row of $\mathbf{A}$, the row which does not occur in $\mathbf{R}$.

III. The reduced system, written in the form (4), becomes

$$
\begin{aligned}
x_1 - x_2 &= -2 - x_3 + x_4 \\
2x_1 + x_2 &= 9 + x_3 - 3x_4
\end{aligned}
$$

IV. Cramer's rule yields

$$
x_1 = \tfrac{1}{3}(7 - 2x_4), \qquad x_2 = \tfrac{1}{3}(13 + 3x_3 - 5x_4),
$$

where x_3 and x_4 are arbitrary.

PROBLEMS

Solve the following systems of linear equations.

1. $2x - 2y + 4z = 6$
$\quad\ 3x - 3y - 7z = -4$

2. $16x + 2y + z = 3$
$\quad\ 7x - 4y - 2z = -6$

3. $x + 3y - 8z = 15$
$-2x + y - 5z = 5$

4. $3x - 20y + 5z = -4$
$-2x + 8y - 2z = 4$

5. $5x - 15y + 7z = 10$
$-x + 3y - 2z = -2$

6. $-3x + 7y - 35z = -18$
$5x + 4y - 20z = -17$

7. $-3w + 3x + 2y - z = 2$
$w - x - 6y + 3z = 2$

8. $3w - x + y - 2z = 8$
$5w + 2x - 2y + 4z = 17$

9. $-3w + 15x + 3y + 11z = 27$
$5w - 25x - 5y - 7z = -45$

10. $-w - 3x + 3y + 9z = 10$
$7w + 2x - 2y - 6z = 6$

11. $2w - 4x + 3y - z = 3$
$-w + 2x - 5y + 3z = 0$
$3w - 6x - y - z = 0$

12. $4w + 3x - 9y + z = 1$
$-w + 2x - 13y + 3z = 3$
$3w - x + 8y - 2z = -2$

13. $x + y + z = 1$
$x - y + 2z = -6$
$3x + y + z = -1$
$2x - 2y + 3z = 2$

14. $x + y + z = 6$
$x - y + 2z = 5$
$3x + y + z = 8$
$2x - 2y + 3z = 7$

7.8   FURTHER PROPERTIES OF SYSTEMS OF LINEAR EQUATIONS

We shall now consider some further basic properties of systems of linear equations. To simplify our notation we may write such a system

$$(1^*) \quad \begin{aligned} a_{11}x_1 + \cdots + a_{1n}x_n &= b_1 \\ a_{21}x_1 + \cdots + a_{2n}x_n &= b_2 \\ \cdots \cdots \cdots \cdots \cdots \cdots \\ a_{m1}x_1 + \cdots + a_{mn}x_n &= b_m \end{aligned}$$

as a single vector equation. In fact, from the definition of matrix multiplication it follows that we may write (1^*) in the form

$$(1) \quad\quad\quad \mathbf{Ax} = \mathbf{b}$$

where $\mathbf{A}$ is the coefficient matrix of the system and $\mathbf{x}$ and $\mathbf{b}$ are column vectors with components $x_1, \cdots, x_n$ and $b_1, \cdots, b_m$, respectively.

If the system is homogeneous, $\mathbf{b} = \mathbf{0}$; otherwise, $\mathbf{b} \neq \mathbf{0}$.

The solutions of the homogeneous system have the following simple but important property.

Theorem 1.   *If* $\mathbf{x}_{(1)}$ *and* $\mathbf{x}_{(2)}$ *are solutions of the homogeneous system*

$$(2) \quad\quad\quad \mathbf{Ax} = \mathbf{0},$$

then $\mathbf{x} = c_1\mathbf{x}_{(1)} + c_2\mathbf{x}_{(2)}$, *where* c_1 *and* c_2 *are any constants, is a solution of the homogeneous system.*

Proof. By assumption, $\mathbf{Ax}_{(1)} = \mathbf{0}$, $\mathbf{Ax}_{(2)} = \mathbf{0}$. Hence

$$\mathbf{Ax} = \mathbf{A}(c_1\mathbf{x}_{(1)} + c_2\mathbf{x}_{(2)}) = c_1\mathbf{Ax}_{(1)} + c_2\mathbf{Ax}_{(2)} = \mathbf{0}.$$

Note that the theorem *does not hold* for nonhomogeneous systems.

p solutions $\mathbf{x}_{(1)}, \cdots, \mathbf{x}_{(p)}$ of the homogeneous system (2) are called *linearly dependent* or *independent*, according to whether these p vectors are linearly dependent or independent in the sense of the usual definition (cf. Sec. 5.7).

We first prove the following useful general criterion for linear dependence and independence of vectors.

Theorem 2. *p vectors $\mathbf{x}_{(1)}, \cdots, \mathbf{x}_{(p)}$ are linearly independent if the matrix with column vectors $\mathbf{x}_{(1)}, \cdots, \mathbf{x}_{(p)}$ has rank p; they are linearly dependent if that rank is less than p.*

Proof. Those vectors are linearly dependent if there are numbers $k_1, \cdots, k_p$, not all zero, such that

$$k_1\mathbf{x}_{(1)} + \cdots + k_p\mathbf{x}_{(p)} = \mathbf{0}.$$

Denoting the components of the vector $\mathbf{x}_{(j)}$ by $x_{1j}, \cdots, x_{nj}$, this vector equation may be written

$$x_{11}k_1 + \cdots + x_{1p}k_p = 0$$
$$x_{21}k_1 + \cdots + x_{2p}k_p = 0$$
$$\cdot \cdot \cdot \cdot \cdot \cdot \cdot \cdot \cdot \cdot \cdot \cdot \cdot \cdot$$
$$x_{n1}k_1 + \cdots + x_{np}k_p = 0$$

In this system we may regard $k_1, \cdots, k_p$ as unknowns. From Theorem 1 in Sec. 7.6 it follows that the system has a nontrivial solution $k_1, \cdots, k_p$ if, and only if, the coefficient matrix has rank less than p. From this the statements follow.

An immediate consequence of Theorem 2 is

Theorem 3. *p vectors with $n < p$ components are always linearly dependent.*

In fact, then the coefficient matrix of the system considered just before has rank $r \leq n < p$, and this proves Theorem 3.

By combining Theorem 2 and Theorem 1 in Sec. 7.4, we also have

Theorem 4. *The rank of a matrix equals the maximum number of linearly independent column vectors or row vectors.*

Returning to our homogeneous system (2), we shall now introduce the following notion.

A set of linearly independent solutions $x_{(1)}, \cdots, x_{(p)}$ *of the homogeneous system* (2) *is called a* **fundamental system** *of solutions of* (2), *if every solution* x *of* (2) *can be written as a linear combin tion of these vectors, that is, in the form*

$$x = c_1 x_{(1)} + \cdots + c_p x_{(p)}$$

where $c_1, \cdots, c_p$ *are suitable constants.*

Theorem 5. *If the coefficient matrix* A *of the homogeneous system* (2) *in* n *unknowns has rank* r ($<n$), *the system has a fundamental system of solutions, consisting of* $n - r$ *independent solutions.*

Proof. If A has rank r then $n - r$ unknowns, say, the unknowns $x_{r+1}, \cdots, x_n$ remain arbitrary. We choose these $n - r$ unknowns in $n - r$ different ways, namely,

(3)
$$x_{r+1} = 1, \text{ and the others zero,}$$
$$x_{r+2} = 1, \text{ and the others zero,}$$
$$\cdots \cdots \cdots \cdots \cdots \cdots \cdots \cdots$$
$$x_n \ \ = 1, \text{ and the others zero.}$$

In each case the unknowns $x_1, \cdots, x_r$ are then uniquely determined (cf. Theorem 1 in Sec. 7.6).

In this way we obtain altogether $n - r$ solutions of (2). We denote these solutions by $y_{(1)}, \cdots, y_{(n-r)}$. To show that they are linearly independent we form the matrix having these solutions as row vectors:

$$\begin{pmatrix} \cdots & 1 & 0 & \cdots & 0 \\ \cdots & 0 & 1 & \cdots & 0 \\ \cdots & \cdot & \cdot & \cdots & \cdot \\ \cdots & 0 & 0 & \cdots & 1 \end{pmatrix};$$

here the dots in the left-hand part denote the values of the unknowns $x_1, \cdots, x_r$ in these solutions. This matrix has rank $n - r$ because the determinant of the $(n - r)$-rowed square submatrix formed of the last $n - r$ columns of the matrix is not zero. This proves linear independence of $y_{(1)}, \cdots, y_{(n-r)}$.

We finally show that these solutions form a fundamental system. We have to prove that any solution x of (2) can be represented as a linear combination of the vectors $y_{(1)}, \cdots, y_{(n-r)}$. For this purpose we introduce the vector

(4)
$$z = x - x_{r+1} y_{(1)} - x_{r+2} y_{(2)} - \cdots - x_n y_{(n-r)}$$

and denote its components by $z_1, \cdots, z_n$. From the form of the last $n - r$ components of the vectors $y_{(j)}$ [cf. (3)], it follows that the last $n - r$ components of z are zero:

(5) $z_{r+1} = x_{r+1} - x_{r+1} \cdot 1 = 0,$ $\cdots,$ $z_n = x_n - x_n \cdot 1 = 0.$

Since the vectors on the right side of (4) are solutions of (2), it follows from Theorem 1 that $\mathbf{z}$ is a solution of (2). Now (2) may be written

$$(6) \qquad \mathbf{a}_{(1)}x_1 + \cdots + \mathbf{a}_{(n)}x_n = 0$$

where $\mathbf{a}_{(j)}$ is a column vector with components $a_{1j}, \cdots, a_{mj}$. By inserting the solution $\mathbf{z}$ and using (5), this becomes

$$(7) \qquad \mathbf{a}_{(1)}z_1 + \cdots + \mathbf{a}_{(r)}z_r = 0.$$

From the assumptions that $\mathbf{A}$ has rank r and $x_{r+1}, \cdots, x_n$ are the unknowns which remain arbitrary, it follows that the matrix with column vectors $\mathbf{a}_{(1)}, \cdots, \mathbf{a}_{(r)}$ has rank r. Hence, by Theorem 2 (with $p = r$), these vectors are linearly independent. From this and (7) we conclude that

$$z_1 = 0, \cdots, z_r = 0.$$

From this and (5) we have $\mathbf{z} = 0$, and (4) yields the desired representation of the arbitrary solution $\mathbf{x}$:

$$\mathbf{x} = x_{r+1}\mathbf{y}_{(1)} + \cdots + x_n\mathbf{y}_{(n-r)}.$$

This completes the proof of Theorem 5.

We now turn to nonhomogeneous systems of linear equations and prove

Theorem 6. *If the nonhomogeneous system* (1) *has solutions* $\mathbf{x}$ *then all these solutions are of the form*

$$\mathbf{x} = \mathbf{x}_0 + \mathbf{x}_h$$

where $\mathbf{x}_0$ *is any fixed solution of* (1) *and* $\mathbf{x}_h$ *runs through all the solutions of the corresponding homogeneous system* (2).

Proof. Let $\mathbf{x}$ be any given solution of (1) and $\mathbf{x}_0$ an arbitrarily chosen solution of (1). Then $\mathbf{A}\mathbf{x} = \mathbf{b}$, $\mathbf{A}\mathbf{x}_0 = \mathbf{b}$ and, therefore,

$$\mathbf{A}(\mathbf{x} - \mathbf{x}_0) = \mathbf{A}\mathbf{x} - \mathbf{A}\mathbf{x}_0 = 0.$$

This shows that the difference $\mathbf{x} - \mathbf{x}_0$ between any solution $\mathbf{x}$ of (1) and any fixed solution $\mathbf{x}_0$ of (1) is a solution of (2), say, $\mathbf{x}_h$. Hence all solutions of (1) are obtained by letting $\mathbf{x}_h$ run through all the solutions of the homogeneous system (2), and the proof is complete.

PROBLEMS

1. Verify Theorem 1 for the two solutions

$$x = 1,\ y = 2,\ z = 3 \qquad \text{and} \qquad x = -2,\ y = -4,\ z = -6$$

of the system

$$
\begin{aligned}
-5x + \ y + \ z &= 0 \\
5x + 2y - 3z &= 0.
\end{aligned}
$$

In each case find whether the given vectors are linearly dependent or independent.

2. $(1, 0)$, $(1, 2)$ **3.** $(1, 3)$, $(-2, -6)$ **4.** $(2, 3)$, $(-4, 1)$, $(-1, 13)$
5. $(0, 0)$, $(1, -1)$ **6.** $(-4, 7, 8)$, $(0, -1, 2)$
7. $(-4, 1, 0)$, $(3, 1, 2)$, $(1, 1, 1)$ **8.** $(4, 1, 3)$, $(9, -1, 1)$, $(-5, 2, 2)$
9. $(1, 0, 0)$, $(3, -1, 2)$, $(-5, 18, 46)$, $(68, 23, 19)$
10. $(16, -4, 13, 8)$, $(-5, 0, 7, 0)$ **11.** $(-3, 0, 4, 1)$, $(0, 1, 14, 1)$, $(-1, 2, 7, 5)$
12. $(1, 0, 0, 0)$, $(0, 1, 0, 0)$, $(0, 0, 1, 0)$

13. In Prob. 12, find a vector x such that x and the three given vectors are linearly independent.

14. Find all values of k such that the vectors $(1, 2, 3)$, $(4, 5, 6)$, and $(7, 8, k)$ are linearly dependent.

15. Find all values of k such that the vectors $(1, 2, 3, 4)$, $(5, 6, 7, 8)$, $(9, 10, 11, 12)$, $(13, 14, 15, k)$ are linearly dependent.

16. Show that in Theorem 2, "column vectors" may be replaced by "row vectors."

7.9   GAUSS'S ELIMINATION METHOD

We have seen that any system of linear algebraic equations can be solved by the use of determinants; the steps of solving such a system are explained on pp. 420 and 425. The last step requires the application of Cramer's rule involving determinants.

Now, if the order of a determinant is large, its evaluation is very tedious. In fact, if an nth order determinant is evaluated by developing it by a row or column, then developing each cofactor in the same fashion, etc., $n!$ multiplications would be required. If these multiplications could be carried out with an electronic computer which can perform 10,000 multiplications per second, the time required would be as follows:

n	5	10	12	14	16	18	20	30
$n! \approx$	10^2	$3 \cdot 10^6$	$5 \cdot 10^8$	$9 \cdot 10^{10}$	$2 \cdot 10^{13}$	$6 \cdot 10^{15}$	$2 \cdot 10^{18}$	$3 \cdot 10^{32}$
Time	0.01 sec.	5 min.	10 hours	3 months	60 years	20,000 years	10^7 years	10^{21} years

Note for comparison that several different physical arguments (arising from nuclear physics, the theory of radioactive decomposition, etc.) lead to the conclusion that the age of the universe cannot be greater than 10^{10} years.

Because the problem of solving linear equations is of great practical importance, various mathematicians have tried to develop simpler and less time-consuming procedures, and various methods for solving systems of linear equations

$$a_{11}x_1 + \cdots + a_{1n}x_n = b_1$$
$$a_{21}x_1 + \cdots + a_{2n}x_n = b_2$$

(1) $$\cdots \cdots \cdots \cdots \cdots \cdots \cdots$$

$$a_{m1}x_1 + \cdots + a_{mn}x_n = b_m$$

have been suggested.   One of the most important methods is the so-called **Gauss algorithm**[1] which is a systematic elimination method.   In this method for solving (1) we proceed stepwise as follows.

First step.   *Elimination of x_1 from the second, third, $\cdots$ mth equation.* We may assume that the order of equations and the order of the unknowns in each equation is such that $a_{11} \neq 0$.   The variable x_1 can then be eliminated from the second, $\cdots$, mth equation by subtracting

a_{21}/a_{11} times the first equation from the second equation,

a_{31}/a_{11} times the first equation from the third equation,

etc.   This gives a new system of equations of the form

(2)
$$a_{11}x_1 + a_{12}x_2 + \cdots + a_{1n}x_n = b_1$$
$$c_{22}x_2 + \cdots + c_{2n}x_n = b_2{}^*$$
$$\cdot$$
$$\cdot$$
$$\cdot$$
$$c_{m2}x_2 + \cdots + c_{mn}x_n = b_m{}^*.$$

Any solution of (1) is a solution of (2) and conversely, because each equation of (2) was derived from two equations of (1) and, by reversing the process, (1) may be obtained from (2).

Second step.   *Elimination of x_2 from the third, $\cdots$, mth equation in (2).* If the coefficients $c_{22}, \cdots, c_{mn}$ in (2) are not all zero, we may assume that the orders of the equations and the unknowns is such that $c_{22} \neq 0$.   Then we may eliminate x_2 from the third, fourth, $\cdots$, mth equation of (2) by subtracting

c_{32}/c_{22} times the second equation from the third equation,

c_{42}/c_{22} times the second equation from the fourth equation,   etc.

The further steps are now obvious.   In the third step we eliminate x_3, in the fourth step we eliminate x_4, etc.

This process will stop only when no equations are left or when the coefficients of all the unknowns in the remaining equations are all zero.   We then have a system of the form

(3)
$$a_{11}x_1 + a_{12}x_2 + \quad \cdots \quad + a_{1n}x_n = b_1$$
$$c_{22}x_2 + \quad \cdots \quad + c_{2n}x_n = b_2{}^*$$
$$\cdot$$
$$\cdot$$
$$\cdot$$
$$k_{rr}x_r + \cdots + k_{rn}x_n = \tilde{b}_r$$

[1] We present the Gauss algorithm in its classical form; further reduction of the amount of computational work was obtained by Banachiewicz and Cholesky.   These and other methods are discussed in Ref. [D1].

where either $r = m$ or $r < m$. If $r < m$, the remaining equations have the form

$$0 = \tilde{b}_{r+1}, \cdots, 0 = \tilde{b}_m,$$

and the system has no solution, unless $\tilde{b}_{r+1} = 0, \cdots, \tilde{b}_m = 0$. If the system has a solution we may obtain it by choosing values at pleasure for the unknowns $x_{r+1}, \cdots, x_n$, solving the last equation in (3) for x_r, the next to the last for x_{r-1}, and so on up to the line.

In the important special case when $m = n = r$, the system (3) has triangular form and there is one, and only one, solution.

Example 1. Solve

$$
\begin{aligned}
w + 2x - 2y + 4z &= 11 \\
2w + x - y + 3z &= 9 \\
w - x + y - z &= -2.
\end{aligned}
$$

(4)

In the first step we eliminate w from the last two equations, finding

$$
\begin{aligned}
w + 2x - 2y + 4z &= 11 \\
-3x + 3y - 5z &= -13 \\
-3x + 3y - 5z &= -13.
\end{aligned}
$$

(5)

We see that the last two equations are identical, and in the second step (elimination of x from the last equation) the last equation will reduce to $0 = 0$. Furthermore, we may choose y and z arbitrarily. Solving the second equation in (5) for x, we have

$$x = \tfrac{13}{3} + y - \tfrac{5}{3}z.$$

By inserting this in the first equation in (5) and solving for w we obtain

$$w = \tfrac{7}{3} - \tfrac{2}{3}z,$$

in agreement with the result at the end of Sec. 7.7 (except for notation).

PROBLEMS

Solve the following systems of linear equations by means of the Gauss algorithm.

1. $3x + 4y = 11$
   $5x - 2y = 1$

2. $-3x - y = 5$
   $2x + 3y = 6$

3. $5x + 3y = -1$
   $-x + 2y = 8$

4. $x - 2y = -4$
   $3x + 4y = 38$

5. $3x + 2y = -4$
   $2x + 3y = 4$

6. $10x + y = 0$
   $3x + 2y = -17$

7. $2x - y + 2z = 8$
   $3x + 2y - 2z = -1$
   $5x + 3y - 3z = 3$

8. $7x + 3y + 4z = 1$
   $5x + y + 2z = 1$
   $9x + 4y + 3z = -1$

9. $2x + 3y + z = 0$
   $x + 5y + 2z = 6$
   $3x - y + z = -2$

10. $2y - z = -1$
    $x + 3z = 11$
    $2x - 4y + 2z = 6$

11. $3x + 2y - 12z = 0$
$2x - 3y + 5z = 0$
$x + 2y - 8z = 0$

12. $-7x + y + 2z = 0$
$9x - y - 3z = 0$
$2x + 4y - 7z = 0$

13. $w + x + y + z = 10$
$w - x + y - z = -2$
$2w + x - 2y + z = 2$
$5w + 7x - 9y + 2z = 0$

14. $w + x + y = 3$
$5x + 2y - z = -1$
$4w + 8y - 5z = 1$
$3w + 17x - y - 2z = -1$

15. $5w + 7x - y + 8z = 1$
$7w + x + y - 3z = 11$
$-w - 2x + 3y - z = 11$
$w + x - y + 3z = -3$

16. $2w + x - y - z = -2$
$w + 3x + 2y - 13z = 4$
$5w + 7x - y - 16z = -2$
$3w + x + y - 8z = 2$

17. $w - x + 3y - 3z = 3$
$2w + 3x + y - 11z = 1$
$5w - 2x + 5y - 4z = 5$
$3w + 4x - 7y + 2z = -7$

18. $3w - 6x + 2y + 4z = 7$
$w + y - z = 0$
$2w - 2x - y + 3z = 5$
$w - 4x + 3y + z = 2$

7.10   THE INVERSE OF A MATRIX

Let $\mathbf{A} = (a_{ik})$ be an n-rowed square matrix and consider the linear transformation

(1) $$\mathbf{y} = \mathbf{A}\mathbf{x}$$

where $\mathbf{x}$ and $\mathbf{y}$ are column vectors with n components $x_1, \cdots, x_n$ and $y_1, \cdots, y_n$, respectively. For given $\mathbf{y} \neq \mathbf{0}$, the equation (1) may be regarded as a nonhomogeneous system of n linear equations in the n unknowns $x_1, \cdots, x_n$. The system has a unique solution if, and only if, $\det \mathbf{A} \neq 0$, and this solution is then given by Cramer's rule:

$$x_1 = D_1/D, \cdots, x_n = D_n/D \quad \text{where} \quad D = \det \mathbf{A}$$

and D_k is obtained from D by replacing the kth column of D by the column $y_1, \cdots, y_n$. By developing D_1 by the first column, D_2 by the second column, etc., the solution may be written

$$x_1 = \frac{1}{\det \mathbf{A}} (y_1 A_{11} + \cdots + y_n A_{n1})$$

(2)
$$\vdots$$

$$x_n = \frac{1}{\det \mathbf{A}} (y_1 A_{1n} + \cdots + y_n A_{nn})$$

where A_{ik} is the cofactor of a_{ik} in $\det \mathbf{A}$. From the definition of matrix multiplication it follows that we may write (2) as a single vector equation,

(3) $$\mathbf{x} = \mathbf{B}\mathbf{y}$$

where

(4)
$$B = \frac{1}{\det A} \begin{pmatrix} A_{11} & A_{21} & \cdots & A_{n1} \\ A_{12} & A_{22} & \cdots & A_{n2} \\ \cdot & \cdot & \cdots & \cdot \\ A_{1n} & A_{2n} & \cdots & A_{nn} \end{pmatrix};$$

note that in B the cofactor A_{ik} occupies the same place as a_{ki} (not a_{ik}) does in A.

Now, by inserting (3) into (1), we obtain

$$y = A(By) = (AB)y,$$

the so-called *identity transformation*, which transforms y into itself. Hence we must have

(5)
$$AB = I,$$

where I is the n-rowed unit matrix. Similarly, by inserting (1) into (3) we obtain

$$x = B(Ax) = (BA)x,$$

and $BA = I$, as before. Altogether,

(6*)
$$AB = BA = I.$$

The matrix B that satisfies (6*) is called the **inverse** or **reciprocal** of A and will be denoted by A^{-1}. Thus

(6)
$$AA^{-1} = A^{-1}A = I.$$

By applying (12) in Sec. 7.3 to this equation we have

$$\det (AA^{-1}) = \det A \det A^{-1} = 1$$

which holds if, and only if, $\det A \neq 0$ and $\det A^{-1} \neq 0$. Since the solution of the system considered before is unique, A^{-1} is unique.

We may sum up our result as follows.

Theorem 1. *The inverse A^{-1} of a square matrix A exists if, and only if, A is nonsingular (that is, $\det A \neq 0$). Then the inverse A^{-1} of A is unique; it is the matrix B in* (4) *which is obtained from A by replacing each element a_{ik} by its cofactor A_{ik} and then transposing the resulting matrix and multiplying it by $1/\det A$.*

For a two-rowed square matrix we obtain from (4)

(7)
$$A = \begin{pmatrix} a_{11} & a_{12} \\ a_{21} & a_{22} \end{pmatrix}, \quad A^{-1} = \frac{1}{\det A} \begin{pmatrix} a_{22} & -a_{12} \\ -a_{21} & a_{11} \end{pmatrix}.$$

In the case of a diagonal matrix we simply have

$$
(8) \quad \mathbf{A} = \begin{pmatrix} a_{11} & \cdots & 0 \\ \cdot & \cdots & \cdot \\ \cdot & \cdots & \cdot \\ 0 & \cdots & a_{nn} \end{pmatrix}, \quad \mathbf{A}^{-1} = \begin{pmatrix} 1/a_{11} & \cdots & 0 \\ \cdot & \cdots & \cdot \\ \cdot & \cdots & \cdot \\ 0 & \cdots & 1/a_{nn} \end{pmatrix};
$$

the elements of $\mathbf{A}^{-1}$ in the principal diagonal are the reciprocals of those of $\mathbf{A}$.

Example 1.

$$
\mathbf{A} = \begin{pmatrix} 3 & 1 \\ 2 & 4 \end{pmatrix}, \quad \mathbf{A}^{-1} = \frac{1}{10}\begin{pmatrix} 4 & -1 \\ -2 & 3 \end{pmatrix} = \begin{pmatrix} 0.4 & -0.1 \\ -0.2 & 0.3 \end{pmatrix}.
$$

Example 2.

$$
\mathbf{A} = \begin{pmatrix} -3 & 6 & -11 \\ 3 & -4 & 6 \\ 4 & -8 & 13 \end{pmatrix}, \quad \det \mathbf{A} = 10, \quad \mathbf{A}^{-1} = \begin{pmatrix} -0.4 & 1.0 & -0.8 \\ -1.5 & 0.5 & -1.5 \\ -0.8 & 0 & -0.6 \end{pmatrix}.
$$

From (6), with $\mathbf{A}$ replaced by $\mathbf{C}$, we have

$$\mathbf{C}\mathbf{C}^{-1} = \mathbf{I}.$$

If we now take for $\mathbf{C}$ the inverse $\mathbf{A}^{-1}$ of a given matrix $\mathbf{A}$, this becomes

$$\mathbf{A}^{-1}(\mathbf{A}^{-1})^{-1} = \mathbf{I}.$$

By premultiplying both sides by $\mathbf{A}$ we obtain

$$(9) \quad (\mathbf{A}^{-1})^{-1} = \mathbf{A};$$

that is, *the inverse of the inverse is the given matrix* $\mathbf{A}$.

The inverse of a product $\mathbf{AC}$ can be obtained by inverting each factor and multiplying the results *in reverse order*:

$$(10) \quad (\mathbf{AC})^{-1} = \mathbf{C}^{-1}\mathbf{A}^{-1}.$$

To prove (10), we start from (6), with $\mathbf{A}$ replaced by $\mathbf{AC}$,

$$\mathbf{AC}(\mathbf{AC})^{-1} = \mathbf{I}.$$

By premultiplying this by $\mathbf{A}^{-1}$ and using $\mathbf{A}^{-1}\mathbf{A} = \mathbf{I}$ we obtain

$$\mathbf{C}(\mathbf{AC})^{-1} = \mathbf{A}^{-1}.$$

By premultiplying this by $\mathbf{C}^{-1}$ the result follows.

Of course, (10) may be generalized to products of more than two matrices; by induction we obtain

$$(11) \qquad (AC \cdots PQ)^{-1} = Q^{-1}P^{-1} \cdots C^{-1}A^{-1}.$$

PROBLEMS

1. Check the results in Exs. 1 and 2 by verifying that $AA^{-1} = A^{-1}A = I$.

2. Find the general formula for the inverse of a three-rowed nonsingular square matrix $A = (a_{jk})$.

In each case find the inverse of the given matrix and check the result.

3. $\begin{pmatrix} 2 & 1 \\ 5 & 3 \end{pmatrix}$ **4.** $\begin{pmatrix} \cos\theta & \sin\theta \\ -\sin\theta & \cos\theta \end{pmatrix}$ **5.** $\begin{pmatrix} a & b \\ b & a \end{pmatrix}$ **6.** $\begin{pmatrix} -1 & 5 \\ 2 & 3 \end{pmatrix}$

7. $\begin{pmatrix} 3 & 0 & 1 \\ 0 & 5 & 0 \\ -1 & 1 & -1 \end{pmatrix}$ **8.** $\begin{pmatrix} 2 & 0 & -1 \\ 5 & 1 & 0 \\ 0 & 1 & 3 \end{pmatrix}$ **9.** $\begin{pmatrix} 2 & -1 & 0 \\ 0 & -2 & 1 \\ 1 & 0 & 1 \end{pmatrix}$

10. $\begin{pmatrix} -4 & 0 & 0 \\ 0 & 3 & 0 \\ 0 & 0 & 0.5 \end{pmatrix}$ **11.** $\begin{pmatrix} 0 & 1 & 0 \\ 1 & 0 & 0 \\ 0 & 0 & 1 \end{pmatrix}$ **12.** $\begin{pmatrix} 0 & 0 & 1 \\ 0 & 1 & 0 \\ 1 & 0 & 0 \end{pmatrix}$

In each case find the inverse of the given linear transformation.

13. $\begin{aligned} x^* &= 2x + 4y + z \\ y^* &= x + 2y + z \\ z^* &= 3x + 4y + 2z \end{aligned}$ **14.** $\begin{aligned} x^* &= 6x + 4y + 3z \\ y^* &= 4x + 3y + 4z \\ z^* &= 3x + 2y + 2z \end{aligned}$

15. $\begin{aligned} x^* &= x + 2y + 5z \\ y^* &= \quad\;\; -y + 2z \\ z^* &= 2x + 4y + 11z \end{aligned}$

16. Show that the inverse of $B = kA$ is $B^{-1} = A^{-1}/k$.

17. Show that the inverse of A^2 is $(A^{-1})^2$.

18. Find the inverse of the square of the matrices in Probs. 3, 4, 8.

Fig. 210. Four-terminal network.

Consider a **four-terminal network** (Fig. 210) in which an input signal is applied to one pair of terminals and the output signal is taken from the other pair. Assume that the network is linear, that is, the currents i_1 and i_2 are linear functions of u_1 and u_2, say,

$$(12) \qquad \begin{aligned} i_1 &= a_{11}u_1 + a_{12}u_2 \\ i_2 &= a_{21}u_1 + a_{22}u_2 \end{aligned}$$

19. Show that (12) may be written $i = Au$ where

$$i = \begin{pmatrix} i_1 \\ i_2 \end{pmatrix}, \qquad A = \begin{pmatrix} a_{11} & a_{12} \\ a_{21} & a_{22} \end{pmatrix}, \qquad u = \begin{pmatrix} u_1 \\ u_2 \end{pmatrix},$$

and $u = A^{-1}i$.

20. If the output terminals are connected, $u_2 = 0$, and then $a_{11} = i_1/u_1$. Find similar relations for the other elements of A.

21. Show that the input potential and current may be expressed as linear functions of the output potential and current, say,

(13)
$$u_1 = t_{11}u_2 + t_{12}i_2,$$
$$i_1 = t_{21}u_2 + t_{22}i_2,$$
or $\quad \mathbf{v}_1 = \mathbf{T}\mathbf{v}_2 \quad$ where $\quad \mathbf{v}_1 = \begin{pmatrix} u_1 \\ i_1 \end{pmatrix}, \; \mathbf{v}_2 = \begin{pmatrix} u_2 \\ i_2 \end{pmatrix},$

and the "transmission matrix" **T** is

$$\mathbf{T} = \begin{pmatrix} t_{11} & t_{12} \\ t_{21} & t_{22} \end{pmatrix} = \frac{1}{a_{21}} \begin{pmatrix} -a_{22} & 1 \\ -\det A & a_{11} \end{pmatrix}.$$

Hint: to verify the last expression, start from (12); express u_1 in terms of u_2 and i_2; then express i_1 in terms of u_2 and i_2; finally, compare the resulting representations with (13).

22. Express **A** in terms of the elements of **T**.

In each case show that the given transmission matrix **T** corresponds to the indicated four-terminal network.

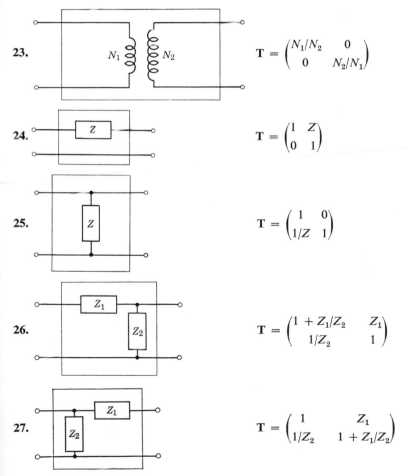

23. $\quad N_1 \quad N_2 \qquad \mathbf{T} = \begin{pmatrix} N_1/N_2 & 0 \\ 0 & N_2/N_1 \end{pmatrix}$

24. $\quad Z \qquad \mathbf{T} = \begin{pmatrix} 1 & Z \\ 0 & 1 \end{pmatrix}$

25. $\quad Z \qquad \mathbf{T} = \begin{pmatrix} 1 & 0 \\ 1/Z & 1 \end{pmatrix}$

26. $\quad Z_1 \quad Z_2 \qquad \mathbf{T} = \begin{pmatrix} 1 + Z_1/Z_2 & Z_1 \\ 1/Z_2 & 1 \end{pmatrix}$

27. $\quad Z_1 \quad Z_2 \qquad \mathbf{T} = \begin{pmatrix} 1 & Z_1 \\ 1/Z_2 & 1 + Z_1/Z_2 \end{pmatrix}$

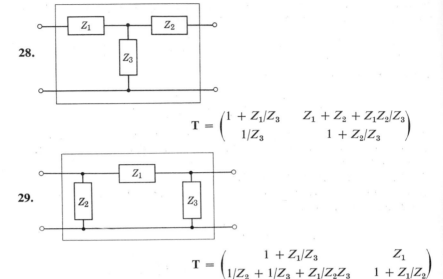

28.

$$T = \begin{pmatrix} 1 + Z_1/Z_3 & Z_1 + Z_2 + Z_1Z_2/Z_3 \\ 1/Z_3 & 1 + Z_2/Z_3 \end{pmatrix}$$

29.

$$T = \begin{pmatrix} 1 + Z_1/Z_3 & Z_1 \\ 1/Z_2 + 1/Z_3 + Z_1/Z_2Z_3 & 1 + Z_1/Z_2 \end{pmatrix}$$

30. If two four-terminal networks are connected in cascade (Fig. 211), show that the resulting network may be regarded as a four-terminal network for which $\mathbf{v}_1 = \mathbf{T}\mathbf{v}_2$ where

$$\mathbf{v}_1 = \begin{pmatrix} u_1 \\ i_1 \end{pmatrix}, \qquad \mathbf{v}_2 = \begin{pmatrix} u_2 \\ i_2 \end{pmatrix}, \qquad \mathbf{T} = \mathbf{T}_1\mathbf{T}_2.$$

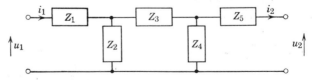

Fig. 211. Problem 30.

Applying the result of Prob. 30, obtain:

31. The matrix in Prob. 26 from those in Prob. 24 (with $Z = Z_1$) and Prob. 25 (with $Z = Z_2$).

32. The matrix in Prob. 27 from those in Probs. 24 and 25.

33. Generalize the result of Prob. 30 to more than two four-terminal networks connected in cascade.

34. Obtain the matrix in Prob. 28 from those in Probs. 24 and 25.

35. Obtain the matrix in Prob. 29 from those in Probs. 24 and 25.

36. Find the transmission matrix of the network in Fig. 212.

Fig. 212. Problem 36.

7.11 EIGENVALUES. EIGENVECTORS

Let $\mathbf{A} = (a_{jk})$ be a given square n-rowed matrix and consider the vector equation

(1) $$\mathbf{A}\mathbf{x} = \lambda\mathbf{x}$$

where λ is a number.

It is clear that the zero vector $\mathbf{x} = \mathbf{0}$ is a solution of (1) for any value of λ. A value of λ for which (1) has a solution $\mathbf{x} \neq \mathbf{0}$ is called an **eigenvalue**[2] or **characteristic value** of the matrix $\mathbf{A}$. The corresponding solutions $\mathbf{x} \neq \mathbf{0}$ of (1) are called **eigenvectors** or **characteristic vectors** of $\mathbf{A}$ corresponding to that eigenvalue λ. The set of the eigenvalues is called the *spectrum* of $\mathbf{A}$.

The problem of determining the eigenvalues and eigenvectors of a matrix is called an *eigenvalue problem*.[3] Problems of this type occur in connection with physical and technical applications. Therefore, the student should know the fundamental ideas and concepts which are important in this field of mathematics. During the last two decades various new methods for the approximate determination of eigenvalues have been developed and other methods which have been known for still a longer time have been put into a form which is suitable for electronic computers. Cf. Ref. [D1] in Appendix 1.

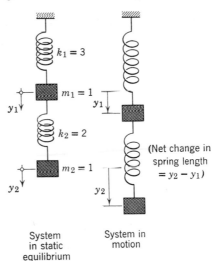

Fig. 213. Example 1.

Let us mention two simple problems which lead to an equation of the form (1).

Example 1. The vertical motion of the mechanical system in Fig. 213 (no damping, masses of springs neglected) is governed by the simultaneous differential equations

(2)
$$\ddot{y}_1 = -3y_1 + 2(y_2 - y_1),$$
$$\ddot{y}_2 = -2(y_2 - y_1),$$

---

[2] German: Eigenwert.

[3] More precisely: an algebraic eigenvalue problem, because there are other eigenvalue problems involving a differential equation (see Secs. 8.12 and 9.3) or an integral equation.

where $y_1(t)$ and $y_2(t)$ are the displacements of the two masses such that $y_1 = 0$, $y_2 = 0$ correspond to the positions of static equilibrium. The derivation of these equations is similar to that in Sec. 2.6. We may write the system in the form

$$\ddot{y}_1 = -5y_1 + 2y_2$$
$$\ddot{y}_2 = 2y_1 - 2y_2$$

or as a single vector equation

$$\ddot{\mathbf{y}} = A\mathbf{y}$$

where

$$\mathbf{y} = \begin{pmatrix} y_1 \\ y_2 \end{pmatrix} \quad \text{and} \quad A = \begin{pmatrix} -5 & 2 \\ 2 & -2 \end{pmatrix}.$$

To solve this equation we substitute

$$(3) \qquad\qquad \mathbf{y} = \mathbf{x}e^{\omega t}.$$

This yields

$$\omega^2 \mathbf{x}e^{\omega t} = A\mathbf{x}e^{\omega t}$$

or

$$A\mathbf{x} = \lambda\mathbf{x} \qquad\qquad \text{where } \lambda = \omega^2.$$

Hence, for (3) to be a solution of (2), not identically zero, $\omega^2 = \lambda$ must be an eigenvalue of A and the vector $\mathbf{x}$ in (3) must be a corresponding eigenvector.

Example 2. Given a linear transformation

$$\mathbf{y} = A\mathbf{x} \qquad\qquad\qquad (A \text{ real}),$$

does there exist a real vector $\mathbf{x} \neq \mathbf{0}$ for which the corresponding vector $\mathbf{y}$ is real and has the same direction and sense as $\mathbf{x}$? This means we want to find a vector $\mathbf{x}$ such that

$$\mathbf{y} = A\mathbf{x} = \lambda\mathbf{x} \qquad\qquad (\lambda \text{ real and positive}).$$

Clearly, such a vector exists if, and only if, A has a real positive eigenvalue. $\mathbf{x}$ is then an eigenvector corresponding to that eigenvalue.

Let us consider (1). If $\mathbf{x}$ is any vector, then the vectors $\mathbf{x}$ and $A\mathbf{x}$ will, in general, be linearly independent. If $\mathbf{x}$ is an eigenvector, then $\mathbf{x}$ and $A\mathbf{x}$ are linearly dependent; corresponding components of $\mathbf{x}$ and $A\mathbf{x}$ are then proportional, the factor of proportionality being the eigenvalue λ.

We shall now demonstrate that *any n-rowed square matrix has at least 1 and at most n distinct (real or complex) eigenvalues.*

For this purpose we write (1) at length:

$$a_{11}x_1 + \cdots + a_{1n}x_n = \lambda x_1$$
$$a_{21}x_1 + \cdots + a_{2n}x_n = \lambda x_2$$
$$\cdots\cdots\cdots\cdots\cdots\cdots\cdots$$
$$a_{n1}x_1 + \cdots + a_{nn}x_n = \lambda x_n.$$

By transferring the terms on the right-hand side to the left-hand side this becomes

$$(a_{11} - \lambda)x_1 + a_{12}x_2 + \cdots + a_{1n}x_n = 0$$
$$a_{21}x_1 + (a_{22} - \lambda)x_2 + \cdots + a_{2n}x_n = 0$$
$$(4) \qquad \cdots\cdots\cdots\cdots\cdots\cdots\cdots\cdots\cdots\cdots$$
$$a_{n1}x_1 + a_{n2}x_2 + \cdots + (a_{nn} - \lambda)x_n = 0.$$

According to Theorem 3 in Sec. 7.6 this homogeneous system of linear equations has a nontrivial solution if, and only if, the corresponding determinant of the coefficients is zero:

$$(5) \quad D(\lambda) = \det(\mathbf{A} - \lambda\mathbf{I}) = \begin{vmatrix} a_{11} - \lambda & a_{12} & \cdots & a_{1n} \\ a_{21} & a_{22} - \lambda & \cdots & a_{2n} \\ \cdot & \cdot & \cdots & \cdot \\ a_{n1} & a_{n2} & \cdots & a_{nn} - \lambda \end{vmatrix} = 0.$$

$D(\lambda)$ is called the *characteristic determinant*, and (5) is called the **characteristic equation** corresponding to the matrix $\mathbf{A}$. By developing $D(\lambda)$ we obtain a polynomial of nth degree in λ. This is called the *characteristic polynomial* corresponding to $\mathbf{A}$.

We have thus obtained the following important result.

Theorem 1. *The eigenvalues of a square matrix* $\mathbf{A}$ *are the roots of the corresponding characteristic equation* (5).

An eigenvalue which is a root of mth order of the characteristic polynomial is called an *eigenvalue of mth order* of the corresponding matrix.

Once the eigenvalues have been determined, the corresponding eigenvectors can be determined from the system (4). Since the system is homogeneous, it is clear that *if* $\mathbf{x}$ *is an eigenvector of* $\mathbf{A}$ *then* $k\mathbf{x}$, *where k is any constant, not zero, is also an eigenvector of* $\mathbf{A}$ *corresponding to the same eigenvalue.*

Example 3. Determine the eigenvalues and eigenvectors of the matrix

$$\mathbf{A} = \begin{pmatrix} 5 & 4 \\ 1 & 2 \end{pmatrix}.$$

The characteristic equation

$$D(\lambda) = \begin{vmatrix} 5 - \lambda & 4 \\ 1 & 2 - \lambda \end{vmatrix} = \lambda^2 - 7\lambda + 6 = 0$$

has the roots $\lambda_1 = 6$ and $\lambda_2 = 1$. For $\lambda = \lambda_1$ the system (4) assumes the form

$$-x_1 + 4x_2 = 0$$
$$x_1 - 4x_2 = 0$$

Thus $x_1 = 4x_2$, and

$$\mathbf{x}_1 = \begin{pmatrix} 4 \\ 1 \end{pmatrix}$$

is an eigenvector of $\mathbf{A}$ corresponding to the eigenvalue λ_1. In the same way we find that an eigenvector of $\mathbf{A}$ corresponding λ_2 is

$$\mathbf{x}_2 = \begin{pmatrix} 1 \\ -1 \end{pmatrix}.$$

$\mathbf{x}_1$ and $\mathbf{x}_2$ are linearly independent vectors.

Example 4. The matrix

$$A = \begin{pmatrix} a & b \\ -b & a \end{pmatrix} \qquad (a, b \text{ real}, b \neq 0)$$

has the conjugate complex eigenvalues $\lambda_1 = a + ib$ and $\lambda_2 = a - ib$. Corresponding eigenvectors are

$$\mathbf{x}_1 = \begin{pmatrix} 1 \\ i \end{pmatrix} \quad \text{and} \quad \mathbf{x}_2 = \begin{pmatrix} 1 \\ -i \end{pmatrix}.$$

If $b = 0$, then $\lambda_1 = \lambda_2 = a$; the matrix A has just one eigenvalue (which is then of the second order), and every vector $\mathbf{x} \neq \mathbf{0}$ with two components is an eigenvector of A.

Example 5. The matrix

$$A = \begin{pmatrix} -2 & 2 & -3 \\ 2 & 1 & -6 \\ -1 & -2 & 0 \end{pmatrix}$$

has the eigenvalues $\lambda_1 = 5$ and $\lambda_2 = \lambda_3 = -3$. The vector

$$\mathbf{x}_1 = \begin{pmatrix} 1 \\ 2 \\ -1 \end{pmatrix}$$

is an eigenvector of A corresponding to the eigenvalue 5, and the vectors

$$\mathbf{x}_2 = \begin{pmatrix} -2 \\ 1 \\ 0 \end{pmatrix} \quad \text{and} \quad \mathbf{x}_3 = \begin{pmatrix} 3 \\ 0 \\ 1 \end{pmatrix}$$

are two linearly independent eigenvectors of A corresponding to the eigenvalue -3. This agrees with the fact that, for $\lambda = -3$, the matrix $A - \lambda I$ has rank 1 and so, by Theorem 5 in Sec. 7.8, a fundamental system of solutions of the corresponding system (4), viz.,

$$x_1 + 2x_2 - 3x_3 = 0$$
$$2x_1 + 4x_2 - 6x_3 = 0$$
$$-x_1 - 2x_2 + 3x_3 = 0$$

consists of two linearly independent vectors.

Example 5 shows that *to an eigenvalue there may correspond several linearly independent eigenvectors*. The maximum number of linearly independent eigenvectors corresponding to an eigenvalue λ is called the **multiplicity** of λ.

PROBLEMS

Find the eigenvalues and eigenvectors of the following matrices.

1. $\begin{pmatrix} 4 & -2 \\ 1 & 1 \end{pmatrix}$ **2.** $\begin{pmatrix} 1 & 0 \\ 1 & 1 \end{pmatrix}$ **3.** $\begin{pmatrix} 0 & 0 \\ 0 & 0 \end{pmatrix}$ **4.** $\begin{pmatrix} 3 & 4 \\ 4 & -3 \end{pmatrix}$

5. $\begin{pmatrix} 1 & 2 \\ -8 & 11 \end{pmatrix}$ **6.** $\begin{pmatrix} 0 & 0 \\ 0 & 2 \end{pmatrix}$ **7.** $\begin{pmatrix} 1 & 0 \\ 2 & -1 \end{pmatrix}$ **8.** $\begin{pmatrix} 1 & 0 \\ 0 & -3 \end{pmatrix}$

9. $\begin{pmatrix} 13 & -3 & 5 \\ 0 & 4 & 0 \\ -15 & 9 & -7 \end{pmatrix}$ **10.** $\begin{pmatrix} 3 & 0 & 0 \\ 0 & 1 & 0 \\ 0 & 0 & 4 \end{pmatrix}$ **11.** $\begin{pmatrix} 15 & -4 & -3 \\ -10 & 12 & -6 \\ -20 & 4 & -2 \end{pmatrix}$

12. $\begin{pmatrix} 3 & 0 & 0 \\ 5 & 4 & 0 \\ 3 & 6 & 1 \end{pmatrix}$ **13.** $\begin{pmatrix} 26 & -2 & 2 \\ 2 & 21 & 4 \\ 4 & 2 & 28 \end{pmatrix}$ **14.** $\begin{pmatrix} 0 & 1 & 0 \\ 1 & 0 & 0 \\ 0 & 0 & 1 \end{pmatrix}$

Let $\lambda_1, \cdots, \lambda_n$ be the eigenvalues of a given matrix $\mathbf{A}$. Prove the following statements.

15. The transpose $\mathbf{A}^\mathsf{T}$ has the eigenvalues $\lambda_1, \cdots, \lambda_n$.

16. If $\mathbf{A}$ is triangular, the elements of the principal diagonal are the eigenvalues of $\mathbf{A}$.

17. The matrix $k\mathbf{A}$ has the eigenvalues $k\lambda_1, \cdots, k\lambda_n$.

18. The matrix $\mathbf{A}^2$ has the eigenvalues $\lambda_1^2, \cdots, \lambda_n^2$.

19. The matrix $\mathbf{A}^m$ (m a nonnegative integer) has the eigenvalues $\lambda_1^m \cdots, \lambda_n^m$.

20. The matrix $k_m\mathbf{A}^m + k_{m-1}\mathbf{A}^{m-1} + \cdots + k_1\mathbf{A} + k_0\mathbf{I}$ has the eigenvalues

$$k_m\lambda_j^m + k_{m-1}\lambda_j^{m-1} + \cdots + k_1\lambda_j + k_0, \qquad j = 1, \cdots, n.$$

21. If $\mathbf{A}$ is nonsingular, the eigenvalues are all different from zero.

22. The inverse has the eigenvalues $1/\lambda_1, \cdots, 1/\lambda_n$.

23. Show that the vertical motion of the mechanical system in Fig. 214 (no damping, masses of springs neglected) is governed by the simultaneous differential equations

$$m_1\ddot{y}_1 = -k_1y_1 + k_2(y_2 - y_1)$$
$$m_2\ddot{y}_2 = -k_2(y_2 - y_1)$$

where dots denote derivatives with respect to the time t.

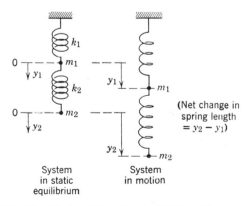

Fig. 214. Mechanical system in Problem 23.

24. Show that the system of equations in Prob. 23 may be written as a single vector equation $\ddot{\mathbf{y}} = \mathbf{A}\mathbf{y}$ where

$$\mathbf{y} = \begin{pmatrix} y_1 \\ y_2 \end{pmatrix} \quad \text{and} \quad \mathbf{A} = \begin{pmatrix} -\dfrac{k_1 + k_2}{m_1} & \dfrac{k_2}{m_1} \\ \dfrac{k_2}{m_2} & -\dfrac{k_2}{m_2} \end{pmatrix}.$$

25. To solve the equation in Prob. 24, substitute

$$\mathbf{y} = \mathbf{x}e^{\omega t}$$

and show that this leads to the eigenvalue problem

$$\mathbf{A}\mathbf{x} = \lambda\mathbf{x} \quad \text{where} \quad \lambda = \omega^2.$$

26. In Prob. 25, let $m_1 = m_2 = 1$, $k_1 = 3$, $k_2 = 2$. Find the eigenvalues and show that corresponding eigenvectors are

$$\mathbf{x}_1 = \begin{pmatrix} 1 \\ 2 \end{pmatrix}, \quad \mathbf{x}_2 = \begin{pmatrix} -2 \\ 1 \end{pmatrix}.$$

Conclude that this leads to the following solution of the equation in Prob. 24 (with m_1, m_2, k_1, k_2 as indicated):

$$\mathbf{y}(t) = a_1\mathbf{x}_1 \cos t + b_1\mathbf{x}_1 \sin t + a_2\mathbf{x}_2 \cos \sqrt{6}t + b_2\mathbf{x}_2 \sin \sqrt{6}t$$

where a_1, b_1, a_2, b_2 are arbitrary constants.

27. Show that by imposing the initial conditions $y_1(0) = 1$, $y_2(0) = 2$, $\dot{y}_1(0) = -2\sqrt{6}$, $\dot{y}_2(0) = \sqrt{6}$ or, in vector form,

$$\mathbf{y}(0) = \begin{pmatrix} 1 \\ 2 \end{pmatrix}, \quad \dot{\mathbf{y}}(0) = \begin{pmatrix} -2\sqrt{6} \\ \sqrt{6} \end{pmatrix},$$

we obtain from the solution in Prob. 26 the particular solution

$$\mathbf{y}(t) = \mathbf{x}_1 \cos t + \mathbf{x}_2 \sin \sqrt{6}t,$$

that is,

$$y_1 = \cos t - 2 \sin \sqrt{6}t, \quad y_2 = 2 \cos t + \sin \sqrt{6}t.$$

Verify by substitution that these functions are solutions of the differential equations in Prob. 23 with $m_1 = m_2 = 1$, $k_1 = 3$, $k_2 = 2$.

28. In Prob. 26, find and graph the solutions satisfying the initial conditions $y_1(0) = 1$, $y_2(0) = 2$, $\dot{y}_1(0) = 0$, $\dot{y}_2(0) = 0$.

Find the solution of the differential equations in Prob. 23, assuming that

29. $m_1 = m_2 = 1, k_1 = 6, k_2 = 4, y_1(0) = 0, y_2(0) = 0, \dot{y}_1(0) = \sqrt{2}, \dot{y}_2(0) = 2\sqrt{2}$

30. $m_1 = m_2 = 1, k_1 = 9, k_2 = 6, y_1(0) = -2, y_2(0) = 1, \dot{y}_1(0) = 0, \dot{y}_2(0) = 0$

31. Show that, for any positive k_1, k_2, m_1, m_2, the eigenvalues of the matrix in Prob. 24 are negative real.

In each case find the solution satisfying the given initial conditions.

32. $\begin{aligned} \dot{y}_1 &= 4y_1 - 2y_2 \\ \dot{y}_2 &= y_1 + y_2 \end{aligned}$ $\qquad y_1(0) = 3, y_2(0) = 2$

33. $\begin{aligned} \dot{y}_1 &= 3y_1 + 4y_2 \\ \dot{y}_2 &= 4y_1 - 3y_2 \end{aligned}$ $\qquad y_1(0) = 1, y_2(0) = 3$

34. $\begin{aligned} \dot{y}_1 &= y_1 + 2y_2 \\ \dot{y}_2 &= -8y_1 + 11y_2 \end{aligned}$ $\qquad y_1(0) = 1, y_2(0) = 1$

35. $\dot{y}_1 = y_2$
$\dot{y}_2 = y_1 + 3y_3$ $y_1(0) = 2, y_2(0) = 0, y_3(0) = 2$
$\dot{y}_3 = y_2$

36. $\dot{y}_1 = 3y_1$
$\dot{y}_2 = 5y_1 + 4y_2$ $y_1(0) = 2, y_2(0) = -10, y_3(0) = -27$
$\dot{y}_3 = 3y_1 + 6y_2 + y_3$

37. Do there exist matrices which have no eigenvalues at all?

38. If **A** is a square matrix whose elements are real, show that the eigenvalues of **A** are real or complex conjugates in pairs.

39. If **A** is an n-rowed square matrix with real elements and n is odd, show that **A** has at least one real eigenvalue.

7.12 BILINEAR, QUADRATIC, HERMITIAN, AND SKEW-HERMITIAN FORMS

An expression of the form

(1)
$$B = \sum_{j=1}^{n} \sum_{k=1}^{n} a_{jk} x_j y_k$$

(where the a_{jk} are numbers) is called a **bilinear form** in the $2n$ variables $x_1, \cdots, x_n$ and $y_1, \cdots, y_n$. Writing B at length, we have

(1′)
$$\begin{aligned}
B = \quad &a_{11}x_1y_1 + a_{12}x_1y_2 + \cdots + a_{1n}x_1y_n \\
+ &a_{21}x_2y_1 + a_{22}x_2y_2 + \cdots + a_{2n}x_2y_n \\
&\cdots\cdots\cdots\cdots\cdots\cdots\cdots\cdots\cdots\cdots \\
+ &a_{n1}x_ny_1 + a_{n2}x_ny_2 + \cdots + a_{nn}x_ny_n.
\end{aligned}$$

The n-rowed square matrix $\mathbf{A} = (a_{jk})$ is called the *coefficient matrix* of the form. Introducing the vectors

$$\mathbf{x} = \begin{pmatrix} x_1 \\ \cdot \\ \cdot \\ \cdot \\ x_n \end{pmatrix} \quad \text{and} \quad \mathbf{y} = \begin{pmatrix} y_1 \\ \cdot \\ \cdot \\ \cdot \\ y_n \end{pmatrix},$$

the form B may be written

(2)
$$B = \mathbf{x}^\mathsf{T}\mathbf{A}\mathbf{y}$$

where $\mathbf{x}^\mathsf{T} = (x_1 \cdots x_n)$ is the transpose of $\mathbf{x}$. This follows immediately from the definition of matrix multiplication.

Example 1. If **A** is the unit matrix **I**, then
$$B = \mathbf{x}^\mathsf{T}\mathbf{I}\mathbf{y} = \mathbf{x}^\mathsf{T}\mathbf{y} = x_1y_1 + x_2y_2 + \cdots + x_ny_n;$$

that is, in this case, B is the scalar product of the vectors **x** and **y**.

If $\mathbf{y} = \mathbf{x}$ then (1) is called a **quadratic form** in the n variables $x_1, \cdots, x_n$. Denoting this form by Q, we have

$$(3) \qquad Q = \sum_{j=1}^{n} \sum_{k=1}^{n} a_{jk} x_j x_k.$$

Writing Q at length and taking corresponding terms $a_{jk} x_j x_k$ and $a_{kj} x_k x_j$ together, we obtain

$$Q = a_{11} x_1{}^2 + (a_{12} + a_{21}) x_1 x_2 + \cdots + (a_{1n} + a_{n1}) x_1 x_n$$
$$+ \; a_{22} x_2{}^2 \qquad + \cdots + (a_{2n} + a_{n2}) x_2 x_n$$
$$+ \cdots \cdots \cdots \cdots \cdots$$
$$+ \; a_{nn} x_n{}^2.$$

We may now set

$$\tfrac{1}{2}(a_{jk} + a_{kj}) = c_{jk}.$$

Then $c_{kj} = c_{jk}$ and $c_{jk} + c_{kj} = a_{jk} + a_{kj}$ so that we may write

$$Q = \sum_{j=1}^{n} \sum_{k=1}^{n} c_{jk} x_j x_k.$$

If $\mathbf{A}$ is real, then the coefficient matrix $\mathbf{C} = (c_{jk})$ in this new representation is a real symmetric matrix. This shows that *any real quadratic form Q in n variables $x_1, \cdots, x_n$ may be written*

$$Q = \mathbf{x}^{\mathsf{T}} \mathbf{C} \mathbf{x}$$

where $\mathbf{C}$ is a real symmetric matrix. The reader may prove that the correspondence between these forms Q and symmetric matrices $\mathbf{C}$ is then one-to-one, that is, to each such form Q there corresponds exactly one symmetric matrix $\mathbf{C}$, and conversely.

Example 2. The quadratic form

$$Q = \mathbf{x}^{\mathsf{T}} \mathbf{A} \mathbf{x} = 2 x_1{}^2 + x_1 x_2 - 3 x_2{}^2$$

has the coefficient matrix

$$\mathbf{A} = (a_{jk}) = \begin{pmatrix} 2 & 1 \\ 0 & -3 \end{pmatrix}.$$

Hence the corresponding symmetric coefficient matrix is

$$\mathbf{C} = \tfrac{1}{2}[\mathbf{A} + \mathbf{A}^{\mathsf{T}}] = \tfrac{1}{2}(a_{jk} + a_{kj}) = \begin{pmatrix} 2 & \tfrac{1}{2} \\ \tfrac{1}{2} & -3 \end{pmatrix}.$$

We introduce the following notation. *Let $\mathbf{A} = (a_{jk})$ be any matrix. Then $\bar{\mathbf{A}}$ denotes the matrix $(\bar{a}_{jk})$ which is obtained from $\mathbf{A}$ by replacing each element a_{jk} by its complex conjugate $\bar{a}_{jk}$.*

A square matrix $\mathbf{A} = (a_{jk})$ for which the transpose equals the complex conjugate, that is,

(4) $$\mathbf{A}^\mathsf{T} = \bar{\mathbf{A}} \qquad (\text{or } a_{kj} = \bar{a}_{jk})$$

is called a **Hermitian[4] matrix**.

From (4) we see that the elements in the principal diagonal of a Hermitian matrix are always real. Furthermore, if all the elements of a Hermitian matrix $\mathbf{A}$ are real, then (4) assumes the form $\mathbf{A}^\mathsf{T} = \mathbf{A}$ which means that *a real Hermitian matrix is a symmetric matrix, and so Hermitian matrices are a natural generalization of real symmetric matrices.*

A form

$$H = \bar{\mathbf{x}}^\mathsf{T}\mathbf{A}\mathbf{x} \qquad \text{(A Hermitian)}$$

is called a **Hermitian form**; here the n components of the vector $\mathbf{x}$ may be real or complex variables. Obviously, this is a generalization of a real quadratic form.

From the definition of matrix multiplication it follows that

$$H = \sum_{j=1}^{n} \sum_{k=1}^{n} a_{jk}\bar{x}_j x_k.$$

Example 3. The matrix

$$\mathbf{A} = \begin{pmatrix} 2 & 3+i \\ 3-i & 1 \end{pmatrix}$$

is Hermitian, and the corresponding Hermitian form is

$$H = \bar{\mathbf{x}}^\mathsf{T}\mathbf{A}\mathbf{x} = (\bar{x}_1 \; \bar{x}_2)\begin{pmatrix} 2 & 3+i \\ 3-i & 1 \end{pmatrix}\begin{pmatrix} x_1 \\ x_2 \end{pmatrix}$$

$$= 2\bar{x}_1 x_1 + (3+i)\bar{x}_1 x_2 + (3-i)\bar{x}_2 x_1 + \bar{x}_2 x_2$$

$$= 2|x_1|^2 + |x_2|^2 + 2\operatorname{Re}[(3+i)\bar{x}_1 x_2]$$

where Re denotes the real part. The last expression shows that for every choice of $\mathbf{x}$ the value of H is a real number. We shall now prove that any Hermitian form has this remarkable property.

Theorem 1. *For every choice of* $\mathbf{x}$ *the value of a Hermitian form*

$$H = \bar{\mathbf{x}}^\mathsf{T}\mathbf{A}\mathbf{x} \qquad \text{(A Hermitian)}$$

is a real number.

Proof. Using (4), we obtain

$$\bar{H} = (\overline{\bar{\mathbf{x}}^\mathsf{T}\mathbf{A}\mathbf{x}}) = \mathbf{x}^\mathsf{T}\bar{\mathbf{A}}\bar{\mathbf{x}} = \mathbf{x}^\mathsf{T}\mathbf{A}^\mathsf{T}\bar{\mathbf{x}}.$$

Since the expression on the right is a scalar, transposition does not change its value. Using (12) in Sec. 7.2, we thus have

$$\mathbf{x}^\mathsf{T}\mathbf{A}^\mathsf{T}\bar{\mathbf{x}} = (\mathbf{x}^\mathsf{T}\mathbf{A}^\mathsf{T}\bar{\mathbf{x}})^\mathsf{T} = \bar{\mathbf{x}}^\mathsf{T}\mathbf{A}\mathbf{x} = H.$$

[4] CHARLES HERMITE (1822–1901), French mathematician.

Hence, $\bar{H} = H$, which means that H is real. This completes the proof.

A square matrix $\mathbf{A} = (a_{jk})$ for which

(5) $\qquad\qquad\qquad \mathbf{A}^\mathsf{T} = -\bar{\mathbf{A}} \qquad\qquad$ (that is, $a_{kj} = -\bar{a}_{jk}$)

is called a **skew-Hermitian matrix**. Obviously this is a generalization of a real skew-symmetric matrix, because if all the elements of a skew-Hermitian matrix $\mathbf{A}$ are real, then (5) assumes the form $\mathbf{A}^\mathsf{T} = -\mathbf{A}$; that is, $\mathbf{A}$ is then a real skew-symmetric matrix.

A form

(6) $\qquad\qquad\qquad\qquad S = \bar{\mathbf{x}}^\mathsf{T}\mathbf{A}\mathbf{x} \qquad\qquad$ (**A** skew-Hermitian)

is called a **skew-Hermitian form**. The reader may prove the following theorem.

Theorem 2. *For every choice of* $\mathbf{x}$ *the value of a skew-Hermitian form is a purely imaginary number or zero.*

PROBLEMS

Find a real symmetric matrix $\mathbf{C}$ such that $Q = \mathbf{x}^\mathsf{T}\mathbf{C}\mathbf{x}$ where Q equals:

1. $6x_1^2 - 4x_1x_2 + 2x_2^2$
2. $x_1^2 - 3x_1x_2 + 5x_2^2$
3. $8x_1x_2 - x_2^2$
4. $(x_1 - x_2)^2$
5. $x_1^2 + 6x_1x_2 - 10x_1x_3 + 4x_3^2$
6. $(x_1 + x_2 + x_3)^2$
7. $-x_1^2 + 6x_1x_2 + 8x_1x_3 + 2x_2^2 - 4x_2x_3 + 5x_3^2$
8. Verify that the right-hand side of (2) is equal to the right-hand side of (1').

Find $H = \bar{\mathbf{x}}^\mathsf{T}\mathbf{A}\mathbf{x}$ where

9. $\mathbf{A} = \begin{pmatrix} 1 & i \\ -i & 1 \end{pmatrix}$, $\mathbf{x} = \begin{pmatrix} 1 \\ i \end{pmatrix}$
     10. $\mathbf{A} = \begin{pmatrix} 1 & 0 \\ 0 & 1 \end{pmatrix}$, $\mathbf{x} = \begin{pmatrix} 2 + i \\ 1 - i \end{pmatrix}$

11. $\mathbf{A} = \begin{pmatrix} 2 & 1 + i \\ 1 - i & 1 \end{pmatrix}$, $\mathbf{x} = \begin{pmatrix} 1 \\ 2 \end{pmatrix}$
     12. $\mathbf{A} = \begin{pmatrix} 0 & 3i \\ -3i & 2 \end{pmatrix}$, $\mathbf{x} = \begin{pmatrix} i \\ -2i \end{pmatrix}$

13. $\mathbf{A} = \begin{pmatrix} 3 & 4 - i \\ 4 + i & 2 \end{pmatrix}$, $\mathbf{x} = \begin{pmatrix} 3 + i \\ 1 - i \end{pmatrix}$

14. $\mathbf{A} = \begin{pmatrix} -2 & 3 + 3i \\ 3 - 3i & 1 \end{pmatrix}$, $\mathbf{x} = \begin{pmatrix} 1 + 2i \\ 2 - i \end{pmatrix}$

15. $\mathbf{A} = \begin{pmatrix} 0 & i & 0 \\ -i & 1 & -2i \\ 0 & 2i & 2 \end{pmatrix}$, $\mathbf{x} = \begin{pmatrix} i \\ 1 \\ -i \end{pmatrix}$
     16. $\mathbf{A} = \begin{pmatrix} 1 & -i & 2i \\ i & 1 & 0 \\ -2i & 0 & 1 \end{pmatrix}$, $\mathbf{x} = \begin{pmatrix} 0 \\ 1 \\ i \end{pmatrix}$

17. $\mathbf{A} = \begin{pmatrix} 2 & 1 + i \\ 1 - i & 1 \end{pmatrix}$, $\mathbf{x} = \begin{pmatrix} x_1 \\ x_2 \end{pmatrix}$
     18. $\mathbf{A} = \begin{pmatrix} 1 & 0 \\ 0 & 1 \end{pmatrix}$, $\mathbf{x} = \begin{pmatrix} x_1 \\ x_2 \end{pmatrix}$

19. $\mathbf{A} = \begin{pmatrix} 1 & 2 + 5i \\ 2 - 5i & 3 \end{pmatrix}$, $\mathbf{x} = \begin{pmatrix} x_1 \\ x_2 \end{pmatrix}$
     20. $\mathbf{A} = \begin{pmatrix} 2 & 3 + 4i \\ 3 - 4i & 1 \end{pmatrix}$, $\mathbf{x} = \begin{pmatrix} x_1 \\ x_2 \end{pmatrix}$

21. $A = \begin{pmatrix} 1 & i & 0 \\ -i & 0 & 3 \\ 0 & 3 & 2 \end{pmatrix}$, $x = \begin{pmatrix} x_1 \\ x_2 \\ x_3 \end{pmatrix}$ **22.** $A = \begin{pmatrix} 0 & 2i & 1+i \\ -2i & 0 & 1 \\ 1-i & 1 & 0 \end{pmatrix}$, $x = \begin{pmatrix} x_1 \\ x_2 \\ x_3 \end{pmatrix}$

23. Show that the elements of the principal diagonal of a skew-Hermitian matrix are purely imaginary or zero.

Find $S = \bar{x}^T A x$ where

24. $A = \begin{pmatrix} i & 1 \\ -1 & i \end{pmatrix}$, $x = \begin{pmatrix} 1 \\ i \end{pmatrix}$ **25.** $A = \begin{pmatrix} 2i & 1+i \\ -1+i & 3i \end{pmatrix}$, $x = \begin{pmatrix} 2+i \\ -i \end{pmatrix}$

26. $A = \begin{pmatrix} 5i & 3+2i \\ -3+2i & 0 \end{pmatrix}$, $x = \begin{pmatrix} 1-i \\ -1+i \end{pmatrix}$

27. $A = \begin{pmatrix} 4i & 1+2i \\ -1+2i & -3i \end{pmatrix}$, $x = \begin{pmatrix} 2-3i \\ 4+2i \end{pmatrix}$

28. Prove Theorem 2. *Hint:* model your work somewhat after that in the proof of Theorem 1.

29. If A and B are n-rowed Hermitian matrices and a and b are any *real* numbers, show that $C = aA + bB$ is a Hermitian matrix.

30. Let A and B be skew-Hermitian matrices. Under what conditions is $C = aA + bB$ a skew-Hermitian matrix? (a and b are numbers.)

31. Show that if the variables of a quadratic form $Q = x^T C x$ undergo a linear transformation, say, $x = Py$, then $Q = y^T A y$ where $A = P^T C P$.

32. Consider the quadratic form $Q = x^T C x$ (C symmetric) in three variables x_1, x_2, x_3. Find $\partial Q/\partial x_1$, $\partial Q/\partial x_2$, $\partial Q/\partial x_3$ and show that grad $Q = 2Cx$.

33. Show that any square matrix may be written as the sum of a Hermitian matrix and a skew-Hermitian matrix.

A real quadratic form $Q = x^T C x$ and its symmetric matrix $C = (c_{jk})$ are said to be **positive definite** if $Q > 0$ for all $(x_1, \cdots, x_n) \neq (0, \cdots, 0)$. A necessary and sufficient condition for positive definiteness is that all the determinants

$$C_1 = c_{11}, \quad C_2 = \begin{vmatrix} c_{11} & c_{12} \\ c_{21} & c_{22} \end{vmatrix}, \quad C_3 = \begin{vmatrix} c_{11} & c_{12} & c_{13} \\ c_{21} & c_{22} & c_{23} \\ c_{31} & c_{32} & c_{33} \end{vmatrix}, \cdots, C_n = \det C$$

are positive (cf. Ref. [D2]).

34. Show that the form in Prob. 1 is positive definite.

35. Test the forms in Probs. 2–4 for positive definiteness.

7.13 EIGENVALUES OF HERMITIAN, SKEW-HERMITIAN, AND UNITARY MATRICES

A square matrix $A = (a_{jk})$ for which

(1) $$A^T = \bar{A}^{-1}$$

is called a **unitary matrix**.

A real unitary matrix $\mathbf{A}$ is called an **orthogonal matrix**. For such a matrix, (1) assumes the form

$$(2) \qquad\qquad \mathbf{A}^\mathsf{T} = \mathbf{A}^{-1},$$

that is, *an orthogonal matrix is a real matrix for which the inverse equals its transpose.*

A system of vectors $\mathbf{x}_1, \cdots, \mathbf{x}_n$ for which

$$(3) \qquad \bar{\mathbf{x}}_j{}^\mathsf{T}\mathbf{x}_k = \delta_{jk} = \begin{cases} 0 & \text{when } j \neq k \\ 1 & \text{when } j = k \end{cases} \qquad (j, k = 1, \cdots, n)$$

is called a **unitary system**.

Clearly, if these vectors are real, then $\bar{\mathbf{x}}_j{}^\mathsf{T}\mathbf{x}_k = \mathbf{x}_j{}^\mathsf{T}\mathbf{x}_k$ is the scalar product of $\mathbf{x}_j$ and $\mathbf{x}_k$ in the elementary sense, and the condition (3) means that $\mathbf{x}_1, \cdots, \mathbf{x}_n$ are orthogonal unit vectors. *Hence a unitary system of real vectors is a system of orthogonal (mutually perpendicular) unit vectors.*

Theorem 1. *The column vectors (and also the row vectors) of a unitary matrix form a unitary system.*

Proof. Let $\mathbf{A}$ be a unitary matrix with column vectors $\mathbf{a}_1, \cdots, \mathbf{a}_n$. Then from (1) it follows that

$$\mathbf{A}^{-1}\mathbf{A} = \bar{\mathbf{A}}^\mathsf{T}\mathbf{A} = \begin{pmatrix} \bar{\mathbf{a}}_1{}^\mathsf{T} \\ \bar{\mathbf{a}}_2{}^\mathsf{T} \\ \cdot \\ \cdot \\ \cdot \\ \bar{\mathbf{a}}_n{}^\mathsf{T} \end{pmatrix} (\mathbf{a}_1 \cdots \mathbf{a}_n) = \begin{pmatrix} \bar{\mathbf{a}}_1{}^\mathsf{T}\mathbf{a}_1 & \bar{\mathbf{a}}_1{}^\mathsf{T}\mathbf{a}_2 & \cdots & \bar{\mathbf{a}}_1{}^\mathsf{T}\mathbf{a}_n \\ \bar{\mathbf{a}}_2{}^\mathsf{T}\mathbf{a}_1 & \bar{\mathbf{a}}_2{}^\mathsf{T}\mathbf{a}_2 & \cdots & \bar{\mathbf{a}}_2{}^\mathsf{T}\mathbf{a}_n \\ \cdot & \cdot & \cdots & \cdot \\ \bar{\mathbf{a}}_n{}^\mathsf{T}\mathbf{a}_1 & \bar{\mathbf{a}}_n{}^\mathsf{T}\mathbf{a}_2 & \cdots & \bar{\mathbf{a}}_n{}^\mathsf{T}\mathbf{a}_n \end{pmatrix} = \mathbf{I}$$

so that

$$\bar{\mathbf{a}}_j{}^\mathsf{T}\mathbf{a}_k = \begin{cases} 0 & \text{when } j \neq k, \\ 1 & \text{when } j = k. \end{cases}$$

This shows that the column vectors of a unitary matrix form a unitary system. From (1) it follows that the inverse $\mathbf{A}^{-1}$ of a unitary matrix $\mathbf{A}$ is unitary (cf. Prob. 1) and, furthermore, the column vectors of $\mathbf{A}^{-1}$ are the conjugates of the row vectors of $\mathbf{A}$. This shows that the row vectors of $\mathbf{A}$ form a unitary system. Theorem 1 is proved.

With respect to orthogonal matrices, Theorem 1 means that *the row vectors (and also the column vectors) of an orthogonal matrix $\mathbf{A} = (a_{jk})$ form a system of orthogonal unit vectors*:

$$(4) \qquad\qquad \sum_{m=1}^{n} a_{jm}a_{km} = \delta_{jk}.$$

For $n = 3$ these relations are identical with (7) in Sec. 5.17. This shows that *transformations of Cartesian coordinate systems into Cartesian coordinate systems (with the same unit of scale) are linear transformations whose coefficient matrices are orthogonal matrices.*

Therefore, these matrices are of great practical importance.

We shall now consider the eigenvalues of Hermitian, skew-Hermitian, and unitary matrices (Fig. 215).

Theorem 2. (a) *The eigenvalues of a Hermitian matrix are real.*
(b) *The eigenvalues of a skew-Hermitian matrix are purely imaginary or zero.*
(c) *The eigenvalues of a unitary matrix have the absolute value 1.*

Proof. (a) Let **A** be Hermitian and λ an eigenvalue of **A**. Then by definition there is a vector $\mathbf{x} \neq \mathbf{0}$ such that $\mathbf{Ax} = \lambda\mathbf{x}$. From this we obtain

$$\bar{\mathbf{x}}^\mathsf{T}\mathbf{Ax} = \bar{\mathbf{x}}^\mathsf{T}\lambda\mathbf{x} = \lambda\bar{\mathbf{x}}^\mathsf{T}\mathbf{x}.$$

Since $\mathbf{x} \neq \mathbf{0}$ it follows that $\bar{\mathbf{x}}^\mathsf{T}\mathbf{x} \neq 0$ and we may divide, finding

$$\lambda = \frac{\bar{\mathbf{x}}^\mathsf{T}\mathbf{Ax}}{\bar{\mathbf{x}}^\mathsf{T}\mathbf{x}}.$$

From Theorem 1 in the last section we conclude that both the numerator and the denominator are real. Hence λ is real.

(b) Let **S** be skew-Hermitian, λ an eigenvalue of **S**, and **x** a corresponding eigenvector. Then $\mathbf{Sx} = \lambda\mathbf{x}$, and by premultiplying this by $\bar{\mathbf{x}}^\mathsf{T}$ we have

$$\bar{\mathbf{x}}^\mathsf{T}\mathbf{Sx} = \bar{\mathbf{x}}^\mathsf{T}\lambda\mathbf{x} = \lambda\bar{\mathbf{x}}^\mathsf{T}\mathbf{x}.$$

Solving for λ we obtain

$$\lambda = \frac{\bar{\mathbf{x}}^\mathsf{T}\mathbf{Sx}}{\bar{\mathbf{x}}^\mathsf{T}\mathbf{x}}.$$

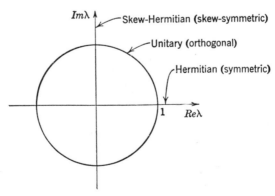

Fig. 215. Location of the eigenvalues of Hermitian, skew-Hermitian, and unitary matrices in the complex λ-plane.

From this and Theorem 2 in the last section the proof follows.

(c) Let U be unitary, λ an eigenvalue of U, and x a corresponding eigenvector. Then

(5) $$Ux = \lambda x.$$

Taking the conjugate transpose and using (12), Sec. 7.2, we obtain

$$(\bar{U}\bar{x})^\mathsf{T} = \bar{x}^\mathsf{T}\bar{U}^\mathsf{T} = \bar{\lambda}\bar{x}^\mathsf{T}.$$

Since U is unitary, $\bar{U}^\mathsf{T} = U^{-1}$, and our equation can be written

(6) $$\bar{x}^\mathsf{T}U^{-1} = \bar{\lambda}\bar{x}^\mathsf{T}.$$

By postmultiplying the left-hand side of (6) by the left-hand side of (5) and the right-hand side of (6) by the right-hand side of (5) we obtain

$$\bar{x}^\mathsf{T}U^{-1}Ux = \bar{\lambda}\bar{x}^\mathsf{T}\lambda x = \lambda\bar{\lambda}\bar{x}^\mathsf{T}x.$$

Since $U^{-1}U = I$ and $\lambda\bar{\lambda} = |\lambda|^2$ this becomes

$$\bar{x}^\mathsf{T}x = |\lambda|^2\,\bar{x}^\mathsf{T}x.$$

Since $x \neq 0$ it follows that $\bar{x}^\mathsf{T}x \neq 0$. Hence we must have $|\lambda|^2 = 1$. Thus $|\lambda| = 1$, and the proof is complete.

An important particular case of Theorem 2 is

Theorem 3. *The eigenvalues of a symmetric matrix are real. The eigenvalues of a skew-symmetric matrix are purely imaginary or zero. The eigenvalues of an orthogonal matrix have the absolute value 1 and are real or complex conjugates in pairs.*

PROBLEMS

1. Show that the inverse of a unitary matrix is unitary.

2. Show that the product of two n-rowed unitary matrices is a unitary matrix.

3. Let A be a given square matrix, and let X be the matrix whose column vectors $x_1, \cdots, x_n$ are eigenvectors of A corresponding to the eigenvalues $\lambda_1, \cdots, \lambda_n$ of A. Show that

$$AX = (\lambda_1 x_1 \cdots \lambda_n x_n) = XD$$

where D is the diagonal matrix with elements $\lambda_1, \cdots, \lambda_n$ in the principal diagonal. (X is called the **modal matrix** and D the **spectral matrix** of A.)

4. If the x_i in Prob. 3 are linearly independent, show that

$$X^{-1}AX = D.$$

5. Verify the formula in Prob. 4 for $A = \begin{pmatrix} 4 & -2 \\ 1 & 1 \end{pmatrix}$.

6. Show that $A = \begin{pmatrix} \cos\theta & -\sin\theta \\ \sin\theta & \cos\theta \end{pmatrix}$ is an orthogonal matrix, and interpret the transformation $y = Ax$ geometrically, assuming that the components of x and y are Cartesian coordinates.

7. Show that the transformation

$$y = Ax, \qquad A = \begin{pmatrix} \cos\theta & -\sin\theta & 0 \\ \sin\theta & \cos\theta & 0 \\ 0 & 0 & 1 \end{pmatrix}, \qquad x = \begin{pmatrix} x_1 \\ x_2 \\ x_3 \end{pmatrix}, \qquad y = \begin{pmatrix} y_1 \\ y_2 \\ y_3 \end{pmatrix}$$

is a rotation about the x_3-axis, and A is orthogonal.

8. In Prob. 7, replace the element 1 by -1. Show that the resulting matrix B is orthogonal and interpret the transformation $y = Bx$ geometrically.

9. If A is orthogonal, show that $\det A = 1$ or $\det A = -1$.

10. Verify the result of Prob. 9 for the matrices in Probs. 6–8.

11. Show that the eigenvectors of a real symmetric matrix corresponding to different eigenvalues are orthogonal.

12. Verify the statement in Prob. 11 for the matrix $\begin{pmatrix} 3 & 4 \\ 4 & -3 \end{pmatrix}$.

13. Consider the linear transformation $y = Ax$ where A is square and set

$$x = T\tilde{x}, \qquad y = T\tilde{y} \qquad \text{(T nonsingular)}.$$

Show that then

$$\tilde{y} = \tilde{A}\tilde{x} \qquad \text{where} \qquad \tilde{A} = T^{-1}AT.$$

(This transformation which transforms A into $\tilde{A}$ is called a **collineatory transformation**.)

14. Show that if $\tilde{A} = T^{-1}AT$ where A is any square matrix, then $\det \tilde{A} = \det A$. *Hint:* use (12), Sec. 7.3.

15. The sum of the elements in the principal diagonal of a square matrix $C = (c_{ik})$ is called the **trace** of C. Thus

$$\text{trace } C = c_{11} + c_{22} + \cdots + c_{nn}.$$

Let $A = (a_{ik})$ and $B = (b_{ik})$ be two n-rowed square matrices. Show that

$$\text{trace } AB = \sum_{i=1}^{n} \sum_{l=1}^{n} a_{il} b_{li}.$$

16. Show that in Prob. 15, trace $AB =$ trace BA.

17. If $\tilde{A} = T^{-1}AT$, show that trace $\tilde{A} =$ trace A.

18. Verify the result of Prob. 16 for the matrices

$$A = \begin{pmatrix} 3 & 4 \\ -1 & 8 \end{pmatrix}, \qquad B = \begin{pmatrix} 1 & -2 \\ 6 & 7 \end{pmatrix}.$$

19. Show that the matrices A and $\tilde{A} = T^{-1}AT$ have the same eigenvalues.

20. Verify the statement of Prob. 19 for the matrices

$$A = \begin{pmatrix} 4 & -2 \\ 1 & 1 \end{pmatrix} \qquad \text{and} \qquad \tilde{A} = T^{-1}AT \qquad \text{where} \qquad T = \begin{pmatrix} 2 & 1 \\ 5 & 3 \end{pmatrix}.$$

21. If x is an eigenvector of A corresponding to an eigenvalue λ, show that $y = T^{-1}x$ is an eigenvector of $\tilde{A} = T^{-1}AT$ corresponding to the same eigenvalue λ.

22. Verify the statement in Prob. 21 for the matrices in Prob. 20.

23. Find a real matrix which has real eigenvalues but is not symmetric. Does this contradict Theorem 3?

24. Prove the last statement of Theorem 3.

25. Show that the matrix $U = \begin{pmatrix} 1/\sqrt{2} & i/\sqrt{2} \\ -i/\sqrt{2} & -1/\sqrt{2} \end{pmatrix}$ is unitary and determine its eigenvalues and eigenvectors.

26. Determine the eigenvalues and eigenvectors of the matrix

$$A = \begin{pmatrix} 1/\sqrt{3} & i\sqrt{2/3} \\ -i\sqrt{2/3} & -1/\sqrt{3} \end{pmatrix}. \quad \text{Is } A \text{ unitary?}$$

Are the following matrices orthogonal?

27. $\begin{pmatrix} 0 & 1 & 0 & 0 \\ 1 & 0 & 0 & 0 \\ 0 & 0 & 0 & 1 \\ 0 & 0 & 1 & 0 \end{pmatrix}$
 28. $\begin{pmatrix} 1/\sqrt{2} & 1/\sqrt{6} & -1/\sqrt{3} \\ 0 & 2/\sqrt{6} & 1/\sqrt{3} \\ 1/\sqrt{2} & -1/\sqrt{6} & 1/\sqrt{3} \end{pmatrix}$

29. Show that the vertical vibrations of the mechanical system in Fig. 216 (masses of springs and damping neglected) are governed by the following system of differential equations:

$$\ddot{y}_1 = -ky_1 + k(y_2 - y_1)$$
$$\ddot{y}_2 = -k(y_2 - y_1) - ky_2$$

30. Show that the system in Prob. 29 may be written

$$\ddot{y} = Ay, \quad \text{where} \quad y = \begin{pmatrix} y_1 \\ y_2 \end{pmatrix} \quad \text{and} \quad A = \begin{pmatrix} -2k & k \\ k & -2k \end{pmatrix}.$$

31. To solve the vector equation in Prob. 30, substitute $y = xe^{\omega t}$. Show that this leads to the eigenvalue problem $Ax = \lambda x$ where $\lambda = \omega^2$. Find the eigenvalues and eigenvectors. Find the solution of the vector equation that satisfies the initial conditions $y_1(0) = 1$, $y_2(0) = 1$, $\dot{y}_1(0) = \sqrt{3k}$, $\dot{y}_2(0) = -\sqrt{3k}$.

32. Show that the vertical vibrations of the mechanical system in Fig. 217 are governed by the equation

$$\ddot{y} = Ay$$

where

$$y = \begin{pmatrix} y_1 \\ y_2 \\ y_3 \end{pmatrix}, \quad A = \begin{pmatrix} -(k_1 + k_2) & k_2 & 0 \\ k_2 & -(k_2 + k_3) & k_3 \\ 0 & k_3 & -(k_3 + k_4) \end{pmatrix}$$

and substitution of $y = xe^{\omega t}$ yields $Ax = \lambda x$ where $\lambda = \omega^2$.

33. Verify that the coefficients of the characteristic equation

$$\lambda^3 + a\lambda^2 + b\lambda + c = 0,$$

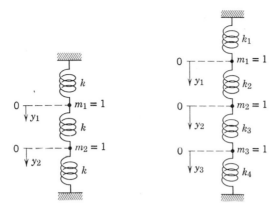

Fig. 216. Problem 29 (System in static equilibrium).

Fig. 217. Problem 32 (System in static equilibrium).

corresponding to the matrix A in Prob. 32, are positive, and conclude that the eigenvalues of A must be negative real. What does this result mean with respect to the motion of the mechanical system in Fig. 217?

34. Let A be the matrix in Prob. 32, with $k_1 = k_2 = k_3 = k_4 = k$. Show that the corresponding matrix $B = A/k + 2I$ has the eigenvalues 0, $+\sqrt{2}$, and $-\sqrt{2}$. Conclude from this that A has the eigenvalues $-2k$, $(-2 + \sqrt{2})k$, and $(-2 - \sqrt{2})k$.

7.14 BOUNDS FOR EIGENVALUES

To compute the eigenvalues of a given n-rowed square matrix we may proceed as follows. We first determine the characteristic polynomial, that is, we develop the characteristic determinant and then collect terms involving the same power of λ. In the second step we determine the roots of the characteristic polynomial; if n is large, this may be done by using an approximation method such as Newton's method. Obviously, for large n both steps require time-consuming computational operations. Therefore, it is desirable to develop more effective numerical methods which yield information about the eigenvalues of a given matrix. There are essentially two types of methods:

1. *Methods for obtaining bounds for eigenvalues,*
2. *Methods for computing approximate values for eigenvalues.*

We shall illustrate both types by some standard examples. For further methods see Ref. [D1] in Appendix 1.

The following interesting theorem by Gershgorin[5] yields a region consisting of closed circular disks and containing all the eigenvalues of a given matrix.

Theorem 1.   *Let λ be an eigenvalue of an arbitrary n-rowed square matrix* $\mathbf{A} = (a_{jk})$. *Then for some k $(1 \leq k \leq n)$,*

(1) $|a_{kk} - \lambda| \leq |a_{k1}| + |a_{k2}| + \cdots + |a_{k,k-1}| + |a_{k,k+1}| + \cdots + |a_{kn}|.$

Proof.   Let $\mathbf{x}$ be an eigenvector corresponding to that eigenvalue λ of $\mathbf{A}$. Then

(2) $\mathbf{Ax} = \lambda\mathbf{x}$ or $(\mathbf{A} - \lambda\mathbf{I})\mathbf{x} = \mathbf{0}.$

Let x_k be a component of $\mathbf{x}$ which is the greatest in absolute value. Then $|x_m/x_k| \leq 1$ $(m = 1, \cdots, n)$. The vector equation (2) is equivalent to a system of n equations for the n components of the vectors on both sides, and the kth of these n equations is

$a_{k1}x_1 + \cdots + a_{k,k-1}x_{k-1} + (a_{kk} - \lambda)x_k + a_{k,k+1}x_{k+1} + \cdots + a_{kn}x_n = 0.$

From this we have

$$a_{kk} - \lambda = -a_{k1}\frac{x_1}{x_k} - \cdots - a_{k,k-1}\frac{x_{k-1}}{x_k} - a_{k,k+1}\frac{x_{k+1}}{x_k} - \cdots - a_{kn}\frac{x_n}{x_k}.$$

By taking absolute values on both sides of this equation, applying the triangle inequality

$$|a + b| \leq |a| + |b| \qquad (a, b \text{ any complex numbers})$$

and observing that

$$\left|\frac{x_1}{x_k}\right| \leq 1, \cdots, \left|\frac{x_n}{x_k}\right| \leq 1$$

we obtain (1), and the theorem is proved.

For each $k = 1, \cdots, n$ the inequality (1) determines a closed circular disk in the complex λ-plane whose center is at a_{kk} and whose radius is given by the expression on the right-hand side of (1). Theorem 1 states that each of the eigenvalues of $\mathbf{A}$ lies in one of these n disks.

Example 1.   From Theorem 1 it follows that the eigenvalues of the matrix

$$\mathbf{A} = \begin{pmatrix} 26 & -2 & 2 \\ 2 & 21 & 4 \\ 4 & 2 & 28 \end{pmatrix}$$

lie in the three disks (Fig. 218)

D_1: center at 26, radius $|-2| + 2 = 4,$

D_2: center at 21, radius $\quad 2 + 4 = 6,$

and D_3: center at 28, radius $\quad 4 + 2 = 6.$

(The eigenvalues of $\mathbf{A}$ are 30, 25, and 20.)

[5] *Bull. Acad. Sciences de l'URSS*, Classe mathém., 7-e série, Leningrad, 1931, p. 749.

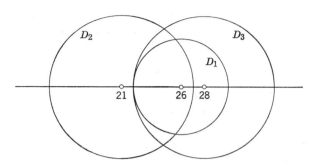

Fig. 218. Example 1.

Bounds for the absolute value of the eigenvalues result from the following theorem by Schur[6] which we shall state without proof.

Theorem 2.   *Let* $\mathbf{A} = (a_{jk})$ *be an n-rowed square matrix, and let* $\lambda_1, \cdots, \lambda_n$ *be its eigenvalues.   Then*

(3)
$$\sum_{i=1}^{n} |\lambda_i|^2 \leq \sum_{j=1}^{n} \sum_{k=1}^{n} |a_{jk}|^2 \qquad (\textit{Schur's inequality}).$$

In (3) *the equality sign holds if, and only if,* $\mathbf{A}$ *is such that*

(4)
$$\bar{\mathbf{A}}^{\mathsf{T}}\mathbf{A} = \mathbf{A}\bar{\mathbf{A}}^{\mathsf{T}}.$$

Matrices which satisfy (4) are called **normal matrices**. It is not difficult to see that Hermitian, skew-Hermitian, and unitary matrices are normal, and so are real symmetric, skew-symmetric, and orthogonal matrices.

Let λ_m be any eigenvalue of the matrix $\mathbf{A}$ in Theorem 2. Then $|\lambda_m|^2$ is less than or equal to the sum on the left side of (3), and by taking square roots we obtain from (3)

(5)
$$|\lambda_m| \leq \sqrt{\sum_{j=1}^{n} \sum_{k=1}^{n} |a_{jk}|^2}.$$

Example 2.   For the matrix $\mathbf{A}$ in Ex. 1 we obtain from (5)

$$|\lambda| \leq \sqrt{1949} < 44.2.$$

(The eigenvalues of $\mathbf{A}$ are 30, 25, and 20; thus $30^2 + 25^2 + 20^2 = 1925 < 1949$; in fact, $\mathbf{A}$ is not normal.)

While the preceding theorems are valid for any real or complex square matrix, there are other theorems which hold for special classes of matrices only. The following theorem by Frobenius,[7] which we state without proof, is of this type.

---

[6] *Mathematische Annalen*, Vol. 66, 1909, p. 488.
[7] *Sitzungsberichte Preuss. Akad. Wiss. Math.-phys. Klasse*, Berlin, 1908, p. 471.

Theorem 3. *Let* **A** *be a real square matrix whose elements are all positive. Then* **A** *has at least one real positive eigenvalue* λ*, and the corresponding eigenvector can be chosen real and such that all its components are positive.*

From this theorem we may derive the following useful result by Collatz.[8]

Theorem 4. *Let* **A** $= (a_{jk})$ *be a real n-rowed square matrix whose elements are all positive. Let* **x** *be any real vector whose components* $x_1, \cdots, x_n$ *are all positive, and let* $y_1, \cdots, y_n$ *be the components of the vector* **y** $=$ **Ax**. *Then the closed interval on the real axis bounded by the smallest and the largest of the n quotients* $q_j = y_j/x_j$ *contains at least one eigenvalue of* **A**.

Proof. We have **Ax** = **y** or

(6) $$\mathbf{y} - \mathbf{Ax} = \mathbf{0}.$$

The transpose $\mathbf{A}^\mathsf{T}$ satisfies the conditions of Theorem 3. Hence $\mathbf{A}^\mathsf{T}$ has a positive eigenvalue λ and, corresponding to this eigenvalue, an eigenvector **u** whose components u_j are all positive. Thus $\mathbf{A}^\mathsf{T}\mathbf{u} = \lambda\mathbf{u}$, and by taking the transpose, $\mathbf{u}^\mathsf{T}\mathbf{A} = \lambda\mathbf{u}^\mathsf{T}$. From this and (6),

$$\mathbf{u}^\mathsf{T}(\mathbf{y} - \mathbf{Ax}) = \mathbf{u}^\mathsf{T}\mathbf{y} - \mathbf{u}^\mathsf{T}\mathbf{Ax} = \mathbf{u}^\mathsf{T}(\mathbf{y} - \lambda\mathbf{x}) = 0$$

or at length

$$\sum_{j=1}^{n} u_j(y_j - \lambda x_j) = 0.$$

Since all the components u_j are positive, it follows that

(7)
$$y_j - \lambda x_j \geq 0, \quad \text{that is,} \quad q_j \geq \lambda \quad \text{for at least one } j, \quad \text{and}$$
$$y_j - \lambda x_j \leq 0, \quad \text{that is,} \quad q_j \leq \lambda \quad \text{for at least one } j.$$

Since **A** and $\mathbf{A}^\mathsf{T}$ have the same eigenvalues, λ is an eigenvalue of **A**, and from (7) the statement of the theorem follows.

Example 3. Let

$$\mathbf{A} = \begin{pmatrix} 1 & 2 & 3 \\ 2 & 4 & 6 \\ 3 & 6 & 1 \end{pmatrix}.$$

Choosing

$$\mathbf{x} = \begin{pmatrix} 1 \\ 1 \\ 1 \end{pmatrix}, \quad \text{we obtain} \quad \mathbf{y} = \mathbf{Ax} = \begin{pmatrix} 6 \\ 12 \\ 10 \end{pmatrix}.$$

[8] L. Collatz, *Eigenwertaufgaben mit technischen Anwendungen.* Leipzig: Akademische Verlagsgesellschaft, 1949, p. 291.

Hence $q_1 = 6$, $q_2 = 12$, $q_3 = 10$. From Theorem 4 it follows that one of the eigenvalues of $\mathbf{A}$ must lie in the interval $6 \leq \lambda \leq 12$.

Of course the length of such an interval depends on the choice of $\mathbf{x}$. Choosing

$$\mathbf{x} = \begin{pmatrix} 1 \\ 2 \\ 2 \end{pmatrix}, \quad \text{we obtain} \quad \mathbf{y} = \mathbf{Ax} = \begin{pmatrix} 11 \\ 22 \\ 17 \end{pmatrix},$$

$q_1 = 11, q_2 = 11, q_3 = 8.5$, and therefore the shorter interval $8.5 \leq \lambda \leq 11$ which must contain an eigenvalue of $\mathbf{A}$. The student may show that $\lambda = 10$ is an eigenvalue of $\mathbf{A}$.

PROBLEMS

Using (5), obtain an upper bound for the absolute value of the eigenvalues of the following matrices.

1. $\begin{pmatrix} 3 & 4 \\ 4 & -3 \end{pmatrix}$ **2.** $\begin{pmatrix} \cos\theta & \sin\theta \\ -\sin\theta & \cos\theta \end{pmatrix}$ **3.** $\begin{pmatrix} 5 & 5 \\ 5 & 5 \end{pmatrix}$

4. $\begin{pmatrix} -9 & 1 & 0 \\ 1 & -9 & 1 \\ 0 & 1 & -9 \end{pmatrix}$ **5.** $\begin{pmatrix} 13 & -3 & 5 \\ 0 & 4 & 0 \\ -15 & 9 & -7 \end{pmatrix}$ **6.** $\begin{pmatrix} 0 & 1 & 0 \\ 1 & 0 & 0 \\ 0 & 0 & 1 \end{pmatrix}$

7. Show that the matrix in Ex. 1 and 2 is not normal.

8. Show that the matrix $\mathbf{A} = \begin{pmatrix} 0 & 1 \\ 0 & 0 \end{pmatrix}$ is not normal and determine its eigenvectors.

9. Show that Hermitian, skew-Hermitian, and unitary matrices are normal.

Using Theorem 1, determine and graph disks which contain the eigenvalues of the given matrix:

10. $\begin{pmatrix} 1 & 2 & 3 \\ 2 & 4 & 6 \\ 1 & 0 & 3 \end{pmatrix}$ **11.** $\begin{pmatrix} 5 & 1 & 0 \\ 1 & 5 & 1 \\ 0 & 1 & 5 \end{pmatrix}$ **12.** $\begin{pmatrix} 0 & 0 & 3i \\ 0 & 2-i & 1+i \\ 1+2i & 0 & 0 \end{pmatrix}$

13. $\begin{pmatrix} 8 & 0 & 1 & 1 \\ 0 & 4 & 0 & 1 \\ 2 & -1 & 0 & 0 \\ 1 & 1 & 0 & -9 \end{pmatrix}$ **14.** $\begin{pmatrix} 13 & 2 & 0 & 0 \\ 1 & 11 & 1 & 0 \\ 0 & 4 & 8 & 1 \\ 0 & 0 & 1 & 3 \end{pmatrix}$

15. Show that $\lambda = 10$ is an eigenvalue of the matrix $\mathbf{A}$ in Ex. 3 and determine a corresponding eigenvector.

16. Verify Theorem 3 for the matrix in Prob. 3.

Apply Theorem 4 to the following matrices, choosing the given vectors as vectors $\mathbf{x}$.

17. $\begin{pmatrix} 17 & 8 & 1 \\ 8 & 18 & 8 \\ 1 & 8 & 17 \end{pmatrix}, \begin{pmatrix} 1 \\ 1 \\ 1 \end{pmatrix}, \begin{pmatrix} 1 \\ 2 \\ 1 \end{pmatrix}, \begin{pmatrix} 2 \\ 3 \\ 2 \end{pmatrix}$ **18.** $\begin{pmatrix} 3 & 1 & 1 \\ 1 & 3 & 1 \\ 1 & 1 & 3 \end{pmatrix}, \begin{pmatrix} 1 \\ 2 \\ 1 \end{pmatrix}, \begin{pmatrix} 1 \\ 1 \\ 1 \end{pmatrix}$

19. If A is normal and U is unitary and both matrices are n-rowed, show that $B = U^{-1}AU$ is normal.

20. Verify that $A = \begin{pmatrix} 6 & 0 & -3 \\ 0 & 6 & 3 \\ -3 & 3 & 2 \end{pmatrix}$ is normal, and for this matrix the equality sign holds in (3).

7.15   DETERMINATION OF EIGENVALUES BY ITERATION

A standard method for computing approximate values of the eigenvalues of matrices is the so-called *iteration method*. We shall first explain the practical procedure, then illustrate it by an example, and finally consider the theoretical background.

Let $A = (a_{jk})$ be a given n-rowed real symmetric matrix. Take an arbitrary real vector x_0 ($\neq 0$) with n components and compute the vectors

(1) $$x_1 = Ax_0, \qquad x_2 = Ax_1, \cdots, x_s = Ax_{s-1}.$$

For simplifying notation, denote x_{s-1} by x and x_s by y so that

(2) $$y = Ax.$$

Compute the scalar products

$$m_0 = x^{\mathsf{T}}x \qquad \text{and} \qquad m_1 = x^{\mathsf{T}}y.$$

Then the quotient

(3) $$q = \frac{m_1}{m_0}$$

is an approximation for one of the eigenvalues of A (in general, for that eigenvalue which has the greatest absolute value among all eigenvalues of A).

Example 1. Let

$$A = \begin{pmatrix} 1 & 2 & 3 \\ 2 & 4 & 6 \\ 3 & 6 & 1 \end{pmatrix} \qquad \text{and choose} \qquad x_0 = \begin{pmatrix} 1 \\ 0 \\ 0 \end{pmatrix}.$$

Then

$$x_1 = \begin{pmatrix} 1 \\ 2 \\ 3 \end{pmatrix}, \qquad x_2 = \begin{pmatrix} 14 \\ 28 \\ 18 \end{pmatrix}, \qquad x_3 = \begin{pmatrix} 124 \\ 248 \\ 228 \end{pmatrix}, \qquad x_4 = \begin{pmatrix} 1304 \\ 2608 \\ 2088 \end{pmatrix}.$$

Taking $x = x_3$ and $y = x_4$, we have

$$m_0 = x^{\mathsf{T}}x = 128\ 864, \qquad m_1 = x^{\mathsf{T}}y = 1\ 284\ 544, \qquad q \approx 9.968.$$

The reader may show that $\lambda = 10$ is an eigenvalue of A.

Taking $\mathbf{x} = \mathbf{x}_2$ and $\mathbf{y} = \mathbf{x}_3$, we obtain

$$m_0 = 1304, \qquad m_1 = 12\ 784, \qquad q \approx 9.80,$$

a less accurate approximation for $\lambda = 10$. In general, the accuracy of q will increase with increasing s; that is, the more vectors (1) we compute, the more accurate q will be. However, by looking at the theoretical basis of the method, we shall now see that this statement is not always true.

The eigenvectors $\mathbf{z}_1, \cdots, \mathbf{z}_n$ of a real symmetric matrix $\mathbf{A} = (a_{jk})$ can be chosen as real unit vectors and such that they are mutually perpendicular:

$$(4) \qquad \mathbf{z}_j^{\mathsf{T}}\mathbf{z}_j = 1, \qquad \mathbf{z}_j^{\mathsf{T}}\mathbf{z}_k = 0 \qquad\qquad (j \neq k).$$

(Proof in Ref. [D7]). Hence our arbitrary vector $\mathbf{x}_0$ can be expressed as a linear combination of the eigenvectors, say,

$$(5) \qquad \mathbf{x}_0 = c_1\mathbf{z}_1 + \cdots + c_n\mathbf{z}_n.$$

It follows that $\mathbf{x}_1$ in (1) then has the representation

$$\mathbf{x}_1 = \mathbf{A}\mathbf{x}_0 = c_1\mathbf{A}\mathbf{z}_1 + \cdots + c_n\mathbf{A}\mathbf{z}_n.$$

Let $\lambda_1, \cdots, \lambda_n$ be the eigenvalues corresponding to $\mathbf{z}_1, \cdots, \mathbf{z}_n$, respectively. Then, by definition,

$$\mathbf{A}\mathbf{z}_1 = \lambda_1\mathbf{z}_1, \cdots, \mathbf{A}\mathbf{z}_n = \lambda_n\mathbf{z}_n,$$

and the representation for $\mathbf{x}_1$ becomes

$$\mathbf{x}_1 = c_1\lambda_1\mathbf{z}_1 + \cdots + c_n\lambda_n\mathbf{z}_n.$$

In the same way it follows from this that

$$\mathbf{x}_2 = \mathbf{A}\mathbf{x}_1 = c_1\lambda_1{}^2\mathbf{z}_1 + \cdots + c_n\lambda_n{}^2\mathbf{z}_n,$$

and for the last two vectors in (1) we similarly obtain

$$(6) \qquad \begin{aligned} \mathbf{x} &\equiv \mathbf{x}_{s-1} = c_1\lambda_1^{s-1}\mathbf{z}_1 + \cdots + c_n\lambda_n^{s-1}\mathbf{z}_n \\ \mathbf{y} &\equiv \mathbf{x}_s \quad = c_1\lambda_1{}^s\mathbf{z}_1 \quad + \cdots + c_n\lambda_n{}^s\mathbf{z}_n. \end{aligned}$$

We now form the scalar products m_0 and m_1; because of the orthogonality (4), we obtain from (6)

$$m_0 = \mathbf{x}^{\mathsf{T}}\mathbf{x} = c_1{}^2\lambda_1^{2s-2} + \cdots + c_n{}^2\lambda_n^{2s-2},$$
$$m_1 = \mathbf{x}^{\mathsf{T}}\mathbf{y} = c_1{}^2\lambda_1^{2s-1} + \cdots + c_n{}^2\lambda_n^{2s-1}.$$

From these expressions it follows that

$$q = \frac{m_1}{m_0} = \frac{c_1{}^2\lambda_1^{2s-1} + \cdots}{c_1{}^2\lambda_1^{2s-2} + \cdots} \approx \lambda_1$$

provided the terms indicated by dots are small compared with the two explicitly written terms. If $c_1 \neq 0$, λ_1 is the greatest eigenvalue in absolute value, and the other eigenvalues are small in absolute value then q will be a good approximation of λ_1 and will become even more accurate for larger s. Now from (5) and (4),

$$\mathbf{z}_1^{\mathsf{T}}\mathbf{x}_0 = c_1\mathbf{z}_1^{\mathsf{T}}\mathbf{z}_1 = c_1$$

and we see that $c_1 \neq 0$, if $\mathbf{x}_0$ and $\mathbf{z}_1$ are not orthogonal. We don't know $\mathbf{z}_1$, but the chance of choosing for $\mathbf{x}_0$ just a vector which is perpendicular to $\mathbf{z}_1$ will be small. A more serious handicap of the method is that another eigenvalue of $\mathbf{A}$ may differ very little from λ_1 in absolute value, and in this case q will be an inaccurate approximation even for large s. The reader may consider the matrix

$$(7) \qquad \mathbf{A} = \begin{pmatrix} 3 & 4 \\ 4 & -3 \end{pmatrix}, \qquad \text{choose} \qquad \mathbf{x}_0 = \begin{pmatrix} 3 \\ -1 \end{pmatrix},$$

and find $q = 0$ for all s, the eigenvalues being 5 and -5. Therefore, to use the iteration method effectively we need bounds for the error of the approximate value q. Such a bound is given by the following theorem.

Theorem 1. *Let $\mathbf{A}$ be an n-rowed real symmetric matrix. Let $\mathbf{x} (\neq \mathbf{0})$ be any real vector with n components. Furthermore, let*

$$\mathbf{y} = \mathbf{A}\mathbf{x}, \qquad m_0 = \mathbf{x}^{\mathsf{T}}\mathbf{x}, \qquad m_1 = \mathbf{x}^{\mathsf{T}}\mathbf{y}, \qquad m_2 = \mathbf{y}^{\mathsf{T}}\mathbf{y}.$$

Then the quotient

$$q = \frac{m_1}{m_0}$$

is an approximation for an eigenvalue λ of $\mathbf{A}$, and if we set $q = \lambda + \epsilon$, so that ϵ is the error of q, then

$$(8) \qquad |\epsilon| \leq \sqrt{\frac{m_2}{m_0} - q^2}.$$

Proof. Let δ^2 denote the radicand in (8). Then, since $m_1 = qm_0$,

$$(9) \quad (\mathbf{y} - q\mathbf{x})^{\mathsf{T}}(\mathbf{y} - q\mathbf{x}) = m_2 - 2qm_1 + q^2m_0 = m_2 - q^2m_0 = \delta^2 m_0.$$

Let $\mathbf{z}_1, \cdots, \mathbf{z}_n$ be real orthogonal unit eigenvectors of $\mathbf{A}$ and let

$$\mathbf{x} = a_1\mathbf{z}_1 + \cdots + a_n\mathbf{z}_n.$$

Then, as before,

$$\mathbf{y} = a_1\lambda_1\mathbf{z}_1 + \cdots + a_n\lambda_n\mathbf{z}_n$$

and

$$(10) \qquad m_0 = \mathbf{x}^{\mathsf{T}}\mathbf{x} = a_1^2 + \cdots + a_n^2.$$

Hence in (9),

$$\mathbf{y} - q\mathbf{x} = a_1(\lambda_1 - q)\mathbf{z}_1 + \cdots + a_n(\lambda_n - q)\mathbf{z}_n.$$

By using the orthogonality of the z_j we thus obtain from (9)

$$\delta^2 m_0 = a_1{}^2(\lambda_1 - q)^2 + \cdots + a_n{}^2(\lambda_n - q)^2.$$

Replacing each $(\lambda_j - q)^2$ by the smallest of these terms and using (10), we have

$$\delta^2 m_0 \geq (\lambda_c - q)^2(a_1{}^2 + \cdots + a_n{}^2) = (\lambda_c - q)^2 m_0$$

where λ_c is the eigenvalue to which q is closest. From this, (8) follows, and the theorem is proved.

Example 2. From (8) we obtain the following bound for the error ϵ of the value $q \approx 9.968$ in Ex. 1:

$$|\epsilon| \leq \sqrt{\frac{12\ 861\ 824}{128\ 864} - 9.968^2} \approx \sqrt{0.45} \approx 0.67.$$

This shows that the exact value of the eigenvalue must lie between 9.29 and 10.64.

PROBLEMS

1. Show that if x and y are eigenvectors, then $\epsilon = 0$ in (8).

2. Determine the eigenvalues and eigenvectors of the matrix (7) and explain the reason why $q = 0$ for all s. Choose another vector x_0 and repeat the iteration.

3. Note that in (7), $x_2 = 25x_0$ and conclude that 25 must be an eigenvalue of A^2. What follows for A from this result?

4. Let

$$A = \begin{pmatrix} 2 & -1 & 1 \\ -1 & 3 & 2 \\ 1 & 2 & 3 \end{pmatrix} \quad \text{and choose} \quad x_0 = \begin{pmatrix} 1 \\ 1 \\ 1 \end{pmatrix}.$$

Compute x_1, x_2, x_3. Take x_2 for x and x_3 for y. Show that q deviates from 5 (the exact value of the largest eigenvalue of A) by 1.7 per cent, approximately. Find a bound for the error of q from (8).

Let A be as in Prob. 4. Compute x_1, the corresponding q and a bound for the error, choosing

5. $x_0 = \begin{pmatrix} 1 \\ 0 \\ 0 \end{pmatrix}$ **6.** $x_0 = \begin{pmatrix} 0 \\ 1 \\ 0 \end{pmatrix}$ **7.** $x_0 = \begin{pmatrix} 0 \\ 0 \\ 1 \end{pmatrix}$ **8.** $x_0 = \begin{pmatrix} 0 \\ 1 \\ 1 \end{pmatrix}$

9. Show that the eigenvalues of the matrix A in Prob. 4 are 0, 3, 5, and indicate which eigenvalue is approximated by the results of Probs. 5–8.

Choosing for x_0, the column vector with components 1, 1, 1, 1, compute x_1, x_2 and approximations $q = x_1{}^T x_0 / x_0{}^T x_0$, $q = x_2{}^T x_1 / x_1{}^T x_1$ and corresponding error bounds for an eigenvalue of each of the following symmetric matrices.

10. $\begin{pmatrix} 1 & 0 & 0 & 1 \\ 0 & 2 & -1 & 0 \\ 0 & -1 & 3 & 0 \\ 1 & 0 & 0 & -1 \end{pmatrix}$ **11.** $\begin{pmatrix} 2 & 0 & 1 & 0 \\ 0 & 0 & 3 & 1 \\ 1 & 3 & 4 & -2 \\ 0 & 1 & -2 & 0 \end{pmatrix}$ **12.** $\begin{pmatrix} 3 & 2 & 0 & 1 \\ 2 & 0 & 5 & -1 \\ 0 & 5 & 2 & 1 \\ 1 & -1 & 1 & 4 \end{pmatrix}$

chapter 8

FOURIER
SERIES AND
INTEGRALS

Periodic functions occur frequently in engineering problems. Their representation in terms of simple periodic functions, such as sine and cosine, is a matter of great practical importance, which leads to Fourier series. These series, named after the French physicist JEAN BAPTISTE FOURIER (1768–1830), represent a very powerful tool in connection with various problems involving ordinary and partial differential equations.

In the present chapter the basic concepts, facts, and techniques in connection with Fourier series will be considered and illustrated by various examples. Some important engineering applications will be included; further applications will occur in the following chapter on partial differential equations and boundary value problems.

While the *theory* of Fourier series is complicated, the *application* of these series is simple. Fourier series are, in a certain sense, more universal than Taylor series, because many *discontinuous* periodic functions of practical interest can be developed in Fourier series, but, of course, do not have Taylor series representations.

Prerequisite for this chapter: elementary integral calculus.

Sections which may be omitted in a shorter course: 8.8, 8.9, 8.11–8.13.

References: Appendix 1, Part E.

Answers to problems: Appendix 2.

8.1 PERIODIC FUNCTIONS. TRIGONOMETRIC SERIES

A function $f(x)$ is said to be **periodic** if it is defined for all real x and if there is some positive number T such that

(1) $$f(x + T) = f(x) \qquad \text{for all } x.$$

The number T is then called a **period**[1] of $f(x)$. The graph of such a function is obtained by periodic repetition of its graph in any interval of length T (Fig. 219).

From (1) it follows that, if n is any integer,

$$f(x + nT) = f(x) \qquad \text{for all } x,$$

so that any integral multiple nT ($n \neq 0$) of T is also a period. Furthermore, if $f(x)$ and $g(x)$ have the period T, then the function

$$h(x) = af(x) + bg(x) \qquad (a, b \text{ constant})$$

has the period T.

Familiar examples of periodic functions are the sine and cosine functions, and we note that the function $f = c = const$ is also a periodic function in the sense of the definition, because it satisfies (1) for any positive T.

Our problem in the first few sections of this chapter will be the representation of various functions of period 2π in terms of the simple functions

$$1, \quad \cos x, \ \sin x, \quad \cos 2x, \ \sin 2x, \cdots, \cos nx, \ \sin nx, \cdots$$

which have the period 2π (Fig. 220). The series which will arise in this connection will be of the form

(2) $$a_0 + a_1 \cos x + b_1 \sin x + a_2 \cos 2x + b_2 \sin 2x + \cdots$$

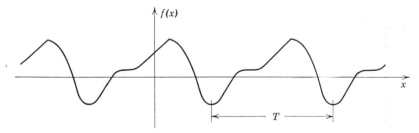

Fig. 219. Periodic function.

[1] The smallest positive period T of a function $f(x)$, not a constant, is often called the *primitive period* of $f(x)$. For example, the primitive periods of $\sin x$ and $\sin 2x$ are 2π and π, respectively.

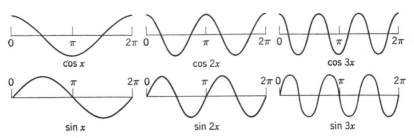

Fig. 220. Cosine and sine functions having the period 2π.

where $a_0, a_1, a_2, \cdots, b_1, b_2, \cdots$ are real constants. Such a series is called a **trigonometric series**, and the a_n and b_n are called the **coefficients** of the series. We see that each term of the series has the period 2π. Hence, *if the series converges, its sum will be a function of period 2π.*

Periodic functions that occur in engineering problems are often rather complicated, and it is therefore desirable to represent these functions in terms of simple periodic functions. We shall see that almost any periodic function $f(x)$ of period 2π that appears in applications, for example, in connection with vibrations, can be represented by a trigonometric series, and we shall derive formulas for the coefficients in (2) in terms of $f(x)$ such that (2) converges and has the sum $f(x)$. Later we shall extend our results to functions of arbitrary period; this extension will turn out to be quite simple.

PROBLEMS

Find the smallest positive period T of the following functions.

1. $\cos 2x$, $\sin 2x$, $\cos \pi x$, $\sin \pi x$, $\cos 2\pi x$, $\sin 2\pi x$

2. $\cos nx$, $\sin nx$, $\cos \dfrac{2\pi x}{k}$, $\sin \dfrac{2\pi x}{k}$, $\cos \dfrac{2\pi n x}{k}$, $\sin \dfrac{2\pi n x}{k}$

3. If T is a period of $f(x)$, show that nT, $n = \pm 2, \pm 3, \cdots$ is a period of that function.

4. If $f(x)$ and $g(x)$ have the period T, show that $h = af + bg$ (a, b constant) has the period T.

5. Show that the function $f(x) = const$ is a periodic function of period T for any value of T.

6. If $f(x)$ is a periodic function of x of period T, show that $f(ax)$, $a \neq 0$, is a periodic function of x of period T/a, and $f(x/b)$, $b \neq 0$, is a periodic function of x of period bT. Verify these results for $f(x) = \sin x$, $a = b = 2$.

Plot accurate graphs of the following functions.

7. $\sin x + \tfrac{1}{3} \sin 3x$, $\sin x + \tfrac{1}{3} \sin 3x + \tfrac{1}{5} \sin 5x$,
$\sin x + \tfrac{1}{3} \sin 3x + \tfrac{1}{5} \sin 5x + \tfrac{1}{7} \sin 7x$,

$$f(x) = \begin{cases} -\pi/4 & \text{when} \quad -\pi < x < 0 \\ \pi/4 & \text{when} \quad\;\; 0 < x < \pi \end{cases} \quad \text{and} \quad f(x + 2\pi) = f(x)$$

8. $\sin x - \frac{1}{2}\sin 2x$, $\sin x - \frac{1}{2}\sin 2x + \frac{1}{3}\sin 3x$

9. $f(x) = x^2$ when $-\pi < x < \pi$ and $f(x + 2\pi) = f(x)$

10. $f(x) = x^3$ when $-\pi < x < \pi$ and $f(x + 2\pi) = f(x)$

11. $f(x) = e^x$ when $-\pi < x < \pi$ and $f(x + 2\pi) = f(x)$

12. $f(x) = \begin{cases} x + \pi & \text{when } -\pi < x < 0 \\ -x + \pi & \text{when } 0 < x < \pi \end{cases}$ and $f(x + 2\pi) = f(x)$

13. $f(x) = \begin{cases} 1 & \text{when } -\pi < x < 0 \\ \cos^2 x & \text{when } 0 < x < \pi \end{cases}$ and $f(x + 2\pi) = f(x)$

14. $f(x) = \begin{cases} 0 & \text{when } -\pi < x < 0 \\ \sin x & \text{when } 0 < x < \pi \end{cases}$ and $f(x + 2\pi) = f(x)$

15. $\sin 2\pi x$, $\sin 2\pi x + \frac{1}{3}\sin 6\pi x$, $\sin 2\pi x + \frac{1}{3}\sin 6\pi x + \frac{1}{5}\sin 10\pi x$

16. $\cos\dfrac{\pi x}{2}$, $\cos\dfrac{\pi x}{2} - \dfrac{1}{2}\cos \pi x$, $\cos\dfrac{\pi x}{2} - \dfrac{1}{2}\cos \pi x + \dfrac{1}{3}\cos\dfrac{3\pi x}{2}$

Evaluate the following integrals where $n = 0, 1, 2, \cdots$. (These are typical examples of integrals which will be needed in our further consideration.)

17. $\displaystyle\int_0^\pi \sin nx \, dx$ **18.** $\displaystyle\int_0^{\pi/2} \cos nx \, dx$ **19.** $\displaystyle\int_{-\pi}^\pi x \sin nx \, dx$

20. $\displaystyle\int_0^\pi x \sin nx \, dx$ **21.** $\displaystyle\int_{-\pi/2}^{\pi/2} x \cos nx \, dx$ **22.** $\displaystyle\int_{-\pi/2}^{\pi/2} x \sin nx \, dx$

23. $\displaystyle\int_{-\pi}^0 e^x \sin nx \, dx$ **24.** $\displaystyle\int_0^\pi e^x \cos nx \, dx$ **25.** $\displaystyle\int_{-\pi}^\pi x^2 \cos nx \, dx$

8.2 FOURIER SERIES. EULER'S FORMULAS

Let us suppose that $f(x)$ is a periodic function with period 2π which can be represented by a trigonometric series

$$(1) \qquad f(x) = a_0 + \sum_{n=1}^\infty (a_n \cos nx + b_n \sin nx).$$

Given such a function $f(x)$, we want to determine the coefficients a_n and b_n in the corresponding series (1).

We first determine a_0. Integrating on both sides of (1) from $-\pi$ to π, we have

$$\int_{-\pi}^\pi f(x) \, dx = \int_{-\pi}^\pi \left[a_0 + \sum_{n=1}^\infty (a_n \cos nx + b_n \sin nx) \right] dx.$$

If term-by-term integration of the series is allowed,[2] then we obtain

$$\int_{-\pi}^\pi f(x) \, dx = a_0 \int_{-\pi}^\pi dx + \sum_{n=1}^\infty \left(a_n \int_{-\pi}^\pi \cos nx \, dx + b_n \int_{-\pi}^\pi \sin nx \, dx \right).$$

[2] This is justified, for instance, in the case of uniform convergence (cf. Theorem 3 in Sec. 11.9).

The first term on the right equals $2\pi a_0$, while all the other integrals are zero, as can be readily seen by performing the integrations. Hence our first result is

$$(2) \qquad a_0 = \frac{1}{2\pi} \int_{-\pi}^{\pi} f(x) \, dx,$$

the area under the curve of $f(x)$ from $-\pi$ to π, divided by 2π.

We now determine $a_1, a_2, \cdots$ by a similar procedure. We multiply (1) by $\cos mx$, where m is any fixed positive integer, and then integrate from $-\pi$ to π, finding

$$(3) \int_{-\pi}^{\pi} f(x) \cos mx \, dx = \int_{-\pi}^{\pi} \left[a_0 + \sum_{n=1}^{\infty} (a_n \cos nx + b_n \sin nx) \right] \cos mx \, dx.$$

By term-by-term integration the right-hand side becomes

$$a_0 \int_{-\pi}^{\pi} \cos mx \, dx$$

$$+ \sum_{n=1}^{\infty} \left[a_n \int_{-\pi}^{\pi} \cos nx \cos mx \, dx + b_n \int_{-\pi}^{\pi} \sin nx \cos mx \, dx \right].$$

The first integral is zero. The other integrals can be transformed by applying the familiar identities (11), Sec. 0.1, finding

$$\int_{-\pi}^{\pi} \cos nx \cos mx \, dx = \frac{1}{2} \int_{-\pi}^{\pi} \cos (n + m)x \, dx + \frac{1}{2} \int_{-\pi}^{\pi} \cos (n - m)x \, dx,$$

$$\int_{-\pi}^{\pi} \sin nx \cos mx \, dx = \frac{1}{2} \int_{-\pi}^{\pi} \sin (n + m)x \, dx + \frac{1}{2} \int_{-\pi}^{\pi} \sin (n - m)x \, dx.$$

Integration shows that the four terms on the right are zero, except for the last term in the first line which equals π when $n = m$. Since in (3) this term is multiplied by a_m the right-hand side in (3) is equal to $a_m \pi$, and our second result is

$$(4) \qquad a_m = \frac{1}{\pi} \int_{-\pi}^{\pi} f(x) \cos mx \, dx, \qquad m = 1, 2, \cdots.$$

We finally determine $b_1, b_2, \cdots$ in (1). If we multiply (1) by $\sin mx$, where m is any fixed positive integer, and then integrate from $-\pi$ to π, we have

$$(5) \int_{-\pi}^{\pi} f(x) \sin mx \, dx = \int_{-\pi}^{\pi} \left[a_0 + \sum_{n=1}^{\infty} (a_n \cos nx + b_n \sin nx) \right] \sin mx \, dx.$$

Integrating term-by-term the right-hand side becomes

$$a_0 \int_{-\pi}^{\pi} \sin mx \, dx$$

$$+ \sum_{n=1}^{\infty} \left[a_n \int_{-\pi}^{\pi} \cos nx \sin mx \, dx + b_n \int_{-\pi}^{\pi} \sin nx \sin mx \, dx \right].$$

The first integral is zero. The next integral is of the type considered before, and we know that it is zero for all $n = 1, 2, \cdots$. The last integral can be transformed by means of (11), Sec. 0.1, finding

$$\int_{-\pi}^{\pi} \sin nx \sin mx \, dx = \frac{1}{2} \int_{-\pi}^{\pi} \cos (n - m)x \, dx - \frac{1}{2} \int_{-\pi}^{\pi} \cos (n + m)x \, dx.$$

The last term is zero. The first term on the right is zero when $n \neq m$ and is π when $n = m$. Since in (5) this term is multiplied by b_m, the right-hand side in (5) is equal to $b_m \pi$, and our last result is

$$b_m = \frac{1}{\pi} \int_{-\pi}^{\pi} f(x) \sin mx \, dx, \qquad m = 1, 2, \cdots.$$

Writing n in place of m in this formula and in (4), we altogether have the so-called **Euler formulas**:

(6)

(a) $\qquad a_0 = \dfrac{1}{2\pi} \displaystyle\int_{-\pi}^{\pi} f(x) \, dx$

(b) $\qquad a_n = \dfrac{1}{\pi} \displaystyle\int_{-\pi}^{\pi} f(x) \cos nx \, dx$

$\qquad\qquad\qquad\qquad\qquad\qquad n = 1, 2, \cdots.$

(c) $\qquad b_n = \dfrac{1}{\pi} \displaystyle\int_{-\pi}^{\pi} f(x) \sin nx \, dx$

A periodic function $f(x)$ with period 2π being given, we may compute the a_n and b_n by (6) and form the trigonometric series

(7) $a_0 + a_1 \cos x + b_1 \sin x + \cdots + a_n \cos nx + b_n \sin nx + \cdots.$

This series is then called the **Fourier series** corresponding to $f(x)$, and its coefficients obtained from (6) are called **Fourier coefficients** of $f(x)$.

Note that because of the periodicity of the integrands the interval of integration in (6) may be replaced by any other interval of length 2π, for instance, by the interval $0 \leq x \leq 2\pi$.

From the definition of a definite integral it follows that, if $f(x)$ is continuous or merely piecewise continuous (continuous except for finitely many finite jumps in the interval of integration), the integrals in (6) exist and we may compute the Fourier coefficients of $f(x)$ by (6). The remaining question, whether the Fourier series thus obtained converges and has the sum $f(x)$, will be considered later in this section.

Let us illustrate the practical use of (6) by a simple example. Numerous other examples will occur in the following sections.

Example 1. Find the Fourier coefficients of the periodic function $f(x)$ in Fig. 221a. The analytic representation is

$$f(x) = \begin{cases} -k & \text{when} & -\pi < x < 0 \\ k & \text{when} & 0 < x < \pi \end{cases} \quad \text{and} \quad f(x + 2\pi) = f(x).$$

Functions of this type may occur as external forces acting on mechanical systems, electromotive forces in electric circuits, etc.

The area under the curve of $f(x)$ between $-\pi$ and π is zero and, therefore, by (6a), $a_0 = 0$. From (6b),

$$a_n = \frac{1}{\pi} \int_{-\pi}^{\pi} f(x) \cos nx \, dx = \frac{1}{\pi} \left[\int_{-\pi}^{0} (-k) \cos nx \, dx + \int_{0}^{\pi} k \cos nx \, dx \right]$$

$$= \frac{1}{\pi} \left[-k \frac{\sin nx}{n} \Big|_{-\pi}^{0} + k \frac{\sin nx}{n} \Big|_{0}^{\pi} \right] = 0$$

because $\sin nx = 0$ at $-\pi, 0,$ and π for all $n = 1, 2, \cdots$. From (6c),

$$b_n = \frac{1}{\pi} \int_{-\pi}^{\pi} f(x) \sin nx \, dx = \frac{1}{\pi} \left[\int_{-\pi}^{0} (-k) \sin nx \, dx + \int_{0}^{\pi} k \sin nx \, dx \right]$$

$$= \frac{1}{\pi} \left[k \frac{\cos nx}{n} \Big|_{-\pi}^{0} - k \frac{\cos nx}{n} \Big|_{0}^{\pi} \right].$$

Since $\cos(-\alpha) = \cos \alpha$ and $\cos 0 = 1$ this yields

$$b_n = \frac{k}{n\pi} [\cos 0 - \cos(-n\pi) - \cos n\pi + \cos 0] = \frac{2k}{n\pi} (1 - \cos n\pi).$$

Now, $\cos \pi = -1$, $\cos 2\pi = 1$, $\cos 3\pi = -1$ etc., in general,

$$\cos n\pi = \begin{cases} -1 & \text{for odd } n, \\ 1 & \text{for even } n, \end{cases} \quad \text{and thus} \quad 1 - \cos n\pi = \begin{cases} 2 & \text{for odd } n, \\ 0 & \text{for even } n. \end{cases}$$

Hence the Fourier coefficients b_n of our function are

$$b_1 = \frac{4k}{\pi}, \qquad b_2 = 0, \qquad b_3 = \frac{4k}{3\pi}, \qquad b_4 = 0, \qquad b_5 = \frac{4k}{5\pi}, \cdots,$$

and since the a_n are zero, the corresponding Fourier series is

$$\frac{4k}{\pi} (\sin x + \tfrac{1}{3} \sin 3x + \tfrac{1}{5} \sin 5x + \cdots).$$

The partial sums are

$$S_1 = \frac{4k}{\pi} \sin x, \qquad S_2 = \frac{4k}{\pi} (\sin x + \tfrac{1}{3} \sin 3x), \qquad \text{etc.,}$$

and their graphs in Fig. 221 seem to indicate that the series is convergent and has the sum $f(x)$, the given function. We notice that at $x = 0$ and $x = \pi$, the points of discontinuity of $f(x)$, all partial sums have the value zero, the arithmetic mean of the values $-k$ and k of our function.

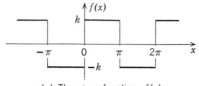

(a) The given function *f(x)*.

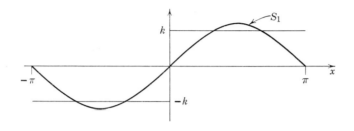

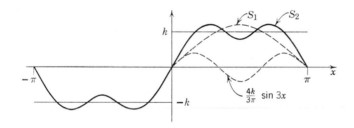

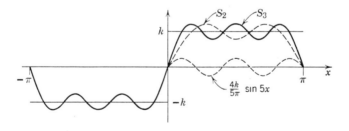

(b) The first three partial sums of the corresponding Fourier series.

Fig. 221. Example 1.

Furthermore, assuming that $f(x)$ is the sum of the series and setting $x = \pi/2$, we have

$$f\left(\frac{\pi}{2}\right) = k = \frac{4k}{\pi}\left(1 - \frac{1}{3} + \frac{1}{5} - + \cdots\right)$$

or

$$1 - \frac{1}{3} + \frac{1}{5} - \frac{1}{7} + - \cdots = \frac{\pi}{4}.$$

This illustrates that the values of various series with constant terms can be obtained by evaluating Fourier series at specific points.

The class of functions which can be represented by Fourier series is surprisingly large and general. Corresponding sufficient conditions covering almost any conceivable engineering application are as follows.

Theorem 1. *If a periodic function $f(x)$ with period 2π is piecewise continuous*[3] *in the interval $-\pi \leq x \leq \pi$ and has a left- and right-hand derivative*[4] *at each point of that interval, then the corresponding Fourier series* (7) [*with coefficients* (6)] *is convergent. Its sum is $f(x)$, except at a point x_0 at which $f(x)$ is discontinuous and the sum of the series is the average of the left- and right-hand limits*[4] *of $f(x)$ at x_0.*

Remark. If the Fourier series *corresponding to* a function $f(x)$ converges with the sum $f(x)$ as characterized in Theorem 1 the series will be called the Fourier series *of $f(x)$*, we write

$$f(x) = a_0 + a_1 \cos x + b_1 \sin x + \cdots + a_n \cos nx + b_n \sin nx + \cdots,$$

and we say that $f(x)$ is *represented* by this Fourier series. Since insertion of parentheses in a convergent series yields a new convergent series having the same sum as the original series (proof in Sec. 10.7), we may write more briefly

$$f(x) = a_0 + \sum_{n=1}^{\infty} (a_n \cos nx + b_n \sin nx).$$

Proof of convergence in Theorem 1 for a continuous function $f(x)$ having continuous first and second derivatives. Integrating (6b) by parts, we obtain

$$a_n = \frac{1}{\pi} \int_{-\pi}^{\pi} f(x) \cos nx \, dx = \frac{f(x) \sin nx}{n\pi} \bigg|_{-\pi}^{\pi} - \frac{1}{n\pi} \int_{-\pi}^{\pi} f'(x) \sin nx \, dx.$$

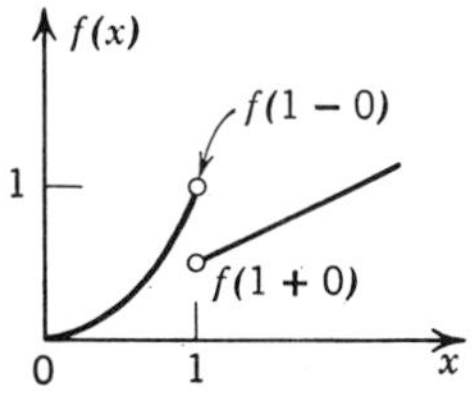

Fig. 222. Left- and right-hand limits

$$f(1 - 0) = 1,$$
$$f(1 + 0) = \tfrac{1}{2}$$

of the function

$$f(x) = \begin{cases} x^2 \text{ when } x < 1 \\ x/2 \text{ when } x > 1. \end{cases}$$

[3] Definition in Sec. 4.1.

[4] The **left-hand limit** of $f(x)$ at x_0 is defined as the limit of $f(x)$ as x approaches x_0 from the left and is frequently denoted by $f(x_0 - 0)$. Thus

$$f(x_0 - 0) = \lim_{h \to 0} f(x_0 - h) \text{ as } h \to 0 \text{ through positive values.}$$

The **right-hand limit** is denoted by $f(x_0 + 0)$ and

$$f(x_0 + 0) = \lim_{h \to 0} f(x_0 + h) \text{ as } h \to 0 \text{ through positive values.}$$

The **left-** and **right-hand derivatives** of $f(x)$ at x_0 are defined as the limits of

$$\frac{f(x_0 - h) - f(x_0 - 0)}{-h} \quad \text{and} \quad \frac{f(x_0 + h) - f(x_0 + 0)}{h},$$

respectively, as $h \to 0$ through positive values. Of course if $f(x)$ is continuous at x_0 the last term in both numerators is simply $f(x_0)$.

The first term on the right is zero. A second integration by parts gives

$$a_n = \frac{f'(x)\cos nx}{n^2\pi}\Big|_{-\pi}^{\pi} - \frac{1}{n^2\pi}\int_{-\pi}^{\pi} f''(x)\cos nx\, dx.$$

The first term on the right is zero because of the periodicity and continuity of $f'(x)$. Since f'' is continuous in the interval of integration,

$$|f''(x)| < M$$

for an appropriate constant M. Furthermore, $|\cos nx| \leq 1$. It follows that

$$|a_n| = \frac{1}{n^2\pi}\left|\int_{-\pi}^{\pi} f''(x)\cos nx\, dx\right| < \frac{1}{n^2\pi}\int_{-\pi}^{\pi} M\, dx = \frac{2M}{n^2}.$$

Similarly, $|b_n| < 2M/n^2$ for all n. Hence each term of the Fourier series corresponding to $f(x)$ is in absolute value at most equal to the corresponding term of the series

$$|a_0| + 2M\left(1 + 1 + \frac{1}{2^2} + \frac{1}{2^2} + \frac{1}{3^2} + \frac{1}{3^2} + \cdots\right)$$

which is convergent. Hence that Fourier series converges and the proof is complete. (Readers already familiar with uniform convergence will see that, by the Weierstrass test in Sec. 11.9, the Fourier series converges uniformly, and our derivation of (6) by integrating term-by-term is then justified by Theorem 3 of that section.)

The proofs of convergence in the case of piecewise continuous function $f(x)$ and of the last statement of Theorem 1 can be found in more advanced texts, for example in Ref. [E2].

PROBLEMS

Find the Fourier series of the function $f(x)$ which is assumed to have the period 2π, and plot accurate graphs of $f(x)$ and the first three partial sums.[5]

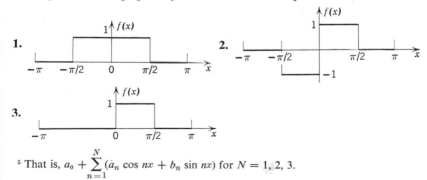

[5] That is, $a_0 + \displaystyle\sum_{n=1}^{N}(a_n \cos nx + b_n \sin nx)$ for $N = 1, 2, 3$.

4. $f(x) = \begin{cases} 0 \text{ if } -\pi < x < 0 \\ -1 \text{ if } \quad 0 < x < \pi/2 \\ 1 \text{ if } \pi/2 < x < \pi \end{cases}$ **5.** $f(x) = \begin{cases} 0 \text{ if } -\pi < x < 0 \\ 1 \text{ if } \quad 0 < x < \pi/2 \\ -1 \text{ if } \pi/2 < x < \pi \end{cases}$

6. $f(x) = \begin{cases} -1 \text{ if } \quad -\pi < x < -\pi/2 \\ 0 \text{ if } -\pi/2 < x < \pi/2 \\ 1 \text{ if } \quad \pi/2 < x < \pi \end{cases}$ **7.** $f(x) = \begin{cases} -1 \text{ if } \quad -\pi < x < -\pi/2 \\ 0 \text{ if } -\pi/2 < x < 0 \\ 1 \text{ if } \quad 0 < x < \pi/2 \\ 2 \text{ if } \quad \pi/2 < x < \pi \end{cases}$

8. $f(x) = x \, (-\pi < x < \pi)$ **9.** $f(x) = x^2 \, (-\pi < x < \pi)$

10. $f(x) = x^3 \, (-\pi < x < \pi)$ **11.** $f(x) = x^4 \, (-\pi < x < \pi)$

12. $f(x) = \begin{cases} -x \text{ if } -\pi < x < 0 \\ x \text{ if } \quad 0 < x < \pi \end{cases}$ **13.** $f(x) = \begin{cases} x + \pi \text{ if } -\pi < x < 0 \\ -x + \pi \text{ if } \quad 0 < x < \pi \end{cases}$

14. $f(x) = \begin{cases} 0 \text{ if } -\pi < x < 0 \\ x \text{ if } \quad 0 < x < \pi \end{cases}$ **15.** $f(x) = \begin{cases} 0 \text{ if } -\pi < x < 0 \\ x^2 \text{ if } \quad 0 < x < \pi \end{cases}$

16. $f(x) = \begin{cases} 0 \text{ if } \quad -\pi < x < -\pi/2 \\ x \text{ if } -\pi/2 < x < \pi/2 \\ 0 \text{ if } \quad \pi/2 < x < \pi \end{cases}$ **17.** $f(x) = \begin{cases} -\pi/2 \text{ if } \quad -\pi < x < -\pi/2 \\ x \text{ if } -\pi/2 < x < \pi/2 \\ \pi/2 \text{ if } \quad \pi/2 < x < \pi \end{cases}$

18. $f(x) = \begin{cases} x^2 \text{ if } -\pi/2 < x < \pi/2 \\ \pi^2/4 \text{ if } \quad \pi/2 < x < 3\pi/2 \end{cases}$ **19.** $f(x) = \begin{cases} x \text{ if } -\pi/2 < x < \pi/2 \\ \pi - x \text{ if } \quad \pi/2 < x < 3\pi/2 \end{cases}$

20. Verify the last statement in Theorem 1 concerning the discontinuities for the functions in Prob. 1 ($x = -\pi/2$, $x = \pi/2$) and Prob. 5 ($x = \pi/2$).

21. If $f(x)$ has the Fourier coefficients a_n, b_n, show that $kf(x)$, where k is a constant, has the Fourier coefficients ka_n, kb_n.

22. Find the Fourier series of

$$f(x) = \begin{cases} k\left(1 + \dfrac{x}{\pi}\right) & \text{when } -\pi < x < 0 \\ \\ k\left(1 - \dfrac{x}{\pi}\right) & \text{when } \quad 0 < x < \pi \end{cases} \qquad f(x + 2\pi) = f(x)$$

(a) by direct calculation, (b) by using the results of Probs. 21 and 13.

8.3   EVEN AND ODD FUNCTIONS

In the first example of the preceding section we wasted time and energy by calculating the a_n which then turned out to be zero. This was disappointing, and we may ask whether this result could have been obtained without performing the integration. In fact, this is possible. We shall see that the a_n are zero because $f(x)$ in Ex. 1 is an odd function.

We first remember that a function $y = g(x)$ is said to be **even** if

$$g(-x) = g(x) \qquad\qquad \text{for all } x.$$

The graph of such a function is symmetric with respect to the y-axis (Fig. 223). A function $h(x)$ is said to be **odd** if

$$h(-x) = -h(x) \qquad\qquad \text{for all } x.$$

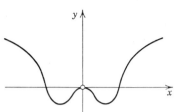

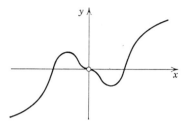

Fig. 223. Even function.   **Fig. 224.** Odd function.

(Cf. Fig. 224). The function $\cos nx$ is even, while $\sin nx$ is odd. (Cf. also Sec. 0.1.)

If $g(x)$ is an even function, then

(1) $$\int_{-\pi}^{\pi} g(x)\,dx = 2\int_{0}^{\pi} g(x)\,dx \qquad (g \text{ even}).$$

If $h(x)$ is an odd function, then

(2) $$\int_{-\pi}^{\pi} h(x)\,dx = 0 \qquad (h \text{ odd}).$$

The formulas (1) and (2) are obvious from the graphs of g and h, and we leave the formal proofs to the student.

The product $q = gh$ of an even function g and an odd function h is odd, because

$$q(-x) = g(-x)h(-x) = g(x)[-h(x)] = -q(x).$$

Hence, if $f(x)$ is even, then $f \sin nx$ in (6c) of the last section is odd, and $b_n = 0$. Similarly, if $f(x)$ is odd, then $f \cos nx$ in (6b) is odd, and $a_n = 0$. From this and (1) we obtain

Theorem 1. *The Fourier series of an even periodic function $f(x)$ having period 2π is a* "Fourier cosine series"

(3) $$f(x) = a_0 + \sum_{n=1}^{\infty} a_n \cos nx \qquad (f \text{ even})$$

with coefficients

(4) $$a_0 = \frac{1}{\pi}\int_{0}^{\pi} f(x)\,dx, \qquad a_n = \frac{2}{\pi}\int_{0}^{\pi} f(x)\cos nx\,dx, \qquad n = 1, 2, \cdots.$$

The Fourier series of an odd periodic function $f(x)$ having period 2π is a "Fourier sine series"

(5) $$f(x) = \sum_{n=1}^{\infty} b_n \sin nx \qquad (f \text{ odd})$$

with coefficients

(6) $$b_n = \frac{2}{\pi}\int_{0}^{\pi} f(x)\sin nx\,dx.$$

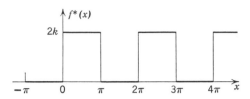

Fig. 225. Example 1.

For instance, $f(x)$ in Ex. 1, Sec. 8.2, is odd and, therefore, is represented by a Fourier sine series.

Further simplifications result from

Theorem 2.   *The Fourier coefficients of a sum $f_1 + f_2$ are the sums of corresponding Fourier coefficients of f_1 and f_2.*

Example 1 (Rectangular pulse).   The function $f^*(x)$ in Fig. 225 is the sum of the function $f(x)$ in Ex. 1 of the last section and the constant k. Hence, from that example and Theorem 2 we conclude that

$$f^*(x) = k + \frac{4k}{\pi}(\sin x + \tfrac{1}{3}\sin 3x + \tfrac{1}{5}\sin 5x + \cdots).$$

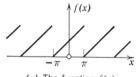

(a) The function $f(x)$.

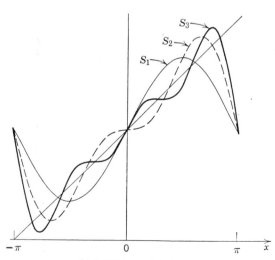

(b) Partial sums $S_n(x)$.

Fig. 226. Example 2.

Example 2. Find the Fourier series of the function (Fig. 226)

$$f(x) = x + \pi \quad \text{when } -\pi < x < \pi \quad \text{and} \quad f(x + 2\pi) = f(x).$$

We may write

$$f = f_1 + f_2 \quad \text{where } f_1 = x \quad \text{and} \quad f_2 = \pi.$$

The Fourier coefficients of f_2 are zero, except for the first one (the constant term), which is π. Hence, by Theorem 2, the Fourier coefficients a_n, b_n are those of f_1, except for a_0 which is π. Since f_1 is odd, $a_n = 0$ for $n = 1, 2, \cdots$, and

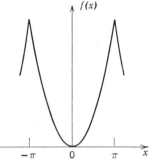

$$b_n = \frac{2}{\pi} \int_0^\pi f_1(x) \sin nx \, dx = \frac{2}{\pi} \int_0^\pi x \sin nx \, dx.$$

Integrating by parts we obtain

$$b_n = \frac{2}{\pi} \left[\frac{-x \cos nx}{n} \bigg|_0^\pi + \frac{1}{n} \int_0^\pi \cos nx \, dx \right]$$

$$= -\frac{2}{n} \cos n\pi.$$

Hence $b_1 = 2$, $b_2 = -2/2$, $b_3 = 2/3$,

Fig. 227. Example 3.

$b_4 = -2/4, \cdots$, and $f(x) = \pi + 2(\sin x - \frac{1}{2} \sin 2x + \frac{1}{3} \sin 3x - + \cdots)$.

Example 3. Find the Fourier series of the function (Fig. 227)

$$f(x) = x^2 \quad \text{when } -\pi < x < \pi \quad \text{and} \quad f(x + 2\pi) = f(x).$$

Since $f(x)$ is even, $b_n = 0$. From (4),

$$a_0 = \frac{1}{\pi} \int_0^\pi x^2 \, dx = \frac{\pi^2}{3},$$

and by integrating by parts,

$$a_n = \frac{2}{\pi} \int_0^\pi x^2 \cos nx \, dx = \frac{2}{\pi} \left[x^2 \frac{\sin nx}{n} \bigg|_0^\pi - \frac{2}{n} \int_0^\pi x \sin nx \, dx \right].$$

The first term on the right is zero. A second integration by parts gives

$$a_n = -\frac{4}{n\pi} \left[-x \frac{\cos nx}{n} \bigg|_0^\pi + \frac{1}{n} \int_0^\pi \cos nx \, dx \right] = \frac{4}{n^2} \cos n\pi.$$

Hence $a_n = -4/n^2$ when n is odd, and $a_n = 4/n^2$ when n is even. Consequently,

$$f(x) = \frac{\pi^2}{3} - 4(\cos x - \tfrac{1}{4} \cos 2x + \tfrac{1}{9} \cos 3x - + \cdots).$$

Setting $x = \pi$, we obtain

$$f(\pi) = \pi^2 = \frac{\pi^2}{3} + 4(1 + \tfrac{1}{4} + \tfrac{1}{9} + \cdots)$$

and from this the following famous result by Euler,

(7) $$\sum_{n=1}^{\infty} \frac{1}{n^2} = 1 + \frac{1}{4} + \frac{1}{9} + \frac{1}{16} + \cdots = \frac{\pi^2}{6}.$$

PROBLEMS

Are the following functions even, odd, or neither even nor odd?

1. e^x, e^{x^2}, $\sin nx$, $x \sin x$, $(\cos x)/x$, $\ln x$, $\sin x^2$, $\sin^2 x$

2. $|x|$, $x \cos nx$, $x^2 \cos nx$, $\sinh 3x$, $1 - x + x^2$, $\sin x + \cos x$

Are the following function $f(x)$ which are assumed to be periodic, of period 2π, even, odd, or neither even nor odd?

3. $f(x) = \begin{cases} x \text{ if } -\pi < x < 0 \\ -x \text{ if } \quad 0 < x < \pi \end{cases}$

4. $f(x) = \begin{cases} 0 \text{ if } -\pi < x < 0 \\ 3x \text{ if } \quad 0 < x < \pi \end{cases}$

5. $f(x) = \begin{cases} e^x \text{ if } -\pi < x < 0 \\ e^{-x} \text{ if } \quad 0 < x < \pi \end{cases}$

6. $f(x) = \begin{cases} -x^3 \text{ if } -\pi < x < 0 \\ x^3 \text{ if } \quad 0 < x < \pi \end{cases}$

7. $f(x) = |\sin x| \ (0 < x < 2\pi)$

8. $f(x) = x \ (0 < x < 2\pi)$

9. $f(x) = \begin{cases} x \text{ if } -\pi/2 < x < \pi/2 \\ 0 \text{ if } \quad \pi/2 < x < 3\pi/2 \end{cases}$

10. $f(x) = \begin{cases} x \text{ if } -\pi < x < \pi/2 \\ 0 \text{ if } \pi/2 < x < \pi \end{cases}$

Prove:

11. The sum and the product of even functions are even functions.

12. The sum of odd functions is odd. The product of two odd functions is even.

13. If $f(x)$ is odd, then $|f(x)|$ is even, and so is $f^2(x)$.

14. If $f(x)$ is even, then $|f(x)|$, $f^2(x)$, and $f^3(x)$ are even functions.

15. If $g(x)$ is any function, defined for all x, then $p(x) = [g(x) + g(-x)]/2$ is even while $q(x) = [g(x) - g(-x)]/2$ is odd.

16. Prove Theorem 2.   **17.** Prove (1).

18. Find all functions which are both even and odd.

Write the following functions as the sum of an even and an odd function.

19. e^x **20.** $1/(1 - x)$ **21.** $(1 + x)/(1 - x)$

Find the Fourier series of the following functions which are assumed to have the period 2π.

22. $f(x) = |x| \ (-\pi < x < \pi)$ **23.** $f(x) = x^2/4 \ (-\pi < x < \pi)$

24. $f(x) = x^3 \ (0 < x < 2\pi)$ **25.** $f(x) = |\sin x| \ (-\pi < x < \pi)$

26. $f(x) = \begin{cases} x \text{ if } 0 < x < \pi \\ \pi - x \text{ if } \pi < x < 2\pi \end{cases}$

27. $f(x) = \begin{cases} x - \pi \text{ if } 0 < x < \pi \\ -x \text{ if } \pi < x < 2\pi \end{cases}$

28. $f(x) = \begin{cases} -x^2 \text{ if } -\pi < x < 0 \\ x^2 \text{ if } \quad 0 < x < \pi \end{cases}$

29. $f(x) = \begin{cases} x \text{ if } -\pi/2 < x < \pi/2 \\ \pi - x \text{ if } \quad \pi/2 < x < 3\pi/2 \end{cases}$

30. Show that the familiar identities

$$\sin^3 x = \tfrac{3}{4} \sin x - \tfrac{1}{4} \sin 3x \quad \text{and} \quad \cos^3 x = \tfrac{3}{4} \cos x + \tfrac{1}{4} \cos 3x$$

can be interpreted as Fourier series expansions.

31. Using the Fourier series in Ex. 3, show that

$$1 - \frac{1}{4} + \frac{1}{9} - \frac{1}{16} + - \cdots = \frac{\pi^2}{12}.$$

8.4 FUNCTIONS HAVING ARBITRARY PERIOD

The transition from functions having period 2π to functions having any period T is quite simple, because it can be effected by a change of scale.

In fact, suppose that $f(t)$ has period T. Then we can introduce a new variable x such that $f(t)$, as a function of x, has period 2π. If we set

$$(1) \qquad (a) \quad t = \frac{T}{2\pi} x \quad \text{so that} \quad (b) \quad x = \frac{2\pi}{T} t,$$

then $x = \pm\pi$ corresponds to $t = \pm T/2$, which means that f, as a function of x, has period 2π and, therefore, a Fourier series of the form

$$(2) \qquad f(t) = f\left(\frac{T}{2\pi} x\right) = a_0 + \sum_{n=1}^{\infty} (a_n \cos nx + b_n \sin nx)$$

whose coefficients are obtained from (6), Sec. 8.2, in the form

$$a_0 = \frac{1}{2\pi} \int_{-\pi}^{\pi} f\left(\frac{T}{2\pi} x\right) dx, \qquad a_n = \frac{1}{\pi} \int_{-\pi}^{\pi} f\left(\frac{T}{2\pi} x\right) \cos nx \, dx,$$

$$b_n = \frac{1}{\pi} \int_{-\pi}^{\pi} f\left(\frac{T}{2\pi} x\right) \sin nx \, dx.$$

We could use these formulas directly, but the change to t simplifies calculation. Since

$$x = \frac{2\pi}{T} t, \qquad \text{we have} \qquad dx = \frac{2\pi}{T} dt,$$

and the interval of integration corresponds to the interval

$$-\frac{T}{2} \le t \le \frac{T}{2}.$$

Consequently, we obtain the **Euler formulas**

$$(3) \qquad (a) \qquad a_0 = \frac{1}{T} \int_{-T/2}^{T/2} f(t) \, dt$$

$$(b) \qquad a_n = \frac{2}{T} \int_{-T/2}^{T/2} f(t) \cos \frac{2n\pi t}{T} \, dt$$

$$n = 1, 2, \cdots$$

$$(c) \qquad b_n = \frac{2}{T} \int_{-T/2}^{T/2} f(t) \sin \frac{2n\pi t}{T} \, dt$$

for the Fourier coefficients of $f(t)$. The Fourier series (2) with x expressed in terms of t becomes

(4) $$f(t) = a_0 + \sum_{n=1}^{\infty} \left(a_n \cos \frac{2n\pi}{T} t + b_n \sin \frac{2n\pi}{T} t \right).$$

The interval of integration in (3) may be replaced by any interval of length T, for example, by the interval $0 \leq t \leq T$.

From Theorem 1 in Sec. 8.3 we now obtain

Theorem 1. *The Fourier series of an even function $f(t)$ having period T is a Fourier cosine series*

(5) $$f(t) = a_0 + \sum_{n=1}^{\infty} a_n \cos \frac{2n\pi}{T} t \qquad\qquad (f \text{ even})$$

with coefficients

(6) $$a_0 = \frac{2}{T} \int_0^{T/2} f(t)\, dt, \quad a_n = \frac{4}{T} \int_0^{T/2} f(t) \cos \frac{2n\pi}{T} t\, dt, \quad n = 1, 2, \cdots.$$

The Fourier series of an odd function $f(t)$ having period T is a Fourier sine series

(7) $$f(t) = \sum_{n=1}^{\infty} b_n \sin \frac{2n\pi}{T} t \qquad\qquad (f \text{ odd})$$

with coefficients

(8) $$b_n = \frac{4}{T} \int_0^{T/2} f(t) \sin \frac{2n\pi}{T} t\, dt.$$

Example 1. Find the Fourier series of the function (Fig. 228)

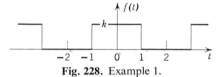

Fig. 228. Example 1.

$$f(t) = \begin{cases} 0 & \text{when} \quad -2 < t < -1, \\ k & \text{when} \quad -1 < t < 1, \qquad T = 4. \\ 0 & \text{when} \quad 1 < t < 2, \end{cases}$$

Since f is even, $b_n = 0$. From (6),

$$a_0 = \frac{1}{2} \int_0^2 f(t)\, dt = \frac{1}{2} \int_0^1 k\, dt = \frac{k}{2},$$

$$a_n = \int_0^2 f(t) \cos \frac{n\pi}{2} t\, dt = \int_0^1 k \cos \frac{n\pi}{2} t\, dt = \frac{2k}{n\pi} \sin \frac{n\pi}{2}.$$

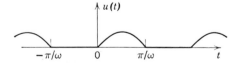

Fig. 229. Half-wave rectifier.

Thus $a_n = 0$ when n is even, $a_n = 2k/n\pi$ when $n = 1, 5, 9, \cdots$, and $a_n = -2k/n\pi$ when $n = 3, 7, 11, \cdots$. Hence

$$f(t) = \frac{k}{2} + \frac{2k}{\pi}\left(\cos\frac{\pi}{2}t - \frac{1}{3}\cos\frac{3\pi}{2}t + \frac{1}{5}\cos\frac{5\pi}{2}t - + \cdots\right).$$

Example 2 (Half-wave rectifier).   A sinusoidal voltage $E\sin \omega t$ is passed through a half-wave rectifier which clips the negative portion of the wave (Fig. 229).   Develop the resulting periodic function

$$u(t) = \begin{cases} 0 & \text{when} \quad -T/2 < t < 0, \\ E\sin \omega t & \text{when} \quad 0 < t < T/2, \end{cases} \qquad T = \frac{2\pi}{\omega}$$

in a Fourier series.

Since $u = 0$ when $-T/2 < t < 0$, we obtain from (3a)

$$a_0 = \frac{\omega}{2\pi}\int_0^{\pi/\omega} E\sin \omega t\, dt = \frac{E}{\pi}$$

and from (3b), by using (11b) in Sec. 0.1, with $x = \omega t$ and $y = n\omega t$,

$$a_n = \frac{\omega}{\pi}\int_0^{\pi/\omega} E\sin \omega t \cos n\omega t\, dt = \frac{\omega E}{2\pi}\int_0^{\pi/\omega}[\sin(1+n)\omega t + \sin(1-n)\omega t]\, dt.$$

When $n = 1$, the integral on the right is zero, and when $n = 2, 3, \cdots$,

$$a_n = \frac{\omega E}{2\pi}\left[-\frac{\cos(1+n)\omega t}{(1+n)\omega} - \frac{\cos(1-n)\omega t}{(1-n)\omega}\right]_0^{\pi/\omega}$$

$$= \frac{E}{2\pi}\left(\frac{-\cos(1+n)\pi + 1}{1+n} + \frac{-\cos(1-n)\pi + 1}{1-n}\right).$$

When n is odd, this is equal to zero, and for even n we obtain

$$a_n = \frac{E}{2\pi}\left(\frac{2}{1+n} + \frac{2}{1-n}\right) = -\frac{2E}{(n-1)(n+1)\pi} \qquad (n = 2, 4, \cdots).$$

In a similar fashion we find from (3c) that $b_1 = E/2$ and $b_n = 0$ for $n = 2, 3, \cdots$. Consequently,

$$u(t) = \frac{E}{\pi} + \frac{E}{2}\sin \omega t - \frac{2E}{\pi}\left(\frac{1}{1\cdot 3}\cos 2\omega t + \frac{1}{3\cdot 5}\cos 4\omega t + \cdots\right).$$

PROBLEMS

1. Show that each term in (4) has the period T.

2. Show that in (3) the interval of integration may be replaced by any other interval of length T.

3. Using (3), prove Theorem 1.

4. Find the Fourier series of the periodic function obtained by passing the voltage $V = 2\cos 100\pi t$ through a half-wave rectifier.

5. Show that in Ex. 2, $b_1 = E/2$, and $b_n = 0$ $(n = 2, 3, \cdots)$ by proving that $u(t) - (E/2)\sin \omega t$ is even.

Find the Fourier series of the periodic function $f(t)$, of period T, and plot accurate graphs of $f(t)$ and the first three partial sums:

6. $f(t) = \begin{cases} -1 \text{ if } -1 < t < 0 \\ 1 \text{ if } 0 < t < 1 \end{cases}$ $(T = 2)$

7. $f(t) = \begin{cases} 1 \text{ if } -1 < t < 1 \\ 0 \text{ if } 1 < t < 3 \end{cases}$ $(T = 4)$

8. $f(\tau) = \begin{cases} 0 \text{ if } -2 < \tau < 0 \\ 1 \text{ if } 0 < \tau < 2 \end{cases}$ $(T = 4)$

9. $f(t) = t^2$ if $-1 < t < 1$ $(T = 2)$

10. $f(t) = \begin{cases} -1 \text{ if } -\pi < t < 0 \\ 1 \text{ if } 0 < t < \pi \\ 0 \text{ if } \pi < t < 3\pi \end{cases}$ $(T = 4\pi)$

11. $f(t) = \begin{cases} -2 \text{ if } -4 < t < -2 \\ t \text{ if } -2 < t < 2 \\ 2 \text{ if } 2 < t < 4 \end{cases}$ $(T = 8)$

12. $f(t) = \begin{cases} 0 \text{ if } -1 < t < 0 \\ t \text{ if } 0 < t < 1 \end{cases}$ $(T = 2)$

13. $f(t) = \begin{cases} t + 1/2 \text{ if } -1/2 < t < 0 \\ -t + 1/2 \text{ if } 0 < t < 1/2 \end{cases}$ $(T = 1)$

14. $f(t) = |t|$ if $-2 < t < 2$ $(T = 4)$

15. $f(t) = t$ if $-1 < t < 1$ $(T = 2)$

16. $f(t) = 1 - t^2$ if $-1 < t < 1$ $(T = 2)$

17. $f(t) = \sin \pi t$ if $0 < t < 1$ $(T = 1)$

18. $f(t) = \begin{cases} -1 \text{ if } -1 < t < 0 \\ 2t \text{ if } 0 < t < 1 \end{cases}$ $(T = 2)$

19. $f(t) = \begin{cases} t \text{ if } 0 < t < 1 \\ 1 - t \text{ if } 1 < t < 2 \end{cases}$ $(T = 2)$

20. $f(t) = \begin{cases} 1 \text{ if } -2 < t < 0 \\ e^{-t} \text{ if } 0 < t < 2 \end{cases}$ $(T = 4)$

21. $f(t) = \begin{cases} t \text{ if } -\pi/8 < t < \pi/8 \\ (\pi/4) - t \text{ if } \pi/8 < t < 3\pi/8 \end{cases}$ $\left(T = \dfrac{\pi}{2}\right)$

22. Obtain the Fourier series of $f(t) = (1 + t)^2$ $(-1 < t < 1)$, $T = 2$, from the results of Probs. 9 and 15.

23. Obtain the Fourier series in Prob. 18 from the results of Probs. 15 and 19.

24. Obtain the Fourier series in Prob. 8 from that in Prob. 7 by setting $\tau = t + 1$.

25. Obtain the Fourier series in Prob. 16 from that in Prob. 9.

8.5   HALF-RANGE EXPANSIONS

Let $f(t)$ have period $T = 2l$. If f is even, we obtain from Theorem 1 in Sec. 8.4 the Fourier cosine series

$$(1) \qquad\qquad f(t) = a_0 + \sum_{n=1}^{\infty} a_n \cos \frac{n\pi}{l} t \qquad\qquad (f \text{ even})$$

with coefficients

(2) $a_0 = \dfrac{1}{l} \displaystyle\int_0^l f(t)\,dt, \quad a_n = \dfrac{2}{l} \displaystyle\int_0^l f(t)\cos\dfrac{n\pi}{l}t\,dt,$ $n = 1, 2, \cdots.$

If f is odd, we obtain the Fourier sine series

(3) $f(t) = \displaystyle\sum_{n=1}^{\infty} b_n \sin\dfrac{n\pi}{l}t$ (f odd)

with coefficients

(4) $b_n = \dfrac{2}{l} \displaystyle\int_0^l f(t)\sin\dfrac{n\pi}{l}t\,dt,$

$n = 1, 2, \cdots.$

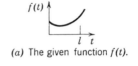

(a) The given function $f(t)$.

Now, (2) and (4) use only the values of $f(t)$ between $t = 0$ and $t = l$. Hence, for a function $f(t)$ given only over this interval, we can form the series (1) and (3). If $f(t)$ satisfies the conditions in Theorem 1, Sec. 8.2, both series will represent the given function in the interval $0 < t < l$. Outside this interval the series (1) will represent the even periodic extension or *continuation* of f having period $T = 2l$ (Fig. 230b) and (3) will represent the odd periodic continuation of

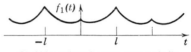

(b) $f(t)$ continued as an even periodic function of period $2l$.

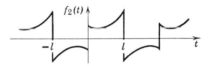

(c) $f(t)$ continued as an odd periodic function of period $2l$.

Fig. 230. Periodic continuations.

f (Fig. 230c). The series (1) and (3) with coefficients given by (2) and (4) are called **half-range expansions** of the given function $f(t)$. They will have important applications in connection with partial differential equations (Secs. 9.3, 9.5).

Example 1. Find the half-range expansions of the function

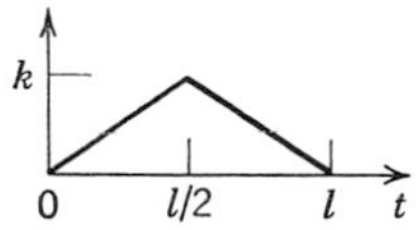

$$f(t) = \begin{cases} \dfrac{2k}{l}t & \text{when} \quad 0 < t < \dfrac{l}{2}, \\[2mm] \dfrac{2k}{l}(l - t) & \text{when} \quad \dfrac{l}{2} < t < l, \end{cases}$$

Fig. 231. The given function in Example 1.

shown in Fig. 231. From (2),

$$a_0 = \frac{1}{l}\left[\frac{2k}{l}\int_0^{l/2} t\,dt + \frac{2k}{l}\int_{l/2}^l (l - t)\,dt\right] = \frac{k}{2},$$

$$a_n = \frac{2}{l}\left[\frac{2k}{l}\int^{l/2} t\cos\frac{n\pi}{l}t\,dt + \frac{2k}{l}\int_{l/2}^l (l - t)\cos\frac{n\pi}{l}t\,dt\right].$$

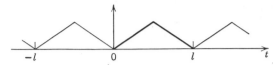

Fig. 232. Even periodic continuation of $f(t)$ in Example 1.

Now by integration by parts,

$$\int_0^{l/2} t \cos \frac{n\pi}{l} t \, dt = \frac{lt}{n\pi} \sin \frac{n\pi}{l} t \Big|_0^{l/2} - \frac{l}{n\pi} \int_0^{l/2} \sin \frac{n\pi}{l} t \, dt$$

$$= \frac{l^2}{2n\pi} \sin \frac{n\pi}{2} + \frac{l^2}{n^2\pi^2} \left(\cos \frac{n\pi}{2} - 1 \right).$$

Similarly,

$$\int_l^{l/2} (l - t) \cos \frac{n\pi}{l} t \, dt = -\frac{l^2}{2n\pi} \sin \frac{n\pi}{2} - \frac{l^2}{n^2\pi^2} \left(\cos n\pi - \cos \frac{n\pi}{2} \right).$$

By inserting these two results we obtain

$$a_n = \frac{4k}{n^2\pi^2} \left(2 \cos \frac{n\pi}{2} - \cos n\pi - 1 \right).$$

Thus,

$$a_2 = -16k/2^2\pi^2, \qquad a_6 = -16k/6^2\pi^2, \qquad a_{10} = -16k/10^2\pi^2, \cdots$$

while $a_n = 0$ when $n \neq 2, 6, 10, 14, \cdots$. Hence the first half-range expansion of $f(t)$ is

$$f(t) = \frac{k}{2} - \frac{16k}{\pi^2} \left(\frac{1}{2^2} \cos \frac{2\pi}{l} t + \frac{1}{6^2} \cos \frac{6\pi}{l} t + \cdots \right).$$

This series represents the even periodic continuation of $f(t)$ shown in Fig. 232.
   Similarly, from (4),

(5)
$$b_n = \frac{8k}{n^2\pi^2} \sin \frac{n\pi}{2}$$

and the other half-range expansion is

$$f(t) = \frac{8k}{\pi^2} \left(\frac{1}{1^2} \sin \frac{\pi}{l} t - \frac{1}{3^2} \sin \frac{3\pi}{l} t + \frac{1}{5^2} \sin \frac{5\pi}{l} t - + \cdots \right).$$

This series represents the odd periodic continuation of $f(t)$ shown in Fig. 233.

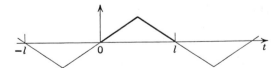

Fig. 233. Odd periodic continuation of $f(t)$ in Example 1.

PROBLEMS

Represent the following functions $f(x)$ by a Fourier sine series and graph the corresponding periodic continuation of $f(x)$.

1. $f(x) = 1 \; (0 < x < \pi)$

2. $f(x) = x \; (0 < x < \pi)$

3. $f(x) = x^2 \; (0 < x < \pi)$

4. $f(x) = x^3 \; (0 < x < \pi)$

5. $f(x) = \begin{cases} x & \text{if } 0 < x < \pi/2 \\ \pi/2 & \text{if } \pi/2 < x < \pi \end{cases}$

6. $f(x) = \begin{cases} \pi/2 & \text{if } 0 < x < \pi/2, \\ \pi - x & \text{if } \pi/2 < x < \pi \end{cases}$

7. $f(x) = \begin{cases} 1/2 & \text{if } 0 < x < \pi/2 \\ 3/2 & \text{if } \pi/2 < x < \pi \end{cases}$

8. $f(x) = \begin{cases} (\pi/2) - x & \text{if } 0 < x < \pi/2 \\ 0 & \text{if } \pi/2 < x < \pi \end{cases}$

9. $f(x) = x \; (0 < x < 1)$

10. $f(x) = x^2 \; (0 < x < l)$

11. $f(x) = \begin{cases} x & \text{if } 0 < x < \pi/8 \\ (\pi/4) - x & \text{if } \pi/8 < x < \pi/4 \end{cases}$

12. $f(x) = \begin{cases} 1 & \text{if } 0 < x < l/2 \\ 0 & \text{if } l/2 < x < l \end{cases}$

Represent the following functions $f(x)$ by a Fourier cosine series and graph the corresponding periodic continuation of $f(x)$.

13. $f(x) = 1 \; (0 < x < l)$

14. $f(x) = x \; (0 < x < l)$

15. $f(x) = x^2 \; (0 < x < l)$

16. $f(x) = x^3 \; (0 < x < l)$

17. $f(x) = \begin{cases} 1 & \text{if } 0 < x < l/2 \\ 0 & \text{if } l/2 < x < l \end{cases}$

18. $f(x) = \begin{cases} 0 & \text{if } 0 < x < l/2 \\ 1 & \text{if } l/2 < x < l \end{cases}$

19. $f(x) = 1 - \dfrac{x}{l} \; (0 < x < l)$

20. $f(x) = e^x \; (0 < x < l)$

21. $f(x) = \sin \dfrac{\pi}{l} x \; (0 < x < l)$

22. $f(x) = \sin \dfrac{\pi x}{2l} \; (0 < x < l)$

23. Using the formula

$$e^{i\theta} = \cos\theta + i\sin\theta, \qquad \text{(cf. Sec. 2.4)}$$

show that

$$\cos nx = \frac{1}{2}(e^{inx} + e^{-inx}), \qquad \sin nx = \frac{1}{2i}(e^{inx} - e^{-inx})$$

and the Fourier series

$$f(x) = a_0 + \sum_{n=1}^{\infty}(a_n \cos nx + b_n \sin nx)$$

may be written in the form

(6)
$$f(x) = c_0 + \sum_{n=1}^{\infty}(c_n e^{inx} + k_n e^{-inx})$$

where $c_0 = a_0$, $c_n = (a_n - ib_n)/2$, $k_n = (a_n + ib_n)/2$, $n = 1, 2, \cdots$.

24. Using (6), Sec. 8.2, show that in Prob. 23,

$$c_n = \frac{1}{2\pi}\int_{-\pi}^{\pi} f(x)e^{-inx}\,dx, \qquad k_n = \frac{1}{2\pi}\int_{-\pi}^{\pi} f(x)e^{inx}\,dx, \qquad n = 1, 2, \cdots.$$

25. Introducing the notation $k_n = c_{-n}$, show that (6) may be written

(7)
$$f(x) = \sum_{n=-\infty}^{\infty} c_n e^{inx}, \qquad c_n = \frac{1}{2\pi}\int_{-\pi}^{\pi} f(x)e^{-inx}\,dx,$$

$$n = 0, \pm 1, \pm 2, \cdots.$$

[This is the so-called **complex form** of the Fourier series, and the c_n are called the **complex Fourier coefficients** of $f(x)$.]

26. Using (7), show that the complex form of the Fourier series of the function

$$f(x) = e^x \quad \text{when} \quad -\pi < x < \pi \quad \text{and} \quad f(x + 2\pi) = f(x)$$
is

$$f(x) = \frac{\sinh \pi}{\pi} \sum_{n=-\infty}^{\infty} (-1)^n \frac{1 + in}{1 + n^2} e^{inx}.$$

27. Obtain from the series in Prob. 26 the real Fourier series

$$f(x) = K\left[\frac{1}{2} - \frac{1}{1 + 1^2}(\cos x - \sin x) + \frac{1}{1 + 2^2}(\cos 2x - 2\sin 2x) - + \cdots\right]$$

where $K = (2 \sinh \pi)/\pi$.

28. Show that the complex Fourier coefficients of an odd function are purely imaginary while those of an even function are real.

8.6 DETERMINATION OF FOURIER COEFFICIENTS WITHOUT INTEGRATION

In Ex. 3, Sec. 8.3, relatively complicated and lengthy integrations led to a simple expression for a_n, and in other cases the situation is quite similar. This raises the question whether there might be a simpler way of obtaining Fourier coefficients. There is, and we want to show that the Fourier coefficients of a periodic function which is represented by polynomials can be obtained in terms of the jumps of the function and its derivatives. Of course, this is a big advantage, and the corresponding formulas are of great practical importance, because by applying them integrations are avoided (except for a_0, which is determined as before).

By a *jump j* of a function $g(x)$ at a point x_0 we mean the difference between the right-hand and left-hand limits (p. 472) of $g(x)$ at x_0; that is (Fig. 234)

(1) $j = g(x_0 + 0) - g(x_0 - 0).$

It follows that an upward jump is positive, while a downward jump is negative.

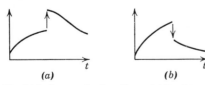

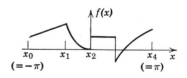

Fig. 234. Jump of a function. (*a*) Positive jump. (*b*) Negative jump.

Fig. 235. Example of a representation of the form (2) (with $m = 4$).

Let $f(x)$ be a function which has period 2π and is represented by polynomials $p_1, \cdots, p_m$ in the interval $-\pi < x < \pi$, say (Fig. 235),

$$
(2) \qquad f(x) = \begin{cases} (p_1 x) \text{ when } x_0 < x < x_1, \quad (x_0 = -\pi) \\ p_2(x) \text{ when } x_1 < x < x_2, \\ \quad \cdot \\ \quad \cdot \\ \quad \cdot \\ p_m(x) \text{ when } x_{m-1} < x < x_m \, (= \pi). \end{cases}
$$

Then f may have jumps at $x_0, x_1, \cdots, x_m$, and the same is true for the derivatives $f', f'', \cdots$. We choose the following notation.

j_s = jump of f at x_s,

(3) j_s' = jump of f' at x_s, $\quad (s = 1, 2, \cdots, m)$

j_s'' = jump of f'' at x_s, $\quad$ etc.

Of course, if f is continuous at x_s, then $j_s = 0$, and for the derivatives the situation is similar, so that some of the numbers $j_s, j_s', \cdots$ in (3) may be zero.

Example 1. Let

$$
f(x) = \begin{cases} 0 & \text{when} & -\pi < x < 0, \\ x^2 & \text{when} & 0 < x < \pi. \end{cases}
$$

We plot graphs of f and its derivatives (Fig. 236),

$$
f' = \begin{cases} 0 \\ 2x \end{cases} \quad f'' = \begin{cases} 0 \\ 2 \end{cases} \quad f''' = 0.
$$

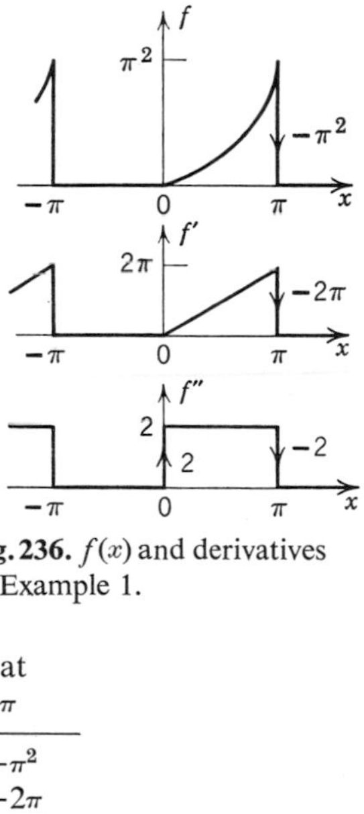

We see that the jumps are:

Fig. 236. $f(x)$ and derivatives in Example 1.

	Jump at $x_1 = 0$	Jump at $x_2 = \pi$
f	$j_1 = 0$	$j_2 = -\pi^2$
f'	$j_1' = 0$	$j_2' = -2\pi$
f''	$j_1'' = 2$	$j_2'' = -2$

Note that the jumps at $x = -\pi$ are not listed, because they are taken into account at $x = \pi$, the other end of the interval of periodicity.

To derive the desired formula for the Fourier coefficients $a_1, a_2, \cdots$ of f, given by (2), we start from the Euler formula (6b) in Sec. 8.2:

$$
(4) \qquad \pi a_n = \int_{-\pi}^{\pi} f \cos nx \, dx.
$$

Since f is represented by (2) we write the integral as the sum of m integrals:

$$(5) \qquad \pi a_n = \int_{x_0}^{x_1} + \int_{x_1}^{x_2} + \cdots + \int_{x_{m-1}}^{x_m} = \sum_{s=1}^{m} \int_{x_{s-1}}^{x_s} f \cos nx \, dx,$$

where $x_0 = -\pi$ and $x_m = \pi$. Integration by parts yields

$$(6) \qquad \int_{x_{s-1}}^{x_s} f \cos nx \, dx = \frac{f}{n} \sin nx \Big|_{x_{s-1}}^{x_s} - \frac{1}{n} \int_{x_{s-1}}^{x_s} f' \sin nx \, dx.$$

Now comes an important point: the evaluation of the first expression on the right. $f(x)$ may be discontinuous at x_s (Fig. 237), and we have to take the left-hand limit $f(x_s - 0)$ of f at x_s. Similarly, at x_{s-1} we have to take the right-hand limit $f(x_{s-1} + 0)$. Hence the first expression on the right-hand side of (6) equals

$$\frac{1}{n} [f(x_s - 0) \sin nx_s - f(x_{s-1} + 0) \sin nx_{s-1}].$$

Consequently, by inserting (6) into (5) and using the short notations $S_0 = \sin nx_0$, $S_1 = \sin nx_1$, etc., we obtain

$$(7) \qquad \pi a_n = \frac{1}{n} [f(x_1 - 0)S_1 - f(x_0 + 0)S_0 + f(x_2 - 0)S_2 - f(x_1 + 0)S_1$$
$$+ \cdots + f(x_m - 0)S_m - f(x_{m-1} + 0)S_{m-1}]$$
$$- \frac{1}{n} \sum_{s=1}^{m} \int_{x_{s-1}}^{x_s} f' \sin nx \, dx.$$

Collecting terms with the same S the expression in brackets becomes

$$(8) \quad -f(x_0 + 0)S_0 + [f(x_1 - 0) - f(x_1 + 0)]S_1$$
$$+ [f(x_2 - 0) - f(x_2 + 0)]S_2 + \cdots + f(x_m - 0)S_m.$$

The expressions in brackets in (8) are the jumps of f, multiplied by -1. Furthermore, because of periodicity, $S_0 = S_m$ and $f(x_0) = f(x_m)$, so that we may combine the first and the last term in (8). Thus (8) is equal to

$$-j_1 S_1 - j_2 S_2 - \cdots - j_m S_m,$$

and from (7) we therefore have the intermediate result

$$(9) \qquad \pi a_n = -\frac{1}{n} \sum_{s=1}^{m} j_s \sin nx_s - \frac{1}{n} \sum_{s=1}^{m} \int_{x_{s-1}}^{x_s} f' \sin nx \, dx.$$

By applying the same procedure to the integrals on the right-hand side of (9) we find

$$(10) \quad \sum_{s=1}^{m} \int_{x_{s-1}}^{x_s} f' \sin nx \, dx = \frac{1}{n} \sum_{s=1}^{m} j_s' \cos nx_s + \frac{1}{n} \sum_{s=1}^{m} \int_{x_{s-1}}^{x_s} f'' \cos nx \, dx.$$

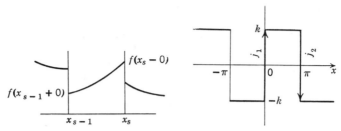

Fig. 237. The formula (6).   **Fig. 238.** Example 2.

Continuing in this fashion, we obtain integrals involving higher and higher derivatives of f. Since f is represented by polynomials and the $(r + 1)$th derivative of a polynomial of degree r is identically zero, we shall reach the point where no integrals are left, and this will happen after finitely many steps. By inserting (10) and the analogous formulas obtained in the further steps into (9) we obtain the desired formula

(11a) $$a_n = \frac{1}{n\pi} \left[- \sum_{s=1}^{m} j_s \sin nx_s - \frac{1}{n} \sum_{s=1}^{m} j_s' \cos nx_s \right.$$

$$\left. + \frac{1}{n^2} \sum_{s=1}^{m} j_s'' \sin nx_s + \frac{1}{n^3} \sum_{s=1}^{m} j_s''' \cos nx_s - - + + \cdots \right].$$

In precisely the same fashion we obtain from (6c) in Sec. 8.2

(11b) $$b_n = \frac{1}{n\pi} \left[\sum_{s=1}^{m} j_s \cos nx_s - \frac{1}{n} \sum_{s=1}^{m} j_s' \sin nx_s \right.$$

$$\left. - \frac{1}{n^2} \sum_{s=1}^{m} j_s'' \cos nx_s + \frac{1}{n^3} \sum_{s=1}^{m} j_s''' \sin nx_s + - - + + \cdots \right].$$

To avoid errors it is practical to graph $f(x)$ and its derivatives and list the jumps in a table as in Ex. 1. The coefficient a_0 must be obtained by integration as before.

Example 2. Find the Fourier coefficients of the function (cf. Fig. 238)

$$f(x) = \begin{cases} -k & \text{when} & -\pi < x < 0, \\ k & \text{when} & 0 < x < \pi. \end{cases}$$

We see that $f' \equiv 0$ and the jumps of f are

	Jump at $x_1 = 0$	Jump at $x_2 = \pi$
f	$j_1 = 2k$	$j_2 = -2k$

Since f is odd, $a_n = 0$, and from (11b),

$$b_n = \frac{1}{n\pi}[j_1 \cos nx_1 + j_2 \cos nx_2] = \frac{1}{n\pi}[2k \cos 0 - 2k \cos n\pi]$$

$$= \frac{2k}{n\pi}(1 - \cos n\pi) = \begin{cases} 4k/n\pi & \text{for odd } n, \\ 0 & \text{for even } n \end{cases}$$

(cf. Ex. 1, Sec. 8.2).

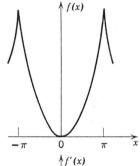

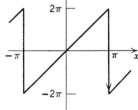

Fig. 239. Example 3.

Example 3. Find the Fourier coefficients of the function (cf. Fig. 239)

$$f(x) = x^2 \ (-\pi < x < \pi), \qquad f(x + 2\pi) = f(x).$$

Here $f' = 2x$, $f'' = 2$, $f''' \equiv 0$, and the jumps are

	Jump at $x_1 = \pi$
f	$j_1 = 0$
f'	$j_1' = -4\pi$
f''	$j_1'' = 0$

Since f is even, $b_n = 0$. By integration, $a_0 = \pi^2/3$. From (11a),

$$a_n = \frac{1}{n\pi}\left(-\frac{1}{n}\right)(-4\pi) \cos n\pi = \frac{4}{n^2} \cos n\pi$$

$$= \begin{cases} -4/n^2 & (n \text{ odd}), \\ 4/n^2 & (n \text{ even}), \end{cases}$$

in agreement with Ex. 3 in Sec. 8.3.

Example 4. Find the Fourier series of the function in Ex. 1 of the current section. By integration,

$$a_0 = \frac{1}{2\pi}\int_0^\pi x^2 \, dx = \frac{\pi^2}{6}.$$

From (11a) we obtain

$$a_n = \frac{1}{n\pi}\left[\pi^2 \sin n\pi + \frac{2\pi}{n} \cos n\pi + \frac{1}{n^2}(2 \sin 0 - 2 \sin n\pi)\right] = \frac{2}{n^2} \cos n\pi.$$

Hence $a_1 = -2/1^2$, $a_2 = 2/2^2$, $a_3 = -2/3^2, \cdots$. From (11b) it follows that

$$b_n = \frac{1}{n\pi}\left[-\pi^2 \cos n\pi + \frac{2\pi}{n} \sin n\pi - \frac{1}{n^2}(2 \cos 0 - 2 \cos n\pi)\right]$$

$$= -\frac{\pi}{n} \cos n\pi + \frac{2}{n^3\pi}(\cos n\pi - 1).$$

Hence,

$$b_1 = \pi - \frac{4}{\pi}, \qquad b_2 = -\frac{\pi}{2}, \qquad b_3 = \frac{\pi}{3} - \frac{4}{3^3\pi}, \qquad b_4 = -\frac{\pi}{4}, \cdots,$$

and the Fourier series is

$$f(x) = \frac{\pi^2}{6} - 2\cos x + \left(\pi - \frac{4}{\pi}\right)\sin x + \tfrac{1}{2}\cos 2x - \frac{\pi}{2}\sin 2x + \cdots.$$

PROBLEMS

1. Derive (11b) from (6c), Sec. 8.2.

2. Show that in the case of a function $f(t)$ having period T the formulas corresponding to (11) are

$$(12a) \quad a_n = \frac{1}{n\pi}\left[-\sum_{s=1}^{m} j_s \sin\frac{2n\pi}{T} t_s - \frac{T}{2n\pi}\sum_{s=1}^{m} j_s' \cos\frac{2n\pi}{T} t_s\right.$$

$$+ \left(\frac{T}{2n\pi}\right)^2 \sum_{s=1}^{m} j_s'' \sin\frac{2n\pi}{T} t_s + \left(\frac{T}{2n\pi}\right)^3 \sum_{s=1}^{m} j_s''' \cos\frac{2n\pi}{T} t_s - - + + \cdots\right]$$

$$(12b) \quad b_n = \frac{1}{n\pi}\left[\sum_{s=1}^{m} j_s \cos\frac{2n\pi}{T} t_s - \frac{T}{2n\pi}\sum_{s=1}^{m} j_s' \sin\frac{2n\pi}{T} t_s\right.$$

$$- \left(\frac{T}{2n\pi}\right)^2 \sum_{s=1}^{m} j_s'' \cos\frac{2n\pi}{T} t_s + \left(\frac{T}{2n\pi}\right)^3 \sum_{s=1}^{m} j_s''' \sin\frac{2n\pi}{T} t_s + - - + + \cdots\right].$$

Using (11) or (12), find the Fourier series of the functions $f(x)$ or $f(t)$ in:

3. Probs. 2–7, Sec. 8.2   **4.** Probs. 8–10, Sec. 8.2
5. Probs. 12–14, Sec. 8.2   **6.** Probs. 16, 17, Sec. 8.2
7. Probs. 6, 7, 10, Sec. 8.4   **8.** Probs. 11–13, Sec. 8.4
9. Probs. 14, 15, Sec. 8.4   **10.** Probs. 9, 16, Sec. 8.4
11. Probs. 19, 21, Sec. 8.4

Using (11) or (12), find the Fourier sine series of the functions $f(x)$ in:

12. Probs. 7, 12, Sec. 8.5   **13.** Probs. 3, 10, Sec. 8.5
14. Probs. 5, 6, Sec. 8.5

Using (11), find the Fourier sine series of the following functions.

15. $f(x) = x(\pi - x)$ if $0 < x < \pi$ **16.** $f(x) = x^3 - x$ if $0 < x < \pi$
17. $f(x) = x(\pi^2 - x^2)$ if $0 < x < \pi$

18. $f(x) = \left(\dfrac{\pi}{2}\right)^4 - \left(x - \dfrac{\pi}{2}\right)^4$ if $0 < x < \pi$

19. Find the Fourier series of $f(x) = x^4$ $(-\pi < x < \pi)$, $f(x + 2\pi) = f(x)$ by the use of (6), Sec. 8.2, and (11), this section, and compare the amount of work.

20. Can (11) be applied to find the Fourier coefficients of the function $f(x) = e^x$ $(0 < x < 2\pi)$, $f(x + 2\pi) = f(x)$?

8.7 FORCED OSCILLATIONS

Fourier series have important applications in connection with differential equations. Let us consider an important practical problem involving an ordinary differential equation. (Partial differential equations will be considered in the next chapter.)

From Sec. 2.13 we know that forced oscillations of a body of mass m on a spring (modulus k) are governed by the equation

(1) $$m\ddot{y} + c\dot{y} + ky = r(t).$$

If the external force $r(t)$ is a sine or cosine function and the damping constant c is not zero, the steady state solution represents a harmonic oscillation having the frequency of the external force.

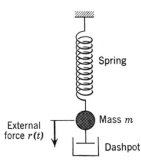

Spring

External force $r(t)$

Mass m

Dashpot

Fig. 240. Vibrating system under consideration.

We shall now see that if $r(t)$ is not a pure sine or cosine function but any other periodic function, then the steady state solution will represent a superposition of harmonic oscillations having the frequency of $r(t)$ and multiples of this frequency. If the frequency of one of these oscillations is close to the resonant frequency of the vibrating system (cf. p. 147), then that oscillation may be the dominant part of the response of the system to the external force. Of course, this is quite surprising to an observer not familiar with the corresponding mathematical theory which is highly important in the study of vibrating systems and resonance. Let us illustrate the situation by an example.

Example 1. In (1), let $m = 1$ (gm), $c = 0.02$ (gm/sec), and $k = 25$ (gm/sec²), so that (1) becomes

(2) $$\ddot{y} + 0.02\dot{y} + 25y = r(t)$$

where $r(t)$ is measured in gm · cm/sec². Let (Fig. 241)

$$r(t) = \begin{cases} t + \dfrac{\pi}{2} & \text{when} \quad -\pi < t < 0, \\[2mm] -t + \dfrac{\pi}{2} & \text{when} \quad 0 < t < \pi, \end{cases} \qquad r(t + 2\pi) = r(t).$$

Find the steady state solution $y(t)$.

We represent $r(t)$ by a Fourier series, finding

(3) $$r(t) = \frac{4}{\pi}\left(\cos t + \frac{1}{3^2}\cos 3t + \frac{1}{5^2}\cos 5t + \cdots\right).$$

Then we consider the differential equation

(4) $$\ddot{y} + 0.02\dot{y} + 25y = \frac{4}{n^2\pi}\cos nt \qquad (n = 1, 3, \cdots)$$

whose right-hand side is a single term of the series (3). From Sec. 2.13, we know that the steady-state solution $y_n(t)$ of (4) is of the form

(5) $$y_n = A_n \cos nt + B_n \sin nt,$$

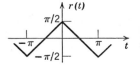

Fig. 241. Force in Example 1.

and by substituting this into (4) we find that

(6) $A_n = \dfrac{4(25 - n^2)}{n^2 \pi D}$, $B_n = \dfrac{0.08}{n\pi D}$ where $D = (25 - n^2)^2 + (0.02n)^2$·

Since (2) is linear, we may expect that the steady state solution is

(7) $y = y_1 + y_3 + y_5 + \cdots$

where y_n is given by (5) and (6). In
fact, this follows readily by substituting (7) into (2) and using the Fourier
series of $r(t)$, provided that termwise
differentiation of (7) is permissible.
(Readers already familiar with the
notion of uniform convergence [Sec.
11.9] may prove that (7) may be differentiated term-by-term.)

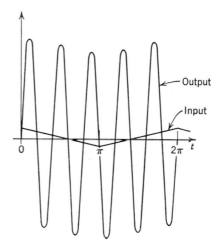

Fig. 242. Input and steady state output
in Example 1.

From (6) we find that the amplitude
of (5) is

$$C_n = \sqrt{A_n^2 + B_n^2} = \frac{4}{n^2 \pi \sqrt{D}}.$$

For $n = 5$ the quantity D is very small
and C_5 is so large that y_5 is the domi-
nating term in (7). This implies that
the steady-state motion is almost a
harmonic oscillation whose frequency
equals five times that of the exciting force (Fig. 242).

TABLE 18. AMPLITUDES IN EXAMPLE 1.

n	C_n
1	0.053
3	0.008 8
5	0.51
7	0.001 1
9	0.000 28
11	0.000 11

PROBLEMS

Find the general solution of the differential equation $\ddot{y} + \omega^2 y = r(t)$ where:
1. $r(t) = \sin t$, $\omega = 0.5, 0.7, 0.9, 1.1, 1.5, 2.0, 10.0$
2. $r(t) = \cos \alpha t + \cos \beta t$ ($\omega^2 \neq \alpha^2, \beta^2$)
3. $r(t) = \sin t + \frac{1}{9} \sin 3t + \frac{1}{25} \sin 5t$, $\omega = 0.5, 0.9, 1.1, 2, 2.9, 3.1, 4, 4.9, 5.1,$
6, 8
4. $r(t) = \displaystyle\sum_{n=1}^{N} b_n \sin nt$, $|\omega| \neq 1, 2, \cdots, N$

5. $r(t) = \begin{cases} t & \text{if } -\pi/2 < t < \pi/2 \\ \pi - t & \text{if } \pi/2 < t < 3\pi/2 \end{cases}$ and $r(t + 2\pi) = r(t)$, $|\omega| \neq 1, 3, 5, \cdots$

6. $r(t) = \dfrac{t^2}{4}$ when $-\pi < t < \pi$ and $r(t + 2\pi) = r(t)$, $|\omega| \neq 0, 1, 2, \cdots$

7. $r(t) = \dfrac{t}{12}(\pi^2 - t^2)$ when $-\pi < t < \pi$ and $r(t + 2\pi) = r(t)$, $|\omega| \neq 1, 2, \cdots$

8. $r(t) = \displaystyle\sum_{n=1}^{N} a_n \cos nt$, $|\omega| \neq 1, 2, \cdots, N$

9. $r(t) = \dfrac{\pi}{4}|\sin t|$ when $-\pi < t < \pi$ and $r(t + 2\pi) = r(t)$, $|\omega| \neq 0, 2, 4, \cdots$

10. $r(t) = \begin{cases} t + \pi & \text{if } -\pi < t < 0 \\ -t + \pi & \text{if } 0 < t < \pi \end{cases}$ and $r(t + 2\pi) = r(t)$, $|\omega| \neq 0, 1, 3, \cdots$

Find the steady-state oscillation corresponding to $\ddot{y} + c\dot{y} + y = r(t)$ where $c > 0$ and

11. $r(t) = K \sin t$ **12.** $r(t) = \sin 3t$ **13.** $r(t) = a_n \cos nt$

14. $r(t) = \displaystyle\sum_{n=1}^{N} b_n \sin nt$

15. $r(t) = \begin{cases} \pi t/4 & \text{if } -\pi/2 < t < \pi/2 \\ \pi(\pi - t)/4 & \text{if } \pi/2 < t < 3\pi/2 \end{cases}$ and $r(t + 2\pi) = r(t)$

16. $r(t) = \dfrac{t}{12}(\pi^2 - t^2)$ when $-\pi < t < \pi$ and $r(t + 2\pi) = r(t)$

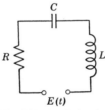

Fig. 243. *RLC*-circuit.

17. Find the steady-state current $I(t)$ in the *RLC*-circuit in Fig. 243 where $R = 100$ ohms, $L = 10$ henrys, $C = 10^{-2}$ farads, $E(t) = 100t(\pi^2 - t^2)$ volts when $-\pi < t < \pi$ and $E(t + 2\pi) = E(t)$. Proceed as follows. Develop $E(t)$ in a Fourier series. $I(t)$ will appear in the form of a trigonometric series. Find the general formulas for the coefficients of this series. Compute numerical values of the first few coefficients with a slide rule. Graph the sum of the first few terms of that series.

18. Same task as in Prob. 17 when

$$E(t) = \begin{cases} 100(\pi t + t^2) & \text{if } -\pi < t < 0 \\ 100(\pi t - t^2) & \text{if } 0 < t < \pi \end{cases} \quad \text{and} \quad E(t + 2\pi) = E(t),$$

the other data being as before.

8.8 NUMERICAL METHODS FOR DETERMINING FOURIER COEFFICIENTS. SQUARE ERROR

The Fourier coefficients of a function $f(x)$ having period 2π are given by the Euler formulas (6), Sec. 8.2, and the occurring integrals may be evaluated by numerical integration, for example, by the rectangular rule (Sec. 0.8).

For this purpose we subdivide the interval of integration $-\pi \leqq x \leqq \pi$ into q equal parts of length $\Delta x = 2\pi/q$, whose common end points will be denoted by

$$x_0(= -\pi), x_1, x_2, \cdots, x_q(= \pi).$$

While in (2), Sec. 0.8, the function values $f(x_m{}^*)$ at the midpoints $x_m{}^*$ of the intervals of subdivision are chosen, we shall now simply choose the function value $f(x_m)$ at the right end point of each interval. Since the integrals in (6) are multiplied by $1/2\pi$ and $1/\pi$, and $\Delta x/2\pi = 1/q$, $\Delta x/\pi = 2/q$ we thus obtain from (6) the following formulas:

$$a_0 = \frac{1}{q}\left[f(x_1) + \cdots + f(x_q)\right]$$

(1)
$$a_n = \frac{2}{q}\left[f(x_1)\cos nx_1 + \cdots + f(x_q)\cos nx_q\right]$$

$$b_n = \frac{2}{q}\left[f(x_1)\sin nx_1 + \cdots + f(x_q)\sin nx_q\right].$$

Since the values of sine and cosine are repeated in the four quadrants it is practical to choose for q a number divisible by 4. A good choice is $q = 24$ because then many terms of the sums in (1) are zero. Let us illustrate the practical procedure by a simple example.

Example 1. Taking $q = 24$ in (1), compute $a_0, \cdots, a_{12}$, in the case of the function (cf. Ex. 3, Sec. 8.3)

$$f(x) = x^2 \quad \text{when} \quad -\pi < x < \pi \quad \text{and} \quad f(x + 2\pi) = f(x).$$

Here $f(x_m) = x_m{}^2$. From (1) and Table 19,

$$a_0 = \frac{1}{24}(x_1{}^2 + \cdots + x_{24}{}^2) = \frac{1}{24}(S_1 + 2S_2) = 3.301 \left(\text{exact}: \frac{\pi^2}{3} \approx 3.290\right).$$

TABLE 19. VALUES OF $f(x)$ IN EXAMPLE 1.

m	x_m		$x_m{}^2$
	degrees	radians	
24	± 180	$\pm \pi$	9.869 60
1 23	± 165	$\pm 11\pi/12$	8.293 21
2 22	± 150	$\pm 5\pi/6$	6.853 89
3 21	± 135	$\pm 3\pi/4$	5.551 65
4 20	± 120	$\pm 2\pi/3$	4.386 49
5 19	± 105	$\pm 7\pi/12$	3.358 41
6 18	± 90	$\pm \pi/2$	2.467 40
7 17	± 75	$\pm 5\pi/12$	1.713 47
8 16	± 60	$\pm \pi/3$	1.096 62
9 15	± 45	$\pm \pi/4$	0.616 85
10 14	± 30	$\pm \pi/6$	0.274 16
11 13	± 15	$\pm \pi/12$	0.068 54
12	0	0	0

Sums $S_1 = 9.869\ 60$ $S_2 = 34.680\ 69$

TABLE 20. VALUES OF $\cos x$
IN EXAMPLE 1.

x	$\cos x$	Notation
$0°$	1	C_0
$15°$	0.965 925 83	C_1
$30°$	0.866 025 40	C_2
$45°$	0.707 106 78	C_3
$60°$	0.5	C_4
$75°$	0.258 819 05	C_5
$90°$	0	C_6

The values of the cosine required in the computation of the further coefficients are contained in Table 20, and (1) yields

$$a_1 = \tfrac{1}{12}[x_1^2 \cos(-165°) + x_2^2 \cos(-150°) + \cdots]$$
$$= \tfrac{1}{12}[x_1^2(-C_1) + x_2^2(-C_2) + \cdots + x_6^2 C_6 + x_7^2 C_5 + \cdots].$$

Collecting terms containing like C, omitting terms which are zero, and using $x_m^2 = x_{24-m}^2$, this becomes

$$a_1 = -\tfrac{1}{6}[\tfrac{1}{2}x_0^2 C_0 + (x_1^2 - x_{11}^2)C_1 + (x_2^2 - x_{10}^2)C_2 + \cdots + (x_5^2 - x_7^2)C_5].$$

Using the function values in Table 20 the numerical result is

$$a_1 = -4.023 \qquad \text{(exact: } -4\text{; cf. Ex. 3 in Sec 8.3.)}$$

The other coefficients $a_2, \cdots, a_{12}$ may be computed from (1) in a similar fashion. The result is shown in Table 21.

TABLE 21. FOURIER COEFFICIENTS
IN EXAMPLE 1.

n	a_n by (1)	a_n exact
0	3.301	3.290
1	−4.023	−4.000
2	1.023	1.000
3	−0.468	−0.444
4	0.274	0.250
5	−0.185	−0.160
6	0.137	0.111
7	−0.109	−0.082
8	0.091	0.063
9	−0.080	−0.049
10	0.073	0.040
11	−0.070	−0.033
12	0.069	0.028

We want to mention that there is another less naive approach to the formulas (1) as follows. Let $f(x)$ be a given function that has period 2π and can be represented by a Fourier series. Then the Nth partial sum is an approximation for $f(x)$:

$$(2) \qquad f(x) \approx a_0 + \sum_{n=1}^{N} (a_n \cos nx + b_n \sin nx).$$

We ask whether we can find a trigonometric polynomial

$$(3) \qquad F(x) = \alpha_0 + \sum_{n=1}^{N} (\alpha_n \cos nx + \beta_n \sin nx)$$

which, for the same fixed N, is a "better" approximation for $f(x)$, that is, an approximation whose *error* is smaller than that of (2).

Of course, we must first define what we mean by an error of such an approximation. We want to choose a definition which measures the goodness of agreement between f and F *on the whole interval* $-\pi \leqq x \leqq \pi$. Obviously, the maximum of $|f - F|$ is not suitable for that purpose: in Fig. 244, the function F is a good approximation of f, but $|f - F|$ is large near x_0. We choose for our consideration

$$(4) \qquad E = \int_{-\pi}^{\pi} (f - F)^2 \, dx.$$

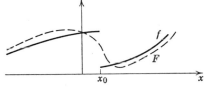

Fig. 244. Error of approximation.

This is the so-called **total square error** of F relative to f over the interval $-\pi \leqq x \leqq \pi$. Clearly, $E \geqq 0$.

N being fixed, we want to determine the coefficients in (3) such that E is minimum. We can write (4) in the form

$$(5) \qquad E = \int_{-\pi}^{\pi} f^2 \, dx - 2 \int_{-\pi}^{\pi} fF \, dx + \int_{-\pi}^{\pi} F^2 \, dx.$$

By inserting (3) into the last integral and evaluating the occurring integrals as in Sec. 8.2, we readily obtain

$$\int_{-\pi}^{\pi} F^2 \, dx = \pi(2\alpha_0^2 + \alpha_1^2 + \cdots + \alpha_N^2 + \beta_1^2 + \cdots + \beta_N^2).$$

By inserting (3) into the second integral in (5) we see that the occurring integrals are those in the Euler formulas (6), Sec. 8.2, and

$$\int_{-\pi}^{\pi} fF \, dx = \pi(2\alpha_0 a_0 + \alpha_1 a_1 + \cdots + \alpha_N a_N + \beta_1 b_1 + \cdots + \beta_N b_N).$$

With these expressions (5) becomes

$$(6) \qquad E = \int_{-\pi}^{\pi} f^2 \, dx - 2\pi \left[2\alpha_0 a_0 + \sum_{n=1}^{N} (\alpha_n a_n + \beta_n b_n) \right]$$
$$+ \pi \left[2\alpha_0^2 + \sum_{n=1}^{N} (\alpha_n^2 + \beta_n^2) \right].$$

If we take $\alpha_n = a_n$ and $\beta_n = b_n$ in (3), then from (6) we see that the square error corresponding to this particular choice of the coefficients of F is

$$(7) \qquad E^* = \int_{-\pi}^{\pi} f^2 \, dx - \pi \left[2a_0^2 + \sum_{n=1}^{N} (a_n^2 + b_n^2) \right].$$

By subtracting (7) from (6) we obtain

$$E - E^* = \pi \left\{ 2(\alpha_0 - a_0)^2 + \sum_{n=1}^{N} [(\alpha_n - a_n)^2 + (\beta_n - b_n)^2] \right\}.$$

The terms on the right are squares of real numbers and therefore non-negative. Hence

$$E - E^* \geqq 0 \qquad \text{or} \qquad E \geqq E^*,$$

and $E = E^*$ if, and only if, $\alpha_0 = a_0, \cdots, \beta_N = b_N$. This proves

Theorem 1. *The total square error of F [cf. (3), N fixed] relative to f on the interval $-\pi \leqq x \leqq \pi$ is minimum if and only if the coefficients of F in (3) are the corresponding Fourier coefficients of f. This minimum value is given by (7).*

The reader may show that the result $\alpha_0 = a_0, \cdots, \beta_N = b_N$ may also be obtained from the conditions (10) (below) which are necessary (but not sufficient) for the minimum.

Let us look at (7). We see that E^* cannot increase as N increases, but may decrease. Hence, *with increasing N, the partial sums of the Fourier series of f yield better and better approximations for $f(x)$,* considered from the view point of the square error.

Since $E^* \geqq 0$ and (7) holds for any N, we obtain the important **Bessel inequality**[6]

$$(8) \qquad 2a_0^2 + \sum_{n=1}^{\infty} (a_n^2 + b_n^2) \leqq \frac{1}{\pi} \int_{-\pi}^{\pi} f^2(x) \, dx$$

for the Fourier coefficients of any function f for which the integral on the right exists.

[6] It can be shown that for such a function f even the equality sign in (8) holds. Proof in Ref. [E3].

In connection with our numerical integration we use only the values of $f(x)$ at certain points, namely at $x_1, \cdots, x_q$. It may even happen that $f(x)$ is not given by a formula at all, but is an empirical function given by those values which are obtained from an experiment or in some other way. In this case we cannot use the integral (4) but may consider the sum

$$(9) \qquad\qquad E = \sum_{m=1}^{q} [f(x_m) - F(x_m)]^2.$$

We may then ask for what choice of the α_m and β_m in (3) this quantity E becomes minimum. Necessary conditions are the $2N + 1$ conditions

$$(10) \qquad \frac{\partial E}{\partial \alpha_0} = 0, \quad \frac{\partial E}{\partial \alpha_n} = 0, \quad \frac{\partial E}{\partial \beta_n} = 0, \quad (n = 1, \cdots, N).$$

$F(x)$ should approximate the $q + 1$ given values $f(x_0), \cdots, f(x_q)$ as closely as possible. But if $2N + 1 > q + 1$ then more than $q + 1$ constants appear in $F(x)$, there are an infinite number of ways that $F(x)$ can take on these $q + 1$ values, and the problem is meaningless. Therefore, we assume that $2N + 1 = q + 1$ or $N = q/2$ where q is even. Then it can be shown that (10) leads to $\alpha_0 = a_0, \alpha_n = a_n, \beta_n = b_n$ $(n = 1, 2, \cdots, N - 1,)$ as given by (1), and

$$(11) \qquad\qquad a_N = \frac{1}{q} \sum_{m=1}^{q} (-1)^m f(x_m) \qquad \left(N = \frac{q}{2}\right).$$

For this choice of the coefficients in (3) the approximating trigonometric polynomial $F(x)$ assumes the values $F(x_m) = f(x_m)$, and the error E in (9) is zero. The proofs are somewhat long and can be found in Ref. [A11] or [A15] in Appendix 1.

Note that a_N obtained from (1) equals twice the value given by (11), as the student may verify, and $b_N = 0$ in (1) because when $n = N = q/2$ all the terms in the formula for b_n are zero.

For example, if $q = 24$, then $N = 12$, and $a_0, \cdots, a_{11}, b_1, \cdots, b_{11}$ should be computed from (1) while a_{12} should be computed from (11).

PROBLEMS

1. Carry out the details of the computations in Ex. 1.

2. Let f be an odd empirical function having period 2π and the following values in the interval $0 \leq x \leq \pi$:

x	0	$\frac{\pi}{12}$	$\frac{2\pi}{12}$	$\frac{3\pi}{12}$	$\frac{4\pi}{12}$	$\frac{5\pi}{12}$	$\frac{6\pi}{12}$	$\frac{7\pi}{12}$	$\frac{8\pi}{12}$	$\frac{9\pi}{12}$	$\frac{10\pi}{12}$	$\frac{11\pi}{12}$	π
$f(x)$	0	0.20	0.36	0.53	0.70	0.84	0.93	0.98	1.00	0.97	0.85	0.50	0

Approximate $f(x)$ by a trigonometric polynomial $F(x)$ [cf. (3)] such that the error (9) is zero.

3. Let $f(x) = \begin{cases} -1 \text{ if } -\pi < x < 0 \\ 1 \text{ if } 0 < x < \pi \end{cases}$ and $f(x + 2\pi) = f(x)$. Find the function $F(x)$ of the form (3) for which the total square error (4) is minimum.

4. Compute the minimum square error in Prob. 3 for $N = 1, 3, 5, 7$. What is the smallest N such that $E^* \leq 0.2$?

5. Show that the minimum square error (7) is a monotone decreasing function of N.

In each case, find the function $F(x)$ of the form (3) for which the total square error E is minimum and compute this minimum value for $N = 1, 2, \cdots, 5$.

6. $f(x) = x \ (-\pi < x < \pi)$ **7.** $f(x) = x^2 \ (-\pi < x < \pi)$

8. Extend the consideration of the present section to functions of period T.

Using (8) with the equality sign, show that:

9. $1 + \dfrac{1}{3^2} + \dfrac{1}{5^2} + \cdots = \dfrac{\pi^2}{8}$. *Hint:* consider $f(x) = \begin{cases} -1 \text{ if } -\pi < x < 0 \\ 1 \text{ if } 0 < x < \pi \end{cases}$

10. $1 + \dfrac{1}{2^2} + \dfrac{1}{3^2} + \dfrac{1}{5^2} + \dfrac{1}{6^2} + \dfrac{1}{7^2} + \dfrac{1}{9^2} + \cdots = \dfrac{5\pi^2}{32}$. *Hint:* consider $f(x)$ in Prob. 7, Sec. 8.2.

11. $1 + \dfrac{1}{2^4} + \dfrac{1}{3^4} + \cdots = \dfrac{\pi^4}{90}$. *Hint:* consider $f(x)$ in Prob. 9, Sec. 8.2.

12. $1 + \dfrac{1}{3^4} + \dfrac{1}{5^4} + \cdots = \dfrac{\pi^4}{96}$. *Hint:* consider $f(x)$ in Prob. 13, Sec. 8.2.

13. Obtain the answer to Prob. 9 directly from Prob. 13, Sec. 8.2.

14. Using the result of Prob. 10, show that

$$1 + \frac{1}{2^2} + \frac{1}{3^2} + \frac{1}{4^2} + \frac{1}{5^2} + \cdots = \frac{\pi^2}{6}.$$

15. Obtain the answer to Prob. 11 directly from the Fourier series of

$$f(x) = x^4 - 2\pi^2 x^2 \text{ when } -\pi < x < \pi \text{ and } f(x + 2\pi) = f(x).$$

8.9 INSTRUMENTAL METHODS FOR DETERMINING FOURIER COEFFICIENTS

In many cases it will be sufficient to determine numerical values of the first few Fourier coefficients of a given periodic function. For this purpose instrumental methods are of considerable help, in particular if the function is an empirical function, given by its graph or by numerical values, or if the corresponding integrals in the Euler formulas cannot be evaluated by elementary methods of integration. We shall discuss two suitable instruments, namely, the planimeter (Sec. 0.8) and the harmonic analyzer.

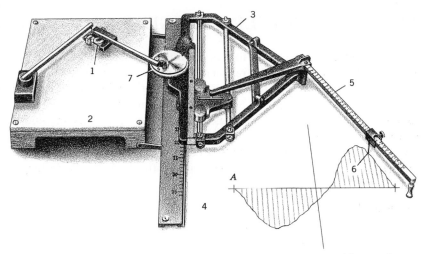

Fig. 245. Harmonic analyzer, manufactured by A. Ott, Kempten (Germany).

For obtaining numerical values of the first few Fourier coefficients of a given function $f(x)$ of period T by means of a planimeter, we have to plot graphs of the functions

$$\frac{1}{T}f(x), \quad \frac{2}{T}f(x)\cos\frac{2\pi x}{T}, \quad \frac{2}{T}f(x)\sin\frac{2\pi x}{T}, \quad \frac{2}{T}f(x)\cos\frac{4\pi x}{T}, \cdots$$

cf. (3) in Sec. 8.4, for $-T/2 \leqq x \leqq T/2$, and determine the areas under these curves.

This procedure can be simplified considerably by means of a **harmonic analyzer** which consists of a planimeter and an additional equipment. In Fig. 245 the planimeter (1) moves on a platform (2). The carriage (3) is moved on a rail (4) by means of a tracing arm (5), carrying the tracing pin (6). The gear (7) is exchangeable. The advantage of the harmonic analyzer is that for determining many Fourier coefficients we have to plot only the graph of the function $f(x)$. To obtain a certain Fourier coefficient of $f(x)$ we have to insert the appropriate gear and then trace around the complete boundary of the shaded area (Fig. 245), starting from the point A and returning to A; the value of the Fourier coefficient is then obtained as the difference of the initial and final readings on the scale of the integrating wheel of the planimeter. To determine another Fourier coefficient of $f(x)$, we have to exchange the gear and proceed as before.[7]

---

[7] The mechanical precision of a harmonic analyzer is of great importance for obtaining satisfactory results. The author has successfully used a Mader-Ott Harmonic Analyzer for many years.

8.10   THE FOURIER INTEGRAL

Fourier series are a powerful tool in treating various problems involving periodic functions. A first illustration of this fact was given in Sec. 8.7, and further important problems in connection with partial differential equations will be considered in Chap. 9. Since, of course, many practical problems do not involve periodic functions, it is desirable to generalize the method of Fourier series to include nonperiodic functions.

Roughly speaking, if we start with a periodic function $f_T(x)$ of period T and let T approach infinity then the resulting function $f(x)$ is no longer periodic.

Example 1. Consider the function

$$f_T(x) = \begin{cases} 0 & \text{when} & -T/2 < x < -1 \\ 1 & \text{when} & -1 < x < 1 \\ 0 & \text{when} & 1 < x < T/2 \end{cases}$$

having period $T > 2$ (Fig. 246). For $T \to \infty$ we obtain the function

$$f(x) = \lim_{T \to \infty} f_T(x) = \begin{cases} 1 & \text{when} & -1 < x < 1, \\ 0 & \text{otherwise.} \end{cases}$$

Example 2. Let

$$f_T(x) = e^{-|x|} \qquad \text{when} \qquad -T/2 < x < T/2 \qquad \text{and} \qquad f_T(x + T) = f_T(x).$$

Then (Fig. 247)

$$f(x) = \lim_{T \to \infty} f_T(x) = e^{-|x|}.$$

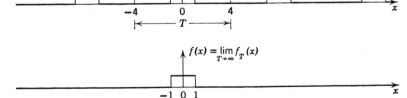

Fig. 246. Example 1.

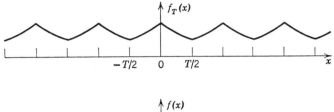

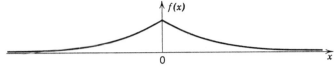

Fig. 247. Example 2.

Now let us start from a periodic function $f_T(x)$ that has period T and can be represented by a Fourier series:

$$f_T(x) = a_0 + \sum_{n=1}^{\infty} \left(a_n \cos \frac{2n\pi}{T} x + b_n \sin \frac{2n\pi}{T} x \right).$$

If we use the short notation

$$w_n = \frac{2n\pi}{T}$$

and insert a_n and b_n according to the Euler formulas (3) in Sec. 8.4, denoting the variable of integration by v, we obtain

$$f_T(x) = \frac{1}{T} \int_{-T/2}^{T/2} f_T(v)\, dv$$

$$+ \frac{2}{T} \sum_{n=1}^{\infty} \left[\cos w_n x \int_{-T/2}^{T/2} f_T(v) \cos w_n v\, dv + \sin w_n x \int_{-T/2}^{T/2} f_T(v) \sin w_n v\, dv \right].$$

Now,

$$w_{n+1} - w_n = \frac{2(n+1)\pi}{T} - \frac{2n\pi}{T} = \frac{2\pi}{T},$$

and we set

$$\Delta w = w_{n+1} - w_n = \frac{2\pi}{T}.$$

Then $2/T = \Delta w / \pi$, and we may write that Fourier series in the form

$$f_T(x) = \frac{1}{T} \int_{-T/2}^{T/2} f_T(v)\, dv$$

(1)

$$+ \frac{1}{\pi} \sum_{n=1}^{\infty} \left[\cos (w_n x)\, \Delta w \int_{-T/2}^{T/2} f_T(v) \cos w_n v\, dv \right.$$

$$\left. + \sin (w_n x)\, \Delta w \int_{-T/2}^{T/2} f_T(v) \sin w_n v\, dv \right].$$

This representation is valid for any fixed T, arbitrarily large, but finite.

We now let T approach infinity and assume that the resulting nonperiodic function

$$f(x) = \lim_{T \to \infty} f_T(x)$$

is absolutely integrable on the x-axis, that is, the integral

$$(2) \qquad\qquad \int_{-\infty}^{\infty} |f(x)| \, dx$$

exists. Then $1/T \to 0$ and the value of the first term on the right side of (1) approaches zero. Furthermore, $\Delta w = 2\pi/T \to 0$ and it seems plausible that the infinite series in (1) becomes an integral from 0 to ∞, which represents $f(x)$, namely,

$$(3) \quad f(x) = \frac{1}{\pi} \int_0^{\infty} \left[\cos wx \int_{-\infty}^{\infty} f(v) \cos wv \, dv \right.$$
$$\left. + \sin wx \int_{-\infty}^{\infty} f(v) \sin wv \, dv \right] dw.$$

If we introduce the short notations

$$(4) \qquad A(w) = \int_{-\infty}^{\infty} f(v) \cos wv \, dv, \quad B(w) = \int_{-\infty}^{\infty} f(v) \sin wv \, dv$$

this may be written in the form

$$(5) \qquad\qquad f(x) = \frac{1}{\pi} \int_0^{\infty} [A(w) \cos wx + B(w) \sin wx] \, dw.$$

This is a representation of $f(x)$ by a so-called **Fourier integral**.

It is clear that our naive approach merely *suggests* the representation (5), but by no means establishes it; in fact, the limit of the series in (1) as Δw approaches zero is not the definition of the integral (3). Sufficient conditions for the validity of (5) are as follows.

Theorem 1. *If $f(x)$ is piecewise continuous (cf. p. 209) in every finite interval and has a right- and left-hand derivative at every point (cf. p. 472) and the integral (2) exists, then $f(x)$ can be represented by a Fourier integral. At a point where $f(x)$ is discontinuous the value of the Fourier integral equals the average of the left- and right-hand limits of $f(x)$ at that point (cf. p. 472).* Proof in Ref. [E2]; cf. Appendix 1.

Example 3 (Single pulse, sine integral). Find the Fourier integral representation of the function (Fig. 248)

$$f(x) = \begin{cases} 1 & \text{when} & |x| < 1, \\ 0 & \text{when} & |x| > 1. \end{cases}$$

From (4) we obtain

$$A(w) = \int_{-\infty}^{\infty} f(v) \cos wv \, dv = \int_{-1}^{1} \cos wv \, dv = \frac{\sin wv}{w} \Big|_{-1}^{1} = \frac{2 \sin w}{w},$$

$$B(w) = \int_{-1}^{1} \sin wv \, dv = 0,$$

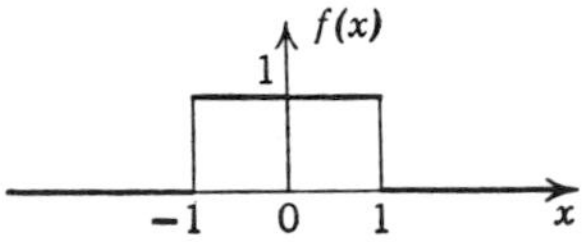

and (5) becomes

(6) $$f(x) = \frac{2}{\pi} \int_0^{\infty} \frac{\cos wx \sin w}{w} \, dw.$$

Fig. 248. Example 3.

The average of the left- and right-hand limits of $f(x)$ at $x = 1$ is equal to $(1 + 0)/2$, that is, $1/2$. Hence, from (6) and Theorem 1,

$$\int_0^{\infty} \frac{\cos wx \sin w}{w} \, dw = \begin{cases} \pi/2 & \text{when} & 0 \le x < 1, \\ \pi/4 & \text{when} & x = 1, \\ 0 & \text{when} & x > 1. \end{cases}$$

This integral is called **Dirichlet's**[8] **discontinuous factor.** In particular, when $x = 0$, then

(7) $$\int_0^{\infty} \frac{\sin w}{w} \, dw = \frac{\pi}{2}.$$

We see that this integral is the limit of the so-called **sine integral**

(8) $$\text{Si}(z) = \int_0^z \frac{\sin w}{w} \, dw$$

as $z \to \infty$ (z real). The graph of Si(z) is shown in Fig. 249.

In the case of a Fourier series the graphs of the partial sums are approximation curves of the curve of the periodic function represented by the series. Similarly,

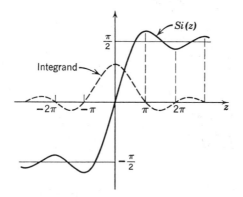

Fig. 249. Sine integral.

[8] PETER GUSTAV LEJEUNE DIRICHLET (1805–1859), German mathematician, known by his important research work on Fourier series and in number theory.

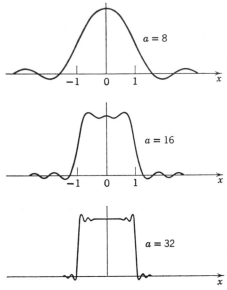

Fig. 250. The integral (9) for $a = 8$, 16, and 32.

in the case of the Fourier integral (5), approximations are obtained by replacing ∞ by numbers a. Hence the integral

$$(9) \qquad\qquad \int_0^a \frac{\cos wx \sin w}{w}\, dw$$

approximates the integral in (6) and therefore $f(x)$. Figure 250 shows oscillations near the points of discontinuity of $f(x)$.

We might expect that these oscillations disappear as a approaches infinity, but this is not true; with increasing a, they are shifted closer to the points $x = \pm 1$. This unexpected behavior, which also occurs in connection with Fourier series, is known as the **Gibbs[9] phenomenon.** It can be explained by representing (9) in terms of the sine integral as follows. Using (11b) in Sec. 0.1 we first have

$$\frac{2}{\pi}\int_0^a \frac{\cos wx \sin w}{w}\, dw = \frac{1}{\pi}\int_0^a \frac{\sin (w + wx)}{w}\, dw + \frac{1}{\pi}\int_0^a \frac{\sin (w - wx)}{w}\, dw.$$

In the first integral on the right we set $w + wx = t$. Then $dw/w = dt/t$, and $0 \leqq w \leqq a$ corresponds to $0 \leqq t \leqq (x + 1)a$. In the last integral we set $w - wx = -t$. Then $dw/w = dt/t$, and the interval $0 \leqq w \leqq a$ corresponds to $0 \leqq t \leqq (x - 1)a$. Since $\sin (-t) = -\sin t$ we thus obtain

$$\frac{2}{\pi}\int_0^a \frac{\cos wx \sin w}{w}\, dw = \frac{1}{\pi}\int_0^{(x+1)a} \frac{\sin t}{t}\, dt - \frac{1}{\pi}\int_0^{(x-1)a} \frac{\sin t}{t}\, dt.$$

[9] JOSIAH WILLARD GIBBS (1839–1903), American mathematician, whose work was of great importance to the development of vector analysis and mathematical physics.

From this and (8) we see that our integral equals

$$\frac{1}{\pi}\mathrm{Si}(a[x+1]) - \frac{1}{\pi}\mathrm{Si}(a[x-1]),$$

and the oscillations in Fig. 250 result from those in Fig. 249. The increase of a amounts to a transformation of the scale on the axis and causes the shift of the oscillations. For further details see Ref. [E1] in Appendix 1.

If $f(x)$ is an even function, then $B(w) = 0$ in (4),

(10) $$A(w) = 2\int_0^\infty f(v)\cos wv\, dv,$$

and (5) reduces to the simpler form

(11) $$f(x) = \frac{1}{\pi}\int_0^\infty A(w)\cos wx\, dw \qquad\qquad (f\text{ even}).$$

If $f(x)$ is odd, then $A(w) = 0$,

(12) $$B(w) = 2\int_0^\infty f(v)\sin wv\, dv,$$

and (5) becomes

(13) $$f(x) = \frac{1}{\pi}\int_0^\infty B(w)\sin wx\, dw \qquad\qquad (f\text{ odd}).$$

These simplifications are quite similar to those in the case of a Fourier series discussed in Sec. 8.3.

Example 4 (Laplace integrals). Find the Fourier integral of

$$f(x) = e^{-kx} \quad\text{when}\quad x > 0 \quad\text{and}\quad f(-x) = f(x), \quad (k > 0)$$

(cf. Fig. 247 in this section, where $k = 1$). Since f is even, we have from (10)

$$A(w) = 2\int_0^\infty e^{-kv}\cos wv\, dv.$$

Now, by integration by parts,

$$\int e^{-kv}\cos wv\, dv = -\frac{k}{k^2+w^2}e^{-kv}\left(-\frac{w}{k}\sin wv + \cos wv\right).$$

When $v = 0$, the expression on the right equals $-k/(k^2 + w^2)$; when v approaches infinity it approaches zero because of the exponential factor. Thus

$$A(w) = \frac{2k}{k^2 + w^2},$$

and by substituting this in (11) we obtain the respresentation

$$f(x) = e^{-kx} = \frac{2k}{\pi}\int_0^\infty \frac{\cos wx}{k^2+w^2}\, dw \qquad\qquad (x > 0, k > 0).$$

From this representation we see that

(14)
$$\int_0^\infty \frac{\cos wx}{k^2 + w^2}\, dw = \frac{\pi}{2k}\, e^{-kx} \qquad (x > 0,\, k > 0).$$

Similarly, from the Fourier integral (13) of the odd function

$$f(x) = e^{-kx} \quad \text{when} \quad x > 0 \quad \text{and} \quad f(-x) = -f(x), \qquad (k > 0)$$

we obtain the result

(15)
$$\int_0^\infty \frac{w \sin wx}{k^2 + w^2}\, dw = \frac{\pi}{2}\, e^{-kx} \qquad (x > 0,\, k > 0).$$

The integrals (14) and (15) are the so-called *Laplace integrals*.

This example illustrates that the Fourier integral representation may be used for evaluating integrals.

PROBLEMS

Using the Fourier integral representation, show that

1. $\displaystyle\int_0^\infty \frac{\cos xw + w \sin xw}{1 + w^2}\, dw = \begin{cases} 0 & \text{when } x < 0 \\ \pi/2 & \text{when } x = 0 \\ \pi e^{-x} & \text{when } x > 0 \end{cases}$ [Use (5).]

2. $\displaystyle\int_0^\infty \frac{\sin w \cos xw}{w}\, dw = \begin{cases} \pi/2 & \text{when } 0 \le x < 1 \\ \pi/4 & \text{when } x = 1 \\ 0 & \text{when } x > 1 \end{cases}$ [Use (11).]

3. $\displaystyle\int_0^\infty \frac{\sin \pi w \sin xw}{1 - w^2}\, dw = \begin{cases} \dfrac{\pi}{2} \sin x & \text{when } 0 \le x \le \pi \\ 0 & \text{when } x > \pi \end{cases}$ [Use (13).]

4. $\displaystyle\int_0^\infty \frac{w^3 \sin xw}{w^4 + 4}\, dw = \frac{\pi}{2}\, e^{-x} \cos x \qquad \text{when } x > 0$ [Use (13).]

5. $\displaystyle\int_0^\infty \frac{\cos (\pi w/2) \cos xw}{1 - w^2}\, dw = \begin{cases} \dfrac{\pi}{2} \cos x & \text{when } |x| < \dfrac{\pi}{2} \\ 0 & \text{when } |x| > \dfrac{\pi}{2} \end{cases}$ [Use (11).]

6. $\displaystyle\int_0^\infty \frac{1 - \cos \pi w}{w} \sin xw\, dw = \begin{cases} \dfrac{\pi}{2} & \text{when } 0 < x < \pi \\ 0 & \text{when } x > \pi \end{cases}$ [Use (13).]

7. $\displaystyle\int_0^\infty \frac{\cos xw}{1 + w^2}\, dw = \frac{\pi}{2}\, e^{-x} \qquad (x > 0)$ [Use (11).]

Represent the following functions $f(x)$ in the form (11).

8. $f(x) = \begin{cases} 1 & \text{when } 0 < x < a \\ 0 & \text{when } x > a \end{cases}$

9. $f(x) = \begin{cases} x & \text{when } 0 < x < 1 \\ 2 - x & \text{when } 1 < x < 2 \\ 0 & \text{when } x > 2 \end{cases}$

10. $f(x) = \dfrac{1}{1 + x^2}$ [cf. (14)]

11. $f(x) = e^{-x} + e^{-2x} \qquad (x > 0)$

12. $f(x) = \begin{cases} x^2 & \text{when } 0 < x < a \\ 0 & \text{when } x > a \end{cases}$ **13.** $f(x) = \begin{cases} x & \text{when } 0 < x < a \\ 0 & \text{when } x > a \end{cases}$

If $f(x)$ has the representation (11), show that:

14. $f(ax) = \dfrac{1}{\pi a} \int_0^\infty A\left(\dfrac{w}{a}\right) \cos xw \, dw \quad (a > 0)$

15. $x^2 f(x) = \dfrac{1}{\pi} \int_0^\infty A^*(w) \cos xw \, dw, \qquad A^* = -\dfrac{d^2 A}{dw^2}$

16. Solve Prob. 12 by applying the formula in Prob. 15 to the result of Prob. 8.

17. Show that $xf(x) = \dfrac{1}{\pi} \int_0^\infty B^*(w) \sin xw \, dw$ where $B^* = -\dfrac{dA}{dw}$ and A is given by (10).

18. Verify the formula in Prob. 17 for $f(x) = 1$ when $0 < x < a$ and $f(x) = 0$ when $x > a$.

19. Show that $f(x) = 1 \ (0 < x < \infty)$ cannot be represented by a Fourier integral.

20. Using the addition formula of the cosine function, show that (5) can be written

(16) $$f(x) = \frac{1}{\pi} \int_0^\infty \left[\int_{-\infty}^\infty f(v) \cos (wx - wv) \, dv \right] dw.$$

21. Show that the integral from $-\infty$ to ∞ in (16) is an even function of w and (16) may be written

$$f(x) = \frac{1}{2\pi} \int_{-\infty}^\infty \left[\int_{-\infty}^\infty f(v) \cos (wx - wv) \, dv \right] dw.$$

Show that

(17) $$\frac{i}{2\pi} \int_{-\infty}^\infty \left[\int_{-\infty}^\infty f(v) \sin (wx - wv) \, dv \right] dw = 0,$$

so that by addition,

(18) $$f(x) = \frac{1}{2\pi} \int_{-\infty}^\infty \left[\int_{-\infty}^\infty f(v) e^{iw(x-v)} \, dv \right] dw.$$

This is the so-called **complex form** of the Fourier integral.

22. Show that (18) can be written

(19) $$f(x) = \frac{1}{\sqrt{2\pi}} \int_{-\infty}^\infty C(w) e^{iwx} \, dw$$

where

$$C(w) = \frac{1}{\sqrt{2\pi}} \int_{-\infty}^\infty f(v) e^{-iwv} \, dv.$$

$f(x)$ is called the **Fourier transform** of $C(w)$, and $C(w)$ is called the *inverse Fourier transform* of $f(x)$. (Elaborate tables of Fourier transforms are listed in Part E of Appendix 1.)

8.11 ORTHOGONAL FUNCTIONS

Two real functions $g_m(x)$ and $g_n(x)$ are said to be **orthogonal** *on an interval* $a \leqq x \leqq b$, if the integral of the product $g_m g_n$ over that interval is zero:

$$(1) \qquad \int_a^b g_m(x) g_n(x) \, dx = 0, \qquad (m \neq n).$$

A set of real functions $g_0, g_1, g_2, \cdots$, satisfying (1) for all pairs of distinct functions in the set, is called an **orthogonal set** *of functions on that interval.*

The integral

$$N(g_m) = \int_a^b g_m{}^2(x) \, dx$$

is called the **norm** of the function $g_m(x)$ on the interval $a \leqq x \leqq b$.

Example 1. The functions $g_m = \cos mx$, $m = 0, 1, \cdots$, form an orthogonal set on the interval $-\pi \leqq x \leqq \pi$, because

$$(2) \qquad \int_{-\pi}^{\pi} \cos mx \cos nx \, dx = 0 \qquad \text{when } m \neq n.$$

The norm of g_m is

$$(3) \qquad N(\cos mx) = \int_{-\pi}^{\pi} \cos^2 mx \, dx = \begin{cases} 2\pi & \text{when } m = 0, \\ \pi & \text{when } m = 1, 2, \cdots. \end{cases}$$

Example 2. The functions

$$1, \cos x, \sin x, \cos 2x, \sin 2x, \cdots$$

occurring in Fourier series form an orthogonal set on the interval $-\pi \leqq x \leqq \pi$ because of (2), the analogous relation for the sine functions, and

$$\int_{-\pi}^{\pi} \cos mx \sin nx \, dx = 0 \qquad \text{for all } m, n = 0, 1, \cdots.$$

The norm of the sine functions on the interval under consideration is π.

Throughout our consideration we shall make the following

General assumption. *All occurring functions are bounded and integrable on the interval under consideration, and their norms are not zero.*

Clearly, an orthogonal set $g_0, g_1, \cdots$ on an interval $a \leqq x \leqq b$ whose functions have norm 1, satisfies the relations

$$(4) \qquad \int_a^b g_m(x) g_n(x) \, dx = \begin{cases} 0 & \text{when } m \neq n, \\ 1 & \text{when } m = n, \end{cases} \qquad \begin{matrix} m = 0, 1, 2, \cdots \\ n = 0, 1, 2, \cdots. \end{matrix}$$

Such a set is called an **orthonormal set** *of functions* on the interval $a \leq x \leq b$.

Obviously, from an *orthogonal* set we may obtain an *orthonormal* set by dividing each function by the square root of its norm on the interval under consideration.

Example 3. From the orthogonal set

$$1, \cos x, \sin x, \cos 2x, \sin 2x, \cdots$$

in Ex. 2 we may obtain the orthonormal set

$$\frac{1}{\sqrt{2\pi}}, \frac{\cos x}{\sqrt{\pi}}, \frac{\sin x}{\sqrt{\pi}}, \frac{\cos 2x}{\sqrt{\pi}}, \frac{\sin 2x}{\sqrt{\pi}}, \cdots.$$

Looking at the derivation of the Euler formulas (6) in Sec. 8.2 for the Fourier coefficients, we see that we used merely the fact that the set in Ex. 2, this section, is orthogonal on an interval of length 2π. This simple observation suggests the attempt to represent given functions $f(x)$ in terms of any other orthogonal set $g_0(x), g_1(x), \cdots$ in the form

$$(5) \qquad f(x) = \sum_{n=0}^{\infty} c_n g_n(x) = c_0 g_0(x) + c_1 g_1(x) + \cdots$$

and determine the coefficients $c_0, c_1, \cdots$ as in Sec. 8.2. If the series (5) converges and represents $f(x)$, it is called a **generalized Fourier series** of $f(x)$, and its coefficients are called the **Fourier constants** *of* $f(x)$ *with respect to that orthogonal set of functions.*

To determine these constants, we proceed as in Sec. 8.2. We multiply both sides of (5) by $g_m(x)$ and integrate over the interval $a \leq x \leq b$ on which the functions are orthogonal; assuming that term-by-term integration is permissible (cf. footnote 2 on p. 467) this yields

$$\int_a^b f g_m \, dx = \sum_{n=0}^{\infty} c_n \int_a^b g_n g_m \, dx.$$

The integral for which $n = m$ is equal to the norm $N(g_m)$, while all the other integrals are zero because the functions are orthogonal. Thus,

$$(6') \qquad \int_a^b f g_m \, dx = c_m N(g_m)$$

and the desired formula for the Fourier constants is

$$(6) \qquad c_m = \frac{1}{N(g_m)} \int_a^b f(x) \, g_m(x) \, dx.$$

Note that for the functions in Ex. 2 this formula becomes identical with the Euler formulas (6) in Sec. 8.2.

As in Sec. 8.8 we conclude that if the set of functions is orthonormal, those Fourier constants satisfy the **Bessel inequality**

(7) $$c_0^2 + c_1^2 + c_2^2 + \cdots \leqq \int_a^b f^2(x)\, dx.$$

Hence the series on the left converges and, therefore,

$$c_n \to 0 \qquad \text{as} \qquad n \to \infty.$$

Some important sets of real functions $g_0, g_1, \cdots$ occurring in applications are not orthogonal but have the property that for some function $p(x)$,

(8) $$\int_a^b p(x)g_m(x)g_n(x)\, dx = 0 \qquad \text{when } m \neq n.$$

Such a set is then said to be *orthogonal with respect to the* **weight function** $p(x)$ *on the interval* $a \leqq x \leqq b$. The *norm* of g_m is now defined as

(9) $$N(g_m) = \int_a^b p(x)g_m^2(x)\, dx,$$

and if the norm of each function g_m is 1, the set is said to be *orthonormal* on that interval with respect to $p(x)$.

If we set $h_m = \sqrt{p}\, g_m$ then (8) becomes

$$\int_a^b h_m(x)h_n(x)\, dx = 0, \qquad\qquad (m \neq n),$$

that is, the functions h_m form an orthogonal set in the usual sense. Clearly, if these functions are to be real, the weight function must be nonnegative. Important examples will be considered in the following sections.

PROBLEMS

In each case, show that the given set is orthogonal on the given interval I and determine the corresponding orthonormal set.

1. $\sin x, \sin 2x, \sin 3x, \cdots, I: -\pi \leqq x \leqq \pi$
2. $\sin x, \sin 2x, \sin 3x, \cdots, I: 0 \leqq x \leqq \pi$
3. $1, \cos x, \sin x, \cos 2x, \sin 2x, \cdots, I: 0 \leqq x \leqq 2\pi$
4. $1, \cos x, \cos 2x, \cos 3x, \cdots, I: 0 \leqq x \leqq \pi$
5. $\sin \pi x, \sin 2\pi x, \sin 3\pi x, \cdots, I: -1 \leqq x \leqq 1$
6. $1, \cos 2x, \cos 4x, \cos 6x, \cdots, I: 0 \leqq x \leqq \pi$
7. $1, \cos \dfrac{2n\pi}{T}x, \sin \dfrac{2n\pi}{T}x\ (n = 1, 2, \cdots), I: -T/2 \leqq x \leqq T/2$
8. $1, x, \frac{1}{2}(3x^2 - 1), \frac{1}{2}(5x^3 - 3x), I: -1 \leqq x \leqq 1$
9. Prove (7).
10. Show that for the functions in Prob. 7 the formula (6) becomes identical with the Euler formulas (3) in Sec. 8.4.

11. Determine constants a_0, b_0, $\cdots$, c_2 so that the functions $g_0 = a_0$, $g_1 = b_0 + b_1 x$, $g_2 = c_0 + c_1 x + c_2 x^2$ form an orthonormal set on the interval $-1 \leq x \leq 1$.

12. Determine the constants in Prob. 11 so that the functions g_0, g_1, g_2 form an orthonormal set on the interval $0 \leq x \leq 1$.

13. The Legendre polynomials $P_n(x)$, $n = 0, 1, \cdots$ [cf. (11') in Sec. 3.3] form an orthogonal set on the interval $-1 \leq x \leq 1$. Find the corresponding orthonormal set. [Use Prob. 7 in Sec. 3.3]. Show that $P_n / \sqrt{N(P_n)} = g_n$, $n = 0, 1, 2$, where g_0, g_1, g_2 are the functions obtained in Prob. 11.

14. If the functions $g_0(x)$, $g_1(x)$, $\cdots$ form an orthogonal set on the interval $a \leq x \leq b$, show that the functions $g_0(cx + k)$, $g_1(cx + k)$, $\cdots$, $c \neq 0$, form an orthogonal set on the interval $(a - k)/c \leq x \leq (b - k)/c$.

15. By applying the result of Prob. 14 to the Legendre polynomials (11') in Sec. 3.3, obtain polynomials $p_n(x)$ which are orthogonal on the interval $0 \leq x \leq 1$. Compare the result with that of Prob. 12.

16. Using the result of Prob. 14, derive the orthogonality property of the set in Prob. 5 from that in Prob. 1.

17. Find an (unbounded) function $f(x)$ such that $\displaystyle\int_0^1 f(x)\, dx$ exists, but $\displaystyle\int_0^1 f^2(x)\, dx$ does not exist.

18. Let $S_N(x)$ be the Nth partial sum of (5). Then if

$$\lim_{N \to \infty} \int_a^b [f(x) - S_N(x)]^2\, dx = 0,$$

the sum $S_N(x)$ is said to **converge in the mean** to the function $f(x)$. If this relation holds for each function $f(x)$ that satisfies the general assumption (p. 510), the set $g_0(x)$, $g_1(x)$, $\cdots$ is said to be **closed**. Show that for a closed orthonormal set,

$$\sum_{n=0}^{\infty} c_n^2 = \int_a^b f^2(x)\, dx \qquad \textbf{(Parseval's formula).}$$

Hint: insert $S_N = \displaystyle\sum_{n=0}^{N} c_n g_n(x)$ into the above integral, use (6'), and show that $\displaystyle\int_a^b \left(\sum_{n=0}^{N} c_n g_n \right)^2 dx = \sum_{n=0}^{N} c_n^2$. Then let $N \to \infty$.

19. Show that a closed orthonormal set of functions is **complete**, that is, there is no function $f(x)$ that satisfies the general assumption on p. 510 and is orthogonal to each function of the set on the interval under consideration.

8.12   STURM-LIOUVILLE PROBLEM

Various important orthogonal sets of functions arise as solutions of second-order differential equations of the form

(1) $$[r(x)y']' + [q(x) + \lambda p(x)]y = 0$$

on some interval $a \leq x \leq b$, satisfying conditions of the form

(2)   (a) $k_1 y + k_2 y' = 0$ at $x = a$ (b) $l_1 y + l_2 y' = 0$ at $x = b$;

here λ is a real parameter, and k_1, k_2, l_1, l_2 are given real constants, at least one in each condition (2) being different from zero.

The equation (1) is known as the **Sturm-Liouville**[10] **equation**, and we shall see that Legendre's equation, Bessel's equation, and other important equations can be written in the form (1). The conditions (2) refer to the boundary points $x = a$ and $x = b$ of that interval and, therefore, are called **boundary conditions**. A differential equation together with boundary conditions constitutes what is known as a **boundary value problem**. Our boundary value problem (1), (2) is called a *Sturm-Liouville problem*.

Of course, this problem has the trivial solution $y = 0$ for any value of the parameter λ. Solutions $y \neq 0$ are called *characteristic functions* or **eigenfunctions** of the problem, and the values of λ for which such solutions exist, are called *characteristic values* or **eigenvalues** of the problem.

Example 1. Find the eigenvalues and eigenfunctions of the Sturm-Liouville problem

$$(3) \qquad (a)\ \ y'' + \lambda y = 0 \qquad (b)\ \ y(0) = 0, \quad y(\pi) = 0.$$

For negative $\lambda = -v^2$ the general solution of the equation is

$$y(x) = c_1 e^{vx} + c_2 e^{-vx}.$$

From (3b), $c_1 = c_2 = 0$ and $y = 0$, which is not an eigenfunction. For $\lambda = 0$ the situation is similar. For positive $\lambda = v^2$ the general solution is

$$y(x) = A \cos vx + B \sin vx.$$

From the boundary conditions we obtain $y(0) = A = 0$ and thus,

$$y(\pi) = B \sin v\pi = 0 \qquad \text{or} \qquad v = 0, \pm 1, \pm 2, \cdots.$$

For $v = 0$, we have $y = 0$. For $\lambda = v^2 = 1, 4, 9, 16, \cdots$, taking $B = 1$, we obtain

$$y(x) = \sin vx \qquad\qquad v = 1, 2, \cdots.$$

These are the eigenfunctions of the problem, and the eigenvalues are $\lambda = v^2$ where $v = 1, 2, \cdots$.

It can be shown that under rather general conditions on the functions p, q, and r in (1) the Sturm-Liouville problem (1), (2) has infinitely many eigenvalues; the corresponding rather complicated theory can be found in Ref. [B5]; cf. Appendix 1.

Furthermore, the eigenfunctions are orthogonal, as follows.

Theorem 1. *Let the functions p, q, and r in the Sturm-Liouville equation (1) be real and continuous on the interval $a \leqq x \leqq b$. Let $y_m(x)$ and $y_n(x)$ be eigenfunctions of the Sturm-Liouville problem (1), (2) corresponding to distinct*

---

[10] JACQUES CHARLES FRANCOIS STURM (1803–1855), Swiss mathematician, JOSEPH LIOUVILLE (1809–1882), French mathematician, known by his important research work in complex analysis.

eigenvalues λ_m and λ_n, *respectively, and let the derivatives* $y_m{}'(x)$ *and* $y_n{}'(x)$ *be continuous on that interval. Then* y_m *and* y_n *are orthogonal on that interval with respect to the weight function p.*

If $r(a) = 0$, *then (2a) can be dropped from the problem. If* $r(b) = 0$, *then (2b) can be dropped. If* $r(a) = r(b)$, *then (2) can be replaced by*

$$(4) \qquad\qquad y(a) = y(b), \qquad y'(a) = y'(b).$$

Proof. y_m satisfies

$$(ry_m{}')' + (q + \lambda_m p)y_m = 0,$$

and y_n satisfies

$$(ry_n{}')' + (q + \lambda_n p)y_n = 0.$$

Multiplying the first equation by y_n and the second by $-y_m$ and adding, we get

$$\begin{aligned}(\lambda_m - \lambda_n)py_m y_n &= y_m(ry_n{}')' - y_n(ry_m{}')' \\ &= [(ry_n{}')y_m - (ry_m{}')y_n]'\end{aligned}$$

where the last equality can be readily verified by carrying out the indicated differentiation in the last expression. Integrating over x from a to b, we obtain

$$(5) \qquad (\lambda_m - \lambda_n)\int_a^b py_m y_n\, dx = \left[r(y_n{}'y_m - y_m{}'y_n)\right]_a^b.$$

The expression on the right equals

$$(6) \qquad \begin{aligned}&r(b)[y_n{}'(b)y_m(b) - y_m{}'(b)y_n(b)] \\ &- r(a)[y_n{}'(a)y_m(a) - y_m{}'(a)y_n(a)].\end{aligned}$$

Case 1. If $r(a) = 0$ and $r(b) = 0$, then the expression in (6) is zero. Hence the expression on the left-hand side of (5) must be zero, and since λ_m and λ_n are distinct, we obtain the desired orthogonality

$$(7) \qquad \int_a^b p(x)y_m(x)y_n(x)\, dx = 0, \qquad\qquad (m \neq n)$$

without the use of the boundary conditions (2).

Case 2. Let $r(b) = 0$, but $r(a) \neq 0$. Then the first line in (6) is zero. We consider the remaining expression in (6). From (2a) we have

$$\begin{aligned}k_1 y_n(a) + k_2 y_n{}'(a) &= 0, \\ k_1 y_m(a) + k_2 y_m{}'(a) &= 0.\end{aligned}$$

Let $k_2 \neq 0$. Then by multiplying the first equation by $y_m(a)$ and the last by $-y_n(a)$ and adding, we have

$$k_2[y_n{}'(a)y_m(a) - y_m{}'(a)y_n(a)] = 0.$$

Since $k_2 \neq 0$, the expression in brackets must be zero. This expression is identical with that in the last line of (6). Hence (6) is zero, and from (5) we obtain (7). If $k_2 = 0$, then by assumption $k_1 \neq 0$, and the argument of proof is similar.

Case 3. If $r(a) = 0$, but $r(b) \neq 0$, the proof is similar to that in Case 2, but instead of (2a) we now have to use (2b).

Case 4. If $r(a) \neq 0$ and $r(b) \neq 0$, we have to use both boundary conditions (2) and proceed as in Cases 2 and 3.

Case 5. Let $r(a) = r(b)$. Then (6) takes the form

$$r(b)[y_n'(b)y_m(b) - y_m'(b)y_n(b) - y_n'(a)y_m(a) + y_m'(a)y_n(a)],$$

and from (4) it follows that the expression in brackets is zero. Hence (5) yields (7), as before. This completes the proof of Theorem 1.

Example 2. The differential equation in Ex. 1 is of the form (1) where $r = 1$, $q = 0$, and $p = 1$. From Theorem 1 it follows that the eigenfunctions are orthogonal on the interval $0 \leq x \leq \pi$.

Example 3. The reader may show that the functions

$$1, \cos x, \sin x, \cos 2x, \sin 2x, \cdots$$

occurring in the Fourier series of a function of period 2π are the eigenfunctions of the Sturm-Liouville problem

$$y'' + \lambda y = 0, \qquad y(\pi) = y(-\pi), \qquad y'(\pi) = y'(-\pi).$$

Hence from Theorem 1 it follows that these functions form an orthogonal set on the interval $-\pi \leq x \leq \pi$. Note that the boundary conditions of our present problem are of the form (4).

We shall now prove a basic theorem concerning the eigenvalues of Sturm-Liouville problems.

Theorem 2. *If the Sturm-Liouville problem* (1), (2) *satisfies the condition stated in Theorem 1 and p is positive in the whole interval* $a \leq x \leq b$ *(or negative everywhere in that interval), then all the eigenvalues of the problem are real.*

Proof. Let $\lambda = \alpha + i\beta$ be an eigenvalue of the problem and let

$$y(x) = u(x) + iv(x)$$

be a corresponding eigenfunction; here, α, β, u, and v are real. Substituting this into (1) we have

$$(ru' + irv')' + (q + \alpha p + i\beta p)(u + iv) = 0.$$

This complex equation is equivalent to the following pair of equations for the real and imaginary parts:

$$(ru')' + (q + \alpha p)u - \beta pv = 0,$$
$$(rv')' + (q + \alpha p)v + \beta pu = 0.$$

Multiplying the first equation by v and the second by $-u$ and adding, we obtain

$$-\beta(u^2 + v^2)p = u(rv')' - v(ru')'$$
$$= [(rv')u - (ru')v]'.$$

Integrating over x from a to b, we find

$$-\beta \int_a^b (u^2 + v^2)p \, dx = \left[r(uv' - u'v) \right]_a^b.$$

From the boundary conditions it follows that the expression on the right is zero; this can be shown in a fashion similar to that in the proof of Theorem 1. Since y is an eigenfunction, $u^2 + v^2 \not\equiv 0$. Since y and p are continuous and $p > 0$ (or $p < 0$) for all x between a and b, the integral on the left is not zero. Hence, $\beta = 0$, which means that $\lambda = \alpha$ is real. This completes the proof.

Theorem 2 is illustrated by Exs. 2, 3, and the following example.

Example 4 (Legendre polynomials).　Legendre's equation (cf. Sec. 3.3) can be written

$$[(1 - x^2)y']' + \lambda y = 0, \qquad \lambda = n(n + 1),$$

and is, therefore, a Sturm-Liouville equation (1) with $r = 1 - x^2$, $q = 0$, and $p = 1$. Since $r = 0$ when $x = \pm 1$, no boundary conditions are needed to form a Sturm-Liouville problem on the interval $-1 \leq x \leq 1$. We know that, for $n = 0, 1, \cdots$, the Legendre polynomials $P_n(x)$ are solutions of the problem. Hence these are the eigenfunctions, and since they have continuous derivatives it follows from Theorem 1 that they are orthogonal on that interval, that is,

$$(8) \qquad \int_{-1}^1 P_m(x)P_n(x) \, dx = 0 \qquad\qquad (m \neq n).$$

The norm is (cf. Prob. 7 in Sec. 3.3)

$$(9) \qquad N(P_m) = \int_{-1}^1 P_m{}^2(x) \, dx = \frac{2}{2m + 1} \qquad m = 0, 1, \cdots.$$

If $g_0(x), g_1(x), \cdots$ are eigenfunctions which are orthogonal on the interval $a \leq x \leq b$ with respect to a weight function $p(x)$, and if a given function $f(x)$ can be represented by a generalized Fourier series

$$(10) \qquad f(x) = c_0 g_0(x) + c_1 g_1(x) + \cdots$$

involving these functions, then the Fourier constants $c_0, c_1, \cdots$ of $f(x)$ in this **eigenfunction expansion** can be determined as in Sec. 8.11; the only difference is that we have to multiply that series by pg_m instead of g_m before integrating. The remaining steps are the same as before and yield

$$(11) \qquad c_m = \frac{1}{N(g_m)} \int_a^b p(x)f(x)g_m(x) \, dx, \qquad m = 0, 1, \cdots,$$

where the norm $N(g_m)$ is now defined by (9), Sec. 8.11.

PROBLEMS

1. Carry out the details of the proof of Theorem 1 in Cases 3 and 4.

Carry out the steps of the proof of Theorem 1 for the Sturm-Liouville problem in:
2. Ex. 1   **3.** Ex. 4

Find the eigenfunctions of the following Sturm-Liouville problems.

4. $y'' + \lambda y = 0,$ $y'(0) = 0,$ $y'(l) = 0$

5. $y'' + \lambda y = 0,$ $y(0) = 0,$ $y'(l) = 0$

Find a Sturm-Liouville problem whose eigenfunctions are:

6. $1, \cos \dfrac{2n\pi}{T} x, \sin \dfrac{2n\pi}{T} x \ (n = 1, 2, \cdots).$ **7.** $1, \cos, \cos 2x, \cos 3x, \cdots$

8. Prove (11).

In each case obtain the first few terms of the representation of $f(x)$ by a generalized Fourier series involving Legendre polynomials and graph the first three partial sums.

9. $f(x) = \begin{cases} 0 \text{ if } -1 < x < 0 \\ 1 \text{ if } \ \ 0 < x < 1 \end{cases}$ **10.** $f(x) = \begin{cases} 0 \text{ if } -1 < x < 0 \\ x \text{ if } \ \ 0 < x < 1 \end{cases}$

11. $f(x) = |x|$ if $-1 < x < 1$ **12.** $f(x) = x^3$

13. If $f(x)$ is odd, show that in $f(x) = c_0 P_0 + c_1 P_1(x) + \cdots$, all c_n with even subscript are zero.

14. State the reason why in Prob. 9, $c_2 = c_4 = c_6 = \cdots = 0.$

15. Show that the functions $P_n(\cos \theta), n = 0, 1, \cdots$, form an orthogonal set on the interval $0 \leqq \theta \leqq \pi$ with respect to the weight function $p(\theta) = \sin \theta$.

16. State why it is true that $\displaystyle\int_{-1}^{1} P_n(x) \, dx = 0 \ (n = 1, 2, \cdots).$

17. The functions

$$L_0 = 1, \qquad L_n(x) = \frac{e^x}{n!} \frac{d^n(x^n e^{-x})}{dx^n}, \qquad n = 1, 2, \cdots$$

are called **Laguerre[11] polynomials.** Show that

$$L_1(x) = 1 - x, \qquad L_2(x) = 1 - 2x + \tfrac{1}{2}x^2, \qquad L_3(x) = 1 - 3x + \tfrac{3}{2}x^2 - \tfrac{1}{6}x^3.$$

18. Show that

$$L_n(x) = \sum_{m=0}^{n} \frac{(-1)^m}{m!} \binom{n}{m} x^m = 1 - nx + \frac{n(n-1)}{4} x^2 - + \cdots + \frac{(-1)^n}{n!} x^n.$$

19. $L_n(x)$ satisfies Laguerre's differential equation

$$xy'' + (1 - x)y' + ny = 0.$$

Verify this fact for $n = 0, 1, 2, 3.$

20. Verify by direct integration that $L_0, L_1(x), L_2(x)$ are orthogonal on the positive axis $0 \leqq x < \infty$ with respect to the weight function $p(x) = e^{-x}.$

[11] EDMOND LAGUERRE (1834–1886), French mathematician who did research work in geometry and the theory of infinite series.

21. Prove that all the Laguerre polynomials have the orthogonality property in Prob. 20. *Hint:* consider $\int_0^\infty e^{-x} L_m(x) L_n(x)\, dx$ for $m < n$. Since the highest power in L_m is x^m, conclude that it suffices to show that $\int_0^\infty e^{-x} x^k L_n(x)\, dx = 0$ ($k < n$). Prove this relation by repeated integration by parts.

22. The functions

$$H_0 = 1, \qquad H_n(x) = (-1)^n\, e^{x^2/2}\, \frac{d^n e^{-x^2/2}}{dx^n}, \qquad n = 1, 2, \cdots$$

are called **Hermite polynomials.** Show that

$$H_1(x) = x, \qquad H_2(x) = x^2 - 1, \qquad H_3(x) = x^3 - 3x, \qquad H_4(x) = x^4 - 6x^2 + 3.$$

(As is true for many special functions, the literature contains more than one notation, and one often defines as Hermite polynomials the expressions

$$H_0^* = 1, \qquad H_n^*(x) = (-1)^n\, e^{x^2}\, \frac{d^n e^{-x^2}}{dx^n}.$$

This differs from our definition which is preferably used in applications.)

23. $H_n(x)$ satisfies $y'' - xy' + ny = 0$. Verify this for $n = 0, 1, \cdots, 4$.

24. Using the equation in Prob. 23, show that $w = e^{-x^2/4}\, H_n(x)$ is a solution of Weber's equation

$$w'' + \left(n + \frac{1}{2} - \frac{x^2}{4}\right) w = 0 \qquad\qquad (n = 0, 1, \cdots).$$

25. Show that the Hermite polynomials satisfy the relation

$$H_{n+1}(x) = x H_n(x) - H_n'(x).$$

26. Show that the Hermite polynomials are related to the coefficients of the Maclaurin series

$$e^{tx - \frac{1}{2}t^2} = \sum_{n=0}^\infty a_n(x) t^n$$

by the formula $H_n(x) = n!\, a_n(x)$. *Hint:* note that $tx - \frac{1}{2}t^2 = \frac{1}{2}x^2 - \frac{1}{2}(x - t)^2$. (The exponential function on the left is called the *generating function* of the H_n).

27. Differentiating the generating function in Prob. 26 with respect to x, show that

$$H_n'(x) = n H_{n-1}(x).$$

28. Using the formula in Prob. 25 (with n replaced by $n - 1$) and the relation in Prob. 27 (and its derivative), prove that $H_n(x)$ satisfies the differential equation in Prob. 23.

29. Show that the Hermite polynomials are orthogonal on the x-axis $-\infty < x < \infty$ with respect to the weight function $p(x) = e^{-x^2/2}$. *Hint:* use the formulas in Probs. 22 and 27 and integrate by parts.

30. The functions

$$T_n(x) = \cos\,(n\, \text{arc cos}\, x), \qquad U_n(x) = \sin\,(n\, \text{arc cos}\, x), \qquad n = 0, 1, \cdots$$

are called **Tchebichef**[12] **polynomials** *of the first and second kind*, respectively. Show that

$$T_0 = 1, \qquad T_1(x) = x, \qquad\qquad T_2(x) = 2x^2 - 1,$$
$$U_0 = 0, \qquad U_1(x) = \sqrt{1 - x^2}, \qquad U_2(x) = 2x\sqrt{1 - x^2}.$$

31. Show that the Tchebichef polynomials $T_n(x)$ are orthogonal on the interval $-1 \leq x \leq 1$ with respect to the weight function $p(x) = 1/\sqrt{1 - x^2}$. *Hint:* to evaluate the integral set arc cos $x = \theta$.

32. Find $T_3(x)$ and $U_3(x)$. Show that $T_n(1) = 1$ and $U_n(1) = 0$.

8.13 ORTHOGONALITY OF BESSEL FUNCTIONS

We shall now consider the orthogonality of the Bessel functions J_n, which is quite important in applications, for example, in connection with vibrations of a circular membrane. We know that the functions $J_n(s)$ satisfy the Bessel equation (Sec. 3.5), that is,

$$s^2 \frac{d^2 J_n}{ds^2} + s \frac{dJ_n}{ds} + (s^2 - n^2)J_n = 0.$$

We assume that n is a nonnegative integer. Setting $s = \lambda x$ where λ is a constant, we have $dx/ds = 1/\lambda$, and

$$\frac{dJ_n}{ds} = \frac{dJ_n}{dx}\frac{dx}{ds} = \frac{J_n{}'}{\lambda}, \qquad \frac{d^2 J_n}{ds^2} = \frac{J_n{}''}{\lambda^2},$$

where primes denote derivatives with respect to x. By substitution,

$$x^2 J_n{}''(\lambda x) + x J_n{}'(\lambda x) + (\lambda^2 x^2 - n^2)J_n(\lambda x) = 0.$$

Dividing by x, this equation may be written

(1) $$[x J_n{}'(\lambda x)]' + \left(-\frac{n^2}{x} + \lambda^2 x\right) J_n(\lambda x) = 0.$$

We see that for each fixed n this is a Sturm-Liouville equation (1), Sec. 8.12, with the parameter written as λ^2 instead of λ, and

$$p(x) = x, \qquad q(x) = -n^2/x, \qquad r(x) = x.$$

Since $r(x) = 0$ at $x = 0$ it follows from Theorem 1 in the last section that those solutions of (1) on a given interval $0 \leq x \leq R$ which satisfy the boundary condition

(2) $$J_n(\lambda R) = 0$$

[12] PAFNUTI TCHEBICHEF (1821–1894), Russian mathematician, particularly known by his important contributions to the theory of numbers.

form an orthogonal set on that interval with respect to the weight function $p(x) = x$. (Note that for $n \neq 0$ the function q is discontinuous at $x = 0$, but this does not affect the proof of that theorem.) It can be shown (Ref. [B9]) that $J_n(s)$ has infinitely many real zeros; let $\alpha_{1n} < \alpha_{2n} < \alpha_{3n} \cdots$ denote the positive zeros of $J_n(s)$. Then (2) holds for

$$(3) \qquad \lambda R = \alpha_{mn} \quad \text{or} \quad \lambda = \lambda_{mn} = \frac{\alpha_{mn}}{R} \qquad (m = 1, 2, \cdots),$$

and since the derivative J_n' is continuous, also at $x = 0$, we obtain the following result.

Theorem 1.   *For each fixed $n = 0, 1, \cdots$ the Bessel functions $J_n(\lambda_{1n}x)$, $J_n(\lambda_{2n}x)$, $J_n(\lambda_{3n}x)$, $\cdots$, with λ_{mn} according to (3), form an orthogonal set on the interval $0 \leq x \leq R$ with respect to the weight function $p(x) = x$, that is,*

$$(4) \qquad \int_0^R x J_n(\lambda_{mn}x) J_n(\lambda_{kn}x)\, dx = 0 \qquad (k \neq m).$$

Hence we have obtained infinitely many orthogonal sets, each corresponding to one of the fixed values of n.

For determining the Fourier constants of a given function with respect to such a set $J_n(\lambda_{mn}x)$ (n fixed, $m = 1, 2, \cdots$), we must know the norms of these functions. The norms can be found as follows.

Multiplying (1) by $2xJ_n'(\lambda x)$, we may write the resulting equation in the form

$$\{[xJ_n'(\lambda x)]^2\}' + (\lambda^2 x^2 - n^2)\{J_n^2(\lambda x)\}' = 0.$$

Integrating over x from 0 to R we find

$$(5) \qquad [xJ_n'(\lambda x)]^2 \Big|_0^R = -\int_0^R (\lambda^2 x^2 - n^2)\{J_n^2(\lambda x)\}'\, dx.$$

From (2') in Sec. 3.6, writing s and n instead of x and ν, we have

$$s^{-n}\frac{dJ_n}{ds} = ns^{-n-1}J_n(s) - s^{-n}J_{n+1}(s).$$

Multiplying by s^{n+1} and setting $s = \lambda x$ we obtain

$$\lambda x \frac{dJ_n(\lambda x)}{d(\lambda x)} = x \frac{dJ_n(\lambda x)}{dx} = nJ_n(\lambda x) - \lambda x J_{n+1}(\lambda x).$$

Hence the left-hand side of (5) equals

$$\left[[nJ_n(\lambda x) - \lambda x J_{n+1}(\lambda x)]^2\right]_{x=0}^R$$

If $\lambda = \lambda_{mn}$ then $J_n(\lambda R) = 0$, and since $J_n(0) = 0$ $(n = 1, 2, \cdots)$, that left-hand side becomes

$$(6) \qquad \lambda_{mn}^2 R^2 J_{n+1}^2(\lambda_{mn}R).$$

Integrating by parts, the right-hand side of (5) becomes

$$-\left[(\lambda^2 x^2 + n^2)J_n^2(\lambda x)\right]_0^R + 2\lambda^2 \int_0^R x J_n^2(\lambda x)\,dx.$$

When $\lambda = \lambda_{mn}$, the first expression is zero, and from this and (6), dividing by λ_{mn}^2, it follows that

$$(7) \qquad N[J_n(\lambda_{mn}x)] = \int_0^R x J_n^2(\lambda_{mn}x)\,dx = \frac{R^2}{2} J_{n+1}^2(\lambda_{mn}R).$$

This is the norm of the functions under consideration; here λ_{mn} is given by (3), and $\lambda_{mn}R = \alpha_{mn}$.

Consequently, if a function $f(x)$ can be represented by a generalized Fourier series of the form

$$(8) \qquad f(x) = c_1 J_n(\lambda_{1n}x) + c_2 J_n(\lambda_{2n}x) + \cdots \qquad (n \text{ fixed})$$

it follows from (11) in Sec. 8.12 that the Fourier constants in this so-called **Fourier-Bessel series** are

$$(9) \qquad c_m = \frac{2}{R^2 J_{n+1}^2(\alpha_{mn})} \int_0^R x f(x) J_n(\lambda_{mn}x)\,dx, \quad m = 1, 2, \cdots.$$

Here $\lambda_{mn} = \alpha_{mn}/R$.

PROBLEMS

1. Graph $J_0(\lambda_{10}x)$, $J_0(\lambda_{20}x)$, $J_0(\lambda_{30}x)$, and $J_0(\lambda_{40}x)$ for $R = 1$ in the interval $0 \leq x \leq 1$. (Use the tables of J_0 and the zeros of J_0 in Secs. 3.5 and 9.10.)

2. Graph $J_1(\alpha_{11}x)$, $J_1(\alpha_{21}x)$, $J_1(\alpha_{31}x)$, and $J_1(\alpha_{41}x)$ in the interval $0 \leq x \leq 1$. Use Table 14 in Sec. 3.5.

Develop the following functions $f(x)$ $(0 < x < R)$ in a Fourier-Bessel series of the form

$$f(x) = c_1 J_0(\lambda_{10}x) + c_2 J_0(\lambda_{20}x) + c_3 J_0(\lambda_{30}x) + \cdots$$

and graph the first few partial sums.

3. $f(x) = 1$. *Hint:* use (1), Sec. 3.6.   **4.** $f(x) = \begin{cases} 1 \text{ if } & 0 < x < R/2 \\ 0 \text{ if } R/2 < x < R \end{cases}$

5. $f(x) = \begin{cases} k \text{ if } 0 < x < a \\ 0 \text{ if } a < x < R \end{cases}$ **6.** $f(x) = \begin{cases} 0 \text{ if } & 0 < x < R/2 \\ k \text{ if } R/2 < x < R \end{cases}$

7. $f(x) = 1 - x^2$ $(R = 1)$. *Hint:* use (1), Sec. 3.6, and integration by parts.

8. $f(x) = R^2 - x^2$ **9.** $f(x) = x^2$ **10.** $f(x) = x^4$

11. Show that $f(x) = x^n$ $(0 < x < 1, n = 0, 1, \cdots)$ can be represented by the Fourier-Bessel series

$$x^n = \frac{2J_n(\alpha_{1n}x)}{\alpha_{1n}J_{n+1}(\alpha_{1n})} + \frac{2J_n(\alpha_{2n}x)}{\alpha_{2n}J_{n+1}(\alpha_{2n})} + \cdots.$$

12. Find a representation of $f(x) = x^n$ $(0 < x < R, n = 0, 1, \cdots)$ similar to that in Prob. 11.

13. It can be shown that the representation in Prob. 11 holds not only for integral $n = 0, 1, \cdots$, but for any $n \geq -1/2$. Using (5) and (6), Sec. 3.6, show that for $n = -1/2$, after multiplying by $\sqrt{x}$, the representation becomes the Fourier series

$$\frac{4}{\pi}\left(\cos\frac{\pi}{2}x - \frac{1}{3}\cos\frac{3\pi}{2}x + \frac{1}{5}\cos\frac{5\pi}{2}x - + \cdots \right)$$

which represents

$$f(x) = \begin{cases} 1 & \text{if } -1 < x < 1 \\ -1 & \text{if } 1 < x < 3 \end{cases} \qquad [f(x + 4) = f(x)].$$

14. Represent $f(x) = x^3$ $(0 < x < 2)$ by a Fourier-Bessel series involving J_3.

chapter 9

PARTIAL DIFFERENTIAL EQUATIONS

Partial differential equations arise in connection with various physical and geometrical problems when the functions involved depend on two or more independent variables. These variables may be the time and one or several coordinates in space. The present chapter will be devoted to some of the most important partial differential equations occurring in engineering applications. We shall derive these equations from physical principles and consider methods for solving initial and boundary value problems, that is, methods for obtaining solutions of those equations corresponding to the given physical situations.

Prerequisites for this chapter: ordinary linear differential equations (Chap. 2) and Fourier series (Chap. 8).

Sections which may be omitted in a shorter course: 9.6, 9.9, 9.10.

References: Appendix 1, Part F.

Answers to problems: Appendix 2.

9.1 BASIC CONCEPTS

An equation involving one or more partial derivatives of an (unknown) function of two or more independent variables is called a **partial differential**

equation. The order of the highest derivative is called the **order** of the equation.

Just as in the case of an ordinary differential equation, we say that a partial differential equation is **linear** if it is of the first degree in the dependent variable and its partial derivatives. If each term of such an equation contains either the dependent variable or one of its derivatives, the equation is said to be **homogeneous**; otherwise it is said to be **nonhomogeneous**.

Example 1. Some important linear partial differential equations of the second order are:

(1)
$$\frac{\partial^2 u}{\partial t^2} = c^2 \frac{\partial^2 u}{\partial x^2} \qquad \text{(one-dimensional wave equation)}$$

(2)
$$\frac{\partial u}{\partial t} = c^2 \frac{\partial^2 u}{\partial x^2} \qquad \text{(one-dimensional heat equation)}$$

(3)
$$\frac{\partial^2 u}{\partial x^2} + \frac{\partial^2 u}{\partial y^2} = 0 \qquad \text{(two-dimensional Laplace equation)}$$

(4)
$$\frac{\partial^2 u}{\partial x^2} + \frac{\partial^2 u}{\partial y^2} = f(x, y) \qquad \text{(two-dimensional Poisson equation)}$$

(5)
$$\frac{\partial^2 u}{\partial x^2} + \frac{\partial^2 u}{\partial y^2} + \frac{\partial^2 u}{\partial z^2} = 0 \qquad \text{(three-dimensional Laplace equation)};$$

here c is a constant, t is the time, and x, y, z are Cartesian coordinates. Equation (4) (with $f \not\equiv 0$) is nonhomogeneous, while the other equations are homogeneous.

A **solution** *of a partial differential equation in some region R of the space of the independent variables* is a function which has all the partial derivatives appearing in the equation and satisfies the equation everywhere in R.

In general, the totality of solutions of a partial differential equation is very large. For example, the functions

(6)
$$u = x^2 - y^2, \qquad u = e^x \cos y, \qquad u = \ln(x^2 + y^2),$$

which are entirely different from each other, are solutions of (3), as the student may verify. We shall see later that the unique solution of a partial differential equation corresponding to a given physical problem will be obtained by the use of additional information arising from the physical situation. For example, in some cases the values of the required solution of the problem on the boundary of some domain will be given ("**boundary conditions**"); in other cases when the time t is one of the variables, the values of the solution at $t = 0$ will be prescribed ("**initial conditions**").

We know that if an *ordinary* differential equation is linear and homogeneous, then from known solutions further solutions can be obtained by superposition. For a homogeneous linear *partial* differential equation the situation is quite similar. In fact, the following theorem holds.

Fundamental Theorem 1.   *If u_1 and u_2 are any solutions of a linear homogeneous partial differential equation in some region, then*

$$u = c_1 u_1 + c_2 u_2,$$

where c_1 and c_2 are any constants, is also a solution of that equation in that region.

The proof of this important theorem is quite similar to that of Theorem 1 in Sec. 2.1 and is left to the student.

PROBLEMS

1. Prove Fundamental Theorem 1 for second-order equations in two and three independent variables.

2. Verify that the functions (6) are solutions of (3).

In each case, verify that the given function is a solution of the given equation and sketch a figure of the solution as a surface in space.

3. $u = x^2 + t^2$, Eq. (1), $c = 1$ **4.** $u = x^2 + 4t^2$, Eq. (1), $c = 2$

5. $u = x^3 + 12xt^2$, Eq. (1), $c = 2$ **6.** $u = x^3 + 3xt^2$, Eq. (1), $c = 1$

7. $u = e^{-t} \sin x$, Eq. (2), $c = 1$ **8.** $u = e^{-2t} \cos 3x$, Eq. (2), $c^2 = 2/9$

9. $u = e^x \sin y$, Eq. (3)   **10.** $u = x^3 - 3xy^2$, Eq. (3)

11. $u = \cos x \cosh y$, Eq. (3)   **12.** $u = \sin x \sinh y$, Eq. (3)

13. $u = \sin x \cosh y$, Eq. (3)   **14.** $u = \arctan (y/x)$, Eq. (3)

15. $u = x^2 + y^2$, Eq. (4), $f = 4$

16. $u = \cos (xy)$, Eq. (4), $f = -(x^2 + y^2) \cos (xy)$

17. $u = y/x$, Eq. (4), $f = 2y/x^3$ **18.** $u = 1/\sqrt{x^2 + y^2 + z^2}$, Eq. (5)

In each case, verify that the given function satisfies the given equation. (Subscripts denote partial derivatives.)

19. $u(x, y) = v(x) + w(y)$, $u_{xy} = 0$

20. $u(x, y) = v(x)w(y)$, $uu_{xy} = u_x u_y$

21. $u(x, t) = v(x + t) + w(x - t)$, $u_{tt} = u_{xx}$

22. $u(x, t) = v(x + 2t) + w(x - 2t)$, $u_{tt} = 4u_{xx}$

23. Show that if the level curves $z = const$ of a surface $z = z(x, y)$ are straight lines parallel to the x-axis, then z is a solution of the differential equation $z_x = 0$. Give examples.

24. Show that the solutions $z = z(x, y)$ of $yz_x - xz_y = 0$ represent surfaces of revolution. Give examples. *Hint:* set $x = r \cos \theta$, $y = r \sin \theta$ and show that the equation becomes $z_\theta = 0$.

A partial differential equation involving derivatives with respect to one variable only may be solved like an ordinary differential equation, treating the other independent variables as parameters. Solve the following equations where $u = u(x, y)$.

25. $u_x = 0$ **26.** $u_y = 0$ **27.** $u_{xx} = 0$

28. $u_{yy} = 0$ **29.** $u_{xx} + u = 0$ **30.** $u_{yy} - u = 0$

Solve the following systems of partial differential equations.

31. (a) $u_{xx} = 0$ (b) $u_{yy} = 0$ **32.** $u_{xx} = 0$, $u_{xy} = 0$

33. $u_{xx} = 0$, $u_{xy} = 0$, $u_{yy} = 0$ **34.** $u_x = 0$, $u_y = 0$

Setting $u_x = p$, solve:

35. $u_{xy} - u_x = 0$ **36.** $u_{xy} + u_x + x + y + 1 = 0$

37. Verify that $u(x, y) = a \ln (x^2 + y^2) + b$ satisfies Laplace's equation (3) and determine a and b so that u satisfies the boundary conditions $u = 0$ on the circle $x^2 + y^2 = 1$ and $u = 3$ on the circle $x^2 + y^2 = 4$. Sketch a figure of the surface represented by this function.

9.2 VIBRATING STRING. ONE-DIMENSIONAL WAVE EQUATION

As a first important partial differential equation, let us derive the equation governing small transverse vibrations of an elastic string, which is stretched to length l and then fixed at the end points. Suppose that the string is distorted and then at a certain instant, say, $t = 0$, it is released and allowed to vibrate. The problem is to determine the vibrations of the string, that is, to find its deflection $u(x, t)$ at any point x and at any time $t > 0$; cf. Fig. 251.

When deriving a differential equation corresponding to a given physical problem, we usually have to make simplifying assumptions in order that the resulting equation does not become too complicated. We know this important fact from our considerations of ordinary differential equations, and for partial differential equations the situation is similar.

In our present case we make the following assumptions.

1. *The mass of the string per unit length is constant ("homogeneous string"). The string is perfectly elastic and does not offer any resistance to bending.*

2. *The tension caused by stretching the string before fixing it at the end points is so large that the action of the gravitational force on the string can be neglected.*

3. *The motion of the string is a small transverse vibration in a vertical plane, that is, each particle of the string moves strictly vertically, and the deflection and the slope at any point of the string are small in absolute value.*

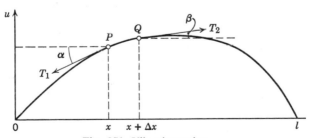

Fig. 251. Vibrating string.

These assumptions are such that we may expect that the solution $u(x, t)$ of the differential equation to be obtained will reasonably well describe small vibrations of the physical "nonidealized" string of small homogeneous mass under large tension.

To obtain the differential equation we consider the forces acting on a small portion of the string (Fig. 251). Since the string does not offer resistance to bending, the tension is tangential to the curve of the string at each point. Let T_1 and T_2 be the tensions at the end points P and Q of that portion. Since there is no motion in horizontal direction the horizontal components of the tension must be constant. Using the notation shown in Fig. 251 we thus obtain

(1) $$T_1 \cos \alpha = T_2 \cos \beta = T = const.$$

In vertical direction we have two forces, namely the vertical components $-T_1 \sin \alpha$ and $T_2 \sin \beta$ of T_1 and T_2; here the minus sign appears because that component at P is directed downward. By Newton's second law the resultant of those two forces is equal to the mass $\rho \Delta s$ of the portion times the acceleration $\partial^2 u / \partial t^2$, evaluated at some point between x and $x + \Delta x$; here ρ is the mass of the string per unit length, and Δs is the length of the portion. Hence

$$T_2 \sin \beta - T_1 \sin \alpha = \rho \Delta s \frac{\partial^2 u}{\partial t^2}.$$

By using (1) we obtain

$$\frac{T_2 \sin \beta}{T_2 \cos \beta} - \frac{T_1 \sin \alpha}{T_1 \cos \alpha} = \frac{\rho \Delta s}{T} \frac{\partial^2 u}{\partial t^2}.$$

Since the slope of the curve of the string is small, we may replace Δs by Δx; then our equation becomes

(2) $$\tan \beta - \tan \alpha = \frac{\rho \Delta x}{T} \frac{\partial^2 u}{\partial t^2}.$$

Now $\tan \alpha$ and $\tan \beta$ are the slopes of the curve of the string at x and $x + \Delta x$, that is,

$$\tan \alpha = \left(\frac{\partial u}{\partial x} \right)_x, \qquad \tan \beta = \left(\frac{\partial u}{\partial x} \right)_{x + \Delta x}.$$

Here we have to write *partial* derivatives because u depends also on t. Dividing (2) by Δx, we thus obtain

$$\frac{1}{\Delta x} \left[\left(\frac{\partial u}{\partial x} \right)_{x + \Delta x} - \left(\frac{\partial u}{\partial x} \right)_x \right] = \frac{\rho}{T} \frac{\partial^2 u}{\partial t^2}.$$

If we let Δx approach zero, we find

$$\frac{\partial^2 u}{\partial x^2} = \frac{\rho}{T}\frac{\partial^2 u}{\partial t^2},$$

both derivatives being evaluated at x. This linear partial differential equation may be written

(3) $$\frac{\partial^2 u}{\partial t^2} = c^2 \frac{\partial^2 u}{\partial x^2} \qquad c^2 = \frac{T}{\rho}.$$

This is the so-called **one-dimensional wave equation**, which governs our problem. The notation c^2 (instead of c) for the physical constant T/ρ has been chosen to indicate that this constant is positive.

Solutions of the equation will be obtained in the following section.

9.3 SEPARATION OF VARIABLES (PRODUCT METHOD)

We have seen that the vibrations of an elastic string are governed by the one-dimensional wave equation

(1) $$\frac{\partial^2 u}{\partial t^2} = c^2 \frac{\partial^2 u}{\partial x^2},$$

where $u(x, t)$ is the deflection of the string. Since the string is fixed at the ends $x = 0$ and $x = l$, we have the two **boundary conditions**

(2) $$u(0, t) = 0, \qquad u(l, t) = 0 \qquad \text{for all } t.$$

Of course the form of the motion of the string will depend on the initial deflection (deflection at $t = 0$) and on the initial velocity (velocity at $t = 0$). Denoting the initial deflection by $f(x)$ and the initial velocity by $g(x)$, we thus obtain the two **initial conditions**

(3) $$u(x, 0) = f(x)$$

and

(4) $$\left.\frac{\partial u}{\partial t}\right|_{t=0} = g(x).$$

Our problem is now to find a solution of (1) satisfying the conditions (2)–(4). We shall proceed step by step, as follows.

First step. By applying the so-called *product method*, or *method of separating variables*, we shall obtain two ordinary differential equations.

Second step. We shall determine solutions of those equations that satisfy the boundary conditions.

Third step. Those solutions will be composed so that the result will be a solution of the wave equation (1), satisfying also the given initial conditions. Let us start in detail with the first step.

First step. The product method yields solutions of (1) of the form

$$(5) \qquad\qquad u(x, t) = F(x)G(t)$$

which are a product of two functions, each depending only on one of the variables x and t. We shall see later that this method has various applications in engineering mathematics.

By differentiating (5), we obtain

$$\frac{\partial^2 u}{\partial t^2} = F\ddot{G} \qquad \text{and} \qquad \frac{\partial^2 u}{\partial x^2} = F''G,$$

where dots denote derivatives with respect to t and primes derivatives with respect to x. By inserting this into (1) we have

$$F\ddot{G} = c^2 F''G.$$

Dividing by $c^2 FG$, we obtain

$$\frac{\ddot{G}}{c^2 G} = \frac{F''}{F}.$$

The expression on the left involves functions depending only on t while the expression on the right involves functions depending only on x. Hence both expressions must be equal to a constant, say, k, because if the expression on the left is not constant, then changing t will presumably change the value of this expression but certainly not that on the right, since the latter does not depend on t. Similarly, if the expression on the right is not constant, changing x will presumably change the value of this expression but certainly not that on the left. Thus

$$\frac{\ddot{G}}{c^2 G} = \frac{F''}{F} = k.$$

This yields immediately the two ordinary linear differential equations

$$(6) \qquad\qquad F'' - kF = 0$$

and

$$(7) \qquad\qquad \ddot{G} - c^2 kG = 0.$$

In these equations, k is still arbitrary.

Second step. We shall now determine solutions F and G of (6) and (7) so that $u = FG$ satisfies (2), that is,

$$u(0, t) = F(0)G(t) = 0, \qquad u(l, t) = F(l)G(t) = 0 \qquad \text{for all } t.$$

Clearly, if $G \equiv 0$, then $u \equiv 0$, which is of no interest. Thus $G \not\equiv 0$ and then

$$(8) \qquad\qquad (a)\ F(0) = 0 \qquad (b)\ F(l) = 0.$$

For $k = 0$ the general solution of (6) is $F = ax + b$, and from (8) we obtain $a = b = 0$. Hence $F \equiv 0$, which is of no interest because then $u \equiv 0$. For positive $k = \mu^2$ the general solution of (6) is

$$F = Ae^{\mu x} + Be^{-\mu x},$$

and from (8) we obtain $F \equiv 0$, as before. Hence we are left with the possibility of choosing k negative, say, $k = -p^2$. Then (6) takes the form

$$F'' + p^2 F = 0,$$

and the general solution is

$$F(x) = A \cos px + B \sin px.$$

From this and (8) we have

$$F(0) = A = 0 \qquad \text{and then} \qquad F(l) = B \sin pl = 0.$$

We must take $B \neq 0$ since otherwise $F \equiv 0$. Hence $\sin pl = 0$, that is,

$$(9) \qquad\qquad pl = n\pi \qquad \text{or} \qquad p = \frac{n\pi}{l} \qquad (n \text{ integral}).$$

Setting $B = 1$, we thus obtain infinitely many solutions $F(x) = F_n(x)$,

$$(10) \qquad\qquad F_n(x) = \sin \frac{n\pi}{l} x \qquad\qquad n = 1, 2, \cdots,$$

which satisfy (8). (For negative integral n, we obtain essentially the same solutions, except for a minus sign, because $\sin(-\alpha) = -\sin \alpha$.)

k is now restricted to the values $k = -p^2 = -(n\pi/l)^2$, resulting from (9). For these k the equation (7) takes the form

$$\ddot{G} = \lambda_n{}^2 G = 0 \qquad \text{where} \qquad \lambda_n = \frac{cn\pi}{l}.$$

The general solution is

$$G_n(t) = B_n \cos \lambda_n t + B_n{}^* \sin \lambda_n t.$$

Hence the functions

$$(11) \quad u_n(x, t) = F_n(x)G_n(t)$$

$$= (B_n \cos \lambda_n t + B_n{}^* \sin \lambda_n t) \sin \frac{n\pi}{l} x \qquad (n = 1, 2, \cdots)$$

are solutions of (1), satisfying the boundary conditions (2). These functions are called the **eigenfunctions**, or *characteristic functions*, and the

Fig. 252. Normal modes of the vibrating string.

values $\lambda_n = cn\pi/l$ are called the **eigenvalues**, or *characteristic values*, of the vibrating string. The set $\lambda_1, \lambda_2, \cdots$ is called the *spectrum*.

We see that each u_n represents a harmonic motion having the frequency $\lambda_n/2\pi = cn/2l$ cycles per unit time. This motion is called the nth **normal mode** of the string. The first normal mode is known as the *fundamental mode* ($n = 1$), and the others as *overtones*; musically they give the octave, octave plus fifth, etc.

Since in (11)

$$\sin \frac{n\pi x}{l} = 0 \quad \text{at} \quad x = \frac{l}{n}, \frac{2l}{n}, \cdots, \frac{n-1}{n} l,$$

the nth normal mode has $n - 1$ so-called **nodes**, that is, points of the string which do not move (Fig. 252).

Figure 253 shows the second normal mode for various values of t. At any instant the string has the form of a sine wave. When the left part of the string is moving downward the other half is moving upward, and conversely. For the other modes the situation is similar.

Third step. Clearly, a single solution $u_n(x, t)$ will, in general, not satisfy the initial conditions (3) and (4). Now, since the equation (1) is linear and homogeneous, it follows from Fundamental Theorem 1 in Sec. 9.1 that the sum of finitely many solutions u_n is a solution of (1). To obtain a solution that satisfies (3) and (4), we consider the infinite series

(12) $\quad u(x, t) = \sum_{n=1}^{\infty} u_n(x, t) = \sum_{n=1}^{\infty} (B_n \cos \lambda_n t + B_n{}^* \sin \lambda_n t) \sin \frac{n\pi}{l} x.$

From this and (3) it follows that

(13) $\quad\quad\quad u(x, 0) = \sum_{n=1}^{\infty} B_n \sin \frac{n\pi}{l} x = f(x).$

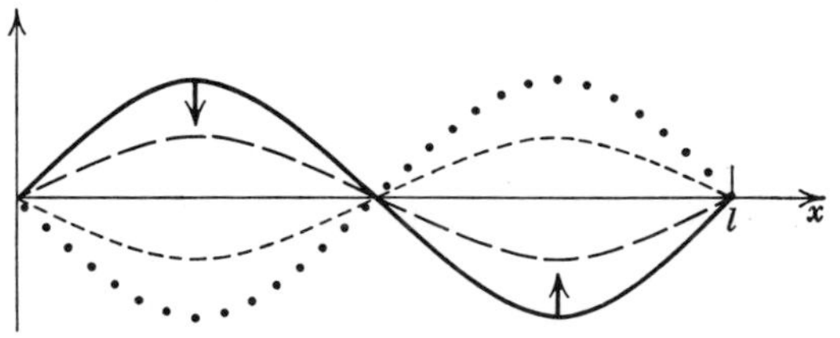

Fig. 253. Second normal mode for various values of t.

Hence, in order that (12) satisfy (3), the coefficients B_n must be chosen so that $u(x, 0)$ becomes a half-range expansion of $f(x)$, namely, the Fourier sine series of $f(x)$; that is [cf. (4) in Sec. 8.5]

$$(14) \qquad B_n = \frac{2}{l} \int_0^l f(x) \sin \frac{n\pi x}{l} \, dx, \qquad n = 1, 2, \cdots.$$

Similarly, by differentiating (12) with respect to t and using (4), we find

$$\frac{\partial u}{\partial t}\Bigg|_{t=0} = \left[\sum_{n=1}^{\infty} (-B_n \lambda_n \sin \lambda_n t + B_n{}^* \lambda_n \cos \lambda_n t) \sin \frac{n\pi x}{l} \right]_{t=0}$$

$$= \sum_{n=1}^{\infty} B_n{}^* \lambda_n \sin \frac{n\pi x}{l} = g(x).$$

Hence, in order that (12) satisfy (4), the coefficients $B_n{}^*$ must be chosen so that, for $t = 0$, $\partial u/\partial t$ becomes the Fourier sine series of $g(x)$; thus, by (4) in Sec. 8.5,

$$B_n{}^* \lambda_n = \frac{2}{l} \int_0^l g(x) \sin \frac{n\pi x}{l} \, dx$$

or, since $\lambda_n = cn\pi/l$,

$$(15) \qquad B_n{}^* = \frac{2}{cn\pi} \int_0^l g(x) \sin \frac{n\pi x}{l} \, dx, \qquad n = 1, 2, \cdots.$$

It follows that $u(x, t)$, given by (12), with coefficients (14) and (15) is a solution of (1) that satisfies the conditions (2)–(4), provided that the series (12) converges and also that the series obtained by differentiating (12) twice (termwise) with respect to x and t, converge and have the sums $\partial^2 u/\partial x^2$ and $\partial^2 u/\partial t^2$, respectively, which are continuous.

Hence the solution (12) is at first a purely formal expression, and we shall now establish it. For the sake of simplicity, we consider only the case when the initial velocity $g(x)$ is identically zero. Then the $B_n{}^*$ are zero, and (12) reduces to the form

$$(16) \qquad u(x, t) = \sum_{n=1}^{\infty} B_n \cos \lambda_n t \sin \frac{n\pi x}{l}, \qquad \lambda_n = \frac{cn\pi}{l}.$$

It is possible to *sum* this series, that is, to write the result in a closed or finite form. From (11*b*) in Sec. 0.1 it follows that

$$\cos \frac{cn\pi}{l} t \sin \frac{n\pi}{l} x = \frac{1}{2} \left[\sin \left\{ \frac{n\pi}{l} (x - ct) \right\} + \sin \left\{ \frac{n\pi}{l} (x + ct) \right\} \right].$$

Fig. 254. Odd periodic extension of $f(x)$.

Hence we may write (16) in the form

$$u(x, t) = \frac{1}{2} \sum_{n=1}^{\infty} B_n \sin \left\{ \frac{n\pi}{l} (x - ct) \right\} + \frac{1}{2} \sum_{n=1}^{\infty} B_n \sin \left\{ \frac{n\pi}{l} (x + ct) \right\}.$$

These two series are those obtained by substituting $x - ct$ and $x + ct$, respectively, for the variable x in the Fourier sine series (13) for $f(x)$. Therefore,

(17) $$u(x, t) = \tfrac{1}{2}[f^*(x - ct) + f^*(x + ct)],$$

where f^* is the odd periodic extension of f with the period $2l$ (Fig. 254). Since the initial deflection $f(x)$ is continuous on the interval $0 \leq x \leq l$ and zero at the end points, it follows from (17) that $u(x, t)$ is a continuous function of both variables x and t for all values of the variables. By differentiating (17) we see that $u(x, t)$ is a solution of (1), provided $f(x)$ is twice differentiable on the interval $0 < x < l$, and has one-sided second derivatives at $x = 0$ and $x = l$, which are zero. Under these conditions $u(x, t)$ is established as a solution of (1), satisfying (2)–(4).

If $f'(x)$ and $f''(x)$ are merely piecewise continuous (cf. p. 209), or if those one-sided derivatives are not zero, then for each t there will be finitely many values of x at which the second derivatives of u appearing in (1) do not exist. Except at these points the wave equation will still be satisfied, and we may then regard $u(x, t)$ as a solution of our problem in a broader sense. For example, the case of a triangular initial deflection (Ex. 1, below) leads to a solution of this type.

Let us mention a very interesting physical interpretation of (17). The graph of $f^*(x - ct)$ is obtained from the graph of $f^*(x)$ by shifting the latter ct units to the right (Fig. 255). This means that $f^*(x - ct)$ $(c > 0)$ represents a wave which is traveling to the right as t increases. Similarly, $f^*(x + ct)$ represents a wave which is traveling to the left, and $u(x, t)$ is the superposition of these two waves.

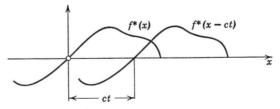

Fig. 255. Interpretation of (17).

Example 1. Find the solution of the wave equation (1) corresponding to the triangular initial deflection

$$f(x) = \begin{cases} \dfrac{2k}{l} x & \text{when} \quad 0 < x < \dfrac{l}{2} \\[2mm] \dfrac{2k}{l} (l - x) & \text{when} \quad \dfrac{l}{2} < x < l \end{cases}$$

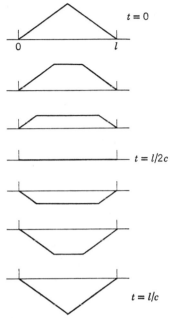

and initial velocity zero. Since $g(x) \equiv 0$ we have $B_n{}^* = 0$ in (12), and from Ex. 1 in Sec. 8.5 we see that the B_n are given by (5), Sec. 8.5. Thus (12) takes the form

$$u(x, t) = \frac{8k}{\pi^2} \left[\frac{1}{1^2} \sin \frac{\pi}{l} x \cos \frac{\pi c}{l} t \right.$$

$$\left. - \frac{1}{3^2} \sin \frac{3\pi}{l} x \cos \frac{3\pi c}{l} t + - \cdots \right].$$

For plotting the graph of the solution we may use $u(x, 0) = f(x)$ and the above interpretation of the two functions in the representation (17). This leads to the graph shown in Fig. 256.

Fig. 256. Solution in Example 1 for various values of t.

PROBLEMS

Find the deflection $u(x, t)$ of the vibrating string (length $l = \pi$, ends fixed, and $c^2 = T/\rho = 1$) corresponding to zero initial velocity and initial deflection:

1. $0.02 \sin x$ **2.** $k \sin 3x$ **3.** $k(\sin x - \sin 2x)$

4.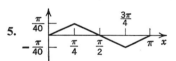

5.

6.

7. $0.01x(\pi - x)$

8. $k\left[\left(\dfrac{\pi}{2}\right)^4 - \left(x - \dfrac{\pi}{2}\right)^4 \right]$

9. $0.01x(\pi^2 - x^2)$

10. In what manner does the frequency of the fundamental mode of the vibrating string depend on the length of the string, the tension, and the mass of the string per unit length?

11. What is the ratio of the amplitudes of the fundamental mode and the second overtone in Prob. 7? The ratio $a_1{}^2/(a_1{}^2 + a_2{}^2 + \cdots)$? *Hint:* use (8) in Sec. 8.8, with the equality sign.

Find solutions $u(x, y)$ of the following equations by separating variables.

12. $u_x - u_y = 0$ **13.** $u_x + u_y = 0$ **14.** $x u_x - y u_y = 0$
15. $u_x - y u_y = 0$ **16.** $a y u_x - b x u_y = 0$ **17.** $u_x + u_y = 2(x + y)u$
18. $u_{xx} + u_{yy} = 0$ **19.** $u_{xy} - u = 0$ **20.** $x^2 u_{xy} + 3y^2 u = 0$

9.4 D'ALEMBERT'S SOLUTION OF THE WAVE EQUATION

It is interesting to note that the solution (17) in the last section of the wave equation

$$(1) \qquad \frac{\partial^2 u}{\partial t^2} = c^2 \frac{\partial^2 u}{\partial x^2} \qquad\qquad c^2 = \frac{T}{\rho}$$

can be immediately obtained by transforming (1) in a suitable way, namely, by introducing the new independent variables[1]

$$(2) \qquad\qquad v = x + ct, \qquad z = x - ct.$$

u then becomes a function of v and z, and the derivatives in (1) can be expressed in terms of derivatives with respect to v and z by the use of the chain rule in Sec. 5.15. Denoting partial derivatives by subscripts, we see from (2) that $v_x = 1$ and $z_x = 1$ and, therefore,

$$u_x = u_v v_x + u_z z_x = u_v + u_z.$$

By applying the chain rule to the right side we find

$$u_{xx} = (u_v + u_z)_x = (u_v + u_z)_v v_x + (u_v + u_z)_z z_x.$$

Since $v_x = 1$ and $z_x = 1$, this becomes

$$u_{xx} = u_{vv} + 2u_{vz} + u_{zz}.$$

The other derivative in (1) is transformed by the same procedure, and the result is

$$u_{tt} = c^2(u_{vv} - 2u_{vz} + u_{zz}).$$

By inserting these two results in (1) we obtain

$$(3) \qquad\qquad u_{vz} \equiv \frac{\partial^2 u}{\partial v\, \partial z} = 0.$$

We may integrate this equation with respect to z, finding

$$\frac{\partial u}{\partial v} = h(v)$$

---

[1] We mention that the general theory of partial differential equations provides a systematic way for finding this transformation which will simplify the equation. Cf. Ref. [F7] in Appendix 1.

where $h(v)$ is an arbitrary function of v. Integrating this with respect to v we have

$$u = \int h(v) \, dv + \psi(z)$$

where $\psi(z)$ is an arbitrary function of z. Since the integral is a function of v, say, $\phi(v)$, the solution u is of the form

$$u = \phi(v) + \psi(z).$$

Because of (2) it takes the form

(4) $$u(x, t) = \phi(x + ct) + \psi(x - ct).$$

This is known as **d'Alembert's solution**[2] of the wave equation (1).

The functions ϕ and ψ can be determined from the initial conditions. Let us illustrate this in the case of zero initial velocity and given initial deflection $u(x, 0) = f(x)$.

By differentiating (4), we have

(5) $$\frac{\partial u}{\partial t} = c\phi'(x + ct) - c\psi'(x - ct)$$

where primes denote derivatives with respect to the *entire* arguments $x + ct$ and $x - ct$, respectively. From (4), (5), and the initial conditions we have

$$u(x, 0) = \phi(x) + \psi(x) = f(x)$$
$$u_t(x, 0) = c\phi'(x) - c\psi'(x) = 0.$$

From the last equation, $\psi' = \phi'$. Hence $\psi = \phi + k$, and from this and the first equation, $2\phi + k = f$ or $\phi = (f - k)/2$. With these functions ϕ and ψ the solution (4) becomes

(6) $$u(x, t) = \tfrac{1}{2}[f(x + ct) + f(x - ct)],$$

in agreement with (17) in Sec. 9.3. The student may show that because of the boundary conditions (2) in that section the function f must be odd and have period $2l$.

Our result shows that the two initial conditions and the boundary conditions determine the solution uniquely.

PROBLEMS

1. Express x and t in terms of v and z [cf. (2)] and use the result for transforming (3) into (1).

2. Verify the dimensions of c^2 in (1) and prove that the equation is dimensionally correct.

[2] JEAN-LE-ROND D'ALEMBERT (1717–1783), French mathematician, who is known for his important work in mechanics.

Using (6), sketch a figure (of the type of Fig. 256 in Sec. 9.3) of the deflection $u(x, t)$ of a vibrating string (length $l = 1$, ends fixed) starting with initial velocity zero and initial deflection $f(x)$, where

3. $f(x) = k \sin 2\pi x$ **4.** $f(x) = kx(1 - x)$ **5.** $f(x) = k(x - x^3)$

6. $f(x) = k(x^2 - x^4)$ **7.** $f(x) = k \sin^2 \pi x$ **8.** $f(x) = k(x^3 - x^5)$

9. $f(x) = \begin{cases} x & \text{if } 0 < x < 1/4 \\ \frac{1}{2} - x & \text{if } 1/4 < x < 1/2 \\ 0 & \text{if } 1/2 < x < 1 \end{cases}$ **10.** $f(x) = \begin{cases} x & \text{if } 0 < x < 1/4 \\ 1/4 & \text{if } 1/4 < x < 3/4 \\ 1 - x & \text{if } 3/4 < x < 1 \end{cases}$

11. Show that substitution of

$$u(x, t) = \sum_{n=1}^{\infty} G_n(t) \sin \frac{n\pi x}{l}$$

into the wave equation (1) leads to the equation .

$$\ddot{G}_n + \lambda_n{}^2 G = 0, \qquad \lambda_n = \frac{cn\pi}{l} \qquad \text{(cf. Sec. 9.3).}$$

12. Show that the forced vibrations of an elastic string under an external force $P(x, t)$ per unit length acting normal to the string are governed by the equation

$$u_{tt} = c^2 u_{xx} + \frac{P}{\rho}.$$

Consider and solve the equation in Prob. 12 for the sinusoidal force $P = A\rho \sin \omega t$, as follows.

13. Show that

$$P/\rho = A \sin \omega t = \sum_{n=1}^{\infty} k_n(t) \sin \frac{n\pi x}{l}$$

where $k_n(t) = (2A/n\pi)(1 - \cos n\pi) \sin \omega t$; hence $k_n = 0$ (n even), and $k_n = (4A/n\pi) \sin \omega t$ (n odd).

14. Show that by substituting the expressions for u in Prob. 11 and P/ρ in Prob. 13 into the equation under consideration we obtain

$$\ddot{G}_n + \lambda_n{}^2 G_n = \frac{2A}{n\pi}(1 - \cos n\pi) \sin \omega t, \qquad\qquad \lambda_n = \frac{cn\pi}{l}.$$

Show that if $\lambda_n{}^2 \neq \omega^2$, the solution is

$$G_n(t) = B_n \cos \lambda_n t + B_n{}^* \sin \lambda_n t + \frac{2A(1 - \cos n\pi)}{n\pi(\lambda_n{}^2 - \omega^2)} \sin \omega t.$$

15. Determine B_n and $B_n{}^*$ in Prob. 14 so that u satisfies the initial conditions $u(x, 0) = f(x)$, $u_t(x, 0) = 0$.

16. Show that in the case of resonance ($\lambda_n = \omega$),

$$G_n(t) = B_n \cos \omega t + B_n{}^* \sin \omega t - \frac{A}{n\pi\omega}(1 - \cos n\pi)t \cos \omega t.$$

Using the indicated transformations of the variables, solve the following equations.

17. $u_{xy} - u_{yy} = 0$ ($v = x$, $z = x + y$)

18. $xu_{xy} = yu_{yy} + u_y$ ($v = x$, $z = xy$)

19. $u_{xx} + u_{xy} - 2u_{yy} = 0$ ($v = x + y$, $z = 2x - y$)

20. $u_{xx} + 2u_{xy} + u_{yy} = 0$ ($v = x$, $z = x - y$)

21. $u_{xx} - 2u_{xy} + u_{yy} = 0$ $(v = x, z = x + y)$

22. An equation of the form

(7) $$Au_{xx} + 2Bu_{xy} + Cu_{yy} = F(x, y, u, u_x, u_y)$$

is said to be **elliptic** if $AC - B^2 > 0$, **parabolic** if $AC - B^2 = 0$, and **hyperbolic** if $AC - B^2 < 0$. (Here A, B, C may be functions of x and y, and the type of (7) may be different in different parts of the xy-plane.) Find whether the equations in Probs. 17–21 are elliptic, parabolic, or hyperbolic.

23. If (7) is *hyperbolic*, it can be transformed to the *normal form*

$$u_{vz} = F^*(v, z, u, u_v, u_z)$$

by setting $v = \Phi(x, y)$, $z = \Psi(x, y)$ where $\Phi = const$ and $\Psi = const$ are the solutions $y = y(x)$ of $Ay'^2 - 2By' + C = 0$ (cf. Ref. [F 7]). Show that in Prob. 19, $\Phi = x + y$, $\Psi = 2x - y$, and in the case of the wave equation (1),

$$\Phi = x + ct, \Psi = x - ct.$$

24. If (7) is *parabolic*, the substitution $v = x$, $z = \Psi(x, y)$, with Ψ defined as in Prob. 23, reduces it to the *normal form* $u_{vv} = F^*(v, z, u, u_v, u_z)$. Verify this result for the equation in Prob. 20.

25. It can be shown that the small free vertical vibrations of a uniform cantilever beam are governed by the fourth-order equation

(8) $$\frac{\partial^2 u}{\partial t^2} + c^2 \frac{\partial^4 u}{\partial x^4} = 0 \quad \text{(Ref. [F 8])}$$

where $c^2 = EI/\rho A$ (E = Young's modulus of elasticity, I = moment of inertia of the cross section with respect to the y-axis in Fig. 257, ρ = density, A = cross-sectional area). Substituting $u = F(x)G(t)$ into (8) and separating variables, show that

$$F^{(4)}/F = -\ddot{G}/c^2 G = \beta^4 = const,$$
$$F(x) = A \cos \beta x + B \sin \beta x$$
$$\quad + C \cosh \beta x + D \sinh \beta x,$$
$$G(t) = a \cos c\beta^2 t + b \sin c\beta^2 t.$$

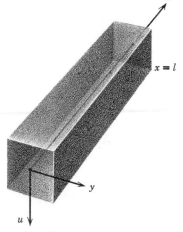

Fig. 257. Undeformed beam.

26. Find solutions $u_n = F_n(x)G_n(t)$ of (8), corresponding to zero initial velocity and satisfying the boundary conditions (Fig. 258)

$u(0, t) = 0$, $u(l, t) = 0$ (ends fixed for all times t),

$u_{xx}(0, t) = 0$, $u_{xx}(l, t) = 0$ (zero moments and, hence, zero curvature at the ends).

Fig. 258. Beam in Problem 26.

27. Find the solution of (8) that satisfies the conditions in Prob. 26 and the initial condition $u(x, 0) = f(x) = x(l - x)$.

28. Compare the results of Prob. 27, this section, and Prob. 7 at the end of Sec. 9.3. What is the basic difference between the frequencies of the normal modes of the vibrating string and the vibrating beam?

29. What are the boundary conditions, if the beam is clamped at both ends (Fig 259)?

$x = 0$ $x = l$

Fig. 259. Beam clamped at both ends.

30. Show that $F(x)$ in Prob. 25 satisfies the conditions in Prob. 29, if βl is a root of the equation

$$(9) \qquad\qquad \cosh \beta l \cos \beta l = 1.$$

31. Determine approximate solutions of (9).

32. If the beam is clamped at the left and free at the other end (Fig. 260), the boundary conditions are

$x = 0$ $x = l$

$$u(0, t) = 0, \qquad u_x(0, t) = 0,$$
$$u_{xx}(l, t) = 0, \qquad u_{xxx}(l, t) = 0.$$

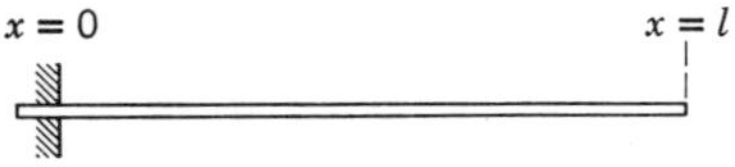

Fig. 260. Beam clamped at one end and free at the other.

Show that $F(x)$ in Prob. 25 satisfies these conditions, if βl is a root of the equation

$$\cosh \beta l \cos \beta l = -1.$$

33. Find approximate solutions of the equation in Prob. 32.

9.5 ONE-DIMENSIONAL HEAT FLOW

The heat flow in a body of homogeneous material is governed by the heat equation (cf. Sec. 6.9)

$$\frac{\partial u}{\partial t} = c^2 \nabla^2 u \qquad\qquad c^2 = \frac{K}{\sigma \rho}$$

where $u(x, y, z, t)$ is the temperature in the body, K is the thermal conductivity, σ is the specific heat, and ρ is the density of material of the body. $\nabla^2 u$ is the Laplacian of u, and with respect to Cartesian coordinates x, y, z,

$$\nabla^2 u = \frac{\partial^2 u}{\partial x^2} + \frac{\partial^2 u}{\partial y^2} + \frac{\partial^2 u}{\partial z^2}.$$

As an important application, let us consider the temperature in a long thin bar or wire of constant cross section and homogeneous material which is oriented along the x-axis (Fig. 261) and is perfectly insulated laterally, so that heat flows in the x-direction only. Then u depends only on x and time t, and the heat equation becomes the so-called **one-dimensional heat equation**

(1)
$$\frac{\partial u}{\partial t} = c^2 \frac{\partial^2 u}{\partial x^2}.$$

While the wave equation (cf. Sec. 9.2) involves the *second* partial derivative $\partial^2 u/\partial t^2$, the heat equation involves the *first* derivative $\partial u/\partial t$, and we shall see that the solutions of (1) are entirely different from those of the wave equation, although the procedure of solving (1) is quite similar to that in the case of the wave equation. We shall solve (1) for some important types of boundary and initial conditions.

Fig. 261. Bar under consideration.

Let us start with the case when the ends $x = 0$ and $x = l$ of the bar are kept at temperature zero. Then the *boundary conditions* are

(2) $u(0, t) = 0, \qquad u(l, t) = 0$ for all t.

Let $f(x)$ be the initial temperature in the bar. Then the *initial condition* is

(3) $u(x, 0) = f(x),$

where $f(x)$ is a given function. We shall determine a solution $u(x, t)$ of (1), satisfying (2) and (3).

First step.   Using the method of separating variables, we first determine solutions of (1) that satisfy the boundary conditions (2). We start from

(4) $u(x, t) = F(x)G(t).$

Differentiating and substituting this into (1), we obtain

$$F\dot{G} = c^2 F'' G,$$

where dots denote derivatives with respect to t and primes denote derivatives with respect to x. Dividing by $c^2 FG$, we have

(5)
$$\frac{\dot{G}}{c^2 G} = \frac{F''}{F}.$$

The expression on the left depends only on t, while the right side depends only on x. As in Sec. 9.3, we conclude that both expressions must be equal to a constant, say, k. The student may show that for $k \geq 0$ the only solution $u = FG$ that satisfies (2) is $u \equiv 0$. For negative $k = -p^2$ we obtain from (5)

$$\frac{\dot{G}}{c^2 G} = \frac{F''}{F} = -p^2$$

and from this the two ordinary differential equations

(6) $$F'' + p^2F = 0$$

and

(7) $$\dot{G} + c^2p^2G = 0.$$

Second step. We consider (6). The general solution is

(8) $$F(x) = A \cos px + B \sin px.$$

From (2) it follows that

$$u(0, t) = F(0)G(t) = 0 \quad \text{and} \quad u(l, t) = F(l)G(t) = 0.$$

Since $G \equiv 0$ implies $u \equiv 0$, we require that $F(0) = 0$ and $F(l) = 0$. By (8), $F(0) = A$. Thus $A = 0$, and, therefore,

$$F(l) = B \sin pl.$$

We must have $B \neq 0$, since otherwise $F \equiv 0$. Hence the condition $F(l) = 0$ leads to

$$\sin pl = 0 \quad \text{or} \quad p = \frac{n\pi}{l}, \qquad n = 1, 2, \cdots.$$

Setting $B = 1$, we thus obtain the solutions

$$F_n(x) = \sin \frac{n\pi x}{l} \qquad n = 1, 2, \cdots,$$

of (6), satisfying (2). (As on p. 531, we need not consider negative integral values of n.)

For the values $p = n\pi/l$, the equation (7) takes the form

$$\dot{G} + \lambda_n^2 G = 0 \qquad \text{where} \qquad \lambda_n = \frac{cn\pi}{l}.$$

The general solution is

$$G_n(t) = B_n e^{-\lambda_n^2 t}, \qquad n = 1, 2, \cdots,$$

where B_n is a constant. Hence the functions

(9) $$u_n(x, t) = F_n(x)\, G_n(t) = B_n \sin \frac{n\pi x}{l} e^{-\lambda_n^2 t} \qquad n = 1, 2, \cdots$$

are solutions of the heat equation (1), satisfying (2).

Third step. To find a solution also satisfying (3), we consider the series

(10) $$u(x, t) = \sum_{n=1}^{\infty} u_n(x, t) = \sum_{n=1}^{\infty} B_n \sin \frac{n\pi x}{l} e^{-\lambda_n^2 t} \qquad \left(\lambda_n = \frac{cn\pi}{l}\right).$$

From this and (3) it follows that

$$u(x, 0) = \sum_{n=1}^{\infty} B_n \sin \frac{n\pi x}{l} = f(x).$$

Hence, for (10) to satisfy (3), the coefficients B_n must be chosen such that $u(x, 0)$ becomes a half-range expansion of $f(x)$, namely, the Fourier sine series of $f(x)$; that is [cf. (4) in Sec. 8.5]

(11) $$B_n = \frac{2}{l} \int_0^l f(x) \sin \frac{n\pi x}{l} \, dx \qquad n = 1, 2, \cdots.$$

The solution of our problem can be established, assuming that $f(x)$ is piecewise continuous on the interval $0 \le x \le l$ (cf. p. 209), and has one-sided derivatives[3] at all interior points of that interval; that is, under these assumptions the series (10) with coefficients (11) is the solution of our physical problem. The proof, which requires the knowledge of uniform convergence of series, will be given at a later occasion (Probs. 19–21 at the end of Sec. 11.9).

Because of the exponential factor all the terms in (11) approach zero as t approaches infinity. The rate of decay varies with n.

Example 1. If the initial temperature is

$$f(x) = \begin{cases} x & \text{when} \quad 0 < x < l/2, \\ l - x & \text{when} \; l/2 < x < l \end{cases}$$

(cf. Fig. 262 where $l = \pi$ and $c = 1$), then we obtain from (11)

(12) $$B_n = \frac{2}{l} \left(\int_0^{l/2} x \sin \frac{n\pi x}{l} \, dx \right.$$

$$+ \left. \int_{l/2}^l (l - x) \sin \frac{n\pi x}{l} \, dx \right).$$

Integration yields $B_n = 0$ when n is even and

$$B_n = \frac{4l}{n^2 \pi^2} \quad (n = 1, 5, 9, \cdots),$$

$$B_n = -\frac{4l}{n^2 \pi^2} \quad (n = 3, 7, 11, \cdots).$$

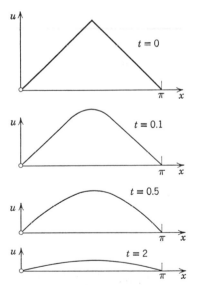

Fig. 262. Solution of Example 1 for various values of t.

[3] Cf. footnote 4 on p. 472.

Hence the solution is

$$u(x, t) = \frac{4l}{\pi^2}\left[\sin\frac{\pi x}{l}\,e^{-(c\pi/l)^2 t} - \frac{1}{9}\sin\frac{3\pi x}{l}\,e^{-(3c\pi/l)^2 t} + \cdots\right].$$

The reader may compare Fig. 262 and Fig. 256 in Sec. 9.3.

PROBLEMS

1. Graph u_1, u_2, u_3 [cf. (9), with $B_n = 1$, $c = 1$, $l = \pi$] as functions of x for $t = 0, 1, 2, 3$. Compare the behavior of these functions.

2. Represent the solutions in Prob. 1 graphically as surfaces over the xt-plane.

3. Show that the one-dimensional heat equation is parabolic, while the one-dimensional wave equation is hyperbolic (cf. Prob. 22 at the end of the last section).

4. How does the rate of decay of (9) for fixed n depend on the specific heat, the density, and the thermal conductivity of the material?

Find the temperature $u(x, t)$ in a bar of silver (length 10 cm, constant cross section of area 1 cm², density 10.6 gm/cm³, thermal conductivity 1.04 cal/cm deg sec, specific heat 0.056 cal/gm deg) which is perfectly insulated laterally, whose ends are kept at temperature 0°C and whose initial temperature (in °C) is $f(x)$, where

5. $f(x) = \sin 0.1\pi x$

6. $f(x) = \sin 0.2\pi x$

7. $f(x) = \begin{cases} x & \text{if } 0 < x < 5 \\ 10 - x & \text{if } 5 < x < 10 \end{cases}$

8. $f(x) = \begin{cases} x & \text{if } 0 < x < 5 \\ 0 & \text{if } 5 < x < 10 \end{cases}$

9. $f(x) = x(10 - x)$

10. $f(x) = x(100 - x^2)$

11. The ends of a rod that satisfies the assumptions in the text are kept at different constant temperatures $u(0, t) = U_1$ and $u(l, t) = U_2$. Find the temperature $u_I(x)$ in the rod after a long time (theoretically: as $t \to \infty$).

12. In Prob. 11, let the initial temperature be $u(x, 0) = f(x)$. Show that the temperature for any time $t > 0$ is $u(x, t) = u_I(x) + u_{II}(x, t)$ with u_I as before and

$$u_{II} = \sum_{n=1}^{\infty} B_n \sin\frac{n\pi x}{l}\,e^{-(cn\pi/l)^2 t},$$

$$B_n = \frac{2}{l}\int_0^l [f(x) - u_I(x)]\sin\frac{n\pi x}{l}\,dx$$

$$= \frac{2}{l}\int_0^l f(x)\sin\frac{n\pi x}{l}\,dx + \frac{2}{n\pi}[(-1)^n U_2 - U_1].$$

13. Consider the bar in Probs. 5–10. Assume that the ends are kept at 100°C for a long time. Then at some instant, say, at $t = 0$, the temperature at $x = l$ is suddenly changed to 0°C and kept at this value, while the temperature at $x = 0$ is kept at 100°C. What are the temperatures in the middle of the bar at $t = 1$, 2, 3, 10, 50 sec?

14. Find the temperature $u(x, t)$ in a bar of length l which is perfectly insulated, also at the ends at $x = 0$ and $x = l$, assuming that $u(x, 0) = f(x)$. Physical information: the flux of heat through the faces at the ends is proportional to the values of $\partial u/\partial x$ there. Show that this situation corresponds to the conditions

$$u_x(0, t) = 0, \qquad u_x(l, t) = 0, \qquad u(x, 0) = f(x).$$

Show that the method of separating variables yields the solution

$$u(x, t) = A_0 + \sum_{n=1}^{\infty} A_n \cos \frac{n\pi x}{l} e^{-(cn\pi/l)^2 t}$$

where, by (2) in Sec. 8.5,

$$A_0 = \frac{1}{l} \int_0^l f(x)\, dx, \qquad A_n = \frac{2}{l} \int_0^l f(x) \cos \frac{n\pi x}{l}\, dx, \qquad n = 1, 2, \cdots.$$

15. In Prob. 14, $u \to A_0$ as $t \to \infty$. Does this agree with your physical intuition? Find the temperature in the bar in Prob. 14, if $l = \pi$, $c = 1$, and

16. $f(x) = 1$ **17.** $f(x) = x^2$ **18.** $f(x) = \sin x$

19. $f(x) = \begin{cases} x & \text{when} \quad 0 < x < \pi/2 \\ 0 & \text{when} \quad \pi/2 < x < \pi \end{cases}$ **20.** $f(x) = \begin{cases} 1 & \text{when} \quad 0 < x < \pi/2 \\ 0 & \text{when} \quad \pi/2 < x < \pi \end{cases}$

9.6 HEAT FLOW IN AN INFINITE BAR

We shall now consider solutions of the heat equation

(1)
$$\frac{\partial u}{\partial t} = c^2 \frac{\partial^2 u}{\partial x^2}$$

in the case of a bar which extends to infinity on both sides (and is laterally insulated, as before). In this case we do not have boundary conditions but only the initial condition

(2)
$$u(x, 0) = f(x) \qquad\qquad (-\infty < x < \infty)$$

where $f(x)$ is the given initial temperature of the bar.

To solve our present problem we start as in the last section, that is, we substitute $u(x, t) = F(x)G(t)$ into (1). This yields the two ordinary differential equations

(3)
$$F'' + p^2 F = 0 \qquad\qquad \text{[cf. (6), Sec. 9.5]}$$

and

(4)
$$\dot{G} + c^2 p^2 G = 0 \qquad\qquad \text{[cf. (7), Sec. 9.5].}$$

The functions

$$F(x) = A \cos px + B \sin px \qquad \text{and} \qquad G(t) = e^{-c^2 p^2 t}$$

are solutions of (3) and (4), respectively; here A and B are arbitrary constants. Hence,

$$(5) \qquad u(x, t; p) = FG = (A \cos px + B \sin px)e^{-c^2 p^2 t}$$

is a solution of (1). (As in the last section, we had to choose the constant of separation k negative, $k = -p^2$, because positive values of k lead to an increasing exponential function in (5), which has no physical meaning.)

Any series of functions (5), found in the usual manner by taking p as multiples of a fixed number, would lead to a function which is periodic in x when $t = 0$. However, since $f(x)$ in (2) is not assumed periodic, it is natural to use Fourier integrals in the present case instead of Fourier series.

Since A and B in (5) are arbitrary, we may consider them as functions of p and write $A = A(p)$ and $B = B(p)$. Since the heat equation is linear and homogeneous, the function

$$(6) \qquad u(x, t) = \int_0^\infty u(x, t; p)\, dp$$
$$= \int_0^\infty [A(p) \cos px + B(p) \sin px]e^{-c^2 p^2 t}\, dp$$

is then a solution of (1), provided this integral exists and can be differentiated twice with respect to x and once with respect to t.

From (6) and the initial condition (2) it follows that

$$(7) \qquad u(x, 0) = \int_0^\infty [A(p) \cos px + B(p) \sin px]\, dp = f(x).$$

Using (4) and (5) in Sec. 8.10, we thus obtain

$$(8) \qquad A(p) = \frac{1}{\pi} \int_{-\infty}^\infty f(v) \cos pv\, dv, \quad B(p) = \frac{1}{\pi} \int_{-\infty}^\infty f(v) \sin pv\, dv.$$

According to (16) in Prob. 20, Sec. 8.10, this Fourier integral may be written

$$u(x, 0) = \frac{1}{\pi} \int_0^\infty \left[\int_{-\infty}^\infty f(v) \cos (px - pv)\, dv \right] dp,$$

and (6), this section, thus becomes

$$u(x, t) = \frac{1}{\pi} \int_0^\infty \left[\int_{-\infty}^\infty f(v) \cos (px - pv)e^{-c^2 p^2 t}\, dv \right] dp.$$

Assuming that we may invert the order of integration, we obtain

$$(9) \qquad u(x, t) = \frac{1}{\pi} \int_{-\infty}^\infty f(v) \left[\int_0^\infty e^{-c^2 p^2 t} \cos (px - pv)\, dp \right] dv.$$

The inner integral can be evaluated by the use of the formula

$$(10) \qquad \int_0^\infty e^{-s^2} \cos 2bs \; ds = \frac{\sqrt{\pi}}{2} e^{-b^2}$$

which will be derived in Sec. 11.15 (Prob. 32). Introducing a new variable of integration p by setting $s = cp\sqrt{t}$ and choosing

$$b = \frac{x - v}{2c\sqrt{t}}$$

the formula (10) becomes

$$\int_0^\infty e^{-c^2 p^2 t} \cos (px - pv) \; dp = \frac{\sqrt{\pi}}{2c\sqrt{t}} e^{-(x-v)^2/4c^2 t}.$$

By inserting this result into (9) we obtain

$$(11) \qquad u(x, t) = \frac{1}{2c\sqrt{\pi t}} \int_{-\infty}^{\infty} f(v) \exp \left\{ -\frac{(x - v)^2}{4c^2 t} \right\} dv.$$

Finally, by introducing the variable of integration $w = (v - x)/2c\sqrt{t}$, this may be written

$$(12) \qquad u(x, t) = \frac{1}{\sqrt{\pi}} \int_{-\infty}^{\infty} f(x + 2cw \sqrt{t}) e^{-w^2} \; dw.$$

If $f(x)$ is bounded for all values of x and integrable in every finite interval, it can be shown (cf. Ref. [E1]) that the function (11) or (12) satisfies (1) and (2). Hence this function is the required solution in the present case.

Example 1. Find the temperature in the infinite bar, if the initial temperature is (Fig. 263)

$$f(x) = \begin{cases} U_0 = const & \text{when} \quad |x| < 1, \\ 0 & \text{when} \quad |x| > 1. \end{cases}$$

From (11) we have

$$u(x, t) = \frac{U_0}{2c\sqrt{\pi t}} \int_{-1}^{1} \exp \left\{ -\frac{(x - v)^2}{4c^2 t} \right\} dv.$$

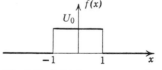

Fig. 263. Initial temperature in Example 1.

If we introduce the above variable of integration w, then the integration over v from -1 to 1 corresponds to the integration over w from $(-1 - x)/2c\sqrt{t}$ to $(1 - x)/2c\sqrt{t}$, and we thus obtain

$$(13) \qquad u(x, t) = \frac{U_0}{\sqrt{\pi}} \int_{-(1+x)/2c\sqrt{t}}^{(1-x)/2c\sqrt{t}} e^{-w^2} \; dw \qquad (t > 0).$$

We shall see later that this integral is not an elementary function, but can be easily expressed in terms of the so-called *error function*, whose values have been tabulated (cf. Sec. 14.2; cf. also Probs. 11–18, this section). Figure 264 shows

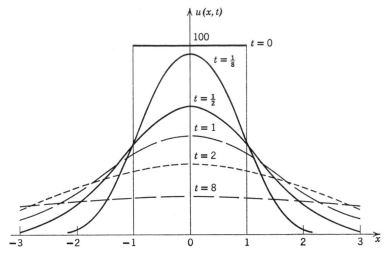

Fig. 264. Solution of Example 1 for $U_0 = 100°C$ and $c^2 = 1$ cm²/sec.

$u(x, t)$ for $U_0 = 100°C$, $c^2 = 1$ cm²/sec, and several values of t. Some of the corresponding function values are given in Table 22.

TABLE 22. SOLUTION OF EXAMPLE 1.

x	$t =$				
	$\frac{1}{8}$	$\frac{1}{2}$	1	2	8
0	96	68	52	38	20
0.25	92	66	51	38	20
0.5	84	62	49	37	20
0.75	69	56	46	36	19
1	50	48	42	34	19
1.5	16	30	32	29	18
2	2	16	22	24	17
2.5	0	7	14	19	16
3	0	2	8	14	15

PROBLEMS

1. Graph the temperatures in Ex. 1 (with $U_0 = 100°C$ and $c^2 = 1$ cm²/sec) at the points $x = 0.5$, 1, and 1.5 as functions of t. Do the results agree with your physical intuition?

2. Find the solution in Ex. 1 by starting from (12).

3. If $f(x) = 1$ when $x > 0$ and $f(x) = 0$ when $x < 0$, show that (12) becomes

$$u(x, t) = \frac{1}{\sqrt{\pi}} \int_{-x/2c\sqrt{t}}^{\infty} e^{-w^2} \, dw \qquad (t > 0).$$

4. Show that for $x = 0$ the solution in Prob. 3 is independent of t. Can this result be expected for physical reasons?

5. If the bar is semi-infinite, extending from 0 to ∞, the end at $x = 0$ is held at temperature 0 and the initial temperature is $f(x)$, show that the temperature in the bar is

(14) $$u(x, t) = \frac{1}{\sqrt{\pi}}\left[\int_{-x/\tau}^{\infty} f(x + \tau w)e^{-w^2}\, dw - \int_{x/\tau}^{\infty} f(-x + \tau w)e^{-w^2}\, dw\right],$$

$$\tau = 2c\sqrt{t}.$$

6. Obtain (14) from (11) by assuming that $f(v)$ in (11) is odd.

7. If in Prob. 5, $f(x) = 1$, show that

$$u(x, t) = \frac{2}{\sqrt{\pi}}\int_0^{x/\tau} e^{-w^2}\, dw \qquad (t > 0).$$

8. What form does (14) take, if $f(x) = 1$ when $a < x < b$ (where $a > 0$) and $f(x) = 0$ otherwise?

9. Show that the result of Prob. 7 can be obtained from (11) or (12) by using $f(x) = 1$ when $x > 0$, and $f(x) = -1$ when $x < 0$. What is the reason?

10. Show that in Prob. 7 the times required for any two points to reach the same temperature are proportional to the squares of their distances from the boundary at $x = 0$.

A detailed treatment of the so-called **error function**

$$\operatorname{erf} x = \frac{2}{\sqrt{\pi}}\int_0^x e^{-w^2}\, dw$$

will be given in Sec. 14.2. For the time being the student may get accustomed to this important function by solving the following problems.

11. Using a table of the exponential function, graph the integrand of erf x (the so-called *bell-shaped curve*).

12. Obtain a small table of erf x for $x = 0, 0.2, 0.4, \cdots, 1.0, 1.5, 2.0$ by counting squares under the curve in Prob. 11 or some other rough method of approximate integration, and compare the result with the actual values whose first two decimal places are 0.00, 0.22, 0.43, 0.60, 0.74, 0.84, 0.97, 1.00.

13. Obtain the Maclaurin series of erf x by term-by-term integration of that of the integrand.

14. Using the result of Prob. 13 compute erf x for the values of x in Prob. 12 (two decimal places).

15. Show that erf x is odd.

16. Show that

$$\int_a^b e^{-w^2}\, dw = \frac{\sqrt{\pi}}{2}(\operatorname{erf} b - \operatorname{erf} a), \qquad \int_{-b}^b e^{-w^2}\, dw = \sqrt{\pi}\,\operatorname{erf} b.$$

17. Show that (13) may be written

$$u(x, t) = \frac{U_0}{2}\left[\operatorname{erf}\frac{1 - x}{2c\sqrt{t}} + \operatorname{erf}\frac{1 + x}{2c\sqrt{t}}\right] \qquad (t > 0).$$

18. Using the representation in Prob. 17 and Table 25 in Sec. 14.2, verify the values in Table 22, this section, for $t = 1$.

19. Show that in Prob. 7, $u(x, t) = \text{erf}\ (x/2c\sqrt{t})\ (t > 0)$.
20. Graph u in Prob. 7 for $x \geqq 0$ and (a) $t = 0$, (b) $t = 0.5$, (c) $t = 1$, and (d) $t = 2$. Choose $c = 1$.

9.7 VIBRATING MEMBRANE. TWO-DIMENSIONAL WAVE EQUATION

As another important problem from the field of vibrations, let us consider the motion of a stretched membrane, such as a drumhead. The reader will notice that our present considerations will be similar to those in the case of the vibrating string in Sec. 9.2.

We make the following assumptions:

1. *The mass of the membrane per unit area is constant ("homogeneous membrane"). The membrane is perfectly flexible and is so thin that it does not offer any resistance to bending.*

2. *The membrane is stretched and then fixed along its entire boundary in the xy-plane. The tension per unit length T caused by stretching the membrane is the same at all points and in all directions and does not change during the motion.*

3. *The deflection u(x, y, t) of the membrane during the motion is small compared with the size of the membrane, and all angles of inclination are small.*

Although these assumptions cannot be realized in practice, small transverse vibrations of a thin physical membrane will satisfy these assumptions relatively accurately.

To derive the differential equation which governs the motion of the membrane, we consider the forces acting on a small portion of the membrane as shown in Fig. 265. Since the deflections of the membrane and the angles of inclination are small, the sides of the portion are approximately equal to Δx and Δy. The tension T is the force per unit length. Hence the forces acting on the edges of the portion are approximately $T\Delta x$ and $T\Delta y$. Since the membrane is perfectly flexible, these forces are tangent to the membrane.

We first consider the horizontal components of the forces. These components are obtained by multiplying the forces by the cosines of the angles of inclination. Since these angles are small, their cosines are close to 1. Hence the horizontal components of the forces at opposite edges are approximately equal. Therefore, the motion of the particles of the membrane in horizontal direction will be negligibly small. From this we conclude that we may regard the motion of the membrane as transversal, that is, each particle moves vertically.

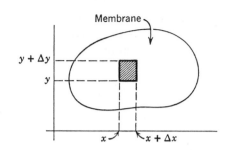

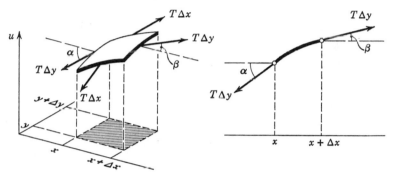

Fig 265. Vibrating membrane.

The vertical components of the forces along the edges parallel to the yu-plane are[4] (Fig. 265)

$$T\Delta y \sin \beta \qquad \text{and} \qquad -T\Delta y \sin \alpha;$$

here the minus sign appears because the force on the left edge is directed downward. Since the angles are small, we may replace their sines by their tangents. Hence the resultant of those two vertical components is

(1)
$$T\Delta y(\sin \beta - \sin \alpha) \approx T\Delta y(\tan \beta - \tan \alpha)$$
$$= T\Delta y[u_x(x + \Delta x, y_1) - u_x(x, y_2)]$$

where subscripts x denote partial derivatives and y_1 and y_2 are values between y and $y + \Delta y$. Similarly, the resultant of the vertical components of the forces acting on the other two edges of the portion is

(2)
$$T\Delta x[u_y(x_1, y + \Delta y) - u_y(x_2, y)],$$

where x_1 and x_2 are values between x and $x + \Delta x$.

---

[4] Note that the angle of inclination varies along the edges, and α and β represent values of that angle at a suitable point of the edges under consideration.

By Newton's second law (cf. Sec. 2.6), the sum of the forces given by (1) and (2) is equal to the mass $\rho \Delta A$ of the portion times the acceleration $\partial^2 u / \partial t^2$; here ρ is the mass of the membrane per unit area and $\Delta A \approx \Delta x \Delta y$ is the area of the portion. Thus

$$\rho \Delta x \Delta y \frac{\partial^2 u}{\partial t^2} = T \Delta y [u_x(x + \Delta x, y_1) - u_x(x, y_2)]$$
$$+ T \Delta x [u_y(x_1, y + \Delta y) - u_y(x_2, y)]$$

where the derivative on the left is evaluated at some suitable point $(\tilde{x}, \tilde{y})$ corresponding to the portion. Division by $\rho \Delta x \Delta y$ yields

$$\frac{\partial^2 u}{\partial t^2} = \frac{T}{\rho} \left[\frac{u_x(x + \Delta x, y_1) - u_x(x, y_2)}{\Delta x} + \frac{u_y(x_1, y + \Delta y) - u_y(x_2, y)}{\Delta y} \right].$$

If we let Δx and Δy approach zero, then we obtain

$$(3) \qquad \frac{\partial^2 u}{\partial t^2} = c^2 \left(\frac{\partial^2 u}{\partial x^2} + \frac{\partial^2 u}{\partial y^2} \right) \qquad\qquad c^2 = \frac{T}{\rho}.$$

This equation is called the **two-dimensional wave equation**. We see that the expression in parentheses is the Laplacian $\nabla^2 u$ of u (cf. Sec. 5.16) and we may write (3) in the form

$$(3') \qquad \frac{\partial^2 u}{\partial t^2} = c^2 \nabla^2 u.$$

9.8   RECTANGULAR MEMBRANE

To solve the problem of a vibrating membrane, we have to determine a solution $u(x, y, t)$ of the two-dimensional wave equation

$$(1) \qquad \frac{\partial^2 u}{\partial t^2} = c^2 \left(\frac{\partial^2 u}{\partial x^2} + \frac{\partial^2 u}{\partial y^2} \right)$$

that satisfies the boundary condition

$(2) \qquad u = 0 \qquad$ on the boundary of the membrane for all $t \geqq 0$

and the initial conditions

$(3) \qquad u(x, y, 0) = f(x, y) \qquad$ [given initial displacement $f(x, y)$]

and

$(4) \qquad \left. \dfrac{\partial u}{\partial t} \right|_{t=0} = g(x, y) \qquad$ [given initial velocity $g(x, y)$].

These conditions are quite similar to those in the case of the vibrating string.

As a first important case, let us consider the rectangular membrane R shown in Fig. 266.

First step. By applying the method of separation of variables we first determine solutions of (1) that satisfy the condition (2). For this purpose we start from

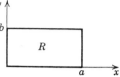

(5) $u(x, y, t) = F(x, y)G(t).$

By substituting this into the wave equation (1) we have

$$F\ddot{G} = c^2(F_{xx}G + F_{yy}G)$$

where subscripts denote partial derivatives and dots denote derivatives with respect to t. Dividing both sides by c^2FG, we find

Fig. 266. Rectangular membrane.

$$\frac{\ddot{G}}{c^2G} = \frac{1}{F}(F_{xx} + F_{yy}).$$

Since the functions on the left depend only on t while the functions on the right do not depend on t, the expressions on both sides must be equal to a constant. A little investigation shows that only negative values of that constant will lead to solutions which satisfy (2) without being identically zero; this is similar to the procedure in Sec. 9.3. Denoting this negative constant by $-\nu^2$, we thus have

$$\frac{\ddot{G}}{c^2G} = \frac{1}{F}(F_{xx} + F_{yy}) = -\nu^2.$$

This yields the two differential equations

(6) $\ddot{G} + \lambda^2 G = 0$ where $\lambda = c\nu,$

and

(7) $F_{xx} + F_{yy} + \nu^2 F = 0.$

Now we consider (7) and apply the method of separating variables once more, that is, we determine solutions of (7) of the form

(8) $F(x, y) = H(x)Q(y)$

which are zero on the boundary of the membrane. Substitution of (8) into (7) yields

$$\frac{d^2H}{dx^2}Q = -\left(H\frac{d^2Q}{dy^2} + \nu^2HQ\right).$$

By dividing both sides by HQ we find

$$\frac{1}{H}\frac{d^2H}{dx^2} = -\frac{1}{Q}\left(\frac{d^2Q}{dy^2} + \nu^2Q\right).$$

The functions on the left depend only on x while the functions on the right depend only on y. Hence the expressions on both sides must be equal to a constant. This constant must be negative, say, $-k^2$, because only negative values will lead to solutions that satisfy (2) without being identically zero. Thus

$$\frac{1}{H}\frac{d^2H}{dx^2} = -\frac{1}{Q}\left(\frac{d^2Q}{dy^2} + v^2Q\right) = -k^2.$$

This yields the ordinary differential equations

(9)
$$\frac{d^2H}{dx^2} + k^2H = 0$$

and

(10)
$$\frac{d^2Q}{dy^2} + p^2Q = 0 \qquad \text{where } p^2 = v^2 - k^2.$$

Second step. The general solutions of (9) and (10) are

$$H(x) = A\cos kx + B\sin kx \quad \text{and} \quad Q(y) = C\cos py + D\sin py,$$

where A, B, C, and D are constants. From (5) and (2) it follows that $F = HQ$ must be zero on the boundary, which corresponds to $x = 0$, $x = a$, $y = 0$, and $y = b$; cf. Fig. 266. This yields the conditions

$$H(0) = 0, \quad H(a) = 0, \qquad Q(0) = 0, \quad Q(b) = 0.$$

Therefore, $H(0) = A = 0$, and then

$$H(a) = B\sin ka = 0.$$

We must take $B \neq 0$ since otherwise $H \equiv 0$ and $F \equiv 0$. Hence $\sin ka = 0$ or

$$ka = m\pi, \qquad k = \frac{m\pi}{a} \qquad (m \text{ integral}).$$

In precisely the same fashion we conclude that $C = 0$ and p must be restricted to the values

$$p = \frac{n\pi}{b} \qquad (n \text{ integral}).$$

In this way we obtain the solutions

$$H_m(x) = \sin\frac{m\pi}{a} x \qquad m = 1, 2, \cdots,$$

and

$$Q_n(y) = \sin\frac{n\pi}{b} y \qquad n = 1, 2, \cdots.$$

(As in the case of the vibrating string, it is not necessary to consider $m, n = -1, -2, \cdots$ because the corresponding solutions are essentially the same as for positive m and n, except for a factor -1.) It follows that the functions

(11) $\qquad F_{mn}(x, y) = H_m(x)Q_n(y) = \sin \dfrac{m\pi x}{a} \sin \dfrac{n\pi y}{b} \qquad \begin{array}{l} m = 1, 2, \cdots, \\ n = 1, 2, \cdots, \end{array}$

are solutions of the equation (7) which are zero on the boundary of the rectangular membrane.

Since $p^2 = v^2 - k^2$ in (10) and $\lambda = cv$ in (6), we have

$$\lambda = c\sqrt{k^2 + p^2}.$$

Hence to $k = m\pi/a$ and $p = n\pi/b$ there corresponds the value

(12) $\qquad \lambda = \lambda_{mn} = c\pi \sqrt{\dfrac{m^2}{a^2} + \dfrac{n^2}{b^2}}$

in (6), and the corresponding general solution of (6) is

$$G_{mn}(t) = B_{mn} \cos \lambda_{mn}t + B_{mn}{}^* \sin \lambda_{mn}t.$$

It follows that the functions

(13) $\quad u_{mn}(x, y, t) = F_{mn}(x, y)G_{mn}(t)$

$$= (B_{mn} \cos \lambda_{mn}t + B_{mn}{}^* \sin \lambda_{mn}t) \sin \dfrac{m\pi x}{a} \sin \dfrac{n\pi y}{b}$$

$$(m = 1, 2, \cdots, n = 1, 2, \cdots)$$

with λ_{mn} according to (12) are solutions of the wave equation (1), which are zero on the boundary of the rectangular membrane in Fig. 266. These functions are called the **eigenfunctions** or *characteristic functions*, and the numbers λ_{mn} are called the **eigenvalues** or *characteristic values* of the vibrating membrane. The frequency of u_{mn} is $\lambda_{mn}/2\pi$.

It is interesting to note that, depending on a and b, several functions F_{mn} may correspond to the same eigenvalue. Physically this means that there may exist vibrations having the same frequency but entirely different **nodal lines** (curves of points on the membrane which do not move). This may be illustrated by the following example.

Example 1. Consider the square membrane for which $a = b = 1$. From (12) we see that the eigenvalues are

(14) $\qquad\qquad\qquad \lambda_{mn} = c\pi \sqrt{m^2 + n^2}.$

Hence,

$$\lambda_{mn} = \lambda_{nm},$$

but for $m \neq n$ the corresponding functions

$$F_{mn} = \sin m\pi x \sin n\pi y \qquad \text{and} \qquad F_{nm} = \sin n\pi x \sin m\pi y$$

are certainly different. For example, to $\lambda_{12} = \lambda_{21} = c\pi\sqrt{5}$ there correspond the two functions

$$F_{12} = \sin \pi x \sin 2\pi y \qquad \text{and} \qquad F_{21} = \sin 2\pi x \sin \pi y.$$

Hence the corresponding solutions

$$u_{12} = (B_{12} \cos c\pi\sqrt{5}t + B_{12}^* \sin c\pi\sqrt{5}t)F_{12}$$

and

$$u_{21} = (B_{21} \cos c\pi\sqrt{5}t + B_{21}^* \sin c\pi\sqrt{5}t)F_{21}$$

have the nodal lines $y = \frac{1}{2}$ and $x = \frac{1}{2}$, respectively (Fig. 267). Taking $B_{12} = 1$ and $B_{12}^* = B_{21}^* = 0$, we obtain

$$(15) \qquad u_{12} + u_{21} = \cos c\pi\sqrt{5}t \, (F_{12} + B_{21}F_{21}),$$

which represents another vibration corresponding to the eigenvalue $c\pi\sqrt{5}$. The nodal line of this function is the solution of the equation

$$F_{12} + B_{21}F_{21} = \sin \pi x \sin 2\pi y + B_{21} \sin 2\pi x \sin \pi y = 0$$

or, since $\sin 2\alpha = 2 \sin \alpha \cos \alpha$,

$$(16) \qquad \sin \pi x \sin \pi y(\cos \pi y + B_{21} \cos \pi x) = 0.$$

This solution depends on the value of B_{21} (Fig. 268).

From (14) we see that even more than two functions may correspond to the same numerical value of λ_{mn}. For example, the four functions F_{18}, F_{81}, F_{47}, and F_{74} correspond to $\lambda_{18} = \lambda_{81} = \lambda_{47} = \lambda_{74} = c\pi\sqrt{65}$, because

$$1^1 + 8^2 = 4^2 + 7^2 = 65.$$

This happens because 65 can be expressed as the sum of two squares of natural numbers in more than one way. According to a theorem by Gauss, this is the case for every sum of two squares among whose prime factors there are at least two different ones of the form $4n + 1$ where n is a positive integer. In our case,

$$65 = 5 \cdot 13 = (4 + 1)(12 + 1).$$

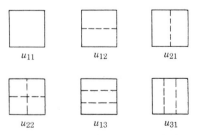

Fig. 267. Nodal lines of the solutions u_{11}, u_{12}, u_{21}, u_{22}, u_{13}, and u_{31} in the case of the square membrane.

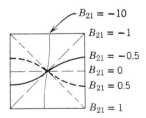

Fig. 268. Nodal lines of the solution (15) for some values of B_{21}.

Third step. To obtain the solution which also satisfies the initial conditions (3) and (4), we proceed in a similar fashion as in Sec. 9.3. We consider the double series[5]

$$(17) \quad u(x, y, t) = \sum_{m=1}^{\infty} \sum_{n=1}^{\infty} u_{mn}(x, y, t)$$

$$= \sum_{m=1}^{\infty} \sum_{n=1}^{\infty} (B_{mn} \cos \lambda_{mn} t + B_{mn}^* \sin \lambda_{mn} t) \sin \frac{m\pi x}{a} \sin \frac{n\pi y}{b}.$$

From this and (3) we obtain

$$(18) \quad u(x, y, 0) = \sum_{m=1}^{\infty} \sum_{n=1}^{\infty} B_{mn} \sin \frac{m\pi x}{a} \sin \frac{n\pi y}{b} = f(x, y).$$

This series is called a **double Fourier series**. Suppose that $f(x, y)$ can be developed in such a series.[6] Then the Fourier coefficients B_{mn} of $f(x, y)$ in (18) can be determined as follows. Setting

$$(19) \quad K_m(y) = \sum_{n=1}^{\infty} B_{mn} \sin \frac{n\pi y}{b}$$

we may write (18) in the form

$$f(x, y) = \sum_{m=1}^{\infty} K_m(y) \sin \frac{m\pi x}{a}.$$

For fixed y this is the Fourier sine series of $f(x, y)$, considered as a function of x, and from (4) in Sec. 8.5, it follows that the coefficients of this expansion are

$$(20) \quad K_m(y) = \frac{2}{a} \int_0^a f(x, y) \sin \frac{m\pi x}{a} dx.$$

Furthermore, (19) is the Fourier sine series of $K_m(y)$, and from (4) in Sec. 8.5 it follows that the coefficients are

$$B_{mn} = \frac{2}{b} \int_0^b K_m(y) \sin \frac{n\pi y}{b} dy.$$

From this and (20) we obtain the *generalized Euler formula*

$$(21) \quad B_{mn} = \frac{4}{ab} \int_0^b \int_0^a f(x, y) \sin \frac{m\pi x}{a} \sin \frac{n\pi y}{b} dx\, dy \qquad \begin{matrix} m = 1, 2, \cdots \\ n = 1, 2, \cdots \end{matrix}$$

for the Fourier coefficients of $f(x, y)$ in the double Fourier series (18).

---

[5] We shall not consider the problems of convergence and uniqueness.

[6] Sufficient conditions: f, $\partial f/\partial x$, $\partial f/\partial y$, $\partial^2 f/\partial x \partial y$ continuous in the rectangle R under consideration.

The B_{mn} in (17) are now determined in terms of $f(x, y)$. To determine the B_{mn}^*, we differentiate (17) termwise with respect to t; using (4), we obtain

$$\frac{\partial u}{\partial t}\bigg|_{t=0} = \sum_{m=1}^{\infty} \sum_{n=1}^{\infty} B_{mn}^* \lambda_{mn} \sin \frac{m\pi x}{a} \sin \frac{n\pi y}{b} = g(x, y).$$

Suppose that $g(x, y)$ can be developed in this double Fourier series. Then, proceeding as before, we obtain

$$(22) \quad B_{mn}^* = \frac{4}{ab\lambda_{mn}} \int_0^b \int_0^a g(x, y) \sin \frac{m\pi x}{a} \sin \frac{n\pi y}{b} \, dx \, dy \quad \begin{array}{l} m = 1, 2, \cdots, \\ n = 1, 2, \cdots. \end{array}$$

The result is that, for (17) to satisfy the initial conditions, the coefficients B_{mn} and B_{mn}^* must be chosen according to (21) and (22).

PROBLEMS

1. Determine and graph the nodal lines of the solutions (13) with $m = 1, 2, 3, 4$ and $n = 1, 2, 3, 4$ in the cases $a = b = 1$ and $a = 2, b = 1$.

2. How does the frequency of a solution (13) change, if the tension of the membrane is increased?

3. Show that, among all rectangular membranes of the same area $A = ab$ and the same c, the square membrane is that for which u_{11} [cf. (13)] has the lowest frequency.

4. Find a similar result as in Prob. 3 for the frequency of any solution (13) (m, n fixed).

5. Find further eigenvalues of the square membrane with side 1 such that four different eigenfunctions correspond to each such eigenvalue.

6. Find eigenvalues of the rectangular membrane of sides $a = 2, b = 1$ such that two or more different eigenfunctions correspond to each such eigenvalue.

Represent the following functions $f(x, y)$ ($0 < x < a, 0 < y < b$) by a double Fourier series of the form (18).

7. $f = g(x)h(y)$, where $g(x) = \begin{cases} x & \text{if } 0 < x < a/2 \\ a - x & \text{if } a/2 < x < a \end{cases}$

and $h(y) = \begin{cases} y & \text{if } 0 < y < b/2 \\ b - y & \text{if } b/2 < y < b \end{cases}$

8. $f = 1$ **9.** $f = xy$ **10.** $f = x + y$
11. $f = xy(a - x)(b - y)$ **12.** $f = xy(a^2 - x^2)(b^2 - y^2)$

Find the deflection $u(x, y, t)$ of the square membrane with $a = b = 1$ and $c = 1$, if the initial velocity is zero and the initial deflection is $f(x, y)$, where

13. $f = 0.01xy(1 - x)(1 - y)$ **14.** $f = kx(1 - x^2)y(1 - y^2)$
15. $f = k \sin \pi x \sin 2\pi y$ **16.** $f = k \sin^2 \pi x \sin^2 \pi y$

17. Show that

$$u_{tt} = c^2 \nabla^2 u + P/\rho$$

governs the forced vibrations of the membrane, where $P(x, y, t)$ is the external force per unit area acting normal to the xy-plane.

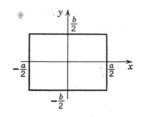

Fig. 269. Rectangular membrane.

Fig. 270. Square plate.

18. Find the eigenfunctions of the rectangular membrane in Fig. 269 which is fixed on the boundary.

19. The four edges of a thin square plate (Fig. 270) are kept at temperature zero and the faces are perfectly insulated. The initial temperature is assumed to be $u(x, y, 0) = f(x, y)$. By applying the method of separating variables to the two-dimensional heat equation $u_t = c^2 \nabla^2 u$, show that the temperature in the plate is

$$u(x, y, t) = \sum_{m=1}^{\infty} \sum_{n=1}^{\infty} B_{mn} \sin mx \sin ny \, e^{-c^2(m^2 + n^2)t}$$

where

$$B_{mn} = \frac{4}{\pi^2} \int_0^\pi \int_0^\pi f(x, y) \sin mx \sin ny \, dx \, dy.$$

20. Find the temperature in the plate of Prob. 19, if $f(x, y) = x(\pi - x)y(\pi - y)$.

9.9 LAPLACIAN
IN POLAR COORDINATES

In connection with boundary value problems for partial differential equations, it is a general principle to use coordinates with respect to which the boundary of the region under consideration has a simple representation. In the next section we shall consider circular membranes. Then polar coordinates r and θ, defined by

$$x = r \cos \theta, \qquad y = r \sin \theta,$$

will be appropriate, because the boundary of the membrane can then be represented by the simple equation $r = const.$

When using r and θ we have to transform the Laplacian

$$\nabla^2 u = \frac{\partial^2 u}{\partial x^2} + \frac{\partial^2 u}{\partial y^2}$$

in the wave equation into these new coordinates.

Transformations of differential expressions from one coordinate system into another are frequently required in applications. Therefore, the student should follow our present consideration with great attention.

As in Sec. 9.4, we shall use the chain rule. For the sake of simplicity we shall denote partial derivatives by subscripts and $u(x, y, t)$, as a function of r, θ, t, by the same letter u.

By applying the chain rule (4), Sec. 5.15, we obtain

$$u_x = u_r r_x + u_\theta \theta_x.$$

By differentiating this again with respect to x we first have

(1)
$$\begin{aligned}
u_{xx} &= (u_r r_x)_x + (u_\theta \theta_x)_x \\
&= (u_r)_x r_x + u_r r_{xx} + (u_\theta)_x \theta_x + u_\theta \theta_{xx}.
\end{aligned}$$

Now, by applying the chain rule again, we find

$$(u_r)_x = u_{rr} r_x + u_{r\theta} \theta_x \qquad \text{and} \qquad (u_\theta)_x = u_{\theta r} r_x + u_{\theta\theta} \theta_x.$$

To determine the partial derivatives r_x and θ_x, we have to differentiate

$$r = \sqrt{x^2 + y^2} \qquad \text{and} \qquad \theta = \arctan \frac{y}{x},$$

finding

$$r_x = \frac{x}{\sqrt{x^2 + y^2}} = \frac{x}{r}, \qquad \theta_x = \frac{1}{1 + (y/x)^2}\left(-\frac{y}{x^2}\right) = -\frac{y}{r^2}.$$

Differentiating these two formulas again, we obtain

$$r_{xx} = \frac{r - x r_x}{r^2} = \frac{1}{r} - \frac{x^2}{r^3} = \frac{y^2}{r^3}, \; \theta_{xx} = -y\left(-\frac{2}{r^3}\right)r_x = \frac{2xy}{r^4}.$$

Substituting all these expressions into (1), using $u_{r\theta} = u_{\theta r}$ (cf. Sec. 0.2), and simplifying, we readily find

(2)
$$u_{xx} = \frac{x^2}{r^2} u_{rr} - 2 \frac{xy}{r^3} u_{r\theta} + \frac{y^2}{r^4} u_{\theta\theta} + \frac{y^2}{r^3} u_r + 2 \frac{xy}{r^4} u_\theta.$$

In a similar fashion we obtain

(3)
$$u_{yy} = \frac{y^2}{r^2} u_{rr} + 2 \frac{xy}{r^3} u_{r\theta} + \frac{x^2}{r^4} u_{\theta\theta} + \frac{x^2}{r^3} u_r - 2 \frac{xy}{r^4} u_\theta.$$

By adding these two expressions we see that the Laplacian in polar coordinates is

(4)
$$\nabla^2 u = \frac{\partial^2 u}{\partial r^2} + \frac{1}{r}\frac{\partial u}{\partial r} + \frac{1}{r^2}\frac{\partial^2 u}{\partial \theta^2}.$$

PROBLEMS

1. Transform (4) back into Cartesian coordinates.

2. Show that (4) may be written

$$\nabla^2 u = \frac{1}{r}\frac{\partial}{\partial r}\left(r\,\frac{\partial u}{\partial r}\right) + \frac{1}{r^2}\frac{\partial^2 u}{\partial \theta^2}.$$

3. If u is independent of θ, then (4) reduces to $\nabla^2 u = u_{rr} + u_r/r$. Derive this result directly from the Laplacian in Cartesian coordinates by assuming that u is independent of θ.

4. Find the Laplacian in *cylindrical coordinates* r, θ, z defined by $x = r\cos\theta$, $y = r\sin\theta$, $z = z$.

5. Let r, θ, ϕ be *spherical coordinates*, defined by

$$x = r\cos\theta\sin\phi, \qquad y = r\sin\theta\sin\phi, \qquad z = r\cos\phi.$$

If $u(x, y, z)$ is a function of $r = \sqrt{x^2 + y^2 + z^2}$ only, show that

$$\nabla^2 u = u_{rr} + \frac{2}{r}u_r.$$

6. Show that the Laplacian of u in spherical coordinates is

$$\nabla^2 u = u_{rr} + \frac{2}{r}u_r + \frac{1}{r^2}u_{\phi\phi} + \frac{\cot\phi}{r^2}u_\phi + \frac{1}{r^2\sin^2\phi}u_{\theta\theta}.$$

7. Show that the Laplacian in spherical coordinates may be written

$$\nabla^2 u = \frac{1}{r^2}\left[\frac{\partial}{\partial r}(r^2 u_r) + \frac{1}{\sin\phi}\frac{\partial}{\partial\phi}(\sin\phi\,u_\phi) + \frac{1}{\sin^2\phi}u_{\theta\theta}\right].$$

8. Transform the Laplacian in Prob. 6 back into Cartesian coordinates.

9. If x, y, are Cartesian coordinates, show that $x^* = x\cos\alpha - y\sin\alpha$, $y^* = x\sin\alpha + y\cos\alpha$ are Cartesian coordinates, and verify by calculation that $\nabla^2 u = u_{x^*x^*} + u_{y^*y^*}$.

10. Express $\nabla^2 u$ in terms of the coordinates $x^* = ax + b$, $y^* = cy + d$ where x, y are Cartesian coordinates.

11. If the surface of the homogeneous solid sphere $x^2 + y^2 + z^2 \leq R^2$ is kept at temperature zero and the initial temperature in the sphere is $f(r)$ where $r = \sqrt{x^2 + y^2 + z^2}$, show that the temperature $u(r, t)$ in the sphere is the solution of $u_t = c^2\left(u_{rr} + \frac{2}{r}u_r\right)$, satisfying the conditions $u(R, t) = 0$, $u(r, 0) = f(r)$.

12. Show that by setting $v = ru$ the formulas in Prob. 11 take the form $v_t = c^2 v_{rr}$, $v(R, t) = 0$, $v(r, 0) = rf(r)$. Include the condition $v(0, t) = 0$ (which holds because u must be bounded at $r = 0$), and solve the resulting problem by separating variables.

9.10   CIRCULAR MEMBRANE. BESSEL'S EQUATION

We shall now consider vibrations of the circular membrane of radius R shown in Fig. 271.   Using polar coordinates defined by

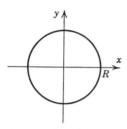

$$x = r \cos \theta \qquad y = r \sin \theta,$$

the wave equation

$$\frac{\partial^2 u}{\partial t^2} = c^2 \nabla^2 u$$

takes the form

$$\frac{\partial^2 u}{\partial t^2} = c^2 \left(\frac{\partial^2 u}{\partial r^2} + \frac{1}{r} \frac{\partial u}{\partial r} + \frac{1}{r^2} \frac{\partial^2 u}{\partial \theta^2} \right),$$

Fig. 271. Circular membrane.

cf. (4) in Sec. 9.9.   In the present section we shall consider solutions $u(r, t)$ of this equation which are radially symmetric, that is, do not depend on θ.   Then the wave equation reduces to the simpler form

(1)
$$\frac{\partial^2 u}{\partial t^2} = c^2 \left(\frac{\partial^2 u}{\partial r^2} + \frac{1}{r} \frac{\partial u}{\partial r} \right).$$

Since the membrane is fixed along the boundary $r = R$, we have the boundary condition

(2) $u(R, t) = 0$ for all $t \geq 0$.

Solutions not depending on θ will occur if the initial conditions do not depend on θ, that is, if they are of the form

(3) $u(r, 0) = f(r)$ [initial deflection $f(r)$]

and

(4) $\left. \dfrac{\partial u}{\partial t} \right|_{t=0} = g(r)$ [initial velocity $g(r)$].

First step.   Using the method of separating variables we first determine solutions of (1) that satisfy the boundary condition (2).   We start from

(5) $u(r, t) = W(r)G(t).$

By differentiating and inserting (5) into (1) and dividing the resulting equation by $c^2 WG$, we obtain

$$\frac{\ddot{G}}{c^2 G} = \frac{1}{W} \left(W'' + \frac{1}{r} W' \right)$$

where dots denote derivatives with respect to t and primes denote derivatives with respect to r. The expressions on both sides must be equal to a constant, and this constant must be negative, say, $-k^2$ in order to obtain solutions that satisfy the boundary condition without being identically zero. Thus,

$$\frac{\ddot{G}}{c^2 G} = \frac{1}{W}\left(W'' + \frac{1}{r}W'\right) = -k^2.$$

This yields the ordinary differential equations

(6) $\ddot{G} + \lambda^2 G = 0$ where $\lambda = ck$

and

(7) $W'' + \frac{1}{r}W' + k^2 W = 0.$

Second step. We first consider (7). Introducing the new independent variable $s = kr$ we have $1/r = k/s$,

$$W' = \frac{dW}{dr} = \frac{dW}{ds}\frac{ds}{dr} = \frac{dW}{ds}k \quad \text{and} \quad W'' = \frac{d^2W}{ds^2}k^2.$$

By substituting this into (7) and omitting the common factor k^2 we obtain

$$\frac{d^2W}{ds^2} + \frac{1}{s}\frac{dW}{ds} + W = 0.$$

This is **Bessel's equation** (1), Sec. 3.5, with $\nu = 0$. The general solution is (cf. Sec. 3.7)

$$W = C_1 J_0(s) + C_2 Y_0(s)$$

where J_0 and Y_0 are the Bessel functions of the first and second kind of order zero. Since the deflection of the membrane is always finite while Y_0 becomes infinite as s approaches zero, we cannot use Y_0 and must choose $C_2 = 0$. Clearly $C_1 \neq 0$ since otherwise $W \equiv 0$. We may set $C_1 = 1$, and then

(8) $W(r) = J_0(s) = J_0(kr).$

On the boundary $r = R$ we must have $u(R, t) = W(R)G(t) = 0$. Since $G \equiv 0$ would imply $u \equiv 0$, we require that

$$W(R) = J_0(kR) = 0.$$

Denoting the positive zeros of $J_0(s)$ by $s = \alpha_1, \alpha_2, \cdots$ (Fig. 272), we thus obtain

(9) $kR = \alpha_m$ or $k = k_m = \dfrac{\alpha_m}{R}$, $m = 1, 2, \cdots$.

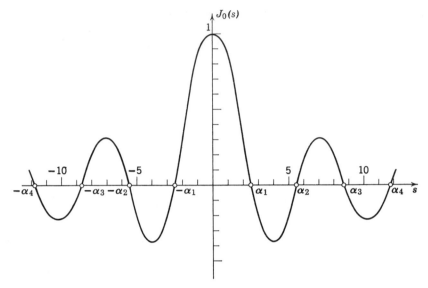

Fig. 272. Bessel function $J_0(s)$.

Hence the functions

(10)
$$W_m(r) = J_0(k_m r) = J_0\left(\frac{\alpha_m}{R} r\right), \qquad m = 1, 2, \cdots$$

are solutions of (7) which vanish at $r = R$.

The corresponding general solutions of (6) with $\lambda = \lambda_m = ck_m$ are

$$G_m(t) = a_m \cos \lambda_m t + b_m \sin \lambda_m t.$$

Hence the functions

(11)
$$\begin{aligned} u_m(r, t) &= W_m(r)G_m(t) \\ &= (a_m \cos \lambda_m t + b_m \sin \lambda_m t)J_0(k_m r) \qquad m = 1, 2, \cdots \end{aligned}$$

are solutions of the wave equation (1), satisfying the boundary condition (2). These are the *eigenfunctions* of our problem, and the corresponding *eigenvalues* are λ_m.

The vibration of the membrane corresponding to u_m is called the *m*th **normal mode**; it has the frequency $\lambda_m/2\pi$ cycles per unit time. Since the zeros of J_0 are not regularly spaced on the axis (in contrast to the zeros of the sine functions appearing in the case of the vibrating string), the sound of a drum is entirely different from that of a violin. The forms of the normal modes can easily be obtained from Fig. 272 and are shown in Fig. 273.

TABLE 23. ZEROS $s = \alpha_m$ OF $J_0(s)$.

m	α_m	m	α_m
1	2.404 825 6	16	49.482 609 9
2	5.520 078 1	17	52.624 051 8
3	8.653 727 9	18	55.765 510 8
4	11.791 534 4	19	58.906 983 9
5	14.930 917 7	20	62.048 469 2
6	18.071 064 0	21	65.189 964 8
7	21.211 636 6	22	68.331 469 3
8	24.352 471 5	23	71.472 981 6
9	27.493 479 1	24	74.614 500 6
10	30.634 606 5	25	77.756 025 6
11	33.775 820 2	26	80.897 555 9
12	36.917 098 4	27	84.039 090 8
13	40.058 425 8	28	87.180 629 8
14	43.199 791 7	29	90.322 172 6
15	46.341 188 4	30	93.463 718 8

For $m = 1$, all the points of the membrane move upward (or downward) at the same time. For $m = 2$, the situation is as follows. The function

$$W_2(r) = J_0\left(\frac{\alpha_2}{R} r\right)$$

is zero for $\alpha_2 r/R = \alpha_1$ or $r = \alpha_1 R/\alpha_2$. The circle $r = \alpha_1 R/\alpha_2$ is, therefore, a nodal line, and when at some instant the central part of the membrane moves upward, the outer part $(r > \alpha_1 R/\alpha_2)$ moves downward, and conversely. The solution $u_m(r, t)$ has $m - 1$ nodal lines which are concentric circles (Fig. 273).

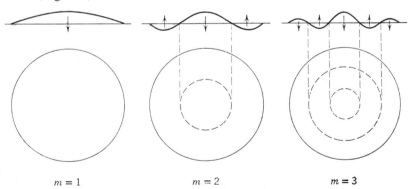

$m = 1$ $m = 2$ $m = 3$

Fig. 273. Normal modes of the circular membrane in the case of vibrations independent of the angle.

Third step.   To obtain a solution that also satisfies the initial conditions (3) and (4), we may proceed as in the case of the vibrating string, that is, we consider the series[7]

(12)
$$u(r, t) = \sum_{m=1}^{\infty} W_m(r)G_m(t)$$
$$= \sum_{m=1}^{\infty} (a_m \cos \lambda_m t + b_m \sin \lambda_m t)J_0\left(\frac{\alpha_m}{R} r\right).$$

Setting $t = 0$ and using (3), we obtain

(13)
$$u(r, 0) = \sum_{m=1}^{\infty} a_m J_0\left(\frac{\alpha_m}{R} r\right) = f(r).$$

Hence, for (12) to satisfy (3), the a_m must be the coefficients of the Fourier-Bessel series which represents $f(r)$ in terms of $J_0(\alpha_m r/R)$, that is [cf. (9) in Sec. 8.13],

$$a_m = \frac{2}{R^2 J_1^{2}(\alpha_m)} \int_0^R rf(r)J_0\left(\frac{\alpha_m}{R} r\right) dr, \qquad m = 1, 2, \cdots .$$

Differentiability of $f(r)$ in the interval $0 \leq r \leq R$ is sufficient for the existence of the development (13), cf. Ref. [B9]. The coefficients b_m in (12) can be determined from (4) in a similar fashion. To obtain numerical values of a_m and b_m, we may apply one of the usual methods of approximate integration, using tables of J_0 and J_1.

PROBLEMS

1. What is the reason for using polar coordinates in the present consideration?

2. If the tension of the membrane is increased how does the frequency of each normal mode (11) change?

3. Determine numerical values of the radii of the nodal lines of u_2 and u_3 [cf. (11)] when $R = 1$.

4. Same question as in Prob. 3, for u_4, u_5, and u_6.

5. Sketch a figure similar to Fig. 273, for u_4, u_5, u_6.

6. Is it possible that, for fixed c and R, two or more functions u_m [cf. (11)] that have different nodal lines correspond to the same eigenvalue?

7. Show that for (12) to satisfy (4),

$$b_m = \frac{2}{c\alpha_m RJ_1^{2}(\alpha_m)} \int_0^R rg(r)J_0(\alpha_m r/R) dr, \qquad m = 1, 2, \cdots .$$

Find the deflection $u(r, t)$ of the circular membrane of radius $R = 1$, if $c = 1$, the initial velocity is zero, and the initial deflection is $f(r)$ where
8. $f = 0.1J_0(\alpha_2 r)$ **9.** $f = k(1 - r^2)$ **10.** $f = k(1 - r^4)$
Hint: remember Probs. 3–10, Sec. 8.13.

[7] We shall not consider the questions of convergence and uniqueness.

Find vibrations of the circular membrane of radius R, depending on r and θ. Proceed as follows.

11. Show that substitution of $u = F(r, \theta)G(t)$ into the wave equation

(14)
$$u_{tt} = c^2\left(u_{rr} + \frac{1}{r}u_r + \frac{1}{r^2}u_{\theta\theta}\right)$$

leads to

(15)
$$\ddot{G} + \lambda^2 G = 0, \qquad \text{where } \lambda = ck,$$

(16)
$$F_{rr} + \frac{1}{r}F_r + \frac{1}{r^2}F_{\theta\theta} + k^2 F = 0.$$

12. Show that substitution of $F = W(r)Q(\theta)$ in (16) yields

(17)
$$Q'' + n^2 Q = 0,$$

(18)
$$r^2 W'' + rW' + (k^2 r^2 - n^2)W = 0.$$

13. Show that $Q(\theta)$ must be periodic with period 2π, and, therefore, $n = 0, 1, \cdots$ in (17) and (18). Show that this yields the solutions $Q_n = \cos n\theta$, $Q_n{}^* = \sin n\theta$, $W_n = J_n(kr)$, $n = 0, 1, \cdots$.

14. Show that the boundary condition

(19)
$$u(R, \theta, t) = 0$$

leads to the values $k = k_{mn} = \alpha_{mn}/R$ where $s = \alpha_{mn}$ is the mth positive zero of $J_n(s)$.

15. Show that solutions of (14) which satisfy (19) are

(20)
$$u_{mn} = (A_{mn} \cos ck_{mn}t + B_{mn} \sin ck_{mn}t)J_n(k_{mn}r) \cos n\theta,$$
$$u_{mn}{}^* = (A_{mn}{}^* \cos ck_{mn}t + B_{mn}{}^* \sin ck_{mn}t)J_n(k_{mn}r) \sin n\theta.$$

16. Show that $u_{m0}{}^* \equiv 0$ and u_{m0} is identical with (11) in the current section.

17. Show that u_{mn} has $m + n - 1$ nodal lines.

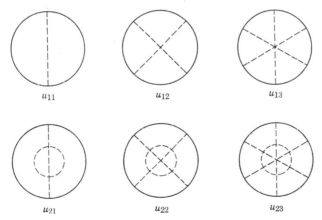

u_{11} $\qquad\qquad$ u_{12} $\qquad\qquad$ u_{13}

u_{21} $\qquad\qquad$ u_{22} $\qquad\qquad$ u_{23}

Fig. 274. Nodal lines of some of the solutions (20).

18. Graph the nodal lines of u_{3m}, $m = 1, 2, 3$.

19. Graph the nodal lines of $u_{mn}{}^*$, $m, n = 1, 2, 3$.

20. Show that the initial condition $u_t(r, \theta, 0) = 0$ leads to $B_{mn} = 0$, $B_{mn}{}^* = 0$ in (20).

9.11 LAPLACE'S EQUATION. POTENTIAL

One of the most important partial differential equations appearing in physics is Laplace's equation

$$(1) \qquad \nabla^2 u = 0.$$

Here $\nabla^2 u$ is the Laplacian of u. With respect to Cartesian coordinates x, y, z in space,

$$(2) \qquad \nabla^2 u = \frac{\partial^2 u}{\partial x^2} + \frac{\partial^2 u}{\partial y^2} + \frac{\partial^2 u}{\partial z^2}.$$

The theory of the solutions of Laplace's equation is called **potential theory**. Solutions of (1) that have *continuous* second-order partial derivatives are called **harmonic functions**.

The two-dimensional case, when u depends on two variables only, can most conveniently be treated by methods of complex analysis and will be considered in Sec. 10.3 and Chap. 13.

To illustrate the importance of Laplace's equation in engineering mathematics, let us mention some basic applications.

Laplace's equation occurs in connection with gravitational forces. In Ex. 4, Sec. 5.16, we have seen that if a particle A of mass M is fixed at a point (ξ, η, ζ) and another particle B of mass m is at a point (x, y, z), then A attracts B, the gravitational force being the gradient of the scalar function

$$u(x, y, z) = \frac{c}{r}, \qquad c = GMm = const,$$

$$r = \sqrt{(x - \xi)^2 + (y - \eta)^2 + (z - \zeta)^2} \qquad (> 0.)$$

This function is called the potential of the gravitational field, and it satisfies Laplace's equation.

The extension to the potential and force due to a continuous distribution of mass is quite direct. If a mass of density $\rho(\xi, \eta, \zeta)$ is distributed throughout a region R in space, then the corresponding potential at a point not occupied by mass is defined to be

$$(3) \qquad u(x, y, z) = k \iiint_R \frac{\rho}{r} \, d\xi \, d\eta \, d\zeta \qquad (k > 0).$$

Since $1/r$ $(r > 0)$ is a solution of (1), that is, $\nabla^2(1/r) = 0$, and ρ does not depend on x, y, z, we obtain

$$\nabla^2 u = k \iiint_R \rho \nabla^2 \left(\frac{1}{r}\right) d\xi \, d\eta \, d\zeta = 0,$$

that is, the gravitational potential defined by (3) satisfies Laplace's equation at any point which is not occupied by matter.

In *electrostatics* the electrical force of attraction or repulsion between charged particles is governed by *Coulomb's law* (cf. Sec. 5.16) which is of the same mathematical form as Newton's law of gravitation. From this it follows that the field created by a distribution of electrical charges can be described mathematically by a potential function which satisfies Laplace's equation at any point not occupied by charges.

In Chap. 13 we shall see that Laplace's equation also appears in the theory of incompressible fluid flow.

Furthermore, the basic equation in problems of heat conduction is the heat equation

$$u_t = c^2 \nabla^2 u \qquad \text{(cf. Sec. 6.9),}$$

and if the temperature u is independent of time t ("*steady state*") this equation reduces to Laplace's equation.

In most applications leading to Laplace's equation, it is required to solve a **boundary value problem**, that is, to determine the solution of (1) satisfying given boundary conditions on certain surfaces. It is then necessary to introduce coordinates in space such that those surfaces can be represented in a simple manner. This requires the transformation of the Laplacian (2) into other coordinate systems. Of course, such a transformation is quite similar to that in the case of the Laplacian of a function of two variables.

From (4) in Sec. 9.9, it follows immediately that the Laplacian of a function u in **cylindrical coordinates**[8] (Fig. 275)

(4) $\qquad r = \sqrt{x^2 + y^2} \qquad \theta = \text{arc tan} \, \dfrac{y}{x}, \qquad z = z$

is

(5) $\qquad \nabla^2 u = \dfrac{\partial^2 u}{\partial r^2} + \dfrac{1}{r}\dfrac{\partial u}{\partial r} + \dfrac{1}{r^2}\dfrac{\partial^2 u}{\partial \theta^2} + \dfrac{\partial^2 u}{\partial z^2}.$

Other important coordinates are **spherical coordinates**[9] r, θ, ϕ which are related to Cartesian coordinates as follows (cf. Fig. 276):

(6) $\qquad x = r \cos \theta \sin \phi, \qquad y = r \sin \theta \sin \phi, \qquad z = r \cos \phi.$

[8] Observe that θ is not completely determined by the ratio y/x but we must also take the signs of x and y into account.

[9] Sometimes also called *polar coordinates*.

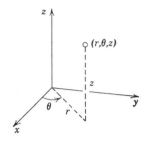

Fig. 275. Cylindrical coordinates.   **Fig. 276.** Spherical coordinates.

The Laplacian of a function u in spherical coordinates is

$$(7) \qquad \nabla^2 u = \frac{\partial^2 u}{\partial r^2} + \frac{2}{r}\frac{\partial u}{\partial r} + \frac{1}{r^2}\frac{\partial^2 u}{\partial \phi^2} + \frac{\cot \phi}{r^2}\frac{\partial u}{\partial \phi} + \frac{1}{r^2 \sin^2 \phi}\frac{\partial^2 u}{\partial \theta^2}.$$

This may also be written

$$(7') \qquad \nabla^2 u = \frac{1}{r^2}\left[\frac{\partial}{\partial r}\left(r^2 \frac{\partial u}{\partial r}\right) + \frac{1}{\sin \phi}\frac{\partial}{\partial \phi}\left(\sin \phi \frac{\partial u}{\partial \phi}\right) + \frac{1}{\sin^2 \phi}\frac{\partial^2 u}{\partial \theta^2}\right].$$

This formula can be derived in a manner similar to that in Sec. 9.9; the details are left as an exercise for the reader.

PROBLEMS

1. Verify that $u = c/r$ satisfies Laplace's equation in spherical coordinates.

2. Show that the only solution of $\nabla^2 u = 0$, depending only on $r = \sqrt{x^2 + y^2 + z^2}$, is $u = c/r + k$; here c and k are constants.

3. Determine c and k in Prob. 2 such that u represents the electrostatic potential between two concentric spheres of radii $r_1 = 10$ cm and $r_2 = 2$ cm kept at the potentials $U_1 = 110$ volts and $U_2 = 10$ volts, respectively.

4. Show that the only solution of the two-dimensional Laplace equation depending only on $r = \sqrt{x^2 + y^2}$, is $u = c \ln r + k$.

5. Find the electrostatic potential between two coaxial cylinders of radii $r_1 = 10$ cm and $r_2 = 2$ cm kept at the potentials $U_1 = 110$ volts and $U_2 = 10$ volts, respectively. Graph and compare the solutions of Probs. 3 and 5.

6. Express the spherical coordinates defined by (6) in terms of Cartesian coordinates.

7. Verify (5) by transforming $\nabla^2 u$ back into Cartesian coordinates.

8. Find the Laplacian in rectangular coordinates $x^* = ax$, $y^* = by$, $z^* = cz$ where x, y, z are Cartesian coordinates.

9. Starting from (2), verify by calculation that with respect to the Cartesian coordinates defined by (9), (10), Sec. 5.17,

$$\nabla^2 u = u_{x^*x^*} + u_{y^*y^*} + u_{z^*z^*}.$$

10. Show that substitution of $u = U(x, y, z)e^{-iwt}$ $(i = \sqrt{-1})$ into the three-dimensional wave equation $u_{tt} = c^2 \nabla^2 u$ yields the so-called *Helmholtz*[10] *equation*

$$\nabla^2 U + k^2 U = 0 \qquad\qquad k = \omega/c.$$

Find the steady-state (time-independent) temperature distribution:

11. Between two parallel plates $x = x_0$ and $x = x_1$ kept at the temperatures u_0 and u_1 respectively.

12. Between two coaxial circular cylinders of radii r_0 and r_1 kept at the temperatures u_0 and u_1, respectively.

13. Between two concentric spheres of radii r_0 and r_1 kept at the temperatures u_0 and u_1, respectively.

Show that the following functions $u = f(x, y)$ satisfy the Laplace equation and plot some of the equipotential lines $u = const.$

14. $x^2 - y^2$ **15.** $x^3 - 3xy^2$ **16.** $x/(x^2 + y^2)$
17. $y/(x^2 + y^2)$ **18.** $(x^2 - y^2)/(x^2 + y^2)^2$

19. If $u(r, \theta)$ satisfies $\nabla^2 u = 0$, show that $v(r, \theta) = u\left(\dfrac{1}{r}, \theta\right)$ satisfies $\nabla^2 v = 0$. (r and θ are polar coordinates.)

20. Let r, θ, ϕ be spherical coordinates. If $u(r, \theta, \phi)$ satisfies $\nabla^2 u = 0$, show that

$$v(r, \theta, \phi) = \frac{1}{r} u\left(\frac{1}{r}, \theta, \phi\right) \text{ satisfies } \nabla^2 v = 0.$$

9.12 LAPLACE'S EQUATION IN SPHERICAL COORDINATES. LEGENDRE'S EQUATION

Let us consider a typical boundary value problem that involves Laplace's equation in spherical coordinates. Suppose that the surface S of a sphere of radius R is kept at a fixed distribution of electric potential

(1) $$u(R, \theta, \phi) = f(\phi)$$

where r, θ, ϕ are the spherical coordinates defined in the last section, with the origin at the center of S, and $f(\phi)$ is a given function. We wish to find the potential u at all points in space which is assumed to be free of further charges. Since the potential on S is independent of θ, so is the potential in space. Thus $\partial^2 u/\partial \theta^2 = 0$, and from (7') in Sec. 9.11 we see that Laplace's equation reduces to

(2) $$\frac{\partial}{\partial r}\left(r^2 \frac{\partial u}{\partial r}\right) + \frac{1}{\sin \phi}\frac{\partial}{\partial \phi}\left(\sin \phi \frac{\partial u}{\partial \phi}\right) = 0.$$

[10] HERMANN VON HELMHOLTZ (1821–1894), German physicist.

Furthermore, at infinity the potential will be zero:

(3) $$\lim_{r \to \infty} u(r, \phi) = 0.$$

We shall solve the boundary value problem consisting of the equation (2) and the boundary conditions (1) and (3) by the method of separating variables. Substituting a solution of the form

$$u(r, \phi) = G(r)H(\phi)$$

into (2), and dividing the resulting equation by GH, we obtain

$$\frac{1}{G} \frac{d}{dr} \left(r^2 \frac{dG}{dr} \right) = - \frac{1}{H \sin \phi} \frac{d}{d\phi} \left(\sin \phi \frac{dH}{d\phi} \right).$$

By the usual argument, the two sides of this equation must be equal to a constant, say, k, so that

(4) $$\frac{1}{\sin \phi} \frac{d}{d\phi} \left(\sin \phi \frac{dH}{d\phi} \right) + kH = 0$$

and

$$\frac{1}{G} \frac{d}{dr} \left(r^2 \frac{dG}{dr} \right) = k.$$

The last equation may be written

$$r^2 G'' + 2rG' - kG = 0.$$

This is Cauchy's equation, and from Sec. 2.7 we know that it has solutions of the form $G = r^\alpha$. These solutions will have a particularly simple form, if we change our notation and write $n(n + 1)$ for k. In fact, then the equation becomes

(5) $$r^2 G'' + 2rG' - n(n + 1)G = 0,$$

where n is still arbitrary. By substituting $G = r^\alpha$ into (5) we have

$$[\alpha(\alpha - 1) + 2\alpha - n(n + 1)]r^\alpha = 0.$$

The zeros of the expression in brackets are $\alpha = n$ and $\alpha = -n - 1$. Hence we obtain the solutions

(6) $$G_n(r) = r^n \quad \text{and} \quad G_n^*(r) = \frac{1}{r^{n+1}}.$$

Introducing $k = n(n + 1)$ in (4) and setting

$$\cos \phi = w,$$

we have $\sin^2 \phi = 1 - w^2$ and

$$\frac{d}{d\phi} = \frac{d}{dw} \frac{dw}{d\phi} = -\sin \phi \frac{d}{dw}.$$

Consequently, (4) takes the form

(7)
$$\frac{d}{dw}\left[(1 - w^2)\frac{dH}{dw}\right] + n(n + 1)H = 0$$

or

(7')
$$(1 - w^2)\frac{d^2H}{dw^2} - 2w\frac{dH}{dw} + n(n + 1)H = 0.$$

This is *Legendre's equation* (cf. Sec. 3.3). For integral[11] $n = 0, 1, \cdots$, the Legendre polynomials

$$H = P_n(w) = P_n(\cos \phi), \qquad n = 0, 1, \cdots,$$

are solutions of (7). We thus obtain the following two sequences of solutions $u = GH$ of Laplace's equation (2):

$$u_n(r, \phi) = A_n r^n P_n(\cos \phi), \qquad u_n{}^*(r, \phi) = \frac{B_n}{r^{n+1}} P_n(\cos \phi), \quad n = 0, 1, \cdots,$$

where A_n and B_n are constants.

To find a solution of (2), valid at points *inside* the sphere and satisfying (1), we consider the series[12]

(8)
$$u(r, \phi) = \sum_{n=0}^{\infty} A_n r^n P_n(\cos \phi).$$

For (8) to satisfy (1) we must have

(9)
$$u(R, \phi) = \sum_{n=0}^{\infty} A_n R^n P_n(\cos \phi) = f(\phi);$$

that is, (9) must be the generalized Fourier series of $f(\phi)$ in terms of Legendre polynomials. From (8)–(11) in Sec. 8.12 [with $p(x) = 1$] it follows that

$$A_n R^n = \frac{2n + 1}{2} \int_{-1}^{1} \tilde{f}(w) P_n(w)\, dw$$

where $\tilde{f}(w)$ denotes $f(\phi)$ as a function of $w = \cos \phi$. Since $dw = -\sin \phi\, d\phi$,

---

[11] So far, n was arbitrary since k was arbitrary. It can be shown that the restriction of n to real integral values is necessary to make the solution of (7) continuous, together with its derivative of the first order, in the interval $-1 \leqq w \leqq 1$ or $0 \leqq \phi \leqq \pi$. Cf. Ref. [E2] in Appendix 1.

[12] Convergence will not be considered. It can be shown that if $f(\phi)$ and $f'(\phi)$ are piecewise continuous in the interval $0 \leqq \phi \leqq \pi$, the series (8) having the coefficients (10) can be differentiated termwise twice with respect to r and with respect to ϕ and the resulting series converge and represent $\partial^2 u/\partial r^2$ and $\partial^2 u/\partial \phi^2$, respectively. Hence the series (8) with coefficients (10) is then the solution of our problem inside the sphere.

and the limits of integration -1 and 1 correspond to $\phi = \pi$ and $\phi = 0$, respectively, we also have

(10) $\qquad A_n = \dfrac{2n + 1}{2R^n} \displaystyle\int_0^\pi f(\phi) P_n(\cos \phi) \sin \phi \, d\phi, \quad n = 0, 1, \cdots.$

Thus the series (8) with coefficients (10) is the solution of our problem for points inside the sphere.

To find the solution *exterior* to the sphere, we cannot use the functions $u_n(r, \phi)$ because these functions do not satisfy (3), but we may use the functions $u_n{}^*(r, \phi)$, which satisfy (3), and proceed as before. This leads to the solution

(11) $\qquad u(r, \phi) = \displaystyle\sum_{n=0}^\infty \dfrac{B_n}{r^{n+1}} P_n(\cos \phi) \qquad\qquad (r \geq R)$

with coefficients

(12) $\qquad B_n = \dfrac{2n + 1}{2} R^{n+1} \displaystyle\int_0^\pi f(\phi) P_n(\cos \phi) \sin \phi \, d\phi.$

PROBLEMS

1. Graph the functions $P_n(\cos \phi)$ for $n = 0, 1, 2, 3$ [cf. (11′), Sec. 3.3].

2. Find the surfaces on which the functions u_1, u_2, u_3 (p. 573) are zero.

Let r, θ, ϕ be the spherical coordinates used in the text. Find the potential in the interior of the sphere $R = 1$, assuming that there are no charges in the interior and the potential on the surface is $f(\phi)$ where

3. $f(\phi) = 1$ **4.** $f(\phi) = \cos \phi$ **5.** $f(\phi) = \cos^2 \phi$

6. $f(\phi) = \cos^3 \phi$ **7.** $f(\phi) = 10 \cos^3 \phi - 3 \cos^2 \phi - 5 \cos \phi - 1$

8. $f(\phi) = \cos 2\phi$ **9.** $f(\phi) = \cos 3\phi$

10. Find the potential exterior to the sphere in Probs. 3–9.

11. Show that in Prob. 3 the potential exterior to the sphere is the same as that of a point charge at the origin.

12. Verify by substitution that $u_n(r, \phi)$ and $u_n{}^*(r, \phi)$, $n = 0, 1, 2$ (p. 573) are solutions of (2).

13. Verify by substitution that the solution of Prob. 5 satisfies (2).

14. Graph the intersections of the equipotential surfaces in Prob. 4 with the xz-plane.

15. Consider the series in Prob. 20, Sec. 3.3 . Writing v for u, setting

$$x = \cos \phi = \tfrac{1}{2}(e^{i\phi} + e^{-i\phi}),$$

and using the binomial theorem, show that

$$(1 - 2v \cos \phi + v^2)^{-1/2} = (1 - ve^{i\phi})^{-1/2}(1 - ve^{-i\phi})^{-1/2}$$

$$= \left(1 + \frac{1}{2} ve^{i\phi} + \frac{1 \cdot 3}{2 \cdot 4} v^2 e^{2i\phi} + \cdots\right)\left(1 + \frac{1}{2} ve^{-i\phi} + \frac{1 \cdot 3}{2 \cdot 4} v^2 e^{-2i\phi} + \cdots\right)$$

$$= P_0 + P_1(\cos \phi)v + P_2(\cos \phi)v^2 + \cdots.$$

16. Show that the coefficient of v^n in the series in Prob. 15 is $P_0 = 1$ when $n = 0$ and

$$P_n(\cos \phi) = \frac{1 \cdot 3 \cdots (2n-1)}{n! \, 2^{n-1}} \left[\cos n\phi + \frac{1 \cdot n}{1 \cdot (2n-1)} \cos (n-2)\phi \right.$$

$$\left. + \frac{1 \cdot 3 \cdot n(n-1)}{1 \cdot 2 \cdot (2n-1)(2n-3)} \cos (n-4)\phi + \cdots + h_n \right] \quad (n = 1, 2, \cdots)$$

where the final term h_n is the term containing $\cos \phi$, if n is odd; but it is half the constant term indicated if n is even. *Hint:* use $e^{in\phi} + e^{-in\phi} = 2 \cos n\phi$, etc.

17. Using the series in Prob. 16, show that $P_0(\cos \phi) = 1$, $P_1(\cos \phi) = \cos \phi$, $P_2(\cos \phi) = (3 \cos 2\phi + 1)/4$.

18. Using the series in Prob. 16, determine $P_n(\cos \phi)$ for $n = 3, 4, 5$.

19. Obtain the representations in Prob. 17 from (11') in Sec. 3.3.

20. Using $P_n(1) = 1$ [cf. Prob. 21, Sec. 3.3], show that $|P_n(\cos \phi)| \leq 1$ for all real values of ϕ.

21. Consider a long cable or telephone wire (Fig. 277) which is imperfectly insulated so that leaks occur along the entire length of the cable. The source S of the current $i(x, t)$ in the cable is at $x = 0$, the receiving end R at $x = l$. The current flows from S to R, through the load, and returns to the ground. Let the constants R, L, C, and G denote the resistance, inductance, capacitance to ground and conductance to ground, respectively, of the cable per unit length. Show that

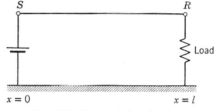

Fig. 277. Transmission line.

$$-\frac{\partial u}{\partial x} = Ri + L\frac{\partial i}{\partial t} \qquad \text{(First transmission line equation)}$$

where $u(x, t)$ is the potential in the cable. *Hint:* apply Kirchhoff's second law to a small portion of the cable between x and $x + \Delta x$ (difference of the potentials at x and $x + \Delta x$ = resistive drop + inductive drop).

22. Show that for the cable in Prob. 21,

$$-\frac{\partial i}{\partial x} = Gu + C\frac{\partial u}{\partial t} \qquad \text{(Second transmission line equation)}$$

Hint: use Kirchhoff's first law (difference of the currents at x and $x + \Delta x$ = loss due to leakage to ground + capacitive loss).

23. Show that elimination of i from the transmission line equations leads to

$$u_{xx} = LCu_{tt} + (RC + GL)u_t + RGu.$$

24. Find a similar second order equation for the current in the cable.

25. Show that in the case of alternating currents of high frequencies the equations in Probs. 23 and 24 can be approximated by the so-called **high frequency line equations**

$$u_{xx} = LCu_{tt}, \qquad i_{xx} = LCi_{tt}.$$

26. Solve the first high frequency line equation assuming that the initial potential is $U_0 \sin(\pi x/l)$, $\partial u/\partial t = 0$ when $t = 0$, and $u = 0$ at the ends $x = 0$ and $x = 1$ for all t.

27. For a submarine cable G is negligible and the frequencies are low. Show that this leads to the so-called *submarine cable equations* or **telegraph equations**

$$u_{xx} = RCu_t, \qquad i_{xx} = RCi_t.$$

28. Find the potential in a submarine cable with ends ($x = 0$, $x = l$) grounded and initial voltage distribution $U_0 = const.$

29. What problem in heat conduction is the analogue of Prob. 28?

30. Under what condition does the problem of a vibrating string lead to the same mathematical formulation as Prob. 26?

chapter 10

COMPLEX
ANALYTIC
FUNCTIONS

Many engineering problems may be treated and solved by methods of complex analysis. Roughly speaking, these problems can be subdivided into two large classes. The first class consists of "elementary problems" for which the knowledge of complex numbers gained in college algebra and calculus is sufficient. For example, many applications in connection with electric circuits and mechanical vibrating systems are of this type. The second class of problems requires a detailed knowledge of the theory of complex analytic functions, ("theory of functions," for short) and the powerful and elegant methods used in this branch of mathematics. Interesting problems in the theory of heat, in fluid dynamics, and in electrostatics belong to this category.

The following chapters will be devoted to the major parts of the theory of complex analytic functions and their applications. We shall see that the importance of these functions in engineering mathematics has the following three main roots.

1. The real and imaginary parts of an analytic function are solutions of Laplace's equation in two independent variables. Consequently, two-dimensional potential problems can be treated by methods developed in connection with analytic functions.

2. Many complicated real and complex integrals that occur in applications can be evaluated by methods of complex integration.

3. The majority of nonelementary functions appearing in engineering mathematics are analytic functions, and the consideration of these functions for complex values of the independent variable leads to a much deeper and more detailed knowledge of their properties.

In the present chapter we shall define analytic functions and consider their fundamental properties. We shall see that power series play a basic role in connection with analytic functions. The last few sections of the chapter will be devoted to the most important elementary complex functions.

Prerequisites for this chapter: elementary calculus, complex numbers (Secs. 0.4 and 0.5).

Sections which may be omitted in a shorter course: 10.4–10.7 (except for the basic notions of a sequence and a series).

References: Appendix 1, Part G.

Answers to problems: Appendix 2.

10.1 COMPLEX NUMBERS. TRIANGLE INEQUALITY

Complex numbers were introduced in Secs. 0.4 and 0.5, and we shall now consider several further properties.

The **real** and **imaginary parts** of a complex number

$$z = x + iy \qquad\qquad (x, y, \text{ real})$$

are x and y, respectively, and we write

$$\operatorname{Re} z = x, \qquad \operatorname{Im} z = y.$$

Introducing polar coordinates r and θ defined by

$$x = r \cos \theta, \qquad y = r \sin \theta,$$

we may represent the complex number z in polar form

$$z = r(\cos \theta + i \sin \theta).$$

r is called the **absolute value**, and θ the **argument** of z, and we write

$$|z| = r \qquad \text{and} \qquad \arg z = \theta.$$

Geometrically, $|z|$ is the distance of the point z from the origin (Fig. 278). Hence the inequality

$$|z_1| > |z_2|$$

means that the point z_1 is farther from the origin than the point z_2, and $|z_1 - z_2|$ is the distance between the points z_1 and z_2 (Fig. 279).

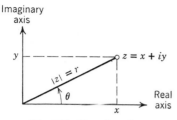

Fig. 278. Complex plane.

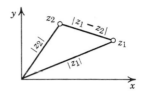

Fig. 279. Distance between two points in the complex plane.

For given z ($\neq 0$), the argument θ is determined only up to integral multiples of 2π. The value of θ which lies in the interval

$$-\pi < \theta \leq \pi$$

is called the **principal value** of the argument of z.

Example 1. Let $z = 1 + i$. Then $z = \sqrt{2}\left(\cos\frac{\pi}{4} + i\sin\frac{\pi}{4}\right)$ and

$$|z| = \sqrt{2}, \qquad \arg z = \frac{\pi}{4} \pm 2n\pi \qquad\qquad (n = 0, 1, \cdots).$$

The principal value of $\arg z$ is $\pi/4$ (Fig. 280).

Example 2. Let $z = 3 + 3\sqrt{3}i$. Then $z = 6\left(\cos\frac{\pi}{3} + i\sin\frac{\pi}{3}\right)$, $|z| = 6$, and the principal value of $\arg z$ is $\pi/3$.

Since for any complex number $z = x + iy$,

$$|z| = \sqrt{x^2 + y^2} \geq |x| \qquad \text{and similarly} \qquad |z| \geq |y|,$$

we obtain the useful inequalities

(1) $$|\mathrm{Re}\, z| \leq |z|, \qquad |\mathrm{Im}\, z| \leq |z|.$$

Let z_1 and z_2 be any complex numbers. Then the origin and the points z_1 and $z_1 + z_2$ are the vertices of a triangle[1] (Fig. 281) whose sides are $|z_1|$, $|z_2|$, and $|z_1 + z_2|$. We thus obtain the important **triangle inequality**

(2) $$|z_1 + z_2| \leq |z_1| + |z_2|,$$

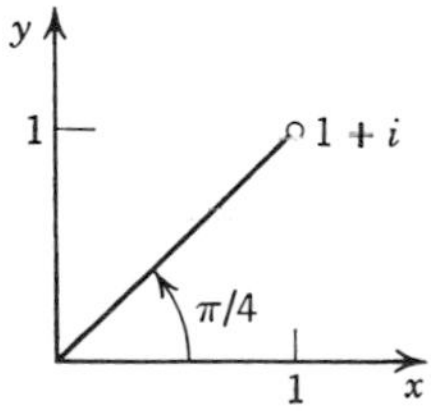

Fig. 280. Example 1. 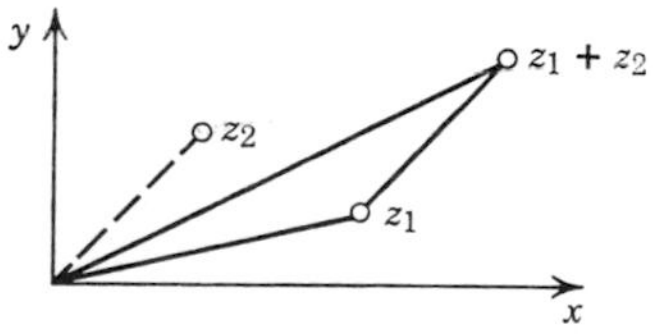   Fig. 281. Triangle inequality.

[1] Which may degenerate if z_1 and z_2 lie on the same straight line through the origin.

which will be frequently used in our considerations. The formal proof is left to the student (Prob. 13).

By induction the triangle inequality can be extended to arbitrary sums:

(3) $|z_1 + z_2 + \cdots + z_n| \leqq |z_1| + |z_2| + \cdots + |z_n|$;

that is, *the absolute value of a sum is at most equal to the sum of the absolute values of the summands.*

We shall now consider some important types of curves and regions in the complex plane and their representations by equations and inequalities.

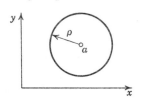

Fig. 282. Circle in the complex plane.

Since the distance between two points z and a is $|z - a|$, it follows that a circle C of radius ρ with center at a point a (Fig. 282) can be represented in the form

(4) $|z - a| = \rho.$

Consequently, the inequality

(5) $|z - a| < \rho$

holds for any point z inside C; that is, (5) represents the interior of C. Such a region is called a **circular disk**, or, more precisely, an *open* circular disk, in contrast to the *closed* circular disk

$$|z - a| \leqq \rho,$$

which consists of the interior of C and C itself. The open circular disk (5) is also called a **neighborhood** of the point a. Obviously, a has infinitely many such neighborhoods, each of which corresponds to a certain value of $\rho \, (>0)$.

Similarly, the inequality

$$|z - a| > \rho$$

represents the exterior of the circle C. Furthermore, the region between two concentric circles of radii ρ_1 and $\rho_2 (> \rho_1)$ can be represented in the form

$$\rho_1 < |z - a| < \rho_2,$$

where a is the center of the circles. Such a region is called an *open circular ring* or *open annulus* (Fig. 283).

The equation

$$|z| = 1$$

represents the so-called **unit circle**, that is, the circle of radius 1 with center at the origin. This circle will play an important role in various considerations.

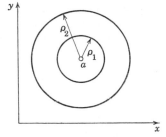

Fig. 283. Annulus in the complex plane.

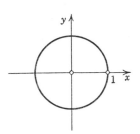

Fig. 284. Unit circle.

It is important that the student becomes completely familiar with representations of curves and regions in the complex plane. Therefore, he should pay particular attention to the problems included in the present section. This will make his future work less difficult.

We finally define some notions which are of general importance and will be used in our further consideration.

The term *set of points* in the complex plane means any sort of collection of finitely or infinitely many points. For example, the solutions of a quadratic equation, the points on a line, and the points in the interior of a circle are sets.

A set S is called *open* if every point of S has a neighborhood every point of which belongs to S. For example, the points in the interior of a circle or a square form an open set, and so do the points of the "right half-plane" Re $z = x > 0$. The set consisting of the points in the interior of a circle C and on C ("closed circular disk") is not open, because no neighborhood of a point of C lies entirely in the set.

A set S in the complex plane is called *closed* if the points of the plane which do not belong to S form an open set. For example, the points on and inside the unit circle form a closed set.

A set is called *bounded* if all of its points lie within a circle of sufficiently large radius. For example, the points in a rectangle form a bounded set, while the points on a straight line do not form a bounded set.

A set S is called *connected* if any two of its points can be joined by a broken line of finitely many linear segments all of whose points belong to S. An open connected set is called a **domain**. Thus the interior of a circle is a domain.

A *boundary point* of a set S is a point every neighborhood of which contains both points which belong to S and points which do not belong to S. For example, the boundary points of an annulus are the points on the two bounding circles. Clearly, if a set S is open, then no boundary point belongs to S; if S is closed, then every boundary point belongs to S.

A **region** is a set consisting of a domain plus, perhaps, some or all of its boundary points. (We should note that some authors use the term "region" for what we call a domain, and others make no distinction between the two terms.)

PROBLEMS

Find

1. Re $\dfrac{3 - i}{4 + 3i}$ **2.** Im $\dfrac{(2 - 3i)^2}{2 + 3i}$ **3.** Re z^4 $(z = x + iy)$

4. Im z^n where n is a positive integer   **5.** Im $(1/z^2)$

6. $|\cos \theta + i \sin \theta|$ **7.** $\left| \dfrac{(3 + 4i)(1 + i)^6}{i^5(2 + 4i)^2} \right|$ **8.** $\left| \dfrac{z + 1}{z - 1} \right|$

Verify (1) for

9. $z = (8 - 2i)^2$ **10.** $z = \dfrac{1 + i}{2 - 3i}$

Verify the triangle inequality for

11. $z_1 = 4 - 3i$, $z_2 = -2 + i$ **12.** $z_1 = 3 + 2i$, $z_2 = 3i$

13. Prove the triangle inequality.

14. Under what conditions will $|z_1 + z_2| = |z_1| + |z_2|$?

Using the triangle inequality prove that

15. $|z_1 + z_2| \geqq |z_1| - |z_2|$ **16.** $|z_1 + z_2| \geqq |z_2| - |z_1|$

Determine and graph the loci represented by the following equations and inequalities.

17. Re $z \geqq -2$ **18.** Re $(z^2) \leqq 1$ **19.** $|\arg z| < \pi/2$

20. $-\pi < \text{Im } z < \pi$ **21.** $|1/z| < 2$

22. $\left| \dfrac{z + 1}{z - 1} \right| = 2$ **23.** $\left| \dfrac{z + 1}{z - 1} \right| = 1$ **24.** $\left| \dfrac{z + i}{z - i} \right| = 1$

25. $|z - 1| + |z + 1| = 3$ **26.** $|z - 1| - |z + 1| = 1$

27. Show that multiplication of a complex number by i corresponds to a counter-clockwise rotation of the corresponding vector through the angle $\pi/2$.

28. Determine the principal values of the arguments of $1 + i\sqrt{3}$, -5, and $-3 - 3i$.

29. Show that the conjugate of a sum (product) of complex numbers is the sum (product) of the conjugates of those numbers.

30. Show that $|z_1 + z_2|^2 + |z_1 - z_2|^2 = 2(|z_1|^2 + |z_2|^2)$.

31. Show that $(|x| + |y|)/\sqrt{2} \leqq |z| \leqq |x| + |y|$. Give examples.

10.2 LIMIT. DERIVATIVE. ANALYTIC FUNCTION

We shall now define some basic concepts of complex analysis. The reader will notice that these definitions are quite similar to those in real calculus.

If x and y are real variables, then $z = x + iy$ is said to be a *complex variable*.

Consider now two complex variables z and w, and suppose that a relation is given so that to each value in some region of the complex z-plane there corresponds one or more values of w in a well-defined manner. Then w is said to be a **function** of z, defined in that region, and we write

$$w = f(z)$$

or $w = g(z)$, etc., or sometimes simply $w(z)$. The set of complex numbers which $w = f(z)$ can assume as z varies in that region, is called the *range of values* of the function $w = f(z)$.

If to each z in that region there corresponds only one value of $w = f(z)$, then the function $f(z)$ is said to be **single-valued**. A function which is not single-valued, is called *multi-valued*.

General assumption. *Unless it is stated otherwise, we shall assume that the functions under consideration are single-valued.*

Let u and v be the real and imaginary parts of w. Then, since w depends on $z = x + iy$, it is clear that in general u depends on x and y, and so does v. We may, therefore, write

$$w = f(z) = u(x, y) + iv(x, y),$$

and this shows that a complex function $f(z)$ is equivalent to two real functions $u(x, y)$ and $v(x, y)$.

Example 1. Let
$$w = f(z) = z^2 + 3z.$$
Then
$$u(x, y) = \operatorname{Re} f(z) = x^2 - y^2 + 3x \quad \text{and} \quad v(x, y) = \operatorname{Im} f(z) = 2xy + 3y.$$

At $z = x + iy = 1 + 3i$, the function has the value
$$(1 + 3i)^2 + 3(1 + 3i) = -5 + 15i,$$
and we may write
$$f(1 + 3i) = -5 + 15i, \quad u(1, 3) = -5, \quad v(1, 3) = 15.$$

Similarly, $f(1 + i) = 3 + 5i$, etc. Obviously, our function is defined for all z.

Example 2. Determine the value of $f(z) = 3\bar{z} = 3x - 3iy$ at $z = 2 + 4i$. Since $x = 2$ and $y = 4$, we obtain $f(2 + 4i) = 6 - 12i$.

A function $f(z)$ is said to have the **limit** l as z approaches z_0 if $f(z)$ is defined in a neighborhood of z_0 (except perhaps at z_0) and if for every positive real number ϵ (no matter how small but not zero) we can find a positive real number δ such that

(1) $$|f(z) - l| < \epsilon$$

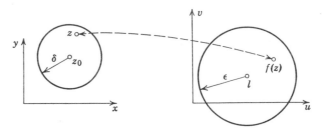

Fig. 285. Limit.

for all values $z \neq z_0$ in the disk $|z - z_0| < \delta$. This means that the values of $f(z)$ are as close as desired to l for all z which are sufficiently close to z_0 (Fig. 285), and we write

$$(2) \qquad \lim_{z \to z_0} f(z) = l.$$

Note well that this definition of a limit implies that z may approach z_0 from *any* direction in the complex plane.

The function $f(z)$ is said to be **continuous** at $z = z_0$ if $f(z_0)$ is defined and

$$(3) \qquad \lim_{z \to z_0} f(z) = f(z_0).$$

Note that by the definition of a limit this implies that $f(z)$ is defined in some neighborhood of z_0. A *continuous function*, without further qualification, is one which is continuous at all points where it is defined.

A function $f(z)$ is said to be *differentiable* at a point $z = z_0$ if the limit

$$(\mathbf{4}) \qquad f'(z_0) = \lim_{\Delta z \to 0} \frac{f(z_0 + \Delta z) - f(z_0)}{\Delta z}$$

exists. This limit is then called the **derivative** of $f(z)$ at the point $z = z_0$.

Setting $z_0 + \Delta z = z$, we have $\Delta z = z - z_0$ and may also write

$$(\mathbf{4'}) \qquad f'(z_0) = \lim_{z \to z_0} \frac{f(z) - f(z_0)}{z - z_0}.$$

Since the notion of a limit implies that z may approach z_0 from any direction, differentiability means that, along whatever path z approaches z_0, the quotient in (4′) always approaches a limit and that the limiting values are the same. This fact will be quite important in our later considerations.

By definition of a limit, (4′) means that there is a complex number $f'(z_0)$ for which, an $\epsilon > 0$ being given, we can find a $\delta > 0$ such that

$$(\mathbf{5}) \qquad \left| \frac{f(z) - f(z_0)}{z - z_0} - f'(z_0) \right| < \epsilon \qquad \text{when} \qquad |z - z_0| < \delta.$$

Example 3. The derivative of the function $f(z) = z^2$ is $2z$ at any point z, since

$$f'(z) = \lim_{\Delta z \to 0} \frac{(z + \Delta z)^2 - z^2}{\Delta z} = \lim_{\Delta z \to 0} (2z + \Delta z) = 2z.$$

All the familiar rules of real differential calculus, such as the rules for differentiating a constant, integer powers of z, sums, products and quotients of differentiable functions, and the chain rule for differentiating a function of a function, continue to hold in complex.

In fact, the corresponding proofs are literally the same.

It is important to note that there are many simple functions which do not have a derivative at any point. For instance, $f(z) = \bar{z} = x - iy$ is such a function, because the limit of the quotient

(6)
$$\frac{f(z + \Delta z) - f(z)}{\Delta z} = \frac{[(x + \Delta x) - i(y + \Delta y)] - (x - iy)}{\Delta x + i \Delta y}$$

$$= \frac{\Delta x - i \Delta y}{\Delta x + i \Delta y} \qquad (\Delta z = \Delta x + i \Delta y)$$

depends on the manner in which Δx and Δy approach zero. In fact, if we let $\Delta y \to 0$ first, and then $\Delta x \to 0$ (path I in Fig. 286), the limit of the quotient is $+1$, but if $\Delta x \to 0$ first, and then $\Delta y \to 0$ (path II in Fig. 286), the limit is -1. This example may be surprising, but it merely illustrates that differentiability of a complex function is a rather severe requirement.

We are now in a position to state the following definition which is basic in our further consideration.

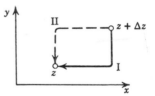

Fig. 286. Paths in (6).

Definition. *A function $f(z)$ is said to be analytic at a point $z = z_0$ if it is defined, and has a derivative, at every point in some neighborhood of z_0. It is said to be analytic in a domain D, if it is analytic at every point in D.*

Example 4. The integral powers $1, z, z^2, \cdots$ and, more generally, **polynomials**, that is, functions of the form

$$f(z) = c_0 + c_1 z + c_2 z^2 + \cdots + c_n z^n$$

where $c_0, \cdots, c_n$ are complex constants, are analytic in the entire plane. The function $1/(1 - z)$ is analytic everywhere except at $z = 1$.

We mention that the terms "holomorphic function" and "regular function" instead of "analytic function" are also used in the literature.

Complex analysis is concerned exclusively with analytic functions, and although many simple functions are not analytic, the large variety of remaining functions will yield a branch of mathematics which is most beautiful from the theoretical point of view and most useful for practical purposes.

PROBLEMS

1. Let $f(z) = z^2 - 2z$. Find $f(3 + i), f(-i), f(-4 + 2i)$.

2. Let $f(z) = (z + 1)/(z - 1)$. Find $f(2 - 4i), f(-1 + i), f(3 + 2i)$.

Find the real and imaginary parts of the following functions.

3. $f(z) = z^2 + 4z - 1$ **4.** $f(z) = 2z^3 - 3z$ **5.** $f(z) = 1/(1 - z)$

Suppose that z varies in a region R in the z-plane. Find the (precise) region in the w-plane in which the corresponding values of $w = f(z)$ lie, and show the two regions graphically.

6. $f(z) = iz$, R: $\operatorname{Re} z \geq 0$

7. $f(z) = 3z - \pi$, R: $-\pi < \operatorname{Re} z < \pi$

8. $f(z) = z^2$, R: $|z| \leq 1, 0 \leq \arg z \leq \pi/4$

9. $f(z) = z^2$, R: $1 \leq |z| \leq 2, 0 \leq \arg z < \pi/2$

10. $f(z) = z^3$, R: $\operatorname{Re} z > 0$, $\operatorname{Im} z > 0$

11. $f(z) = z^4$, R: $0 \leq \arg z < \pi/2$

Differentiate

12. $f(z) = z^3 - 4z^2 + 3z + 2$ **13.** $f(z) = (z^2 - 4)^3$

14. $f(z) = 1/(1 - z)$ **15.** $f(z) = (z^2 - 4)/(z^2 + 1)$

Find the value of the derivative at z_0:

16. $f(z) = 2z^2 - 4z + 3i, z_0 = 1 + i$ **17.** $f(z) = (z^2 - i)^2, z_0 = 3 - 2i$

18. $f(z) = (z + i)/(z - i), z_0 = -i$ **19.** $f(z) = (1 + i)z^2 - 2iz, z_0 = 1 - i$

20. If $\lim\limits_{z \to z_0} f(z) = l$ and $\lim\limits_{z \to z_0} g(z) = p$ show that

$$\lim_{z \to z_0} [f(z) + g(z)] = \lim_{z \to z_0} f(z) + \lim_{z \to z_0} g(z) = l + p,$$

$$\lim_{z \to z_0} [f(z)g(z)] = \lim_{z \to z_0} f(z) \lim_{z \to z_0} g(z) = lp.$$

21. Prove that (2) is equivalent to the pair of relations

$$\lim_{z \to z_0} \operatorname{Re} f(z) = \operatorname{Re} l, \qquad \lim_{z \to z_0} \operatorname{Im} f(z) = \operatorname{Im} l.$$

22. The function $f(z) = 3(z^2 - 1)/(z - 1)$ is not defined for $z = 1$, but for all other values of z it is equal to $3(z + 1)$. Using the definition of the limit, show that $\lim\limits_{z \to 1} f(z) = 6$. (Note that the limit is established when some formula is found for δ as a function of ϵ.)

Using the definition of the limit, prove that the following functions are continuous.

23. $f(z) = z^2$ **24.** $f(z) = z^3$

Are the following functions continuous at the origin?

25. $f(z) = \begin{cases} 0 & \text{when } z = 0 \\ \operatorname{Re} z/|z| & \text{when } z \neq 0 \end{cases}$ **26.** $f(z) = \begin{cases} 0 & \text{when } z = 0 \\ \operatorname{Re} (z^2)/|z^2| & \text{when } z \neq 0 \end{cases}$

27. $f(z) = \begin{cases} 0 & \text{when } z = 0 \\ (\operatorname{Re} z)^2/|z| & \text{when } z \neq 0 \end{cases}$

28. $f(z) = \begin{cases} 0 & \text{when } z = 0 \\ \text{Im } z/(1 + |z|) & \text{when } z \neq 0 \end{cases}$

29. If $z_1, z_2, \cdots$ are complex numbers for which $\lim\limits_{n \to \infty} z_n = a$ and $f(z)$ is continuous at $z = a$, show that $\lim\limits_{n \to \infty} f(z_n) = f(a)$.

Show that

30. $[af(z) + bg(z)]' = af'(z) + bg'(z)$

31. $[f(z)g(z)]' = f'(z)g(z) + f(z)g'(z)$

32. Show that $f(z) = |z|^2$ is differentiable only at $z = 0$. *Hint:* use the relation $|z + \Delta z|^2 = (z + \Delta z)(\bar{z} + \overline{\Delta z})$.

10.3 CAUCHY-RIEMANN EQUATIONS. LAPLACE'S EQUATION

We shall now derive a simple basic criterion for analyticity of a complex function

$$(1) \qquad w = f(z) = u(x, y) + iv(x, y).$$

We first suppose that $f(z)$ is analytic in a domain D of the z-plane. Then, by definition, $f(z)$ has a derivative

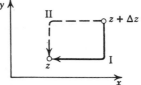

$$(2) \qquad f'(z) = \lim_{\Delta z \to 0} \frac{f(z + \Delta z) - f(z)}{\Delta z}$$

Fig. 287. Paths in (2).

everywhere in D, and the limit in (2) is independent of the choice of the path along which $\Delta z \to 0$. We may set $\Delta z = \Delta x + i\Delta y$. Choosing path I in Fig. 287, we let $\Delta y \to 0$ first and then $\Delta x \to 0$. After Δy becomes zero, $\Delta z = \Delta x$, and by (1),

$$f'(z) = \lim_{\Delta x \to 0} \frac{u(x + \Delta x, y) + iv(x + \Delta x, y) - [u(x, y) + iv(x, y)]}{\Delta x}$$

$$= \lim_{\Delta x \to 0} \frac{u(x + \Delta x, y) - u(x, y)}{\Delta x} + i \lim_{\Delta x \to 0} \frac{v(x + \Delta x, y) - v(x, y)}{\Delta x}.$$

Since $f'(z)$ exists, the last two limits exist. They are the partial derivatives of u and v with respect to x. Hence $f'(z)$ can be written

$$(3) \qquad f'(z) = \frac{\partial u}{\partial x} + i \frac{\partial v}{\partial x}.$$

Similarly, if we choose path II in Fig. 287, we let $\Delta x \to 0$ first and then $\Delta y \to 0$. After Δx becomes zero, $\Delta z = i\Delta y$, and

$$f'(z) = \lim_{\Delta y \to 0} \frac{u(x, y + \Delta y) - u(x, y)}{i\Delta y} + i \lim_{\Delta y \to 0} \frac{v(x, y + \Delta y) - v(x, y)}{i\Delta y} ;$$

that is,

$$(4) \qquad f'(z) = -i\frac{\partial u}{\partial y} + \frac{\partial v}{\partial y}$$

because $1/i = -i$. The existence of $f'(z)$ thus implies the existence of the four partial derivatives in (3) and (4).

By equating the real and the imaginary parts of the right-hand sides of (3) and (4) we obtain

$$(5) \qquad \frac{\partial u}{\partial x} = \frac{\partial v}{\partial y} \qquad \text{and} \qquad \frac{\partial u}{\partial y} = -\frac{\partial v}{\partial x}.$$

These basic relations are called the **Cauchy-Riemann differential equations.**[2,3]

We may sum up our result as follows.

Theorem 1. *The real and imaginary parts of an analytic function $f(z) = u(x, y) + iv(x, y)$ satisfy the Cauchy-Riemann equations (5) at each point where $f(z)$ is analytic.*

Example 1. The function $f(z) = z^2 = x^2 - y^2 + 2ixy$ is analytic for all z, and $f'(z) = 2z$. We have $u = x^2 - y^2$, $v = 2xy$,

$$\frac{\partial u}{\partial x} = 2x, \qquad \frac{\partial u}{\partial y} = -2y, \qquad \frac{\partial v}{\partial x} = 2y, \qquad \frac{\partial v}{\partial y} = 2x,$$

and the Cauchy-Riemann equations are satisfied for all x, y.

The Cauchy-Riemann equations are fundamental because they are not only necessary but also sufficient for a function to be analytic; more precisely:

Theorem 2. *If two real (single-valued) functions $u(x, y)$ and $v(x, y)$ of the real variables x and y have continuous first partial derivatives that satisfy the Cauchy-Riemann equations in some domain D, then the complex function $f(z) = u(x, y) + iv(x, y)$ is analytic in D.*

[2] Cf. the footnote on p. 92.

[3] BERNHARD RIEMANN (1826–1866), German mathematician, who developed what may be called the "geometrical approach" to complex analysis, based upon the Cauchy-Riemann equations and conformal mapping, in contrast to the German mathematician KARL WEIERSTRASS (1815–1897), who based complex analysis on power series (cf. Sec. 10.9, 11.7). Riemann developed also the so-called Riemannian geometry, which is the mathematical base of Einstein's theory of relativity.

Proof. Let P: (x, y) be any fixed point in D. Since D is a domain, it contains a neighborhood of P. In this neighborhood we choose a point Q: $(x + \Delta x, y + \Delta y)$. Then the segment PQ is in D, and from the mean-value theorem in Sec. 5.15 it follows that

(6)

$$u(x + \Delta x, y + \Delta y) - u(x, y) = \Delta x \frac{\partial u}{\partial x} + \Delta y \frac{\partial u}{\partial y},$$

$$v(x + \Delta x, y + \Delta y) - v(x, y) = \Delta x \frac{\partial v}{\partial x} + \Delta y \frac{\partial v}{\partial y},$$

the derivatives being evaluated at a suitable point of that segment. We set

$$f(z) = u(x, y) + iv(x, y) \quad \text{and} \quad \Delta z = \Delta x + i\Delta y.$$

Then we obtain from (6)

$$f(z + \Delta z) - f(z) = \frac{\partial u}{\partial x} \Delta x + \frac{\partial u}{\partial y} \Delta y + i\left(\frac{\partial v}{\partial x} \Delta x + \frac{\partial v}{\partial y} \Delta y\right).$$

Using the Cauchy-Riemann equations, we may replace $\partial u/\partial y$ by $-\partial v/\partial x$ and $\partial v/\partial y$ by $\partial u/\partial x$, finding

$$f(z + \Delta z) - f(z) = \frac{\partial u}{\partial x}(\Delta x + i\Delta y) + i\frac{\partial v}{\partial x}(\Delta x + i\Delta y) = \left(\frac{\partial u}{\partial x} + i\frac{\partial v}{\partial x}\right)\Delta z.$$

Dividing both sides by Δz, we obtain

$$\frac{f(z + \Delta z) - f(z)}{\Delta z} = \frac{\partial u}{\partial x} + i\frac{\partial v}{\partial x}.$$

If we let Δz approach zero then the derivatives on the right become $\partial u/\partial x$ and $\partial v/\partial x$, evaluated at (x, y); hence the limit of the quotient on the left exists, and from (3) we see that it is $f'(z)$. This means that $f(z)$ is analytic in D, and the proof is complete.

These theorems are of great practical importance, and we may now easily decide whether or not a given complex function is analytic.

Example 2. Let
$$f(z) = \operatorname{Re} z = x.$$
Then
$$u = x \quad \text{and} \quad v = 0.$$

The equations (5) are not satisfied, that is, $\operatorname{Re} z$ is not analytic. Similarly, $\operatorname{Im} z$ is not analytic.

Example 3. Let
$$f(z) = |z|^2 = x^2 + y^2.$$
Then
$$u = x^2 + y^2 \quad \text{and} \quad v = 0.$$

The Cauchy-Riemann equations are satisfied only at the origin $x = y = 0$.

Example 4. Let
$$f(z) = \bar{z} = x - iy.$$
Then
$$u = x \quad \text{and} \quad v = -y.$$
Hence $\partial u/\partial x = 1$ and $\partial v/\partial y = -1$, which shows that the first equation (5) is not satisfied at any point, that is, $\bar{z}$ is not an analytic function. This reestablishes our result in Sec. 10.2.

We mention that if we use the polar form $z = r(\cos \theta + i \sin \theta)$ and set
$$f(z) = u(r, \theta) + iv(r, \theta),$$
then the Cauchy-Riemann equations are:

(7)
$$\frac{\partial u}{\partial r} = \frac{1}{r}\frac{\partial v}{\partial \theta}, \qquad \frac{\partial v}{\partial r} = -\frac{1}{r}\frac{\partial u}{\partial \theta}.$$

We shall prove later (in Sec. 11.6) that the derivative of an analytic function $f(z) = u(x, y) + iv(x, y)$ is itself analytic. By this important fact $u(x, y)$ and $v(x, y)$ will have continuous partial derivatives of all orders. In particular the mixed second derivatives of these functions will be equal:
$$\frac{\partial^2 u}{\partial x \partial y} = \frac{\partial^2 u}{\partial y \partial x}, \qquad \frac{\partial^2 v}{\partial x \partial y} = \frac{\partial^2 v}{\partial y \partial x}.$$

Differentiating the Cauchy-Riemann equations, we thus obtain
$$\frac{\partial^2 u}{\partial x^2} = \frac{\partial^2 v}{\partial x \partial y}, \qquad \frac{\partial^2 u}{\partial y^2} = -\frac{\partial^2 v}{\partial x \partial y},$$
$$\frac{\partial^2 u}{\partial x \partial y} = \frac{\partial^2 v}{\partial y^2}, \qquad \frac{\partial^2 u}{\partial x \partial y} = -\frac{\partial^2 v}{\partial x^2}.$$

This yields the following important result.

Theorem 3. *The real and imaginary parts of a complex function $f(z) = u(x, y) + iv(x, y)$ which is analytic in a domain D are solutions of Laplace's equation,*
$$\nabla^2 u = \frac{\partial^2 u}{\partial x^2} + \frac{\partial^2 u}{\partial y^2} = 0, \qquad \nabla^2 v = \frac{\partial^2 v}{\partial x^2} + \frac{\partial^2 v}{\partial y^2} = 0,$$
in D and have continuous second partial derivatives in D.

This is one of the main reasons for the great practical importance of complex analysis in engineering mathematics, as we shall see in Chaps. 12 and 13.

A solution of Laplace's equation having *continuous* second-order partial derivatives is called a **harmonic function** (cf. also Sec. 9.11). Hence the real and imaginary parts of an analytic function are harmonic functions.

If two harmonic functions $u(x, y)$ and $v(x, y)$ satisfy the Cauchy-Riemann equations in a domain D, that is, if u and v are the real and imaginary parts of an analytic function $f(z)$ in D, then $v(x, y)$ is said to be a **conjugate harmonic function** of $u(x, y)$ in D, and the pair u, v is called a *pair of conjugate harmonic functions* in D. (Of course this use of the word "conjugate" is different from that employed in defining $\bar{z}$, the conjugate of a complex number z.)

A conjugate of a given harmonic function can be obtained from the Cauchy-Riemann equations, as may be illustrated by the following example.

Example 5. The function $u = x^2 - y^2$ is harmonic, and we have $\partial u / \partial x = 2x$, $\partial u / \partial y = -2y$. Hence a conjugate of u must satisfy

$$\frac{\partial v}{\partial y} = 2x, \qquad \frac{\partial v}{\partial x} = 2y.$$

By integrating the first equation with respect to y we obtain

$$v = 2xy + h(x)$$

where $h(x)$ depends only on x. Substituting this in the last equation, we have $h'(x) = 0$ and, therefore, $h = c = const$. Hence, the most general conjugate function of $x^2 - y^2$ is $2xy + c$, where c is a real constant, and the most general analytic function with the real part $x^2 - y^2$ is $x^2 - y^2 + i(2xy + c) = z^2 + ic$.

PROBLEMS

Using (3) or (4), find the derivative of the following functions.

1. $f(z) = az + b$　　　　**2.** $f(z) = z + \dfrac{1}{z}$　　　　**3.** $f(z) = \dfrac{1}{1 - z}$

4. $f(z) = z^3 + 3z^2 - z$　　　**5.** $f(z) = \dfrac{z + 1}{z - 2}$　　　**6.** $f(z) = (z^2 + 3z)^2$

7. Show that

$$f'(z) = \frac{\partial u}{\partial x} - i \frac{\partial u}{\partial y}, \qquad f'(z) = \frac{\partial v}{\partial y} + i \frac{\partial v}{\partial x}.$$

Are the following functions analytic?
8. $f(z) = z^3$　　　**9.** $f(z) = 1/(1 - z)$, $z \neq 1$　　　**10.** $f(z) = z + \bar{z}$
11. $f(z) = |z|^2$　　**12.** $f(z) = e^x(\cos y + i \sin y)$
13. $f(z) = \sin x \cosh y + i \cos x \sinh y$

Using (5), find the most general analytic function $f(z) = u(x, y) + iv(x, y)$ for which:
14. $u = x$　　**15.** $v = y$　　　　**16.** $v = xy$
17. $u = xy$　　**18.** $u = 2x^3 - 6xy^2$　　**19.** $u = e^x \cos y$

Show that the following functions are harmonic and find a corresponding analytic function $f(z) = u(x, y) + iv(x, y)$.
20. $v = 2xy + 2y$　　**21.** $u = \ln(x^2 + y^2)$　　**22.** $v = \cos x \sinh y$

Find the most general real harmonic polynomial of the form

23. $u = ax^2 + bxy + cy^2$ **24.** $u = ax^3 + bx^2y + cxy^2 + ky^3$

25. If $f(z)$ is analytic and $|f(z)| = const$, show that $f(z) = const$.

26. If $f(z)$ is analytic and $\operatorname{Re} f(z) = const$, show that $f = const$.

27. If $f(z)$ is analytic in a domain D and $f'(z) = 0$ everywhere in D, show that $f(z) = const$.

28. Derive (7) from (5).

Using (7), show that the following functions are analytic.

29. $f(z) = z^6$ **30.** $f(z) = 1/z^4$ $(z \neq 0)$ **31.** $f(z) = \ln r + i\theta$

10.4 SEQUENCES

Infinite sequences and series play a basic role in complex analysis and its applications. We shall see that most of the definitions and theorems relating to complex sequences and series are quite similar to those in the case of real sequences and series.

If to each positive integer n there is assigned a number z_n, then these numbers

$$z_1, z_2, \cdots, z_n, \cdots$$

are said to form an *infinite sequence* or, briefly, a **sequence**, and the numbers z_n are called the **terms** of the sequences.

A sequence whose terms are real is called a *real sequence*.

At times it is convenient to number the terms of a sequence starting with 0, with 2, or with some other integer.

A sequence $z_1, z_2, \cdots$ is said to **converge** *to the number c*, or to *be convergent with the limit c*, if to each positive number ϵ (no matter how small but not zero) we can find a number N such that

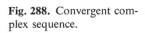

(1) $|z_n - c| < \epsilon$ for each $n > N$,

and then we write

$$\lim_{n \to \infty} z_n = c.$$

Fig. 288. Convergent complex sequence.

A sequence which is not convergent is said to be **divergent** or to **diverge**.

The geometrical interpretation of the condition (1) is simple enough. It means that each term z_n with $n > N$ lies in the open circular disk of radius ϵ with center at c (Fig. 288), and at most finitely many terms z_n do not lie in

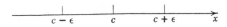

Fig. 289. Convergent real sequence.

that disk no matter how small the radius ϵ of the disk is chosen. Of course, N will depend on the choice of ϵ, in general.

In the case of a *real* sequence, the condition (1) means geometrically that each term z_n with $n > N$ lies between $c - \epsilon$ and $c + \epsilon$ (Fig. 289), and at most finitely many terms of the sequence do not lie in that interval.

Example 1. The sequence whose terms are $z_n = 1 + \dfrac{2}{n}, (n = 1, 2, \cdots)$, that is,

$$3, 2, \tfrac{5}{3}, \tfrac{6}{4}, \tfrac{7}{5}, \cdots$$

is convergent with the limit $c = 1$. In fact, in (1),

$$z_n - c = 1 + \frac{2}{n} - 1 = \frac{2}{n} \quad \text{and} \quad \frac{2}{n} < \epsilon \quad \text{when} \quad \frac{n}{2} > \frac{1}{\epsilon} \quad \text{or} \quad n > \frac{2}{\epsilon}.$$

For example, choosing $\epsilon = \dfrac{1}{100}$ we have $\dfrac{2}{n} < \dfrac{1}{100}$ when $n > 200$.

Example 2. The sequences $1, 2, 3, \cdots$ and $\tfrac{1}{4}, \tfrac{3}{4}, \tfrac{1}{5}, \tfrac{4}{5}, \tfrac{1}{6}, \tfrac{5}{6}, \cdots$ are divergent.

Example 3. The sequence whose terms are $z_n = \dfrac{2n - 1}{n} + i\,\dfrac{n + 2}{n}$ is

$$1 + 3i, \qquad \tfrac{3}{2} + 2i, \qquad \tfrac{5}{3} + \tfrac{5}{3}i, \qquad \tfrac{7}{4} + \tfrac{3}{2}i, \cdots.$$

It converges to $c = 2 + i$. In fact, in (1),

$$|z_n - c| = \left| \frac{2n - 1}{n} + i\,\frac{n + 2}{n} - (2 + i) \right| = \left| -\frac{1}{n} + \frac{2i}{n} \right| = \frac{\sqrt{5}}{n}$$

and $\dfrac{\sqrt{5}}{n} < \epsilon$ when $\dfrac{n}{\sqrt{5}} > \dfrac{1}{\epsilon}$ or $n > \dfrac{\sqrt{5}}{\epsilon} = \dfrac{2.236 \cdots}{\epsilon}$.

For example, choosing $\epsilon = 1/100$ we thus obtain

$$|z_n - c| < \epsilon \quad \text{when} \quad n = 224, 225, \cdots.$$

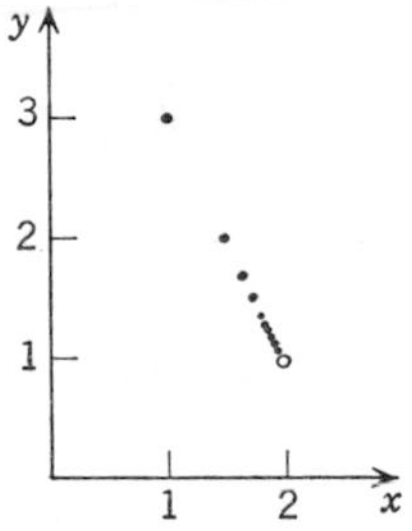

A complex sequence $z_1, z_2, \cdots$ being given, we may consider the sequence of the real parts and the sequence of the imaginary parts. Setting

$$z_n = x_n + iy_n,$$

these sequences are

Fig. 290. Sequence in Example 3.

$$x_1, x_2, x_3, \cdots \qquad \text{and} \qquad y_1, y_2, y_3, \cdots.$$

For instance, in Ex. 3 the two sequences are

$$1, \tfrac{3}{2}, \tfrac{5}{3}, \tfrac{7}{4}, \cdots \qquad \text{and} \qquad 3, 2, \tfrac{5}{3}, \tfrac{3}{2}, \cdots,$$

and we observe that the sequence of the real parts converges to 2, the real part of c, while the sequence of the imaginary parts converges to 1, the imaginary part of c. This illustrates

Theorem 1. *A sequence $z_1, z_2, \cdots, z_n, \cdots$ of complex numbers $z_n = x_n + iy_n$ ($n = 1, 2, \cdots$) converges to the limit $c = a + ib$ if and only if the sequence of the real parts $x_1, x_2, \cdots$ converges to a and the sequence of the imaginary parts $y_1, y_2, \cdots$ converges to b.*

Proof. If $|z_n - c| < \epsilon$ then $z_n = x_n + iy_n$ is within the circle of radius ϵ about $c = a + ib$ so that necessarily (Fig. 291a)

$$|x_n - a| < \epsilon, \qquad |y_n - b| < \epsilon.$$

Thus convergence of z_n to c as $n \to \infty$ implies convergence of x_n to a and y_n to b.

Conversely, if $x_n \to a$ and $y_n \to b$ as $n \to \infty$, then for given $\epsilon > 0$ we can choose N so large that

$$|x_n - a| < \frac{\epsilon}{2}, \qquad |y_n - b| < \frac{\epsilon}{2} \qquad \text{for every } n > N.$$

These two inequalities imply that $z_n = x_n + iy_n$ lies in a square with center c and side ϵ. Hence, z_n must lie within a circle of radius ϵ about c (Fig. 291b). This completes the proof.

This theorem shows that, by studying the real and imaginary parts, the convergence of complex sequences can be referred back to that of real sequences.

A point a is called a **limit point** of a sequence $z_1, z_2, \cdots$ if, given an $\epsilon > 0$ (no matter how small),

(2) $$|z_n - a| < \epsilon \qquad \text{for infinitely many } n.$$

Geometrically speaking, this means that infinitely many terms of the sequence lie within the circle of radius ϵ about a, no matter how small the radius ϵ is chosen.

Note that if (2) holds, there may still be infinitely many terms which do not lie within that circle, and the sequence may not be convergent. In fact, if a sequence has more than one limit point, it diverges. The following example may illustrate the situation.

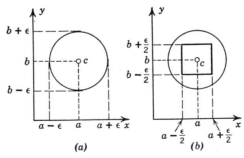

Fig. 291. Proof of Theorem 1.

Example 4.

Sequence	Limit points at:	Convergent or divergent
$1, 2, 3, \cdots$	(none)	divergent
$\frac{1}{2}, \frac{2}{3}, \frac{3}{4}, \frac{4}{5}, \cdots$	1	convergent
$\frac{1}{2}, 2, \frac{1}{3}, 3, \frac{1}{4}, 4, \cdots$	0	divergent
$\frac{1}{4}, \frac{3}{4}, \frac{1}{5}, \frac{4}{5}, \frac{1}{6}, \frac{5}{6}, \cdots$	0 and 1	divergent

A number which appears infinitely often in a sequence is to be regarded as a limit point; this is a matter of convenience and convention.

A sequence $z_1, z_2, \cdots$ is said to be **bounded**, if there is a positive number

Fig. 292. Last sequence in Example 4.

K such that all the terms of the sequence lie in a disk of radius K about the origin, that is,

$$|z_n| < K \qquad \text{for all } n.$$

For example, the second and the last sequences in Ex. 4 are bounded while the first and third are not. We observe that the two bounded sequences have limit points. This illustrates the following important theorem.

Theorem 2 (*Bolzano*[4] and *Weierstrass*[5]). *A bounded infinite sequence has at least one limit point.*

Proof. It is obvious that both conditions are necessary: a finite sequence cannot have a limit point, and the sequence $1, 2, 3, \cdots$, though infinite, has no limit point because it is not bounded. To prove the theorem, consider a bounded infinite sequence $z_1, z_2, \cdots$ and let K be such that $|z_n| < K$ for all n. If only finitely many values of the z_n are different, then, since the sequence is infinite, some number z must occur infinitely many times in the sequence, and, by definition, this number is a limit point of the sequence.

We may now turn to the case when the sequence contains infinitely many different terms. We draw the large square Q_0 in Fig. 293 which contains all z_n. We subdivide Q_0 into four congruent squares. Clearly, at least one of these squares (each taken with its

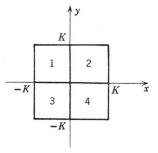

Fig. 293. Proof of Theorem 2.

[4] BERNHARD BOLZANO (1781–1848), German mathematician, a pioneer in the study of point sets.

[5] Cf. footnote 3 in Sec. 10.3.

complete boundary) must contain infinitely many terms of the sequence. The square of this type with the lowest number $(1, 2, 3,$ or $4)$ will be denoted by Q_1. This is the first step. In the next step we subdivide Q_1 into four congruent squares and select a square Q_2 according to the same rule, and so on. This yields an infinite sequence of squares $Q_0, Q_1, Q_2, \cdots, Q_n, \cdots$ with the property that the side of Q_n approaches zero as n approaches infinity, and Q_m contains all Q_n with $n > m$. It is not difficult to see that the number which belongs to all these squares,[6] call it $z = a$, is a limit point of the sequence. In fact, given an $\epsilon > 0$, we can choose an N so large that the side of the square Q_N is less than ϵ and, since Q_N contains infinitely many z_n we have $|z_n - a| < \epsilon$ for infinitely many n. This completes the proof.

By the use of this theorem we shall now establish a general criterion for convergence which will be fundamental in our further consideration.

Theorem 3 (*Cauchy's convergence principle*). *A sequence* $z_1, z_2, \cdots$ *is convergent if, and only if, for every positive number* ϵ *we can find a number* N *(which may depend on* ϵ*) such that*

$$(3) \qquad\qquad |z_m - z_n| < \epsilon \qquad\qquad \text{when } m > N, n > N;$$

(that is, any two terms z_m, z_n *with* $m > N, n > N$ *must have a distance of less than* ϵ *from each other).*

Proof. **(a)** Let the sequence $z_1, z_2, \cdots$ be convergent with the limit c. Then, for a given $\epsilon > 0$, we can find an N such that

$$|z_n - c| < \frac{\epsilon}{2} \qquad\qquad \text{for every } n > N.$$

Hence, when $m > N, n > N$, then by the triangle inequality

$$|z_m - z_n| = |(z_m - c) - (z_n - c)| \leq |z_m - c| + |z_n - c| < \frac{\epsilon}{2} + \frac{\epsilon}{2} = \epsilon,$$

which shows that, if the sequence converges, then (3) holds.

(b) Conversely, consider a sequence $z_1, z_2, \cdots$ for which (3) holds. We first show that the sequence is bounded. In fact, choose a fixed ϵ and a fixed $n = n_0 > N$ in (3). Then (3) implies that every z_m with $m > N$ lies in a disk of radius ϵ about z_{n_0}, and only finitely many terms of the sequence do not lie in that disk. It is clear that we can find a circle about the origin so large that the disk and those finitely many z_n lie within the circle. This shows that the sequence is bounded, and from the Bolzano-Weierstrass theorem we conclude that it has at least one limit point, call it L.

---

[6] The fact that such a unique number $z = a$ exists seems to be obvious, but it actually follows from an axiom of the real number system, the so-called *Cantor-Dedekind axiom*. Cf. footnote 7 on p. 598.

We show that the sequence is convergent with the limit L. The definition of a limit point implies that, an $\epsilon > 0$ being given, $|z_n - L| < \epsilon/2$ for infinitely many n. Since (3) holds for any $\epsilon > 0$, when an $\epsilon > 0$ is given we can find an N^* such that $|z_m - z_n| < \epsilon/2$ for $m > N^*, n > N^*$. Choose a fixed $n > N^*$ such that $|z_n - L| < \epsilon/2$, and let m be any integer greater than N^*. Then, by the triangle inequality,

$$|z_m - L| = |(z_m - z_n) + (z_n - L)| \leq |z_m - z_n| + |z_n - L| < \frac{\epsilon}{2} + \frac{\epsilon}{2} = \epsilon$$

that is, $|z_m - L| < \epsilon$ for all $m > N^*$; by definition, this means that the sequence is convergent with the limit L. This completes the proof.

This theorem will play an important role in our considerations of infinite series.

The following property of a convergent sequence is almost obvious.

Theorem 4. *A convergent sequence is bounded. Consequently, if a sequence is not bounded, it diverges.*

Proof.   Let the sequence $z_1, z_2, \cdots$ be convergent with the limit c. Then we may choose an $\epsilon > 0$ and find a corresponding N such that every z_n with $n > N$ lies in the disk of radius ϵ with center c, and at most finitely many terms may not lie in that disk. It is clear that we can find a circle of radius K about the origin so large that the disk as well as those finitely many terms lie within that circle. This proves that the sequence is bounded.

Note well that the condition of Theorem 4 is only necessary for convergence but not sufficient. This is illustrated by the last sequence in Ex. 4, which is bounded but has two limit points and, therefore, is divergent. The first and third sequences in Ex. 4 are not bounded, and from Theorem 4 it follows that they are divergent.

In the case of a *real sequence* we may find a simple condition sufficient for convergence. For this purpose we need the following concepts.

A real sequence $x_1, x_2, \cdots, x_n, \cdots$ is said to be **monotone increasing**, if

$$x_1 \leq x_2 \leq x_3 \leq \cdots.$$

Similarly, the sequence is said to be **monotone decreasing**, if

$$x_1 \geq x_2 \geq x_3 \geq \cdots.$$

A sequence which is either monotone increasing or monotone decreasing is called a *monotone sequence*.

For example, the first two sequences in Ex. 4 are monotone, while the last two are not monotone. We observe that the second sequence in Ex. 4

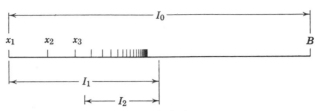

Fig. 294. Proof of Theorem 5.

is bounded and monotone, and we shall now prove that these two properties together are sufficient for convergence.

Theorem 5.   *If a real sequence is bounded and monotone, it converges.*

Proof. Let $x_1, x_2, \cdots$ be a bounded monotone increasing sequence. Then its terms are smaller than some number B and, since $x_1 \leqq x_n$ for all n, they lie in the interval $x_1 \leqq x_n \leqq B$, which will be denoted by I_0. We bisect I_0, that is, we subdivide it into two parts of equal length. If the right half (together with its end points) contains terms of the sequence, we denote it by I_1. If it does not contain terms of the sequence, then the left half of I_0 (together with its end points) is called I_1. This is the first step.

In the second step we bisect I_1, select one half by the same rule, and call it I_2, and so on (Fig. 294).

In this way we obtain shorter and shorter intervals $I_0, I_1, I_2, \cdots$ with the following properties. Each I_m contains all I_n for $n > m$. No term of the sequence lies to the right of I_m, and, since the sequence is monotone increasing, all x_n with n greater than some number N lie in I_m; of course, N will depend on m, in general. The lengths of the I_m approach zero as m approaches infinity. Hence, there is precisely one number, call it L, which lies in all those intervals,[7] and we may now easily prove that the sequence is convergent with the limit L.

In fact, given an $\epsilon > 0$, we choose an m such that the length of I_m is less than ϵ. Then L and all the x_n with $n > N(m)$ lie in I_m, and, therefore, $|x_n - L| < \epsilon$ for all those n. This completes the proof for an increasing sequence. For a decreasing sequence the proof is the same, except for a suitable interchange of "left" and "right" in the construction of those intervals.

---

[7] This statement seems to be obvious, but actually it is not; it may be regarded as an axiom of the real number system in the following form. Let $J_1, J_2, \cdots$ be closed intervals such that each J_m contains all J_n with $n > m$, and the lengths of the J_m approach zero as m approaches infinity. Then there is precisely one real number which is contained in all those intervals. This is the so-called **Cantor-Dedekind Axiom,** named after the German mathematicians, GEORG CANTOR (1845–1918), the creator of set theory, and RICHARD DEDEKIND (1831–1916). For further details see Ref. [A9] in Appendix 1. (An interval I is said to be **closed** if its two end points are regarded as points belonging to I. It is said to be **open** if the end points are not regarded as points of I.)

PROBLEMS

Write the first few terms of the sequence $z_1, z_2, \cdots$ where

1. $z_n = n/(n + 1)$ **2.** $z_n = n^2/(3n - 2)$ **3.** $z_n = (-1)^{n+1} + 2n\pi i$

4. $z_n = i^n/n^2$ **5.** $z_1 = 1, z_2 = 1, z_n = z_{n-1} + z_{n-2}$ $(n = 3, 4, \cdots)$

6. $z_1 = 1/2, z_2 = 1/3, z_n = z_{n-1}z_{n-2}$ $(n = 3, 4, \cdots)$

7. $z_{2n-1} = \dfrac{n+1}{n}, z_{2n} = \dfrac{n-1}{n}$ $(n = 1, 2, \cdots)$ **8.** $z_n = \sin \dfrac{n\pi}{2}$

Are the following real sequences bounded or not, convergent or not, monotone or not? Determine their limit points.

9. $\frac{1}{2}, \frac{1}{4}, \frac{1}{8}, \frac{1}{16}, \cdots$ **10.** $1, -\frac{1}{3}, \frac{1}{9}, -\frac{1}{27}, \frac{1}{81}, \cdots$

11. $1, -2, 3, -4, 5, -6, \cdots$ **12.** $\dfrac{4n^2 - 2}{2n^2 + n}$ $(n = 1, 2, \cdots)$

13. $\frac{1}{5}, \frac{1}{2}, \frac{4}{5}, \frac{1}{2}, \frac{1}{6}, \frac{5}{2}, \frac{1}{2}, \frac{1}{7}, \frac{1}{2}, \frac{6}{7}, \cdots$ **14.** $\frac{1}{2}, 2, \frac{1}{3}, 3, \frac{1}{4}, 4, \cdots$

15. $1, \sqrt{2}, \sqrt[3]{3}, \sqrt[4]{4}, \cdots$ **16.** $a, a^2, a^3, \cdots$

17. $c, 2c^2, 3c^3, \cdots (|c| < 1)$ **18.** $c, 2^2c^2, 3^2c^3, 4^2c^4, \cdots (|c| < 1)$

19. If the sequence $z_1, z_2, \cdots$ is convergent with the limit 0, and the sequence $b_1, b_2, \cdots$ is such that $|b_n| \leq K|z_n|$ for some fixed $K > 0$ and all n, show that the sequence $b_1, b_2, \cdots$ is convergent with the limit 0.

20. Show that changing the values of finitely many terms of a convergent sequence does not affect the convergence.

Find all the limit points of the sequence $z_1, z_2, \cdots$ where

21. $z_n = (-1)^n + 2$ **22.** $z_n = (-2)^n$ **23.** $z_n = i^n/n$ **24.** $z_n = i^n$

25. $z_n = \cos n\pi$ **26.** $z_n = 4 \sin (n\pi/2)$ **27.** $z_n = (\cos n\pi)/\sqrt{n}$

28. $z_n = \dfrac{1}{n^2} - \dfrac{i}{2n}$ **29.** $z_n = (-1)^n + \dfrac{i}{n}$ **30.** $z_n = \dfrac{i^n}{n^2}$

10.5 SERIES

Let $w_1, w_2, \cdots, w_m, \cdots$ be a sequence of numbers, complex or real. Then we may consider the **infinite series**

(1) $$\sum_{m=1}^{\infty} w_m = w_1 + w_2 + w_3 + \cdots.$$

The w_m are called the **terms** of the series. The sum of the first n terms is

(2) $$s_n = w_1 + w_2 + \cdots + w_n.$$

This expression is called the *nth* **partial sum** of the series (1). Clearly if we omit the terms of s_n from (1) the remaining expression is

(3) $$R_n = w_{n+1} + w_{n+2} + w_{n+3} + \cdots.$$

This is called the **remainder** *of the series* (1) *after the nth term.*

In this way we have now associated with the series (1) the sequence of its partial sums $s_1, s_2, s_3, \cdots$. If this sequence is convergent, say,

$$\lim_{n \to \infty} s_n = s,$$

then the series (1) is said to **converge** or to *be convergent*, the number s is called its **value** or *sum*, and we write

$$s = \sum_{m=1}^{\infty} w_m = w_1 + w_2 + \cdots.$$

If the sequence of the partial sums diverges, the series (1) is said to **diverge** or to *be divergent*.

If the series (1) converges and has the value s, then

(4) $$s = s_n + R_n \qquad \text{or} \qquad R_n = s - s_n.$$

Example 1. The series

$$\sum_{m=1}^{\infty} \frac{1}{2^m} = \tfrac{1}{2} + \tfrac{1}{4} + \tfrac{1}{8} + \cdots$$

converges, because

$$s_n = \frac{1}{2} + \frac{1}{4} + \cdots + \frac{1}{2^n} = 1 - \frac{1}{2^n} \qquad \text{and} \qquad \lim_{n \to \infty} s_n = 1;$$

the series has the value 1.

Example 2. The series

$$\sum_{m=1}^{\infty} m = 1 + 2 + 3 + \cdots$$

diverges.

Example 3. The series

$$\sum_{m=0}^{\infty} (-1)^m = 1 - 1 + 1 - + \cdots$$

diverges, because

$$s_0 = 1, \qquad s_1 = 1 - 1 = 0, \qquad s_2 = 1 - 1 + 1 = 1, \qquad \text{etc.,}$$

and the sequence $1, 0, 1, 0, \cdots$ is divergent.

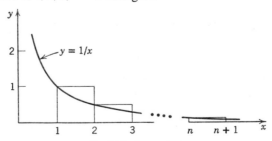

Fig. 295. Example 4.

Example 4. The harmonic series

$$\sum_{m=1}^{\infty} \frac{1}{m} = 1 + \tfrac{1}{2} + \tfrac{1}{3} + \cdots$$

diverges. In fact,

$$s_n = 1 + \frac{1}{2} + \cdots + \frac{1}{n},$$

and s_n equals the sum of the areas of the n rectangles in Fig. 295. This area is greater than the area A_n under the corresponding portion of the curve $y = 1/x$, and

$$A_n = \int_1^{n+1} \frac{dx}{x} = \ln(n+1) \to \infty \qquad \text{as } n \to \infty.$$

Since $s_n > A_n$, it follows that $s_n \to \infty$ as $n \to \infty$, which means divergence.

Theorem 1. *If the series* $w_1 + w_2 + \cdots$ *converges, then*

$$(5) \qquad\qquad\qquad \lim_{m \to \infty} w_m = 0.$$

Consequently, a series which does not satisfy (5) *diverges.*

Proof. Let $w_1 + w_2 + \cdots$ be convergent with the sum s. Then

$$w_{n+1} = s_{n+1} - s_n,$$

and

$$\lim_{n \to \infty} (s_{n+1} - s_n) = \lim_{n \to \infty} s_{n+1} - \lim_{n \to \infty} s_n = s - s = 0.$$

Note well that the condition (5) is only necessary for convergence, but not sufficient. In fact, the harmonic series satisfies (5), but diverges. The series in Ex. 2 and 3 do not satisfy (5) and, therefore, are divergent.

If a given series $w_1 + w_2 + \cdots$ converges and has the value s, then

$$s = s_n + R_n \qquad \text{or} \qquad R_n = s - s_n \qquad\qquad [\text{cf. } (4)]$$

and from the definition of convergence of a sequence it follows that $|R_n|$ can be made as small as we please, by taking n large enough. In many cases it will be impossible to find the sum s of a convergent series. Then for computational purposes we must use a partial sum s_n as an approximation of s, and by estimating the remainder R_n we may obtain information about the degree of accuracy of the approximation.

In the case of a *real series* whose terms have alternating sign and decrease in absolute value, the following useful theorem may be applied for that purpose.

Theorem 2 (Leibniz test for real series). *Let* $u_1, u_2, \cdots$ *be real and*

$$(6) \qquad (a) \quad u_1 \geqq u_2 \geqq u_3 \geqq \cdots, \qquad (b) \quad \lim_{m \to \infty} u_m = 0.$$

Then the series

$$u_1 - u_2 + u_3 - u_4 + - \cdots$$

converges, and for the remainder R_n after the nth term we have the estimate

(7) $$|R_n| \leqq u_{n+1}.$$

Proof. Let s_n be the nth partial sum of the series. Then, because of (6a),

$$s_1 = u_1, \qquad\qquad s_2 = u_1 - u_2 \leqq s_1,$$
$$s_3 = s_2 + u_3 \geqq s_2, \qquad s_3 = s_1 - (u_2 - u_3) \leqq s_1,$$

so that $s_2 \leqq s_3 \leqq s_1$. Proceeding in this fashion, we conclude that (Fig. 296)

(8) $$s_1 \geqq s_3 \geqq s_5 \geqq \cdots \geqq s_6 \geqq s_4 \geqq s_2,$$

which shows that the odd partial sums form a bounded monotone sequence, and so do the even partial sums. Hence, by Theorem 5, Sec. 10.4, both sequences converge, say,

$$\lim_{n \to \infty} s_{2n+1} = s, \qquad \lim_{n \to \infty} s_{2n} = s^*.$$

Now, since $s_{2n+1} - s_{2n} = u_{2n+1}$, we obtain from (6b)

$$s - s^* = \lim_{n \to \infty} s_{2n+1} - \lim_{n \to \infty} s_{2n} = \lim_{n \to \infty} (s_{2n+1} - s_{2n}) = \lim_{n \to \infty} u_{2n+1} = 0.$$

Hence $s^* = s$, and the series converges with the sum s.

We prove (7). Since $s_n \to s$, it follows from (8) that

$$s_{2n+1} \geqq s \geqq s_{2n} \qquad \text{and also} \qquad s_{2n-1} \geqq s \geqq s_{2n}.$$

By subtracting s_{2n} and s_{2n-1}, respectively, we obtain

$$s_{2n+1} - s_{2n} \geqq s - s_{2n} \geqq 0, \qquad 0 \geqq s - s_{2n-1} \geqq s_{2n} - s_{2n-1}.$$

In these inequalities, the first expression is equal to u_{2n+1}, the last is equal to $-u_{2n}$, and the expressions between the inequality signs are the remainders R_{2n} and R_{2n-1}. Thus the inequalities may be written

$$u_{2n+1} \geqq R_{2n} \geqq 0, \qquad 0 \geqq R_{2n-1} \geqq -u_{2n}$$

and imply (7). This completes the proof of Theorem 2.

Example 5. The series
$$1 - \tfrac{1}{2} + \tfrac{1}{3} - \tfrac{1}{4} + - \cdots$$
is convergent, as follows from Theorem 2.

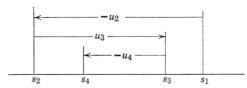

Fig. 296. Proof of Theorem 2 (Leibniz test).

Example 6. Compute e, the base of the natural logarithm with an error less than 1/2 unit of the sixth decimal place. From the familiar Maclaurin series,

$$e^{-1} = 1 - 1 + \frac{1}{2!} - \frac{1}{3!} + - \cdots.$$

From (7), $|R_n| < 1/(n + 1)!$, and if we choose n such that

(9) $1/(n + 1)! < 0.5 \cdot 10^{-7}$ or $(n + 1)! > 20{,}000{,}000,$

the error of the corresponding approximation for $1/e$ will be less than 1/2 unit of the seventh decimal place and, since e is about ten times $1/e$, the error of the approximation for e obtained from that for $1/e$ will meet the requirement. Since $11! = 39{,}916{,}800$, condition (9) is satisfied when $n = 10$. From the corresponding computation shown in the table, $1/e \approx 0.367\ 879\ 47$ and the reciprocal is

$$e \approx 2.718\ 282 \qquad \text{(cf. Sec. 0.1)}.$$

n	$(-1)^n/n!$
0	1.000 000 00
1	−1.000 000 00
2	0.500 000 00
3	−0.166 666 67
4	0.041 666 67
5	−0.008 333 33
6	0.001 388 89
7	−0.000 198 41
8	0.000 024 80
9	−0.000 002 76
10	0.000 000 28
Sum	0.367 879 47

The student may show that this computation may be simplified by using the formula $(e^a)^b = e^{ab}$.

From Theorem 1, Sec. 10.4, we immediately obtain the following relation between a complex series and the series of its real and imaginary parts.

Theorem 3.   *Let $w_m = u_m + iv_m$. Then the series*

$$\sum_{m=1}^{\infty} w_m = w_1 + w_2 + w_3 + \cdots$$

converges and has the value $s = a + ib$ if, and only if, the series of the real parts and the series of the imaginary parts

$$\sum_{m=1}^{\infty} u_m = u_1 + u_2 + \cdots \quad \text{and} \quad \sum_{m=1}^{\infty} v_m = v_1 + v_2 + \cdots$$

converge and have the values a and b, respectively.

Furthermore, we may apply Theorem 3 in Sec. 10.4 to the sequence of the partial sums s_n of a given series $w_1 + w_2 + \cdots$. Then the inequality in that theorem becomes

$$|s_m - s_n| < \epsilon \qquad\qquad (m > N, n > N)$$

or, if we set $m = n + p$,

$$|s_{n+p} - s_n| < \epsilon \qquad (n > N, p = 1, 2, \cdots).$$

Now by definition of a partial sum,

$$s_{n+p} - s_n = w_{n+1} + w_{n+2} + \cdots + w_{n+p},$$

and we immediately obtain the following basic result.

Theorem 4. *A series $w_1 + w_2 + \cdots$ is convergent if, and only if, for any given $\epsilon > 0$ (no matter how small) we can find an N (which will depend on ϵ, in general) such that*

$$|w_{n+1} + w_{n+2} + \cdots + w_{n+p}| < \epsilon \text{ for every } n > N \text{ and } p = 1, 2, \cdots.$$

Theorem 3 establishes a relation between complex and real series. A far more important relation can be gained by the use of the following basic notion.

A series $w_1 + w_2 + \cdots$ is said to be **absolutely convergent**, if the corresponding series

$$(10) \qquad \sum_{m=1}^{\infty} |w_m| = |w_1| + |w_2| + \cdots$$

(whose terms are real and nonnegative) converges.

If the series $w_1 + w_2 + \cdots$ converges but (10) diverges, then the series is called, more precisely, *conditionally convergent*.

For instance, the series in Ex. 5 is conditionally convergent because the corresponding series (10) is the harmonic series (Ex. 4), which diverges. The series in Ex. 6 is absolutely convergent, because the corresponding series (10) is convergent (with the sum e).

The following property of an absolutely convergent series is almost obvious.

Theorem 5. *If a series $w_1 + w_2 + \cdots$ is absolutely convergent, it is convergent.*

Proof. By the generalized triangle inequality (3) in Sec. 10.1 we have

$$(11) \qquad |w_{n+1} + \cdots + w_{n+p}| \le |w_{n+1}| + |w_{n+2}| + \cdots + |w_{n+p}|.$$

Since, by assumption the series $|w_1| + |w_2| + \cdots$ converges, it follows from Theorem 4 that the right-hand side of (11) becomes less than any given $\epsilon > 0$ for each $n > N$ (N sufficiently large) and $p = 1, 2, \cdots$. Hence, the same is true for the left-hand side of (11), and by the same theorem, this proves convergence of the series $w_1 + w_2 + \cdots$.

10.6 TESTS FOR CONVERGENCE AND DIVERGENCE OF SERIES

Of course, before we can use a series for computational or other purposes we must know whether it converges. In most cases that arise in engineering mathematics, this question may be answered by applying one of the various tests for convergence and divergence. These tests, therefore, are of great practical interest.

A simple test for divergence (Theorem 1 in the last section) and the so-called Leibniz test for real series have already been considered. The following theorem is a source of various criteria for convergence.

Theorem 1 (Comparison test). *If a series $w_1 + w_2 + \cdots$ is given and we can find a converging series $b_1 + b_2 + \cdots$ with nonnegative real terms such that*

$$(1) \qquad\qquad |w_n| \leq b_n \qquad \text{for } n = 1, 2, \cdots,$$

then the given series is absolutely convergent.

Proof. Since the series $b_1 + b_2 + \cdots$ converges, it follows from Theorem 4 in the last section that for any given $\epsilon > 0$ we can find an N such that

$$b_{n+1} + \cdots + b_{n+p} < \epsilon \qquad \text{for every } n > N \text{ and } p = 1, 2, \cdots.$$

From this and (1) we conclude that

$$|w_{n+1}| + \cdots + |w_{n+p}| \leq b_{n+1} + \cdots + b_{n+p} < \epsilon$$

for those n and p. Hence, by Theorem 4 in the last section, the series $|w_1| + |w_2| + \cdots$ is convergent, and the given series converges absolutely.

For deriving two important tests from Theorem 1 let us prove

Theorem 2. *The geometric series*

$$\sum_{m=0}^{\infty} q^m = 1 + q + q^2 + \cdots$$

converges with the sum $1/(1 - q)$ when $|q| < 1$ and diverges when $|q| \geq 1$.

Proof. When $|q| \geq 1$, then $|q|^n \geq 1$ and divergence follows from Theorem 1 in the last section. Now let $|q| < 1$. The nth partial sum is

$$s_n = 1 + q + \cdots + q^n.$$

From this, $$qs_n = \qquad q + \cdots + q^n + q^{n+1}.$$

By subtraction, $\qquad s_n - qs_n = (1-q)s_n = 1 - q^{n+1}$

since the other terms cancel in pairs. Now $q - 1 \neq 0$ because $q \neq 1$, and we may solve for s_n, finding

$$(2) \qquad s_n = \frac{1-q^{n+1}}{1-q} = \frac{1}{1-q} - \frac{q^{n+1}}{1-q}.$$

Since $|q| < 1$, the last term approaches zero as $n \to \infty$. Hence the series is convergent and has the value $1/(1-q)$. This completes the proof.

From Theorems 1 and 2 we shall now derive two important tests, the ratio test and the root test.

Theorem 3 (Ratio test). *Suppose that $w_n \neq 0$ for $n = 1, 2, \cdots$ and the sequence*

$$\left| \frac{w_{n+1}}{w_n} \right| \qquad\qquad n = 1, 2, \cdots$$

converges with the limit L. Then the series

$$w_1 + w_2 + w_3 + \cdots$$

is
$$\text{absolutely convergent, if } L < 1,$$
$$\text{divergent, if } L > 1.$$

(If $L = 1$, the test fails).

Proof. By assumption

$$\lim_{n \to \infty} b_n = L \qquad \text{where} \qquad b_n = \left| \frac{w_{n+1}}{w_n} \right|.$$

Clearly, the b_n and L are real. By definition of limit, for given $\epsilon > 0$ we can find an N such that every b_n with $n > N$ lies between $L - \epsilon$ and $L + \epsilon$, that is,

$$(3) \qquad (a)\ b_n < L + \epsilon \qquad (b)\ b_n > L - \epsilon \qquad (n > N).$$

We first consider the case $L < 1$. We set $L + \epsilon = q$ and choose $\epsilon = (1 - L)/2$. Then $\epsilon > 0$, and (3a) becomes

$$b_n < q = L + \frac{1-L}{2} = \frac{1+L}{2}.$$

Since $L < 1$ we have $q < 1$. Now we can write

$$|w_{N+1}| + |w_{N+2}| + |w_{N+3}| + \cdots$$
$$(4) \qquad = |w_{N+1}| \left(1 + \left| \frac{w_{N+2}}{w_{N+1}} \right| + \left| \frac{w_{N+3}}{w_{N+2}} \right| \left| \frac{w_{N+2}}{w_{N+1}} \right| + \cdots \right)$$
$$= |w_{N+1}|(1 + b_{N+1} + b_{N+2}b_{N+1} + b_{N+3}b_{N+2}b_{N+1} + \cdots).$$

Since $b_n < q < 1$, each term of this series is less than the corresponding term of the geometric series

$$|w_{N+1}| (1 + q + q^2 + q^3 + \cdots).$$

By Theorem 2 this series converges because $q < 1$. From Theorem 1 it follows that the series in (4) is convergent. From this we conclude that the series $|w_1| + |w_2| + \cdots$ is convergent. This implies that the series $w_1 + w_2 + \cdots$ is absolutely convergent.

We now consider the case $L > 1$. We choose $\epsilon = (L - 1)/2$. Clearly, $\epsilon > 0$, and (3b) becomes

$$b_n > L - \epsilon = \frac{1 + L}{2} > 1 \qquad (n > N),$$

that is,

$$b_n = \left| \frac{w_{n+1}}{w_n} \right| > 1 \quad \text{or} \quad |w_{n+1}| > |w_n| \qquad (n > N).$$

The last inequality shows that the terms are increasing in absolute value. From this and Theorem 1, Sec. 10.5, it follows that the series is divergent.

For $L = 1$, the series may converge or diverge so that the test fails. This is illustrated by the harmonic series (Ex. 4 in Sec. 10.5)

$$\sum_{n=1}^{\infty} \frac{1}{n} = 1 + \frac{1}{2} + \frac{1}{3} + \cdots$$

which diverges and for which

$$\frac{w_{n+1}}{w_n} = \frac{n}{n+1} \to L = 1 \qquad \text{as } n \to \infty$$

and by the series

(5) $$\sum_{n=1}^{\infty} \frac{1}{n^2} = 1 + \frac{1}{4} + \frac{1}{9} + \cdots$$

which converges and for which

$$\frac{w_{n+1}}{w_n} = \frac{n^2}{(n+1)^2} \to L = 1 \qquad \text{as } n \to \infty.$$

Convergence of (5) may be shown as follows. The nth partial sum is

$$s_n = 1 + \frac{1}{4} + \frac{1}{9} + \cdots + \frac{1}{n^2}.$$

Clearly, $s_n > 0$ and (Fig. 297)

$$s_n \le 1 + \int_1^n \frac{dx}{x^2} = 2 - \frac{1}{n},$$

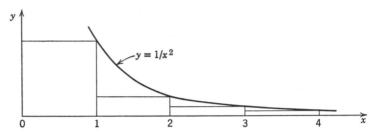

Fig. 297. Convergence of the series (5).

which shows that the sequence of the partial sums is bounded. Since the terms of the series are positive, the sequence is monotone increasing, and convergence follows from Theorem 5 in Sec. 10.4.

The following test is more general than the ratio test, but its application is often more difficult.

Theorem 4 (Root test). *Suppose that the sequence*

$$\sqrt[n]{|w_n|} \qquad\qquad n = 1, 2, \cdots$$

is convergent with the limit L. Then the series

$$w_1 + w_2 + w_3 + \cdots$$

is

absolutely convergent, if $L < 1$,

divergent, if $L > 1$.

(*If $L = 1$, the test fails*).

Proof. If $L < 1$, then, as in the proof for the ratio test, we can choose $q < 1$ and find a corresponding N such that

$$b_n{}^* \equiv \sqrt[n]{|w_n|} < q < 1 \qquad\qquad \text{for every } n > N.$$

From this we obtain

$$|w_n| < q^n < 1 \qquad\qquad (n > N),$$

and the series $|w_N| + |w_{N+1}| + \cdots$ converges by comparison with the geometric series. Hence, the series $w_1 + w_2 + \cdots$ converges absolutely.

If $L > 1$, then $\sqrt[n]{|w_n|} > 1$ for all sufficiently large n. Hence, $|w_n| > 1$ for those n, and divergence follows from Theorem 1 in the last section.

If $L = 1$, the test fails. This is illustrated by the harmonic series for which

$$\sqrt[n]{\frac{1}{n}} = \frac{1}{n^{1/n}} = \frac{1}{e^{(1/n)\,\ln n}} \to \frac{1}{e^0} = 1 \qquad\qquad (n \to \infty)$$

since $(1/n) \ln n \to 0$, and the series (5), for which

$$\sqrt[n]{\frac{1}{n^2}} = \frac{1}{n^{2/n}} = \frac{1}{e^{(2/n)\ln n}} \to \frac{1}{e^0} = 1 \qquad (n \to \infty)$$

since $(2/n) \ln n \to 0$ as $n \to \infty$.

Example 1. Test the series

$$\sum_{n=1}^{\infty} \frac{n^2}{2^n} = \tfrac{1}{2} + 1 + \tfrac{9}{8} + 1 + \tfrac{25}{32} + \cdots.$$

We have

$$w_n = \frac{n^2}{2^n}, \qquad w_{n+1} = \frac{(n+1)^2}{2^{n+1}}, \qquad \frac{w_{n+1}}{w_n} = \frac{(n+1)^2}{2n^2} \to \tfrac{1}{2} \qquad (n \to \infty),$$

and convergence follows from the ratio test. We may also apply the root test:

$$\sqrt[n]{\frac{n^2}{2^n}} = \frac{n^{2/n}}{2} = \frac{e^{(2/n)\ln n}}{2} \to \frac{e^0}{2} = \tfrac{1}{2} \qquad (n \to \infty).$$

This confirms our result.

Example 2. Is the series

$$\sum_{n=0}^{\infty} \frac{6^n}{n!} = 1 + 6 + 18 + 36 + 54 + \cdots$$

convergent or divergent? We have

$$w_n = \frac{6^n}{n!}, \qquad w_{n+1} = \frac{6^{n+1}}{(n+1)!}, \qquad \frac{w_{n+1}}{w_n} = \frac{6}{n+1} \to 0 \qquad (n \to \infty),$$

and convergence follows from the ratio test. (What is the sum of the series?)

Example 3. Is the series

$$\sum_{n=1}^{\infty} \frac{n^n}{n!} = 1 + 2 + \tfrac{9}{2} + \tfrac{32}{3} + \cdots$$

convergent or divergent? We have

$$\frac{w_{n+1}}{w_n} = \frac{(n+1)^{n+1} n!}{(n+1)! \, n^n} = \frac{(n+1)(n+1)^n}{(n+1) \, n^n} = \left(1 + \frac{1}{n}\right)^n \to e,$$

and since $e > 1$, it follows from the ratio test that the series diverges.

We finally mention that both the ratio test and the root test can be generalized to the case when the sequences $|w_{n+1}/w_n|$ and $\sqrt[n]{|w_n|}$, respectively, are not convergent.

Theorem 5 (Ratio test). *If $w_n \neq 0$ for $n = 1, 2, \cdots$, and if for every n greater than some number N*

$$(6) \qquad \left| \frac{w_{n+1}}{w_n} \right| \leq q,$$

where q is some fixed number less than 1, *then the series*

$$w_1 + w_2 + w_3 + \cdots$$

converges absolutely. If

(7)
$$\left| \frac{w_{n+1}}{w_n} \right| \geqq 1 \qquad\qquad \text{for every } n > N$$

the series diverges.

Proof. In the first part of the proof of Theorem 3, convergence followed from the existence of a number $q < 1$ such that (6) holds for all $n > N$. Hence, for the present theorem, convergence follows by the same argument. The last statement of the theorem follows from the fact that, by (7), $|w_{n+1}| \geqq |w_n|$ and Theorem 1 in the last section.

Example 4.   In the series

$$1 + \frac{1}{2} + \frac{1}{8} + \frac{1}{16} + \frac{1}{64} + \frac{1}{128} + \frac{1}{512} + \cdots$$

the odd terms and the even terms each form a geometric series with ratio 1/8. Convergence follows from Theorem 5, because the ratios of successive terms are

$$\frac{1}{2}, \frac{1}{4}, \frac{1}{2}, \frac{1}{4}, \cdots.$$

We see that the sequence of these ratios does not converge. Hence Theorem 3 cannot be applied, and our example illustrates that Theorem 5 is more general than Theorem 3.

Theorem 6 (Root test).   *If for every n greater than some number N*

(8)
$$\sqrt[n]{|w_n|} \leqq q,$$

where q is some fixed number less than 1, *then the series*

$$w_1 + w_2 + w_3 + \cdots$$

converges absolutely. If for infinitely many n

(9)
$$\sqrt[n]{|w_n|} \geqq 1,$$

the series diverges.

Proof.   If (8) holds, then

$$|w_n| \leqq q^n < 1 \qquad\qquad (n > N)$$

and the series $|w_N| + |w_{N+1}| + \cdots$ converges by comparison with the geometric series. Hence, the series $w_1 + w_2 + \cdots$ converges absolutely. If (9) holds, then $|w_n| \geqq 1$ for infinitely many n, and divergence follows from Theorem 1 in the last section.

In the last two theorems it is essential for convergence that $|w_{n+1}/w_n|$ *and* $\sqrt[n]{|w_n|}$, *respectively, should be ultimately less than or equal to a definite number* $q < 1$. *It does not at all suffice for convergence that we should have*

$$\left| \frac{w_{n+1}}{w_n} \right| < 1 \quad \text{or} \quad \sqrt[n]{|w_n|} < 1$$

for sufficiently large n. For example, in the case of the harmonic series (Ex. 4 in Sec. 10.5) we have

$$\frac{w_{n+1}}{w_n} = \frac{1/(n+1)}{1/n} = \frac{n}{n+1} < 1 \quad \text{and} \quad \sqrt[n]{\frac{1}{n}} < 1,$$

but the series diverges.

PROBLEMS

Show that the following series converge. How many terms are needed to compute s with an error less than 0.01?

1. $s = \frac{1}{2} - \frac{1}{4} + \frac{1}{8} - + \cdots$

2. $s = 1 - 1 + \frac{1}{2!} - \frac{1}{3!} + \frac{1}{4!} - + \cdots$

3. $s = 1 - \frac{1}{3!} + \frac{1}{5!} - \frac{1}{7!} + - \cdots$

4. $s = 1 - \frac{1}{2!} + \frac{1}{4!} - \frac{1}{6!} + - \cdots$

5. $s = 1 - \frac{1}{3} + \frac{1}{9} - \frac{1}{27} + - \cdots$

6. $s = 1 - \frac{1}{3} + \frac{1}{6} - \frac{1}{12} + \frac{1}{24} - + \cdots$

Are the following series convergent or divergent?

7. $1 - 2 + 3 - 4 + - \cdots$

8. $1 - \frac{1}{\sqrt{2}} + \frac{1}{\sqrt{3}} - \frac{1}{\sqrt{4}} + - \cdots$

9. $1 + \frac{1}{\sqrt{2}} + \frac{1}{\sqrt{3}} + \frac{1}{\sqrt{4}} + \cdots$

10. $1 + \frac{1}{2} + \frac{1}{4} + \frac{1}{8} + \cdots$

11. $2 + \frac{2}{3} + \frac{2}{9} + \frac{2}{27} + \cdots$

12. $1 + 1 + \frac{1}{2!} + \frac{1}{3!} + \frac{1}{4!} + \cdots$

13. $\frac{1}{1 \cdot 2} + \frac{1}{2 \cdot 3} + \frac{1}{3 \cdot 4} + \cdots$

14. $1 + \frac{1}{4} + \frac{1}{9} + \frac{1}{16} + \cdots$

15. $1 + \frac{1}{2^a} + \frac{1}{3^a} + \cdots (a \geq 2)$

16. $\frac{1}{1 + 1^2} + \frac{1}{1 + 2^2} + \frac{1}{1 + 3^2} + \cdots$

17. $\frac{1}{\sqrt{1 \cdot 2}} + \frac{1}{\sqrt{2 \cdot 3}} + \frac{1}{\sqrt{3 \cdot 4}} + \cdots$

18. $\frac{1}{\ln 2} + \frac{1}{\ln 3} + \frac{1}{\ln 4} + \cdots$

19. $\frac{d_1}{10} + \frac{d_2}{10^2} + \frac{d_3}{10^3} + \frac{d_4}{10^4} + \cdots$ where $d_1, d_2, \cdots$ are nonnegative integers ≤ 9

20. $1 + 2 + \frac{2^2}{2!} + \frac{2^3}{3!} + \cdots$

21. $1 + 10 + \frac{10^2}{2!} + \frac{10^3}{3!} + \cdots$

22. $\sum_{n=1}^{\infty} \frac{n!}{2^n}$

23. $\sum_{n=1}^{\infty} \frac{n^{2n}}{n!}$

24. $\sum_{n=1}^{\infty} n(\frac{3}{4})^n$

25. Determine how many terms are needed to compute the sum s of the geometric series $1 + q + q^2 + \cdots$ with an error less than 0.01, when $q = \frac{1}{4}$, $q = \frac{1}{2}$, $q = 0.9$.

26. If $|w_{n+1}/w_n| \leq q < 1$, so that the series $w_1 + w_2 + \cdots$ converges by the ratio test (Theorem 5), show that the remainder $R_n = w_{n+1} + w_{n+2} + \cdots$ satisfies $|R_n| \leq |w_{n+1}|/(1 - q)$. *Hint:* use the fact that the ratio test is a comparison of the series $w_1 + w_2 + \cdots$ with the geometric series.

27. Using the inequality in Prob. 26, determine how many terms are sufficient to compute $s = \sum_{n=1}^{\infty} \dfrac{n + 1}{2^n n}$ with an allowed error 0.05 and find s to this accuracy.

28. A ball is dropped from a height of 10 ft. Each time it strikes the ground after falling from a height of h feet it rebounds a distance $h/2$ ft. Find the total distance traveled by the ball.

29. Show that a real series whose terms are nonnegative converges if, and only if, the sequence of its partial sums is bounded.

30. Work out the proof of Theorem 3 in Sec. 10.5.

10.7 OPERATIONS ON SERIES

We shall now consider some simple operations which are frequently used in working with series.

We start with the addition of series and show that two convergent series may be added term by term.

Theorem 1. *If the series $w_1 + w_2 + \cdots$ and $z_1 + z_2 + \cdots$ are convergent with the respective sums s and s^*, then the series*

$$(1) \qquad \sum_{n=1}^{\infty} (w_n + z_n), \qquad \sum_{n=1}^{\infty} (w_n - z_n), \qquad and \qquad \sum_{n=1}^{\infty} k w_n,$$

where k is any constant, are convergent and have the sums $s + s^*$, $s - s^*$, and ks, respectively.

Proof. The partial sums of the two given series are

$$s_n = w_1 + \cdots + w_n, \qquad s_n^* = z_1 + \cdots + z_n,$$

and by definition of convergence of a series,

$$\lim_{n \to \infty} s_n = s, \qquad \lim_{n \to \infty} s_n^* = s^*.$$

Now the nth partial sum of the first series in (1) is

$$S_n = s_n + s_n^* = (w_1 + z_1) + \cdots + (w_n + z_n).$$

From this we obtain

$$\lim_{n \to \infty} S_n = \lim_{n \to \infty} (s_n + s_n^*) = \lim_{n \to \infty} s_n + \lim_{n \to \infty} s_n^* = s + s^*.$$

Hence this series converges and has the sum $s + s^*$. The other statements can be proved by a similar argument.

The next operation to be considered is that of inserting parentheses in a given series. This operation is called **grouping**.

For example, by grouping the terms of the series $w_1 + w_2 + w_3 + \cdots$ we may obtain the series $(w_1 + w_2) + (w_3 + w_4) + \cdots$ whose terms are $W_n = w_{2n-1} + w_{2n}$ where $n = 1, 2, \cdots$.

Of course, in the case of a *finite* series (that is, a series with only finitely many terms) we may insert parentheses without changing the sum of the series. However, this is not true in general for an infinite series. For instance, by grouping the divergent series

$$1 - 1 + 1 - 1 + - \cdots \qquad \text{(cf. Ex. 3 in Sec. 10.5)}$$

we may obtain the convergent series

$$(1 - 1) + (1 - 1) + \cdots = 0 + 0 + \cdots$$

whose sum is zero.

We shall now prove that, in the case of a convergent series, grouping is permissible.

Theorem 2. *If a series converges, then insertion of parentheses yields a new convergent series having the same sum as the original series.*

Proof. Obviously, the partial sums of the new series are obtained by skipping certain partial sums of the given series. For example, the partial sums of the series

$$(w_1 + w_2 + w_3) + (w_4 + w_5 + w_6) + \cdots$$

are the partial sums $s_3, s_6, s_9, \cdots$ of the series $w_1 + w_2 + \cdots$. Now, if the sequence of the partial sums s_n of the given series converges to s, it follows immediately from the definition of convergence of a sequence that the new sequence obtained by skipping must also converge to s. This proves the theorem.

Example 1. By the Leibniz test (cf. Sec. 10.5) the series

$$\sum_{n=1}^{\infty} \frac{(-1)^{n+1}}{n} = 1 - \tfrac{1}{2} + \tfrac{1}{3} - \tfrac{1}{4} + - \cdots$$

converges. Let s be its sum. Then by Theorem 2,

$$(2) \qquad \frac{1}{1 \cdot 2} + \frac{1}{3 \cdot 4} + \frac{1}{5 \cdot 6} + \cdots = (1 - \tfrac{1}{2}) + (\tfrac{1}{3} - \tfrac{1}{4}) + \cdots$$

$$= \sum_{m=1}^{\infty} \left(\frac{1}{2m - 1} - \frac{1}{2m} \right) = s$$

and, similarly,

$$\frac{1 \cdot 2 + 3 \cdot 4}{1 \cdot 2 \cdot 3 \cdot 4} + \frac{5 \cdot 6 + 7 \cdot 8}{5 \cdot 6 \cdot 7 \cdot 8} + \cdots = (1 - \tfrac{1}{2} + \tfrac{1}{3} - \tfrac{1}{4}) + (\tfrac{1}{5} - \tfrac{1}{6} + \tfrac{1}{7} - \tfrac{1}{8}) + \cdots$$

$$(3) \qquad = \sum_{m=1}^{\infty} \left(\frac{1}{4m - 3} - \frac{1}{4m - 2} + \frac{1}{4m - 1} - \frac{1}{4m} \right) = s.$$

The last operation to be considered in this section is that of changing the order of the terms in a series.

Clearly, if a series is finite, the order of its terms may be changed without altering the sum. Also we may change the order of finitely many terms of a given infinite series: if the given series is divergent, so will be the new series, and if the given series converges, the new series will be convergent with the same sum. This follows immediately from the definitions of convergence and divergence.

We may now ask what happens if we "change the order of infinitely many terms" of a series. Of course we must first define what we mean by such an operation. This can be done as follows.

A series

$$\sum_{n=1}^{\infty} w_n{}^* = w_1{}^* + w_2{}^* + \cdots$$

is said to be a **rearrangement** of a series

$$\sum_{m=1}^{\infty} w_m = w_1 + w_2 + \cdots$$

if there is a one-to-one correspondence between the indices n and m such that $w_n{}^* = w_m$ for corresponding indices.

For example, the series

$$\tfrac{1}{2} + 1 + \tfrac{1}{4} + \tfrac{1}{3} + \tfrac{1}{6} + \tfrac{1}{5} + \cdots$$

is a rearrangement of the harmonic series

$$1 + \tfrac{1}{2} + \tfrac{1}{3} + \tfrac{1}{4} + \tfrac{1}{5} + \tfrac{1}{6} + \cdots .$$

The following example illustrates that, by rearranging a convergent series, we may obtain a convergent series whose sum is different from that of the original series.

Example 2. We rearrange the series

$$s = 1 - \tfrac{1}{2} + \tfrac{1}{3} - \tfrac{1}{4} + \tfrac{1}{5} - \tfrac{1}{6} + \tfrac{1}{7} - \tfrac{1}{8} + \tfrac{1}{9} - + \cdots$$

by writing first two positive terms, then one negative, then again two positive, etc., in the order of their occurrence. This yields the rearrangement

$$s^* = 1 + \tfrac{1}{3} - \tfrac{1}{2} + \tfrac{1}{5} + \tfrac{1}{7} - \tfrac{1}{4} + \tfrac{1}{9} + \tfrac{1}{11} - \tfrac{1}{6} + \tfrac{1}{13} + \cdots .$$

We want to show that the sums s and s^* are different. By inserting parentheses in the rearrangement we have

$$s^* = (1 + \tfrac{1}{3} - \tfrac{1}{2}) + (\tfrac{1}{5} + \tfrac{1}{7} - \tfrac{1}{4}) + \cdots = \sum_{m=1}^{\infty} \left(\frac{1}{4m-3} + \frac{1}{4m-1} - \frac{1}{2m} \right).$$

On the other hand, by multiplying the series (2) by $\frac{1}{2}$ and adding the resulting series and the series (3) term by term (cf. Theorem 1), we get

$$\tfrac{3}{2}s = \sum_{m=1}^{\infty} \left(\frac{1}{4m-3} - \frac{1}{4m-2} + \frac{1}{4m-1} - \frac{1}{4m} + \frac{\frac{1}{2}}{2m-1} - \frac{\frac{1}{2}}{2m} \right)$$

$$= \sum_{m=1}^{\infty} \left(\frac{1}{4m-3} + \frac{1}{4m-1} - \frac{1}{2m} \right) = s^*.$$

Hence, $s^* = 3s/2$.

We note that the series in Ex. 2 is not absolutely convergent. Let us prove that an absolutely convergent series can always be rearranged without altering the sum.

Theorem 3. *If a series converges absolutely, then any of its rearrangements converges absolutely and has the same sum as the original series.*

Proof. Let $w_1^* + w_2^* + w_3^* + \cdots$ be any rearrangement of an absolutely convergent series $w_1 + w_2 + w_3 + \cdots$. Then, since every w_m^* equals a w_n for appropriate n and no two m's correspond to the same n we clearly have

$$\sum_{m=1}^{n} |w_m^*| \leq \sum_{k=1}^{\infty} |w_k| \qquad \text{for every } n.$$

The expression on the left is the nth partial sum of the series $|w_1^*| + |w_2^*| + \cdots$. Since these partial sums are nonnegative, the inequality shows that they form a bounded sequence. Since $|w_m^*| \geq 0$ the sequence is monotone increasing and, therefore, convergent (cf. Theorem 5 in Sec. 10.4). Hence the rearrangement $w_1^* + w_2^* + \cdots$ converges absolutely. Let s^* be its sum, and let s be the sum of the original series. We show that $s^* = s$.

From the definition of convergence and from Theorem 4 in Sec. 10.5 when applied to the series $|w_1| + |w_2| + \cdots$ it follows that, when $\epsilon > 0$ is given, we can find an N such that

$$(4) \qquad (a) \quad |s_n - s| < \frac{\epsilon}{2} \qquad (b) \quad |w_{n+1}| + \cdots + |w_{n+p}| < \frac{\epsilon}{2}$$

for every $n > N$ and $p = 1, 2, \cdots$; here s_n is the nth partial sum of the original series. Now for sufficiently large m, the mth partial sum s_m^* of the rearrangement will contain all the terms $w_1, \cdots, w_n$ ($n > N$ and fixed) and perhaps some more terms w_r ($r > n$) of the original series. Hence s_m^* will be of the form

$$(5) \qquad\qquad s_m^* = s_n + A_{mn}$$

where A_{mn} is the sum of those additional terms. Let $n + p$ be the greatest subscript of the terms in A_{mn}. Then by (4b), since $n > N$,

$$|A_{mn}| \leq |w_{n+1}| + \cdots + |w_{n+p}| < \frac{\epsilon}{2}.$$

From this and (5) it follows that

$$|s_m{}^* - s_n| = |A_{mn}| < \frac{\epsilon}{2}.$$

Using (4a) and the triangle inequality we thus obtain

$$|s_m{}^* - s| = |(s_m{}^* - s_n) + (s_n - s)| \leq |s_m{}^* - s_n| + |s_n - s| < \frac{\epsilon}{2} + \frac{\epsilon}{2} = \epsilon$$

for every sufficiently large m. Hence, $s_m{}^*$ converges to s and, therefore, $s^* = s$. This completes the proof.

10.8 POWER SERIES

We have made the definitions for series of *constant* terms. If the terms of a series are *variable*, say, functions of a variable z, they assume definite values when z is given a fixed value, and then all those definitions apply. It is obvious that in the case of such a series of functions of z the partial sums, the remainders, and the sum will be functions of z. Usually such a series will be convergent for some values of z, for example, for all z in some region, and divergent for the other values of z.

In complex analysis, the most important series with variable terms are power series. A **power series**[8] *in powers of* $z - a$ is an infinite series of the form

(1) $$\sum_{m=0}^{\infty} c_m(z - a)^m = c_0 + c_1(z - a) + c_2(z - a)^2 + \cdots$$

where z is a variable, $c_0, c_1, \cdots$ are constants, called the **coefficients**, and a is a constant, called the **center** of the series.

If $a = 0$, we obtain as a particular case a *power series in powers of* z:

(2) $$\sum_{m=0}^{\infty} c_m z^m = c_0 + c_1 z + c_2 z^2 + \cdots.$$

The convergence behavior of a power series can be characterized in a very simple way. Let us start with three examples, which will turn out to be typical.

Example 1. The **geometric series**

$$\sum_{m=0}^{\infty} z^m = 1 + z + z^2 + \cdots$$

converges absolutely when $|z| < 1$ and diverges when $|z| \geq 1$ (cf. Theorem 2 in Sec. 10.6).

---

[8] It should be noted that the term "power series" alone usually refers to series of the form (1), including the particular case (2), but *does not include* series of negative powers of z such as $c_1 z^{-1} + c_2 z^{-2} + \cdots$ or series involving fractional powers of z.

Example 2. The power series

$$\sum_{n=0}^{\infty} \frac{z^n}{n!} = 1 + z + \frac{z^2}{2!} + \frac{z^3}{3!} + \cdots$$

is absolutely convergent for each (finite) z, as follows from the ratio test, because

$$\left| \frac{z^{n+1}/(n+1)!}{z^n/n!} \right| = \frac{|z|}{n+1} \to 0 \qquad \text{as} \qquad n \to \infty \qquad (z \text{ fixed}).$$

Example 3. The power series

$$\sum_{n=0}^{\infty} n! \, z^n = 1 + z + 2z^2 + 6z^3 + \cdots$$

converges only at the center $z = 0$, but diverges for any $z \neq 0$. In fact, this follows from the ratio test because

$$\left| \frac{(n+1)! \, z^{n+1}}{n! \, z^n} \right| = (n+1)|z| \to \infty \qquad \text{as} \qquad n \to \infty \qquad (z \text{ fixed and} \neq 0).$$

The power series (1) converges when $z = a$ because then $z - a = 0$, and the series reduces to the single term c_0. Example 3 illustrates that in some cases this may be the only value of z for which the series converges. However, if the series converges for some $z_0 \neq a$, then it converges for all z whose distances from the center are less than that of z_0. In fact, the following theorem holds.

Theorem 1. *If the power series* (1) *converges for* $z = z_0$, *it converges absolutely for every* z *for which* $|z - a| < |z_0 - a|$, *that is, for each* z *within the circle through* z_0 *about* a.

Proof. Since the series (1) converges for z_0, Theorem 1 in Sec. 10.5 shows that

$$c_n(z_0 - a)^n \to 0 \qquad \text{as} \qquad n \to \infty.$$

This implies that for $z = z_0$ the terms of (1) are bounded, say,

$$|c_n(z_0 - a)^n| < M \qquad \text{for every } n = 0, 1, \cdots.$$

From this we obtain

$$|c_n(z - a)^n| = \left| c_n(z_0 - a)^n \left(\frac{z-a}{z_0-a} \right)^n \right| < M \left| \frac{z-a}{z_0-a} \right|^n$$

and, therefore,

(3) $$\sum_{n=0}^{\infty} |c_n(z - a)^n| < \sum_{n=0}^{\infty} M \left| \frac{z-a}{z_0-a} \right|^n = M \sum_{n=0}^{\infty} \left| \frac{z-a}{z_0-a} \right|^n.$$

From the assumption $|z - a| < |z_0 - a|$ we have

$$\left| \frac{z-a}{z_0-a} \right| < 1,$$

and the series on the right-hand side of (3) is a geometric series which converges. Hence, the series on the left-hand side of (3) converges, and the series (1) converges absolutely when $|z - a| < |z_0 - a|$. This completes the proof.

Examples 2 and 3 illustrate that a power series may converge for all z or only for $z = a$. Let us exclude these two cases from our consideration for a moment. Then, if a power series (1) is given, we may consider all the points z in the complex plane for which the series converges. Let R be the smallest real number so that the distance of any of these points from the center a is at most equal to R. (For instance, in Ex. 1, $R = 1$.) Then from Theorem 1 it follows that the series converges for all z within the circle of radius R about the center a, that is, for all z for which

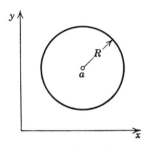

Fig. 298. Circle of convergence.

(4) $$|z - a| < R$$

and diverges for all z for which

$$|z - a| > R.$$

The circle

$$|z - a| = R$$

is called the **circle of convergence**, and its radius R is called the **radius of convergence** of (1). Cf. Fig. 298.

At the points on the circle of convergence the series may converge or diverge. For instance, in Ex. 1 we have $R = 1$, and the series diverges at each point of the circle of convergence $|z| = 1$. The series

$$\sum_{n=1}^{\infty} \frac{z^n}{n} = z + \frac{z^2}{2} + \frac{z^3}{3} + \cdots$$

converges for $|z| < 1$ and diverges for $|z| > 1$, as follows by the ratio test. Thus $R = 1$. At $z = 1$ it becomes the harmonic series and diverges, while at $z = -1$ it becomes the series in Ex. 5, Sec. 10.5, and converges. This illustrates that a series may converge at some points on the circle of convergence, while at others it may diverge.

Clearly, if we consider a *real* power series (1), that is, if the variable

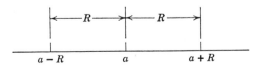

Fig. 299. Interval of convergence of a real power series.

$z = x$, the center, and the coefficients are real, then (4) represents an interval of length $2R$ with midpoint at a on the x-axis, the so-called **interval of convergence** (Fig. 299).

If the series (1) converges for all z (as in Ex. 2), then we set

$$R = \infty \qquad \text{(and } 1/R = 0\text{);}$$

if it converges only at the center $z = a$ (as in Ex. 3), then we set

$$R = 0 \qquad \text{(and } 1/R = \infty\text{).}$$

Using these conventions, the radius of convergence R of the power series (1) may be determined from the coefficients of the series as follows.

Theorem 2. *If the sequence* $\sqrt[n]{|c_n|}$, $n = 1, 2, \cdots$ *converges with the limit* L, *then the radius of convergence R of the power series* (1) *is*

(5a)
$$R = \frac{1}{L} \qquad \textbf{(Cauchy-Hadamard formula),}[9]$$

including the case $L = 0$ where $R = \infty$ and the series (1) *converges for all z. If that sequence does not converge but is bounded, then*

(5b)
$$R = \frac{1}{l}$$

where l is the greatest of the limit points of the sequence.

If that sequence is not bounded, then $R = 0$, and the series converges only for $z = a$.

Proof. If

$$\lim_{n \to \infty} \sqrt[n]{|c_n|} = L \neq 0,$$

then

$$\lim_{n \to \infty} \sqrt[n]{|c_n(z - a)^n|} = |z - a| \lim_{n \to \infty} \sqrt[n]{|c_n|} = |z - a| L.$$

Since the terms of the series (1) are $w_n = c_n(z - a)^n$, the root test (p. 608) shows that the series converges absolutely when

$$|z - a| L < 1 \qquad \text{or} \qquad |z - a| < \frac{1}{L} = R$$

but diverges when

$$|z - a| L > 1 \qquad \text{or} \qquad |z - a| > \frac{1}{L} = R.$$

If

$$\lim_{n \to \infty} \sqrt[n]{|c_n|} = L = 0,$$

[9] Named after the French mathematicians, A. L. CAUCHY (cf. the footnote on p. 92) and JAQUES HADAMARD (1865–   ).

it follows from the definition of limit that for any given $\epsilon > 0$, for example, for $\epsilon = 1/(2 |z_1 - a|)$ with arbitrary fixed z_1, we can find an N such that

$$\sqrt[n]{|c_n|} < \frac{1}{2 |z_1 - a|} \qquad \text{for every } n > N.$$

From this we immediately obtain

$$|c_n| < \frac{1}{(2 |z_1 - a|)^n} \qquad \text{or} \qquad |c_n(z_1 - a)^n| < \frac{1}{2^n}.$$

Now, since $\Sigma\, 2^{-n}$ converges, the comparison test (cf. Sec. 10.6) shows that the series (1) converges absolutely for $z = z_1$. Since z_1 was arbitrary, this means absolute convergence for every finite z, and the proof of the statement involving (5a) is complete.

We next prove the statement involving (5b). The existence of l follows from the Bolzano-Weierstrass theorem (Sec. 10.4), and since $\sqrt[n]{|c_n|} \geqq 0$, we clearly have $l > 0$. From the definition of a limit point it follows that, an $\epsilon > 0$ being given,

$$l - \epsilon < \sqrt[n]{|c_n|} < l + \epsilon \qquad \text{for infinitely many } n.$$

By multiplying this by the positive quantity $|z - a|$ we have

$$(6) \qquad |z - a| (l - \epsilon) < \sqrt[n]{|c_n(z - a)^n|}$$

and

$$(7) \qquad \sqrt[n]{|c_n(z - a)^n|} < |z - a| (l + \epsilon).$$

The inequality (7) holds even for all sufficiently large n, say, for $n > N$, because l is the greatest limit point and, therefore, at most finitely many terms can be greater than the expression on the right. We prove that for

$$(8) \qquad |z - a| < \frac{1}{l}$$

convergence follows from (7). In fact, if we choose

$$\epsilon = \frac{1 - l\,|z - a|}{2\,|z - a|},$$

then, by (8), $\epsilon > 0$, and (7) becomes

$$\sqrt[n]{|c_n(z - a)^n|} < \frac{1 + l\,|z - a|}{2} \qquad (n > N).$$

From (8) we see that the expression on the right is less than 1, and convergence follows by means of the root test (Theorem 6, Sec. 10.6). On the other hand, when

$$|z - a| > \frac{1}{l},$$

then, choosing

$$\epsilon = \frac{l\,|z - a| - 1}{2\,|z - a|},$$

we have $\epsilon > 0$ and (6) becomes

$$\sqrt[n]{|c_n(z - a)^n|} > \frac{|z - a|\,l + 1}{2} > 1.$$

Hence, by Theorem 6 in Sec. 10.6 the series diverges for those z. This proves the statement involving (5b).

Finally if the sequence $\sqrt[n]{|c_n|}$ is not bounded, then, by definition, any K being given,

$$\sqrt[n]{|c_n|} > K \qquad \text{for infinitely many } n.$$

Choosing $K = 1/|z - a|$ where $z \neq a$, this becomes

$$\sqrt[n]{|c_n|} > \frac{1}{|z - a|} \qquad \text{or} \qquad \sqrt[n]{|c_n(z - a)^n|} > 1,$$

and divergence follows from Theorem 6 in Sec. 10.6. This completes the proof of Theorem 2.

We shall now consider the operations of addition and multiplication of power series.

From Theorem 1, Sec. 10.7, it is clear that *two power series may be added term by term for any z for which both series are convergent.*

Let us consider the term-by-term multiplication of two power series

$$(9) \quad \sum_{k=0}^{\infty} a_k z^k = a_0 + a_1 z + \cdots \qquad \text{and} \qquad \sum_{m=0}^{\infty} c_m z^m = c_0 + c_1 z + \cdots.$$

If we multiply each term of the first series by each term of the second series and collect products of like powers of z, we obtain

$$
\begin{aligned}
&a_0 c_0 + (a_0 c_1 + a_1 c_0)z + (a_0 c_2 + a_1 c_1 + a_2 c_0)z^2 + \cdots \\
\textbf{(10)} \quad &= \sum_{n=0}^{\infty} (a_0 c_n + a_1 c_{n-1} + \cdots + a_n c_0)z^n.
\end{aligned}
$$

This series is called the **Cauchy product** of the series (9).

Theorem 3.   *The Cauchy product of the two power series* (9) *is absolutely convergent for each z within the circle of convergence of each of the series* (9). *If the series have the sums g(z) and h(z), respectively, the Cauchy product has the sum*

$$(11) \qquad\qquad s(z) = g(z)h(z).$$

Proof. The general term of the product series (10) is

$$p_n = (a_0 c_n + a_1 c_{n-1} + \cdots + a_n c_0) z^n.$$

Now, by the generalized triangle inequality (3) in Sec. 10.1,

$$|p_0| + |p_1| = |a_0 c_0| + |(a_0 c_1 + a_1 c_0) z| \leq (|a_0| + |a_1 z|)(|c_0| + |c_1 z|),$$

$$|p_0| + |p_1| + |p_2| \leq (|a_0| + |a_1 z| + |a_2 z^2|)(|c_0| + |c_1 z| + |c_2 z^2|),$$

as can be readily verified by performing the multiplication on the right; in general,

$$|p_0| + |p_1| + \cdots + |p_n|$$
$$\leq (|a_0| + |a_1 z| + \cdots + |a_n z^n|)(|c_0| + |c_1 z| + \cdots + |c_n z^n|).$$

If z lies within the circle of convergence of each of the series (9), the sequence of the expressions on the right is bounded, and so is the sequence of the partial sums of the series $|p_0| + |p_1| + \cdots$. Since $|p_n| \geq 0$, that sequence is monotone increasing, and from Theorem 5 in Sec. 10.4 if follows that it converges. Hence that series is convergent, and the product series (10) converges absolutely.

We prove (11). By Theorem 3 in Sec. 10.7, any rearrangement of (10) is absolutely convergent for precisely those z and has the same sum as (10). We consider the particular rearrangement $p_0{}^* + p_1{}^* + \cdots$ where (Fig. 300)

$$p_n{}^* = (a_n c_0 + a_0 c_n) z^n + (a_n c_1 + a_1 c_n) z^{n+1} + \cdots$$
$$+ (a_n c_{n-1} + a_{n-1} c_n) z^{2n-1} + a_n c_n z^{2n}.$$

Obviously,

$$a_0 c_0 = p_0{}^*, \qquad (a_0 + a_1 z)(c_0 + c_1 z) = p_0{}^* + p_1{}^*$$

and, in general,

$$(a_0 + a_1 z + \cdots + a_n z^n)(c_0 + c_1 z + \cdots + c_n z^n) = p_0{}^* + p_1{}^* + \cdots + p_n{}^*.$$

By letting n approach infinity, (11) follows, and Theorem 3 is proved.

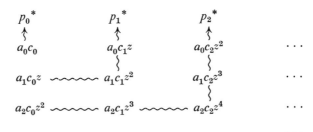

Fig. 300. Proof of Theorem 3.

Example 4. The geometric series $1 + z + z^2 + \cdots$ has the sum $1/(1 - z)$ when $|z| < 1$ (cf. Theorem 2 in Sec. 10.6), and from Theorem 3 it follows that

$$\left(\frac{1}{1-z}\right)^2 = \sum_{k=0}^{\infty} z^k \sum_{m=0}^{\infty} z^m = (1 + z + z^2 + \cdots)(1 + z + z^2 + \cdots)$$

$$= 1 + 2z + 3z^2 + \cdots = \sum_{n=0}^{\infty} (n + 1)z^n \qquad (|z| < 1).$$

PROBLEMS

Find the radius of convergence of the following series.

1. $\displaystyle\sum_{n=0}^{\infty} \frac{(z - 1)^n}{4^n}$

2. $\displaystyle\sum_{n=1}^{\infty} \frac{n}{2^n} (z - i)^n$

3. $\displaystyle\sum_{n=0}^{\infty} (n + 1)z^n$

4. $\displaystyle\sum_{n=0}^{\infty} (n + 2)(n + 1)z^n$

5. $\displaystyle\sum_{n=0}^{\infty} (3z)^n$

6. $\displaystyle\sum_{n=0}^{\infty} 5^n(z + 2i)^n$

7. $\displaystyle\sum_{n=0}^{\infty} \left(\frac{\pi}{2}\right)^n \left(z - \frac{i\pi}{2}\right)^n$

8. $\displaystyle\sum_{n=2}^{\infty} \frac{n + 1}{n - 1} (z - 2i)^n$

9. $\displaystyle\sum_{n-1}^{\infty} n^{2n} z^n$

10. $\displaystyle\sum_{n-1}^{\infty} \frac{z^n}{n^n}$

11. $\displaystyle\sum_{n=1}^{\infty} \frac{(z + 2)^n}{n}$

12. $\displaystyle\sum_{n=1}^{\infty} \frac{z^n}{n^2}$

13. Show that if the sequence

$$\left| \frac{c_{n+1}}{c_n} \right| \qquad\qquad n = 1, 2, \cdots$$

is convergent with the limit L then the radius of convergence R of the power series (1) is $R = 1/L$, including the case $L = 0$ where $R = \infty$.

Using the result of Prob. 13, find the radius of convergence of the following series.

14. $\displaystyle\sum_{n=0}^{\infty} \frac{(-1)^n}{n!} z^n$

15. $\displaystyle\sum_{n=1}^{\infty} nz^{n-1}$

16. $\displaystyle\sum_{n=1}^{\infty} \frac{(3n)!}{(n!)^3} z^n$

17. $\displaystyle\sum_{n=1}^{\infty} \frac{(-1)^n(2n)!}{(n!)^2} z^n$

18. $\displaystyle\sum_{n=1}^{\infty} \frac{(n!)^2}{(2n)!} z^n$

19. $\displaystyle\sum_{n=1}^{\infty} \frac{z^n}{n^2}$

20. If the radius of convergence of $\Sigma c_n z^n$ is R, show that the radius of convergence of $\Sigma\, c_n z^{2n}$ is $\sqrt{R}$.

10.9 FUNCTIONS REPRESENTED BY POWER SERIES

Power series are basic in complex analysis, and the main objective of this section is to show the reasons for this fact.

Let $\displaystyle\sum_{n=0}^{\infty} c_n z^n$ be an arbitrary power series with nonzero radius of convergence R. Then the sum of this series is a function of z, say, $f(z)$, and we write

$$(1) \qquad f(z) = \sum_{n=0}^{\infty} c_n z^n = c_0 + c_1 z + c_2 z^2 + \cdots \qquad (|z| < R).$$

We say that $f(z)$ *is represented by the power series* or that *it is developed in the power series.* For example, the geometric series (4) in Ex. 1, Sec. 10.8, represents the function $f(z) = 1/(1 - z)$ in the interior of the unit circle $|z| = 1$.

We shall now show that each power series with a nonzero radius of convergence represents an analytic function. In Sec. 11.7 we shall prove that, conversely, every analytic function can be represented by power series. For these reasons power series play a basic role in connection with analytic functions and their practical applications.

We subdivide our consideration into several steps, starting with the following theorem.

Theorem 1. *The function $f(z)$ in (1) is continuous at $z = 0$.*

Proof. We have to show that

$$(2) \qquad\qquad \lim_{z \to 0} f(z) = f(0) = c_0.$$

We choose an arbitrary positive number $r < R$. Since the series in (1) is absolutely convergent in the disk $|z| < R$, it follows that the series

$$\sum_{n=1}^{\infty} |c_n| \, r^{n-1} = \frac{1}{r} \sum_{n=1}^{\infty} |c_n| \, r^n \qquad\qquad (0 < r < R)$$

is convergent. Let K denote its sum. Then

$$|f(z) - c_0| = \left| z \sum_{n=1}^{\infty} c_n z^{n-1} \right| \le |z| \sum_{n=1}^{\infty} |c_n| |z|^{n-1} \le |z| \, K \qquad (0 < |z| \le r).$$

An $\epsilon > 0$ being given, $|f(z) - c_0| < \epsilon$ for all $|z| < \delta$ where δ is a positive real number less than both r and ϵ/K. By definition of a limit, this means that (2) holds, and the proof is complete.

Next we consider the question of **uniqueness** and show that *the same function $f(z)$ cannot be represented by two different power series with the same center.* If $f(z)$ can be developed in a power series with center a, the development is unique. This important fact is frequently used in real and complex analysis. We may formulate it as follows (assuming that $a = 0$, without loss of generality).

Theorem 2 (Identity theorem for power series). *Suppose that*

$$\sum_{n=0}^{\infty} a_n z^n \qquad and \qquad \sum_{n=0}^{\infty} b_n z^n$$

are power series which are convergent for $|z| < R$ where R is positive, and have the same sum for all these z. Then the series are identical, that is,

$$(3) \qquad\qquad a_n = b_n \qquad\qquad for\ all\ n = 0, 1, \cdots .$$

Proof. We proceed by induction. By assumption,

$$(4) \qquad a_0 + a_1 z + a_2 z^2 + \cdots = b_0 + b_1 z + b_2 z^2 + \cdots \qquad (|z| < R).$$

Let z approach zero. Then, by Theorem 1, $a_0 = b_0$. Assume that $a_n = b_n$ for $n = 0, 1, \cdots, m$. Then, by omitting the first $m + 1$ terms on both sides of (4) and dividing by z^{m+1} ($\neq 0$), we obtain

$$a_{m+1} + a_{m+2} z + a_{m+3} z^2 + \cdots = b_{m+1} + b_{m+2} z + b_{m+3} z^2 + \cdots.$$

By Theorem 1, each of these power series represents a function which is continuous at $z = 0$. Hence $a_{m+1} = b_{m+1}$. This completes the proof.

We shall now consider **developments around different centers.** Let us show that the function $f(z)$ represented by the power series (1) (with non-zero radius of convergence R) can also be represented by a power series with center $z = b$, where b is any point whose distance from the origin is less than R.

To derive such a power series, we set $z - b = Z$. Then $z = b + Z$, and (1) takes the form

$$
\begin{aligned}
(5) \qquad f(z) &= \sum_{n=0}^{\infty} c_n z^n = \sum_{n=0}^{\infty} c_n (b + Z)^n \\
&= c_0 + c_1(b + Z) + c_2(b^2 + 2bZ + Z^2) + \cdots.
\end{aligned}
$$

We consider the corresponding series

$$(6) \quad \sum_{n=0}^{\infty} |c_n| (|b| + |Z|)^n = |c_0| + |c_1| (|b| + |Z|) + |c_2| (|b| + |Z|)^2 + \cdots.$$

Since the original series converges absolutely when $|z| < R$, it follows that if

$$|b| + |Z| < R, \qquad \text{that is,}$$
$$|Z| = |z - b| < R - |b|,$$

the series (6) is convergent. The corresponding values of z lie in the open disk D^* in Fig. 301. For these values of z we may thus arrange the series on the right-hand side of (5) in powers of $Z = z - b$ without altering its sum. In this way we obtain a representation of the form

$$(7) \qquad f(z) = \sum_{n=0}^{\infty} a_n (z - b)^n,$$

valid (at least) in the disk

$$|z - b| < R - |b|.$$

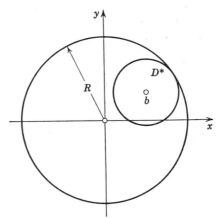

Fig. 301. Development around different centers.

We shall see later (in Sec. 11.7) that in general the radius of convergence of (7) will be greater than $R - |b|$, so that (7) will yield a *"continuation"* of the function $f(z)$ in (1) to points outside the disk $|z| < R$. This process of continuing a function, at first given by a power series in a region of convergence $|z| < R$, beyond that region is called **analytic continuation**.

By direct calculation it follows that the coefficients a_n can be represented in terms of the coefficients c_n of the original representation (1) in the form

$$(8) \quad a_n = \sum_{m=0}^{\infty} \binom{m+n}{n} c_{m+n} b^m \quad \text{where} \quad \binom{m+n}{n} = \frac{(m+n)!}{n!\,m!}.$$

The practical application of (8) will be difficult in general. We shall see later (in Sec. 11.8) that in the case where $f(z)$ in (1) is a known function, there are various other methods for determining the coefficients of the corresponding series (7).

Let us now consider termwise differentiation and integration of power series. By differentiating the series $c_0 + c_1 z + c_2 z^2 + \cdots$ we obtain the series

$$(9) \qquad \sum_{n=1}^{\infty} n c_n z^{n-1} = c_1 + 2c_2 z + 3c_3 z^2 + \cdots$$

which is called the *derived series* of the given series.

Theorem 3. *The derived series of a power series has the same radius of convergence as the original series.*

Proof. Let $n c_n = c_n^{*}$. Then $\sqrt[n]{|c_n^{*}|} = \sqrt[n]{n}\,\sqrt[n]{|c_n|}$. Since $\sqrt[n]{n} \to 1$ as $n \to \infty$ it follows that the sequences $\sqrt[n]{|c_n^{*}|}$ and $\sqrt[n]{|c_n|}$ either both converge with the same limit or both diverge. If they diverge, they are both unbounded or bounded, and in the latter case their greatest limit points are the same. From this and Theorem 2 in the last section the statement of our present theorem follows.

Theorem 4. *The series*

$$\sum_{n=0}^{\infty} \frac{c_n}{n+1} z^{n+1} = c_0 z + \frac{c_1}{2} z^2 + \frac{c_2}{3} z^3 + \cdots$$

obtained by integrating the series $c_0 + c_1 z + c_2 z^2 + \cdots$ term by term has the same radius of convergence as the original series.

The proof is similar to that of Theorem 3.

Example 1. The power series

$$\sum_{n=1}^{\infty} (n+1) z^n$$

has the radius of convergence $R = 1$ since, by integrating term by term we obtain the geometric series $\sum_{n=1}^{\infty} z^{n+1}$.

Power series represent analytic functions. More precisely:

Theorem 5. *A power series with a nonzero radius of convergence R represents an analytic function at every point interior to its circle of convergence. The derivatives of this function are obtained by differentiating the original series term by term; all the series thus obtained have the same radius of convergence as the original series.*

Proof. We consider the representation

$$f(z) = \sum_{n=0}^{\infty} c_n z^n,$$

assuming that the radius of convergence R is not zero. Then we may represent $f(z)$ in the form (7), and from Theorem 1 it follows that $f(z)$ is continuous at the center b. Since b is any point in the disk $|z| < R$, the function $f(z)$ is continuous everywhere in this disk. From (7) we obtain $f(b) = a_0$ and, therefore,

$$\frac{f(z) - f(b)}{z - b} = a_1 + a_2(z - b) + a_3(z - b)^2 + \cdots.$$

According to Theorem 1, the function represented by the power series on the right is continuous at b. Hence by (8),

(10)
$$f'(b) = \lim_{z \to b} \frac{f(z) - f(b)}{z - b} = a_1 = \sum_{m=0}^{\infty} (m + 1)c_{m+1}b^m$$

$$= \sum_{k=1}^{\infty} kc_k b^{k-1}.$$

That is, the first derivative of $f(z)$ exists at any point $z = b$ in the disk $|z| < R$ and can be obtained by differentiating the original series term by term; indeed, the series on the right has the radius of convergence R, as was proved in Theorem 3. Hence $f(z)$ is analytic in the disk $|z| < R$, and the proof is complete.

Since the derivative

$$f'(z) = \sum_{n=1}^{\infty} nc_n z^{n-1}$$

of $f(z)$ is now represented by a power series, we may apply Theorem 5 to $f'(z)$ and conclude that $f''(z)$ exists in the disk $|z| < R$, and

$$f''(z) = \sum_{n=2}^{\infty} n(n - 1)c_n z^{n-2}.$$

More generally, the mth derivative $f^{(m)}(z)$ of $f(z)$ exists in that disk, and

(11) $$f^{(m)}(z) = \sum_{n=m}^{\infty} n(n-1) \cdots (n-m+1)c_n z^{n-m}.$$

This means that $f(z)$ *has derivatives of all orders in that disk.* We shall see later (in Secs. 11.6 and 11.7) that *every analytic function has derivatives of all orders and, moreover, can be represented by power series.*

PROBLEMS

Using Theorem 2, prove the following statements and formulas.

1. If $f(z)$ in (1) is an even function, then $c_n = 0$ for $n = 1, 3, \cdots$.

2. If $f(z)$ in (1) is odd, then $c_n = 0$ for $n = 0, 2, 4, \cdots$.

3. $f(z) = \sum_{n=0}^{\infty} z^n/n!$ is neither even nor odd.

4. $\binom{k}{0}^2 + \binom{k}{1}^2 + \cdots + \binom{k}{k}^2 = \binom{2k}{k}$. *Hint:* consider

$$(1 + z)^k (1 + z)^k = (1 + z)^{2k} \qquad (k > 0, \text{integral}).$$

5. $\sum_{n=0}^{r} \binom{p}{n} \binom{q}{r-n} = \binom{p+q}{r}$. *Hint:* consider

$$(1 + z)^p (1 + z)^q = (1 + z)^{p+q} \qquad (p > 0, q > 0, \text{integral}).$$

6. Verify the statements in Probs. 1 and 2 for some elementary real functions.

7. Explain the use of Theorems 2 and 5 in connection with the power series method for solving differential equations (Sec. 3.1).

8. Verify Theorem 3 for $\quad \sum_{n=0}^{\infty} z^{2n} \quad$ and $\quad \sum_{n=0}^{\infty} \dfrac{z^{2n}}{(2n)!}$.

9. Verify Theorem 4 for $\quad \sum_{n=0}^{\infty} \dfrac{z^n}{2^n} \quad$ and $\quad \sum_{n=0}^{\infty} \dfrac{z^{2n+1}}{(2n+1)!}$.

Using the geometric series and Theorems 3 and 4, find the radius of convergence of the following series.

10. $\sum_{n=k}^{\infty} \binom{n}{k} z^{n-k}$ **11.** $\sum_{n=k}^{\infty} \binom{n}{k} \dfrac{z^n}{2^n}$

12. $\sum_{n=0}^{\infty} \dfrac{1}{\binom{n+k}{n}} z^{n+k}$ **13.** $\sum_{n=0}^{\infty} \dfrac{1}{\binom{n+k}{n}} \dfrac{z^n}{3^n}$

Using Theorem 5, prove the following formulas and statements.

14. $\dfrac{1}{(1-z)^2} = \sum_{n=1}^{\infty} nz^{n-1}, \qquad \dfrac{1}{(1-z)^3} = 2 \sum_{n=2}^{\infty} \binom{n}{2} z^{n-2}$ $(|z| < 1)$

15. $f(z) = \sum_{n=0}^{\infty} \dfrac{z^n}{n!}$ satisfies $f'(z) = f(z)$.

16. $f(z) = \sum_{n=0}^{\infty} \dfrac{(-kz)^n}{n!}$ satisfies $f'(z) + kf(z) = 0$.

17. $f(z) = z - \dfrac{z^3}{3!} + \dfrac{z^5}{5!} - + \cdots$ satisfies $f''(z) + f(z) = 0$.

10.10   RATIONAL FUNCTIONS. ROOT

The remaining sections of this chapter will be devoted to the most important elementary complex functions, such as powers, exponential function, logarithm, trigonometric functions, etc. We shall see that these functions can easily be defined in such a way that, for real values of the independent variable, the functions become identical with the familiar real functions. Some of the complex functions have interesting properties, which do not show when the independent variable is restricted to real values. The student should follow the consideration with great care, because these elementary functions will frequently be needed in applications. Furthermore, a detailed knowledge of these special functions will be helpful later for a better understanding of our more general considerations.

The powers

$$(1) \qquad\qquad w = z^n \qquad\qquad n = 0, 1, \cdots$$

are analytic in the entire plane, and the same is true for a function of the form

$$(2) \qquad w = c_0 + c_1 z + c_2 z^2 + \cdots + c_n z^n$$

where $c_0, \cdots, c_n$ are (complex or real) constants. Such a function is called a **polynomial** or an *entire rational function*. The exponent n is called the *degree* of the polynomial. The study of these functions is the principal subject of classical algebra.

A quotient of two polynomials $p(z)$ and $q(z)$ is called a (*fractional*) **rational function**. Such a function

$$(3) \qquad\qquad w = \frac{p(z)}{q(z)}$$

is analytic for every z for which $q(z)$ is not zero. A rational function of the particularly simple form

$$\frac{c}{(z - z_0)^m} \qquad\qquad (c \neq 0)$$

where both c and z_0 are complex numbers and m is a positive integer, is called a *partial fraction*. It is proved in algebra that every rational function can be represented as the sum of a polynomial and finitely many partial fractions.

If $z = w^n$ ($n = 1, 2, \cdots$), then to each value of w there corresponds one value of z. We shall immediately see that to a given $z \neq 0$ there correspond precisely n distinct values of w. Each of these values is called an **nth root** of z, and we write

$$(4) \qquad\qquad w = \sqrt[n]{z}.$$

Hence this symbol is *multi-valued*, namely, *n-valued*, in contrast to the usual conventions made in real calculus.

The n values of $\sqrt[n]{z}$ can easily be determined as follows. We set

$$w = R(\cos \phi + i \sin \phi) \qquad \text{and} \qquad z = r(\cos \theta + i \sin \theta).$$

Then from de Moivre's formula (cf. Sec. 0.5) it follows that

$$z = w^n = R^n(\cos n\phi + i \sin n\phi) = r(\cos \theta + i \sin \theta).$$

By equating the absolute values on both sides we have

$$R^n = r \qquad \text{or} \qquad R = \sqrt[n]{r}$$

where the root is real positive and thus uniquely determined. By equating the arguments we obtain

$$n\phi = \theta + 2k\pi \qquad \text{or} \qquad \phi = \frac{\theta}{n} + \frac{2k\pi}{n}$$

where k is an integer. Consequently, $\sqrt[n]{z}$, for $z \neq 0$, has the n distinct values

$$(5) \qquad \sqrt[n]{z} = \sqrt[n]{r} \left(\cos \frac{\theta + 2k\pi}{n} + i \sin \frac{\theta + 2k\pi}{n} \right),$$
$$k = 0, 1, \cdots, n - 1.$$

These n values lie on a circle of radius $\sqrt[n]{r}$ with center at the origin and constitute the vertices of a regular polygon of n sides.

The value of $\sqrt[n]{z}$ obtained by taking the principal value of arg z (cf. Sec. 10.1) and $k = 0$ in (5) is called the **principal value** *of the n-valued function* $w = \sqrt[n]{z}$.

Example 1. $w = \sqrt{z}$ has the values

$$z_1 = \sqrt{r}\left(\cos \frac{\theta}{2} + i \sin \frac{\theta}{2} \right)$$

$$\text{and} \qquad z_2 = \sqrt{r}\left[\cos \left(\frac{\theta}{2} + \pi \right) + i \sin \left(\frac{\theta}{2} + \pi \right) \right] = -z_1,$$

which lie symmetric with respect to the origin. For instance,

$$\sqrt{4i} = \pm 2\left(\cos \frac{\pi}{4} + i \sin \frac{\pi}{4} \right) = \pm(\sqrt{2} + i\sqrt{2}) \qquad \text{(Fig. 302)}.$$

Example 2. If z is *positive real*, then $w = \sqrt[3]{z}$ has the real value $\sqrt[3]{r}$ and the conjugate complex values

$$\sqrt[3]{r}\left(\cos \frac{2\pi}{3} + i \sin \frac{2\pi}{3} \right) = \sqrt[3]{r}\left(-\frac{1}{2} + \frac{\sqrt{3}}{2}i \right)$$

$$\text{and} \qquad \sqrt[3]{r}\left(\cos \frac{4\pi}{3} + i \sin \frac{4\pi}{3} \right) = \sqrt[3]{r}\left(-\frac{1}{2} - \frac{\sqrt{3}}{2}i \right).$$

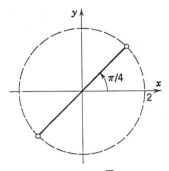

Fig. 302. $\sqrt{4i}$.

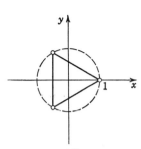

Fig. 303. $\sqrt[3]{1}$.

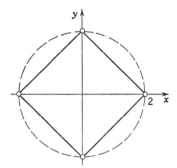

Fig. 304. $\sqrt[4]{16}$.

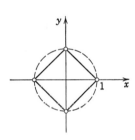

Fig. 305. $\sqrt[4]{1}$.

For instance, $\sqrt[3]{1} = 1, -\dfrac{1}{2} \pm \dfrac{\sqrt{3}}{2} i$ (Fig. 303). Clearly these are the roots of the equation $w^3 - 1 = 0$.

Example 3. $\sqrt[4]{16}$ has the four values 2, $2i$, -2, $-2i$ (Fig. 304), and the principal value is 2.

Example 4. From (5) it follows that the **nth root of unity** is given by the formula

$$\sqrt[n]{1} = \cos\frac{2k\pi}{n} + i\sin\frac{2k\pi}{n}, \qquad k = 0, 1, \cdots n - 1.$$

If ω denotes the value corresponding to $k = 1$, then the n values of $\sqrt[n]{1}$ can be written as 1, ω, ω^2, $\cdots$, ω^{n-1}. These values are the vertices of a regular polygon of n sides inscribed in the unit circle, with one vertex at the point 1. For instance, $\sqrt[4]{1}$ has the values 1, i, -1, and $-i$ (Fig. 305). Fig. 306 shows $\sqrt[5]{1}$.

If w_1 is any nth root of an arbitrary complex number z, then

$$w_1, \qquad w_1\omega, \qquad w_1\omega^2, \qquad \cdots, \qquad w_1\omega^{n-1}$$

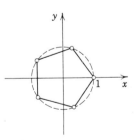

Fig. 306. $\sqrt[5]{1}$.

are the n values of $\sqrt[n]{z}$, because the multiplication of a number w_1 by ω^k corresponds to an increase of the argument of w_1 by $2k\pi/n$.

PROBLEMS

Determine all values of the following roots and plot the corresponding points in the complex plane.

1. $\sqrt{i}$ 2. $\sqrt[3]{-1}$ 3. $\sqrt{-i}$ 4. $\sqrt{-25}$

5. $\sqrt{\tfrac{1}{2}(1 + i\sqrt{3})}$ 6. $\sqrt{1 - i\sqrt{3}}$ 7. $\sqrt[3]{i}$ 8. $\sqrt[4]{1}$

9. $\sqrt[4]{-1}$ 10. $\sqrt[3]{-i}$ 11. $\sqrt[6]{-1}$ 12. $\sqrt[8]{1}$

13. $\sqrt[5]{-1}$ 14. $\sqrt[7]{-128}$ 15. $\sqrt[3]{1 + i}$

Find and plot all solutions of the following equations.

16. $z^4 + 81 = 0$ 17. $z^3 = 64$ 18. $z^2 - 6z + 13 = 0$

19. $z^4 + 5z^2 = 36$ 20. $z^6 + 7z^3 = 8$ 21. $z^4 - (1 + 4i)z^2 + 4i = 0$

22. Solve the system of simultaneous equations

$$x^4 - 6x^2y^2 + y^4 = 4, \qquad xy(x^2 - y^2) = 1 \qquad\qquad (x, y \text{ real})$$

by transforming it into a single complex equation for $z = x + iy$.

23. Prove that

$$\sqrt{z} = \pm[\sqrt{(|z| + x)/2} + (\text{sign } y)i\sqrt{(|z| - x)/2}] \qquad (z = x + iy)$$

where sign $y = 1$ if $y \geq 0$, sign $y = -1$ if $y < 0$, and all square roots of positive numbers are taken with the positive sign. *Hint:* set $\sqrt{z} = w = u + iv$, square, separate into two real equations, express u^2 and v^2 in terms of x and y.

Using the result of Prob. 23, find

24. $\sqrt{2i}$ 25. $\sqrt{-2i}$ 26. $\sqrt{-5 + 12i}$ 27. $\sqrt{3 - 4i}$

28. $\sqrt{-8i}$ 29. $\sqrt{-6i - 8}$ 30. $\sqrt{5 + 12i}$ 31. $\sqrt{21 - 20i}$

Using the result of Prob. 23, solve the following equations.

32. $z^2 - 3z + 3 = i$ 33. $z^2 - (5 + i)z + 8 + i = 0$ 34. $z^2 + z + 1 = i$

35. $z^4 - 3(1 + 2i)z^2 = 8 - 6i$ 36. $z^4 + (1 + 2i)z^2 + 2i = 0$

10.11 EXPONENTIAL FUNCTION

The real exponential function e^x has the Maclaurin[10] series

(1) $$e^x = \sum_{n=0}^{\infty} \frac{x^n}{n!} = 1 + x + \frac{x^2}{2!} + \cdots .$$

[10] COLIN MACLAURIN (1698–1746), Scotch mathematician.

The exponential function for complex $z = x + iy$ will be denoted by e^z, and (1) suggests that we define this function by the power series

$$(2) \qquad e^z = \sum_{n=0}^{\infty} \frac{z^n}{n!} = 1 + z + \frac{z^2}{2!} + \cdots$$

which is obtained from (1) by replacing the real variable x by the complex variable z. We say that in this way we *continue* the real exponential function analytically into the complex domain. We know that the series in (2) converges for all z (cf. Ex. 2 in Sec. 10.8). Hence from Theorem 5 in Sec. 10.9, it follows that e^z is *analytic in the entire plane.*

Differentiating (2) term by term and using Theorem 5 in Sec. 10.9, we find that the derivative is

$$(3) \qquad \frac{d}{dz} e^z = e^z.$$

Furthermore, let us show that

$$(4) \qquad e^{z_1} e^{z_2} = e^{(z_1 + z_2)}.$$

To prove (4), we use (2) and start from

$$e^{z_1} e^{z_2} = \sum_{k=0}^{\infty} \frac{z_1^k}{k!} \sum_{m=0}^{\infty} \frac{z_2^m}{m!}.$$

Since both series converge absolutely, we may multiply them term by term; the sum of the products for which $k + m = n$ is

$$\frac{z_1^n}{n!} + \frac{z_1^{n-1}}{(n-1)!} \frac{z_2}{1!} + \cdots + \frac{z_1}{1!} \frac{z_2^{n-1}}{(n-1)!} + \frac{z_2^n}{n!}$$

$$= \frac{1}{n!} \left[z_1^n + \binom{n}{1} z_1^{n-1} z_2 + \binom{n}{2} z_1^{n-2} z_2^2 + \cdots + z_2^n \right] = \frac{(z_1 + z_2)^n}{n!}.$$

Hence the product of the two series may be written

$$\sum_{n=0}^{\infty} \frac{(z_1 + z_2)^n}{n!} = e^{z_1 + z_2},$$

and (4) is proved.

From (4) it follows that

$$e^z = e^{x+iy} = e^x e^{iy}.$$

By setting $z = iy$ in (2) and applying Theorem 1 in Sec. 10.7 we obtain

$$(5) \qquad e^{iy} = \sum_{n=0}^{\infty} \frac{(iy)^n}{n!} = \sum_{k=0}^{\infty} (-1)^k \frac{y^{2k}}{(2k)!} + i \sum_{k=0}^{\infty} (-1)^k \frac{y^{2k+1}}{(2k+1)!},$$

as the reader may easily verify. The series on the right are the familiar Maclaurin expansions of the real cosine and sine functions. This proves the **Euler formula**

(6)
$$e^{iy} = \cos y + i \sin y.$$

We thus obtain the result

(7)
$$e^z = e^{x+iy} = e^x e^{iy} = e^x(\cos y + i \sin y).$$

Furthermore, the trigonometric representation of a complex number $z = x + iy$ may now be written

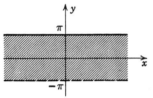

Fig. 307. Fundamental region of the exponential function e^z.

(8)
$$z = r(\cos \theta + i \sin \theta) = re^{i\theta}.$$

From (7) we see that

(9)
$$\text{Re } e^z = e^x \cos y, \quad \text{Im } e^z = e^x \sin y,$$

$$|e^z| = e^x \sqrt{\cos^2 y + \sin^2 y} = e^x,$$

$$\arg e^z = y.$$

Since $\cos 2\pi = 1$ and $\sin 2\pi = 0$, we obtain from (6)

(10)
$$e^{2\pi i} = 1.$$

Similarly,

(11)
$$e^{\pi i} = e^{-\pi i} = -1, \quad e^{\pi i/2} = i, \quad e^{-\pi i/2} = -i.$$

From (10) and (4) it follows that

$$e^{z+2\pi i} = e^z e^{2\pi i} = e^z,$$

which shows that e^z *is periodic with the imaginary period $2\pi i$.* Thus

(12)
$$e^{z \pm 2n\pi i} = e^z \qquad\qquad (n = 0, 1, \cdots)$$

Because of the periodicity, all the values which $w = e^z$ can assume are already assumed in the strip (Fig. 307)

(13)
$$-\pi < y \leq \pi.$$

This infinite strip is called a **fundamental region** of the function e^z.
The reader may prove that (Prob. 27)

(14)
$$e^z \neq 0 \qquad\qquad \text{for all } z.$$

PROBLEMS

1. Using the Cauchy-Riemann equations, show that e^z is analytic for all z.
Find the value of e^z when

2. $z = \pi i/4$ **3.** $z = -\pi i/4$ **4.** $z = 3\pi i/4$ **5.** $z = \pi i/3$
6. $z = -\pi i/3$ **7.** $z = (2 + \pi i)/4$ **8.** $z = 1 + i$ **9.** $z = 2 + 5\pi i$

Find the real and imaginary parts of
10. e^{-3z} **11.** e^{z^2} **12.** e^{z^3} **13.** $e^{(e^z)}$

14. Show that e^z and $e^{\bar{z}}$ are conjugates.
15. Write $z = \sqrt{i}$, $\sqrt{-i}$, $3 + 4i$, and $2 - 2i$ in the form (8).
Let $z_1 = r_1 e^{i\theta_1}$ and $z_2 = e^{i\theta_2}$ ($\neq 0$). Write the following expressions in the
form (8).
16. $z_1 z_2$, z_1^n ($n > 0$, integral), z_1/z_2, $\sqrt{z_1}$ **17.** $\sqrt[n]{z_1}$

Using tables of the real exponential function and sine and cosine, calculate
18. $e^{2+3\pi i}$ **19.** e^{2+i} **20.** $e^{-3+1.5i}$ **21.** $e^{4-0.8i}$

22. Show that $f(z) = e^x(\cos ky + i \sin ky)$, $z = x + iy$, is analytic if, and only if,
$k = 1$.
Show that the following functions are harmonic and find a conjugate.

23. $u = 2e^x \cos y$ **24.** $u = e^{(x^2-y^2)/2} \cos xy$ **25.** $u = e^{xy} \cos \dfrac{x^2 - y^2}{2}$

26. Prove (3) by the use of (3), Sec. 10.3.   **27.** Prove (14).
Find all solutions of the following equations, and plot some of the solutions in
the complex plane.
28. $e^z = 3$ **29.** $e^z = -2$ **30.** $e^{z^2} = 1$
31. Show that $f(z) = ce^z$ ($c = const$) is the only analytic function for which
$f'(z) - f(z)$.
32. Determine the values of z for which $|e^{-2z}| < 1$.
33. Using (2), show that $|e^z - 1| < 2|z|$ for all z in the region $0 < |z| < 1$.
34. Consider the behavior of e^z as $|z| \to \infty$ along different rays, say, for
$\arg z = 0, \pi/2$, and π.

10.12 TRIGONOMETRIC AND HYPERBOLIC FUNCTIONS

From Euler's formula (6) in the last section we obtain

$$\cos x = \tfrac{1}{2}(e^{ix} + e^{-ix}), \qquad \sin x = \frac{1}{2i}(e^{ix} - e^{-ix}) \qquad (x \text{ real}).$$

This suggests the following definitions for complex $z = x + iy$:

(1) $$\cos z = \tfrac{1}{2}(e^{iz} + e^{-iz}), \qquad \sin z = \frac{1}{2i}(e^{iz} - e^{-iz}).$$

Furthermore, in agreement with the familiar definitions from real calculus we define

$$\text{(2)} \qquad \tan z = \frac{\sin z}{\cos z}, \qquad \cot z = \frac{\cos z}{\sin z}$$

and

$$\text{(3)} \qquad \sec z = \frac{1}{\cos z}, \qquad \csc z = \frac{1}{\sin z}.$$

Since e^z is analytic for all z, the same is true for the functions $\cos z$ and $\sin z$. The functions $\tan z$ and $\sec z$ are analytic except at the points where $\cos z$ is zero, and $\cot z$ and $\csc z$ are analytic except where $\sin z$ is zero.

The functions $\cos z$ and $\sec z$ are even, while the other functions are odd:

$$\text{(4)} \qquad \begin{aligned} \cos(-z) &= \cos z & \sin(-z) &= -\sin z \\ \cot(-z) &= -\cot z & \tan(-z) &= -\tan z, \end{aligned}$$

etc. Since the exponential function is periodic, the trigonometric functions are also periodic, and we have

$$\text{(5)} \qquad \begin{aligned} \cos(z \pm 2n\pi) &= \cos z & \sin(z \pm 2n\pi) &= \sin z \\ \tan(z \pm n\pi) &= \tan z & \cot(z \pm n\pi) &= \cot z \end{aligned}$$

where $n = 0, 1, \cdots$.

From the definitions it follows immediately that *all the familiar formulas for the real trigonometric functions continue to hold for complex values.* For example,

$$\text{(6)} \qquad \frac{d}{dz}\cos z = -\sin z, \quad \frac{d}{dz}\sin z = \cos z, \quad \frac{d}{dz}\tan z = \sec^2 z,$$

$$\text{(7)} \qquad \begin{aligned} \cos(z_1 \pm z_2) &= \cos z_1 \cos z_2 \mp \sin z_1 \sin z_2 \\ \sin(z_1 \pm z_2) &= \sin z_1 \cos z_2 \pm \sin z_2 \cos z_1 \\ \sin^2 z + \cos^2 z &= 1, \end{aligned}$$

and so on.

From (1) we see that *Euler's formula is valid for complex values:*

$$\text{(8)} \qquad e^{iz} = \cos z + i \sin z.$$

By substituting (2), Sec. 10.11, into (1) of this section, we obtain the power series developments

$$\cos z = \sum_{n=0}^{\infty} (-1)^n \frac{z^{2n}}{(2n)!} = 1 - \frac{z^2}{2!} + \frac{z^4}{4!} - + \cdots$$

(9)

$$\sin z = \sum_{n=0}^{\infty} (-1)^n \frac{z^{2n+1}}{(2n+1)!} = z - \frac{z^3}{3!} + \frac{z^5}{5!} - + \cdots.$$

If z is real, these are the familiar Maclaurin series of the real cosine and sine functions.

Using (7), we may readily represent $\cos z$ and $\sin z$ in terms of real functions. We first have

(10)
$$\cos (x + iy) = \cos x \cos iy - \sin x \sin iy$$
$$\sin (x + iy) = \sin x \cos iy + \cos x \sin iy.$$

Now from (1) it follows that [cf. (16), Sec. 0.1]

$$\cos iy = \tfrac{1}{2}(e^{-y} + e^{y}) = \cosh y, \qquad \sin iy = \frac{1}{2i} (e^{-y} - e^{y}) = i \sinh y.$$

This altogether yields the desired representations

(11)
$$\cos (x + iy) = \cos x \cosh y - i \sin x \sinh y$$
$$\sin (x + iy) = \sin x \cosh y + i \cos x \sinh y,$$

which are useful for numerical computation of $\cos z$ and $\sin z$.

The **hyperbolic cosine** and **sine** of a complex variable z are defined by the formulas

(12)
$$\cosh z = \tfrac{1}{2}(e^{z} + e^{-z}), \qquad \sinh z = \tfrac{1}{2}(e^{z} - e^{-z}),$$

in agreement with the familiar definitions (16), Sec. 0.1, for a real variable. These functions are analytic in the entire plane.

By substituting (2), Sec. 10.11, into (12) we obtain the power series developments

(13)
$$\cosh z = \sum_{n=0}^{\infty} \frac{z^{2n}}{(2n)!} = 1 + \frac{z^2}{2!} + \frac{z^4}{4!} + \cdots$$
$$\sinh z = \sum_{n=0}^{\infty} \frac{z^{2n+1}}{(2n + 1)!} = z + \frac{z^3}{3!} + \frac{z^5}{5!} + \cdots.$$

From (12) and (1) it follows that

(14)
$$\cosh z = \cos (iz), \qquad \sinh z = -i \sin (iz).$$

As in real calculus we define

(15)
$$\tanh z = \frac{\sinh z}{\cosh z}, \qquad \coth z = \frac{\cosh z}{\sinh z},$$

(16)
$$\operatorname{sech} z = \frac{1}{\cosh z}, \qquad \operatorname{csch} z = \frac{1}{\sinh z}.$$

The absolute value $|f(z)|$ of an analytic function $f(z)$, $z = x + iy$, is a real function of the two real variables x and y and can, therefore, be

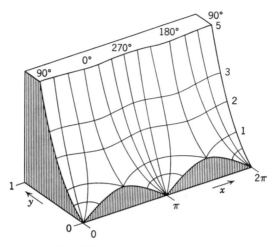

Fig. 308. Modular surface of sin z.

represented by a surface in three-dimensional space; to each point (x, y) in the xy-plane there corresponds a point with Cartesian coordinates $(x, y, |f|)$ in space, and these points form that surface which is called the **modular surface** of $f(z)$. On this surface we may draw some of the curves $|f| = const$ and $\arg f = const$; this yields a useful graphical representation of an analytic function and a geometrical illustration of its behavior.

Figure 308 shows a portion of the modular surface of $f(z) = \sin z$ and some curves $|\sin z| = const$ and $\arg(\sin z) = const$ on the surface. Figure 309 shows the orthogonal projection of these curves into the xy-plane; this graphical representation of the complex sine function is well known and used in electrical engineering.

Modular surfaces have interesting geometrical properties which are considered in Ref. [C4] in Appendix 1.

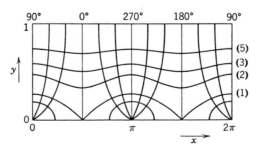

Fig. 309. Curves $|\sin z| = const$ and $\arg(\sin z) = const$ in the z-plane.

PROBLEMS

1. Using (1), prove (4), (6), and (7).
2. Show that cos z and sin z are analytic for all z.
3. Show that Re cos z, Im cos z, Re sin z, and Im sin z are harmonic functions.

Find
4. $|\cos z|$ 5. $|\sin z|$ 6. $|\sec z|$ 7. $|\tan z|$
8. Re tan z 9. Re cot z 10. Im csc z 11. Re sec z

12. Show that $\cos \bar{z} = \overline{\cos z}$, $\sin \bar{z} = \overline{\sin z}$, $\tan \bar{z} = \overline{\tan z}$.
13. Using (1) and (2), prove (5).
14. Determine all values of z for which (a) cos z, (b) sin z, has real values.
15. Show that all the values for which (a) cos $z = 0$, (b) sin $z = 0$, are real.
16. Using (1), show that $\cos^4 \theta = \frac{1}{8}(\cos 4\theta + 4 \cos 2\theta + 3)$.

Using tables of the real trigonometric and hyperbolic functions, calculate:
17. $\cos (1.7 + 1.5i)$ 18. $\cos (1 + 2i)$ 19. $\sin (1.7 + 1.5i)$
20. $\sin (2 - 2i)$ 21. $\cos 10i$ 22. $\sin 10i$

Find all solutions of the following equations.
23. $\sin z = \cosh 3$ 24. $\sin z = i \sinh 1$ 25. $\cos z = 5$
26. $\sin z = 2$ 27. $\sin z = 1000$

28. Show that $1 + \dfrac{1}{2} \cos \theta + \dfrac{1}{4} \cos 2\theta + \dfrac{1}{8} \cos 3\theta + \cdots = \dfrac{4 - 2 \cos \theta}{5 - 4 \cos \theta}$.

Hint: Using Euler's formula, consider the real part of

$$1 + z + z^2 + \cdots = 1/(1 - z), \qquad z = e^{i\theta}/2.$$

Show that:
29. $\cosh^2 z - \sinh^2 z = 1$ 30. $(\cosh z)' = \sinh z$
31. $\cosh z = \cosh x \cos y + i \sinh x \sin y$
32. $\sinh z = \sinh x \cos y + i \cosh x \sin y$
33. Derive (13).   34. Prove (14).

Find all solutions of the following equations.
35. $\cosh z = 1/2$ 36. $\cosh z = 0$ 37. $\sinh z = 0$
38. Show that $\tanh (z + i\pi) = \tanh z$.
39. Show that $\cot z \neq \pm i$ for all z.
40. Show that $\tan z \neq \pm i$ for all z.

10.13 LOGARITHM. GENERAL POWER

The *natural logarithm* of $z = x + iy$ is denoted by ln z (sometimes also by log z) and is defined as the inverse of the exponential function; that is, $w = \ln z$ is the function which satisfies the relation

(1) $$e^w = z$$

for each $z \neq 0$.

Setting $w = u + iv$ and $z = |z|\, e^{i\theta} = re^{i\theta}$ in (1) we have

$$e^w = e^{u+iv} = e^u e^{iv} = re^{i\theta}.$$

It follows that

$$e^u = |z| = r \qquad \text{or} \qquad u = \ln |z|$$

where $\ln |z|$ is the elementary real natural logarithm of the positive number $|z|$, and

$$v = \theta = \arg z.$$

Therefore,

(2) $\ln z = \ln |z| + i \arg z = \ln \sqrt{x^2 + y^2} + i \arg (x + iy).$

Since the argument of z is determined only up to multiples of 2π, *the complex natural logarithm is infinitely many-valued.*

The value of $\ln z$ corresponding to the principal value of $\arg z$, that is,

$$-\pi < \arg z \le \pi \qquad\qquad \text{(p. 579)}$$

is called the **principal value** of $\ln z$ and is often denoted by $\operatorname{Ln} z$.

Obviously the other values of $\ln z$ are then of the form

(3) $\ln z = \operatorname{Ln} z \pm 2n\pi i \qquad\qquad (n = 1, 2, \cdots);$

they have the same real part, and their imaginary parts differ by multiples of 2π, in agreement with the fact that e^z is periodic with the imaginary period $2\pi i$.

Also, if z is real positive, the principal value of $\arg z$ is zero, and the principal value $\operatorname{Ln} z$ is identical with the real natural logarithm known from elementary calculus. If z is real negative, the principal value of $\arg z$ is π, and then

$$\operatorname{Ln} z = \ln |z| + \pi i.$$

Example 1.

$$\ln (-1) = \pm \pi i, \pm 3\pi i, \pm 5\pi i, \cdots, \qquad \operatorname{Ln} (-1) = \pi i$$

$$\ln i = \frac{\pi}{2} i, \; -\frac{3\pi}{2} i, \frac{5\pi}{2} i, \; -\frac{7\pi}{2} i, \frac{9\pi}{2} i, \cdots, \qquad \operatorname{Ln} i = \frac{\pi}{2} i$$

$$\operatorname{Ln} (-i) = -\frac{\pi}{2} i, \qquad \operatorname{Ln} (-2 - 2i) = \ln \sqrt{8} - \frac{3}{4} \pi i.$$

The familiar relations for the natural logarithm continue to hold for complex values:

(4)   (*a*) $\ln (z_1 z_2) = \ln z_1 + \ln z_2,$ (*b*) $\ln (z_1/z_2) = \ln z_1 - \ln z_2,$

but these relations are to be understood in the sense that each value of one side is also contained among the values of the other side.

Example 2. Let

$$z_1 = z_2 = e^{\pi i} = -1.$$

Taking

$$\ln z_1 = \ln z_2 = \pi i,$$

then (4a) holds provided we write $\ln (z_1 z_2) = \ln 1 = 2\pi i$; it is not true for the principal value, $\text{Ln} (z_1 z_2) = \text{Ln} 1 = 0$.

Since for real positive $z = x$ the principal value $\text{Ln} z$ becomes the elementary real natural logarithm $\ln x$, it follows that the familiar power series for $\ln (1 + x)$ corresponds to a similar development of $\text{Ln} z$; we have

(5)
$$\text{Ln} (1 + z) = z - \frac{z^2}{2} + \frac{z^3}{3} - + \cdots \qquad (|z| < 1).$$

Replacing z by $-z$ and multiplying both sides by -1, we get

(6)
$$-\text{Ln} (1 - z) = \text{Ln} \frac{1}{1 - z} = z + \frac{z^2}{2} + \frac{z^3}{3} + \cdots \qquad (|z| < 1).$$

By adding both series we obtain

(7)
$$\text{Ln} \frac{1 + z}{1 - z} = 2\left(z + \frac{z^3}{3} + \frac{z^5}{5} + \cdots\right) \qquad (|z| < 1).$$

By applying (3), Sec. 10.3, to (2), this section, we find

$$\frac{d}{dz} \ln z = \frac{\partial}{\partial x} \ln \sqrt{x^2 + y^2} + i \frac{\partial}{\partial x} (\arg z)$$

$$= \frac{x}{x^2 + y^2} + i \frac{1}{1 + (y/x)^2} \left(-\frac{y}{x^2}\right) = \frac{x - iy}{x^2 + y^2} = \frac{1}{z};$$

that is, the derivative of the natural logarithm is

(8)
$$\frac{d}{dz} \ln z = \frac{1}{z} \qquad (z \neq 0).$$

Hence the principal value $\text{Ln} z$ ($z \neq 0$), which is a single-valued function, is analytic in the domain $-\pi < \arg z < \pi$ of the z-plane, that is, everywhere except at points of the negative real axis (where its imaginary part is not even continuous but has a jump of magnitude 2π).

General powers of a complex number $z = x + iy$ ($\neq 0$) are defined by the formula

(9)
$$z^c = e^{c \ln z} \qquad (c \text{ complex}, z \neq 0).$$

Since $\ln z$ is infinitely many-valued, z^c will, in general, be multi-valued. The particular value

$$z^c = e^{c \, \text{Ln} z}$$

is called the *principal value* of z^c.

If $c = n = 1, 2, \cdots$, then z^n is single-valued and identical with the usual nth power of z. If $c = -1, -2, \cdots$, the situation is similar.

If $c = 1/n$ where $n = 1, 2, \cdots$, then

$$z^c = \sqrt[n]{z} = e^{(1/n) \ln z} \qquad\qquad (z \neq 0),$$

the exponent is determined up to multiples of $2\pi i/n$, and we obtain the n distinct values of the nth root, in agreement with the result in Sec. 10.10. If $c = p/q$, the quotient of two positive integers, the situation is similar, and z^c has only finitely many distinct values. However, if c is real irrational or genuinely complex, then z^c is infinitely many-valued.

Example 3.

$$i^i = e^{i \ln i} = e^{i[(\pi/2)i \pm 2n\pi i]} = e^{-(\pi/2) \mp 2n\pi}.$$

All these values are real, and the principal value ($n = 0$) is $e^{-\pi/2}$.

It is a *convention* that for real positive $z = x$ the expression z^c means $e^{c \ln x}$ where $\ln x$ is the elementary real natural logarithm (that is, the principal value of $\ln z$ ($z = x > 0$) in the sense of our definition). Also, if $z = e$, the base of the natural logarithm, $z^c = e^c$ is *conventionally* regarded as the unique value given by the power series development (2), Sec. 10.11, of the exponential function.

According to (9), the *general exponential function* with a complex constant a as its base can be written

$$\textbf{(10)} \qquad\qquad a^z = e^{z \ln a}.$$

PROBLEMS

Determine all values of the given expressions and plot some of them in the complex plane.

1. $\ln 1$ **2.** $\ln e$ **3.** $\ln (-e^2)$ **4.** $\ln (e^{-2})$

5. $\ln (ie)$ **6.** $\ln (-ie)$ **7.** $\ln (e^i)$ **8.** $\ln (-e^{-i})$

Using tables of the real logarithm, calculate the principal value $\text{Ln } z$ for

9. $z = 1 + i$ **10.** $z = (1 - i)^2$ **11.** $z = -5$

12. $z = 2 - 2i$ **13.** $z = 3 + i3\sqrt{3}$ **14.** $z = -2 - i2\sqrt{3}$

15. Verify (4) for $z_1 = i$, $z_2 = -1$.

16. Using (7), Sec. 10.3, show that $\text{Ln } z$ ($z \neq 0$) is analytic in the region $-\pi < \theta < \pi$ where θ is the principal value of arg z.

17. Show that $\text{Ln } z$ is not continuous on the negative real axis.

18. Find a conjugate harmonic function of $u = \ln (x^2 + y^2)$.

19. Show that $e^{\ln z} = z$, $\ln (e^z) = z \pm 2n\pi i$, $n = 0, 1, \cdots$.

Solve the following equations for z.

20. $\ln z = \pi i/2$ **21.** $\ln z = -\pi i/2$ **22.** $\ln z = 1 + i\pi$

Find the principal value of

23. $(1 + i)^{2-i}$ **24.** $(2 - i)^{1+i}$ **25.** $(1 + i)^{i}$
26. $(2i)^{1/2}$ **27.** $(1 - i)^{1+i}$ **28.** $(1 + i)^{1-i}$
29. 2^{2i} **30.** 2^{3+2i} **31.** 3^{3-i}

The **inverse sine** $w = \sin^{-1} z$ is defined as the function which satisfies the relation $\sin w = z$.

32. Show that $w = \sin^{-1} z$ is infinitely many-valued, and if w_1 is one of these values, the others are of the form $w_1 \pm 2n\pi$ and $\pi - w_1 \pm 2n\pi$, $n = 0, 1, \cdots$.

33. Using $\sin w = (e^{iw} - e^{-iw})/2i$, show that

$$(11) \qquad\qquad \sin^{-1} z = -i \ln (iz + \sqrt{1 - z^2}).$$

34. Replacing x by z in the Maclaurin series of the real inverse sine function, we obtain

$$(12) \qquad \sin^{-1} z = z + \left(\frac{1}{2}\right)\frac{z^3}{3} + \left(\frac{1 \cdot 3}{2 \cdot 4}\right)\frac{z^5}{5} + \left(\frac{1 \cdot 3 \cdot 5}{2 \cdot 4 \cdot 6}\right)\frac{z^7}{7} + \cdots \qquad (|z| < 1).$$

Show that this series represents the principal value which is defined as that value $w = u + iv$ for which $-\pi/2 \leq u \leq \pi/2$ when $v \geq 0$ and $-\pi/2 < u < \pi/2$ when $v < 0$.

35. The **inverse cosine** is the function $w = \cos^{-1} z$ which satisfies the relation $\cos w = z$. Show that

$$(13) \qquad\qquad \cos^{-1} z = -i \ln (z + \sqrt{z^2 - 1}).$$

36. The **inverse tangent** is the function $w = \tan^{-1} z$ which satisfies the relation $\tan w = z$. Show that

$$(14) \qquad\qquad \tan^{-1} z = \frac{i}{2} \ln \frac{i + z}{i - z}.$$

37. Using (14) and (7), show that

$$(15) \qquad\qquad \tan^{-1} z = z - \frac{z^3}{3} + \frac{z^5}{5} - + \cdots \qquad (|z| < 1).$$

(This series represents the principal value, defined as that value $w = u + iv$ for which $-\pi/2 < u < \pi/2$.)

38. Show that

$$(16) \qquad \cosh^{-1} z = \ln (z + \sqrt{z^2 - 1}), \qquad \sinh^{-1} z = \ln (z + \sqrt{z^2 + 1}),$$

$$\tanh^{-1} z = \frac{1}{2} \ln \frac{1 + z}{1 - z}.$$

chapter 11

COMPLEX INTEGRALS. TAYLOR AND LAURENT SERIES

There are two main reasons why integrals in the complex plane are so important. The practical reason is that in applications there occur real integrals which can be evaluated by complex integration, while the usual methods of real integral calculus are not successful. The other reason is of a theoretical nature and results from the fact that some basic properties of analytic functions (such as the existence of higher derivatives) cannot be proved by other methods. In other words, questions which superficially concern only the complex *differential* calculus must be considered by means of *integration*. This fact indicates basic differences between real and complex calculus.

In this chapter we shall first define complex integrals. The most fundamental result in the first part of the chapter will be Cauchy's integral theorem (Sec. 11.3) from which the important Cauchy integral formula (Sec. 11.5) will follow. In Sec. 11.6 we shall prove that, if a function is analytic, it has derivatives of any order. This means that in this respect complex analytic functions behave much more simply than real functions of a real variable.

We know from Sec. 10.9 that a power series with nonzero radius of convergence represents an analytic function. In Sec. 11.7 we shall prove that, conversely, every analytic function can be represented by power series. These considerations will lead to the Taylor and Laurent expansions, and we shall see that some of them will be natural generalizations of familiar ideas in real calculus.

The coefficients of those expansions will be given by integral formulas. However, we shall see that there are various methods for determining the coefficients without integration. This will enable us to use these integral formulas for evaluating complex integrals by a very elegant and powerful method, known as the integration by means of the theory of residues.

Prerequisite for this chapter: Chap. 10.
Sections which may be omitted in a shorter course: 11.9, 11.11, 11.12.
References: Appendix 1, Part G.
Answers to problems: Appendix 2.

11.1 LINE INTEGRAL IN THE COMPLEX PLANE

As in real calculus, we distinguish between definite integrals and indefinite integrals or antiderivatives. An **indefinite integral** is a function whose derivative equals a given analytic function in a region. By inversion of known differentiation formulas we may find many types of indefinite integrals.

Let us now define *definite integrals*, or *line integrals*, of a complex function $f(z)$ where $z = x + iy$. We shall see that this definition will be a natural generalization of the familiar definition of a real definite integral, and the consideration will be similar to that in Sec. 6.1. In the case of a definite integral the path of integration is an interval of the real axis. In the case of a complex definite integral we shall integrate along a curve[1] in the complex plane.

Let C be a curve in the complex z-plane. We *orient* C by choosing one of the two directions along C as the positive direction and denote the initial and terminal points of the oriented curve by z_0 and Z, respectively. We may represent C in the form

$$\textbf{(1)} \qquad\qquad z = z(t) = x(t) + iy(t) \qquad\qquad (a \leq t \leq b)$$

where the positive direction along C corresponds to increasing values of the real parameter t.

---

[1] Actually along a portion, or arc, of a curve. For the sake of simplicity we shall use the single term "curve" to denote an entire curve as well as a portion of it.

We assume that $x(t)$ and $y(t)$ are continuous and have continuous first derivatives, and $\dot{z}(t) \neq 0$ in the interval $a \leq t \leq b$. Then C is rectifiable (cf. Sec. 5.12) and has a unique tangent at each of its points, as is known from real calculus. A curve satisfying these assumptions will be called a **smooth curve**.

Let $f(z)$ be a single-valued and continuous function which is defined (at least) at each point of C. We subdivide C by points $z_1, z_2, \cdots, z_{n-1}$, $z_n(=Z)$, cf. Fig. 310. On each portion of subdivision we choose an arbitrary point, say, a point ζ_1 between z_0 and z_1, a point ζ_2 between z_1 and z_2, etc., and form the sum

(2)
$$S_n = \sum_{m=1}^{n} f(\zeta_m) \, \Delta z_m$$

where

$$\Delta z_m = z_m - z_{m-1}.$$

This we do for each $n = 2, 3, \cdots$ in a completely independent manner, but such that the greatest $|\Delta z_m|$ approaches zero as n approaches infinity. In this way we obtain a sequence of complex numbers $S_2, S_3, \cdots$. The limit of this sequence is called the **line integral** (or simply the integral) of $f(z)$ along the oriented curve C and is denoted by

(3)
$$\int_C f(z) \, dz.$$

The curve C is called the **path of integration**.

Throughout the following considerations all paths of integration for complex line integrals will be assumed to be piecewise smooth, that is, will consist of finitely many smooth curves.

From our assumptions the existence of the line integral (3) follows. In fact, let $f(z) = u(x, y) + iv(x, y)$ and set

$$\zeta_m = \xi_m + i\eta_m \qquad \text{and} \qquad \Delta z_m = \Delta x_m + i\Delta y_m.$$

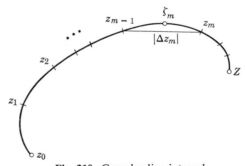

Fig. 310. Complex line integral.

Then (2) may be written

(4) $$S_n = \sum (u + iv)(\Delta x_m + i\Delta y_m)$$

where $u = u(\xi_m, \eta_m)$, $v = v(\xi_m, \eta_m)$ and we sum over m from 1 to n. We may now split up S_n into four sums:

$$S_n = \sum u\Delta x_m - \sum v\Delta y_m + i[\sum u\Delta y_m + \sum v\Delta x_m].$$

These sums are real. Since f is continuous, u and v are continuous. Hence, if we let n approach infinity in the aforementioned way, then the greatest Δx_m and Δy_m will approach zero and each sum on the right becomes a real line integral:

(5) $$\lim_{n \to \infty} S_n = \int_C f(z)\, dz = \int_C u\, dx - \int_C v\, dy + i\left[\int_C u\, dy + \int_C v\, dx\right].$$

This shows that the line integral (3) exists and its value is independent of the choice of subdivisions and intermediate points ζ_m.

Furthermore, as in Sec. 6.2 we may convert each of those real line integrals to a definite integral by the use of the representation (1) of the curve C:

(6) $$\int_C f(z)\, dz = \int_a^b u\dot{x}\, dt - \int_a^b v\dot{y}\, dt + i\left[\int_a^b u\dot{y}\, dt + \int_a^b v\dot{x}\, dt\right]$$

where $u = u[x(t), y(t)]$, $v = v[x(t), y(t)]$, and dots denote derivatives with respect to t.

Without causing misinterpretation, we may also write

$$\int_C f(z)\, dz = \int_a^b (u + iv)(\dot{x} + i\dot{y})\, dt$$

or more briefly

(6*) $$\int_C f(z)\, dz = \int_a^b f[z(t)]\, \dot{z}(t)\, dt.$$

Let us consider some basic examples.

Example 1. Integrate $f(z) = 1/z$ once around the unit circle C in the counter-clockwise sense, starting from $z = 1$. We may represent C in the form

(7) $$z(t) = \cos t + i \sin t \qquad (0 \le t \le 2\pi).$$

Then we have

$$\dot{z}(t) = -\sin t + i \cos t,$$

and by (6*) the integral under consideration becomes

$$\int_C \frac{dz}{z} = \int_0^{2\pi} \frac{1}{\cos t + i \sin t}(-\sin t + i \cos t)\, dt = i\int_0^{2\pi} dt = 2\pi i,$$

a fundamental result which we shall use in our further consideration.

Clearly, instead of (7) we may write more simply

(7') $$z(t) = e^{it} \qquad (0 \le t \le 2\pi).$$

Then we obtain by differentiation

$$\dot{z}(t) = ie^{it}, \qquad d = ie^{it}\, dt,$$

and from this the same result as before:

(8) $$\int_C \frac{dz}{z} = \int_0^{2\pi} \frac{1}{e^{it}} ie^{it}\, dt = i\int_0^{2\pi} dt = 2\pi i.$$

Example 2. Integrate $f(z) = \mathrm{Re}\, z = x$ along the segment from $z_0 = 0$ to $Z = 1 + i$ (path C_1 in Fig. 311).

The segment may be represented in the form

$$z(t) = x(t) + iy(t) = (1 + i)t \qquad (0 \le t \le 1).$$

Then

$$f[z(t)] = \mathrm{Re}\, z(t) = x(t) = t, \qquad dz = (1 + i)\, dt.$$

Therefore, we obtain the result

$$\int_{C_1} \mathrm{Re}\, z\, dz = \int_0^1 t(1 + i)\, dt = (1 + i)\int_0^1 t\, dt = \tfrac{1}{2}(1 + i).$$

Let us now integrate $f(z) = \mathrm{Re}\, z = x$ along the real axis from 0 to 1, and then vertically to $1 + i$ (path C_2 in Fig. 311). We may represent the first part of C_2 by

$$z = z(t) = t \qquad (0 \le t \le 1)$$

and the last part in the form

$$z(t) = 1 + i(t - 1) \qquad (1 \le t \le 2).$$

Then the entire path corresponds to the interval $0 \le t \le 2$. On the first part, $\mathrm{Re}\, z = t$, $dz = dt$, and on the last part, $\mathrm{Re}\, z = 1$, $dz = i\, dt$. Therefore,

$$\int_{C_2} \mathrm{Re}\, z\, dz = \int_0^1 t\, dt + \int_1^2 i\, dt = \tfrac{1}{2} + i.$$

We note that the last part of C_2 could be represented equally well in the form

$$z(t) = 1 + it \qquad (0 \le t \le 1);$$

then the limits of the last integral are 0 and 1, and its value is the same as before.

By comparing our two results we see that in the case of the function $\mathrm{Re}\, z$ (which is not analytic) the value of the integral depends not only on the end points of the path, but also on its geometric shape.

Example 3. Let $f(z) = (z - z_0)^m$ where m is an integer and z_0 is a constant. Integrate counterclockwise around the circle C of radius ρ with center at z_0.

We may represent C in the form

$$z(t) = z_0 + \rho(\cos t + i \sin t) = z_0 + \rho e^{it} \qquad (0 \le t \le 2\pi).$$

Then we have

$$(z - z_0)^m = \rho^m e^{imt}, \qquad dz = i\rho e^{it}\, dt,$$

and we obtain

$$\int_C (z - z_0)^m\, dz = \int_0^{2\pi} \rho^m e^{imt} i\rho e^{it}\, dt = i\rho^{m+1}\int_0^{2\pi} e^{i(m+1)t}\, dt.$$

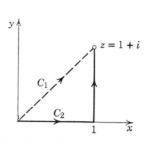

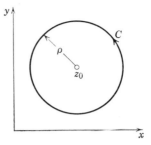

Fig. 311. Paths in Example 2.   **Fig. 312.** Path in Example 3.

The case $m = -1$ was considered in Ex. 2, and when $m \neq -1$, we obtain [cf. (12) in Sec. 10.11]

$$\int_0^{2\pi} e^{i(m+1)t}\, dt = \left[\frac{e^{i(m+1)t}}{i(m+1)}\right]_0^{2\pi} = 0 \qquad (m \neq -1).$$

The result is

(9)
$$\int_C (z - z_0)^m\, dz = \begin{cases} 2\pi i & (m = -1), \\ 0 & (m \neq -1 \text{ and integral}). \end{cases}$$

Example 4. Let $f(z) = k = const$, and C be any curve joining two points z_0 and Z. In this case we may use the definition of the line integral as the limit of the sum S_n given by (2). We have

$$S_n = \sum_{m=1}^{n} k\Delta z_m = k[(z_1 - z_0) + (z_2 - z_1) + \cdots + (Z - z_{n-1})] = k(Z - z_0).$$

From this we immediately have the result

$$\int_C k\, dz = \lim_{n \to \infty} S_n = k(Z - z_0).$$

We note that the value of this integral depends only on z_0 and Z, not on the geometric shape of the path joining these points. If in particular C is closed, then $z_0 = Z$ and the integral is zero.

Example 5. Let $f(z) = z$ and C be any curve joining two points z_0 and Z. We again use (2). Taking $\zeta_m = z_m$ we obtain

$$S_n = \sum_{m=1}^{n} z_m\Delta z_m = z_1(z_1 - z_0) + z_2(z_2 - z_1) + \cdots + Z(Z - z_{n-1}).$$

Taking $\zeta_m = z_{m-1}$ we find

$$S_n^* = \sum_{m=1}^{n} z_{m-1}\Delta z_m = z_0(z_1 - z_0) + z_1(z_2 - z_1) + \cdots + z_{n-1}(Z - z_{n-1}).$$

Addition of these two sums yields

$$S_n + S_n^* = Z^2 - z_0^2,$$

as can easily be verified. From this we have

$$\lim_{n \to \infty} (S_n + S_n^*) = 2\int_{z_0}^{Z} z\, dz = Z^2 - z_0^2.$$

Hence,

$$\int_{z_0}^{Z} z \, dz = \tfrac{1}{2}(Z^2 - z_0^2)$$

along every path joining z_0 and Z. If, in particular, C is a closed path, then $z_0 = Z$ and

(10)
$$\int_{C} z \, dz = 0.$$

Note that this result follows also from Green's theorem (cf. Sec. 6.4) by the use of the formula (6) in the current section.

PROBLEMS

Represent the line segments from A to B in the form $z = z(t)$ where
1. $A: z = 0$, $B: z = 3 - 12i$ **2.** $A: z = 0$, $B: z = 5 + 10i$
3. $A: z = 1 - i$, $B: z = 9 - 5i$ **4.** $A: z = -3 + 2i$, $B: z = -4 + 5i$
5. $A: z = 4 + 2i$, $B: z = 3 + 5i$ **6.** $A: z = -4i$, $B: z = -7 + 38i$
Represent the circle of radius r with center at P in the form $z = z(t)$ where
7. $r = 2$, $P: z = i$ **8.** $r = 4$, $P: z = 3 - 4i$ **9.** $r = 6$, $P: z = -4 + 6i$
Represent the following curves in the form $z = z(t)$.
10. The parabola $y = x^2$ from $(0, 0)$ to $(2, 4)$
11. The parabola $y = 4x^2 + 3$ from $(1, 7)$ to $(3, 39)$
12. The hyperbola $y = 1/x$ from $(1, 1)$ to $(3, 1/3)$
13. The hyperbola $y = 1 + 2/x$ from $(1, 3)$ to $(3, 5/3)$
14. The ellipse $x^2 + 4y^2 = 4$ **15.** The ellipse $9(x - 2)^2 + 4(y + 1)^2 = 36$
What curves are represented by the following functions?
16. $z(t) = 2 - 3t + (4 + t)i \ (0 \le t \le 1)$
17. $z(t) = 1 + t - (2 - 2t)i \ (-1 \le t \le 1)$
18. $z(t) = 1 + i + 3e^{-it} \ (0 \le t \le 2\pi)$
19. $z(t) = -2 + 3i + 4e^{-it} \ (0 \le t \le 2\pi)$
20. $z(t) = t + 2t^3 i \ (-2 \le t \le 2)$
21. $z(t) = t - 2 + (t - 1)^4 i \ (0 \le t \le 2)$

Evaluate $\int_{C} z^2 \, dz$ where C is:

22. The line segment from 0 to i **23.** The line segment from 0 to $2 + i$
24. The line segment in Prob. 1 **25.** The line segment in Prob. 4
26. The circle $|z| = 3$ **27.** The parabola in Prob. 10
28. The boundary of the square with vertices $0, 1, 1 + i$, and i

29. Evaluate $\int_{C} (z - 3)^{-1} \, dz$, $C: |z - 3| = 2$. Integrate (a) counterclockwise, (b) clockwise.

30. Evaluate $\int_{C} |z| \, dz$ from $A: z = -i$ to $B: z = i$ along (a) the line segment AB, (b) the unit circle in the left half plane, (c) the unit circle in the right half plane.

31. Evaluate $\int_{C} \operatorname{Re} z \, dz$ around the circle $|z| = r$ in the counterclockwise sense, starting from $z = r$.

32. Evaluate $\displaystyle\int_C (1/\sqrt{z})\,dz$ from 1 to -1 (a) along the upper semicircle $|z| = 1$, (b) along the lower semicircle $|z| = 1$, where $\sqrt{z}$ is the principal value of the square root.

11.2 BASIC PROPERTIES OF THE COMPLEX LINE INTEGRAL

From the definition of a complex line integral as the limit of a sum we may immediately obtain the following properties.

If we decompose the path C into two portions C_1 and C_2 (Fig. 313), then

(1) $\displaystyle\int_C f(z)\,dz = \int_{C_1} f(z)\,dz + \int_{C_2} f(z)\,dz.$

If we reverse the sense of integration, the sign of the value of the integral changes:

(2) $\displaystyle\int_{z_0}^{Z} f(z)\,dz = -\int_{Z}^{z_0} f(z)\,dz;$

Fig. 313. Formula (1).

here the path C with end points z_0 and Z is the same; on the left we integrate from z_0 to Z, and on the right in the opposite sense.

A sum of two (or more) functions may be integrated term by term, and constants may be taken out from under the integral sign:

(3) $\displaystyle\int_C [k_1 f_1(z) + k_2 f_2(z)]\,dz = k_1 \int_C f_1(z)\,dz + k_2 \int_C f_2(z)\,dz.$

There will be a frequent necessity for estimating the absolute value of complex line integrals. The basic formula is

(4) $$\left| \int_C f(z)\,dz \right| \leq Ml$$

where l is the length of the path C and M is a real constant such that $|f(z)| \leq M$ everywhere on C.

To prove (4), we apply (3), Sec. 10.1, to the sum S_n defined by (2), Sec. 11.1, finding

$$|S_n| = \left| \sum_{m=1}^{n} f(\zeta_m)\Delta z_m \right| \leq \sum_{m=1}^{n} |f(\zeta_m)|\,|\Delta z_m| \leq M \sum_{m=1}^{n} |\Delta z_m|.$$

Now $|\Delta z_m|$ is the length of the chord whose end points are z_{m-1} and z_m, cf. Fig. 310 in Sec. 11.1. The sum on the right thus represents the length L of the broken line of chords whose end points are $z_0, z_1, \cdots, z_n(=Z)$. If n approaches infinity such that the greatest $|\Delta z_m|$ approaches zero, then L

approaches the length l of the curve C, by definition of the length of a curve (cf. Sec. 5.12). From this, formula (4) follows.

Example 1. Let $f(z) = 1/z$ and integrate once around the circle $|z| = \rho$. Then $l = 2\pi\rho$ and $|f(z)| = 1/\rho$ on the circle. Hence, by (4),

$$\left| \int_C \frac{dz}{z} \right| \leq \frac{1}{\rho} 2\pi\rho = 2\pi. \qquad \text{(cf. Ex. 1, Sec. 11.1).}$$

Example 2. The path C_2 in Ex. 2, Sec. 11.1, has the length $l = 2$, and $|\text{Re } z| \leq 1$ on C_2. Therefore, by (4),

$$\left| \int_{C_2} \text{Re } z \, dz \right| \leq 2.$$

PROBLEMS

1. Verify (1) for $f(z) = 1/z$ where C is the unit circle, C_1 its upper half and C_2 its lower half.

2. Verify (2) for $\int_C z^2 \, dz$ where C is the line segment from $1 + i$ to $2 + 2i$.

3. Verify (3) for $\int_C \left(\frac{4}{z} - 2z \right) dz$ where C is the shorter arc of the unit circle from 1 to i.

Without evaluating the integrals show that:

4. $\left| \int_C z^{-2} \, dz \right| \leq 4$ where C is the line segment from i to $4 + i$

5. $\left| \int_C z^4 \, dz \right| \leq 8\sqrt{2}$ where C is the line segment from $-1 - i$ to $1 + i$

6. $\left| \int_C \frac{z + 1}{z - 1} \, dz \right| \leq 8\pi$ where C is the circle $|z - 1| = 2$

Find an upper bound for the absolute values of the following integrals.

7. $\int_C \frac{e^z}{z} \, dz$ where C is the circle $|z| = 2$

8. $\int_C \frac{\sin z}{z} \, dz$ where C is the line segment from 1 to 2

9. $\int_C \frac{\sin z}{z} \, dz$ where C is the line segment from i to $2 + i$

10. $\int_C \frac{1 + z}{2 - z} \, dz$ where C is the boundary of the square with vertices $1 - i$, $3 - i$, $3 + i$, and $1 + i$

11. Find a better bound in Prob. 4 by decomposing C into two arcs.

Evaluate:

12. $\int_C (az + b) \, dz$ where C is the segment from 0 to $-4 - 4i$

13. $\int_C (z^4 - z^2 + z^{-1})\, dz$ where C is the unit circle (counterclockwise)

14. $\int_C 4 \sin z\, dz$ where C is the line segment from 0 to i

15. $\int_C \sin z\, dz$ where C is the line segment from i to $\pi + i$

16. $\int_C e^z\, dz$ where C is the line segment from 1 to $1 + \pi i/2$

17. $\int_C [(z - 1)^{-1} + 2(z - 1)^{-2}]\, dz$ where C is the circle $|z - 1| = 4$ (clockwise)

18. $\int_C (z^{-5} + z^3)\, dz$ where C is the upper arc of the unit circle from 1 to -1

19. $\int_C (z^{-5} + z^3)\, dz$ where C is the lower arc of the unit circle from 1 to -1

20. $\int_C \left(2z^2 - \dfrac{1}{z} + \dfrac{2}{z^2}\right)\, dz$ where C is the unit circle (clockwise)

11.3   CAUCHY'S INTEGRAL THEOREM

Cauchy's integral theorem is very important in complex analysis and has various theoretical and practical consequences. To state this theorem, we shall need the following concept.

The interior of a simple closed curve (that is, a curve which is closed and has no self-intersections) is called a **simply connected domain**. A domain which is not simply connected is said to be *multiply connected*. For example the interior of a circle ("circular disk"), ellipse, square etc. is simply connected while a circular ring (cf. Sec. 10.1) is multiply connected (more precisely: doubly[2] connected).

Cauchy's integral theorem.   *If $f(z)$ is analytic[3] in a simply connected bounded domain D, then*

(1) $$\int_C f(z)\, dz = 0$$

on every simple closed path C in D.

---

[2] A domain is said to be *p-fold connected* if its boundary consists of p parts without common points. For the annulus, $p = 2$, because the boundary consists of two circles having no points in common.

[3] Remember our general assumption that the functions under consideration are single-valued. Actually, if a function is analytic in a *simply connected* domain D, it is single-valued in D. The proof of this fact is rather difficult.

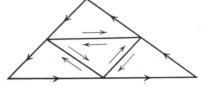

Fig. 314. Cauchy's integral theorem.   **Fig. 315.** Proof of Cauchy's integral theorem.

Cauchy's proof. From (5), Sec. 11.1, we have

$$\int_C f(z)\,dz = \int_C (u\,dx - v\,dy) + i\int_C (u\,dy + v\,dx).$$

$f(z)$ is analytic and, therefore $f'(z)$ exists. Cauchy made the *additional assumption* that $f'(z)$ is continuous. Then u and v have continuous first partial derivatives in D, as follows from (3) and (4), Sec. 10.3. Green's theorem (cf. Sec. 6.4) (with u and $-v$ instead of f and g) is applicable, and

$$\int_C (u\,dx - v\,dy) = \iint_R \left(-\frac{\partial v}{\partial x} - \frac{\partial u}{\partial y}\right) dx\,dy$$

where R is the region bounded by C. The second Cauchy-Riemann equation (Sec. 10.3) shows that the integrand on the right is identically zero. Hence, the integral on the left is zero. In the same fashion it follows by the use of the first Cauchy-Riemann equation that the last integral in the above formula is zero. This completes Cauchy's proof.

Goursat's[4] proof. Goursat proved Cauchy's theorem without assuming that $f'(z)$ is continuous. This progress is quite important. We start with the case when C is the boundary of a triangle. By joining the midpoints of the sides of the triangle we subdivide it into four congruent triangles (Fig. 315). Then

$$\int_C f\,dz = \int_{C_{\mathrm{I}}} f\,dz + \int_{C_{\mathrm{II}}} f\,dz + \int_{C_{\mathrm{III}}} f\,dz + \int_{C_{\mathrm{IV}}} f\,dz$$

where $C_{\mathrm{I}}, \cdots, C_{\mathrm{IV}}$ are the boundaries of the triangles; in fact, on the right side we integrate along each of the three segments of subdivision in both possible directions, the corresponding integrals cancel out in pairs, and the sum of the integrals on the right equals the integral on the left. Among the four integrals on the right there must be one, call its path C_1, for which

$$\left|\int_C f\,dz\right| \le 4\left|\int_{C_1} f\,dz\right|$$

[4] EDOUARD GOURSAT (1858–1936), French mathematician.

because not each of the absolute values of the four integrals can be smaller than $\frac{1}{4}$ of the absolute value of the sum of those integrals. This follows readily from (3) in Sec. 10.1.

We subdivide the triangle bounded by C_1 as before and select a triangle of subdivision with boundary C_2 for which

$$\left| \int_{C_1} f \, dz \right| \leq 4 \left| \int_{C_2} f \, dz \right|, \quad \text{and then} \quad \left| \int_C f \, dz \right| \leq 4^2 \left| \int_{C_2} f \, dz \right|.$$

Continuing in this fashion, we obtain a sequence of triangles $T_1, T_2, \cdots$ with boundaries $C_1, C_2, \cdots$ which are similar and such that T_n lies in T_m when $n > m$, and

$$(2) \qquad \left| \int_C f \, dz \right| \leq 4^n \left| \int_{C_n} f \, dz \right|, \qquad n = 1, 2, \cdots.$$

Let z_0 be the point which belongs to all these triangles. Since f is differentiable at $z = z_0$, the derivative $f'(z_0)$ exists, and we may write

$$(3) \qquad f(z) = f(z_0) + (z - z_0)f'(z_0) + h(z)(z - z_0).$$

By integrating over the boundary C_n of the triangle T_n we have

$$\int_{C_n} f(z) \, dz = \int_{C_n} f(z_0) \, dz + \int_{C_n} (z - z_0)f'(z_0) \, dz + \int_{C_n} h(z)(z - z_0) \, dz.$$

Since $f(z_0)$ and $f'(z_0)$ are constants, it follows from the results in Ex. 4 and 5, Sec. 11.1, that the first two integrals on the right are zero. Hence,

$$\int_{C_n} f(z) \, dz = \int_{C_n} h(z)(z - z_0) \, dz.$$

By dividing (3) by $z - z_0$, transposing two terms to the left, and taking absolute values we obtain

$$\left| \frac{f(z) - f(z_0)}{z - z_0} - f'(z_0) \right| = |h(z)|.$$

From this and (5) in Sec. 10.2 we see that for given $\epsilon > 0$ we can find a $\delta > 0$ such that

$$|h(z)| < \epsilon \quad \text{when} \quad |z - z_0| < \delta.$$

We may now take n so large that the triangle T_n lies in the disk $|z - z_0| < \delta$. Let l_n be the length of C_n. Then $|z - z_0| \leq l_n/2$ for all z on C_n and z_0 in T_n. By applying (4) in Sec. 11.2 we thus obtain

$$(4) \qquad \left| \int_{C_n} f(z) \, dz \right| = \left| \int_{C_n} h(z)(z - z_0) \, dz \right| < \epsilon \frac{l_n}{2} l_n = \frac{\epsilon}{2} l_n^2.$$

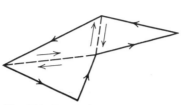

Fig. 316. Proof of Cauchy's integral theorem for a polygon.

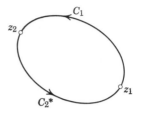

Fig. 317. Formula (5′).

Let l be the length of C. Then the path C_1 has the length $l_1 = l/2$, the path C_2 has the length $l_2 = l_1/2 = l/4$, etc., and C_n has the length

$$l_n = \frac{l}{2^n}.$$

From (2) and (4) we thus obtain

$$\left| \int_C f \, dz \right| \le 4^n \left| \int_{C_n} f \, dz \right| < 4^n \frac{\epsilon}{2} l_n{}^2 = 4^n \frac{\epsilon}{2} \frac{l^2}{4^n} = \frac{\epsilon}{2} l^2.$$

By choosing ϵ (>0) sufficiently small, the expression on the right can be made as small as we please, while the expression on the left is the definite value of an integral. From this we conclude that this value must be zero, and the proof is complete.

The proof for *the case in which C is the boundary of a polygon* follows from the previous proof by subdividing the polygon into triangles (Fig. 316). The integral corresponding to each such triangle is zero. The sum of these integrals is equal to the integral over C, because we integrate along each segment of subdivision in both directions, the corresponding integrals cancel out in pairs, and we are left with the integral over C.

The case of a general simple closed path C can be reduced to the preceding one by inscribing in C a closed polygon P of chords, which approximates C "sufficiently accurately," and it can be shown that one can find a polygon P such that the integral over P differs from that over C by less than any pre-assigned positive real number ϵ, no matter how small. The details of this proof are somewhat involved and can be found in Ref. [G5] in Appendix 1.

Example 1.

$$\int_C e^z \, dz = 0$$

for any closed path, because e^z is analytic for all z.

Example 2.

$$\int_C \frac{dz}{z^2} = 0,$$

where C is the unit circle (cf. Sec. 11.1). This result does not follow from Cauchy's theorem, because $f(z) = 1/z^2$ is not analytic at $z = 0$. It illustrates that *the condition that f be analytic in D is sufficient rather than necessary for* (1) *to be true.*

Example 3.

$$\int_C \frac{dz}{z} = 2\pi i,$$

the integration being taken around the unit circle in the counterclockwise sense (cf. Sec. 11.1). C lies in the annulus $\frac{1}{2} < |z| < \frac{3}{2}$ where $1/z$ is analytic, but this domain is not simply connected, so that Cauchy's theorem cannot be applied. Hence, *the condition that the domain D be simply connected, is quite essential.*

If we subdivide the path C in Cauchy's theorem into two arcs C_1 and $C_2{}^*$ (Fig. 317) then (1) takes the form

$$\int_C f\, dz = \int_{C_1} f\, dz + \int_{C_2{}^*} f\, dz = 0.$$

Consequently,

(5')
$$-\int_{C_2{}^*} f\, dz = \int_{C_1} f\, dz.$$

If we reverse the sense of integration along $C_2{}^*$, then the integral over $C_2{}^*$ is multiplied by -1, and we obtain (cf. Fig. 318)

(5)
$$\int_{C_2} f(z)\, dz = \int_{C_1} f(z)\, dz.$$

Hence, if f is analytic in D, and C_1 and C_2 are any paths in D joining two points in D and having no further points in common, then (5) holds.

If those paths C_1 and C_2 have finitely many points in common (Fig. 319), then (5) continues to hold; this follows by applying the previous result to the portions of C_1 and C_2 between each pair of consecutive points of intersection.

It is even true that (5) *holds for any paths entirely in the domain D where $f(z)$ is analytic and joining any points z_1 and z_2 in D. Then we say that the integral of $f(z)$ from z_1 to z_2 is* **independent of path in D.** (Of course the value of the integral depends on the choice of z_1 and z_2.)

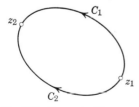

Fig. 318. Formula (5).

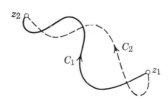

Fig. 319. Paths having finitely many intersections.

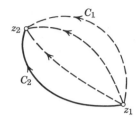

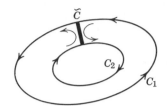

Fig. 320. Continuous deformation of path.   **Fig. 321.** Doubly connected domain.

The *proof* would require an additional consideration of the case in which C_1 and C_2 have infinitely many points of intersection, and will not be presented here.

We may imagine that the path C_2 in (5) was obtained from C_1 by a continuous deformation (Fig. 320). It follows that in a given integral we may impose a continuous deformation on the path of integration (keeping the end points fixed); as long as we do not pass through a point where $f(z)$ is not analytic, the value of the line integral will not change under such a deformation. This is often called the **principle of deformation of path.**

A *multiply connected domain* can be cut such that the resulting domain becomes simply connected. For a doubly connected domain D^* we need one cut $\tilde{C}$ (Fig. 321). If $f(z)$ is analytic in D^* and at each point of C_1 and C_2 then, since C_1, C_2, and $\tilde{C}$ bound a simply connected region, it follows from Cauchy's theorem that the integral of f taken over C_1, $\tilde{C}$, C_2 in the sense indicated by the arrows in Fig. 321, has the value zero. Since we integrate along $\tilde{C}$ in both directions, the corresponding integrals cancel out, and we obtain

(6) $$\int_{C_1} f(z)\, dz + \int_{C_2} f(z)\, dz = 0$$

where one of the curves is traversed in the counterclockwise sense and the other in the opposite sense.

Equation (6) may also be written

(7) $$\int_{C_1} f(z)\, dz = \int_{C_2} f(z)\, dz$$

where C_1 and C_2 are now traversed in the same direction (Fig. 322). We remember that (7) holds under the assumption that $f(z)$ is analytic in the domain bounded by C_1 and C_2 and at each point of C_1 and C_2.

For more complicated domains we may need more than one cut, but the basic idea remains the same as before. For instance, for the domain in Fig. 323,

$$\int_{C_1} f(z)\, dz + \int_{C_2} f(z)\, dz + \int_{C_3} f(z)\, dz = 0$$

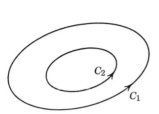

Fig. 322. Paths in (7).

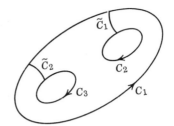

Fig. 323. Triply connected domain.

where C_2 and C_3 are traversed in the same sense while C_1 is traversed in the opposite sense.

We mention that a simple closed path is sometimes called a *contour*, and integrals along such a path are known as **contour integrals**.

Example 4. Let C_1 be the unit circle $|z| = 1$ and C_2 the circle $|z| = \frac{1}{2}$. Then, by (7),

$$\int_{C_2} \frac{dz}{z} = \int_{C_1} \frac{dz}{z} = 2\pi i \qquad \text{(cf. Ex. 1 in Sec. 11.1)}$$

where both paths are traversed in the counterclockwise sense.

Example 5. Integrate $f(z) = (2z - 1)/(z^2 - z)$ around any contour C containing the points 0 and 1 in its interior, in the counter-clockwise sense (Fig. 324). Since

$$\frac{2z - 1}{z^2 - z} = \frac{1}{z} + \frac{1}{z - 1} \qquad \text{we obtain} \qquad \int_C \frac{2z - 1}{z^2 - z} \, dz = \int_C \frac{dz}{z} + \int_C \frac{dz}{z - 1}.$$

Now, the integral of $1/z$ taken around the unit circle in the counterclockwise sense has the value $2\pi i$. The function $1/z$ is analytic at each point $z \neq 0$. The path C as well as the unit circle encloses the point $z = 0$. Consequently, C may be deformed continuously into the unit circle without passing over a point where $1/z$ is not analytic. Hence,

$$\int_C \frac{dz}{z} = 2\pi i.$$

Similarly, the integral of $1/(z - 1)$ over C has the value $2\pi i$, because $1/(z - 1)$ is analytic at each point $z \neq 1$ and C is assumed to include this point in its interior. Hence the integral under consideration has the value $4\pi i$.

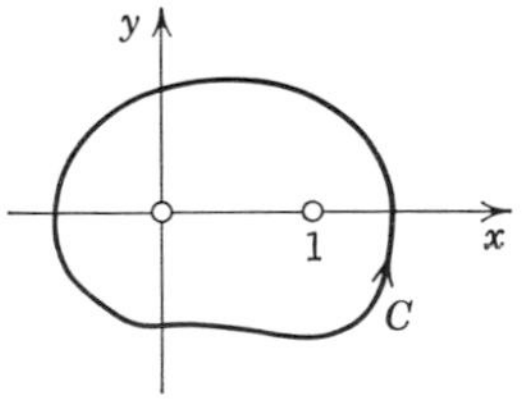

Fig. 324. Path in Example 5.

Example 6. From Ex. 3 in Sec. 11.1 it follows that

$$\int_C (z - z_0)^m \, dz = \begin{cases} 2\pi i & (m = -1) \\ 0 & (m \neq -1 \text{ and integral}) \end{cases}$$

where C is any contour containing the point z_0 in its interior and the integration is taken around C in the counterclockwise sense.

PROBLEMS

1. For what simple closed paths is $\displaystyle\int_C z^{-1}\,dz = 0$?

2. Verify Cauchy's theorem for $\displaystyle\int_C z^3\,dz$ where C is the boundary of the rectangle with vertices $-1,\ 1,\ 1+i,\ -1+i$.

3. Show that $\displaystyle\int_C z^{-4}\,dz = 0$ around the unit circle. Does this follow from Cauchy's theorem?

To which of the following integrals does Cauchy's theorem apply?

4. $\displaystyle\int_C \frac{z^2}{\cos z}\,dz,\ C:|z|=1$ **5.** $\displaystyle\int_C \frac{z^2}{\cos z}\,dz,\ C:|z|=2$

6. $\displaystyle\int_C \frac{\sin z}{z}\,dz,\ C:|z|=1$ **7.** $\displaystyle\int_C \frac{\sin z}{z^2}\,dz,\ C:|z|=1$

8. Evaluate $\displaystyle\int_C \frac{dz}{z}$ where C is the shorter arc of the unit circle from i to -1. For what paths from i to -1 does the integral have the same value?

9. Integrate $\int z^2\,dz$ from 0 to $1+i$ along $C_1, C_2,$ and C_3 (Fig. 325).

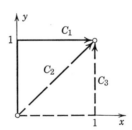

Fig. 325. Problem 9.

Evaluate the following integrals. (*Hint:* if necessary, represent the integrand in terms of partial fractions.)

10. $\displaystyle\int_C \frac{2z+1}{z^2+z}\,dz$ where C is the circle   (a) $|z|=\tfrac{1}{4}$,   (b) $|z-\tfrac{1}{2}|=\tfrac{1}{4}$, (c) $|z-1|=\tfrac{1}{4}$, (d) $|z|=2$ (clockwise)

11. $\displaystyle\int_C \frac{z^2-\tfrac{1}{3}}{z^3-z}\,dz$ where C is the circle $|z-\tfrac{1}{2}|=1$ (counterclockwise)

12. $\displaystyle\int_C \frac{z^2-z+2}{z^3-2z^2}\,dz$ where C is the boundary of the rectangle with vertices $3\pm i,\ -1\pm i$ (clockwise)

13. $\int_C \dfrac{dz}{1 + z^2}$ where C is the circle (a) $|z| = 2$, (b) $|z - i| = 1$, (c) $|z + i| = 1$
(clockwise)

14. $\int_C \dfrac{dz}{1 + z^3}$ where C is the circle $|z + 1| = 1$ (counterclockwise)

15. $\int_C \dfrac{dz}{z}$ where C consists of the circles $|z| = 2$ (clockwise) and $|z| = 1$ (counterclockwise)

16. $\int_C \dfrac{dz}{z - i}$ where C consists of the circles $|z - i| = 2$ (counterclockwise) and $|z - i| = 1$ (clockwise)

17. $\int_C \dfrac{dz}{z^2(z^2 + 4)}$ where C consists of the circles $|z| = \frac{3}{2}$ (counterclockwise) and $|z| = 1$ (clockwise)

18. $\int_C \dfrac{dz}{z^2(z^2 + 4)}$ where C consists of the circles $|z| = 3$ (counterclockwise) and $|z| = 1$ (clockwise)

19. $\int_C \dfrac{e^z}{z} \, dz$ where C is the unit circle (counterclockwise)

20. $\int_C \dfrac{\cos z}{z} \, dz$ where C is the unit circle (clockwise)

21. $\int_C \dfrac{\cos z}{z^2} \, dz$ where C is the unit circle (counterclockwise)

11.4   EVALUATION OF LINE INTEGRALS BY INDEFINITE INTEGRATION

Using Cauchy's integral theorem, we want to show that in many cases complex line integrals can be evaluated by a very simple method, namely, by indefinite integration.

Suppose that $f(z)$ is analytic in a simply connected domain D, and let z_0 be any fixed point in D. Then the integral

$$\int_{z_0}^{z} f(z^*) \, dz^*$$

is a function of z for all paths which lie in D and join z_0 and z, and we may write

(1) $$F(z) = \int_{z_0}^{z} f(z^*) \, dz^*.$$

Let us prove that $F(z)$ *is an analytic function of z in D, and $F'(z) = f(z)$.*
We keep z fixed. Since D is a domain, a neighborhood N of z belongs to D. In N we choose a point $z + \Delta z$. Then the line segment with end points z and $z + \Delta z$ is in D, and from (1) we obtain

$$F(z + \Delta z) - F(z) = \int_{z_0}^{z+\Delta z} f(z^*)\,dz^* - \int_{z_0}^{z} f(z^*)\,dz^* = \int_{z}^{z+\Delta z} f(z^*)\,dz^*,$$

where we may integrate from z to $z + \Delta z$ along that segment (Fig. 326). Hence,

$$\frac{F(z + \Delta z) - F(z)}{\Delta z} - f(z) = \frac{1}{\Delta z} \int_{z}^{z+\Delta z} [f(z^*) - f(z)]\,dz^*$$

because z is kept fixed and, therefore,

$$-\frac{1}{\Delta z} \int_{z}^{z+\Delta z} f(z)\,dz^*$$
$$= -\frac{f(z)}{\Delta z} \int_{z}^{z+\Delta z} dz^* = -f(z).$$

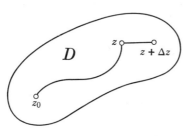

Fig. 326. Path of integration.

Now $f(z)$ is continuous. Hence, an $\epsilon > 0$ being given, we can find a number $\delta > 0$ such that

$$|f(z^*) - f(z)| < \epsilon$$
$$\text{when} \qquad |z^* - z| < \delta.$$

Consequently, if $|\Delta z| < \delta$, then

$$\left| \frac{F(z + \Delta z) - F(z)}{\Delta z} - f(z) \right| = \frac{1}{|\Delta z|} \left| \int_{z}^{z+\Delta z} [f(z^*) - f(z)]\,dz^* \right|$$

$$< \frac{\epsilon}{|\Delta z|} \left| \int_{z}^{z+\Delta z} dz^* \right| = \epsilon;$$

that is,

$$(2) \qquad F'(z) = \lim_{\Delta z \to 0} \frac{F(z + \Delta z) - F(z)}{\Delta z} = f(z).$$

From (1) it follows that if z_0 is replaced by another fixed point in D, the function $F(z)$ is changed by an additive constant. From (2) we see that $F(z)$ is an indefinite integral or antiderivative of $f(z)$, written

$$F(z) = \int f(z)\,dz;$$

that is, $F(z)$ is an analytic function in D whose derivative is $f(z)$.

If $F'(z) = f(z)$ and $G'(z) = f(z)$, then $F'(z) - G'(z) \equiv 0$ in D. Hence, the function $F(z) - G(z)$ is constant (cf. Prob. 27 at the end of Sec. 10.3).

That is, the two indefinite integrals $F(z)$ and $G(z)$ differ only by a constant. In view of (1), we have for any points a and b in D and any path in D from a to b,

$$\int_a^b f(z)\, dz = \int_{z_0}^b f(z)\, dz - \int_{z_0}^a f(z)\, dz = F(b) - F(a),$$

as in the case of real definite integrals, but *it is important that the paths of integration lie in a simply connected domain D where $f(z)$ is analytic.*

We may sum up our result as follows.

Theorem 1. *If $f(z)$ is analytic in a simply connected domain D, and if $F(z)$ is an indefinite integral of $f(z)$, then for all paths in D joining two points a and b in D,*

(3)
$$\int_a^b f(z)\, dz = F(b) - F(a).$$

This theorem enables us to evaluate complex line integrals by means of indefinite integration.

Example 1.
$$\int_i^{1+4i} z^2\, dz = \left[\frac{z^3}{3}\right]_i^{1+4i} = \tfrac{1}{3}[(1+4i)^3 - i^3] = -\frac{47}{3} - 17i.$$

Example 2.
$$\int_i^{\pi/2} \cos z\, dz = \sin z \Big|_i^{\pi/2} = \sin\frac{\pi}{2} - \sin i = 1 - i\sinh 1.$$

PROBLEMS

Evaluate:

1. $\displaystyle\int_0^{1+i} z^2\, dz$

2. $\displaystyle\int_i^{1+3i} (2z^2 - z + 1)\, dz$

3. $\displaystyle\int_{1+i}^{1-i} (z^3 - 6z)\, dz$

4. $\displaystyle\int_{2i}^{3i} (z+4)^2\, dz$

5. $\displaystyle\int_i^{2i} (z^2 - 1)^3\, dz$

6. $\displaystyle\int_i^{1+3i} (8z^3 + 2z)\, dz$

7. $\displaystyle\int_0^{\pi i} e^z\, dz$

8. $\displaystyle\int_{-\pi i}^{3\pi i} e^{2z}\, dz$

9. $\displaystyle\int_{1-\pi i}^{1+\pi i} e^{z/2}\, dz$

10. $\displaystyle\int_{-\pi i}^{\pi i} \cos z\, dz$

11. $\displaystyle\int_\pi^{\pi i} \sin 2z\, dz$

12. $\displaystyle\int_0^i \sinh \pi z\, dz$

13. $\displaystyle\int_0^{\pi i/6} \cosh 3z\, dz$

14. $\displaystyle\int_0^{\pi i} z\cos z\, dz$

15. $\displaystyle\int_{-\pi i}^{\pi i} \sin^2 z\, dz$

16. $\displaystyle\int_0^{2-\pi i} ze^{z^2}\, dz$

17. $\displaystyle\int_{-i}^i z\cosh(z^2)\, dz$

18. $\displaystyle\int_{-\pi i}^{\pi i} z\cosh z\, dz$

11.5 CAUCHY'S INTEGRAL FORMULA

The most important consequence of Cauchy's integral theorem is Cauchy's integral formula. This formula and its conditions of validity may be stated as follows

Theorem 1. *Let $f(z)$ be analytic and single-valued in a simply connected domain D. Then for any point z_0 in D and any simple closed path C in D which encloses z_0 (Fig. 327),*

(1) $$\int_C \frac{f(z)}{z - z_0}\, dz = 2\pi i f(z_0) \qquad \text{(Cauchy's integral formula),}$$

the integration being taken in the counterclockwise sense.

Proof. Writing $f(z) = f(z_0) + [f(z) - f(z_0)]$ and remembering that a constant may be taken out from under the integral sign, we have

(2) $$\int_C \frac{f(z)}{z - z_0}\, dz = f(z_0) \int_C \frac{dz}{z - z_0} + \int_C \frac{f(z) - f(z_0)}{z - z_0}\, dz.$$

From Ex. 6 in Sec. 11.3 it follows that the first term on the right is equal to $2\pi i f(z_0)$. Hence we see that (1) holds, provided the last integral is zero. Now the integrand of this integral is analytic in D except at the point z_0. We may thus replace C by a small circle K with center at z_0, without changing the value of the integral (Fig. 328). Since $f(z)$ is analytic, it is continuous. Hence, an $\epsilon > 0$ being given we can find a $\delta > 0$ such that

$$|f(z) - f(z_0)| < \epsilon \qquad \text{for all } z \text{ in the disk } |z - z_0| < \delta.$$

Choosing the radius ρ of K smaller than δ, we thus have

$$\left| \frac{f(z) - f(z_0)}{z - z_0} \right| < \frac{\epsilon}{\rho}$$

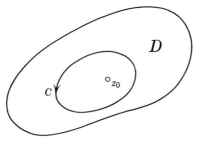

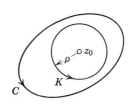

Fig. 327. Cauchy's integral formula.

Fig. 328. Proof of Cauchy's integral formula.

at each point of K. The length of K is $2\pi\rho$. Hence, by (4) in Sec. 11.2,

$$\left| \int_K \frac{f(z) - f(z_0)}{z - z_0} \, dz \right| < \frac{\epsilon}{\rho} \, 2\pi\rho = 2\pi\epsilon.$$

Since ϵ can be made arbitrarily small, it follows that the last integral on the right side of (2) has the value zero, and the theorem is proved.

Example 1. Integrate

$$\frac{z^2 + 1}{z^2 - 1}$$

along a circle of radius 1 with center at

$$(a) \, z = 1 \quad (b) \, z = \tfrac{1}{2} \quad (c) \, z = -1 \quad (d) \, z = i,$$

the integration being taken in the counterclockwise sense.

(a) The integral under consideration may be written as

$$\int_C \frac{z^2 + 1}{z^2 - 1} \, dz = \int_C \frac{z^2 + 1}{z + 1} \frac{dz}{z - 1}.$$

The expression on the right is of the form (1) where $z_0 = 1$ and

$$f(z) = \frac{z^2 + 1}{z + 1}.$$

The point $z_0 = 1$ lies inside the circle C under consideration, and $f(z)$ is analytic inside and on C. (The point $z = -1$, where $f(z)$ is not analytic, lies outside C.) Hence, by Cauchy's integral formula,

$$\int_C \frac{z^2 + 1}{z^2 - 1} \, dz = \int_C \frac{z^2 + 1}{z + 1} \frac{dz}{z - 1} = 2\pi i \left[\frac{z^2 + 1}{z + 1}\right]_{z=1} = 2\pi i.$$

(b) We obtain the same result as before because the given function is analytic except at the points $z = 1$ and $z = -1$, and we may obtain the circle (b) from that in the case (a) by a continuous deformation (even a translation) without passing over a point where the given function is not analytic.

(c) We may write

$$\int_C \frac{z^2 + 1}{z^2 - 1} \, dz = \int_C \frac{z^2 + 1}{z - 1} \frac{dz}{z + 1}.$$

The integral on the right is of the form (1) where $z_0 = -1$ and

$$f(z) = \frac{z^2 + 1}{z - 1}.$$

The point $z_0 = -1$ lies inside the circle C now under consideration, and $f(z)$ is analytic inside and on C. Therefore, by (1),

$$\int_C \frac{z^2 + 1}{z^2 - 1} \, dz = \int_C \frac{z^2 + 1}{z - 1} \frac{dz}{z + 1} = 2\pi i \left[\frac{z^2 + 1}{z - 1}\right]_{z=-1} = -2\pi i.$$

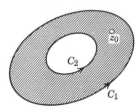

Fig. 329. Formula (3).

(d) The given function is analytic everywhere inside the circle now under consideration and on that circle. Hence, by Cauchy's integral theorem, the integral has the value zero.

In the case of a *multiply connected domain* we may proceed in a manner similar to that in Sec. 11.3. For instance, if $f(z)$ is analytic (and single-valued) on C_1 and C_2 and in the ring-shaped domain bounded by C_1 and C_2 (Fig. 329) and z_0 is any point in that domain, then

$$(3) \qquad f(z_0) = \frac{1}{2\pi i} \int_{C_1} \frac{f(z)}{z - z_0}\, dz - \frac{1}{2\pi i} \int_{C_2} \frac{f(z)}{z - z_0}\, dz,$$

where both integrals are taken in the counterclockwise sense.

PROBLEMS

Integrate $(z^2 - 1)/(z^2 + 1)$ in the counterclockwise sense around the circle
1. $|z - i| = 1$ **2.** $|z + i| = 1$ **3.** $|z| = 1/2$ **4.** $|z - 2i| = 2$
Integrate $1/(z^4 - 1)$ in the counterclockwise sense around the circle
5. $|z - i| = 1$ **6.** $|z - 1| = 1$ **7.** $|z + 1| = 1$ **8.** $|z + 3| = 1$
Integrate the following functions in the counterclockwise sense around the unit circle.
9. e^z/z **10.** $(\sin z)/z$ **11.** $(\cos z)/2z$
12. $z/(z^2 - 2z + \frac{3}{4})$ **13.** $e^z/(z + \frac{1}{2})$ **14.** $(z^2 + 1)/(z^2 - 2z)$
15. $(\cos z)\Big/\Big(z + \dfrac{\pi}{4}\Big)$ **16.** $z^3\Big/\Big(z - \dfrac{i}{2}\Big)$ **17.** $(z^4 + 1)/(z^2 - 2iz)$

18. $e^{z^2}\Big/\Big(z + \dfrac{i}{2}\Big)$ **19.** $(\cosh \pi z)/\pi z$ **20.** $(e^z - 1)/z$

11.6 THE DERIVATIVES OF AN ANALYTIC FUNCTION

From the assumption that a *real* function of a real variable is once differentiable nothing follows about the existence of derivatives of higher order. We shall now see that from the assumption that a *complex* function has a first derivative in a domain D there follows the existence of derivatives of all orders in D. This means that in this respect complex analytic functions behave much simpler than real functions which are once differentiable.

Theorem 1. *If $f(z)$ is analytic in a domain D, then it has derivatives of all orders in D which are then also analytic functions in D. The values of these* *derivatives at a point z_0 of D are given by the formulas*

(1')
$$f'(z_0) = \frac{1}{2\pi i} \int_C \frac{f(z)}{(z - z_0)^2} \, dz,$$

(1'')
$$f''(z_0) = \frac{2!}{2\pi i} \int_C \frac{f(z)}{(z - z_0)^3} \, dz,$$

and in general

(1)
$$f^{(n)}(z_0) = \frac{n!}{2\pi i} \int_C \frac{f(z)}{(z - z_0)^{n+1}} \, dz \qquad (n = 1, 2, \cdots);$$

here C is any simple closed path in D which encloses z_0 and whose full interior belongs to D; the curve C is traversed in the counterclockwise sense (Fig. 330).

Remark. For memorizing (1), it is useful to observe that these formulas are obtained formally by differentiating the Cauchy formula (1), Sec. 11.5, under the integral sign *with respect to z_0.*

Proof of Theorem 1. We prove (1'). By definition,

$$f'(z_0) = \lim_{\Delta z \to 0} \frac{f(z_0 + \Delta z) - f(z_0)}{\Delta z}.$$

From this and (1), Sec. 11.5, it follows that

(2)
$$f'(z_0) = \lim_{\Delta z \to 0} \frac{1}{2\pi i \Delta z} \left[\int_C \frac{f(z)}{z - (z_0 + \Delta z)} \, dz - \int_C \frac{f(z)}{z - z_0} \, dz \right].$$

Straightforward calculation shows that

$$\frac{1}{\Delta z} \left[\frac{1}{z - (z_0 + \Delta z)} - \frac{1}{z - z_0} \right] = \frac{1}{(z - z_0)^2} + \frac{\Delta z}{(z - z_0 - \Delta z)(z - z_0)^2}.$$

Hence, we may write (2) in the form

$$f'(z_0) = \frac{1}{2\pi i} \int_C \frac{f(z)}{(z - z_0)^2} \, dz + \lim_{\Delta z \to 0} \frac{\Delta z}{2\pi i} \int_C \frac{f(z)}{(z - z_0 - \Delta z)(z - z_0)^2} \, dz.$$

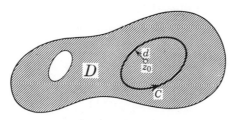

Fig. 330. Theorem 1.

Consequently, (1′) will be established if we show that the last expression on the right has the value zero. On C, $f(z)$ is continuous and, therefore, bounded in absolute value, say, $|f(z)| < M$. Let d be the distance of the point (or points) of C which are closest to z_0. Then for all z on C,

$$|z - z_0| \geq d \qquad \text{and} \qquad \frac{1}{|z - z_0|} \leq \frac{1}{d}.$$

Furthermore, if $|\Delta z| \leq d/2$, then for all these z,

$$|z - z_0 - \Delta z| \geq \frac{d}{2} \qquad \text{and} \qquad \frac{1}{|z - z_0 - \Delta z|} \leq \frac{2}{d}.$$

Denoting the length of C by L and using (4) in Sec. 11.2 we thus obtain

$$\left| \frac{\Delta z}{2\pi i} \int_C \frac{f(z)}{(z - z_0 - \Delta z)(z - z_0)^2} \, dz \right| < \frac{|\Delta z|}{2\pi} \frac{M}{\frac{1}{2}dd^2} L \qquad \left(|\Delta z| \leq \frac{d}{2} \right).$$

If Δz approaches zero, the expression on the right approaches zero. This proves (1′). Formula (1″) can be proved by a similar argument, using (1′), and the general formula (1) follows by induction.

Using Theorem 1, let us prove the converse of Cauchy's theorem.

Morera's[5] theorem. *If $f(z)$ is continuous in a simply connected domain D and if*

(3) $$\int_C f(z) \, dz = 0$$

for every closed path in D, then $f(z)$ is analytic in D.

Proof. In Sec. 11.4 it was shown that if $f(z)$ is analytic in D, then

$$F(z) = \int_{z_0}^z f(z^*) \, dz^*$$

is analytic in D and $F'(z) = f(z)$. In the proof we used only the continuity of $f(z)$ and the property that its integral around every closed path in D is zero; from these assumptions we concluded that $F(z)$ is analytic. By Theorem 1 the derivative of $F(z)$ is analytic, that is, $f(z)$ is analytic in D, and Morera's theorem is proved.

We shall now derive an important inequality. In (1), let C be a circle of radius r with center at z_0, and let M be the maximum of $|f(z)|$ on C. Then, by applying (4), Sec. 11.2, to (1) we find

$$|f^{(n)}(z_0)| = \frac{n!}{2\pi} \left| \int_C \frac{f(z) \, dz}{(z - z_0)^{n+1}} \right| \leq \frac{n!}{2\pi} M \frac{1}{r^{n+1}} 2\pi r.$$

[5] GIACINTO MORERA (1856–1909), Italian mathematician.

This yields **Cauchy's inequality**

(4)
$$|f^{(n)}(z_0)| \leqq \frac{n!\,M}{r^n}.$$

Using (4), let us prove the following interesting and basic result.

Liouville's theorem. *If $f(z)$ is analytic and bounded in absolute value for all (finite) z, then $f(z)$ is a constant.*

Proof. By assumption, $|f(z)|$ is bounded, say, $|f(z)| < K$ for all z. Using (4), it follows that $|f'(z_0)| < K/r$. Since this is true for every r, we can take r as large as we please and conclude that $f'(z_0) = 0$. Since z_0 is arbitrary, $f'(z) = 0$ for all finite z, and $f(z)$ is a constant (cf. Prob. 27 at the end of Sec. 10.3). This completes the proof.

PROBLEMS

Using Theorem 1, integrate the following functions in the counterclockwise sense around the circle $|z| = 2$.

1. $(z^4 + z)/(z - 1)^2$　　**2.** e^z/z^2　　**3.** e^z/z^3　　**4.** $(\cos z)/z^2$
5. $(\sin z)/z^2$　　**6.** $z^3/(z + i)^3$　　**7.** $(z^3 - 2z + 1)/(z - i)^2$
8. e^z/z^n ($n > 0$, integral)　　　**9.** $(\sin z)/z^{2n}$ ($n > 0$, integral)
10. $(\cos z)/z^{2n}$ ($n > 0$, integral)　**11.** $(z^3 + 3z + 1)/(z^4 - 5z^2)$
12. $(z \cos z)/(z - \pi/2)^2$　**13.** $(z + 1)^2 e^z/(z - 1)^2$　**14.** $ze^z/(z - 4)^3$
15. $(z^4 + 1)/(z + 1)^4$　　**16.** $z^3/[(z + 3)(z - i)^2]$.　　**17.** $(e^{-z} \sin z)/z^2$

18. If $f(z)$ is not a constant and is analytic for all (finite) z, and R and M are any positive real numbers (no matter how large), show that there exist values of z for which $|z| > R$ and $|f(z)| > M$. *Hint:* use Liouville's theorem.

19. If $f(z)$ is a polynomial of degree $n > 0$ and M an arbitrary positive real number (no matter how large), show that there exists a positive real number R such that $|f(z)| > M$ for all $|z| > R$.

20. Show that $f(z) = e^z$ has the property characterized in Prob. 18, but does not have that characterized in Prob. 19.

21. Prove the Fundamental Theorem of Algebra: If $f(z)$ is a polynomial in z, not a constant, then $f(z) = 0$ for at least one value of z. *Hint:* assume $f(z) \neq 0$ for all z and apply the result of Prob. 18 to $g = 1/f$.

11.7 TAYLOR SERIES

The familiar Taylor expansion is an effective tool in real calculus and its applications. We shall see that in complex analysis the Taylor expansion, which is a generalization of the aforementioned expansion, is even more important.

We consider a function $f(z)$ which is analytic in a neighborhood of a point $z = a$. Let C be a circle which lies in this neighborhood and has the center a. Then we may apply Cauchy's integral formula (1), Sec. 11.5; writing z and z^* in place of z_0 and z, we have

$$(1) \qquad f(z) = \frac{1}{2\pi i} \int_C \frac{f(z^*)}{z^* - z} \, dz^*$$

where z is an arbitrary fixed point inside C and z^* is the complex variable of integration. Now,

$$(2) \qquad \frac{1}{z^* - z} = \frac{1}{z^* - a - (z - a)} = \frac{1}{(z^* - a)\left(1 - \dfrac{z - a}{z^* - a}\right)} \cdot$$

We note that since z^* is on C while z is inside C,

$$(3) \qquad \left| \frac{z - a}{z^* - a} \right| < 1.$$

From the geometric progression

$$1 + q + q^2 + \cdots + q^n = \frac{1 - q^{n+1}}{1 - q} \qquad (q \neq 1)$$

we obtain the relation

$$\frac{1}{1 - q} = 1 + q + \cdots + q^n + \frac{q^{n+1}}{1 - q} \cdot$$

By setting $q = (z - a)/(z^* - a)$ it follows that

$$\frac{1}{1 - [(z - a)/(z^* - a)]} = 1 + \frac{z - a}{z^* - a} + \left(\frac{z - a}{z^* - a}\right)^2 + \cdots$$
$$+ \left(\frac{z - a}{z^* - a}\right)^n + \frac{[(z - a)/(z^* - a)]^{n+1}}{(z^* - z)/(z^* - a)} \cdot$$

We insert this into (2), and then (2) into (1). Since z and a are constant, we may take the powers of $z - a$ out from under the integral sign, and (1) takes the form

$$(4) \quad f(z) = \frac{1}{2\pi i} \int_C \frac{f(z^*)}{z^* - a} \, dz^* + \frac{z - a}{2\pi i} \int_C \frac{f(z^*)}{(z^* - a)^2} \, dz^* + \cdots$$
$$+ \frac{(z - a)^n}{2\pi i} \int_C \frac{f(z^*)}{(z^* - a)^{n+1}} \, dz^* + R_n(z)$$

where the last term is given by the formula

$$(5) \qquad R_n(z) = \frac{(z - a)^{n+1}}{2\pi i} \int_C \frac{f(z^*)}{(z^* - a)^{n+1}(z^* - z)} \, dz^*.$$

Using (1), Sec. 11.6, we may write this expansion in the form

(6) $f(z) = f(a) + \dfrac{z-a}{1!}f'(a) + \dfrac{(z-a)^2}{2!}f''(a) + \cdots + \dfrac{(z-a)^n}{n!}f^{(n)}(a)$

$$+ R_n(z).$$

This representation is called **Taylor's[6] formula.** $R_n(z)$ is called the *remainder.*

Since the analytic function $f(z)$ has derivatives of all orders, we may take n in (6) as large as we please. If we let n approach infinity, we obtain from (6) the power series

(7) $$f(z) = \sum_{m=0}^{\infty} \frac{f^{(m)}(a)}{m!}(z-a)^m.$$

This series is called the **Taylor series** *of $f(z)$ with center at a.* The particular case where $a = 0$ is called the **Maclaurin[7] series** of $f(z)$.

Clearly, the series (7) will converge and represent $f(z)$ if, and only if,

(8) $$\lim_{n \to \infty} R_n(z) = 0.$$

To prove (8), we consider (5). Since z^* is on C while z is inside C, we have $|z^* - z| > 0$. Since $f(z)$ is analytic inside C and on C, it follows that the absolute value of $f(z^*)/(z^* - z)$ is bounded, say,

$$\left| \frac{f(z^*)}{z^* - z} \right| < \tilde{M}$$

for all z^* on C. Let r be the radius of C. Then C has the length $2\pi r$, and $|z^* - a| = r$ for all z^* on C. Hence, by applying (4) in Sec. 11.2 to (5) in the current section we obtain

$$|R_n| = \frac{|z-a|^{n+1}}{2\pi} \left| \int_C \frac{f(z^*)}{(z^*-a)^{n+1}(z^*-z)} \, dz^* \right|$$

$$< \frac{|z-a|^{n+1}}{2\pi} \tilde{M} \frac{1}{r^{n+1}} 2\pi r = \tilde{M}r \left| \frac{z-a}{r} \right|^{n+1}$$

If we let n approach infinity, it follows from (3) that the expression on the right approaches zero. This proves (8) for all z inside C. Since, by Theorem 2 in Sec. 10.9, the representation of $f(z)$ in the form (7) is unique in the sense that (7) is the only power series with center at a which represents the given function $f(z)$, we may sum up our result as follows.

---

[6] BROOK TAYLOR (1685–1731), English mathematician, who introduced this formula for functions of a real variable.

[7] COLIN MACLAURIN (1698–1746), Scotch mathematician.

Taylor's theorem. *Let $f(z)$ be analytic in a domain D and let $z = a$ be any point in D. Then there exists precisely one power series with center at a which represents $f(z)$; this series is of the form*

$$(9) \qquad f(z) = \sum_{n=0}^{\infty} b_n(z - a)^n$$

where

$$b_n = \frac{1}{n!} f^{(n)}(a) \qquad\qquad n = 0, 1, \cdots ;$$

it converges at least in a circle with center a which encloses only points of D. The precise circle of convergence of (9) is the largest circle around a as center such that $f(z)$ is analytic throughout its interior. The remainders $R_n(z)$ of (9) can be represented in the form (5). The coefficients satisfy the inequality

$$(10) \qquad |b_n| \leq \frac{M}{r^n}$$

where M is the maximum of $|f(z)|$ on the circle $|z - a| = r$.

Relation (10) follows from Cauchy's inequality (4) in the last section.

Various examples of Taylor series are included in Chap. 10. From our theorem we see that each of those series defines the corresponding elementary function uniquely.

Practically speaking, (8) means that for all z for which (9) converges, the nth partial sum of (9) will approximate $f(z)$ to any assigned degree of accuracy; we just have to choose n large enough.

One surprising property of complex analytic functions is that they have derivatives of all orders, and now we have discovered the other surprising property that they can always be represented by power series of the form (9). This is not true in general for real functions; there are real functions which have derivatives of all orders but cannot be represented by a power series.

The relation between our present consideration and that in Sec. 10.9 about power series may be established by the following theorem.

Theorem 2. *Every power series with a nonzero radius of convergence is the Taylor series of the function represented by this series.*

Proof. Let the power series

$$\sum_{n=0}^{\infty} b_n(z - a)^n$$

have a nonzero radius of convergence R. Then it represents some analytic function $f(z)$ in the disk $|z - a| < R$, that is,

$$f(z) = b_0 + b_1(z - a) + b_2(z - a)^2 + \cdots .$$

From Theorem 5 in Sec. 10.9 it follows that

$$f'(z) = b_1 + 2b_2(z - a) + \cdots$$

and more generally

$$f^{(n)}(z) = n!\, b_n + (n + 1)n \cdots 3 \cdot 2 b_{n+1}(z - a) + \cdots;$$

all these series converge in the disk $|z - a| < R$. By setting $z = a$ we obtain the following representations for the coefficients of our power series:

$$f(a) = b_0, \qquad f'(a) = b_1, \qquad \cdots, \qquad f^{(n)}(a) = n!\, b_n, \cdots.$$

Since these formulas are identical with those in Taylor's theorem, the proof is complete.

A point at which a function $f(z)$ ceases to be analytic is called a **singular point** of $f(z)$; we also say that $f(z)$ has a **singularity** at such a point. More precisely: a point $z = z_0$ is called a *singular point* of $f(z)$, if $f(z)$ is not differentiable at z_0 but if every neighborhood of z_0 contains points at which $f(z)$ is differentiable.

Using this concept, we may say that there is at least one singular point of $f(z)$ on the circle of convergence of the development (9); that is, *the radius of convergence of* (9) *is equal to the distance from the point a to the nearest singular point of* $f(z)$.

Example 1. Let $f(z) = 1/(1 - z)$. Then $f^{(n)}(z) = n!/(1 - z)^{n+1}$, $f^{(n)}(0) = n!$. Hence, the Maclaurin expansion of $1/(1 - z)$ is the geometric series

$$(11) \qquad \frac{1}{1 - z} = \sum_{n=0}^{\infty} z^n = 1 + z + z^2 + \cdots \qquad (|z| < 1).$$

$f(z)$ is singular at $z = 1$; this point lies on the circle of convergence.

Example 2. The series

$$\sum_{n=0}^{\infty} \frac{z^n}{n!} = 1 + z + \frac{z^2}{2!} + \cdots$$

is the Maclaurin expansion of e^z. It converges for all finite z, in agreement with the fact that e^z is analytic for every such z.

PROBLEMS

Find the Taylor series expansion of the given function about $z = a$ and determine the radius of convergence R.

1. $\sqrt{2} \cos z$, $a = -\pi/4$	2. $\sin z$, $a = \pi/2$	3. $1/z$, $a = -1$
4. e^{-z}, $a = 0$	5. e^z, $a = \pi i$	6. e^{z-1}, $a = 1$
7. $\operatorname{Ln} z$, $a = 1$	8. $\operatorname{Ln}(1 + z)$, $a = 0$	9. $1/(1 - z)$, $a = i$
10. $1/(1 - z)$, $a = -1$	11. $\cos^2 z$, $a = 0$	12. $\sin^2 z$, $a = 0$

Find the Maclaurin series by integrating that of the integrand term by term.

13. $\int_0^z e^{t^2}\, dt$ **14.** $\int_0^z \cos t\, dt$ **15.** $\int_0^z \frac{\sin t}{t}\, dt$

16. $\int_0^z \frac{e^t - 1}{t}\, dt$ **17.** $\int_0^z \cos t^2\, dt$ **18.** $\int_0^z \sin t^2\, dt$

Find the first three terms of the Maclaurin series of the following functions.
19. $\tan z$ **20.** $z \cot z$ **21.** $e^z \sin z$
22. Find a function which has more than one singularity on the circle of convergence of its Maclaurin series.

11.8 PRACTICAL METHODS FOR OBTAINING POWER SERIES

In most practical cases the determination of the coefficients of a Taylor series by means of the formula in Taylor's theorem will be complicated or time-consuming. There are a number of simpler practical procedures for that purpose which may be illustrated by the following examples. The uniqueness of the representations thus obtained follows from Theorem 2 in Sec. 10.9.

Example 1 (Substitution). Find the Maclaurin series of $f(z) = 1/(1 + z^2)$. By substituting $-z^2$ for z in (11), Sec. 11.7, we obtain

$$(1) \quad \frac{1}{1 + z^2} = \frac{1}{1 - (-z^2)} = \sum_{n=0}^{\infty} (-z^2)^n = \sum_{n=0}^{\infty} (-1)^n z^{2n}$$
$$= 1 - z^2 + z^4 - z^6 + \cdots \qquad (|z| < 1).$$

Example 2 (Integration). Let $f(z) = \tan^{-1} z$. We have $f'(z) = 1/(1 + z^2)$. By integrating (1) term by term and noting that $f(0) = 0$, we find

$$\tan^{-1} z = \sum_{n=0}^{\infty} \frac{(-1)^n}{2n + 1} z^{2n+1} = z - \frac{z^3}{3} + \frac{z^5}{5} - + \cdots \qquad (|z| < 1);$$

this series represents the principal value of $\tan^{-1} z$ [cf. (15) in Sec. 10.13].

Example 3 (Development by using the geometric series). Develop $1/(c - bz)$ in powers of $z - a$ where $c - ab \neq 0$ and $b \neq 0$. Obviously,

$$\frac{1}{c - bz} = \frac{1}{c - ab - b(z - a)} = \frac{1}{(c - ab)\left[1 - \dfrac{b(z - a)}{c - ab}\right]}.$$

To the last expression we apply (11) in Sec. 11.7 with z replaced by $b(z - a)/(c - ab)$, finding

$$\frac{1}{c - bz} = \frac{1}{c - ab} \sum_{n=0}^{\infty} \left[\frac{b(z - a)}{(c - ab)}\right]^n = \sum_{n=0}^{\infty} \frac{b^n}{(c - ab)^{n+1}} (z - a)^n.$$

Writing the last series at length we have

$$\frac{1}{c - bz} = \frac{1}{c - ab} + \frac{b}{(c - ab)^2}(z - a) + \frac{b^2}{(c - ab)^3}(z - a)^2 + \cdots.$$

This series converges for

$$\left| \frac{b(z - a)}{c - ab} \right| < 1 \qquad \text{that is,} \qquad |z - a| < \left| \frac{c - ab}{b} \right| = \left| \frac{c}{b} - a \right|.$$

Example 4 (Binomial series, reduction by partial fractions). Find the Taylor series of the function

$$f(z) = \frac{2z^2 + 9z + 5}{z^3 + z^2 - 8z - 12}$$

with center at $z = 1$.

Given a rational function, we may first represent it as a sum of partial fractions and then apply the *binomial series*

(2)
$$\frac{1}{(1 + z)^m} = (1 + z)^{-m} = \sum_{n=0}^{\infty} \binom{-m}{n} z^n$$

$$= 1 - mz + \frac{m(m + 1)}{2!} z^2 - \frac{m(m + 1)(m + 2)}{3!} z^3 + \cdots.$$

Since the function on the left is singular at $z = -1$, the series converges in the disk $|z| < 1$. In our case we obtain

$$f(z) = \frac{1}{(z + 2)^2} + \frac{2}{z - 3} = \frac{1}{[3 + (z - 1)]^2} - \frac{2}{2 - (z - 1)}.$$

This may be written in the form

$$f(z) = \frac{1}{9}\left(\frac{1}{[1 + \frac{1}{3}(z - 1)]^2}\right) - \frac{1}{1 - \frac{1}{2}(z - 1)}.$$

By using the binomial series we obtain

$$f(z) = \frac{1}{9} \sum_{n=0}^{\infty} \binom{-2}{n} \left(\frac{z - 1}{3}\right)^n - \sum_{n=0}^{\infty} \left(\frac{z - 1}{2}\right)^n.$$

We may add the two series on the right term by term. Since the binomial coefficient in the first series equals $(-1)^n(n + 1)$ we find

$$f(z) = \sum_{n=0}^{\infty} \left[\frac{(-1)^n(n + 1)}{3^{n+2}} - \frac{1}{2^n} \right](z - 1)^n.$$

Writing this result at length we have

$$f(z) = -\tfrac{8}{9} - \tfrac{31}{54}(z - 1) - \tfrac{23}{108}(z - 1)^2 - \cdots.$$

Since $z = 3$ is the singular point of $f(z)$ which is nearest to the center $z = 1$, the series converges in the disk $|z - 1| < 2$.

Example 5 (Use of differential equations). Find the Maclaurin series of $f(z) = \tan z$. We have $f'(z) = \sec^2 z$ and, therefore,

$$f'(z) = 1 + f^2(z), \qquad f'(0) = 1.$$

Observing that $f(0) = 0$, we obtain by successive differentiation

$$f'' = 2ff', \qquad\qquad f''(0) = 0,$$
$$f''' = 2f'^2 + 2ff'', \qquad f'''(0) = 2, \qquad f'''(0)/3! = \tfrac{1}{3},$$
$$f^{(4)} = 6f'f'' + 2ff''', \qquad f^{(4)}(0) = 0,$$
$$f^{(5)} = 6f''^2 + 8f'f''' + 2ff^{(4)}, \qquad f^{(5)}(0) = 16, \qquad f^{(5)}(0)/5! = \tfrac{2}{15}, \qquad \text{etc.}$$

Hence, we obtain the result

$$(3) \qquad\qquad \tan z = z + \tfrac{1}{3} z^3 + \tfrac{2}{15} z^5 + \tfrac{17}{315} z^7 + \cdots \qquad\qquad \left(|z| < \frac{\pi}{2}\right).$$

Example 6 (Undetermined coefficients). Find the Maclaurin series of $\tan z$ by using those of $\cos z$ and $\sin z$ (Sec. 10.12). Since $\tan z$ is odd, the desired expansion will be of the form

$$\tan z = b_1 z + b_3 z^3 + b_5 z^5 + \cdots.$$

Using $\sin z = \tan z \cos z$, we obtain by inserting those developments

$$z - \frac{z^3}{3!} + \frac{z^5}{5!} - + \cdots = (b_1 z + b_3 z^3 + b_5 z^5 + \cdots)\left(1 - \frac{z^2}{2!} + \frac{z^4}{4!} - + \cdots\right).$$

Since $\tan z$ is analytic except at $z = \pm\dfrac{\pi}{2}, \pm\dfrac{3\pi}{2}, \cdots$, its Maclaurin series converges in the disk $|z| < \pi/2$, and for these z we may multiply the two series on the right term by term and arrange the resulting series in powers of z (cf. Theorem 3 in Sec. 10.8). By Theorem 2 in Sec. 10.9 the coefficient of each power of z is the same on both sides. This yields

$$1 = b_1, \qquad -\frac{1}{3!} = -\frac{b_1}{2!} + b_3, \qquad \frac{1}{5!} = \frac{b_1}{4!} - \frac{b_3}{2!} + b_5, \qquad \text{etc.}$$

Therefore $b_1 = 1$, $b_3 = \tfrac{1}{3}$, $b_5 = \tfrac{2}{15}$, etc., as before.

We mention that there exist tables[8] of the so-called **Bernoulli numbers** B_n from which the coefficients of (3) can easily be calculated. The numbers $B_n/n!$ are, by definition, the coefficients in the Maclaurin series

$$(4) \qquad\qquad \frac{z}{e^z - 1} = 1 + B_1 z + \frac{B_2}{2!} z^2 + \frac{B_3}{3!} z^3 + \cdots.$$

By the method of undetermined coefficients we obtain

$$(5) \qquad B_1 = -\frac{1}{2}, \quad B_2 = \frac{1}{6}, \quad B_3 = 0, \quad B_4 = -\frac{1}{30}, \quad B_5 = 0, \quad B_6 = \frac{1}{42}, \cdots.$$

From (1), (2), Sec. 10.12, it follows that

$$\tan z = \frac{2i}{e^{2iz} - 1} - \frac{4i}{e^{4iz} - 1} - i.$$

as the student may verify. From this and (4) we obtain

$$(6) \qquad \tan z = \frac{4 \cdot 3}{2!} B_2 z + \cdots + (-1)^{n-1} \frac{2^{2n}(2^{2n} - 1)}{(2n)!} B_{2n} z^{2n-1} + \cdots.$$

[8] Cf. Glaisher, *Trans. Cambridge Philos. Soc.*, vol. 12, 1873, 384–391.

PROBLEMS

Find the Maclaurin series of the following functions.

1. $\dfrac{1}{1 + z^3}$ **2.** $\dfrac{1}{1 - z^5}$ **3.** $\cos z^3$ **4.** $e^{z^2 - z}$

5. $\dfrac{1}{(1 + z^2)^2}$ **6.** $\dfrac{z^2}{(1 - z^3)^2}$ **7.** $\dfrac{4 - 3z}{(1 - z)^2}$ **8.** $\dfrac{4z^2 + 30z + 68}{(z + 4)^2(z - 2)}$

9. $\dfrac{\sqrt{z}}{2} \displaystyle\int_0^z \dfrac{\sin t}{\sqrt{t}}\, dt$ **10.** $\dfrac{\sqrt{z}}{2} \displaystyle\int_0^z \dfrac{\cos t}{\sqrt{t}}\, dt$ **11.** $f(z) = e^{z^2} \displaystyle\int_0^z e^{-t^2}\, dt$

12. $\dfrac{\cos z}{1 - z^2}$ **13.** $\dfrac{e^{z^2}}{\cos z}$

Find the Taylor series expansion of the given function about $z = a$.

14. $\dfrac{1}{1 - z}$, $a = 2i$ **15.** $\dfrac{1}{4 - 3z}$, $a = 1 + i$ **16.** $\dfrac{1}{2z - i}$, $a = -1$

17. $\dfrac{1}{(1 + z)^2}$, $a = -i$ **18.** $\dfrac{1}{(2 + 3z^3)^2}$, $a = 0$ **19.** $\dfrac{2 - 3z}{2z^2 - 3z + 1}$, $a = -1$

20. $\dfrac{z^2 - z}{z^3 + z^2 + z + 1}$, $a = 0$ **21.** $\tan z$, $a = \dfrac{\pi}{4}$

22. The expansion $\sec z = E_0 - \dfrac{E_2}{2!} z^2 + \dfrac{E_4}{4!} z^4 + - \cdots$

defines the **Euler numbers** E_{2n}. Show that $E_0 = 1$, $E_2 = -1$, $E_4 = 5$, $E_6 = -61$.

Find the first few terms of the Maclaurin series of the following functions.

23. $e^{1/(1-z)}$ **24.** $\cos \left(\dfrac{z}{1 - z} \right)$ **25.** $e^{(e^z)}$

26. Derive (6) from (4).

11.9 UNIFORM CONVERGENCE

Suppose we know that a given series converges in a certain region R, the remaining question is whether the convergence is sufficiently rapid throughout the whole region or whether there are points near which the convergence becomes poor. The practical importance of this question in connection with computations is obvious, but we shall see that the theoretical aspect of the question is even more important. To illustrate the situation, let us start with some examples.

Example 1. Suppose we want to compute a table of e^x for real x in the interval $0 \leq x \leq 1$, for example, for $x = 0, 0.1, 0.2, \cdots$ and the absolute value of the error of each value should be less than a given number ϵ, say, less than $\frac{1}{2}$ unit of the sixth decimal place. We may use a suitable partial sum

$$s_n = 1 + x + \cdots + \frac{x^n}{n!}$$

of the Maclaurin series. Then the absolute value of the error is equal to $|R_n| = |s - s_n|$ where $s = e^x$, the sum of the series, and we have to choose n such that

$$|s(x) - s_n(x)| < \epsilon \ (= 5 \cdot 10^{-7}).$$

From Ex. 6 in Sec. 10.5 we see that when $x = 1$, then for $n = 10$, and thus for any $n > N = 9$, we obtain the required accuracy. Now the remainder decreases in absolute value as $x \ (\geq 0)$ decreases, and, therefore,

$$|s(x) - s_n(x)| < \epsilon \qquad \text{for} \qquad n > N(\epsilon) \ (= 9) \qquad \text{and all } x$$

under consideration. Note that, of course, N depends on ϵ, and if we want more accurate values so that ϵ is smaller, then N will be larger.

Example 2. In the case of the geometric series $1 + z + z^2 + \cdots$ the remainder is

$$R_n(z) = s(z) - s_n(z) = \sum_{m=n+1}^{\infty} z^m = \frac{z^{n+1}}{1 - z}$$

and becomes arbitrarily large for real $z = x \ (< 1)$ and sufficiently close to 1. Hence, a maximum error ϵ being prescribed, we cannot find an N *depending only on ϵ* such that $|R_n(x)| = |s(x) - s_n(x)| < \epsilon$ for $n > N$ and *all x* in the interval $0 \leq x < 1$. Cf. also Prob. 25 at the end of Sec. 10.6.

The result in Ex. 2 is not quite unexpected, because the series diverges at $z = 1$. A really surprising situation arises in the case of the following series.

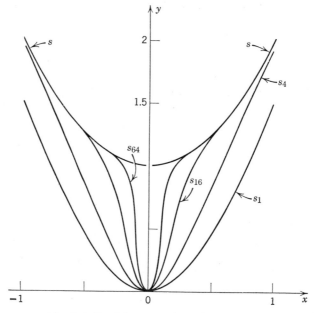

Fig. 331. Partial sums and sum in Example 3.

Example 3. Consider the series

$$x^2 + \frac{x^2}{1 + x^2} + \frac{x^2}{(1 + x^2)^2} + \frac{x^2}{(1 + x^2)^3} + \cdots .$$

Using the formula for the sum of a geometric progression, the student may readily verify that the nth partial sum is

$$s_n(x) = 1 + x^2 - \frac{1}{(1 + x^2)^n} .$$

Hence, if $x \neq 0$, the series has the sum

$$s(x) = \lim_{n \to \infty} s_n(x) = 1 + x^2.$$

If $x = 0$, then $s_n = 0$ for all n and, therefore,

$$s(0) = \lim_{n \to \infty} s_n(0) = 0.$$

This shows that the series converges for all x (even absolutely), but we have the surprising result that the sum is discontinuous (at $x = 0$), although all the terms of the series are continuous functions. Furthermore, when $x \neq 0$ the absolute value of the remainder is

$$|R_n(x)| = |s(x) - s_n(x)| = \frac{1}{(1 + x^2)^n}$$

and we see that for a given ϵ (< 1) we cannot find an N depending only on ϵ such that $|R_n| < \epsilon$ for all $n > N(\epsilon)$ and all x in the interval $0 \leq x \leq 1$.

The series in the examples are of the form

(1) $$\sum_{n=0}^{\infty} f_n(z) = f_0(z) + f_1(z) + f_2(z) + \cdots .$$

We assume that (1) converges for all z in a region R. Let $s(z)$ be the sum and $s_n(z)$ the nth partial sum of (1). We know that convergence of (1) at a point z means that, an $\epsilon > 0$ being given, we can find an $N = N(\epsilon, z)$ such that

$$|s(z) - s_n(z)| < \epsilon \qquad \text{for all } n > N(\epsilon, z).$$

N depends on ϵ and will, in general, also depend on the point z which has been selected for consideration. Now, any $\epsilon > 0$ being given, it may happen that we can find a number $N(\epsilon)$, *independent of z*, such that

$$|s(z) - s_n(z)| < \epsilon \qquad \text{for all } n > N(\epsilon) \text{ and all } z \text{ in } R.$$

Then the series is said to be **uniformly convergent** *in R*.

Uniformity of convergence is thus a property that depends on a whole set of values of z, whereas the convergence of a series may be considered for various particular values of z, without reference to other values.

The series in Ex. 1 is uniformly convergent in the interval $0 \leq x \leq 1$ (and, in fact, in any bounded region of the z-plane), while the series in

Ex. 3 is not uniformly convergent in a region containing the point 0. This shows that *an absolutely convergent series may not be uniformly convergent.* Conversely, *uniformly convergent series may not be absolutely convergent.* This is illustrated by

Example 4. The series

$$\sum_{n=1}^{\infty} \frac{(-1)^{n-1}}{x^2+n} = \frac{1}{x^2+1} - \frac{1}{x^2+2} + \frac{1}{x^2+3} - + \cdots \qquad (x \text{ real})$$

is uniformly convergent for all real x, but not absolutely convergent (cf. Prob. 17).

Example 2 is typical for power series, because for such a series the situation is very simple, as follows.

Theorem 1. *A power series*

(2)
$$\sum_{n=0}^{\infty} c_n(z-a)^n$$

with a nonzero radius of convergence R is uniformly convergent in every circular disk $|z-a| \leq r$ of radius $r < R$.

Proof. For $|z-a| \leq r$ we have

(3)
$$|c_{n+1}(z-a)^{n+1} + \cdots + c_{n+p}(z-a)^{n+p}|$$
$$\leq |c_{n+1}|r^{n+1} + \cdots + |c_{n+p}|r^{n+p}.$$

Since (2) converges absolutely at $z = r$, it follows from Theorem 4 in Sec. 10.5 that, and $\epsilon > 0$ being given, we can find an $N(\epsilon)$ such that

$$|c_{n+1}|r^{n+1} + \cdots + |c_{n+p}|r^{n+p} < \epsilon \quad \text{for} \quad n > N(\epsilon) \quad \text{and} \quad p = 1, 2, \cdots.$$

From this and (3) we obtain

$$|c_{n+1}(z-a)^{n+1} + \cdots + c_{n+p}(z-a)^{n+p}| < \epsilon$$

for all z in the disk $|z-a| \leq r$, every $n > N(\epsilon)$, and every $p = 1, 2, \cdots$. Since $N(\epsilon)$ is independent of z, this shows uniform convergence, and the theorem is proved.

While, of course, the sum of finitely many continuous functions is continuous, Ex. 3 illustrates that the sum of an infinite series of continuous functions may be discontinuous, even if it converges absolutely. But if series converges *uniformly*, this cannot happen. In fact the following important theorem holds.

Theorem 2. *Let the series*

$$\sum_{m=0}^{\infty} f_m(z) = f_0(z) + f_1(z) + \cdots$$

be uniformly convergent in a region R and let $F(z)$ be its sum. Then, if each term $f_m(z)$ is continuous at a point z_0 in R, the function $F(z)$ is continuous at z_0.

Proof. Let $s_n(z)$ be the nth partial sum of the series and $R_n(z)$ the corresponding remainder:

$$s_n = f_0 + f_1 + \cdots + f_n, \qquad R_n = f_{n+1} + f_{n+2} + \cdots .$$

An $\epsilon > 0$ being given, we can find an $n = N(\epsilon)$ such that

$$|R_N(z)| < \frac{\epsilon}{3} \qquad\qquad \text{for all } z \text{ in } R,$$

because the series converges uniformly. Since $s_N(z)$ is a sum of finitely many functions which are continuous at z_0, this sum is continuous at z_0. Therefore we can find a $\delta > 0$ such that

$$|s_N(z) - s_N(z_0)| < \frac{\epsilon}{3} \qquad\qquad \text{for all } z \text{ in } R \text{ for which } |z - z_0| < \delta.$$

By the triangle inequality (Sec. 10.1) for these z we thus obtain

$$|F(z) - F(z_0)| = |s_N(z) + R_N(z) - [s_N(z_0) + R_N(z_0)]|$$

$$\leq |s_N(z) - s_N(z_0)| + |R_N(z)| + |R_N(z_0)| < \frac{\epsilon}{3} + \frac{\epsilon}{3} + \frac{\epsilon}{3} = \epsilon.$$

This implies that $F(z)$ is continuous at z_0, and the theorem is proved.

We want to mention that in this theorem uniformity of convergence is a sufficient rather than a necessary condition. This may be illustrated by the following example.

Example 5. Let

$$u_m(x) = \frac{mx}{1 + m^2 x^2}$$

and consider the series

$$\sum_{m=1}^{\infty} f_m(x) \qquad \text{where} \qquad f_m(x) = u_m(x) - u_{m-1}(x).$$

The nth partial sum is

$$s_n = u_1 - u_0 + u_2 - u_1 + \cdots + u_n - u_{n-1} = u_n - u_0 = u_n.$$

Hence the series has the sum

$$F(x) = \lim_{n \to \infty} s_n(x) = \lim_{n \to \infty} u_n(x) = 0,$$

which is a continuous function. However, the series is not uniformly convergent in an interval $0 \leq x \leq a$, where $a > 0$. In fact, from

$$|F(x) - s_n(x)| = \frac{nx}{1 + n^2 x^2} < \epsilon$$

we obtain

$$\frac{nx}{\epsilon} < 1 + n^2 x^2 \qquad \text{or} \qquad n^2 x^2 - \frac{nx}{\epsilon} + 1 > 0$$

and from this

$$n > \frac{1}{2x\epsilon} (1 + \sqrt{1 - 4\epsilon^2}).$$

For fixed ϵ the right side approaches infinity as x approaches zero, which shows that the series is not uniformly convergent in that interval.

Under what conditions may we integrate a series term by term?

Let us start our consideration with an example which illustrates the important fact that term by term integration of series is not always permissible.

Example 6. Let

$$u_m(x) = mxe^{-mx^2}$$

and consider the series

$$\sum_{m=1}^{\infty} f_m(x) \qquad \text{where} \qquad f_m(x) = u_m(x) - u_{m-1}(x)$$

in the interval $0 \leq x \leq 1$. The nth partial sum is

$$s_n = u_1 - u_0 + u_2 - u_1 + \cdots + u_n - u_{n-1} = u_n - u_0 = u_n.$$

Hence the series has the sum

$$F(x) = \lim_{n \to \infty} s_n(x) = \lim_{n \to \infty} u_n(x) = 0 \qquad (0 \leq x \leq 1).$$

From this we obtain

$$\int_0^1 F(x) \, dx = 0.$$

On the other hand, by integrating term by term,

$$\sum_{m=1}^{\infty} \int_0^1 f_m(x) \, dx = \lim_{n \to \infty} \sum_{m=1}^{n} \int_0^1 f_m(x) \, dx = \lim_{n \to \infty} \int_0^1 s_n(x) \, dx.$$

Now $s_n = u_n$ and the expression on the right becomes

$$\lim_{n \to \infty} \int_0^1 u_n(x) \, dx = \lim_{n \to \infty} \int_0^1 nxe^{-nx^2} \, dx = \lim_{n \to \infty} \tfrac{1}{2}(1 - e^{-n}) = \tfrac{1}{2},$$

but not 0. This shows that the series under consideration cannot be integrated term by term from $x = 0$ to $x = 1$.

The series in Ex. 6 is not uniformly convergent in that interval, and we shall now prove that in the case of a uniformly convergent series of continuous functions we may integrate term by term.

Theorem 3. *Let*

$$F(z) = \sum_{n=0}^{\infty} f_n(z) = f_0(z) + f_1(z) + \cdots$$

be a uniformly convergent series of continuous functions within a region R.

Let C be any path in R. Then the series

(4)
$$\sum_{n=0}^{\infty} \int_C f_n(z)\, dz = \int_C f_0(z)\, dz + \int_C f_1(z)\, dz + \cdots$$

is convergent and has the sum $\int_C F(z)\, dz.$

Proof. From Theorem 2 it follows that $F(z)$ is continuous. Let $s_n(z)$ be the nth partial sum of the given series and $R_n(z)$ the corresponding remainder. Then $F = s_n + R_n$ and

$$\int_C F(z)\, dz = \int_C s_n(z)\, dz + \int_C R_n(z)\, dz.$$

Let l be the length of C. Since the given series converges uniformly, to every given $\epsilon > 0$ we can find a number N such that

$$|R_n(z)| < \frac{\epsilon}{l} \qquad \text{for all } n > N \text{ and all } z \text{ in } R.$$

By applying (4), Sec. 11.2, we thus obtain

$$\left| \int_C R_n(z)\, dz \right| < \frac{\epsilon}{l}\, l = \epsilon \qquad \text{for all } n > N.$$

Since $R_n = F - s_n$, this means that

$$\left| \int_C F(z)\, dz - \int_C s_n(z)\, dz \right| < \epsilon \qquad \text{for all } n > N.$$

Hence, the series (4) converges and has the sum indicated in the theorem. This completes the proof.

Theorem 2 and 3 characterize the two most important properties of uniformly convergent series.

Of course, since differentiation and integration are inverse processes, we readily conclude from Theorem 3 that a convergent series may be differentiated term by term, provided the terms of the given series have continuous derivatives and the resulting series is uniformly convergent; more precisely:

Theorem 4. *Suppose that the series* $f_0(z) + f_1(z) + f_2(z) + \cdots$ *is convergent in a region R and has the sum* $F(z)$, *the derivatives* $f_n{}'(z)$ *are continuous in R, and the series* $f_0{}'(z) + f_1{}'(z) + f_2{}'(z) + \cdots$ *converges uniformly in R. Then*

$$F'(z) = f_0{}'(z) + f_1{}'(z) + f_2{}'(z) + \cdots \qquad \textit{for all } z \textit{ in } R.$$

The simple proof is left to the student (Prob. 18).

Usually uniform convergence is established by a comparison test, namely, by the so-called

Weierstrass M-test. *If, for all values of z within a region R, the absolute value of the terms of a given series of the form* (1) *are, respectively, less than the corresponding terms in a convergent series of constant terms,*

$$(5) \qquad\qquad M_0 + M_1 + M_2 + \cdots,$$

then the series (1) *converges uniformly in R.*

The simple proof is left to the student (Prob. 7).

Example 7. The Weierstrass test shows that the series

$$\sum_{m=1}^{\infty} \frac{\sin mx}{m^2} \qquad\qquad (x \text{ real})$$

converges uniformly in any interval, because for real x,

$$\left| \frac{\sin mx}{m^2} \right| \leq \frac{1}{m^2}$$

and Σm^{-2} is convergent [cf. (5) in Sec. 10.6].

Differentiating the series term by term we obtain

$$\sum_{m=1}^{\infty} \frac{\cos mx}{m}.$$

At $x = 0$ this series becomes the harmonic series which is not convergent. This shows that the last assumption in Theorem 4 cannot be omitted.

PROBLEMS

1. Prove that the series in Ex. 3 is not uniformly convergent in any interval containing the point $x = 0$.

2. Determine the smallest integer n such that $|R_n| < 0.01$ in Ex. 2, when $x = 0.5, 0.6, 0.7, 0.8, 0.9$. What does the result mean from the viewpoint of computing $1/(1 - x)$ with an absolute error less than 0.01 by means of the geometric series?

3. Graph $s_1, s_2, \cdots, s_5$, and s in Ex. 2 for $-1 < x < 1$.

4. In Ex. 2, show that $\lim_{x \to -1} R_{2n}(x) = -\frac{1}{2}$ while $\lim_{x \to -1} R_{2n+1}(x) = \frac{1}{2}$ and conclude from the result that the convergence of the geometric series is not uniform in the interval $-1 < x < 0$.

5. Show that $1 + \sum_{n=1}^{\infty} (x^n - x^{n-1})$ is not uniformly convergent in the interval $0 \leq x \leq 1$. Graph the partial sums s_1, s_2, s_3, s_4.

6. Show that $\sum_{n=1}^{\infty} \left(\dfrac{x^{2n}}{1 + x^{2n}} - \dfrac{x^{2n-2}}{1 + x^{2n-2}} \right) = \begin{cases} -1 & \text{when } |x| < 1 \\ -\frac{1}{2} & \text{when } x = \pm 1 \\ 0 & \text{when } |x| > 1 \end{cases}$

Hint: consider the partial sums.

7. Give a proof of the Weierstrass M-test.

Prove that the following series converge uniformly in the given regions R. (Here x is real.)

8. $\sum_{n=0}^{\infty} z^n$, R: $|z| \leq 0.9$

9. $\sum_{n=1}^{\infty} \dfrac{\cos^n x}{n^2}$, R: all x

10. $\sum_{n=1}^{\infty} \dfrac{\sin n |z|}{n(n+1)}$, R: all z

11. $\sum_{n=1}^{\infty} \dfrac{1}{|z| + n^2}$, R: all z

12. $\sum_{n=1}^{\infty} \dfrac{\cos nx}{2^n}$, R: all x

13. $\sum_{n=1}^{\infty} \dfrac{z^n}{n^2}$, R: $|z| \leq 1$

14. $\sum_{n=1}^{\infty} \dfrac{\tanh^n x}{n!}$, R: all x

15. $\sum_{n=0}^{\infty} \dfrac{z^n}{n!}$, R: $|z| \leq 10^{50}$

16. Show that if the series (1) is uniformly convergent in some region R, it is uniformly convergent in any portion of R.

17. Prove the statement in Ex. 4.

18. Derive Theorem 4 from Theorem 3.

Show that (10), Sec. 9.5, with coefficients (11) is a solution of the heat equation for $t > 0$, assuming that $f(x)$ is continuous on the interval $0 \leq x \leq l$ and has one-sided derivatives at all interior points of that interval. Proceed as follows.

19. Show that $|B_n|$ is bounded, say, $|B_n| < K$ for all n. Conclude that

$$|u_n| < Ke^{-\lambda_n^2 t_0} \qquad \text{when} \qquad t \geq t_0 > 0$$

and, by the Weierstrass test, the series (10) converges uniformly with respect to x and t when $t \geq t_0$, $0 \leq x \leq l$. Using Theorem 2, show that $u(x, t)$ is continuous when $t \geq t_0$ and thus satisfies the boundary conditions (2) when $t \geq t_0$.

20. Show that $|\partial u_n / \partial t| < \lambda_n^2 K e^{-\lambda_n^2 t_0}$ when $t \geq t_0$ and the series of the expressions on the right converges, by the ratio test. Conclude from this, the Weierstrass test, and Theorem 4 that the series (10) can be differentiated term by term with respect to t and the resulting series has the sum $\partial u / \partial t$.

21. Show that (10) can be differentiated twice with respect to x and the resulting series has the sum $\partial^2 u / \partial x^2$. Conclude from this and the results of Probs. 19 and 20 that (10) is a solution of the heat equation for all $t \geq t_0$. (The proof that (10) satisfies the given initial condition can be found in Ref. [E2].)

11.10 LAURENT SERIES

In various applications it is necessary to expand a function $f(z)$ around points where $f(z)$ is singular. Taylor's theorem cannot be applied in such cases. A new type of series, known as *Laurent series* is necessary. This will be a representation which is valid in an annulus bounded by two concentric circles C_1 and C_2 such that $f(z)$ is analytic in the annulus and at each point of C_1 and C_2 (Fig. 332). As in the case of the Taylor series, $f(z)$ may be singular at some points outside C_1 and, as the essentially new feature, it may also be singular at some points inside C_2.

Laurent's theorem.[9] *If $f(z)$ is analytic and single-valued on two concentric circles C_1 and C_2 with center a and in the annulus between them, then $f(z)$ can be represented by the Laurent series*

(1)
$$f(z) = \sum_{n=0}^{\infty} b_n(z-a)^n + \sum_{n=1}^{\infty} \frac{c_n}{(z-a)^n}$$

$$= b_0 + b_1(z-a) + b_2(z-a)^2 + \cdots + \frac{c_1}{z-a} + \frac{c_2}{(z-a)^2} + \cdots$$

where[10]

(2) $b_n = \dfrac{1}{2\pi i} \displaystyle\int_C \dfrac{f(z^*)}{(z^*-a)^{n+1}} \, dz^*, \qquad c_n = \dfrac{1}{2\pi i} \displaystyle\int_C (z^*-a)^{n-1} f(z^*) \, dz^*,$

each integral being taken counterclockwise around any simple closed path C which lies in the annulus and encircles the inner circle (Fig. 332).

This series converges and represents $f(z)$ in the open annulus obtained from the given annulus by continuously increasing the circle C_1 and decreasing C_2 until each of the two circles reaches a point where $f(z)$ is singular.

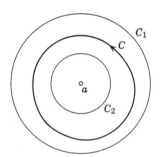

Remark. Obviously, instead of (1) and (2) we may write simply

(1′) $f(z) = \displaystyle\sum_{n=-\infty}^{\infty} A_n(z-a)^n$

where

(2′) $A_n = \dfrac{1}{2\pi i} \displaystyle\int_C \dfrac{f(z^*)}{(z^*-a)^{n+1}} \, dz^*.$

Fig. 332. Laurent's theorem.

Proof of Laurent's theorem. Let z be any point in the given annulus. Then from Cauchy's integral formula [cf. (3) in Sec. 11.5], it follows that

(3)
$$f(z) = \frac{1}{2\pi i} \int_{C_1} \frac{f(z^*)}{z^*-z} \, dz^* - \frac{1}{2\pi i} \int_{C_2} \frac{f(z^*)}{z^*-z} \, dz^*,$$

where both integrals are taken counterclockwise. These integrals will now be transformed in a fashion similar to that in the case of the Taylor expansion in Sec. 11.7. Since z lies inside C_1, the first of these integrals is precisely of the same type as the integral (1), Sec. 11.7. By expanding it and estimating the remainder as in Sec. 11.7, we obtain

(4)
$$\frac{1}{2\pi i} \int_{C_1} \frac{f(z^*)}{z^*-z} \, dz^* = \sum_{n=0}^{\infty} b_n(z-a)^n$$

[9] HERMANN LAURENT (1841–1908), French mathematician.
[10] We denote the variable of integration by z^* since z is used in $f(z)$.

where the coefficients are given by the formula

$$(5) \qquad b_n = \frac{1}{2\pi i} \int_{C_1} \frac{f(z^*)}{(z^* - a)^{n+1}} \, dz^*$$

and the integral is taken in the counterclockwise sense. Since a is not a point of the annulus, the functions $f(z^*)/(z^* - a)^{n+1}$ are analytic in the annulus. Hence, we may integrate along the path C (cf. in the theorem) instead of C_1, without altering the value of b_n. This proves (2) for all $n \geqq 0$.

In the case of the last integral in (3), the situation is different since z lies outside C_2. Instead of (3), Sec. 11.7, we now have

$$(6) \qquad \left| \frac{z^* - a}{z - a} \right| < 1,$$

that is, we now have to develop $1/(z^* - z)$ in powers of $(z^* - a)/(z - a)$ for the resulting series to be convergent. We find

$$\frac{1}{z^* - z} = \frac{1}{z^* - a - (z - a)} = \frac{-1}{(z - a)\left(1 - \dfrac{z^* - a}{z - a}\right)}.$$

By applying the formula for a finite geometric progression to the last expression this becomes

$$\frac{1}{z^* - z} = -\frac{1}{z - a}\left\{1 + \frac{z^* - a}{z - a} + \left(\frac{z^* - a}{z - a}\right)^2 + \cdots + \left(\frac{z^* - a}{z - a}\right)^n\right\}$$
$$- \frac{1}{z - z^*}\left(\frac{z^* - a}{z - a}\right)^{n+1}.$$

From this development we readily obtain

$$-\frac{1}{2\pi i} \int_{C_2} \frac{f(z^*)}{z^* - z} \, dz^*$$

$$= \frac{1}{2\pi i}\left\{\frac{1}{z - a} \int_{C_2} f(z^*) \, dz^* + \frac{1}{(z - a)^2} \int_{C_2} (z^* - a)f(z^*) \, dz^* + \cdots\right.$$

$$\left. + \frac{1}{(z - a)^{n+1}} \int_{C_2} (z^* - a)^n f(z^*) \, dz^*\right\} + R_n^*(z);$$

in this representation the last term is of the form

$$(7) \qquad R_n^*(z) = \frac{1}{2\pi i(z - a)^{n+1}} \int_{C_2} \frac{(z^* - a)^{n+1}}{z - z^*} f(z^*) \, dz^*.$$

In the integrals on the right we may replace the circle C_2 by the aforementioned path C, without altering their values. This establishes Laurent's theorem provided that

(8)
$$\lim_{n \to \infty} R_n^*(z) = 0.$$

We prove (8). Since $z - z^* \neq 0$ and $f(z)$ is analytic in the annulus and on C_2 the absolute value of the expression $f(z^*)/(z - z^*)$ in (7) is bounded, say,

$$\left| \frac{f(z^*)}{z - z^*} \right| < \tilde{M} \qquad \text{for all } z^* \text{ on } C_2.$$

By applying (4) in Sec. 11.2 to (7) and denoting the length of C_2 by l we thus obtain

$$|R_n^*(z)| < \frac{1}{2\pi |z - a|^{n+1}} |z^* - a|^{n+1} \tilde{M} l = \frac{\tilde{M} l}{2\pi} \left| \frac{z^* - a}{z - a} \right|^{n+1}$$

From (6) we see that the expression on the right approaches zero as n approaches infinity. This proves (8). The representation (1) with coefficients (2) is now established in the given annulus.

Finally let us prove convergence of (1) in the open annulus characterized at the end of the theorem.

We denote the sums of the two series in (1) by $g(z)$ and $h(z)$, and the radii of C_1 and C_2 by r_1 and r_2, respectively. Then $f = g + h$. The first series is a power series. Since it converges in the annulus, it must converge in the entire disk bounded by C_1, and g is analytic in that disk.

Setting $Z = 1/(z - a)$, the last series becomes a power series in Z. The annulus $r_2 < |z - a| < r_1$ then corresponds to the annulus $1/r_1 < |Z| < 1/r_2$, the new series converges in this annulus and, therefore, in the entire disk $|Z| < 1/r_2$. Now, since this disk corresponds to $|z| > r_2$, the exterior of C_2, the given series converges for all z outside C_2, and h is analytic for all these z.

Since $f = g + h$, it follows that g must be singular at all those points outside C_1 where f is singular, and h must be singular at all those points inside C_2 where f is singular. Consequently, the radius of convergence of the first series is equal to the distance of that singularity of f outside C_1 which is closest to a. Similarly, the second series converges for all z outside the circle about a whose radius is equal to the maximum distance of the singularities of f inside C_2. The domain common to both of those domains of convergence is the open annulus characterized at the end of the theorem, and the proof is complete.

It follows that if $f(z)$ is analytic inside C_2, the Laurent series reduces to the Taylor series of $f(z)$ with center a. In fact, by applying Cauchy's integral theorem to (2) we see that in this case all the coefficients of the negative powers in (1) are zero.

Furthermore, if $z = a$ is the only singular point of $f(z)$ in C_2, then the Laurent expansion (1) converges for all z in C_1 except at $z = a$. This case occurs frequently and, therefore, is of particular importance.

The Laurent series of a given analytic function $f(z)$ in its annulus of convergence is unique (cf. Prob. 19, this section). *However, $f(z)$ may have different Laurent series in two annuli with the same center* (cf. Ex. 2, below).

The uniqueness is important, because Laurent series usually are not obtained by using (2) for determining the coefficients, but by various other methods. Some of these methods are illustrated by the following examples. If a Laurent series is found by any such process, it must be *the* Laurent series of the given function in the given annulus.

Example 1. The Laurent series of $z^2 e^{1/z}$ with center 0 can be obtained from (2) in Sec. 10.11. Replacing z by $1/z$ in that series, we find

$$z^2 e^{1/z} = z^2 \left(1 + \frac{1}{1!\,z} + \frac{1}{2!\,z^2} + \cdots \right) = z^2 + z + \frac{1}{2} + \frac{1}{3!\,z} + \frac{1}{4!\,z^2} + \cdots$$
$$(|z| > 0).$$

Example 2. Find all Laurent series of $f(z) = 1/(1 - z^2)$ with center at $z = 1$. We have $1 - z^2 = -(z - 1)(z + 1)$. Using the geometric series

$$\frac{1}{1 - q} = \sum_{n=0}^{\infty} q^n \qquad (|q| < 1),$$

we find

(a)
$$\frac{1}{z + 1} = \frac{1}{2 + (z - 1)} = \frac{1}{2} \frac{1}{\left[1 - \left(-\dfrac{z - 1}{2} \right) \right]}$$

$$= \frac{1}{2} \sum_{n=0}^{\infty} \left(-\frac{z - 1}{2} \right)^n = \sum_{n=0}^{\infty} \frac{(-1)^n}{2^{n+1}} (z - 1)^n;$$

this series converges in the disk $|(z - 1)/2| < 1$, that is, $|z - 1| < 2$. Similarly,

(b)
$$\frac{1}{z + 1} = \frac{1}{(z - 1) + 2} = \frac{1}{(z - 1)} \frac{1}{\left(1 + \dfrac{2}{z - 1} \right)}$$

$$= \frac{1}{z - 1} \sum_{n=0}^{\infty} \left(-\frac{2}{z - 1} \right)^n = \sum_{n=0}^{\infty} \frac{(-2)^n}{(z - 1)^{n+1}};$$

this series converges for $|2/(z - 1)| < 1$, that is, $|z - 1| > 2$. Therefore, from (a) we obtain

$$f(z) = \frac{-1}{(z - 1)(z + 1)} = \sum_{n=0}^{\infty} \frac{(-1)^{n+1}}{2^{n+1}} (z - 1)^{n-1}$$

$$= \frac{-1/2}{z - 1} + \frac{1}{4} - \frac{1}{8} (z - 1) + \frac{1}{16} (z - 1)^2 - + \cdots;$$

this series converges in the domain $0 < |z - 1| < 2$. From (b),

$$f(z) = -\sum_{n=0}^{\infty} \frac{(-2)^n}{(z - 1)^{n+2}} = -\frac{1}{(z - 1)^2} + \frac{2}{(z - 1)^3} - \frac{4}{(z - 1)^4} + - \cdots$$

$$(|z - 1| > 2).$$

Example 3. From Prob. 20 at the end of Sec. 11.7 we obtain the Laurent series

$$\cot z = \frac{1}{z} - \frac{1}{3} z - \frac{1}{45} z^3 - \frac{2}{945} z^5 - \cdots \qquad (0 < |z| < \pi).$$

PROBLEMS

Expand the following functions in Laurent series which converge for $0 < |z| < R$ and determine the precise region of convergence.

1. $\dfrac{e^{1/z^2}}{z^4}$ **2.** $\dfrac{1}{z^2(1 - z)}$ **3.** $\dfrac{\sin 4z}{z^3}$

4. $\dfrac{1}{z^5(1 + z)^2}$ **5.** $\dfrac{1}{z^8 + z^4}$ **6.** $\dfrac{1}{z^3 - 3z^2}$

Find all Taylor series and Laurent series with center at $z = a$ and determine the precise regions of convergence:

7. $\dfrac{1}{1 + z^2}, a = i$ **8.** $\dfrac{1}{1 + z^2}, a = -i$ **9.** $\dfrac{1}{1 - z^4}, a = -1$

10. $\dfrac{1}{1 - z^4}, a = 0$ **11.** $\dfrac{4z - 1}{z^4 - 1}, a = 0$ **12.** $\dfrac{1}{z(1 - z)^2}, a = 0$

13. $\dfrac{7z^2 + 9z - 18}{z^3 - 9z}, a = 0$ **14.** $\dfrac{4z^2 + 2z - 4}{z^3 - 4z}, a = 2$ **15.** $\dfrac{e^z}{(z - 1)^2}, a = 1$

16. $\dfrac{\sin z}{\left(z - \dfrac{\pi}{4}\right)^3}, a = \dfrac{\pi}{4}$ **17.** $\dfrac{1}{z^4}, a = 1$ **18.** $\dfrac{1}{z^3}, a = i$

19. Prove that the Laurent expansion of a given analytic function in a given annulus is unique.

11.11 THE "POINT" AT INFINITY

We shall see in the next section that the Laurent series can be used for classifying the singularities of analytic functions. In this connection we shall also consider the behavior of analytic functions $f(z)$ as $|z|$ approaches infinity.

For investigating a function $f(z)$ for large $|z|$, it seems to be natural to introduce a new variable w by setting $z = 1/w$ because large $|z|$ then corresponds to small $|w|$, and $|z| \to \infty$ corresponds to $|w| \to 0$.

The transformation $z = 1/w$ is defined for all $w \neq 0$, and it is a one-to-one transformation. That is, to each $z \neq 0$ there corresponds precisely one $w \neq 0$ and, conversely, to each $w \neq 0$ there corresponds precisely one $z \neq 0$. However, we see that the point $w = 0$ in the complex w-plane does not correspond to any point in the z-plane. This situation suggests that we attach an "improper point" to the z-plane; this point is called the **point at infinity** and is denoted by the symbol ∞ (*infinity*). The complex plane plus the point ∞ is called the **extended complex plane**. The complex plane without that improper point is called the *finite complex plane*.

Reconsidering the transformation $z = 1/w$, we see that we may now let $z = \infty$ correspond to $w = 0$, and $w = \infty$ to $z = 0$, so that the transformation becomes one-to-one with respect to the extended w and z planes.

The idea of attaching just one improper point to the complex plane at infinity may also be motivated by the following simple geometrical consideration. The usual representation of complex numbers z in the complex plane is convenient as long as the absolute values of the numbers are not too large. For large $|z|$ the situation becomes inconvenient, and in this case we may prefer a representation of the complex numbers on a sphere, which was suggested by Riemann and is obtained as follows.

Let S be a sphere of diameter 1 which touches the complex z-plane at the origin (Fig. 333). Let N be the "North pole" of S (the point diametrically opposite to the point of contact between the sphere and the plane). Let P be any point in the complex plane. Then the straight segment with end points P and N intersect S at a point P^*. We let P and P^* correspond to each other. In this way we obtain a correspondence between the points in the complex plane and the points on S. This correspondence is called a **mapping** of the points of the z-plane onto the sphere S, and P^* is called the *image point* of P with respect to the mapping. The complex numbers, first represented in the plane, are now represented by points on S. To

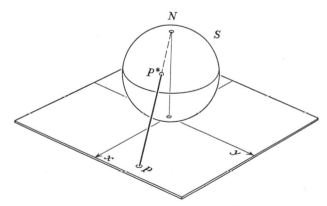

Fig. 333. Riemann number sphere.

each z there corresponds a point on S. Conversely, each point on S represents a complex number z, except for the point N which does not correspond to any point in the complex plane. But if we introduce the improper point $z = \infty$ and let this point correspond to N, the mapping becomes a one-to-one mapping of the extended plane onto S. The sphere S is called the **Riemann number sphere**. The particular mapping which we have used is called a *stereographic projection*.

Obviously, the unit circle is mapped onto the "equator" of S. The interior of the unit circle corresponds to the "Southern hemisphere" and the exterior to the "Northern hemisphere." Numbers z, whose absolute values are large, lie close to the North pole N. The x and y axes (and, more generally, all the straight lines through the origin) are mapped onto "meridians," while circles with center at the origin are mapped onto "parallels." It can be shown that any circle or straight line in the z-plane is mapped onto a circle on S, and, furthermore, that stereographic projection is *conformal*, that is, any two intersecting curves have images whose angle of intersection is equal to that of the curves.

Given a function $f(z)$ to be investigated for large $|z|$, we may now set $z = 1/w$ and investigate $f(z) = f(1/w) \equiv g(w)$ in a neighborhood of $w = 0$. We define

$$g(0) = \lim_{w \to 0} g(w),$$

and we say that $f(z)$ *is analytic or singular at infinity according as $g(w)$ is analytic or singular, respectively, at $w = 0$.*

Example 1. The function $f(z) = 1/z^2$ is analytic at infinity since $g(w) = f(1/w) = w^2$ is analytic at $w = 0$. The function $f(z) = z^3$ is singular at infinity because $g(w) = f(1/w) = 1/w^3$ is singular at $w = 0$. The exponential function e^z is singular at infinity since $e^{1/w}$ is singular at $w = 0$. Similarly, the trigonometric functions $\sin z$ and $\cos z$ are singular at infinity.

Let $f(z)$ be analytic outside a circle C, say, in the domain $|z - a| > R$, also at infinity. If we set

$$z = \frac{1}{w} + a, \qquad \text{then} \qquad z - a = \frac{1}{w},$$

and

$$f(z) = f\left(\frac{1}{w} + a\right) \equiv h(w)$$

is analytic in the disk $|w| < 1/R$. Let the Maclaurin series of $h(w)$ be

$$h(w) = \sum_{n=0}^{\infty} c_n w^n = c_0 + c_1 w + c_2 w^2 + \cdots \qquad \left(|w| < \frac{1}{R}\right).$$

Then by inserting $w = 1/(z - a)$ we obtain the Laurent series

$$(1) \qquad f(z) = \sum_{n=0}^{\infty} \frac{c_n}{(z - a)^n} = c_0 + \frac{c_1}{z - a} + \frac{c_2}{(z - a)^2} + \cdots$$

$$(|z - a| > R).$$

PROBLEMS

Are the following functions analytic at infinity or not?

1. e^z 2. $\cos z$, $\sin z$ 3. $e^{1/z}$ 4. z^{-4}

5. $z^3 - z^{-1}$ 6. $1/(z^2 - 4z)$ 7. $z^2 e^{-z}$ 8. $z^2 e^{1/z}$

9. $(z^2 + 1)/(z^2 - 1)$

Describe and sketch the images of the following regions on the Riemann number sphere.

10. $|z| > 10$ 11. $2 < |z| < 3$ 12. $\mathrm{Re}\, z > 0$, $\mathrm{Im}\, z > 0$

13. $0 < \arg z < \pi/4$ 14. $1/2 < |z| < 1$ 15. $2 < |z| < 3$, $|\arg z| < \pi/4$

16. $\mathrm{Re}\, z > 1$ 17. $\mathrm{Re}\, z > -1$ 18. $-\pi < \mathrm{Im}\, z < \pi$

19. $\pi < \mathrm{Re}\, z < 2\pi$ 20. $|\arg z| < 3\pi/4$ 21. $|z| > 1$, $|\arg z| < \pi/4$

22. Using the method described at the end of this section, show that

$$\frac{1}{z^4} = \sum_{n=0}^{\infty} \binom{-4}{n} (z - 1)^{-n-4} = \frac{1}{(z - 1)^4} - \frac{4}{(z - 1)^5} + \cdots \qquad (|z - 1| > 1).$$

11.12 ZEROS AND SINGULARITIES

If a function $f(z)$ is analytic in a domain D and is zero at a point $z = a$ in D, then $f(z)$ is said to have a *zero* at that point $z = a$. If not only f but also the derivatives $f', \cdots, f^{(n-1)}$ are all zero at $z = a$ and $f^{(n)}(a) \neq 0$, then $f(z)$ is said to have a *zero of the order n* at the point $z = a$.

For example, if $f(a) = 0$, $f'(a) \neq 0$, then f has a zero of the first order or *simple zero* at $z = a$. If $f(a) = f'(a) = 0$, $f''(a) \neq 0$, then the zero of f at $z = a$ is of the second order, etc.

Furthermore, our consideration in the last section suggests the following definition.

An analytic function $f(z)$ is said to have a *zero of nth order at infinity*, if $f(1/z)$ has such a zero at $z = 0$.

Example 1. The function $\sin z$ has simple zeros at $z = 0$, $\pm\pi$, $\pm 2\pi$, $\cdots$. The function $(z - a)^3$ has a zero of the third order at $z = a$. The function $1 - \cos z$ has second-order zeros at $z = 0$, $\pm 2\pi$, $\pm 4\pi$, $\cdots$. The function $1/(1 - z)$ has a simple zero at infinity.

Clearly, if $f(z)$ is analytic in some neighborhood of a point $z = a$ and has a zero of nth order at a, it follows from Taylor's theorem in Sec. 11.7 that the coefficients $b_0, \cdots, b_{n-1}$ of its Taylor series with center $z = a$ are zero, and the series is of the form

$$f(z) = b_n(z - a)^n + b_{n+1}(z - a)^{n+1} + \cdots$$

(1)
$$\qquad\qquad\qquad\qquad\qquad\qquad (b_n \neq 0).$$

$$= (z - a)^n[b_n + b_{n+1}(z - a) + b_{n+2}(z - a)^2 + \cdots]$$

A point of a point set S is called an **isolated point** of S, if it has a neighborhood which does not contain further points of S. A point b is called a **limit point** of S, if every neighborhood of b (no matter how small) contains at least one point ($\neq b$) of S (and hence infinitely many points of S).

Example 2. The set of the points $z = n \, (n = 1, 2, \cdots)$ consists wholly of isolated points and has no limit point in the finite plane. The set of the points $z = i/n \, (n = 1, 2, \cdots)$ on the imaginary axis consists wholly of isolated points and has one limit point, namely, $z = 0$; this point does not belong to the set. The set of all complex numbers z for which $|z| < 1$ has no isolated points. Every point of the set and also the points on the unit circle $|z| = 1$ (which do not belong to the set) are limit points of the set.

Theorem 1. *The zeros of an analytic function $f(z)$ ($\neq 0$) are isolated.*

Proof. We consider (1). Let $g(z)$ be the analytic function represented by the series in brackets $[\cdots]$. Since $b_n \neq 0$, we have $g(a) \neq 0$. Consequently, since $g(z)$ is continuous, it is not zero in some neighborhood of $z = a$. It follows that $f(z)$ is not zero in that neighborhood (except at $z = a$), so that $z = a$ is the only zero of $f(z)$ in that neighborhood and is, therefore, isolated. This completes the proof.

Analytic functions may have different types of singularities.[11] We first remember that a *singular point* of an analytic function $f(z)$ is a point where $f(z)$ ceases to be analytic (cf. Sec. 11.7). We also say that $f(z)$ *is singular*, or *has a singularity*, at that point. The function $f(z)$ is said to be *singular at infinity*, if $f(1/z)$ is singular at $z = 0$.

If $f(z)$ has an isolated singularity at a point $z = a$, then we can represent it by its Laurent series

(2)
$$f(z) = \sum_{n=0}^{\infty} b_n(z - a)^n + \sum_{n=1}^{\infty} \frac{c_n}{(z - a)^n}$$

valid throughout some neighborhood of $z = a$ (except at $z = a$ itself). The last series in (2) is called the **principal part** of $f(z)$ near $z = a$.

It may happen that from some n on, all the coefficients c_n are zero, say, $c_m \neq 0$ and $c_n = 0$ for all $n > m$. Then (2) reduces to the form

(3)
$$f(z) = \sum_{n=0}^{\infty} b_n(z - a)^n + \frac{c_1}{z - a} + \cdots + \frac{c_m}{(z - a)^m} \qquad (c_m \neq 0).$$

In this case, where the principal part consists of finitely many terms, the

[11] By our general assumption the functions under consideration are single-valued.

singularity of f at $z = a$ is called a **pole**, and m is called the *order* of the pole. Poles of the first order are also known as *simple poles*.

Any singularity of a single-valued analytic function other than a pole is called an **essential singularity**.

Poles are, by definition, isolated singularities. All singularities which are not isolated (for instance, the limit point of a sequence of poles) are thus essential singularities. An essential singularity may be isolated or not. If in (2) infinitely many c_n are different from zero, then the singularity of $f(z)$ at $z = a$ is not a pole but an isolated essential singularity.

Example 3. The function

$$f(z) = \frac{1}{z(z - 2)^5} + \frac{3}{(z - 2)^2}$$

has a simple pole at $z = 0$ and a pole of the fifth order at $z = 2$. The functions

$$(4) \qquad e^{1/z} = \sum_{n=0}^{\infty} \frac{1}{n!\, z^n} = 1 + \frac{1}{z} + \frac{1}{2!\, z^2} + \cdots$$

and

$$(5) \qquad \sin\frac{1}{z} = \sum_{n=0}^{\infty} \frac{(-1)^n}{(2n + 1)!\, z^{2n+1}} = \frac{1}{z} - \frac{1}{3!\, z^3} + \frac{1}{5!\, z^5} - + \cdots$$

have an isolated essential singularity at $z = 0$.

The function $\tan\dfrac{1}{z}$ has poles at

$$\frac{1}{z} = \pm\frac{\pi}{2}, \pm\frac{3\pi}{2}, \cdots \qquad \text{that is,} \qquad z = \pm\frac{2}{\pi}, \pm\frac{2}{3\pi}, \cdots.$$

The limit point $z = 0$ of these points is thus a nonisolated essential singularity of $\tan\dfrac{1}{z}$.

Example 4. The polynomial $f(z) = 2z + 6z^3$ has a pole of the third order at infinity, because $f\left(\dfrac{1}{z}\right) = \dfrac{2}{z} + \dfrac{6}{z^3}$ has such a pole at $z = 0$. More generally, a polynomial of nth degree has a pole of nth order at infinity.

The functions e^z, $\sin z$, $\cos z$ have an isolated essential singularity at infinity, since $e^{1/z}$, $\sin\dfrac{1}{z}$, and $\cos\dfrac{1}{z}$ have an isolated essential singularity at $z = 0$.

A function $f(z)$ which is not analytic at a point $z = a$ but can be made analytic there by assigning some value to $f(z)$ at $z = a$, is said to have a *removable singularity* at $z = a$. Such singularities are not of interest, because they can be removed.

A function which is analytic everywhere in the finite plane is called an **entire function**.

If such a function is also analytic at infinity, it is bounded for all z, and from Liouville's theorem (cf. Sec. 11.6) it follows that it must be a constant. Hence, any entire function which is not a constant must be singular at infinity. For instance, polynomials (of at least the first degree), e^z, sin z, and cos z are entire functions, and they are singular at infinity.

An analytic function, whose only singularities in the finite plane are poles, is called a **meromorphic function**.

Example 5. Rational functions with nonconstant denominator, tan z, cot z, sec z, and csc z are meromorphic functions.

The classification of singularities into poles and essential singularities is not merely a formal matter; the behavior of an analytic function in a neighborhood of an essential singularity is entirely different from that in the neighborhood of a pole.

Example 6. The function $f(z) = 1/z^2$ has a pole at $z = 0$, and $|f| \to \infty$ as $z \to 0$ in any manner.

This example illustrates

Theorem 2. *If $f(z)$ is analytic and has a pole at $z = a$, then $|f(z)| \to \infty$ as $z \to a$ in any manner.* (Cf. Prob. 25.)

Example 7. The function $f(z) = e^{1/z}$ has an essential singularity at $z = 0$. It has no limit for approach along the imaginary axis; it becomes infinite if $z \to 0$ through positive real values, but it approaches zero if $z \to 0$ through negative real values. It takes on any given value $c = c_0 e^{i\alpha} \neq 0$ in an arbitrarily small neighborhood of $z = 0$. In fact, setting $z = re^{i\theta}$, we have to solve the equation

$$e^{1/z} = e^{(\cos\theta - i\sin\theta)/r} = c_0 e^{i\alpha}$$

for r and θ. Equating the absolute values and the arguments, we have

$$e^{(\cos\theta)/r} = c_0 \quad \text{or} \quad \cos\theta = r\ln c_0 \quad \text{and} \quad \sin\theta = -\alpha r.$$

From these two equations and $\cos^2\theta + \sin^2\theta = 1$ we obtain

$$r^2 = \frac{1}{(\ln c_0)^2 + \alpha^2} \quad \text{and} \quad \tan\theta = -\frac{\alpha}{\ln c_0}.$$

We see that r can be made arbitrarily small by adding multiples of 2π to α, leaving c unaltered.

This example illustrates the famous

Picard's theorem. *If $f(z)$ is analytic and has an isolated essential singularity at a point a, it takes on every value, with at most one exceptional value, in an arbitrarily small neighborhood of a.*

In Ex. 7, the exceptional value is $z = 0$. The proof of Picard's theorem is rather complicated; it can be found in Ref. [G9].

PROBLEMS

Determine the location and order of the zeros of the following functions.

1. $1 - z^4$ **2.** $(1 - z)^4$ **3.** $\sin^3 z$ **4.** $\left(\sin \dfrac{z}{2} - 1\right)^2$

5. $\dfrac{z + 1}{z^2 + 3}$ **6.** $\dfrac{(z - 6)^2}{z^5}$ **7.** $e^z - e^{2z}$ **8.** $\tan^2 z$

9. $z^4 \sin^2 \dfrac{1}{z}$ **10.** $\cot^3 z$ **11.** $\dfrac{(4 - z^2)^2}{(1 - z^2)^3}$ **12.** $\dfrac{(9 + z^2)^2}{(1 + z)^4}$

Determine the location and type of the singularities of the following functions.

13. $z^4 - 3z^2 + 1$ **14.** $z^2 - \dfrac{1}{z^2}$ **15.** $\sinh z$

16. $\dfrac{e^{1/z}}{(z + 1)(z + 2)^2}$ **17.** $\cosh^2 \dfrac{1}{z - \pi}$ **18.** $\csc^2 z$

19. $\cos z - \sin z$ **20.** $\left(z^4 + \dfrac{1}{z}\right)e^{-z}$ **21.** $\dfrac{e^{1/(z-1)}}{e^z - 1}$

22. $\dfrac{1}{\cos z - \sin z}$ **23.** $e^{z^2 + z^{-2}}$

24. If $f(z)$ has a zero of order n at $z = a$, prove that $f^2(z)$ has a zero of order $2n$ at $z = a$. Give examples.

25. Verify Theorem 2 for $f(z) = z^{-2} + z^{-1}$. Prove Theorem 2.

26. If $f(z)$ has a zero of order n at $z = a$, prove that $1/f(z)$ has a pole of order n at $z = a$. Give examples.

11.13 RESIDUES

If $f(z)$ is analytic in a neighborhood of a point $z = a$, then, by Cauchy's integral theorem,

$$(1) \qquad \int_C f(z)\, dz = 0$$

for any contour in that neighborhood. If, however, $f(z)$ has a pole or an isolated essential singularity (cf. Sec. 11.12) at $z = a$ and a lies in the interior of C then the integral in (1) will, in general, be different from zero. In this case we may represent $f(z)$ by a Laurent series

$$(2) \qquad f(z) = \sum_{n=0}^{\infty} b_n (z - a)^n + \sum_{n=1}^{\infty} \frac{c_n}{(z - a)^n}$$

which converges in the domain $0 < |z - a| < R$, where R is the distance from a to the nearest singular point of $f(z)$. From (2) in Sec. 11.10 we see that the coefficient c_1 of the power $1/(z - a)$ in this development is

$$c_1 = \frac{1}{2\pi i} \int_C f(z)\, dz,$$

and, therefore,

(3)
$$\int_C f(z)\, dz = 2\pi i c_1,$$

the integration being taken in the counterclockwise sense around a simple closed path C which lies in the domain $0 < |z - a| < R$ and contains the point $z = a$ in its interior. The coefficient c_1 in the development (2) of $f(z)$ is called the **residue** of $f(z)$ at $z = a$, and we shall use the notation

(4)
$$c_1 = \operatorname*{Res}_{z=a} f(z).$$

We have seen that Laurent expansions can be obtained by various methods, without using the integral formulas for the coefficients. *Hence, we may determine the residue by one of those methods and then use the formula (3) for evaluating contour integrals.*

Example 1. Integrate the function $f(z) = z^{-4} \sin z$ around the unit circle C in the counterclockwise sense.

From (9) in Sec. 10.12 we obtain the Laurent series

$$f(z) = \frac{\sin z}{z^4} = \frac{1}{z^3} - \frac{1}{3!\,z} + \frac{z}{5!} - \frac{z^3}{7!} + - \cdots.$$

We see that the residue is $c_1 = -1/3!$, and from (3) it follows that

$$\int_C \frac{\sin z}{z^4}\, dz = 2\pi i c_1 = -\frac{\pi i}{3}.$$

Before we proceed in evaluating integrals we shall develop a simple standard method for determining the residue in the case of a pole.

If $f(z)$ has a **simple pole** at a point $z = a$, the corresponding Laurent series is of the form [cf. (3) in the last section]

$$f(z) = \frac{c_1}{z - a} + b_0 + b_1(z - a) + b_2(z - a)^2 + \cdots$$
$$(0 < |z - a| < R,\ c_1 \neq 0).$$

Multiplying both sides by $z - a$, we have

(5)
$$(z - a)f(z) = c_1 + (z - a)[b_0 + b_1(z - a) + \cdots].$$

If we let z approach a, the right-hand side approaches c_1 and we obtain

(6)
$$\operatorname*{Res}_{z=a} f(z) = c_1 = \lim_{z \to a} (z - a) f(z).$$

In the case of a simple pole, another useful formula is obtained as follows. If $f(z)$ has a simple pole at $z = a$, we may set

$$f(z) = \frac{p(z)}{q(z)}$$

where $p(z)$ and $q(z)$ are analytic at $z = a$, $p(a) \neq 0$, and $q(z)$ has a simple zero at $z = a$. Consequently, $q(z)$ can be expanded in a Taylor series of the form

$$q(z) = (z - a)q'(a) + \frac{(z - a)^2}{2!} q''(a) + \cdots.$$

From (6) it follows that

$$\operatorname*{Res}_{z=a} f(z) = \lim_{z \to a} (z - a) \frac{p(z)}{q(z)} = \lim_{z \to a} \frac{(z - a)p(z)}{(z - a)[q'(a) + (z - a)q''(a)/2 + \cdots]};$$

that is, in the case of a simple pole we also have

(7) $$\operatorname*{Res}_{z=a} f(z) = \operatorname*{Res}_{z=a} \frac{p(z)}{q(z)} = \frac{p(a)}{q'(a)}.$$

Example 2. The function $f(z) = (4 - 3z)/(z^2 - z)$ has simple poles at $z = 0$ and $z = 1$. From (7) we obtain

$$\operatorname*{Res}_{z=0} f(z) = \left[\frac{4 - 3z}{2z - 1}\right]_{z=0} = -4, \qquad \operatorname*{Res}_{z=1} f(z) = \left[\frac{4 - 3z}{2z - 1}\right]_{z=1} = 1.$$

We shall now consider **poles of higher order**. If $f(z)$ has a pole of order $m > 1$ at a point $z = a$, the corresponding Laurent expansion is of the form

$$f(z) = \frac{c_m}{(z - a)^m} + \frac{c_{m-1}}{(z - a)^{m-1}} + \cdots + \frac{c_2}{(z - a)^2} + \frac{c_1}{z - a}$$
$$+ b_0 + b_1(z - a) + \cdots$$

where $c_m \neq 0$ and the series converges in some neighborhood of $z = a$, except at the point a itself. By multiplying both sides by $(z - a)^m$ we obtain

$$(z - a)^m f(z) = c_m + c_{m-1}(z - a) + \cdots + c_2(z - a)^{m-2} + c_1(z - a)^{m-1}$$
$$+ b_0(z - a)^m + b_1(z - a)^{m+1} + \cdots.$$

This shows that the residue c_1 of $f(z)$ at $z = a$ is now the coefficient of the power $(z - a)^{m-1}$ in the Taylor expansion of the function $g(z) = (z - a)^m f(z)$ with center at $z = a$. Therefore, from Taylor's theorem (Sec. 11.7),

$$c_1 = \frac{g^{(m-1)}(a)}{(m - 1)!};$$

that is,

(8) $$\operatorname*{Res}_{z=a} f(z) = \frac{1}{(m - 1)!} \lim_{z \to a} \left\{ \frac{d^{m-1}}{dz^{m-1}} \left[(z - a)^m f(z) \right] \right\}.$$

Example 3. The function

$$f(z) = \frac{2z}{(z + 4)(z - 1)^2}$$

has a pole of the second order at $z = 1$, and from (8) we obtain the corresponding residue

$$\operatorname*{Res}_{z=1} f(z) = \lim_{z \to 1} \frac{d}{dz} [(z-1)^2 f(z)] = \lim_{z \to 1} \frac{d}{dz} \left(\frac{2z}{z+4} \right) = \frac{8}{25}.$$

Of course, in the case of a rational function $f(z)$, the residues can also be determined from the representation of $f(z)$ in terms of partial fractions.

PROBLEMS

Determine the residues at the singular points of the following functions.

1. $\dfrac{4}{1-z}$ 2. $\dfrac{z-1}{z+1}$ 3. $\dfrac{3e^z}{z^4}$

4. $\dfrac{\cos z}{z^6}$ 5. $\dfrac{4z-1}{z^2+3z+2}$ 6. $\dfrac{z}{1+z^2}$

7. $\dfrac{z^2}{1-z^4}$ 8. $\sec z$ 9. $\csc \pi z$

10. $\tan z$ 11. $\cot z$ 12. $\coth 2z$

13. $\dfrac{1}{z^2}$ 14. $\dfrac{\sin z}{z^2}$ 15. $\dfrac{1}{(z^2-1)^2}$

16. $\dfrac{1}{(z^4-1)^2}$ 17. $\dfrac{e^{1/z}}{z^2}$ 18. $\dfrac{4-3z}{z^3-3z^2+2z}$

19. $\dfrac{z+1}{(z^2-16)(z+2)}$ 20. $\dfrac{\cos z}{z^2-4\pi z+3\pi^2}$ 21. $\dfrac{1}{1-e^z}$

22. $\dfrac{e^z}{(z-\pi i)^5}$ 23. $\csc^2 z$

Evaluate the following integrals where C is the unit circle (counterclockwise).

24. $\displaystyle\int_C \frac{z+1}{2z+i}\, dz$ 25. $\displaystyle\int_C \frac{z^2+1}{z^2-2z}\, dz$ 26. $\displaystyle\int_C \frac{z^3-3z}{z^2+2z+\frac{3}{4}}\, dz$

27. $\displaystyle\int_C e^{1/z}\, dz$ 28. $\displaystyle\int_C z^2 e^{1/z}\, dz$ 29. $\displaystyle\int_C \frac{e^{1/z}}{z}\, dz$

30. $\displaystyle\int_C \cot z\, dz$ 31. $\displaystyle\int_C \frac{dz}{\sin z}$ 32. $\displaystyle\int_C \frac{dz}{\sinh z}$

33. $\displaystyle\int_C \frac{dz}{\cosh z}$ 34. $\displaystyle\int_C \frac{(z^2+1)e^{-z}}{\sin z}\, dz$ 35. $\displaystyle\int_C \frac{z^2-4}{(z-2)^2}\, dz$

11.14 THE RESIDUE THEOREM

So far we are in a position to evaluate contour integrals whose integrands have only one isolated singularity inside the contour of integration. We shall now see that our simple method may easily be extended to the case when the integrand has several isolated singularities inside the contour.

Residue theorem. *Let $f(z)$ be a single-valued function which is analytic inside a simple closed path C and on C, except for finitely many singular points $a_1, a_2, \cdots, a_m$ inside C. Then*

(1)
$$\int_C f(z)\, dz = 2\pi i \sum_{j=1}^{m} \operatorname*{Res}_{z=a_j} f(z),$$

the integral being taken in the counterclockwise sense around C.

Proof. We enclose each of the singular points a_j in a circle C_j with radius small enough that those m circles and C are all separated (Fig. 334). Then $f(z)$ is analytic in the multiply connected domain D bounded by C and $C_1, \cdots, C_m$ and on the entire boundary of D. From Cauchy's integral theorem it follows that

$$(2) \quad \int_C f(z)\, dz + \int_{C_1} f(z)\, dz + \int_{C_2} f(z)\, dz + \cdots + \int_{C_m} f(z)\, dz = 0,$$

the integral along C being taken in the counterclockwise sense and the other integrals in the clockwise sense (cf. p. 658). We now reverse the sense of integration along $C_1, \cdots, C_m$. Then the signs of the values of these integrals change, and we obtain from (2)

$$(3) \qquad \int_C f(z)\, dz = \int_{C_1} f(z)\, dz + \int_{C_2} f(z)\, dz + \cdots + \int_{C_m} f(z)\, dz,$$

all integrals now being taken in the counterclockwise sense. Since, by (3) in the last section,

$$\int_{C_j} f(z)\, dz = 2\pi i \operatorname*{Res}_{z=a_j} f(z),$$

formula (3) yields (1), and the theorem is proved.

This important theorem has various applications in connection with complex and real integrals. We shall first consider some complex integrals.

Example 1. The function $(4 - 3z)/(z^2 - z)$ is analytic except at the points 0 and 1 where it has simple poles; the residues are -4 and 1, respectively (cf. Ex. 2 in

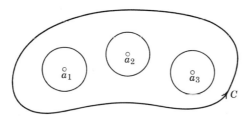

Fig. 334. Residue theorem.

the last section). Therefore,

$$\int_C \frac{4 - 3z}{z^2 - z}\, dz = 2\pi i(-4 + 1) = -6\pi i$$

for every simple closed path C which encloses the points 0 and 1, and

$$\int_C \frac{4 - 3z}{z^2 - z}\, dz = 2\pi i(-4) = -8\pi i$$

for any simple closed path C for which $z = 0$ lies inside C while $z = 1$ lies outside C, the integrations being taken in the counterclockwise sense.

Example 2. Integrate $1/(z^3 - 1)^2$ in the counterclockwise sense around the circle $|z - 1| = 1$. The function has poles of second order at $z = 1$, $z = e^{2\pi i/3}$, and $z = e^{-2\pi i/3}$. Only the pole at $z = 1$ lies inside C. Using (8), Sec. 11.13, thus obtain

$$\int_C \frac{dz}{(z^3 - 1)^2} = 2\pi i \operatorname*{Res}_{z=1} \frac{1}{(z^3 - 1)^2} = 2\pi i\left(-\frac{2}{9}\right) = -\frac{4\pi i}{9}.$$

Example 3. Integrate $1/(z - a)^m$ (m a positive integer) in the counterclockwise sense around any simple closed path C enclosing the point $z = a$. We find

$$\operatorname*{Res}_{z=a} \frac{1}{z - a} = 1 \quad \text{and} \quad \operatorname*{Res}_{z=a} \frac{1}{(z - a)^m} = 0 \quad (m = 2, 3, \cdots).$$

Therefore, the result is

$$\int_C \frac{dz}{(z - a)^m} = \begin{cases} 2\pi i & (m = 1) \\ 0 & (m = 2, 3, \cdots), \end{cases}$$

in agreement with Ex. 3 in Sec. 11.1.

PROBLEMS

Using the residue theorem, evaluate the following integrals where C is the unit circle (counterclockwise).

1. $\displaystyle\int_C \frac{dz}{1 + 4z^2}$ **2.** $\displaystyle\int_C \frac{z}{1 + 9z^2}\, dz$ **3.** $\displaystyle\int_C \frac{(z^2 + 2)^3}{2z^2 - z}\, dz$

4. $\displaystyle\int_C \frac{z^4 - 2z}{z^2 - 2z}\, dz$ **5.** $\displaystyle\int_C \frac{(2z + 1)^2}{4z^3 + z}\, dz$ **6.** $\displaystyle\int_C \frac{z^5 - 3z^3 + 1}{(2z + 1)(z^2 + 4)}\, dz$

7. $\displaystyle\int_C \tan \pi z\, dz$ **8.** $\displaystyle\int_C \cot \frac{z}{4}\, dz$ **9.** $\displaystyle\int_C \tan 2\pi z\, dz$

10. $\displaystyle\int_C \frac{e^z}{\sin z}\, dz$ **11.** $\displaystyle\int_C \frac{e^z}{\cos \pi z}\, dz$ **12.** $\displaystyle\int_C \frac{e^{z^2}}{\cos \pi z}\, dz$

13. $\displaystyle\int_C \frac{(z + 4)^3}{z^4 + 5z^3 + 6z^2}\, dz$ **14.** $\displaystyle\int_C \frac{z + 1}{z^4 - 2z^3}\, dz$ **15.** $\displaystyle\int_C \frac{10z^5 - 2z^4 + 2z - 1}{2z^6 - z^5}\, dz$

16. $\displaystyle\int_C \frac{27z^3 - 18z^2 - 5z + 2}{9z^4 - z^2}\, dz$ **17.** $\displaystyle\int_C \frac{4z^4 - 3z^3 + 17z^2 + 4}{z^3(z^2 + 4)}\, dz$

18. $\displaystyle\int_C \frac{6z^2 - 4z + 1}{(z - 2)(1 + 4z^2)}\, dz$ **19.** $\displaystyle\int_C \frac{\tan \pi z}{z^3}\, dz$

20. Evaluate $\displaystyle\int_C \frac{z + 1}{z(z - 1)(z - 2)}\, dz$ along different paths (counterclockwise), namely, (a) $|z| = \frac{1}{2}$, (b) $|z - 1| = \frac{1}{4}$, (c) $|z - 2| = \frac{1}{2}$, (d) $|z| = \frac{3}{2}$, (e) $|z| = 3$, (f) $|z - \frac{1}{2}| = \frac{1}{4}$, and (g) $|z - \frac{3}{2}| = 1$.

11.15   EVALUATION OF REAL INTEGRALS

The residue theorem yields a very elegant and simple method for evaluating certain classes of complicated real integrals, and we shall see that in many cases this method of integration can be made a routine matter.

A. Integrals of rational functions of $\cos \theta$ and $\sin \theta$.   We first consider integrals of the type

$$(1) \qquad\qquad I = \int_0^{2\pi} R(\cos \theta, \sin \theta)\, d\theta$$

where $R(\cos \theta, \sin \theta)$ is a real rational function of $\cos \theta$ and $\sin \theta$ finite on the interval $0 \leq \theta \leq 2\pi$.   Setting $e^{i\theta} = z$, we obtain

$$\cos \theta = \tfrac{1}{2}(e^{i\theta} + e^{-i\theta}) = \frac{1}{2}\left(z + \frac{1}{z}\right),$$

$$\sin \theta = \frac{1}{2i}(e^{i\theta} - e^{-i\theta}) = \frac{1}{2i}\left(z - \frac{1}{z}\right),$$

and we see that the integrand becomes a rational function of z, say, $f(z)$. As θ ranges from 0 to 2π, the variable z ranges around the unit circle, $|z| = 1$ in the counterclockwise sense.   Since $dz/d\theta = ie^{i\theta}$, we have $d\theta = dz/iz$, and the given integral takes the form

$$(2) \qquad\qquad I = \int_C f(z)\,\frac{dz}{iz},$$

the integration being taken in the counterclockwise sense around the unit circle.

Example 1.   Let p be a fixed real number in the interval $0 < p < 1$.   We consider

$$\int_0^{2\pi} \frac{d\theta}{1 - 2p \cos \theta + p^2} = \int_C \frac{dz/iz}{1 - 2p\,\frac{1}{2}\left(z + \frac{1}{z}\right) + p^2} = \int_C \frac{dz}{i(1 - pz)(z - p)}.$$

The integrand has simple poles at $z = 1/p > 1$ and $z = p < 1$. Only the last pole lies inside the unit circle C, and the residue is

$$\operatorname*{Res}_{z=p} \frac{1}{i(1 - pz)(z - p)} = \left[\frac{1}{i(1 - pz)} \right]_{z=p} = \frac{1}{i(1 - p^2)}.$$

The residue theorem yields

$$\int_0^{2\pi} \frac{d\theta}{1 - 2p \cos \theta + p^2} = 2\pi i \frac{1}{i(1 - p^2)} = \frac{2\pi}{1 - p^2} \qquad (0 < p < 1).$$

B. Improper integrals of rational functions. We consider real integrals of the type

$$(3) \qquad\qquad \int_{-\infty}^{\infty} f(x)\, dx.$$

Such an integral, for which the interval of integration is not finite, is called an **improper integral**, and it has the meaning

$$(4') \qquad \int_{-\infty}^{\infty} f(x)\, dx = \lim_{a \to -\infty} \int_a^0 f(x)\, dx + \lim_{b \to \infty} \int_0^b f(x)\, dx.$$

If both limits exist, we may couple the two independent passages to $-\infty$ and ∞, and write[12]

$$(4) \qquad\qquad \int_{-\infty}^{\infty} f(x)\, dx = \lim_{r \to \infty} \int_{-r}^{r} f(x)\, dx.$$

We assume that the function $f(x)$ in (3) is a real rational function whose denominator is different from zero for all real x and is of degree at least two units higher than the degree of the numerator. Then the limits in (4') exist, and we may start from (4). We consider the corresponding contour integral

$$(4^*) \qquad\qquad \int_C f(z)\, dz$$

around a path C, as shown in Fig. 335. Since $f(x)$ is rational, $f(z)$ has finitely many poles in the upper half-plane, and by choosing r large enough, C encloses all these poles. By the residue theorem we then obtain

$$\int_C f(z)\, dz = \int_S f(z)\, dz + \int_{-r}^{r} f(x)\, dx = 2\pi i \sum \operatorname{Res} f(z)$$

where the sum consists of all the residues of $f(z)$ at the points in the upper half-plane where $f(z)$ has a pole. From this we have

$$(5) \qquad \int_{-r}^{r} f(x)\, dx = 2\pi i \sum \operatorname{Res} f(z) - \int_S f(z)\, dz.$$

---

[12] The expression on the right side of (4) is called the *Cauchy principal value* of the integral; it may exist even if the limits in (4') do not exist. For instance,

$$\lim_{r \to \infty} \int_{-r}^{r} x\, dx = \lim_{r \to \infty} \left(\frac{r^2}{2} - \frac{r^2}{2} \right) = 0, \qquad \text{but} \qquad \lim_{b \to \infty} \int_0^b x\, dx = \infty.$$

We prove that, if $r \to \infty$, the value of the integral over the semicircle S approaches zero. Setting $z = re^{i\theta}$, the path S is represented by $r = const$, and as z ranges along S the variable θ ranges from 0 to π. Since the degree of the denominator of $f(z)$ is at least two units higher than the degree of the numerator, we have

$$|f(z)| < \frac{k}{|z|^2} \qquad\qquad (|z| = r > r_0)$$

for sufficiently large constants k and r_0. By applying (4) in Sec. 11.2 we thus obtain

$$\left| \int_S f(z)\, dz \right| < \frac{k}{r^2}\, \pi r = \frac{k\pi}{r} \qquad\qquad (r > r_0).$$

Hence, as r approaches infinity, the value of the integral over S approaches zero, and (4) and (5) yield the result

(6)
$$\int_{-\infty}^{\infty} f(x)\, dx = 2\pi i \sum \operatorname{Res} f(z),$$

the sum being extended over all the residues of $f(z)$ corresponding to poles of $f(z)$ in the upper half-plane.

Example 2.

$$\int_0^\infty \frac{dx}{1 + x^4} = \frac{\pi}{2\sqrt{2}}.$$

Indeed, $f(z) = 1/(1 + z^4)$ has four simple poles at the points

$$z_1 = e^{\pi i/4}, \qquad z_2 = e^{3\pi i/4}, \qquad z_3 = e^{-3\pi i/4}, \qquad z_4 = e^{-\pi i/4}.$$

The first two of these poles lie in the upper half-plane (Fig. 336). From (7) in Sec. 11.13 we find

$$\operatorname*{Res}_{z=z_1} f(z) = \left[\frac{1}{(1 + z^4)'} \right]_{z=z_1} = \left[\frac{1}{4z^3} \right]_{z=z_1} = \frac{1}{4} e^{-3\pi i/4} = -\frac{1}{4} e^{\pi i/4},$$

$$\operatorname*{Res}_{z=z_2} f(z) = \left[\frac{1}{4z^3} \right]_{z=z_2} = \frac{1}{4} e^{-9\pi i/4} = \frac{1}{4} e^{-\pi i/4}.$$

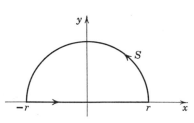

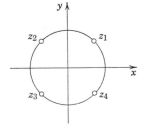

Fig. 335. Path of the contour integral in (4*).

Fig. 336. Example 2.

By (1) in Sec. 10.12 and (6) in the current section,

$$(7) \qquad \int_{-\infty}^{\infty} \frac{dx}{1 + x^4} = \frac{2\pi i}{4} (-e^{\pi i/4} + e^{-\pi i/4}) = \pi \sin \frac{\pi}{4} = \frac{\pi}{\sqrt{2}}.$$

Since $1/(1 + x^4)$ is an even function,

$$\int_0^{\infty} \frac{dx}{1 + x^4} = \frac{1}{2} \int_{-\infty}^{\infty} \frac{dx}{1 + x^4}.$$

From this and (7) the result follows.

C. Fourier integrals. Real integrals of the form

$$(8) \qquad \int_{-\infty}^{\infty} f(x) \cos sx \, dx \qquad \text{and} \qquad \int_{-\infty}^{\infty} f(x) \sin sx \, dx \qquad (s \text{ real})$$

occur in connection with the Fourier integral (cf. Sec. 8.10).

If $f(x)$ is a rational function satisfying the assumptions stated in connection with (3) then the integrals (8) may be evaluated in a similar way as the integrals (3).

In fact we may then consider the corresponding integral

$$\int_C f(z) e^{isz} \, dz \qquad (s \text{ real and positive})$$

over the contour C in Fig. 335, and instead of (6) we now obtain the formula

$$(9) \qquad \int_{-\infty}^{\infty} f(x) e^{isx} \, dx = 2\pi i \sum \text{Res} \left[f(z) e^{isz} \right] \qquad (s > 0)$$

where the sum consists of the residues of $f(z)e^{isz}$ at its poles in the upper half-plane. Equating the real and the imaginary parts on both sides of (9) we have

$$\int_{-\infty}^{\infty} f(x) \cos sx \, dx = -2\pi \sum \text{Im Res} \left[f(z) e^{isz} \right],$$

$$(10) \qquad\qquad\qquad\qquad\qquad\qquad\qquad\qquad (s > 0)$$

$$\int_{-\infty}^{\infty} f(x) \sin sx \, dx = 2\pi \sum \text{Re Res} \left[f(z) e^{isz} \right].$$

We remember that (6) was established by proving that the value of the integral over the semicircle S in Fig. 335 approaches zero as $r \to \infty$. To establish (9) we should now prove the same fact for our present contour integral. This can be done as follows. Since S lies in the upper half-plane $y \geq 0$ and $s > 0$ we obtain

$$|e^{isz}| = |e^{isx}| \, |e^{-sy}| = e^{-sy} \leq 1 \qquad (s > 0, y \geq 0).$$

From this we obtain the inequality

$$|f(z)e^{isz}| = |f(z)| \, |e^{isz}| \leq |f(z)| \qquad (s > 0, y \geq 0)$$

which reduces our present problem to that in Part B of this section. Continuing as before, we see that the value of the integral under consideration approaches zero as r approaches infinity, and (9) is now established.

Example 3.

$$\int_{-\infty}^{\infty} \frac{\cos sx}{k^2 + x^2}\, dx = \frac{\pi}{k} e^{-ks}, \qquad \int_{-\infty}^{\infty} \frac{\sin sx}{k^2 + x^2}\, dx = 0 \qquad (s > 0,\, k > 0).$$

In fact, $e^{isz}/(k^2 + z^2)$ has only one pole in the upper half-plane, namely, a simple pole at $z = ik$, and from (7) in Sec. 11.13 we obtain

$$\operatorname*{Res}_{z=ik} \frac{e^{isz}}{k^2 + z^2} = \left[\frac{e^{isz}}{2z}\right]_{z=ik} = \frac{e^{-ks}}{2ik}.$$

Therefore,

$$\int_{-\infty}^{\infty} \frac{e^{isx}}{k^2 + x^2}\, dx = 2\pi i \frac{e^{-ks}}{2ik} = \frac{\pi}{k} e^{-ks},$$

and this yields the above results (cf. also (14) in Sec. 8.10).

D. Other types of real improper integrals are definite integrals

$$(11) \qquad\qquad \int_A^B f(x)\, dx$$

whose integrand becomes infinite at a point a in the interval of integration, that is,

$$\lim_{x\to a} |f(x)| = \infty.$$

Then the integral (11) means

$$(12) \qquad \int_A^B f(x)\, dx = \lim_{\epsilon\to 0} \int_A^{a-\epsilon} f(x)\, dx + \lim_{\eta\to 0} \int_{a+\eta}^B f(x)\, dx$$

where both ϵ and η approach zero independently and through positive values. It might happen that neither of these limits exists when $\epsilon,\ \eta \to 0$ independently, but

$$(13) \qquad \lim_{\epsilon\to 0} \left[\int_A^{a-\epsilon} f(x)\, dx + \int_{a+\epsilon}^B f(x)\, dx\right]$$

exists; this is called the **Cauchy principal value** of the integral and is often written

$$\text{pr. v.} \int_A^B f(x)\, dx.$$

For example,

$$\text{pr. v.} \int_{-1}^{1} \frac{dx}{x^3} = \lim_{\epsilon\to 0} \left[\int_{-1}^{-\epsilon} \frac{dx}{x^3} + \int_{\epsilon}^{1} \frac{dx}{x^3}\right] = 0;$$

the principal value exists although the integral itself has no meaning. The whole situation is quite similar to that discussed in Part B of this section.

To evaluate improper integrals whose integrands have poles on the real axis, we use a path which avoids these singularities by following small semicircles with centers at the singular points; the procedure may be illustrated by the following example.

Example 4. Show that

$$\int_0^\infty \frac{\sin x}{x}\, dx = \frac{\pi}{2} \qquad\qquad \text{(cf. Sec. 8.10).}$$

We do not consider $\dfrac{\sin z}{z}$ since this function does not behave suitably at infinity.

We consider e^{iz}/z which has a simple pole at $z = 0$, and integrate around the contour shown in Fig. 337. Since e^{iz}/z is analytic inside and on C, it follows from Cauchy's integral theorem that

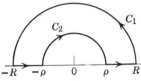

Fig. 337. Example 4.

$$(14) \qquad \int_C \frac{e^{iz}}{z}\, dz = 0.$$

We show that the value of the integral over the large semicircle C_1 approaches zero as R approaches infinity. Setting $z = Re^{i\theta}$ we have $dz = iRe^{i\theta}\, d\theta,\ dz/z = i\, d\theta$ and therefore

$$\left| \int_{C_1} \frac{e^{iz}}{z}\, dz \right| = \left| \int_0^\pi e^{iz} i\, d\theta \right| \leq \int_0^\pi |e^{iz}|\, d\theta \qquad (z = Re^{i\theta}).$$

In the integrand on the right,

$$|e^{iz}| = |e^{iR(\cos\theta + i\sin\theta)}| = |e^{iR\cos\theta}|\, |e^{-R\sin\theta}| = e^{-R\sin\theta}.$$

By inserting this and using the fact that in the interval of integration,

$$\sin(\pi - \theta) = \sin\theta$$

we obtain

$$\int_0^\pi |e^{iz}|\, d\theta = \int_0^\pi e^{-R\sin\theta}\, d\theta = 2\int_0^{\pi/2} e^{-R\sin\theta}\, d\theta$$

$$= 2\left[\int_0^\epsilon e^{-R\sin\theta}\, d\theta + \int_\epsilon^{\pi/2} e^{-R\sin\theta}\, d\theta \right]$$

where ϵ is any value between 0 and $\pi/2$. The absolute value of the integrand in the first and the last integral on the right is at most equal to 1 and $e^{-R\sin\epsilon}$, respectively, because the integrand is a monotone decreasing function of θ in the interval of integration. Consequently the whole expression on the right is smaller than

$$2\left[\int_0^\epsilon d\theta + e^{-R\sin\epsilon} \int_\epsilon^{\pi/2} d\theta \right] = 2\left[\epsilon + e^{-R\sin\epsilon}\left(\frac{\pi}{2} - \epsilon\right) \right] < 2\epsilon + \pi e^{-R\sin\epsilon}.$$

Altogether,

$$\left| \int_{C_1} \frac{e^{iz}}{z}\, dz \right| < 2\epsilon + \pi e^{-R\sin\epsilon}.$$

We first take ϵ arbitrarily small. Then, having fixed ϵ, the last term can be made as small as we please by choosing R sufficiently large. Hence, the value of the integral along C_1 approaches zero as R approaches infinity.

For the integral over the small semicircle C_2 in Fig. 337 we have

$$\int_{C_2} \frac{e^{iz}}{z}\, dz = \int_{C_2} \frac{dz}{z} + \int_{C_2} \frac{e^{iz}-1}{z}\, dz.$$

The first integral on the right has the value $-\pi i$. The integrand of the last integral is analytic at $z = 0$ and, therefore, bounded in absolute value as $\rho \to 0$. From this and (4) in Sec. 11.2 we conclude that the value of that integral approaches zero as $\rho \to 0$. From (14) we thus obtain

$$\text{pr. v.} \int_{-\infty}^{\infty} \frac{e^{ix}}{x}\, dx = -\lim_{\rho \to 0} \int_{C_2} \frac{e^{iz}}{z}\, dz = +\pi i,$$

and by taking the imaginary parts on both sides

(15) $$\text{pr. v.} \int_{-\infty}^{\infty} \frac{\sin x}{x}\, dx = \pi.$$

Now the integrand in (15) is not singular at $x = 0$. Furthermore, since for positive x the function $1/x$ decreases, the areas under the curve of the integrand between two consecutive positive zeros decrease in a monotone fashion, that is, the absolute values of the integrals

$$I_n = \int_{n\pi}^{n\pi + \pi} \frac{\sin x}{x}\, dx \qquad\qquad n = 0, 1, \cdots$$

form a monotone decreasing sequence $|I_1|, |I_2|, \cdots$, and $I_n \to 0$ as $n \to \infty$. Since these integrals have alternating sign, it follows from the Leibniz criterion in Sec. 10.5 that the series $I_0 + I_1 + I_2 + \cdots$ converges. Clearly, the sum of the series is the integral

$$\int_{0}^{\infty} \frac{\sin x}{x}\, dx = \lim_{b \to \infty} \int_{0}^{b} \frac{\sin x}{x}\, dx,$$

which therefore exists. Similarly, the integral from 0 to $-\infty$ exists. Hence we need not take the principal value in (15), and

$$\int_{-\infty}^{\infty} \frac{\sin x}{x}\, dx = \pi.$$

Since the integrand is an even function, the desired result follows.

E. Reduction of integrals to other known integrals. By means of contour integration, certain real improper integrals may be reduced to other real integrals whose values are known. This may be illustrated by

Example 5. We shall see in Sec. 14.2 that

(16) $$\int_{0}^{\infty} e^{-x^2}\, dx = \frac{\sqrt{\pi}}{2}.$$

Using this formula show that

(17) $$\int_0^\infty \cos (x^2) \, dx = \frac{1}{2} \sqrt{\frac{\pi}{2}}, \qquad \int_0^\infty \sin (x^2) \, dx = \frac{1}{2} \sqrt{\frac{\pi}{2}}.$$

(These integrals are of importance in connection with the so-called Fresnel integrals to be considered in Sec. 14.2.)

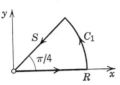

To prove (17), we integrate the function e^{-z^2} along the contour shown in Fig. 338. By Cauchy's integral theorem,

(18) $$\int_C e^{-z^2} \, dz = \int_0^R e^{-x^2} \, dx + \int_{C_1} e^{-z^2} \, dz$$

$$+ \int_S e^{-z^2} \, dz = 0.$$

Fig. 338. Path in Example 5.

We prove that the value of the integral along C_1 approaches zero as R approaches infinity. Setting $z = Re^{i\theta}$, we have

$$\left| \int_{C_1} e^{-z^2} \, dz \right| = \left| \int_0^{\pi/4} e^{-R^2(\cos 2\theta + i \sin 2\theta)} iRe^{i\theta} \, d\theta \right|$$

$$\leqq R \int_0^{\pi/4} e^{-R^2 \cos 2\theta} \, d\theta < R \int_0^{\pi/4} e^{-R^2(1 - 4\theta/\pi)} \, d\theta = \frac{\pi}{4R} (1 - e^{-R^2}),$$

where the last inequality follows from

$$\cos 2\theta \geqq 1 - \frac{4\theta}{\pi} \qquad \left(0 \leqq \theta \leqq \frac{\pi}{4} \right).$$

If $R \to \infty$, the expression on the right approaches zero.
    Since the segment S may be represented in the form

$$z(t) = te^{i\pi/4} \qquad (0 \leqq t \leqq R),$$

we have $z^2 = it^2$, $dz = e^{i\pi/4} \, dt$, and

$$\int_S e^{-z^2} \, dz = e^{i\pi/4} \int_R^0 e^{-it^2} \, dt.$$

From (18) and (16) we thus obtain

$$\int_0^\infty e^{-it^2} \, dt = \lim_{R \to \infty} \int_0^R e^{-it^2} \, dt = e^{-i\pi/4} \lim_{R \to \infty} \int_0^R e^{-x^2} \, dx = \tfrac{1}{2} \sqrt{\pi} \, e^{-i\pi/4}$$

$$= \frac{1}{2} \sqrt{\frac{\pi}{2}} (1 - i).$$

By separating the real and the imaginary parts, (17) follows.

PROBLEMS

Evaluate the following integrals.

1. $\displaystyle\int_0^{2\pi} \frac{d\theta}{5 - 3 \cos \theta}$

2. $\displaystyle\int_0^{2\pi} \frac{d\theta}{25 - 24 \cos \theta}$

3. $\displaystyle\int_0^{2\pi} \frac{d\theta}{2 + \cos\theta}$

4. $\displaystyle\int_0^{2\pi} \frac{\cos\theta}{17 - 8\cos\theta}\, d\theta$

5. $\displaystyle\int_0^{\pi} \frac{d\theta}{k + \cos\theta},\ k > 1$

6. $\displaystyle\int_0^{\pi} \frac{d\theta}{1 + k\cos\theta},\ k^2 < 1$

7. $\displaystyle\int_0^{2\pi} \frac{\cos\theta}{3 + \sin\theta}\, d\theta$

8. $\displaystyle\int_0^{2\pi} \frac{\sin^2\theta}{5 - 4\cos\theta}\, d\theta$

9. $\displaystyle\int_0^{2\pi} \frac{\cos^2\theta}{26 - 10\cos 2\theta}\, d\theta$

10. $\displaystyle\int_0^{2\pi} \frac{\cos^2 3\theta}{5 - 4\cos 2\theta}\, d\theta$

11. $\displaystyle\int_0^{2\pi} \frac{d\theta}{1 - 2k\sin\theta + k^2}\ (k^2 < 1)$

12. $\displaystyle\int_0^{2\pi} \frac{\cos\theta}{13 - 12\cos 2\theta}\, d\theta$

13. $\displaystyle\int_0^{\pi} \frac{\cos^2 3\theta}{5 - 4\cos 2\theta}\, d\theta$

14. $\displaystyle\int_{-\infty}^{\infty} \frac{dx}{1 + x^2}$

15. $\displaystyle\int_{-\infty}^{\infty} \frac{dx}{(1 + x^2)^3}$

16. $\displaystyle\int_0^{\infty} \frac{1 + x^2}{1 + x^4}\, dx$

17. $\displaystyle\int_{-\infty}^{\infty} \frac{x^3}{1 + x^8}\, dx$

18. $\displaystyle\int_{-\infty}^{\infty} \frac{dx}{x^4 + 16}$

19. $\displaystyle\int_{-\infty}^{\infty} \frac{dx}{1 + x^6}$

20. $\displaystyle\int_{-\infty}^{\infty} \frac{x}{(4 + x^2)^2}\, dx$

21. $\displaystyle\int_{-\infty}^{\infty} \frac{x}{(x^2 - 2x + 2)^2}\, dx$

22. $\displaystyle\int_{-\infty}^{\infty} \frac{dx}{(x^2 + 1)(x^2 + 9)}$

23. $\displaystyle\int_{-\infty}^{\infty} \frac{dx}{(x^2 + 1)(x^2 + 4)(x^2 + 9)}$

24. $\displaystyle\int_{-\infty}^{\infty} \frac{dx}{(x^2 + 1)(x^2 + 4)^2}$

25. $\displaystyle\int_{-\infty}^{\infty} \frac{\sin 2x}{x^2 + x + 1}\, dx$

26. $\displaystyle\int_{-\infty}^{\infty} \frac{\sin 3x}{1 + x^4}\, dx$

27. $\displaystyle\int_{-\infty}^{\infty} \frac{\cos x}{1 + x^4}\, dx$

28. $\displaystyle\int_{-\infty}^{\infty} \frac{\cos 4x}{(x^2 + 1)(x^2 + 4)}\, dx$

29. $\displaystyle\int_{-\infty}^{\infty} \frac{\cos x}{(x^2 + 1)^2}\, dx$

30. $\displaystyle\int_{-\infty}^{\infty} \frac{\cos 2x}{(x^2 + 4)^2}\, dx$

31. $\displaystyle\int_0^{\infty} e^{-x^2}\cos 2x\, dx$. *Hint:* integrate e^{-z^2} around the contour in Fig. 339, let $a \to \infty$, and use (16).

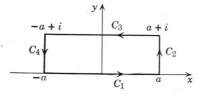

Fig. 339. Problem 31.

32. $\displaystyle\int_0^{\infty} e^{-x^2}\cos 2bx\, dx$. *Hint:* integrate e^{-z^2} around the boundary of the rectangle with vertices at a, $-a$, $a + ib$, $-a + ib$, let $a \to \infty$, and use (16).

33. pr. v. $\int_{-\infty}^{\infty} \dfrac{dx}{(x+1)(x^2+2)}$. *Hint:* integrate $f(z) = 1/[(z+1)(z^2+2)]$ along the contour in Fig. 340.

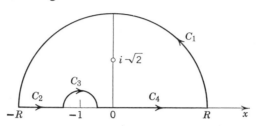

Fig. 340. Problem 33.

34. Derive (10) from (9).

35. Solve Prob. 14 by elementary methods. How can the answers to Probs. 17, 20, and 26 be found without any calculation?

chapter 12

CONFORMAL MAPPING

If a complex function $w = f(z)$ is defined in a domain D of the z-plane, then to each point in D there corresponds a point in the w-plane. In this way we obtain a correspondence or *mapping* between D and the range of values of $f(z)$ in the w-plane. We shall see that, if $f(z)$ is an analytic function, the mapping given by $f(z)$ is *conformal* (angle-preserving), except at points where the derivative $f'(z)$ is zero.

Conformal mapping is important in engineering mathematics, because it is a standard method for solving boundary value problems in potential theory by transforming a given complicated region into a simpler one.

We shall first define and explain the concept of mapping and then consider the mappings corresponding to elementary analytic functions. Applications will be included in this chapter as well as in the following one.

Prerequisites for this chapter: Chaps. 10 and 11.

References: Appendix 1, Part G.

Answers to problems: Appendix 2.

12.1 MAPPING

A continuous *real* function $y = f(x)$ of a real variable x can be exhibited graphically by plotting a curve in the Cartesian xy-plane; this curve is called the *graph* of the function. In the case of a *complex* function

(1) $$w = f(z) = u(x, y) + iv(x, y) \qquad (z = x + iy)$$

the situation is more complicated, since each of the complex variables w and z is represented geometrically by the points in the complex plane. This suggests the use of two separate complex planes for the two variables: one the z-plane, in which the point $z = x + iy$ is to be plotted, and the other the w-plane, in which the corresponding point $w = u + iv$ is to be plotted. In this way the function $w = f(z)$ defines a correspondence between points of these two planes. This correspondence is called a **mapping** (or *transformation*) of points in the z-plane onto points in the w-plane, and we say that $f(z)$ *maps* its domain of definition in the z-plane onto its range of values in the w-plane.

The point $w_0 = f(z_0)$ corresponding to a point z_0 is called the *image point* or **image** of the point z_0 with respect to the mapping defined by $f(z)$. If z moves along some curve C and $f(z)$ is continuous (not a constant), the corresponding point $w = f(z)$ will in general travel along a curve C^* in the w-plane. This curve is then called the *image* of the curve C, and the word "image" applies also to regions or other point sets.

We shall see that the properties of such mappings can be investigated by considering curves (and regions) in the z-plane and their images in the w-plane, and conversely. This will give more information about the functions than the consideration of individual points and their images.

Although two separate planes are used to represent w and z it is sometimes convenient to think of the mapping as effected in one plane and use such familiar terms as translation and rotation. For example, the mapping $w = z + 3$ may be interpreted as a translation which moves each point and configuration in the z-plane three units to the right.

To investigate the specific properties of a mapping defined by a given analytic function $w = u + iv = f(z)$, we may consider the images of the straight lines $x = const$ and $y = const$ in the w-plane. Another possibility is the study of the images of the circles $|z| = const$ and the straight lines through the origin. Conversely, we may consider the curves defined by $u(x, y) = const$ and $v(x, y) = const$ in the z-plane. These curves are called the *level curves* of u and v.

Example 1. Let us illustrate these various possibilities in the case of the mapping

(2) $$w = z^2.$$

In this case the simplest procedure is to set $z = re^{i\theta}$ and $w = Re^{i\phi}$. Then

$$R = r^2 \qquad \text{and} \qquad \phi = 2\theta.$$

We see that circles $r = r_0 = const$ are mapped onto circles $R = r_0^2 = const$, and

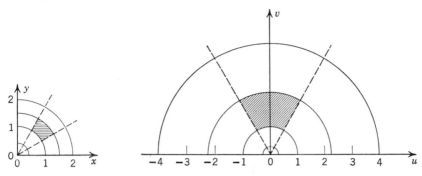

Fig. 341. Mapping $w = z^2$

rays $\theta = \theta_0 = const$ onto rays $\phi = 2\theta_0 = const$. In particular, the positive real axis ($\theta = 0$) is mapped onto the positive real axis in the w-plane, and the positive imaginary axis ($\theta = \pi/2$) in the z-plane is mapped onto the negative real axis in the w-plane. The angles at the origin are doubled under the mapping. The first quadrant $0 \leq \theta \leq \pi/2$ is mapped upon the entire upper half of the w-plane (Fig. 341).

In rectangular coordinates the transformation $w = z^2$ becomes

$$u + iv = x^2 - y^2 + 2xyi.$$

By separating the real and the imaginary parts we obtain

(3) $$u = x^2 - y^2, \qquad v = 2xy.$$

We see that the level curves of u and v are equilateral hyperbolas with the lines $y = \pm x$ and the coordinate axes for asymptotes. We observe that these curves are the orthogonal trajectories of each other (cf. Sec. 1.10.) In Fig. 342, the two shaded domains in the z-plane are both mapped onto the shaded rectangle in the w-plane. Clearly, every point $w \neq 0$ is the image of precisely two points in the z-plane.

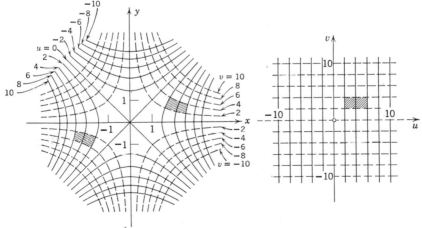

Fig. 342. Level curves of u and v in the case of the mapping $w = z^2$.

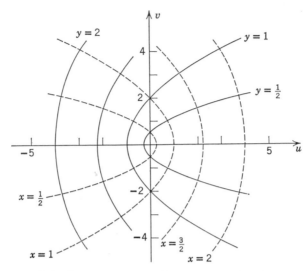

Fig. 343. Images of the lines $x = const$ and $y = const$ under the mapping $w = z^2$.

Finally, we may use (3) for determining the images of the straight lines $x = const$ and $y = const$. The line $x = c = const$ has the image

$$u = c^2 - y^2, \qquad v = 2cy.$$

We may eliminate y from these equations, finding

$$v^2 = 4c^2(c^2 - u).$$

This is a parabola with focus at the origin and opening to the left. Similarly, the image of a line $y = k = const$ can be represented in the form

$$v^2 = 4k^2(k^2 + u).$$

This is a parabola with focus at the origin and opening to the. right (Fig 343).

The other powers

(4) $$w = z^n, \qquad n = 3, 4, \cdots$$

may be considered in a similar fashion. Of course, the level curves, etc., are then represented by more complicated equations. The angular region $0 \leqq \arg z \leqq \pi/n$ is mapped onto the upper half of the w-plane (Fig. 344).

Fig. 344. Mapping defined by $w = z^n$.

PROBLEMS

Consider the mapping $w = u + iv = z^2$. Find and plot the images of the following curves.

1. $x = 1, 2, 3, 4$ **2.** $y = 1, 2, 3, 4$ **3.** $y = x, y = -x$
4. $y = x + 1$ **5.** $y = 1 - x$ **6.** $y^2 = x^2 + 1$

In each case plot the image of the given region under the mapping $w = z^2$.

7. $|\arg z| < \pi/4$ and $|z| > 1$ **8.** $1/2 < x < 3/2$ and $1/2 < y < 3/2$
9. $2 < |z| < 3$ and $|\arg z| < \pi/3$ **10.** $1/2 < |z| < 3/2$ and $\operatorname{Re} z \geq 0$

Determine the images of the curves $x = const$, $y = const$, $|z| = const$, $\arg z = const$, and the level curves of u and v in the case of the following functions.

11. $w = 2iz$ **12.** $w = (1 + i)z/\sqrt{2}$ **13.** $w = (2 + 2i)z$
14. $w = 1/z$ **15.** $w = iz^2$ **16.** $w = i/z$

17. Determine and plot the images of the angular region $0 \leq \arg z \leq \pi/8$ in the case of the mappings $w = iz$, $w = z^2$, $w = iz^2$, $w = -z^2$, $w = z^3$, $w = iz^3$, $w = z^2 + c$, $w = kz^2 + c$, and $w = 1/z$.

18. Determine and plot the images of the region $y > -1$ under the transformations $w = iz$, $w = (1 + i)z$, $w = (1 - i)z + 2i$, $w = 2iz - 4$, $w = z^2$, and $w = iz^2$.

19. Determine and plot the image of the region $x > 0$, $-\pi < y < \pi$ under the transformation $w = u + iv = i\left(\dfrac{z}{\pi} + 1\right)$.

20. Find an analytic function $w = u + iv = f(z)$ which maps the half plane $x \geq 0$ onto the region $u \geq 2$ such that $z = 0$ corresponds to $w = 2 + i$.

21. Find an analytic function $w = u + iv = f(z)$ which maps the angular region $0 < \arg z < \pi/3$ onto the region $u < 1$.

12.2 CONFORMAL MAPPING

We shall now consider the most important geometrical property of the mappings defined by analytic functions, namely, their conformality.

A mapping in the plane is said to be *angle-preserving*, or **conformal**, if it preserves angles between oriented curves in magnitude as well as in sense, that is, the images of any two intersecting oriented curves, taken with their corresponding orientation, make the same angle of intersection as the curves, both in magnitude and direction. Here the angle between two oriented curves is defined as the angle $\alpha\,(0 \leq \alpha \leq \pi)$ between their oriented tangents (Fig. 345).

We know that a smooth curve C (cf. Sec. 11.1) in the complex z-plane can be represented in the form

$$z = z(t) = x(t) + iy(t)$$

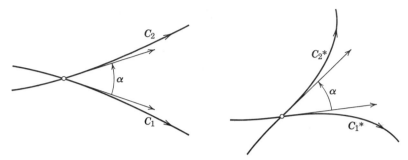

Fig. 345. Curves C_1 and C_2 and their respective images $C_1{}^*$ and $C_2{}^*$ under a conformal mapping.

where $z(t)$ is a differentiable function of t, and $\dot z(t) \neq 0$. The representation defines an orientation on C; the positive sense on C corresponds to the direction of increasing values of t.

The tangent to C at a point $z_0 = z(t_0)$ is defined as the limiting position of the straight line through z_0 and another point $z_1 = z(t_0 + \Delta t)$ as z_1 approaches z_0 along C, that is, as $\Delta t \to 0$. (Cf. also Sec. 5.13). Now the number $z_1 - z_0$ can be represented by the vector from z_0 to z_1 (Fig. 346), and the vector corresponding to $(z_1 - z_0)/\Delta t$, where $\Delta t > 0$, has the same direction as that vector. It follows that the vector corresponding to

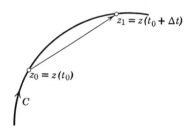

Fig. 346. Derivation of formula (1).

$$(1) \quad \dot z(t_0) = \frac{dz}{dt}\bigg|_{t_0} = \lim_{\Delta t \to 0} \frac{z_1 - z_0}{\Delta t}$$

$$= \lim_{\Delta t \to 0} \frac{z(t_0 + \Delta t) - z(t_0)}{\Delta t}$$

is tangent to C at z_0, and the angle between this vector and the positive x-axis is $\arg \dot z(t_0)$.

Consider now the mapping given by a nonconstant analytic function $w = f(z) = u(x, y) + iv(x, y)$ defined in a domain containing C. Then the image of C under this mapping is a curve C^* in the w-plane represented by

$$w = w(t) = f[z(t)].$$

The point $z_0 = z(t_0)$ corresponds to the point $w(t_0)$ of C^*, and $\dot w(t_0)$ represents a tangent vector to C^* at this point. Now by the chain rule,

$$(2) \qquad\qquad\qquad \frac{dw}{dt} = \frac{df}{dz}\frac{dz}{dt}.$$

Hence, if $f'(z_0) \neq 0$, we see that $\dot{w}(t_0) \neq 0$ and C^* has a unique tangent at $w(t_0)$, the angle between the tangent vector $\dot{w}(t_0)$ and the positive u-axis being arg $\dot{w}(t_0)$. Since the argument of a product equals the sum of the arguments of the factors, we have from (2)

$$\arg \dot{w}(t_0) = \arg f'(z_0) + \arg \dot{z}(t_0).$$

Thus under the mapping the directed tangent to C at z_0 is rotated through the angle

(3) $\arg \dot{w}(t_0) - \arg \dot{z}(t_0) = \arg f'(z_0),$

the angle between those two tangent vectors to C and C^*. Since the expression on the right is independent of the choice of C, we see that this angle is independent of C; that is, the transformation $w = f(z)$ rotates the tangents of all the curves through z_0 through the *same* angle $\arg f'(z_0)$. Hence, two curves through z_0 which form a certain angle at z_0 are mapped upon curves forming the same angle, in sense as well as in magnitude, at the image point w_0 of z_0. This proves the following basic result.

Theorem 1. *The mapping defined by an analytic function $f(z)$ is conformal, except at points where the derivative $f'(z)$ is zero.*

A point at which $f'(z) = 0$ is sometimes called a **critical point**. At such a point the mapping is not conformal, as may be illustrated by the following example.

Example 1. The mapping $w = z^2$ is conformal except at $z = 0$ where $w' = 2z = 0$. The conformality can be seen from the curves considered in the last section. At $z = 0$ the angles are doubled under the mapping, because each ray $\arg z = c = const$ transforms into a ray $\arg w = 2c$.

We further note that, by the definition of a derivative,

$$\lim_{z \to z_0} \left| \frac{f(z) - f(z_0)}{z - z_0} \right| = |f'(z_0)|.$$

Therefore, the mapping $w = f(z)$ magnifies the lengths of short lines by approximately the factor $|f'(z_0)|$. The image of a small figure *conforms* to the original figure in the sense that it has approximately the same shape. However, since $f'(z)$ varies from point to point, a *large* figure may have an image whose shape is quite different from that of the original figure.

We want to mention that, by the Cauchy-Riemann equations,

$$|f'(z)|^2 = \left| \frac{\partial u}{\partial x} + i \frac{\partial v}{\partial x} \right|^2 = \left(\frac{\partial u}{\partial x} \right)^2 + \left(\frac{\partial v}{\partial x} \right)^2 = \frac{\partial u}{\partial x} \frac{\partial v}{\partial y} - \frac{\partial u}{\partial y} \frac{\partial v}{\partial x},$$

that is,

$$(4) \qquad |f'(z)|^2 = \begin{vmatrix} \dfrac{\partial u}{\partial x} & \dfrac{\partial u}{\partial y} \\[2mm] \dfrac{\partial v}{\partial x} & \dfrac{\partial v}{\partial y} \end{vmatrix} = \frac{\partial(u, v)}{\partial(x, y)},$$

where the determinant is the so-called *Jacobian* (cf. Sec. 6.3) of the transformation $w = f(z)$, written in real form,

$$u = u(x, y), \qquad v = v(x, y).$$

Hence, the condition $f'(z_0) \neq 0$ implies that the Jacobian is not zero at z_0, and it can be shown (cf. Ref. [A8] in Appendix 1) that this is a sufficient condition for the mapping given by $w = f(z)$ to be one-to-one in a sufficiently small neighborhood of z_0. The important notion of a one-to-one mapping appearing in this connection is defined as follows.

A mapping of a region R onto a region R^* is said to be **one-to-one** if each point in R^* is the image of precisely one point in R, so that different points in R are mapped onto different points in R^*.

Example 2. The mapping $w = z^2$ is one-to-one in a sufficiently small neighborhood of any point $z \neq 0$. In a neighborhood of $z = 0$ it is not one-to-one. The full z-plane is mapped onto the w-plane so that each point $w \neq 0$ is the image of two points in the z-plane. For instance, the points $z = 1$ and $z = -1$ are both mapped onto $w = 1$, and, more generally, z_1 and $-z_1$ have the same image point $w = z_1^2$.

The practical importance of conformal mapping results from the fact that harmonic functions of two real variables (cf. Sec. 10.3) remain harmonic under a change of variables arising from a conformal transformation (Theorem 2, below). This has important consequences. Suppose that it is required to solve a **boundary value problem** in connection with a two-dimensional potential, that is, to find a solution of Laplace's equation (of two independent variables) in a given region D, assuming given values on the boundary of D. It may be possible to find a conformal mapping which transforms D into some simpler region D^* such as a circular disk or a half-plane. Then we may solve Laplace's equation subject to the transformed boundary conditions in D^*. The resulting solution when carried back to D by the inverse transformation will be the solution of the original problem. This powerful method is justified by the following theorem.

Theorem 2. *A harmonic function $h(x, y)$ remains harmonic under a change of the variables arising from a one-to-one conformal transformation $w = f(z)$.*

Proof. Let $h(x, y)$ be harmonic in a region D. Let $w = u + iv = f(z)$ be an analytic function which maps D one-to-one and conformally onto a region D^* in the w-plane. Since the mapping is one-to-one and conformal, $f'(z) \neq 0$ in D, and the inverse function $z = F(w)$ which maps D^* onto D exists. This function is analytic, that is, it has a derivative in D^*, namely

$$\frac{dF}{dw} = \frac{1}{df/dz}.$$

The proof of this formula is similar as in real calculus. Let $g(x, y)$ be a conjugate harmonic function of $h(x, y)$ (cf. Sec. 10.3). Then $h + ig$ is an analytic function of $z = x + iy$, say, $H(z)$. Since the function

$$z = F(w) = x(u, v) + iy(u, v)$$

is analytic, $H[F(w)]$ is an analytic function of $w = u + iv$. Its real part $h[x(u, v), y(u, v)]$ is thus a harmonic function of u and v in D^*, and the proof is complete.

When using the method of conformal mapping in potential theory the difficulty is to find an analytic function which maps a given region onto a simpler one. For this purpose one needs some experience and a detailed knowledge of the mapping properties of the elementary analytic functions. Therefore, we shall consider the most important elementary functions from this point of view.

PROBLEMS

1. Does the mapping $w = \bar{z} = x - iy$ preserve angles in size as well as in sense?

2. What is the reason that the level curves $u = const$ and $v = const$ of an analytic function $w = u + iv = f(z)$ intersect at right angles at each point at which $f'(z) \neq 0$?

3. Why do the images of the curves $|z| = const$ and arg $z = const$ under a mapping by an analytic function intersect at right angles?

Verify the formula (4) for the following functions.

4. $f(z) = u + iv = 4z^2 - z$ **5.** $f(z) = e^z$ **6.** $f(z) = \sin z$

7. Verify Theorem 2 for $h(x, y) = \ln (x^2 + y^2)$, $f(z) = 1/z$ $(z \neq 0)$.

Determine the points in the z-plane at which the mapping $w = f(z)$ fails to be conformal, where

8. $w = az^2 + bz + c$ **9.** $w = z + \dfrac{1}{z}$ $(z \neq 0)$

10. $w = z^2 + \dfrac{1}{z^2}$ $(z \neq 0)$ **11.** $w = e^{z^2}$

12.3 LINEAR TRANSFORMATIONS

We shall now consider an important class of conformal mappings, starting with the simplest types of transformations in this class.

The mapping

(1) $$w = z + b$$

may be regarded as a *translation* in the direction defined by the argument of b through a distance equal to $|b|$. If $b = 0$, then we obtain the **identity transformation**

$$w = z.$$

A transformation of the form

(2) $w = az$ $(a \neq 0)$

is a *rotation* through a fixed angle equal to arg a *combined with a uniform dilatation or contraction* such that $|w| = |a|\,|z|$. If a is real and positive,

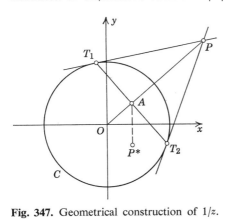

then (2) is a pure dilatation or contraction. If $|a| = 1$, then (2) is a pure rotation.

In the case of the transformation

(3) $w = \dfrac{1}{z}$

it is useful to introduce polar coordinates by setting

$$z = re^{i\theta} \qquad \text{and} \qquad w = Re^{i\phi}.$$

Then our mapping may be written

(3′) $R = \dfrac{1}{r}$, $\phi = -\theta$.

Fig. 347. Geometrical construction of $1/z$.

From this we see that a point $w = 1/z$ lies on the ray from the origin through $\bar{z}$, at the distance $1/|z|$ from the origin.

We mention that the image $w = 1/z$ of a given point z can be obtained by a simple geometric construction shown in Fig. 347. In this figure, P represents the given number z. The points T_1 and T_2 are those points of the unit circle C for which the tangents to C pass through P, and A is the point of intersection of the segments OP and T_1T_2. It can be shown by elementary methods that if OP has the length l, then OA has the length $1/l$. We say that A is obtained from P by **inversion** *with respect to the unit circle* (or "reflection" in the unit circle). Obviously, A represents the complex number $1/\bar{z}$. Hence, the point P^*, representing $w = 1/z$, is obtained by reflecting A in the real axis. This means that *the transformation $w = 1/z$ is an inversion with respect to the unit circle combined with a reflection in the real axis.*

The function $w = 1/z$ maps the interior of the unit circle $|z| = 1$ onto the exterior of the unit circle $|w| = 1$ and the exterior of $|z| = 1$ onto the interior of $|w| = 1$. As in Sec. 11.11 we let the point $z = 0$ correspond to the improper point $w = \infty$, and the improper point $z = \infty$ to the point $w = 0$.

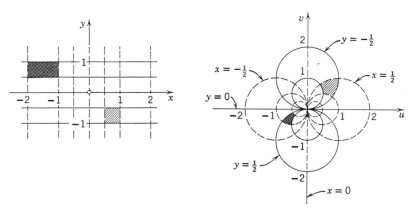

Fig. 348. Mapping $w = 1/z$.

A **fixed point** of a mapping $w = f(z)$ is a point whose image is the same complex number; that is, the fixed points are obtained from

$$w = f(z) = z.$$

The mapping $w = 1/z$ has the fixed points $z = \pm 1$, since these points are the solutions of the equation $z = 1/z$.

A transformation of the form

(4)
$$w = \frac{az + b}{cz + d} \qquad (ad - bc \neq 0)$$

is called a *linear fractional transformation*, or briefly, a **linear transformation** or *linear mapping*. The constants a, b, c, and d in (4) are real or complex numbers.

The derivative is

$$w' = \frac{a(cz + d) - c(az + b)}{(cz + d)^2} = \frac{ad - bc}{(cz + d)^2},$$

and this shows that the condition $ad - bc \neq 0$ implies $w' \neq 0$, which entails conformality, while $ad - bc = 0$ leads to the uninteresting case $w' \equiv 0$ or $w = const$, which will be excluded in our further consideration.

From (4) we see that to each z for which $cz + d \neq 0$ there corresponds precisely one complex number w. If z is such that $cz + d = 0$, then we let $w = \infty$ be the corresponding image point, that is, we consider the mapping in the extended complex plane (cf. Sec. 11.11).

The inverse mapping of (4) is obtained by solving (4) for z, finding

(5)
$$z = \frac{-dw + b}{cw - a}.$$

It follows that every mapping (4) is a one-to-one conformal mapping of the extended z-plane onto the extended w-plane; we say, that *every linear transformation* (4) *maps "the extended plane in a one-to-one and conformal manner onto itself."* It can be shown that, conversely, every one-to-one conformal mapping of the plane onto itself is a linear transformation; cf. Ref. [G2] in Appendix 1. This property is the reason for the importance of linear mappings in various applications.

The fixed points of the mapping (4) are obtained from the equation

$$z = \frac{az + b}{cz + d}$$

or

(6) $$cz^2 - (a - d)z - b = 0.$$

This is a quadratic equation in z whose coefficients all vanish if, and only if, the mapping is the identity (in this case, $a = d \neq 0, b = c = 0$). Hence we obtain the following result.

Theorem 1. *A linear transformation, not the identity, has at most two fixed points. If a linear transformation is known to have three or more fixed points, it must be the identity.*

Linear transformations have the following interesting property.

Theorem 2. *Any linear transformation* (4) *maps the totality of circles and straight lines in the z-plane onto the totality of circles and straight lines in the w-plane.*

Proof. Let $w = u + iv$. Any straight line or circle in the w-plane can be represented in the form

$$A(u^2 + v^2) + B_1 u + B_2 v + C = 0$$

where A, B_1, B_2, and C are real constants. Since

$$u^2 + v^2 = |w|^2 = w\bar{w}, \qquad u = \frac{1}{2}(w + \bar{w}), \qquad v = \frac{1}{2i}(w - \bar{w})$$

we may write this representation in the form

(7) $$Aw\bar{w} + Bw + \bar{B}\bar{w} + C = 0$$

where $B = \frac{1}{2}(B_1 - iB_2)$. If we insert w and $\bar{w}$ according to (4) and multiply the resulting equation by $(cz + d)\overline{(cz + d)}$, we obtain

$$A(az + b)\overline{(az + b)} + B(az + b)\overline{(cz + d)}$$

$$+ \bar{B}\overline{(az + b)}(cz + d) + C(cz + d)\overline{(cz + d)} = 0.$$

By performing the multiplication this equation becomes

(8) $$\alpha z \bar{z} + \beta z + \bar{\beta} \bar{z} + \gamma = 0$$

where the coefficients are given by the formulas

$$\alpha = A\,|a|^2 + 2\mathrm{Re}\,(Ba\bar{c}) + C\,|c|^2$$
$$\beta = Aa\bar{b} + Ba\bar{d} + \bar{B}\bar{b}c + Cc\bar{d}$$
$$\gamma = A\,|b|^2 + 2\mathrm{Re}\,(Bb\bar{d}) + C\,|d|^2.$$

Since α and γ are real, (8) represents a circle or straight line in the z-plane. Conversely, starting from (8) and using the inverse transformation (5), we obtain (7), and the proof is complete.

The calculations in the proof show that a straight line may very well be mapped onto a circle, but never onto any other curve. For example, $w = 1/z$ maps a straight line or a circle through the origin onto a straight line in the w-plane, while a straight line or circle not passing through $z = 0$ is mapped onto a circle in the w-plane.

Obviously, the mappings (1), (2), and (3) are special cases of (4). Conversely, *any mapping* (4) *is a composite of mappings of the forms* (1), (2), *and* (3). In fact, if $c = 0$, this is immediately clear. If $c \neq 0$, then we can write (4) in the form

(9) $$w = K\,\frac{1}{cz + d} + \frac{a}{c} \qquad \text{where} \qquad K = -\frac{ad - bc}{c}.$$

Setting

$$w_1 = cz, \qquad w_2 = w_1 + d, \qquad w_3 = \frac{1}{w_2}, \qquad w_4 = Kw_3,$$

we have $w = w_4 + a/c$, and the statement is proved.

Special linear transformations of practical importance and further general properties of linear transformations will be considered in the following section.

PROBLEMS

1. Prove that $w = 1/z$ maps circles onto circles (straight lines regarded as degenerate cases of circles).

Find the images of the following circles and straight lines under the mapping $w = 1/z$.

2. $|z - 2| = 1$ **3.** $|z - 2i| = 1$ **4.** $x = 1$
5. $y = x + 1$ **6.** $|z - 1| = 1$ **7.** $|z - 2i| = 2$

8. Find $1/(3 + 4i)$ from $3 + 4i$ by means of the geometric construction explained in connection with the transformation $w = 1/z$.

Find the images of the following regions under the mapping $w = 1/z$.

9. $1 < x < 2$ **10.** $-2 < x < -1,\; -1 < y < 1$

Determine the fixed points of the following mappings.

11. $w = z^2$ **12.** $w = z^3$ **13.** $w = z^{n+1}$ ($n > 0$, integral)

14. $w = iz^2$ **15.** $w = \dfrac{3z + 2}{z - 1}$ **16.** $w = \dfrac{3z - 1}{z + 3}$

Find a linear mapping whose fixed points are:

17. $-2, 2$ **18.** $-i, i$ **19.** 1 **20.** i

21. Find all linear mappings whose fixed points are -1 and 1.

22. Show that a mapping (4) with $c = 0$ can be represented as a composite of simpler mappings of the types (1), (2), and (3).

23. Represent $w = \dfrac{z + i}{iz + 4}$ as a composite of mappings of the types (1), (2), and (3).

12.4 SPECIAL LINEAR TRANSFORMATIONS

In applying conformal mapping to practical problems it is often required to map the interior of the unit circle or a half-plane onto itself, or the interior of the unit circle onto a half-plane. We want to show that this can be done by linear transformations, and these transformations can be found in a systematic way.

We start with the following *general remark* about linear transformations

$$(1) \qquad w = \frac{az + b}{cz + d} \qquad (ad - bc \neq 0).$$

If $z = \infty$, the right-hand side of (1) becomes $(a \cdot \infty + b)/(c \cdot \infty + d)$, which is a meaningless expression. Now, from the inverse (5) in the last section we see that $w = a/c$ corresponds to $z = \infty$, and this suggests to assign the meaning a/c to that expression.

The linear transformation (1) depends on three essential constants, namely, the ratios of any three of the constants a, b, c, d to the fourth. The requirement that three distinct points in the z-plane have specified images in the w-plane leads to a unique linear transformation, as follows.

Theorem 1. *Three given distinct points z_1, z_2, z_3 can always be mapped onto three prescribed distinct points w_1, w_2, w_3 by one, and only one, linear mapping $w = f(z)$. This mapping is given implicitly by the equation*

$$(2) \qquad \frac{w - w_1}{w - w_3} : \frac{w_2 - w_1}{w_2 - w_3} = \frac{z - z_1}{z - z_3} : \frac{z_2 - z_1}{z_2 - z_3}.$$

(If one of these points is the point ∞, the quotient of those two differences which contain this point is to be replaced by 1).

Proof. Equation (2) is of the form $F(w) = G(z)$ where F and G denote fractional linear functions of the respective variables. From this we obtain $w = f(z) = F^{-1}[G(z)]$ where F^{-1} denotes the inverse function of F. Since the inverse of a linear transformation and the composite of linear transformations are linear transformations (cf. Prob. 1 at the end of the section), $w = f(z)$ is a linear transformation. Furthermore, from (2) we see that

$$F(w_1) = 0, \qquad F(w_2) = 1, \qquad F(w_3) = \infty,$$

$$G(z_1) = 0, \qquad G(z_2) = 1, \qquad G(z_3) = \infty.$$

Hence, $w_1 = f(z_1)$, $w_2 = f(z_2)$, $w_3 = f(z_3)$. This proves the existence of a linear transformation $w = f(z)$ which maps z_1, z_2, z_3 onto w_1, w_2, w_3, respectively.

We prove that $w = f(z)$ is uniquely determined. Suppose that $w = g(z)$ is another linear mapping which maps z_1, z_2, z_3 onto w_1, w_2, w_3, respectively. Then its inverse $g^{-1}(w)$ maps w_1 onto z_1, w_2 onto z_2, and w_3 onto z_3. Consequently, the composite mapping $H = g^{-1}[f(z)]$ maps each of the points z_1, z_2, and z_3 onto itself; that is, it has three distinct fixed points z_1, z_2, z_3. From Theorem 1 in the last section it follows that H is the identity mapping, and, therefore, $g(z) \equiv f(z)$.

The last statement of the theorem follows from the general remark at the beginning of this section. This completes the proof.

We shall now consider *linear mappings of the upper half plane $y \geqq 0$ onto the unit disk $|w| \leqq 1$*. Clearly the x-axis, which is the boundary of that half-plane, must correspond to the unit circle $|w| = 1$ of that disk, and we have to make sure that the upper half-plane is mapped onto the interior but not onto the exterior of that unit circle.

Example 1. Find the linear transformation (1) which maps $z_1 = -1$, $z_2 = 0$, $z_3 = 1$ onto $w_1 = -1$, $w_2 = -i$, $w_3 = 1$, respectively. From (2) we obtain

$$\frac{w - (-1)}{w - 1} : \frac{-i - (-1)}{-i - 1} = \frac{z - (-1)}{z - 1} : \frac{0 - (-1)}{0 - 1}$$

or

(3)
$$w = \frac{z - i}{-iz + 1}.$$

Let us show that we can determine the specific properties of such a mapping without difficult calculations. The images of the lines $x = const$ and $y = const$ are obtained as follows. The point $z = i$ corresponds to $w = 0$, and $z = \infty$ corresponds to $w = i$. If $z = iy$ then $w = i(y - 1)/(y + 1)$; that is, the positive imaginary axis is mapped onto the segment $u = 0$, $-1 \leqq v \leqq 1$. Since the mapping is conformal and straight lines are mapped onto circles or straight lines, the lines $y = const$ are mapped onto circles through the image of $z = \infty$, that is, onto circles through $w = i$ and with center on the v-axis. It follows that, for the same reasons, the lines $x = const$ are mapped onto circles which are orthogonal

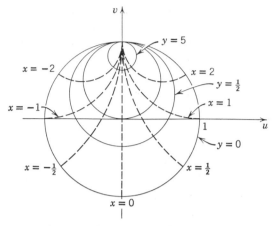

Fig. 349. Linear mapping in Example 1.

to the image circles of the lines $y = const$ (Fig. 349). The lower half plane corresponds to the exterior of the unit circle $|w| = 1$.

Example 2. Determine the linear transformation which maps $z_1 = 0$, $z_2 = 1$, $z_3 = \infty$ onto $w_1 = i$, $w_2 = -1$, $w_3 = -i$, respectively.

From (2) we find that the desired mapping is

$$(4) \qquad\qquad w = -i\,\frac{z - i}{z + i}\,;$$

in this case we have to replace the quotient $(1 - \infty)/(z - \infty)$, which first occurs, by 1.

We shall now consider *linear mappings of the upper half-plane $y \geq 0$ onto the upper half-plane $v \geq 0$.* In this case the x-axis must be mapped onto the u-axis.

Example 3. Find the linear transformation which maps the points $z_1 = -2$, $z_2 = 0$, $z_3 = 2$ onto the points $w_1 = \infty$, $w_2 = \frac{1}{4}$, $w_3 = \frac{3}{8}$, respectively. From (2) we obtain

$$(5) \qquad\qquad w = \frac{z + 1}{2z + 4}\,.$$

We leave the discussion of the properties of this mapping to the reader (Prob. 15).

As another important class of linear mappings let us consider the *transformations which map the unit disk in the z-plane onto the disk in the w-plane.* We may readily verify that the function

$$(6) \qquad\qquad w = \frac{z - z_0}{cz - 1}\,, \qquad c = \bar{z}_0, \qquad |z_0| < 1$$

belongs to this class and maps the point z_0 onto $w = 0$ (cf. Prob. 17).

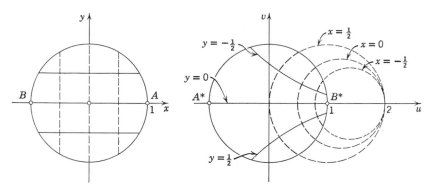

Fig. 350. Mapping in Example 4.

Example 4. Let $z_0 = \frac{1}{2}$. Then by (6),

$$w(z) = \frac{2z - 1}{z - 2} \, .$$

The real axes correspond to each other; in particular,

$$w(-1) = 1, \qquad w(0) = \tfrac{1}{2}, \qquad w(1) = -1.$$

Since the mapping is conformal and straight lines are mapped onto circles or straight lines and $w(\infty) = 2$, the images of the lines $x = const$ are circles through $w = 2$ with centers on the u-axis; the lines $y = const$ are mapped onto circles which are orthogonal to the aforementioned circles (Fig. 350).

By combining linear transformations and transformations of the form $w = z^n$ ($n > 1$ and integral) we may obtain *mappings of angular regions onto the unit disk*.

Example 5. Map the angular region D: $-\pi/6 \leq \arg z \leq \pi/6$ onto the unit disk $|w| \leq 1$. We may proceed as follows. The mapping $t = z^3$ maps D onto the right half of the t-plane. Then we may apply a linear transformation which maps this half-plane onto the unit disk, for example, the transformation

$$w = i \frac{t - 1}{t + 1} \, .$$

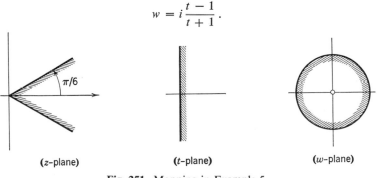

(z-plane)   (t-plane)   (w-plane)

Fig. 351. Mapping in Example 5.

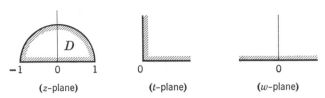

Fig. 352. Mapping in Example 6.

By inserting $t = z^3$ into this mapping we find

$$w = i\,\frac{z^3 - 1}{z^3 + 1} \; ;$$

this mapping has the required properties (Fig. 351).

Example 6. Find an analytic function which maps the region D defined by $|z| \leq 1$, $\operatorname{Im} z \geq 0$ onto the upper half of the w-plane such that $z = -1$ and $z = 0$ correspond to $w = 0$ and $w = 1$, respectively. We first apply a linear transformation $t = t(z)$ which maps the unit disk $|z| \leq 1$ onto the right half of the t-plane so that D is mapped onto the first quadrant; this can be done by requiring that $z_1 = -1$, $z_2 = 0$, $z_3 = 1$ correspond to $t_1 = 0$, $t_2 = 1$, $t_3 = \infty$, respectively. The mapping is

$$t = -\frac{z + 1}{z - 1}\,.$$

The transformation $w = t^2$ maps the first quadrant of the t-plane onto the upper half of the w-plane; the points $t = 0$ and $t = 1$ are fixed points under this transformation. The composed mapping

$$w = \left(\frac{z + 1}{z - 1}\right)^2$$

has the required properties.

PROBLEMS

1. Show that the composite of two linear transformations is a linear transformation.

Find the linear mapping $w = w(z)$ which maps:

2. $0, 1, 2$ onto $2, 5, 8$, respectively

3. $0, 2, 4$ onto $-1, 3, \frac{5}{3}$, respectively

4. $-1, 0, 1$ onto $-(3 - i)/5$, $-\frac{3}{4}$, $-1 - i/3$, respectively

5. $0, 1, 2$ onto ∞, $1 + i/2$, $\frac{3}{4} + i/2$, respectively

6. $\infty, 1, -1$ onto $1, (3 + 2i)/5$, $3 - 2i$, respectively

7. $1, i, -1$ onto $i, 1, -i$, respectively

8. $\infty, 0, -1$ onto $1, 0, (1 + i)/2$, respectively

9. $0, 2, 4$ onto ∞, $-5i$, $-4i$, respectively

10. $i, -i, \infty$ onto $1 - 2i$, $(1 + 2i)/3$, $\frac{1}{2}$, respectively

11. Find the inverse of (3). Show that (3) maps the lines $x = c = const$ onto circles with centers on the line $v = 1$.

12. Derive (4) from (2). Graph the curves corresponding to the lines $u = const$ and $v = const$.

13. Find the inverse of (4) and graph the images of the lines $x = const$ and $y = const$.

14. Find and graph the images of the lines $x = -3, -2, \cdots, 2, 3$ and $y = -3, -2, \cdots, 2, 3$, under the mapping (5).

15. Derive (5) from (2). Find the inverse of (5) and graph the curves corresponding to $u = const$ and $v = const$.

16. Find a linear mapping which maps $|z| \leq 1$ onto $|w| \leq 1$ such that $z = i/4$ is mapped onto $w = 0$ and graph the images of the lines $x = const$ and $y = const$ under this mapping.

17. Prove the statement involving (6).

18. Find an analytic function which maps the second quadrant of the z-plane onto the interior of the unit circle in the w-plane.

19. Find an analytic function $w = f(z)$ which maps the region $2 \leq y \leq x + 1$ onto the unit disk $|w| \leq 1$.

20. Find an analytic function $w = f(z)$ which maps the region $0 \leq \arg z \leq \pi/4$ onto the unit disk $|w| \leq 1$.

12.5 MAPPING BY OTHER ELEMENTARY FUNCTIONS

We shall now consider the mapping properties of some further important special functions.

The **exponential function** (Sec. 10.11)

$$(1) \qquad\qquad w = e^z$$

defines a mapping which is conformal everywhere, because its derivative is different from zero at any point. If we set $w = Re^{i\phi}$, then

$$Re^{i\phi} = e^{x+iy} = e^x e^{iy},$$

and (1) can be written in the form

$$(2) \qquad\qquad R = e^x, \qquad \phi = y.$$

From this we see that the lines $x = a = const$ are mapped onto the circles $R = e^a$, and the lines $y = c$ are mapped onto the rays $\phi = c$. Since $e^z \neq 0$ for all z, the point $w = 0$ is not an image of any point z. A rectangular region, say, $a \leq x \leq b$, $c \leq y \leq d$ is mapped onto the region

$$e^a \leq R \leq e^b, \qquad c \leq \phi \leq d$$

bounded by portions of rays and circles (Fig. 353).

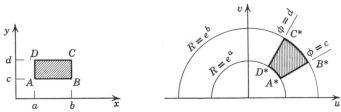

Fig. 353. Mapping by $w = e^z$.

The fundamental strip $-\pi < y \leqq \pi$ is mapped upon the full w-plane (cut along the negative real axis). More generally, every horizontal strip bounded by two lines $y = c$ and $y = c + 2\pi$ is mapped upon the full w-plane. This illustrates the fact that e^z is periodic with period $2\pi i$.

The horizontal strip $0 \leqq y \leqq \pi$ is mapped onto the upper half of the w-plane. The boundary $y = 0$ is mapped onto the positive half of the u-axis, and the line $y = \pi$ onto the negative half of the u-axis, as follows from (2). The segment from 0 to πi is mapped onto the semicircle $|w| = 1, v \geqq 0$. The left half ($x \leqq 0$) of our strip is mapped onto the region $|w| \leqq 1, v \geqq 0$, while the right half ($x \geqq 0$) of the strip is mapped onto the exterior of that semicircle $|w| = 1$ in the upper half of the w-plane (Fig. 354).

Since the **logarithmic function** $w = u + iv = \ln z$ is the inverse of the exponential function, the properties of the corresponding conformal mapping can be easily obtained from those of the exponential function by interchanging the roles of the z and the w planes in the preceding considerations. The principal value $w = \operatorname{Ln} z$ thus maps the z-plane (cut along the negative real axis) onto the horizontal strip $-\pi < v \leqq \pi$ of the w-plane. Further details of the mapping will be discussed in Ex. 2 of the next section.

The **sine function** (Sec. 10.12)

(3) $w = u + iv = \sin z = \sin x \cosh y + i \cos x \sinh y$

where

(4) $u = \sin x \cosh y, \qquad v = \cos x \sinh y,$

is periodic. Hence, the mapping (4) is certainly not one-to-one if we consider it in the full xy-plane. We restrict our consideration to the infinite

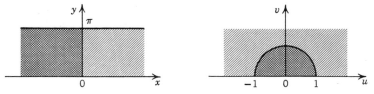

Fig. 354. Mapping by $w = e^z$.

strip D defined by $-\pi/2 \leq x \leq \pi/2$. Since $f'(z) = \cos z$ is zero at $z = \pm\pi/2$, the mapping is not conformal at these two points. From (4) we see that the boundary of D is mapped onto the u-axis. The segment $-\pi/2 \leq x \leq \pi/2$ of the x-axis maps onto the segment $-1 \leq u \leq 1$ of the u-axis, the line $x = -\pi/2$ maps onto $u \leq -1$, $v = 0$, and the line $x = \pi/2$ maps onto $u \geq 1$, $v = 0$. The line segment $y = c > 0$, $-\pi/2 \leq x \leq \pi/2$ maps onto the semi-ellipse

$$u = \cosh c \sin x, \qquad v = \sinh c \cos x$$

or

(5)
$$\frac{u^2}{\cosh^2 c} + \frac{v^2}{\sinh^2 c} = 1$$

in the upper half of the w-plane. The line segment $y = -c$ $(c > 0)$, $-\pi/2 \leq x \leq \pi/2$ maps onto the lower half of the ellipse (5). The foci of the ellipse are at $w = \pm 1$, and we see that they are independent of c. Consequently, if we let c vary, we obtain a family of confocal ellipses. The rectangular region D defined by $-\pi/2 < x < \pi/2$, $-c < y < c$ is thus mapped onto the interior of the ellipse (5); but note that the image of the boundary consists of the ellipse and the two segments of the x-axis, as shown in Fig. 355 (where $c = 1$). The image points of points on the vertical parts of the boundary coincide in pairs. In particular, $B^* = F^*$ and $C^* = E^*$.

Similarly, the rectangle $-\pi < x < \pi$, $c < y < d$ maps onto an elliptic ring cut along the negative v-axis (Fig. 356). The lines

$$x = const \qquad (-\pi/2 < x < \pi/2)$$

map onto confocal hyperbolas which intersect those ellipses at right angles, and the y-axis maps onto the v-axis.

The **cosine function**

(6)
$$w = \cos z = \sin\left(z + \frac{\pi}{2}\right)$$

defines the same mapping as $\sin z$, preceded by a translation to the right through $\pi/2$ units.

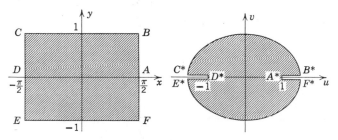

Fig. 355. Mapping by $w = \sin z$.

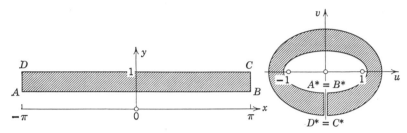

Fig. 356. Mapping by $w = \sin z$.

The **hyperbolic function**

(7) $$w = \sinh z = -i \sin (iz)$$

defines a transformation which is a rotation $t = iz$ followed by the mapping $p = \sin t$ and another rotation $w = -ip$.

Similarly, the transformation

(8) $$w = \cosh z = \cos (iz)$$

is a rotation $t = iz$ followed by the mapping $w = \cos t$.

Example 1. Find the image of the semi-infinite strip $x \geq 0$, $0 \leq y \leq \pi$ (Fig. 357) under the mapping (8). We set $w = u + iv$. Since $\cosh 0 = 1$ the point $z = 0$ is mapped onto $w = 1$. For real $z = x \geq 0$, $\cosh z$ is real and increases monotone from 1 as x increases. Hence the positive x-axis is mapped onto the portion $u \geq 1$ of the u-axis. For purely imaginary $z = iy$, we have

$$\cosh iy = \cos y.$$

It follows that the left boundary of the strip is mapped onto the segment $1 \geq u \geq -1$ of the u-axis, the point $z = \pi i$ corresponding to

$$w = \cosh i\pi = \cos \pi = -1.$$

On the upper boundary of the strip, $y = \pi$, and since $\sin \pi = 0$, $\cos \pi = -1$, it follows that this part of the boundary is mapped onto the portion $u \leq -1$ of the u-axis. Hence the boundary of the strip is mapped onto the u-axis. It is not difficult to see that the interior of the strip is mapped onto the upper half of the w-plane, and the mapping is one-to-one.

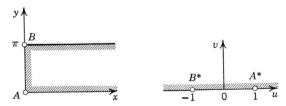

Fig. 357. Mapping in Example 1.

Example 2. Find the temperature $T(x, y)$ in the strip considered in Ex. 1, if the temperature on the boundary is

$$T = T_0 \text{ on the segment from } 0 \text{ to } \pi i,$$

$$T = 0 \text{ on the upper and lower boundaries.}$$

Since T does not depend on time ("steady state temperature distribution"), the heat equation reduces to Laplace's equation (cf. Sec. 9.11)

$$\nabla^2 T = \frac{\partial^2 T}{\partial x^2} + \frac{\partial^2 T}{\partial y^2} = 0,$$

and we have to find a solution of this equation satisfying those boundary conditions.

To solve this problem we map the strip by means of (8) onto the upper half of the w-plane. Since the segment $0 \leq y \leq \pi i$ of the y-axis is mapped onto the segment $-1 \leq u \leq 1$ of the u-axis, the boundary conditions in the w-plane are (Fig. 358):

$$T = T_0 \text{ on the segment from } -1 \text{ to } 1,$$

$$T = 0 \text{ on the other parts of the } u\text{-axis.}$$

The real and imaginary parts of analytic functions are solutions of Laplace's equation, and we have to find such a solution $T(u, v)$ in the upper half of the w-plane which satisfies those boundary conditions. For this purpose we consider the functions

(9*)
$$\text{Ln } (w + 1) = \ln |w + 1| + i\phi_1, \qquad \phi_1 = \arg (w + 1) = \arctan \frac{v}{u + 1},$$

$$\text{Ln } (w - 1) = \ln |w - 1| + i\phi_2, \qquad \phi_2 = \arg (w - 1) = \arctan \frac{v}{u - 1}.$$

Since $\phi_1(u, v)$ and $\phi_2(u, v)$ are harmonic functions, $\phi_2 - \phi_1$ is harmonic. If $w = u$ is real and smaller than -1, then $\phi_2 - \phi_1 = \pi - \pi = 0$; for real $w = u$ in the interval $-1 < u < 1$ we have $\phi_2 - \phi_1 = \pi - 0 = \pi$, and for real $w = u > 1$ we have $\phi_2 - \phi_1 = 0 - 0 = 0$. Hence, the function

(9)
$$T(u, v) = \frac{T_0}{\pi} (\phi_2 - \phi_1)$$

is harmonic in the half-plane $v > 0$ and satisfies those boundary conditions in the w-plane. Since $\tan \phi_1 = v/(u + 1)$ and $\tan \phi_2 = v/(u - 1)$, it follows that

$$\tan (\phi_2 - \phi_1) = \frac{\tan \phi_2 - \tan \phi_1}{1 + \tan \phi_1 \tan \phi_2} = \frac{2v}{u^2 + v^2 - 1},$$

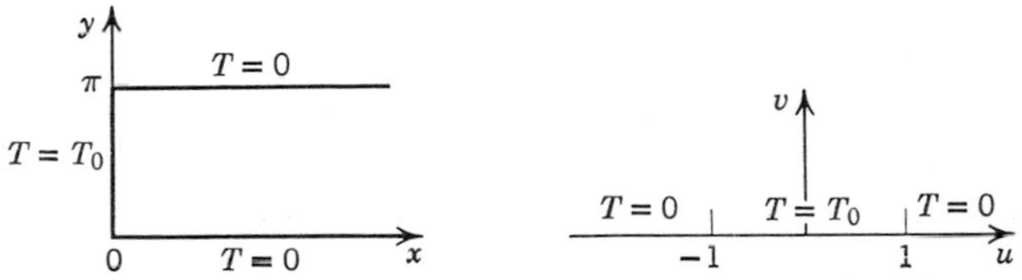

Fig. 358. Boundary conditions in Example 2.

and (9) takes the form

$$(10) \qquad T(u, v) = \frac{T_0}{\pi} \arctan \frac{2v}{u^2 + v^2 - 1}.$$

The function $w = \cosh z$ maps the strip under consideration onto the half-plane $v \geq 0$, and we have

$$w = u + iv = \cosh(x + iy) = \cosh x \cos y + i \sinh x \sin y.$$

Separating the real and imaginary parts on both sides, this may be written

$$u = \cosh x \cos y, \qquad v = \sinh x \sin y.$$

From these expressions for u and v it follows that in (10),

$$u^2 + v^2 - 1 = \cosh^2 x \cos^2 y + \sinh^2 x \sin^2 y - 1 = \sinh^2 x - \sin^2 y.$$

By inserting this and the expression for v into (10) and denoting $T(u(x, y), v(x, y))$ by $T^*(x, y)$ we have

$$T^*(x, y) = \frac{T_0}{\pi} \arctan \frac{2 \sinh x \sin y}{\sinh^2 x - \sin^2 y}.$$

Noting that the numerator and the denominator are the imaginary part and the real part of the function $(\sinh x + i \sin y)^2$ we may write

$$T^*(x, y) = \frac{T_0}{\pi} \arg [(\sinh x + i \sin y)^2] = \frac{2T_0}{\pi} \arg (\sinh x + i \sin y).$$

Hence the solution of our problem is

$$(11) \qquad T^*(x, y) = \frac{2T_0}{\pi} \arctan \frac{\sin y}{\sinh x}.$$

This function is harmonic in the interior of our strip (cf. Theorem 2 in Sec. 12.2) and it satisfies the boundary conditions. Indeed, $T^* = 0$ when $y = 0$ or $y = \pi$, and $T^* = T_0$ when $x = 0$. The isotherms ($=$ curves of constant temperature) are the curves

$$\frac{\sin y}{\sinh x} = const.$$

In Ex. 2 we transformed the real potential $T(u, v)$ into the real potential $T^*(x, y)$ by using the function $w = u(x, y) + iv(x, y)$ which maps the half-plane onto the given region. In many cases problems of this type become simpler by working with a **complex potential**, that is, by taking a complex analytic function $F(w)$ such that the real potential $T(u, v)$ is the real or imaginary part of $F(w)$, and transforming F instead of T. It is clear that such a complex potential F may be readily obtained from T by determining a conjugate harmonic function of T (cf. at the end of Sec. 10.3). Let us illustrate this "method of complex potentials" in the case of our previous example. A detailed consideration of complex potentials will be presented later (in Chap. 13).

Example 3. From (9*) we see that the real potential

$$T(u, v) = \frac{T_0}{\pi} (\phi_2 - \phi_1)$$

in Ex. 2 (cf. (9)) is the imaginary part of the complex potential

(12) $$F(w) = \frac{T_0}{\pi} [\text{Ln } (w - 1) - \text{Ln } (w + 1)] = \frac{T_0}{\pi} \text{Ln } \frac{w - 1}{w + 1}.$$

The mapping function in Ex. 2 is

$$w = \cosh z = \tfrac{1}{2}(e^z + e^{-z}).$$

From this we see that in (12),

$$\frac{w - 1}{w + 1} = \frac{\cosh z - 1}{\cosh z + 1} = \frac{e^z + e^{-z} - 2}{e^z + e^{-z} + 2} = \frac{(e^{z/2} - e^{-z/2})^2}{(e^{z/2} + e^{-z/2})^2} = \tanh^2 \frac{z}{2}.$$

By inserting this into (12) and denoting $F(w(z))$ by $F^*(z)$ we have

(13) $$F^*(z) = \frac{T_0}{\pi} \text{Ln } \tanh^2 \frac{z}{2} = \frac{2T_0}{\pi} \text{Ln } \tanh \frac{z}{2}.$$

This is the complex potential in the strip in Ex. 2, and its imaginary part is the solution of our problem. This solution may be obtained as follows.

Denoting $\tanh \dfrac{z}{2}$ by $H(z)$ and using (2) in Sec. 10.13, we first have

(14) $$F^*(z) = \frac{2T_0}{\pi} \text{Ln } H = \frac{2T_0}{\pi} \left(\ln |H| + i \text{ arc tan } \frac{\text{Im } H}{\text{Re } H} \right).$$

To determine the real and imaginary part of H we may start from

$$H = \tanh \frac{z}{2} = \frac{\sinh \dfrac{z}{2}}{\cosh \dfrac{z}{2}} = \frac{\sinh \dfrac{z}{2} \overline{\cosh \dfrac{z}{2}}}{\cosh \dfrac{z}{2} \overline{\cosh \dfrac{z}{2}}}.$$

By using the definitions of the hyperbolic sine and cosine in terms of exponential functions, noting that $\overline{\cosh \dfrac{z}{2}} = \cosh \dfrac{\bar{z}}{2}$, and carrying out the multiplications this becomes

$$H = \frac{\sinh x + i \sin y}{\cosh x + \cos y}.$$

From this we readily obtain

(15) $$\text{Re } H = \frac{\sinh x}{\cosh x + \cos y}, \qquad \text{Im } H = \frac{\sin y}{\cosh x + \cos y}.$$

By inserting these expressions into (14) we have

$$T^*(x, y) = \text{Im } F^*(z) = \frac{2T_0}{\pi} \text{ arc tan } \frac{\sin y}{\sinh x},$$

in agreement with our result in Ex. 2.

Furthermore, from (15) it follows that

$$|H|^2 = \frac{\sinh^2 x + \sin^2 y}{(\cosh x + \cos y)^2},$$

and from (14) we see that the real part of $F^*(z)$ becomes

$$S^*(x, y) = \operatorname{Re} F^*(z) = \frac{T_0}{\pi} \ln \frac{\sinh^2 x + \sin^2 y}{(\cosh x + \cos y)^2}.$$

The curves $S^* = const$ intersect the isotherms $T^* = const$ at right angles and, therefore, are the curves along which the heat flows.

PROBLEMS

Find and graph the images of the following regions under the mapping $w = e^z$.
1. $0 \leq x \leq 1, 0 \leq y \leq \pi/2$ 2. $1 < x < 2, -\pi/2 < y < \pi/2$
3. $-2 < x < -1, 0 < y < \pi$ 4. $-1 < x < 1, \pi/4 < y < 3\pi/4$

5. Find an analytic function which maps the region R bounded by the positive y and x axes and the hyperbola $xy = \pi/2$ in the first quadrant onto the upper half-plane. *Hint:* first map R onto a horizontal strip.

6. Same question as in Prob. 5, with $xy = \pi/2$ replaced by $xy = c$ where c is any positive constant.

7. Determine all the points where the mapping $w = \sin z$ is not conformal.

Find and graph the images of the following regions under the mapping $w = \sin z$.
8. $-\pi/2 < x < \pi/2, 0 < y < 1$ 9. $-\pi/2 < x < \pi/2, 1 < y < 2$
10. $0 < x < \pi/2, 0 < y < 2$ 11. $0 < x < 2\pi, 1 < y < 2$

12. Find and plot the images of the lines $x = 0, \pm\pi/6, \pm\pi/3, \pm\pi/2$ under the mapping $w = \sin z$.

13. Describe the transformation $w = \cosh z$ in terms of the transformation $w = \sin z$ and rotations and translations.

14. Investigate the mapping $w = \sin^{-1} z$.

15. Verify by differentiation that (11) is harmonic.

16. Find the temperature $T(x, y)$ in the strip in Ex. 1, assuming that $T = 0$ on the left boundary and $T = 1$ on the upper and lower boundaries of the strip.

17. Show that $w = \operatorname{Ln} \dfrac{z - 1}{z + 1}$ maps the upper half plane onto the horizontal strip $0 \leq \operatorname{Im} w \leq \pi$ as shown in Fig. 359.

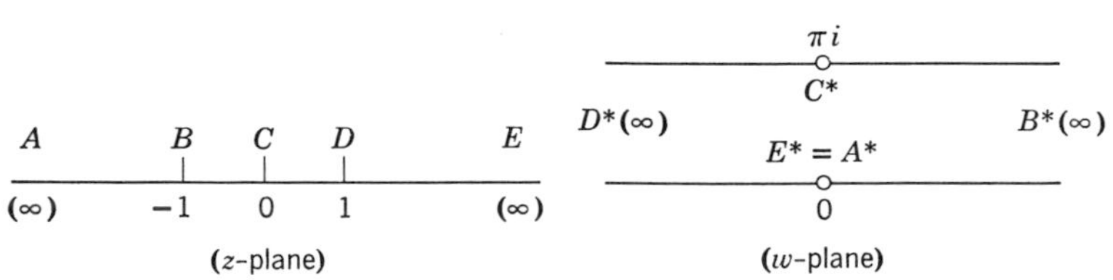

Fig. 359. Problem 17.

18. Find the image of the region $0 < \arg z < \pi/4$ under the mapping $w = \sqrt{z^2 - 1}$ (where w is the principal value of the root).

Find the image of the first quadrant of the z-plane under the mapping

19. $w = 1/(z^3 + 1)$ **20.** $w = 1/(z^2 + i)$

12.6   RIEMANN SURFACES

We consider the mapping defined by

(1) $$w = u + iv = z^2$$

(cf. Sec. 12.1). This mapping is conformal, except at $z = 0$ where $w' = 2z$ is zero. The angles at $z = 0$ are doubled under the mapping. The right half of the z-plane (including the positive y-axis) maps onto the full w-plane cut along the negative half of the u-axis; the mapping is one-to-one. Similarly, the left half of the z-plane (including the negative y-axis) is mapped onto the cut w-plane in a one-to-one manner.

Obviously, the mapping of the full z-plane is not one-to-one, because every point $w \neq 0$ corresponds to precisely two points z. In fact, if z_1 is one of these points, then the other is $-z_1$. For example, $z = i$ and $z = -i$ have the same image, namely, $w = -1$, etc. Hence, the w-plane is "covered twice" by the image of the z-plane. We say that the full z-plane is mapped onto the *doubly covered* w-plane. We can still give our imagination the necessary support as follows.

We imagine one of the two previously obtained copies of the cut w-plane to be placed upon the other such that the upper sheet is the image of the right half of the z-plane, and the lower sheet is the image of the left half of the z-plane; we denote these half-planes by R and L, respectively. When passing from R to L, the corresponding image point should pass from the upper to the lower sheet. For this reason we join the two sheets crosswise along the cut, that is, along the negative real axis. (This construction can be carried out only in imagination, since the penetration of the two sheets of a material model can only be imperfectly realized.) The two origins are fastened together. The configuration thus obtained is called a **Riemann surface.** On it every point $w \neq 0$ appears twice, at superposed positions, and the origin appears precisely once. The function $w = z^2$ now maps the full z-plane onto this Riemann surface in a one-to-one manner, and the mapping is conformal, except for the "winding point" or **branch point** at $w = 0$ (Fig. 360). This branch point is said to be of the *second order*, since it connects two sheets.

Fig. 360. Example of a Riemann surface.

We now consider the double-valued function

$$(2) \qquad\qquad w = \sqrt{z}.$$

To each $z \neq 0$ there correspond two values w, one of which is the principal value. If we replace the z-plane by the two-sheeted Riemann surface just considered, then each complex number $z \neq 0$ is represented by two points of the surface at superposed positions. We let one of these points correspond to the principal value—for example, the point in the upper sheet—and the other to the other value. Then our function becomes a single-valued function of the points of the Riemann surface, and to any continuous motion of z on the surface there corresponds a continuous motion of the corresponding point in the w-plane. The function maps the sheet corresponding to the principal value onto the right half of the w-plane and the other sheet onto the left half of the w-plane.

Let us consider some further important examples.

Example 1. In the case of the function

$$(3) \qquad\qquad w = \sqrt[n]{z} \qquad\qquad n = 3, 4, \ldots$$

we need a Riemann surface consisting of n sheets and having a branch point of order n at $z = 0$. One of the sheets corresponds to the principal value and the other $n - 1$ sheets to the other $n - 1$ values of the function.

Example 2. The Riemann surface of the infinitely many-valued function

$$(4) \qquad\qquad w = \ln z = \text{Ln } z + 2n\pi i \qquad (n = 0, \pm 1, \pm 2, \ldots, z \neq 0)$$

consists of infinitely many sheets. The single-valued function $w = \text{Ln } z$ corresponds to one of these sheets. On this sheet the argument θ of z ranges in the interval $-\pi < \theta \leq \pi$ (cf. Sec. 10.13). The sheet is cut along the negative ray of the real axis, and the upper edge of the slit is joined to the lower edge of the next sheet which corresponds to the interval $\pi < \theta \leq 3\pi$, that is, to the single-valued function $w = \text{Ln } z + 2\pi i$. In this way each value of n in (4) corresponds to precisely one of these infinitely many sheets. The function $w = \text{Ln } z$ maps the corresponding sheet onto the horizontal strip $-\pi < v \leq \pi$ in the w-plane. The next sheet is mapped onto the neighboring strip $\pi < v \leq 3\pi$, etc. The function $w = \ln z$ thus maps all the sheets of the corresponding Riemann surface onto the entire w-plane, the correspondence between the points $z \neq 0$ of the Riemann surface and those of the w-plane being one-to-one.

Example 3. Let us consider the mapping defined by

$$(5) \qquad\qquad w = z + \frac{1}{z} \qquad\qquad (z \neq 0)$$

which is important in aerodynamics (see below). Since

$$w' = 1 - \frac{1}{z^2} = \frac{(z + 1)(z - 1)}{z^2}$$

the mapping is conformal except at the points $z = 1$ and $z = -1$; these points correspond to $w = 2$ and $w = -2$, respectively. From (5) we find

$$(6) \qquad\qquad z = \frac{w}{2} \pm \sqrt{\frac{w^2}{4} - 1} = \frac{w}{2} \pm \frac{1}{2} \sqrt{(w + 2)(w - 2)}.$$

Hence, the points $w = 2$ and $w = -2$ are branch points of the second order of this function $z = z(w)$. To any value w ($\neq 2$, $\neq -2$) there correspond two values of z. Consequently, (5) maps the z-plane onto a two-sheeted Riemann surface, the two sheets being connected crosswise from $w = -2$ to $w = 2$ (Fig. 361), and this mapping is one-to-one. We set $z = re^{i\theta}$ and determine the images of the curves $r = const$ and $\theta = const$. From (5) we obtain

$$w = u + iv = re^{i\theta} + \frac{1}{r}e^{-i\theta} = \left(r + \frac{1}{r}\right)\cos\theta + i\left(r - \frac{1}{r}\right)\sin\theta.$$

By equating the real and imaginary parts on both sides we have

(7) $$u = \left(r + \frac{1}{r}\right)\cos\theta, \qquad v = \left(r - \frac{1}{r}\right)\sin\theta.$$

From this we find

$$\frac{u^2}{a^2} + \frac{v^2}{b^2} = 1 \qquad \text{where} \qquad a = r + \frac{1}{r}, \qquad b = \left|r - \frac{1}{r}\right|.$$

The circles $r = const$ are thus mapped onto ellipses whose principal axes lie in the u and v axes and have the lengths $2a$ and $2b$, respectively. Since $a^2 - b^2 = 4$, independent of r, these ellipses are confocal, with foci at $w = -2$ and $w = 2$. The unit circle $r = 1$ maps onto the line segment from $w = -2$ to $w = 2$. For every $r \neq 1$ the two circles with radii r and $1/r$ map onto the same ellipse in the w-plane, corresponding to the two sheets of the Riemann surface. Hence, the interior of the unit circle $|z| = 1$ corresponds to one sheet, and the exterior to the other.

Furthermore, from (7) we obtain

(8) $$\frac{u^2}{\cos^2\theta} - \frac{v^2}{\sin^2\theta} = -4.$$

The lines $\theta = const$ are thus mapped onto the hyperbolas which are the orthogonal trajectories of those ellipses. The real axis, that is, the rays $\theta = 0$ and $\theta = \pi$, are mapped onto the part of the real axis from $w = 2$ via ∞ to $w = -2$. The y-axis is mapped onto the v-axis. Any other pair of rays $\theta = \theta_0$ and $\theta = \theta_0 + \pi$ is mapped onto the two branches of the same hyperbola.

An exterior region of one of the above ellipses is free of branch points and corresponds to either the interior or the exterior of the corresponding circle in the

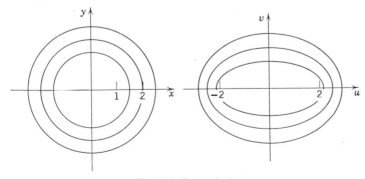

Fig. 361. Example 3.

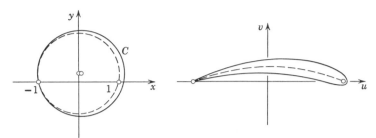

Fig. 362. Jukowski airfoil.

z-plane, depending on the sheet of the Riemann surface to which the region belongs. In particular the full w-plane corresponds to the interior or the exterior of the unit circle $|z| = 1$, as was mentioned before.

The mapping (5) transforms suitable circles into airfoils with a sharp trailing edge whose interior angle is zero; these airfoils are known as **Jukowski airfoils.** Since the airfoil to be obtained has a sharp edge it is clear that the circle to be mapped must pass through one of the points $z = \pm 1$ where the mapping is not conformal. Let us choose a circle C through $z = -1$ and such that $z = 1$ lies inside C. The simplest way of determining the image is the graphical vector addition of the vectors corresponding to z and $1/z$ (where the latter can be obtained from the former as shown in Sec. 12.3). This leads to the result shown in Fig. 362. Further details can be found in Ref. [G7] in Appendix 1.

A more elaborate treatment of Riemann surfaces can be found in Ref. [G8].

PROBLEMS

1. Show that the Riemann surface of $w = \sqrt[3]{z}$ consists of three sheets and has a branch point of third order at $z = 0$. Find the path of the image point w of a point z which moves three times around the unit circle starting from the initial position $z = 1$.

2. Consider the Riemann surfaces of $w = \sqrt[4]{z}$ and $w = \sqrt[5]{z}$ in a fashion similar to that in Prob. 1.

3. Determine the path of the image of a point z under the mapping $w = \ln z$ as z moves several times around the unit circle.

4. Show that the Riemann surface of $w = \sqrt{(z - 1)(z - 4)}$ has branch points at $z = 1$ and $z = 4$ and consists of two sheets which may be cut along the line segment from 1 to 4 and joined crosswise. *Hint:* introduce polar coordinates $z - 1 = r_1 e^{i\theta_1}, \ z - 4 = r_2 e^{i\theta_2}$

Determine the location of the branch points and the number of sheets of the Riemann surfaces of the following functions.

5. $w = \sqrt{z^2 - 1}$ **6.** $w = \sqrt[3]{z - i}$ **7.** $w = \sqrt{z(z - 1)(z + 1)}$

8. Find the images of the annuli $\frac{1}{2} < |z| < 1$, $1 < |z| < 2$, and $2 < |z| < 3$ under the mapping $w = z + 1/z$.

9. Show that the Riemann surface of $w = \sqrt{(1 - z^2)(4 - z^2)}$ has four branch points and two sheets which may be joined crosswise along the segments $-2 \leq x \leq -1$ and $1 \leq x \leq 2$ of the x-axis.

chapter 13

COMPLEX ANALYTIC FUNCTIONS AND POTENTIAL THEORY

Laplace's equation $\nabla^2 u = 0$ is one of the most important partial differential equations in engineering mathematics, because it occurs in connection with gravitational fields (Sec. 5.16), electrostatic fields (Sec. 9.11), steady-state heat conduction (Sec. 12.5), incompressible fluid flow, etc. The theory of the solutions of this equation is called *potential theory*.

In the "two-dimensional case" when u depends only on two Cartesian coordinates x and y, Laplace's equation becomes

$$\nabla^2 u = u_{xx} + u_{yy} = 0.$$

We know that then its solutions are closely related to complex analytic functions (cf. Sec. 10.3).[1] We shall now consider this connection and its consequences in more detail and illustrate it by practical examples taken from hydrodynamics and electrostatics. In Sec. 13.4 we shall see that results about analytic functions can be used for characterizing various general properties of harmonic functions. Finally we shall derive an important general formula for the solution of boundary value problems involving Laplace's equation in a circular disk.

Prerequisites for this chapter: Chap. 10–12.

References: Appendix 1, Part G.

Answers to problems: Appendix 2.

[1] No such close relation exists in the three-dimensional case.

13.1 ELECTROSTATIC FIELDS

The electrical force of attraction or repulsion between charged particles is governed by Coulomb's law. This force is the gradient of a function u, called the *electrostatic potential*, and at any points free of charges u is a solution of Laplace's equation

$$\nabla^2 u = 0.$$

Cf. Sec. 9.11. The surfaces $u = const$ are called **equipotential surfaces**. At each point P the gradient of u is perpendicular to the surface $u = const$ through P, that is, the electrical force has the direction perpendicular to the equipotential surface.

Example 1. Find the potential of the field between two parallel conducting plates extending to infinity (Fig. 363), which are kept at potentials U_1 and U_2, respectively. From the shape of the plates it follows that u depends only on x, and Laplace's equation becomes $u'' = 0$. By integrating twice, $u = ax + b$ where the constants a and b are determined by the given boundary values of u on the plates. For example, if the plates correspond to $x = -1$ and $x = 1$, the solution is

$$u(x) = \tfrac{1}{2}(U_2 - U_1)x + \tfrac{1}{2}(U_2 + U_1).$$

The equipotential surfaces are parallel planes.

Example 2. Find the potential between two coaxial conducting cylinders which extend to infinity on both sides (Fig. 364), and are kept at potentials U_1 and U_2, respectively. Here u depends only on $r = \sqrt{x^2 + y^2}$, for reasons of symmetry, and Laplace's equation becomes

$$ru'' + u' = 0 \qquad \text{[cf. (4) in Sec. 9.9].}$$

By separating variables and integrating we obtain

$$\frac{u''}{u'} = -\frac{1}{r}, \qquad \ln u' = -\ln r + \tilde{a}, \qquad u' = \frac{a}{r}, \qquad u = a \ln r + b,$$

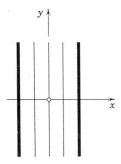

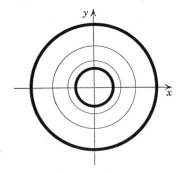

Fig. 363. Potential in Example 1.   **Fig. 364.** Potential in Example 2.

and a and b are determined by the given values of u on the cylinders. Although no infinitely extended conductors exist, the field in our idealized conductor will approximate the field in a long finite conductor in that part which is far away from the ends of the two cylinders.

If the potential u depends only on two Cartesian coordinates x and y, then Laplace's equation becomes

(1) $$\nabla^2 u = \frac{\partial^2 u}{\partial x^2} + \frac{\partial^2 u}{\partial y^2} = 0.$$

The equipotential surfaces $u = const$ appear as *equipotential lines* in the xy-plane.

We make the general assumption that $u(x, y)$ is *harmonic*, that is, its second partial derivatives are continuous. Then, if $v(x, y)$ is a conjugate harmonic function of $u(x, y)$ (cf. Sec. 10.3), the function

$$F(z) = u(x, y) + iv(x, y)$$

is an analytic function of $z = x + iy$. This function is called the **complex potential** corresponding to the real potential u. Remember that for a given u the conjugate is uniquely determined, except for an additive real constant.

Since the lines $v = const$ intersect the equipotential lines $u = const$ at right angles [except at points where $F'(z) = 0$], they have the direction of the electrical force and, therefore, are called **lines of force**.

Example 3. In Ex. 1, a conjugate is $v = ay$. The complex potential is

$$F(z) = az + b = ax + b + iay,$$

and the lines of force are straight lines parallel to the x-axis.

Example 4. In Ex. 2 we have

$$u = a \ln r + b = a \ln |z| + b.$$

A conjugate is $v = a \arg z$. The complex potential is $F(z) = a \ln z + b$, and the lines of force are straight lines through the origin. The function $F(z)$ may also be interpreted as the complex potential of a source line whose trace with the xy-plane is the origin.

Often more complicated potentials can be obtained by superposition. This may be illustrated by

Example 5. Determine the complex potential of a pair of oppositely charged source lines of the same strength at the points $z = x_1$ and $z = x_2$. From Exs. 2 and 4 it follows that the potential of each of the source lines is

$$u_1 = -c \ln |z - x_1| \quad \text{and} \quad u_2 = c \ln |z - x_2|,$$

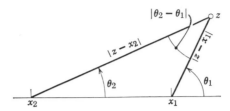

Fig. 365. Example 5.

respectively. These are the real parts of the complex potentials

$$F_1(z) = -c \ln (z - x_1) \qquad \text{and} \qquad F_2(z) = c \ln (z - x_2).$$

Hence, the complex potential of the combination of the two source lines is

$$(2) \qquad\qquad F(z) = F_1(z) + F_2(z) = c \ln \frac{z - x_2}{z - x_1}$$

The equipotential lines are the circles

$$u = \operatorname{Re} F(z) = c \ln \frac{|z - x_2|}{|z - x_1|} = const,$$

and the lines of force are the curves

$$v = \operatorname{Im} F(z) = c \ \arg \frac{z - x_2}{z - x_1} = c \left[\arg (z - x_2) - \arg (z - x_1) \right] = const,$$

that is,

$$v = c(\theta_2 - \theta_1) = const$$

(cf. Fig. 365). Now, $|\theta_2 - \theta_1|$ is the angle between the line segments from z to x_1 and x_2. The lines of force, therefore, are curves along each of which the line segment $x_1 x_2$ appears under a constant angle; these curves are the totality of circular arcs over $x_1 x_2$, as is well known from elementary geometry. The function (2) may also be interpreted as the complex potential of a capacitor consisting of two circular cylinders whose axes are parallel but do not coincide (Fig. 366).

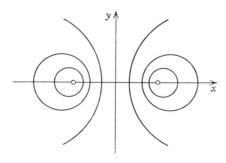

Fig. 366. Potential field of two oppositely charged source lines of the same strength (which have the same distance from the origin).

PROBLEMS

Find the potential u between the infinite concentric cylinders (Fig. 367) of radi i r_1 and r_2 which are kept on the potentials U_1 and U_2, respectively, where

1. $r_1 = 1$, $r_2 = 2$, $U_1 = 20$ volts, $U_2 = 40$ volts

2. $r_1 = \frac{1}{2}$, $r_2 = 3$, $U_1 = 0$, $U_2 = 110$ volts

3. $r_1 = 1/10$, $r_2 = 1$, $U_1 = 100$ volts, $U_2 = 10$ volts

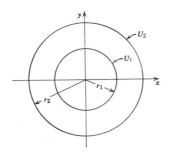

Fig. 367. Problems 1–3.

4. Find the potential of two oppositely charged source lines at the points $z = a$ and $z = -a$. Show the equipotential lines graphically.

5. Find the potential of two source lines at $z = a$ and $z = -a$ having the same charge.

6. Find the potential u between the infinite plates in Fig. 368 and show the equipotential lines graphically.

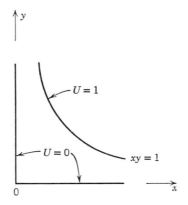

Fig. 368. Problem 6.

7. Show that $F(z) = \cos^{-1} z$ may be interpreted as the complex potential of the configurations in Figs. 369–371.

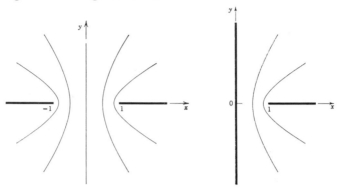

Fig. 369. Problem 7.   Fig. 370. Problem 7.

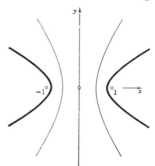

Fig. 371. Problem 7.

8. Show that $F(z) = \cosh^{-1} z$ may be interpreted as the complex potential between two confocal elliptic cylinders.

9. Find the potential u between the infinite cylinders in Fig. 372, if on the left cylinder, $u = -1$ and on the right, $u = 1$. *Hint:* use the potential in Prob. 4.

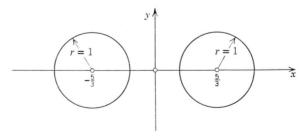

Fig. 372. Problem 9.

10. Find the equipotential lines of the complex potential $F(z) = 1/z$, and show these lines graphically.

13.2   TWO-DIMENSIONAL FLUID FLOW

Harmonic functions play an important role in hydrodynamics. To illustrate this, let us consider the two-dimensional steady motion of a non-viscous fluid. Here "two-dimensional" means that the motion of the fluid is the same in all planes parallel to the xy-plane, the velocity being parallel to that plane. It then suffices to consider the motion of the fluid in the xy-plane. "Steady" means that the velocity is independent of the time.

At any point (x, y) the flow has a certain velocity which is determined by its magnitude and its direction and is thus a vector. Since in the complex plane any number a represents a vector (the vector from the origin to the point corresponding to a) we may represent the velocity of the flow by a complex variable, say,

$$(1) \qquad\qquad V = V_1 + iV_2.$$

Then V_1 and V_2 are the components of the velocity in the x and y directions, and V is tangential to the paths of the moving particles of the fluid. Such a path is called a **streamline** of the motion.

Consider now an arbitrary given smooth curve C, whose arc length is denoted by s, and let the real variable V_t be the component of the velocity V tangent to C (Fig. 374). Then the value of the line integral

$$(2) \qquad\qquad \int_C V_t \, ds$$

taken along C in the sense of increasing values of s is called the **circulation** of the fluid along C. By dividing the circulation by the length of C we obtain the mean velocity[2] of the flow along the curve C. Now

$$V_t = |V| \cos \alpha \qquad\qquad (\text{cf. Fig. 374}).$$

Consequently, V_t is the scalar product (Sec. 5.4) of V and the unit tangent vector (cf. Sec. 12.2)

$$\frac{dz}{ds} = \frac{dx}{ds} + i\frac{dy}{ds}$$

[2] *Definitions:* $\dfrac{1}{l} \displaystyle\int_a^b f(x)\, dx$ = mean value of f on the interval $a \leqq x \leqq b$.

(l = length of that interval).

$\dfrac{1}{l} \displaystyle\int_C f(s)\, ds$ = mean value of f on C. (l = length of C).

$\dfrac{1}{A} \displaystyle\iint_D f(x, y)\, dx\, dy$ = mean value of f on D. (A = area of D).

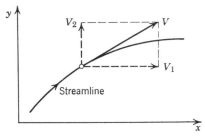

Fig. 373. Velocity.

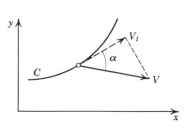

Fig. 374. Tangential component of the velocity with respect to a curve C.

to C, where $z(s) = x(s) + iy(s)$ is a representation of C. Therefore, the product $V_t \, ds$ may be written

$$V_t \, ds = V \cdot dz = V_1 \, dx + V_2 \, dy \qquad (dz = dx + i \, dy).$$

Now let C be a *closed* curve, namely, the boundary curve of a simply connected domain D. Then, if V has continuous partial derivatives in a region containing D in its interior, it follows from Green's theorem (Sec. 6.4) that the circulation around C can be represented by a double integral,

$$(3) \qquad \int_C (V_1 \, dx + V_2 \, dy) = \iint_D \left(\frac{\partial V_2}{\partial x} - \frac{\partial V_1}{\partial y} \right) dx \, dy.$$

The function in the integral on the right permits a simple physical interpretation as follows. Let C be a circle of radius r. The circulation, divided by $2\pi r$ then represents the mean velocity of the fluid along C, and the mean angular velocity ω_0 of the fluid about the axis of the circle is obtained by dividing the mean velocity by the radius r; thus

$$\omega_0 = \frac{1}{\pi r^2} \iint_D \frac{1}{2} \left(\frac{\partial V_2}{\partial x} - \frac{\partial V_1}{\partial y} \right) dx \, dy.$$

The expression on the right is the mean value[3] of the function

$$(4) \qquad \omega = \frac{1}{2} \left(\frac{\partial V_2}{\partial x} - \frac{\partial V_1}{\partial y} \right)$$

on the disk D bounded by the circle C. The function ω is called the **rotation**, and 2ω is called the **vorticity** of the motion. If $r \to 0$, the limit of that expression is the value of ω at the center of C. Hence, $\omega(x, y)$ is the limiting angular velocity of a circular element of the fluid as the circle shrinks to the point (x, y). Roughly speaking, if a spherical element of the

---

[3] Cf. the previous footnote.

fluid were suddenly solidified and the surrounding fluid simultaneously annihilated, the element would rotate with the angular velocity ω (cf. also Sec. 5.19).

We consider only *irrotational flows*, that is, flows for which ω is zero everywhere in the region D of the flow, that is,

$$(5) \qquad \frac{\partial V_2}{\partial x} - \frac{\partial V_1}{\partial y} = 0,$$

the existence and continuity of the derivatives being assumed.

We further assume that the fluid is *incompressible*. Then

$$(6) \qquad \frac{\partial V_1}{\partial x} + \frac{\partial V_2}{\partial y} = 0 \qquad \text{[cf. (9), Sec. 5.18]}$$

in every region which is free of **sources** or **sinks**, that is, points at which fluid is produced or disappears.

If D is a simply connected region and the flow is irrotational, it follows from Theorem 3 in Sec. 6.12, that the line integral

$$(7) \qquad \int_C (V_1\, dx + V_2\, dy)$$

is independent of path in D. Integrating from a fixed point (a, b) in D to a variable point (x, y) in D the integral thus becomes a function of the point (x, y), say, $\Phi(x, y)$:

$$(8) \qquad \Phi(x, y) = \int_{(a,b)}^{(x,y)} (V_1\, dx + V_2\, dy).$$

The function $\Phi(x, y)$ is called the **velocity potential**[4] of the motion. Since the integral is independent of path, $V_1\, dx + V_2\, dy$ is an exact differential (Sec. 6.12), namely, the differential of the function $\Phi(x, y)$, that is,

$$(9) \qquad V_1\, dx + V_2\, dy = \frac{\partial \Phi}{\partial x}\, dx + \frac{\partial \Phi}{\partial y}\, dy.$$

It follows that

$$(10) \qquad V_1 = \frac{\partial \Phi}{\partial x}, \qquad V_2 = \frac{\partial \Phi}{\partial y},$$

and we see that the velocity vector is the gradient of $\Phi(x, y)$:

$$(\mathbf{11}) \qquad V = V_1 + iV_2 = \frac{\partial \Phi}{\partial x} + i\frac{\partial \Phi}{\partial y} \qquad \text{(cf. Sec. 5.16).}$$

The curves $\Phi(x, y) = const$ are called **equipotential lines**. Since V is the gradient of Φ, at each point V is perpendicular to the equipotential line through that point (provided $V \neq 0$).

---

[4] Some authors use $-\Phi$ (instead of Φ) as the velocity potential.

Furthermore, by inserting (10) into (6) we see that Φ satisfies Laplace's equation

$$\nabla^2\Phi = \frac{\partial^2\Phi}{\partial x^2} + \frac{\partial^2\Phi}{\partial y^2} = 0.$$

Let $\Psi(x, y)$ be a conjugate harmonic function of $\Phi(x, y)$. Then at each point the curves

$$\Psi(x, y) = const$$

are perpendicular[5] to the equipotential lines $\Phi(x, y) = const$. Hence, their tangents have the direction of the velocity of the fluid, and *the curves $\psi(x, y) = const$ are, therefore, the streamlines of the flow.* The function $\psi(x, y)$ is called the **stream function** of the flow.

Assuming that both Φ and Ψ have continuous second partial derivatives, the complex function

(12) $$F(z) = \Phi(x, y) + i\Psi(x, y)$$

is analytic in the region of the flow. This function is called the **complex potential** of the flow. Working with the complex potential is simpler than working with Φ and Ψ separately.

The velocity of the flow can be obtained by differentiating (12) and using the Cauchy-Riemann equations, finding

$$F'(z) = \frac{\partial\Phi}{\partial x} + i\frac{\partial\Psi}{\partial x} = \frac{\partial\Phi}{\partial x} - i\frac{\partial\Phi}{\partial y} = V_1 - iV_2.$$

From this it follows that

(13) $$V = V_1 + iV_2 = \overline{F'(z)}.$$

In this way *two-dimensional irrotational steady flows of incompressible fluids may be described in terms of analytic functions*, and the methods of complex analysis, such as conformal mapping, may be employed.

In connection with boundary value problems the stream function Ψ is important, because a boundary across which fluid cannot flow is a streamline. Under conformal mapping, a streamline transforms into a streamline in the image plane. Another possibility for obtaining and investigating complicated flows is the *superposition of simple flows*. The sum $F = F_1 + F_2$ of the complex potentials F_1, F_2 of two flows is the complex potential of the flow which is obtained by vector addition of the velocity vectors of the two flows. Clearly, since Laplace's equation is linear and homogeneous, the sum of two harmonic functions is a harmonic function.

Special examples will be considered in the next section.

[5] Except for points where $F'(z) = 0$ [cf. (12)].

Note that while in electrostatics the given boundaries (conducting plates) are equipotential lines, in hydrodynamics the boundaries are streamlines and thus are orthogonal to the equipotential lines.

13.3   SPECIAL COMPLEX POTENTIALS

The following examples may illustrate that even the simplest analytic functions correspond to interesting flow patterns.

Note that some functions considered in Sec. 13.1 now reappear, but have an entirely different physical interpretation. The problem of uniqueness is discussed in Ref. [C5] and will not be considered here.

Example 1 (Parallel flow).   The complex potential

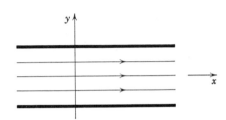

(1) $F(z) = Kz$ (K positive real)

describes a uniform flow to the right whose potential lines are

$$\operatorname{Re} F(z) = Kx = const$$

and whose streamlines are

$$\operatorname{Im} F(z) = Ky = const,$$

Fig. 375. Parallel flow.

that is, horizontal straight lines. From (13), Sec. 13.2, we obtain

$$V = V_1 + iV_2 = K, \qquad \text{that is,} \qquad V_1 = K, \quad V_2 = 0;$$

the velocity vector is constant and parallel to the x-axis, and the flow can be interpreted as a uniform flow between two parallel lines (between two parallel planes in three-dimensional space). Cf. Fig. 375.

Example 2 (Flow around a corner).   The complex potential

(2) $$F(z) = z^2 = x^2 - y^2 + 2ixy$$

describes a flow whose equipotential lines are the hyperbolas

$$\Phi = x^2 - y^2 = const$$

and whose streamlines are the hyperbolas

$$\Psi = 2xy = const.$$

From (13) in the last section we obtain the velocity vector

$$V = 2\bar{z} = 2(x - iy), \qquad \text{that is,} \qquad V_1 = 2x, \quad V_2 = -2y.$$

The speed (magnitude of the velocity) is

$$|V| = \sqrt{V_1{}^2 + V_2{}^2} = 2\sqrt{x^2 + y^2}.$$

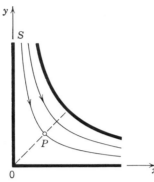

Fig. 376. Flow around a corner.

The flow may be interpreted as the flow in a channel bounded by the positive coordinate axes and a hyperbola, say, $xy = 1$ (Fig. 376). We note that the speed along a streamline S has a minimum at the point P where the cross section of the channel is large.

Example 3 (Source and sink). The complex potential

$$(3) \qquad F(z) = \frac{c}{2\pi} \ln z \qquad (c \text{ positive real})$$

corresponds to a **point source** at $z = 0$ (this means a **source line** $x = 0$, $y = 0$ in space). The constant c is called the **strength** or **discharge** of the source. The equipotential lines

$$\Phi = \operatorname{Re} F(z) = \frac{c}{2\pi} \ln r = const \qquad (r = \sqrt{x^2 + y^2})$$

are concentric circles, and the streamlines

$$\Psi = \operatorname{Im} F(z) = \frac{c\theta}{2\pi} = const \qquad (\theta = \arg z)$$

are straight lines through the origin. Since

$$V = \overline{F'(z)} = \frac{c}{2\pi \bar{z}} = \frac{c}{2\pi r^2}(x + iy)$$

we see that the flow is directed radially outward. Cf. Fig. 377.

If c is negative real, then the flow described by (3) is said to have a **sink** at $z = 0$; the flow is directed radially inward, and fluid disappears at the singular point $z = 0$ of the complex potential.

Example 4 (Vortex line). If in (3) the constant c is purely imaginary, say, $c = -iK$ where $K > 0$, then

$$(4) \qquad F(z) = -\frac{iK}{2\pi} \ln z.$$

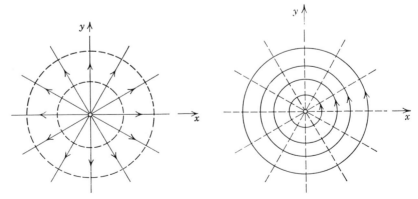

Fig. 377. Point source.   **Fig. 378.** Vortex flow.

The equipotential lines are the straight lines

$$\Phi = \operatorname{Re} F(z) = \frac{K}{2\pi}\theta = const,$$

and the streamlines are the concentric circles

$$\Psi = \operatorname{Im} F(z) = -\frac{K}{2\pi}\ln r = const.$$

Hence, the flow circles around the origin in the counterclockwise sense. The point $z = 0$ is a **vortex**. The potential increases by the value K each time we travel around the vortex.

Example 5 (Flow around a cylinder). We shall now consider the complex potential

$$F(z) = z + \frac{1}{z}.$$

Setting $z = re^{i\theta}$, we obtain

$$F(z) = re^{i\theta} + \frac{1}{r}e^{-i\theta}$$

$$= \left(r + \frac{1}{r}\right)\cos\theta + i\left(r - \frac{1}{r}\right)\sin\theta.$$

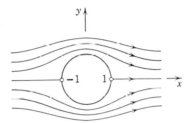

Fig. 379. Flow around a cylinder.

Consequently, the streamlines are

$$\Psi(x, y) = \left(r - \frac{1}{r}\right)\sin\theta = const.$$

The particular streamline

$$\left(r - \frac{1}{r}\right)\sin\theta = 0$$

consists of the x-axis ($\theta = 0$ and $\theta = \pi$) and the unit circle $r = 1$. For large $|z|$ we have $F(z) \approx z$ and the flow is then nearly uniform and parallel. It may be interpreted as the flow around a long circular cylinder of unit radius (Fig. 379). The velocity is

$$V = \overline{F'(z)} = 1 - \frac{1}{\bar{z}^2}.$$

At $z = -1$ and $z = 1$ we have $V = 0$. Such points are called **stagnation points** of the flow.

Example 6 (Flow with circulation around a cylinder). This flow can be obtained by superposition of the flows in Exs. 4 and 5. In both flows the cylinder wall $|z| = 1$ is a streamline. By adding the two corresponding complex potentials we obtain

(5) $$F(z) = z + \frac{1}{z} - \frac{iK}{2\pi}\ln z.$$

The streamlines are

$$\Psi = \operatorname{Im} F(z) = y - \frac{y}{x^2 + y^2} - \frac{K}{2\pi}\ln\sqrt{x^2 + y^2} = const.$$

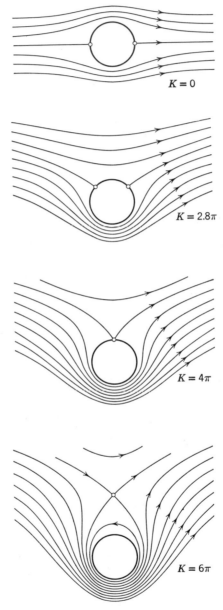

$K = 0$

$K = 2.8\pi$

$K = 4\pi$

$K = 6\pi$

Fig. 380. Flow around a cylinder with circulation.

Depending on the magnitude of K, we may distinguish between three types of flow having either two or one or no stagnation points on the cylinder wall. The speed is

$$|V| = |\overline{F'(z)}| = |F'(z)| = \left|\left(1 - \frac{1}{z^2}\right) - \frac{iK}{2\pi z}\right|.$$

We first note that $|V| \to 1$ as $|z| \to \infty$; that is, for points at a great distance from the cylinder the flow is nearly parallel and uniform. The stagnation points are the solutions of the equation $V = 0$, that is,

(6) $$z^2 - \frac{iK}{2\pi} z - 1 = 0.$$

We obtain

$$z = \frac{iK}{4\pi} \pm \sqrt{\frac{-K^2}{16\pi^2} + 1}.$$

If $K = 0$ (no circulation), then $z = \pm 1$, as in Ex. 5. As K increases from 0 to 4π, the stagnation points move from $z = \pm 1$ up on the unit circle until they unite at $z = i$. The value $K = 4\pi$ corresponds to a double root of the equation (6). If $K > 4\pi$, the roots of (6) become imaginary, so that one of the stagnation points lies on the imaginary axis in the field of flow while the other one lies inside the cylinder, thus loosing its physical meaning (Fig. 380).

PROBLEMS

Consider the flow that corresponds to the given complex potential $F(z)$. Show the streamlines and equipotential lines graphically. Find the velocity vector, and determine all points at which it is parallel to the x-axis.

1. $F(z) = iz$ **2.** $F(z) = -3iz$ **3.** $F(z) = z^2 + z$
4. $F(z) = z^3$ **5.** $F(z) = z^4$ **6.** $F(z) = iz^3$

7. Find a representation of the curves along which the speed (magnitude of the velocity) of a flow corresponding to a complex potential $F(z)$ is constant.

8. Prove that under conformal mapping the stream function transforms into a harmonic function of the new variables.

9. Show that vector addition of the velocity vectors of two flows leads to a flow whose complex potential is obtained by adding those of the two flows.

10. Obtain the flow in Ex. 2 from that in Ex. 1 by a conformal mapping of the first quadrant onto the upper half-plane.

11. Determine the complex potential of a flow which has a point source of strength 1 at $z = -a$ and a sink of strength 1 at $z = a$. Show the streamlines graphically.

12. In Ex. 5 determine the velocity at the points ± 1, ± 2, ± 3, ± 4, and on the wall of the cylinder.

13. Show that $F(z) = \cosh^{-1} z$ corresponds to a flow whose streamlines are confocal hyperbolas with foci at $z = \pm 1$, and the flow may be interpreted as a flow through an aperture (Fig. 381).

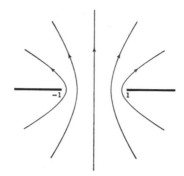

Fig. 381. Flow through an aperture.

14. Show that $F(z) = \cos^{-1} z$ can be interpreted as the complex potential of a flow circulating around an elliptic cylinder or around a plate (the straight segment from $z = -1$ to $z = 1$). Show that the streamlines are confocal ellipses with foci at $z = \pm 1$. (Cf. Fig. 382.)

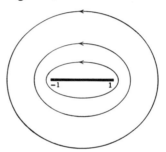

Fig. 382. Flow around a plate.

15. Find the streamlines of the flow corresponding to $F(z) = 1/z$. Show that for small $|a|$ the streamlines in Prob. 11 look similar to those in the present problem.

16. How does the flow in Prob. 15 transform under the mapping $w = \sqrt{z}$? Show the streamlines qualitatively.

13.4   GENERAL PROPERTIES
OF HARMONIC FUNCTIONS

In this section we want to show how results about complex analytic functions can be used for deriving general properties of harmonic functions.

If $u(x, y)$ is any given harmonic function, we may determine a conjugate harmonic function $v(x, y)$ by the use of the Cauchy-Riemann equations, and $f(z) = u(x, y) + iv(x, y)$ is then an analytic function (cf. Sec. 10.3).

This shows that any harmonic function can be regarded as the real part of a suitable analytic function. Since analytic functions have derivatives of all orders, we immediately obtain the following result.

Theorem 1.   *A function $u(x, y)$ which is harmonic in a domain D has partial derivatives of all orders in D.*

If $f(z)$ is analytic in a simply connected domain D, then, by Cauchy's integral formula (Sec. 11.5),

(1*)
$$f(z_0) = \frac{1}{2\pi i} \int_C \frac{f(z)}{z - z_0}\, dz$$

where C is a simple closed path in D and z_0 lies inside C. Choosing for C a circle

$$z = z_0 + re^{i\phi}$$

in D we have

$$z - z_0 = re^{i\phi}, \qquad dz = ire^{i\phi}\, d\phi$$

and the integral formula becomes

(1)
$$f(z_0) = \frac{1}{2\pi} \int_0^{2\pi} f(z_0 + re^{i\phi})\, d\phi.$$

Fig. 383. Proof of Theorem 3.

The right side is the mean value of f on the circle (= value of the integral divided by the length of the interval of integration). This proves

Theorem 2 (Mean value property).   *Let $f(z)$ be analytic in a simply connected domain D. Then the value of $f(z)$ at a point z_0 in D is equal to the mean value of $f(z)$ on any circle in D with center at z_0.*

Another important property of analytic functions is the following one.

Theorem 3 (Maximum modulus theorem).   *If $f(z)$ is analytic and nonconstant in a bounded region D and on the boundary of D, then its absolute value $|f(z)|$ cannot have a maximum at an interior point of D. Consequently, the maximum of $|f(z)|$ is taken on the boundary of D. If $f(z) \neq 0$ in D, the same is true with respect to the minimum of $|f(z)|$.*

Proof.   We show that the assumption that $|f(z)|$ has a maximum at an interior point of D leads to a contradiction. Let z_0 be that point, and let $|f(z_0)| = M$ be that maximum. Since $f(z)$ is not constant, $|f(z)|$ is not constant. Consequently, we can find a circle C of radius r with center at z_0 such that the interior of C is in D and $|f(z)|$ is smaller than M at some point P of C. Since $|f(z)|$ is continuous, it will be smaller than M on an arc C_1 of C which contains P, say, $|f(z)| \leq M - \epsilon$ ($\epsilon > 0$) for all z on C_1 (Fig. 383). If C_1 has the length l_1, the complementary arc C_2 of C has the length $2\pi r - l_1$. By applying (4), Sec. 11.2, to (1*), this section, and noting that $|z - z_0| = r$, we thus obtain

$$M = |f(z_0)| \leq \frac{1}{2\pi} \left| \int_{C_1} \frac{f(z)}{z - z_0} \, dz \right| + \frac{1}{2\pi} \left| \int_{C_2} \frac{f(z)}{z - z_0} \, dz \right|$$

$$\leq \frac{1}{2\pi} (M - \epsilon) \frac{1}{r} l_1 + \frac{1}{2\pi} M \frac{1}{r} (2\pi r - l_1) = M - \frac{\epsilon l_1}{2\pi r} < M,$$

that is, $M < M$ which is impossible. Hence, our assumption is false and the first statement of the theorem is proved.

We prove the last statement. If $f(z) \neq 0$ in D, then $1/f(z)$ is analytic in D. From the statement already proved it follows that the maximum of $1/|f(z)|$ lies on the boundary of D. But this maximum corresponds to a minimum of $|f(z)|$. This completes the proof.

From these theorems we shall now derive corresponding results about harmonic functions.

Theorem 4. *Let D be a simply connected bounded domain and let C be its boundary curve. Then if $u(x, y)$ is harmonic in a region containing D in its interior, it has the following properties.*

I. The value of $u(x, y)$ at an interior point (x_0, y_0) of D is equal to the mean value of $u(x, y)$ on any circle in D with center at (x_0, y_0).

II. The value of $u(x, y)$ at the point (x_0, y_0) is equal to the mean value of $u(x, y)$ in any circular disk in D with center at (x_0, y_0). [Cf. footnote 2 on p. 749].

III. If $u(x, y)$ is nonconstant, it has neither a maximum nor a minimum in D. Consequently, the maximum and the minimum are taken on the boundary of D. **(Maximum principle)**

IV. If $u(x, y)$ is constant on C, then $u(x, y)$ is a constant.

V. If $v(x, y)$ is harmonic in D and on C and if $v(x, y) = u(x, y)$ on C, then $v(x, y) = u(x, y)$ everywhere in D.

Proof. Statement I follows from (1) by taking the real parts on both sides, that is,

$$u(x_0, y_0) = \mathrm{Re}\, f(x_0 + iy_0) = \frac{1}{2\pi} \int_0^{2\pi} u(x_0 + r \cos \phi, y_0 + r \sin \phi) \, d\phi.$$

If we multiply both sides by r and integrate over r from 0 to r_0 where r_0 is the radius of a circular disk in D with center at (x_0, y_0), then we obtain on the left-hand side $\frac{1}{2} r_0^2 u(x_0, y_0)$ and therefore

$$u(x_0, y_0) = \frac{1}{\pi r_0^2} \int_0^{r_0} \int_0^{2\pi} u(x_0 + r \cos \phi, y_0 + r \sin \phi) r \, d\phi \, dr.$$

This proves the second statement.

We prove the statement III. Let $v(x, y)$ be a conjugate harmonic function of $u(x, y)$ in D. Then $f(z) = u(x, y) + iv(x, y)$ is analytic in D, and so is

$$F(z) = e^{f(z)}.$$

The absolute value is

$$|F(z)| = e^{\operatorname{Re} f(z)} = e^{u(x,y)}.$$

From Theorem 3 it follows that $|F(z)|$ cannot have a maximum at an interior point of D. Since e^u is a monotone increasing function of the real variable u, the statement III about the maximum of u follows. From this, the statement about the minimum follows by replacing u by $-u$.

If u is constant on C, say, $u = k$, then by III the maximum and the minimum of u are equal. From this, the statement IV follows.

If u and v are harmonic in D and on C, then $u - v$ is also harmonic in D and on C, and by assumption, $u - v = 0$ everywhere on C. Hence, by IV, $u - v = 0$ everywhere in D, and the statement V is proved. This completes the proof of Theorem 4.

The last statement of Theorem 4 is very important. It means that *a harmonic function is uniquely determined in D by its values on the boundary of D*. Usually $u(x, y)$ is required to be harmonic in D and continuous on the boundary[6] of D. Under these circumstances the maximum principle (Theorem 4, III) is still applicable. The problem of determining $u(x, y)$ when the boundary values are given is known as **Dirichlet's problem**. From Theorem 4, V we have

Theorem 5. *If for a given region and given boundary values the Dirichlet problem has a solution, the solution is unique.*

PROBLEMS

1. Verify Theorem 2 for $f(z) = (z + 2)^2$, $z_0 = 1$ and a circle of radius 1 with center at z_0.

Verify Theorem 3 for:

2. $f(z) = z^2$ and D: $-2 \leq x \leq 2$, $-1 \leq y \leq 1$

3. $f(z) = e^z$ and any bounded region R.

4. The function $f(x) = \cos x$ has a maximum at $x = 0$. Using Theorem 3, conclude that the modular surface of $f(z) = \cos z$ (cf. Sec. 10.12) cannot have a summit at $z = 0$.

5. If $f(z)$ is analytic (not a constant) in a simply connected domain D, and the curve given by $|f(z)| = c$ (c any fixed constant) lies in D and is closed, show that $f(z) = 0$ at a point in the interior of that curve. Give examples.

[6] That is, $\lim\limits_{\substack{x \to x_0 \\ y \to y_0}} u(x, y) = u(x_0, y_0)$ where (x_0, y_0) is on the boundary and (x, y) is in D.

13.5 POISSON'S INTEGRAL FORMULA

The Dirichlet problem for a circular disk can be solved by the use of the so-called Poisson[7] formula which represents a harmonic function in terms of its values given on the boundary circle of the disk. We shall derive this formula, starting from Cauchy's integral formula

(1) $$f(z) = \frac{1}{2\pi i} \int_C \frac{f(z^*)}{z^* - z}\, dz^*;$$

here C is the circle represented by

$$z^* = Re^{i\phi} \qquad\qquad (0 \leq \phi \leq 2\pi)$$

and the function

$$f(z) = u(r, \theta) + iv(r, \theta), \qquad\qquad (z = re^{i\theta})$$

is assumed to be analytic in a simply connected region containing C in its interior.

Since $dz^* = iRe^{i\phi}\, d\phi = iz^*\, d\phi$ we obtain from (1)

(2) $$f(z) = \frac{1}{2\pi} \int_0^{2\pi} f(z^*) \frac{z^*}{z^* - z}\, d\phi \qquad\qquad (z^* = Re^{i\phi},\, z = re^{i\theta}).$$

On the other hand, if we consider a point Z outside C, say, the point $Z = z^*\bar{z}^*/\bar{z}$ (whose absolute value is $R^2/r > R$), then the integrand in (1) is analytic in the disk $|z| \leq R$ and the integral is zero:

$$0 = \frac{1}{2\pi i} \int_C \frac{f(z^*)}{z^* - Z}\, dz^* = \frac{1}{2\pi} \int_0^{2\pi} f(z^*) \frac{z^*}{z^* - Z}\, d\phi.$$

By inserting $Z = z^*\bar{z}^*/\bar{z}$ and simplifying the fraction, the integral becomes

$$0 = \frac{1}{2\pi} \int_0^{2\pi} f(z^*) \frac{\bar{z}}{\bar{z} - \bar{z}^*}\, d\phi.$$

We subtract this from (2); then, since

(3) $$\frac{z^*}{z^* - z} - \frac{\bar{z}}{\bar{z} - \bar{z}^*} = \frac{z^*\bar{z}^* - z\bar{z}}{(z^* - z)(\bar{z}^* - \bar{z})},$$

we obtain

(4) $$f(z) = \frac{1}{2\pi} \int_0^{2\pi} f(z^*) \frac{z^*\bar{z}^* - z\bar{z}}{(z^* - z)(\bar{z}^* - \bar{z})}\, d\phi.$$

---

[7] SIMÉON DENIS POISSON (1781–1840), French mathematician and physicist.

From the polar representations of z and z^* we see that the quotient in the integrand is equal to

$$\frac{R^2 - r^2}{(Re^{i\phi} - re^{i\theta})(Re^{-i\phi} - re^{-i\theta})} = \frac{R^2 - r^2}{R^2 - 2Rr \cos(\theta - \phi) + r^2}.$$

Hence, by taking the real parts on both sides of (4) we obtain **Poisson's integral formula**

$$(5) \qquad u(r, \theta) = \frac{1}{2\pi} \int_0^{2\pi} u(R, \phi) \frac{R^2 - r^2}{R^2 - 2Rr \cos(\theta - \phi) + r^2} \, d\phi$$

which represents the harmonic function u in the disk $|z| \leq R$ in terms of its values $u(R, \phi)$ on the circle which bounds the disk.

It is of practical interest to note that in (5) we may use for $u(R, \phi)$ any function which is merely piecewise continuous on the interval of integration. Formula (5) then *defines* a function $u(r, \theta)$ which is harmonic in the open disk $|z| < R$ and continuous on the circle $|z| = R$. On this circle this function is equal to $u(R, \phi)$, except at points where $u(R, \phi)$ is discontinuous. The proof can be found in Ref. [G1].

From (5) we may obtain an important series development of u in terms of simple harmonic functions. We remember that the quotient in the integrand of (5) was obtained from (3), and it is not difficult to see that the right side of (3) is the real part of $(z^* + z)/(z^* - z)$. By the use of the geometric series we obtain

$$(6) \qquad \frac{z^* + z}{z^* - z} = \frac{1 + (z/z^*)}{1 - (z/z^*)} = \left(1 + \frac{z}{z^*}\right) \sum_{n=0}^{\infty} \left(\frac{z}{z^*}\right)^n = 1 + 2 \sum_{n=1}^{\infty} \left(\frac{z}{z^*}\right)^n.$$

Since $z = re^{i\theta}$ and $z^* = Re^{i\phi}$, we have

$$(7) \qquad \mathrm{Re}\left(\frac{z}{z^*}\right)^n = \mathrm{Re}\left[\frac{r^n}{R^n} e^{in\theta} e^{-in\phi}\right] = \left(\frac{r}{R}\right)^n \cos(n\theta - n\phi)$$

$$= \left(\frac{r}{R}\right)^n (\cos n\theta \cos n\phi + \sin n\theta \sin n\phi).$$

From (6) and (7) we obtain

$$\mathrm{Re}\,\frac{z^* + z}{z^* - z} = 1 + 2 \sum_{n=1}^{\infty} \frac{r^n}{R^n} (\cos n\theta \cos n\phi + i \sin n\theta \sin n\phi).$$

This expression is equal to the quotient in (5), as we have mentioned before, and by inserting the series into (5) and integrating term by term we find

$$(8) \qquad u(r, \theta) = a_0 + \sum_{n=1}^{\infty} \left(\frac{r}{R}\right)^n (a_n \cos n\theta + b_n \sin n\theta)$$

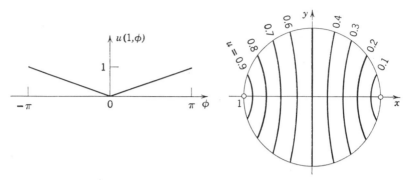

Fig. 384. Potential in Example 1.

where the coefficients are

$$a_0 = \frac{1}{2\pi} \int_0^{2\pi} u(R, \phi) \, d\phi, \qquad a_n = \frac{1}{\pi} \int_0^{2\pi} u(R, \phi) \cos n\phi \, d\phi,$$

(9)

$$b_n = \frac{1}{\pi} \int_0^{2\pi} u(R, \phi) \sin n\phi \, d\phi, \qquad n = 1, 2, \cdots,$$

the Fourier coefficients of $u(R, \phi)$. Note that for $r = R$ the series (8) becomes the Fourier series of $u(R, \phi)$, and therefore the representation (8) will be valid whenever $u(R, \phi)$ can be represented by a Fourier series.

Example 1. Find the potential $u(r, \theta)$ in the unit disk $r < 1$ having the boundary values (Fig. 384)

$$u(1, \phi) = \begin{cases} -\phi/\pi & \text{when } -\pi < \phi < 0 \\ \phi/\pi & \text{when } 0 < \phi < \pi. \end{cases}$$

Since $u(1, \phi)$ is even, $b_n = 0$, and from (9) we obtain $a_0 = \frac{1}{2}$ and

$$a_n = \frac{1}{\pi}\left[-\int_{-\pi}^0 \frac{\phi}{\pi} \cos n\phi \, d\phi + \int_0^\pi \frac{\phi}{\pi} \cos n\phi \, d\phi \right] = \frac{2}{n^2\pi^2}(\cos n\pi - 1).$$

Hence, $a_n = -4/n^2\pi^2$ when n is odd, $a_n = 0$ when $n = 2, 4, \cdots$, and the potential is

$$u(r, \theta) = \frac{1}{2} - \frac{4}{\pi^2}\left[r \cos \theta + \frac{r^3}{3^2} \cos 3\theta + \frac{r^5}{5^2} \cos 5\theta + \cdots \right].$$

PROBLEMS

1. Derive Theorem 4 I, Sec. 13.4, from (5).

2. Verify (3).

3. Show that each term in (8) is a harmonic function in the disk $r^2 < R^2$.

4. Using (8), show that the potential $u(r, \theta)$ in the unit disk $r < 1$ having the boundary values

$$u(1, \theta) = \begin{cases} -1 \text{ when } -\pi < \theta < 0 \\ 1 \text{ when } 0 < \theta < \pi \end{cases}$$

is given by the series

$$u(r, \theta) = \frac{4}{\pi}\left(r \sin \theta + \frac{r^3}{3} \sin 3\theta \right.$$

$$\left. + \frac{r^5}{5} \sin 5\theta + \cdots \right).$$

Compute some values of u by the use of the first few terms of this series and draw some of the equipotential lines (Fig. 385).

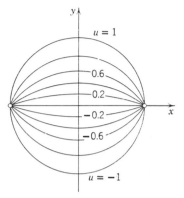

Fig. 385. Problem 4.

5. Using (7), Sec. 10.13, show that in Prob. 4,

$$u(r, \theta) = \frac{2}{\pi} \text{Im Ln} \frac{1 + z}{1 - z} = \frac{2}{\pi} [\arg (1 + z) - \arg (1 - z)].$$

6. Applying a familiar theorem of elementary geometry to the result of Prob. 5, show that the curves $u = const$ in Fig. 385 are circular arcs.

7. Show that

$$U = 1 + \frac{2}{\pi} \text{Im Ln} \frac{w + 1}{w - 1} \qquad (w = u + iv)$$

is harmonic in the upper half-plane $v > 0$ and has the values -1 for $-1 < u < 1$ and $+1$ on the remaining part of the u-axis.

8. Show that the linear transformation which maps $w_1 = -1$, $w_2 = 0$, $w_3 = 1$ onto $z_1 = -1$, $z_2 = -i$, $z_3 = 1$, respectively, is

$$z = \frac{w - i}{-iw + 1}.$$

Find the inverse $w = w(z)$, insert it into U in Prob. 7, and show that the resulting harmonic function is that in Prob. 5.

Using (8), find the potential $u(r, \theta)$ in the unit disk $r < 1$ having the given boundary values $u(1, \theta)$. Sketch a figure of the equipotential lines as explained in Prob. 4, assuming that:

9. $u(1, \theta) = \begin{cases} 0 \text{ if } -\pi < \theta < 0 \\ 1 \text{ if } 0 < \theta < \pi \end{cases}$ **10.** $u(1, \theta) = \dfrac{\theta}{\pi}$ $(-\pi < \theta < \pi)$

11. $u(1, \theta) = \left(\dfrac{\theta}{\pi}\right)^2$ $(-\pi < \theta < \pi)$

12. $u(1, \theta) = \begin{cases} \theta \text{ if } -\pi/2 < \theta < \pi/2 \\ \pi - \theta \text{ if } \pi/2 < \theta < 3\pi/2 \end{cases}$

13. $u(1, \theta) = \begin{cases} 0 \text{ if } -\pi < \theta < 0 \\ 1 \text{ if } 0 < \theta < \pi/2 \\ -1 \text{ if } \pi/2 < \theta < \pi \end{cases}$

14. $u(1, \theta) = \begin{cases} -\pi/2 \text{ if } & -\pi < \theta < -\pi/2 \\ \theta \quad \text{ if } & -\pi/2 < \theta < \pi/2 \\ \pi/2 \text{ if } & \pi/2 < \theta < \pi \end{cases}$

15. $u(1, \theta) = 1 + \cos 2\theta \qquad (-\pi < \theta < \pi)$

16. $u(1, \theta) = 4 \sin^3 \theta \qquad (-\pi < \theta < \pi)$

17. $u(1, \theta) = \sin 3\theta \qquad (-\pi < \theta < \pi)$

18. $u(1, \theta) = \cos 4\theta \qquad (-\pi < \theta < \pi)$

19. Using (7), Sec. 10.13, show that the result in Prob. 13 may be written

$$u(r, \theta) = \frac{1}{\pi} \operatorname{Im} \operatorname{Ln} \frac{(1 + iz)(1 + z^2)}{(1 - iz)(1 - z^2)}.$$

20. Show that the potential in Prob. 10 may be written

$$u(r, \theta) = \frac{2}{\pi} \operatorname{Im} \operatorname{Ln} (1 + z).$$

chapter 14

SPECIAL FUNCTIONS. ASYMPTOTIC EXPANSIONS

Two classes of nonelementary functions play an important role in engineering mathematics. The first class consists of functions arising in connection with linear differential equations; examples of such functions were considered in Chap. 3. The second class consists of functions defined by integrals which cannot be evaluated in terms of finitely many elementary functions. It includes the Gamma function, Beta function, error function, sine and cosine integrals, and Fresnel integrals, which will be considered in the present chapter.

We shall see that some of these functions (and other functions) have so-called *asymptotic expansions*. These are series which may not converge, but can nevertheless be used for computing numerical values of the functions for large values of the independent variable. We shall see that, roughly speaking, the greater the values of the independent variable are, the less work will be required in those computations. Important examples of asymptotic series will be considered in Sec. 14.3 and general properties of these series in Sec. 14.4.

Prerequisites for this chapter: elementary integral calculus.

References: Appendix 1, Part H.

Answers to problems: Appendix 2.

14.1 GAMMA AND BETA FUNCTIONS

One of the most important nonelementary functions is the **Gamma function** written $\Gamma(\alpha)$ and defined by the integral

(1) $$\Gamma(\alpha) = \int_0^\infty e^{-t} t^{\alpha-1}\, dt \qquad (\alpha > 0).$$

The Gamma function occurs in connection with various practical and theoretical considerations in physics, engineering, and mathematical statistics, and therefore the student should become familiar with its properties.

The integral representation (1) is meaningful only when α is positive.[1] To show this, write

(2) $$\Gamma(\alpha) = \int_0^c e^{-t} t^{\alpha-1}\, dt + \int_c^\infty e^{-t} t^{\alpha-1}\, dt,$$

where c is any positive number. While the last integral on the right exists for all $c > 0$ and all α (as the reader may prove), the situation with respect to the first integral is different. By using the mean-value theorem for integrals we obtain

$$\int_0^c e^{-t} t^{\alpha-1}\, dt = e^{-b} \int_0^c t^{\alpha-1}\, dt = e^{-b} \left.\frac{t^\alpha}{\alpha}\right|_0^c \qquad (\alpha \ne 0),$$

where b is some real number between 0 and c. If $\alpha > 0$, then $t^\alpha \to 0$ as $t \to 0$ so that the expression on the right and, therefore, also the integral on the left, exists. On the other hand, for $\alpha < 0$ we have $t^\alpha \to \infty$ as $t \to 0$, and that integral does not exist. For $\alpha = 0$ we obtain $e^{-b} \ln t$ which becomes infinite as $t \to 0$.

By integration by parts we find

$$\Gamma(\alpha + 1) = \int_0^\infty e^{-t} t^\alpha\, dt = -e^{-t} t^\alpha \Big|_0^\infty + \alpha \int_0^\infty e^{-t} t^{\alpha-1}\, dt \qquad (\alpha > 0).$$

The first expression on the right is zero, and the integral on the right is $\Gamma(\alpha)$. We thus obtain the important *functional relation of the Gamma function,*

(3) $$\Gamma(\alpha + 1) = \alpha\Gamma(\alpha).$$

Let α be a positive integer, say, k. Then repeated application of (3) yields

$$\Gamma(k + 1) = k\Gamma(k) = k(k - 1)\Gamma(k - 1)$$

$$\cdots\cdots\cdots$$

$$= k(k - 1) \cdots 3 \cdot 2 \cdot 1 \cdot \Gamma(1).$$

[1] Or, more generally, if we consider also complex values, for those α whose real part is positive.

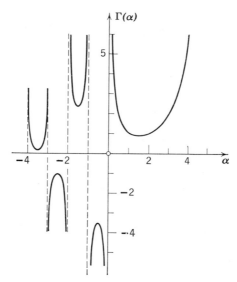

Fig. 386. Gamma function.

Now, for the remaining function $\Gamma(1)$ we obtain by integration

(4)
$$\Gamma(1) = \int_0^\omega e^{-t}\, dt = 1.$$

This proves the basic relation

(5)
$$\Gamma(k + 1) = k! \qquad\qquad (k = 0, 1, \cdots).$$

Hence, *the Gamma function can be regarded as a generalization of the elementary factorial function*; in fact, this property was the historical reason for introducing the Gamma function.[2]

By repeated application of (3) we obtain

$$\Gamma(\alpha) = \frac{\Gamma(\alpha + 1)}{\alpha} = \frac{\Gamma(\alpha + 2)}{\alpha(\alpha + 1)} = \cdots = \frac{\Gamma(\alpha + k + 1)}{\alpha(\alpha + 1)(\alpha + 2)\cdots(\alpha + k)},$$

and this relation

(6)
$$\Gamma(\alpha) = \frac{\Gamma(\alpha + k + 1)}{\alpha(\alpha + 1)\cdots(\alpha + k)} \qquad (\alpha \neq 0, -1, -2, \cdots)$$

may be used for defining the Gamma function for negative α ($\neq 0, -1, -2, \cdots$), choosing for k the smallest integer such that $\alpha + k + 1 > 0$. *Together with* (1), *this then gives a definition of* $\Gamma(\alpha)$ *for all* α *not equal to zero or a negative integer* (Fig. 386).

---

[2] Sometimes the notation $(\alpha - 1)!$ for $\Gamma(\alpha)$ is used, even for noninteger values of α, and the Gamma function is also known as the **factorial function.**

Tables of $\Gamma(\alpha)$ for $1 \leq \alpha \leq 2$ have been computed (cf. Refs. [A7], [H5]), and for other values of α the values of $\Gamma(\alpha)$ can be obtained from these tables by using (3).

It can be shown that the Gamma function may also be represented as the limit of a product,[3] namely, by the formula

$$(7) \qquad \Gamma(\alpha) = \lim_{n \to \infty} \frac{n! \, n^\alpha}{\alpha(\alpha + 1)(\alpha + 2) \cdots (\alpha + n)} \qquad (\alpha \neq 0, -1, \cdots).$$

From (6) or (7) we see that, for complex α, the Gamma function $\Gamma(\alpha)$ is a meromorphic function which has simple poles at $\alpha = 0, -1, -2, \cdots$.

Since the Gamma function increases very rapidly as α increases, it is sometimes convenient to use approximation formulas for $\Gamma(\alpha)$ when α is large. An important such formula is the **Stirling[4] formula**

$$(8) \qquad \Gamma(\alpha + 1) \approx \sqrt{2\pi\alpha} \left(\frac{\alpha}{e}\right)^\alpha \qquad (\alpha \text{ a large positive number})$$

where e is the base of the natural logarithm. The derivation of (8) (and similar more accurate but more complicated formulas) can be found in Ref. [A14] in Appendix 1.

Example 1. The following simple computation may illustrate the goodness of the approximation obtained by the Stirling formula. The values were computed by using (8) in the form

$$(9) \qquad \ln k! \approx A_k + \tfrac{1}{2} \ln 2\pi \qquad \text{where} \qquad A_k = (k + \tfrac{1}{2}) \ln k - k$$

and a five-place table of natural logarithms.

k	$\ln k$	A_k	Approximation		$k!$	Error	
			$\ln k!$	$k!$		abs.	rel.
4	1.386 29	2.238 31	3.157 25	23.5	24	0.5	2.0%
6	1.791 76	5.646 44	6.565 38	710	720	10	1.4%
8	2.079 44	9.675 24	10.594 18	39 900	40 320	4.10^2	1.0%
10	2.302 59	14.177 20	15.096 14	3 600 000	3 628 800	3.10^4	0.8%

We see that with increasing k the relative error decreases while the absolute error increases. It can be shown that, *as k approaches infinity the relative error approaches zero while the absolute error approaches infinity*, a property which should be kept in mind when using the Stirling formula.

The values of $\Gamma(k + \tfrac{1}{2})$ where k is an integer can easily be computed by using (3) and

$$(10) \qquad \Gamma(\tfrac{1}{2}) = \sqrt{\pi}.$$

[3] Cf. Ref. [A14]. Gauss introduced and used (7) as a definition of the Gamma function, while (1) was introduced by Euler.

[4] JAMES STIRLING (1692–1770), English mathematician.

To prove (10), we start from (1) and set $t = u^2$. Then $dt = 2u\, du$ and

$$(10^*) \qquad \Gamma(\tfrac{1}{2}) = \int_0^\infty e^{-t} t^{-\frac{1}{2}} \, dt = 2 \int_0^\infty e^{-u^2} \, du.$$

We square on both sides, writing v instead of u in the second integral and then writing the product of the two integrals as a double integral:

$$[\Gamma(\tfrac{1}{2})]^2 = 4 \int_0^\infty e^{-u^2} \, du \int_0^\infty e^{-v^2} \, dv = 4 \int_0^\infty \int_0^\infty e^{-(u^2 + v^2)} \, du \, dv.$$

We now introduce polar coordinates r and ϕ by setting

$$u = r \cos \phi, \qquad v = r \sin \phi.$$

The element of area in polar coordinates is $r\, dr\, d\phi$, and the limits 0 and ∞ for u and v correspond to the limits 0 and ∞ for r and 0 and $\pi/2$ for ϕ. Thus,

$$[\Gamma(\tfrac{1}{2})]^2 = 4 \int_0^{\pi/2} \int_0^\infty e^{-r^2} r \, dr \, d\phi = 4 \cdot \frac{\pi}{2} \int_0^\infty e^{-r^2} r \, dr$$

$$= 2\pi(-\tfrac{1}{2}) e^{-r^2} \bigg|_0^\infty = \pi.$$

By taking square roots on both sides we obtain (10).

We finally mention the so-called *multiplication formula*[5]

$$(11) \qquad \Gamma(\alpha)\Gamma(1 - \alpha) = \frac{\pi}{\sin \pi\alpha} \qquad (\alpha \neq 0, \pm 1, \pm 2, \cdots).$$

We now consider functions which are closely related to the Gamma function.

The functions

$$(12) \quad P(\alpha, x) = \int_0^x e^{-t} t^{\alpha-1} \, dt \quad \text{and} \quad Q(\alpha, x) = \int_x^\infty e^{-t} t^{\alpha-1} \, dt \qquad (\alpha > 0)$$

are called the **incomplete Gamma functions**. These functions of the two variables x and α occur occasionally in applications and play a certain role in mathematical statistics; we shall see later that they are related to other important special functions. From (1) we obtain the relation

$$(13) \qquad \Gamma(\alpha) = P(\alpha, x) + Q(\alpha, x).$$

Euler's **Beta function** $B(x, y)$ is defined by the integral

$$\textbf{(14)} \qquad B(x, y) = \int_0^1 t^{x-1}(1 - t)^{y-1} \, dt \qquad (x > 0, y > 0).$$

[5] For the proof see, e.g., Ref. [G5] in Appendix 1.

It can be represented in terms of Gamma functions as follows:

(15)
$$B(x, y) = \frac{\Gamma(x)\,\Gamma(y)}{\Gamma(x + y)}.$$

To derive (15), we start from

$$\Gamma(x)\,\Gamma(y) = \int_0^\infty e^{-t}t^{x-1}\,dt \int_0^\infty e^{-u}u^{y-1}\,du$$

$$= \int_0^\infty \int_0^\infty e^{-(t+u)}t^{x-1}u^{y-1}\,dt\,du.$$

We introduce new variables of integration r and ϕ by setting

(16)
$$t = r\sin^2\phi, \qquad u = r\cos^2\phi.$$

Expressing the integrand in terms of r and ϕ and replacing $dt\,du$ by $dr\,d\phi$ times the absolute value of the Jacobian (cf. Sec. 6.3)

$$\frac{\partial(t, u)}{\partial(r, \phi)} = \begin{vmatrix} \dfrac{\partial t}{\partial r} & \dfrac{\partial t}{\partial \phi} \\[2mm] \dfrac{\partial u}{\partial r} & \dfrac{\partial u}{\partial \phi} \end{vmatrix} = \begin{vmatrix} \sin^2\phi & 2r\sin\phi\cos\phi \\[1mm] \cos^2\phi & -2r\cos\phi\sin\phi \end{vmatrix} = -2r\cos\phi\sin\phi$$

corresponding to (16), we obtain

(17)
$$\Gamma(x)\,\Gamma(y) = 2\int_0^{\pi/2}\int_0^\infty e^{-r}(r\sin^2\phi)^{x-1}(r\cos^2\phi)^{y-1}r\cos\phi\sin\phi\,dr\,d\phi$$

$$= 2\int_0^\infty e^{-r}r^{x+y-1}\,dr\int_0^{\pi/2}\sin^{2x-1}\phi\,\cos^{2y-1}\phi\,d\phi.$$

The first integral on the right is $\Gamma(x + y)$. Furthermore, by setting $t = \sin^2\phi$ in (14) we have $1 - t = \cos^2\phi$, $dt = 2\sin\phi\cos\phi\,d\phi$ and, therefore,

(18)
$$B(x, y) = \int_0^1 t^{x-1}(1 - t)^{y-1}\,dt = 2\int_0^{\pi/2}\sin^{2x-1}\phi\,\cos^{2y-1}\phi\,d\phi.$$

Hence (17) assumes the form

$$\Gamma(x)\Gamma(y) = \Gamma(x + y)B(x, y),$$

and (15) is proved.

There are various integrals which can be expressed in terms of Beta functions. We mention two examples.

Example 2. From (18), (15), and (10) it follows that

(19)
$$\int_0^{\pi/2}\cos^\alpha\phi\,d\phi = \tfrac{1}{2}\,B\!\left(\tfrac{1}{2}, \frac{\alpha + 1}{2}\right) = \frac{\Gamma(\tfrac{1}{2})\Gamma\!\left(\dfrac{\alpha + 1}{2}\right)}{2\Gamma\!\left(\dfrac{\alpha}{2} + 1\right)} = \frac{\sqrt{\pi}}{2}\,\frac{\Gamma\!\left(\dfrac{\alpha + 1}{2}\right)}{\Gamma\!\left(\dfrac{\alpha}{2} + 1\right)}.$$

Example 3. Evaluate

$$I_n = \int_{-1}^{1} (1 - t^2)^n \, dt \qquad\qquad n = 0, 1, \cdots .$$

Since the integrand is an even function,

$$I_n = 2 \int_{0}^{1} (1 - t^2)^n \, dt.$$

Setting $1 - t^2 = u$ we have $t^2 = 1 - u$, $-2t \, dt = du$, and

$$I_n = 2 \int_{1}^{0} u^n \, \frac{du}{-2\sqrt{1 - u}} = \int_{0}^{1} u^n (1 - u)^{-\frac{1}{2}} \, du = B(n + 1, \tfrac{1}{2}) = \frac{\Gamma(n + 1)\,\Gamma(\tfrac{1}{2})}{\Gamma(n + \tfrac{3}{2})}$$

$$= \frac{n!\,\Gamma(\tfrac{1}{2})}{(n + \tfrac{1}{2})(n - \tfrac{1}{2})\ldots\tfrac{3}{2}\cdot\tfrac{1}{2}\Gamma(\tfrac{1}{2})} = \frac{2^{n+1}\,n!}{(2n + 1)(2n - 1)\cdots 3 \cdot 1}.$$

The student may show that by setting $t = \sin\phi$ the present integral may be transformed into that occurring in Ex. 2.

TABLE 24. GAMMA FUNCTION

α	$\Gamma(\alpha)$	α	$\Gamma(\alpha)$	α	$\Gamma(\alpha)$	α	$\Gamma(\alpha)$	α	$\Gamma(\alpha)$
1.00	1.000 000	1.20	0.918 169	1.40	0.887 264	1.60	0.893 515	1.80	0.931 384
1.02	0.988 844	1.22	0.913 106	1.42	0.886 356	1.62	0.895 924	1.82	0.936 845
1.04	0.978 438	1.24	0.908 521	1.44	0.885 805	1.64	0.898 642	1.84	0.942 612
1.06	0.968 744	1.26	0.904 397	1.46	0.885 604	1.66	0.901 668	1.86	0.948 687
1.08	0.959 725	1.28	0.900 718	1.48	0.885 747	1.68	0.905 001	1.88	0.955 071
1.10	0.951 351	1.30	0.897 471	1.50	0.886 227	1.70	0.908 639	1.90	0.961 766
1.12	0.943 590	1.32	0.894 640	1.52	0.887 039	1.72	0.912 581	1.92	0.968 774
1.14	0.936 416	1.34	0.892 216	1.54	0.888 178	1.74	0.916 826	1.94	0.976 099
1.16	0.929 803	1.36	0.890 185	1.56	0.889 639	1.76	0.921 375	1.96	0.983 743
1.18	0.923 728	1.38	0.888 537	1.58	0.891 420	1.78	0.926 227	1.98	0.991 708
1.20	0.918 169	1.40	0.887 264	1.60	0.893 515	1.80	0.931 384	2.00	1.000 000

PROBLEMS

1. Express $\Gamma(k + \tfrac{1}{2})$ where k is a positive integer, in terms of $\Gamma(\tfrac{1}{2})$ and compute $\Gamma(k + \tfrac{1}{2})$ for $k = 1, 2, 3, 4$.

2. Prove that the last integral in (2) exists for all real α and all $c > 0$.

Using Table 24, compute

3. $\Gamma(2.1)$ **4.** $\Gamma(4.2)$ **5.** $\Gamma(-1.5)$ **6.** $\Gamma(-0.3)$ **7.** $\Gamma(-2.6)$

8. Using (19), evaluate

$$\int_{0}^{\pi/2} \cos^{2n}\phi \, d\phi \qquad \text{where} \qquad n = 1, 2, \cdots .$$

9. Using (19), show that

$$\int_0^{\pi/2} \cos^{2n+1}\phi \, d\phi = \frac{\sqrt{\pi}\, n!}{2\Gamma\left(\dfrac{2n+3}{2}\right)} = \frac{2^{2n}\,(n!)^2}{(2n+1)!} \qquad (n = 0, 1, \cdots).$$

10. Using (18), evaluate $\displaystyle\int_0^{\pi/2} \sin^2 \phi \cos^2 \phi \, d\phi$.

11. Show that

$$\int_0^{\pi/2} \sin^5 \phi \cos^7 \phi \, d\phi = \tfrac{1}{120}, \qquad \int_0^1 \frac{dx}{\sqrt{x(1-x)}} = \pi.$$

12. Express $\displaystyle\int_0^{\pi/2} \sin^\alpha \phi \, d\phi \;(\alpha > 0)$ in terms of Gamma functions. Discuss in particular the cases $\alpha = 2n$ and $\alpha = 2n+1$, where $n = 0, 1, \cdots$.

13. Show that $B(x, y) = B(y, x)$.

Compute
14. $B(2, 3)$ **15.** $B(4, 3)$ **16.** $B(1, 1)$ **17.** $B(1.9, 0.6)$ **18.** $B(2.5, 1.5)$

19. Prove that the residue of $\Gamma(\alpha)$ at $\alpha = -k$ (k a non-negative integer) is $(-1)^k/k!$.

20. Derive (3) from (7).

21. Obtain the result in Ex. 3 from that in Ex. 2 by setting $t = \sin \phi$.

14.2   ERROR FUNCTION
FRESNEL INTEGRALS
SINE AND COSINE INTEGRALS

The function e^{-x^2} is an even function whose graph, the so-called *bell-shaped curve*, is shown in Fig. 387. This function and its integral frequently appear in applied mathematics. The function

(1) $$\operatorname{erf} x = \frac{2}{\sqrt{\pi}} \int_0^x e^{-t^2} \, dt$$

is called the **error function** (Fig. 388).

From (10) and (10*) in the last section we see that

(2) $$\int_0^\infty e^{-t^2} \, dt = \tfrac{1}{2}\Gamma(\tfrac{1}{2}) = \tfrac{1}{2}\sqrt{\pi}.$$

From this and (1) it follows that

(3) $$\operatorname{erf} \infty = \lim_{x \to \infty} \operatorname{erf} x = 1,$$

and this is the reason for choosing the "normalizing factor" $2/\sqrt{\pi}$ in (1).

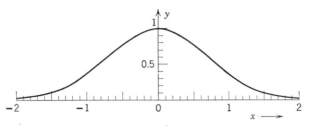

Fig. 387. Graph of $y = e^{-x^2}$ ("bell-shaped curve").

The error function cannot be represented in terms of finitely many elementary functions. Tables of function values of erf x are available (see Ref. [A7] in Appendix 1). For computing erf x for small values of $|x|$ we may use the Maclaurin series

(4) $$\text{erf } x = \frac{2}{\sqrt{\pi}} \left(x - \frac{x^3}{1!\,3} + \frac{x^5}{2!\,5} - \frac{x^7}{3!\,7} + - \cdots \right)$$

which is obtained by integrating the Maclaurin series of e^{-x^2} term by term. For large values of x we may use the asymptotic expansion of erf x, which will be derived in the next section.

Example 1.   Compute the first three decimals of erf 0.5. The terms in (4) have alternating sign and decrease in a monotone fashion when $|x|$ is sufficiently small. Hence, for those x the absolute value of the remainder after some term is less than the absolute value of the first term of the remainder (cf. Theorem 2 in Sec. 10.5). For $x = 0.5$ we have $(2/\sqrt{\pi})x^7/3!\,7 \approx 0.0002$ which shows that for our purpose it suffices to use the first three terms of (4). Thus,

$$\text{erf } 0.5 \approx 1.1284(0.5 - 0.0417 + 0.0031) = 0.521.$$

Example 2 (Relation to the normal distribution).   Express erf x in terms of the function

(5) $$\Phi(\xi) = \frac{1}{\sqrt{2\pi}} \int_{-\infty}^{\xi} e^{-\tau^2/2}\, d\tau.$$

Fig. 388. Error function.

TABLE 25. ERROR FUNCTION AND ITS DERIVATIVE.

x	erf x	$(2/\sqrt{\pi})e^{-x^2}$	x	erf x	$(2/\sqrt{\pi})e^{-x^2}$
0.00	0.000 000	1.128 379	1.00	0.842 701	0.415 107
0.05	0.056 372	1.125 562	1.1	0.880 205	0.336 480
0.10	0.112 463	1.117 152	1.2	0.910 314	0.267 344
0.15	0.167 996	1.103 274	1.3	0.934 008	0.208 208
0.20	0.222 703	1.084 135	1.4	0.952 285	0.158 942
0.25	0.276 326	1.060 014	1.5	0.966 105	0.118 930
0.30	0.328 627	1.031 261	1.6	0.976 348	0.087 229
0.35	0.379 382	0.998 284	1.7	0.983 790	0.062 711
0.40	0.428 392	0.961 541	1.8	0.989 091	0.044 192
0.45	0.475 482	0.921 532	1.9	0.992 790	0.030 525
0.50	0.520 500	0.878 783	2.0	0.995 322	0.020 667
0.55	0.563 323	0.833 837	2.2	0.998 137	0.008 922
0.60	0.603 856	0.787 243	2.4	0.999 311	0.003 556
0.65	0.642 029	0.739 547	2.6	0.999 764	0.001 308
0.70	0.677 801	0.691 275	2.8	0.999 925	0.000 444
0.75	0.711 156	0.642 931	3.0	0.999 978	0.000 139
0.80	0.742 101	0.594 986	3.2	0.999 994	0.000 040
0.85	0.770 668	0.547 870	3.4	0.999 998	0.000 011
0.90	0.796 908	0.501 969	3.6	1.000 000	0.000 003
0.95	0.820 891	0.457 619	3.8	1.000 000	0.000 001
1.00	0.842 701	0.415 107	4.0	1.000 000	0.000 000

We mention that this function $\Phi(\xi)$ is fundamental in statistics, because it is the so-called cumulative distribution function of the standardized normal distribution, and for this reason extensive tables of the function were computed.

The reader may show that $\Phi(\infty) = 1$ (see Prob. 1 at the end of this section). Since the integrand in (5) is even we thus have $\Phi(0) = \frac{1}{2}$. Consequently,

$$(6) \qquad \frac{1}{\sqrt{2\pi}}\int_0^\xi e^{-\tau^2/2}\,d\tau = \Phi(\xi) - \Phi(0) = \Phi(\xi) - \tfrac{1}{2}.$$

On the other hand, by setting $t^2 = \tau^2/2$ in (1) we obtain

$$\operatorname{erf} x = \sqrt{\frac{2}{\pi}}\int_0^{x\sqrt{2}} e^{-\tau^2/2}\,d\tau.$$

From this and (6),

$$(7) \qquad \operatorname{erf} x = 2\Phi(x\sqrt{2}) - 1.$$

TABLE 26. THE FUNCTION $\Phi(\xi)$ DEFINED BY (5).

ξ	$\Phi(\xi)$	ξ	$\Phi(\xi)$	ξ	$\Phi(\xi)$
0.0	0.5000	1.0	0.8413	2.0	0.9772
0.1	0.5398	1.1	0.8643	2.1	0.9821
0.2	0.5793	1.2	0.8849	2.2	0.9861
0.3	0.6179	1.3	0.9032	2.3	0.9893
0.4	0.6554	1.4	0.9192	2.4	0.9918
0.5	0.6915	1.5	0.9332	2.5	0.9938
0.6	0.7257	1.6	0.9452	2.6	0.9953
0.7	0.7580	1.7	0.9554	2.7	0.9965
0.8	0.7881	1.8	0.9641	2.8	0.9974
0.9	0.8159	1.9	0.9713	2.9	0.9981
1.0	0.8413	2.0	0.9772	3.0	0.9987

The function

(8)
$$\text{erfc } x = \frac{2}{\sqrt{\pi}} \int_x^\infty e^{-t^2} \, dt$$

is called the **complementary error function.** From (3) it follows that

(9)
$$\text{erfc } x = 1 - \text{erf } x.$$

Example 3 (Relations to incomplete Gamma functions). By setting $t^2 = \tau$ in (1) we have $dt = d\tau/2\sqrt{\tau}$. Therefore,

$$\text{erf } x = \frac{1}{\sqrt{\pi}} \int_0^{x^2} e^{-\tau} \tau^{-\frac{1}{2}} \, d\tau.$$

From this and (12) in the last section we obtain the relation

(10)
$$\text{erf } x = \frac{1}{\sqrt{\pi}} P(\tfrac{1}{2}, x^2).$$

The reader may derive a similar relation between erfc x and $Q(\alpha, x)$.

We finally mention some other important integrals which cannot be evaluated in terms of finitely many elementary functions.

The **Fresnel integrals**[6] (Fig. 389)

(11)
$$C(x) = \int_0^x \cos (t^2) \, dt, \qquad S(x) = \int_0^x \sin (t^2) \, dt$$

---

[6] AUGUSTIN FRESNEL (1788–1827), French physicist and mathematician. For tables see Ref. [A6], [A7]; cf. also *Acta mathematica*, vol. 85 (1951), p. 180, and vol. 89 (1953), p. 130.

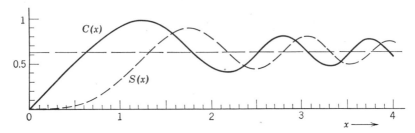

Fig. 389. Fresnel integrals.

and their complementary functions

$$(12) \qquad c(x) = \int_x^\infty \cos(t^2)\, dt, \qquad s(x) = \int_x^\infty \sin(t^2)\, dt$$

appear in various applications, for example, in optics and in antenna theory. We have shown that

$$(13) \quad C(\infty) = \int_0^\infty \cos(t^2)\, dt = \frac{1}{2}\sqrt{\frac{\pi}{2}}, \quad S(\infty) = \int_0^\infty \sin(t^2)\, dt = \frac{1}{2}\sqrt{\frac{\pi}{2}},$$

see (17) in Sec. 11.15. Therefore,

$$(14) \qquad c(x) = \frac{1}{2}\sqrt{\frac{\pi}{2}} - C(x), \qquad s(x) = \frac{1}{2}\sqrt{\frac{\pi}{2}} - S(x).$$

The **sine integral** (Fig. 390) is defined as follows:

$$(15) \qquad\qquad\qquad \mathrm{Si}(x) = \int_0^x \frac{\sin t}{t}\, dt.$$

(The corresponding integral involving $\cos t$ instead of $\sin t$ does not exist. Why?) Its complementary function is

$$(16) \qquad\qquad\qquad \mathrm{si}(x) = \int_x^\infty \frac{\sin t}{t}\, dt.$$

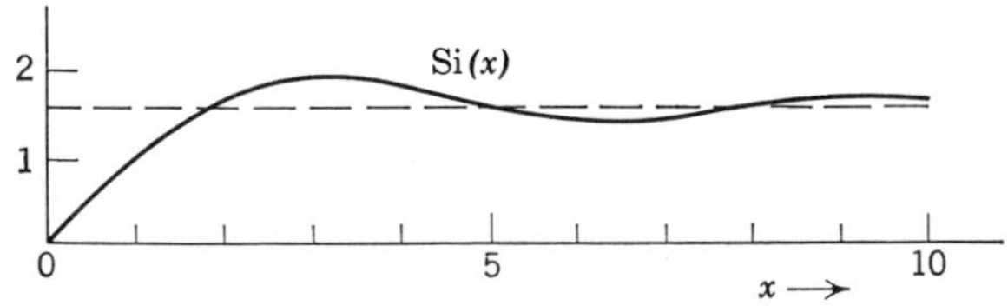

Fig. 390. Sine integral.

Since

(17) $$\text{Si}(\infty) = \int_0^{\infty} \frac{\sin t}{t}\, dt = \frac{\pi}{2} \qquad \text{(see p. 708)},$$

we have

(18) $$\text{si}(x) = \frac{\pi}{2} - \text{Si}(x).$$

The function

(19) $$\text{ci}(x) = \int_x^{\infty} \frac{\cos t}{t}\, dt$$

is called the **cosine integral**.

TABLE 27. SINE AND COSINE INTEGRALS

x	$\text{Si}(x)$	$\text{ci}(x)$	x	$\text{Si}(x)$	$\text{ci}(x)$	x	$\text{Si}(x)$	$\text{ci}(x)$
0.0	0.0000	∞	2.0	1.6054	−0.4230	5	1.5499	0.1900
0.2	0.1996	1.0422	2.2	1.6876	−0.3751	6	1.4247	0.0681
0.4	0.3965	0.3788	2.4	1.7525	−0.3173	7	1.4546	−0.0767
0.6	0.5881	0.0223	2.6	1.8004	−0.2533	8	1.5742	−0.1224
0.8	0.7721	−0.1983	2.8	1.8321	−0.1865	9	1.6650	−0.0554
1.0	0.9461	−0.3374	3.0	1.8487	−0.1196	10	1.6583	0.0455
1.2	1.1080	−0.4205	3.2	1.8514	−0.0553	11	1.5783	0.0896
1.4	1.2562	−0.4620	3.4	1.8419	0.0045	12	1.5050	0.0498
1.6	1.3892	−0.4717	3.6	1.8219	0.0580	13	1.4994	−0.0268
1.8	1.5058	−0.4568	3.8	1.7934	0.1038	14	1.5562	−0.0694
2.0	1.6054	−0.4230	4.0	1.7582	0.1410	15	1.6182	−0.0463

PROBLEMS

1. Show that

$$\int_{-\infty}^{\infty} e^{-t^2}\, dt = \sqrt{\pi}, \qquad \int_{-\infty}^{\infty} e^{-t^2/2}\, dt = \sqrt{2\pi}, \qquad \int_{0}^{\infty} e^{-t^2/2}\, dt = \sqrt{\frac{\pi}{2}}.$$

2. Show that erf x, $C(x)$, $S(x)$, and Si(x) are odd functions.

3. Derive (4) as indicated in the text. Why is term-by-term integration permissible?

4. Compute the first three decimals of erf 1.0.

5. Carry out the derivation of (9).

6. Determine the points of inflection of the curve $y = e^{-x^2}$.

7. Express

$$F(x) = \frac{1}{\sqrt{2\pi}\,\sigma} \int_{-\infty}^{x} e^{-\frac{1}{2}((t-\mu)/\sigma)^2} \, dt$$

where μ and $\sigma(\neq 0)$ are constants, in terms of the function $\Phi(\xi)$ defined by (5).

8. Plot graphs of erfc x and si(x).

9. Find the Maclaurin series of $C(x)$.

10. Find the Maclaurin series of $S(x)$.

11. Show that Si(x) does not have real zeros (except at $x = 0$).

12. Determine the location of the maxima and minima of $C(x)$, $S(x)$, and Si(x).

13. Express $C(x)$ and $S(x)$ in terms of error functions. *Hint:* consider the functions $C(x) + i\,S(x)$ and $C(x) - i\,S(x)$.

14. Find the Maclaurin series of Si(x).

15. Show that

$$C(x) = \frac{1}{2} \int_{0}^{x^2} \frac{\cos \tau}{\sqrt{\tau}} \, d\tau, \quad S(x) = \frac{1}{2} \int_{0}^{x^2} \frac{\sin \tau}{\sqrt{\tau}} \, d\tau.$$

16. Determine the points at which the mappings defined by $C(z)$, $S(z)$, and Si(z), $z = x + iy$, are not conformal.

17. Show that $C(z)$, $S(z)$, and Si(z) are entire functions of $z = x + iy$.

18. Show that erfc $x = \dfrac{1}{\sqrt{\pi}} Q(\frac{1}{2}, x^2)$ where $Q(\alpha, x)$ is the incomplete Gamma function (Sec. 14.1).

19. Show that $\Phi(-\xi) = 1 - \Phi(\xi)$ where $\Phi(\xi)$ is defined by (5).

20. Prove that the maxima of Si(x) on the positive x-axis form a monotone decreasing sequence.

21. Show that for small $|x|$, $S(x) \approx x^3/3$ and determine those x for which the error of this approximation is less than 1 per cent.

14.3 ASYMPTOTIC EXPANSIONS

Asymptotic expansions are (in general divergent) series which are of great practical importance for computing values of a function $f(x)$ for large x. It is clear that the Maclaurin series of $f(x)$, if it exists and converges for large x, is not suitable for that purpose, because the number of terms to be used for obtaining a prescribed accuracy increases rapidly as x increases. For a Taylor series with center at a, where a is large, the situation will be similar for all those x which are far apart from a. We shall see that the larger x is, the fewer terms of an asymptotic expansion we need for obtaining a required accuracy. On the other hand, the accuracy is limited, and it decreases as x decreases so that asymptotic expansions can be used for large x only.

The variables and functions to be considered in this section are assumed to be real.

A series of the form

$$c_0 + \frac{c_1}{x} + \frac{c_2}{x^2} + \cdots \qquad (c_0, c_1, \cdots \text{ constant})$$

(which need not converge for any value of x) *is called an* **asymptotic expansion**, *or* **asymptotic series**, *of a function $f(x)$ which is defined for every sufficiently large value of x if, for every fixed $n = 0, 1, 2, \cdots$,*

(1)
$$\left[f(x) - \left(c_0 + \frac{c_1}{x} + \frac{c_2}{x^2} + \cdots + \frac{c_n}{x^n} \right) \right] x^n \to 0 \quad \text{as } x \to \infty,$$

and we shall then write

$$f(x) \sim c_0 + \frac{c_1}{x} + \frac{c_2}{x^2} + \cdots.$$

If a function $f(x)$ has an asymptotic expansion, then this expansion is unique, because its coefficients $c_0, c_1, \cdots$ are uniquely determined by (1). In fact, from (1) we obtain

(1*)
$$f(x) - c_0 \to 0 \qquad \text{or} \qquad c_0 = \lim_{x \to \infty} f(x),$$
$$\left[f(x) - c_0 - \frac{c_1}{x} \right] x \to 0 \qquad \text{or} \qquad c_1 = \lim_{x \to \infty} [f(x) - c_0] x, \quad \text{etc.}$$

On the other hand, different functions may have the same asymptotic expansion. In fact, let $f(x) = e^{-x}$. Then, since $e^{-x} \to 0$, $x e^{-x} \to 0$, etc., we see from (1*) that $c_0 = 0$, $c_1 = 0$, etc. Hence,

$$e^{-x} \sim 0 + \frac{0}{x} + \cdots.$$

Thus, if $g(x)$ has an asymptotic expansion, then $g(x) + e^{-x}$ has certainly the same asymptotic expansion.

For applications it is advantageous to *extend the definition* by writing

$$f(x) \sim g(x) + h(x) \left(c_0 + \frac{c_1}{x} + \frac{c_2}{x^2} + \cdots \right)$$

whenever

$$\frac{f(x) - g(x)}{h(x)} \sim c_0 + \frac{c_1}{x} + \frac{c_2}{x^2} + \cdots$$

in the sense of the above definition.

Only in rare cases may we determine the coefficients of an asymptotic expansion directly from (1*). In general, other methods will be more suitable, for example, successive integration by parts. We shall illustrate this procedure by Ex. 1, and we shall also compare the typical behavior of the terms of an asymptotic series with that of the terms of a Maclaurin series.

Example 1 (Asymptotic series of the error function).   We have

$$\operatorname{erf} x = 1 - \operatorname{erfc} x,$$

and by setting $t^2 = \tau$, $dt = d\tau/2\sqrt{\tau}$,

$$\operatorname{erfc} x = \frac{2}{\sqrt{\pi}} \int_x^\infty e^{-t^2}\, dt = \frac{1}{\sqrt{\pi}} \int_{x^2}^\infty e^{-\tau} \tau^{-\frac12}\, d\tau.$$

Repeated integration by parts will lead to integrals of the form

(2)
$$F_n(x) = \int_{x^2}^\infty e^{-\tau} \tau^{-(2n+1)/2}\, d\tau, \qquad n = 0, 1, \cdots.$$

Note that $\operatorname{erfc} x = F_0(x)/\sqrt{\pi}$. By integration by parts we obtain

$$F_n(x) = -e^{-\tau}\, \tau^{-(2n+1)/2} \Big|_{x^2}^\infty - \frac{2n+1}{2} \int_{x^2}^\infty e^{-\tau} \tau^{-(2n+3)/2}\, d\tau.$$

The integral on the right is $F_{n+1}(x)$ and, therefore,

$$F_n(x) = \frac{1}{x^{2n+1}}\, e^{-x^2} - \frac{2n+1}{2}\, F_{n+1}(x), \qquad n = 0, 1, \cdots.$$

By multiplying by e^{x^2} on both sides this recurrence relation becomes

$$e^{x^2} F_n(x) = \frac{1}{x^{2n+1}} - \frac{2n+1}{2}\, e^{x^2} F_{n+1}(x).$$

Repeated application of this formula yields

$$e^{x^2} F_0(x) = \frac{1}{x} - \tfrac12\, e^{x^2} F_1(x)$$

$$= \frac{1}{x} - \frac{1}{2x^3} + \frac12 \cdot \frac32\, e^{x^2} F_2(x)$$

(3)
$$\cdots\cdots\cdots\cdots\cdots\cdots$$

$$= \left[\frac{1}{x} - \frac{1}{2x^3} + \frac{1\cdot 3}{2^2 x^5} - + \cdots + (-1)^{n-1} \frac{1\cdot 3\cdots(2n-3)}{2^{n-1} x^{2n-1}} \right]$$

$$+ (-1)^n\, \frac{1\cdot 3\cdots(2n-1)}{2^n}\, e^{x^2} F_n(x).$$

We show that the series obtained in this way is an asymptotic expansion,

(4)
$$e^{x^2} F_0(x) \sim \frac{1}{x} - \frac{1}{2x^3} + \frac{1\cdot 3}{2^2 x^5} - + \cdots.$$

Let S_{2n-1} denote the expression in brackets in (3). Then from (3) we obtain

(5)
$$[e^{x^2} F_0(x) - S_{2n-1}]\, x^{2n-1} = K_n e^{x^2} x^{2n-1} F_n(x)$$

where
$$K_n = (-1)^n\, \frac{1\cdot 3\cdots(2n-1)}{2^n}.$$

We have to show that for each fixed $n = 1, 2, \cdots$ the expression on the right approaches zero as x approaches infinity. In (2),

$$\frac{1}{\tau^{(2n+1)/2}} \leq \frac{1}{x^{2n+1}} \qquad \text{for all } \tau \geq x^2.$$

Hence we obtain the following inequality:

$$(6) \qquad F_n(x) = \int_{x^2}^{\infty} \frac{e^{-\tau}}{\tau^{(2n+1)/2}} \, d\tau < \frac{1}{x^{2n+1}} \int_{x^2}^{\infty} e^{-\tau} \, d\tau = \frac{e^{-x^2}}{x^{2n+1}}.$$

From this we immediately see that

$$|K_n| \, e^{x^2} x^{2n-1} F_n(x) < \frac{|K_n|}{x^2} \to 0 \qquad\qquad (x \to \infty).$$

This proves that the series in (4) is an asymptotic expansion of the function on the left-hand side of (4). Since

$$\operatorname{erf} x = 1 - \operatorname{erfc} x = 1 - \frac{F_0(x)}{\sqrt{\pi}}$$

it follows that the desired asymptotic series of the error function is

$$(7) \qquad \operatorname{erf} x \sim 1 - \frac{1}{\sqrt{\pi}} e^{-x^2} \left(\frac{1}{x} - \frac{1}{2x^3} + \frac{1 \cdot 3}{2^2 x^5} - \frac{1 \cdot 3 \cdot 5}{2^3 x^7} + - \cdots \right).$$

For large x we thus have the simple approximation

$$(7^*) \qquad\qquad\qquad \operatorname{erf} x \approx 1 - \frac{1}{\sqrt{\pi} \, x} e^{-x^2}.$$

We now want to illustrate the use of (7) in numerical computation. From (5) and (6) it follows that

$$|e^{x^2} F_0(x) - S_{2n-1}| = \frac{1 \cdot 3 \cdots (2n-1)}{2^n} e^{x^2} F_n(x) < \frac{1 \cdot 3 \cdots (2n-1)}{2^n} \frac{1}{x^{2n+1}},$$

and for sufficiently large x the expression on the right is very small. This shows that for such x, S_{2n-1} is a very good approximation to $e^{x^2} F_0(x)$, and so, for large x, the error function can be computed very accurately by means of (7). It turns out that even for relatively small $|x|$ the results are surprisingly accurate.

For instance, let us take $x = 2$ and show that by taking the sum of a suitable number of terms in (7) we obtain three digit accuracy of erf 2 ($= 0.99532$). Table 28 shows that the terms in (7) first decrease in absolute value and then (for $n > 5$) again increase (cf. Fig. 391). This is typical for an asymptotic expansion. In general, the greatest accuracy is obtained by taking the sum of the terms up to the smallest in absolute value. In our case, this is the sum of the first five terms (corresponding to $n = 1, \cdots, 5$); by taking more terms the error again increases and, therefore, the accuracy is limited to three digits. This limited accuracy is in contrast to the situation in the case of a Maclaurin series where, for every fixed x for which the series converges, we can reach any degree of accuracy by taking the sum of sufficiently many terms. Hence, for fixed x, when using an asymptotic expansion we have a limited degree of accuracy. However, the advantage of the asymptotic expansion is obvious. In our case we

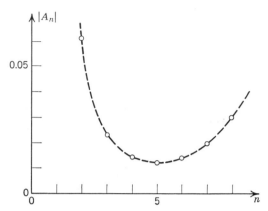

Fig. 391. Absolute values of the terms A_n of the asymptotic expansion (7) for $x = 2$.

need only two terms (the constant term and the term involving $1/x$) to obtain the first three decimals of erf 2, and the error of this approximation is $1/2$ unit of the third decimal (0.000 49). Table 29 shows the values of the terms of the Maclaurin series

$$(8) \qquad \frac{\sqrt{\pi}}{2} \operatorname{erf} x = x - \frac{x^3}{1!\,3} + \frac{x^5}{2!\,5} - \frac{x^7}{3!\,7} + - \cdots$$

when $x = 2$ and Fig. 392 their absolute values. We see that to compute the first three decimals of erf 2 from (8) we must use the sum of the first fourteen terms, the last one of which contains x^{27}. If four or more correct digits of erf 2 are needed, then we cannot use the asymptotic expansion, as we see from the error in Table 28.

TABLE 28. COMPUTATION OF erf x FOR $x = 2$ BY MEANS OF THE
ASYMPTOTIC EXPANSION

n	$A_1 = 1/x$ $A_n = (-1)^{n-1} \dfrac{1.3 \cdots (2n-3)}{2^{n-1} x^{2n-1}}$	$1 - \dfrac{1}{\sqrt{\pi}} e^{-x^2}(A_1 + \cdots + A_n)$	Absolute value of error
1	0.500 000	0.994 83	0.000 49
2	−0.062 500	0.995 48	0.000 16
3	0.023 438	0.995 24	0.000 08
4	−0.014 648	0.995 39	0.000 07
5	0.012 817	0.995 26	0.000 06
6	−0.014 420	0.995 40	0.000 08
7	0.019 827	0.995 20	0.000 12
8	−0.032 219	0.995 53	0.000 21

TABLE 29. TERMS OF THE MAC-
LAURIN SERIES (8) FOR $x = 2$

n	$\dfrac{(-1)^n 2^{2n+1}}{n!\,(2n+1)}$
0	2.000 00
1	−2.666 67
2	3.200 00
3	−3.047 62
4	2.370 37
5	−1.551 52
6	0.875 21
7	−0.433 44
8	0.191 22
9	−0.076 04
10	0.027 52
11	−0.009 14
12	0.002 80
13	−0.000 80

TABLE 30. ERROR ESTIMATE FOR THE COMPUTATION OF erf x
FROM THE ASYMPTOTIC EXPANSION (7) WHEN $x = 2$
AND THE SUM OF THE FIRST $n + 1$ TERMS IS USED

n	Error bound $k(2, n)$	Absolute value of actual error
1	0.000 65	0.000 49
2	0.000 25	0.000 16
3	0.000 16	0.000 08
4	0.000 14	0.000 07
5	0.000 15	0.000 06
6	0.000 21	0.000 08
7	0.000 34	0.000 12
8	0.000 63	0.000 21

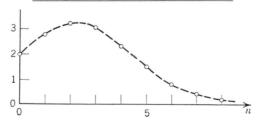

Fig. 392. Absolute values of the terms of the Maclaurin series (8) for $x = 2$ shown in Table 29.

We mention that we can obtain a bound for the absolute value of the error of our approximate values in Table 28 as follows. From (3) and

$$\operatorname{erf} x = 1 - \operatorname{erfc} x = 1 - \frac{1}{\sqrt{\pi}} F_0(x)$$

we see that the absolute value of the error is

$$\frac{1 \cdot 3 \cdots (2n-1)}{2^n \sqrt{\pi}} |F_n(x)|.$$

From (6) it follows that this expression is less than

$$k(x, n) = \frac{1 \cdot 3 \cdots (2n-1)}{2^n \sqrt{\pi}} \frac{e^{-x^2}}{x^{2n+1}} \qquad (x > 0, \ n = 1, 2, \cdots),$$

and this is the desired bound. Numerical values for $x = 2$ are shown in Table 30.

To understand completely our result concerning the asymptotic expansion, the reader should keep in mind that $x = 2$ is relatively small; for $x = 5$, for example, we obtain from (7*)

$$\operatorname{erf} 5 \approx 1 - \frac{1}{\sqrt{\pi}} \frac{e^{-25}}{5} = 0.99999\ 99999\ 98433;$$

the first thirteen decimals are correct, the error is three units of the fourteenth decimal. However, we wish to warn the reader that the present case may be misleading; for other asymptotic expansions a similarly favourable situation may arise not at $x = 2$ or 5, but only for much larger x, perhaps for $x = 20$ or $x = 100$.

PROBLEMS

1. Compute a table of erf x for $x = 0, 0.5, 1.0, \cdots, 5.0$ (two decimal places).

2. Which term of (7) is the smallest in absolute value when $x = 1$? When $x = 2$? When $x = 3$?

3. Find a method for determining the smallest term in absolute value of the asymptotic series $c_0 + c_1/x + \cdots$, where x is fixed.

4. Why is it important to determine the smallest term in absolute value of an asymptotic series to be used for computations?

5. Find a method for determining the largest term in absolute value of a Maclaurin series $a_0 + a_1 x + a_2 x^2 + \cdots$, where x is fixed.

6. Which term of the Maclaurin series of e^x is the largest when $x = 2$? When $x = 3$? When $x = n$?

7. Draw figures similar to Figs. 391 and 392 for erf x when $x = 1$.

8. Same task as in Prob. 7, for $x = 3$.

9. Show that the series $1 + \frac{1}{x} + \frac{1}{2! \, x^2} + \cdots$ [which converges for $|x| > 0$ and represents $e^{1/x}$] is an asymptotic expansion of $e^{1/x}$.

10. Show that $\sin \frac{1}{x} \sim \frac{1}{x} - \frac{1}{3! \, x^3} + \frac{1}{5! \, x^5} - + \cdots$.

11. Integrating by parts, find the asymptotic expansion of the incomplete Gamma function $Q(0, x)$ defined by (12) in Sec. 14.1.

12. Find the asymptotic expansion of $Q(\alpha, x)$ where α is a fixed positive number and the variable x is real.

13. Find the asymptotic expansion of the incomplete Gamma function $P(\alpha, x)$ where α is fixed and positive and the variable x is real.

14.4 FURTHER PROPERTIES OF ASYMPTOTIC EXPANSIONS

For practical applications it is useful to know that asymptotic series may be added, multiplied, and under certain restrictions also integrated and differentiated term by term. Let us formulate these properties in a precise manner.

Theorem 1. *If*

$$f(x) \sim a_0 + \frac{a_1}{x} + \frac{a_2}{x^2} + \cdots \qquad and \qquad g(x) \sim b_0 + \frac{b_1}{x} + \frac{b_2}{x^2} + \cdots$$

then the function $Af + Bg$, where A and B are constants, has the asymptotic expansion

(1) $$Af(x) + Bg(x) \sim Aa_0 + Bb_0 + \frac{Aa_1 + Bb_1}{x} + \frac{Aa_2 + Bb_2}{x^2} + \cdots$$

and the function fg has the asymptotic expansion

(2) $$f(x)g(x) \sim c_0 + \frac{c_1}{x} + \frac{c_2}{x^2} + \cdots$$

whose coefficients are given by the formula

$$c_n = a_0 b_n + a_1 b_{n-1} + \cdots + a_n b_0.$$

Proof.   The simple proof of (1) is left to the reader. We prove the last statement. We must show that for any fixed nonnegative integer n,

(3) $(fg - S_n)x^n \to 0$ as $x \to \infty$

where

$$S_n(x) = c_0 + \frac{c_1}{x} + \cdots + \frac{c_n}{x^n}$$

with the coefficients $c_0, \cdots, c_n$ given in the theorem.
   We choose an arbitrary fixed n and write

$$f(x) = s_n(x) + \frac{h(x)}{x^n} \qquad where \qquad s_n(x) = a_0 + \frac{a_1}{x} + \cdots + \frac{a_n}{x^n}.$$

Then we immediately have

$$[f(x) - s_n(x)]x^n = h(x).$$

From this and the definition of an asymptotic expansion it follows that $h(x)$ must approach zero as $x \to \infty$. Similarly, if we write

$$g(x) = s_n^*(x) + \frac{l(x)}{x^n} \qquad \text{where} \qquad s_n^*(x) = b_0 + \frac{b_1}{x} + \cdots + \frac{b_n}{x^n},$$

then $l(x) \to 0$ as $x \to \infty$. From these representations we obtain

$$fg = s_n s_n^* + \frac{h+l}{x^n} + \frac{hl}{x^{2n}}.$$

By multiplying term by term and collecting like powers of x we can readily verify that

$$s_n s_n^* = S_n + T_n$$

where T_n is the sum of terms involving the powers $1/x^{n+1}, \cdots, 1/x^{2n}$. Clearly, $x^n T_n \to 0$ as $x \to \infty$. Consequently, in (3),

$$fg - S_n = T_n + \frac{h+l}{x^n} + \frac{hl}{x^{2n}}.$$

We multiply by x^n on both sides. Then the resulting expression on the right approaches zero as $x \to \infty$, because $x^n T_n \to 0$, $l \to 0$, and $h \to 0$. Hence, the expression on the left-hand side of (3) approaches zero, and the proof is complete.

We now consider the term by term integration of asymptotic expansions.

Theorem 2. *Let $f(x)$ be continuous for all sufficiently large x, and let*

$$f(x) \sim \frac{c_2}{x^2} + \frac{c_3}{x^3} + \cdots.$$

Then for those x,

(4)
$$\int_x^\infty f(t)\, dt \sim \frac{c_2}{x} + \frac{c_3}{2x^2} + \frac{c_4}{3x^3} + \cdots.$$

Proof. Let $F(x)$ denote the integral in (4) and let $S_{n-1}(x)$ denote the integral of

$$s_n(x) = \frac{c_2}{x^2} + \cdots + \frac{c_n}{x^n},$$

that is,

$$S_{n-1}(x) = \int_x^\infty s_n(t)\, dt = \frac{c_2}{x} + \frac{c_3}{2x^2} + \cdots + \frac{c_n}{(n-1)x^{n-1}}.$$

By definition of an asymptotic expansion, for every $n = 0, 1, \cdots,$

$$|f(x) - s_n(x)| \, x^n \to 0 \qquad\qquad \text{as } x \to \infty.$$

Because of continuity of f this implies that, given any $\epsilon > 0$ we can find an x_0 such that for all $x > x_0$,

$$|f(x) - s_n(x)| x^n < \epsilon \qquad \text{or} \qquad |f(x) - s_n(x)| < \frac{\epsilon}{x^n}.$$

From this we obtain for all $x > x_0$

$$|F(x) - S_{n-1}(x)| = \left| \int_x^\infty f(t)\, dt - \int_x^\infty s_n(t)\, dt \right| = \left| \int_x^\infty [f(t) - s_n(t)]\, dt \right|$$

$$\leq \int_x^\infty |f(t) - s_n(t)|\, dt < \epsilon \int_x^\infty \frac{dt}{t^n} = \frac{\epsilon}{(n-1)x^{n-1}}.$$

By multiplying on both sides by the positive quantity x^{n-1} we have

$$|F(x) - S_{n-1}(x)| x^{n-1} < \frac{\epsilon}{n-1} \qquad \text{when } x > x_0(\epsilon).$$

Since $\epsilon \, (>0)$ may be chosen as small as we please, it follows that

$$|F(x) - S_{n-1}(x)| \, x^{n-1} \to 0 \qquad\qquad \text{as } x \to \infty,$$

and the proof is complete.

If $f(x)$ is continuous for all sufficiently large x and

$$f(x) \sim c_0 + \frac{c_1}{x} + \frac{c_2}{x^2} + \cdots,$$

then we conclude from Theorem 2 that

$$(4^*) \qquad \int_x^\infty \left[f(t) - c_0 - \frac{c_1}{t} \right] dt \sim \frac{c_2}{x} + \frac{c_3}{2x^2} + \frac{c_4}{3x^2} + \cdots.$$

If $f(x)$ has an asymptotic expansion, it does not follow that the derivative $f'(x)$ has an asymptotic expansion. For example, from (1^*) in the last section we obtain

$$f(x) = e^{-x} \sin(e^x) \sim 0 + \frac{0}{x} + \frac{0}{x^2} + \cdots$$

but the derivative of $f(x)$, which is given by the formula

$$f'(x) = -e^{-x} \sin(e^x) + e^{-x} \cos(e^x) e^x = -f(x) + \cos(e^x)$$

does not have an asymptotic expansion. (Why?) However, if the derivative $f'(x)$ of a function $f(x)$ has an asymptotic expansion, it can be obtained by termwise differentiation of that of $f(x)$. In fact, the following theorem holds true.

Theorem 3. *If*

$$f(x) \sim c_0 + \frac{c_1}{x} + \frac{c_2}{x^2} + \cdots \tag{5}$$

and $f(x)$ has a continuous derivative $f'(x)$ which has an asymptotic expansion, then this expansion is

$$f'(x) \sim -\frac{c_1}{x^2} - \frac{2c_2}{x^3} - \frac{3c_3}{x^4} - \cdots . \tag{6}$$

Proof. By assumption,

$$f'(x) \sim a_0 + \frac{a_1}{x} + \frac{a_2}{x^2} + \cdots \tag{7}$$

and we have to show that the coefficients a_n are such that (6) and (7) are identical. We first show that $a_0 = 0$ and $a_1 = 0$. From (5) and the definition of an asymptotic expansion we have

$$(8) \qquad (a) \quad \lim_{x \to \infty} f(x) = c_0, \qquad (b) \quad \lim_{x \to \infty} [f(x) - c_0]x = c_1.$$

The corresponding relations for the asymptotic series (7) are

$$(9) \qquad (a) \quad \lim_{x \to \infty} f'(x) = a_0, \qquad (b) \quad \lim_{x \to \infty} [f'(x) - a_0]x = a_1.$$

We may relate f and f' by the formula

$$f(x) = \int_{x_0}^{x} f'(t)\, dt + k \qquad [x_0 (>0) \text{ and } k \text{ constant}]. \tag{10}$$

From this and (8a) it follows that

$$\lim_{x \to \infty} \int_{x_0}^{x} f'(t)\, dt + k = c_0.$$

Now (9a) shows that if a_0 were not zero, the limit of the integral would not exist. Hence $a_0 = 0$. Then (9b) becomes

$$(9b*) \qquad \lim_{x \to \infty} xf'(x) = a_1.$$

By definition this means that for any preassigned $\epsilon > 0$ and all sufficiently large x,

$$(11) \quad a_1 - \epsilon < xf'(x) < a_1 + \epsilon \quad \text{or} \quad \frac{a_1 - \epsilon}{x} < f'(x) < \frac{a_1 + \epsilon}{x} .$$

From (8b) and (10) we obtain

$$\lim_{x \to \infty} \left(\int_{x_0}^{x} f'(t)\, dt + k - c_0 \right) x = c_1.$$

From (11) we see that for $a_1 \neq 0$ this limit does not exist. Hence $a_1 = 0$, and (7) becomes

$$f'(x) \sim \frac{a_2}{x^2} + \frac{a_3}{x^3} + \cdots .$$

Consequently, from (10) and Theorem 2 we now obtain

$$(12) \qquad f(x) = \int_{x_0}^{\infty} f'(t)\, dt - \int_x^{\infty} f'(t)\, dt + k$$

$$\sim \int_{x_0}^{\infty} f'(t)\, dt + k - \frac{a_2}{x} - \frac{a_3}{x^2} - \cdots ,$$

the first integral on the right being a constant. If a given function has an asymptotic expansion, it is unique. We may thus compare corresponding terms in (5) and (12), finding $a_2 = -c_1$, $a_3 = -2c_2$, etc. With these coefficients the series (6) and (7) become identical, and the theorem is proved.

If we know that a function $f(x)$ satisfies the assumptions of Theorem 3 and is a solution of a first-order differential equation, then we may determine the coefficients of its asymptotic expansion by substituting (5) and (6) in the differential equation.

Example 1. Let

$$y = f(x) = e^x \int_x^{\infty} \frac{e^{-t}}{t}\, dt \qquad (x > 0).$$

Then

$$y' = f'(x) = e^x \int_x^{\infty} \frac{e^{-t}}{t}\, dt - e^x \frac{e^{-x}}{x} = y - \frac{1}{x}.$$

Hence, $f(x)$ satisfies the linear differential equation

$$(13) \qquad y' - y + \frac{1}{x} = 0.$$

It may be proved directly that this equation has only one solution y such that y and y' exist for positive x and have an asymptotic expansion. By substituting (5) and (6) into (13) and equating the coefficient of each power to x to zero we obtain

$$-c_0 = 0, \quad -c_1 + 1 = 0, \quad -c_1 - c_2 = 0, \quad \cdots , \quad -nc_n - c_{n+1} = 0, \cdots ,$$

that is,

$$c_0 = 0, \quad c_1 = 1, \quad c_2 = -1, \quad \cdots , \quad c_{n+1} = (-1)^n n! , \cdots$$

and, therefore,

$$(14) \qquad f(x) \sim \frac{1}{x} - \frac{1}{x^2} + \frac{2!}{x^3} - \frac{3!}{x^4} + - \cdots .$$

The special incomplete Gamma function [cf. (12) in Sec. 14.1]

$$\mathrm{Ei}(x) = \int_x^{\infty} \frac{e^{-t}}{t}\, dt \qquad (x > 0)$$

is called the **exponential integral**; clearly $\text{Ei}(x) = Q(0, x)$. From (14) we obtain the asymptotic expansion

$$(15) \qquad \text{Ei}(x) = e^{-x} f(x) \sim e^{-x} \left(\frac{1}{x} - \frac{1}{x^2} + \frac{2!}{x^3} - \frac{3!}{x^4} + - \cdots \right).$$

We finally derive the asymptotic expansion of another important function, namely of the sine integral.

Example 2. From (18) in Sec. 14.2 we obtain

$$\text{Si}(x) = \int_0^x \frac{\sin t}{t} \, dt = \frac{\pi}{2} - \text{si}(x).$$

We want to apply repeated integration by parts to $\text{si}(x)$. This will lead to integrals of the form

$$F_n(x) = \int_x^\infty \frac{\sin t}{t^n} \, dt, \qquad\qquad n = 1, 3, 5, \cdots.$$

By integrating twice by parts we obtain the recurrence relation

$$F_n(x) = - \left. \frac{\cos t}{t^n} \right|_x^\infty - n \int_x^\infty \frac{\cos t}{t^{n+1}} \, dt$$

$$= \frac{\cos x}{x^n} + n \frac{\sin x}{x^{n+1}} - n(n + 1) F_{n+2}(x).$$

In particular,

$$\text{si}(x) = F_1(x) = \frac{\cos x}{x} + \frac{\sin x}{x^2} - 1 \cdot 2 F_3(x),$$

$$F_3(x) = \frac{\cos x}{x^3} + 3 \frac{\sin x}{x^4} - 3 \cdot 4 F_5(x),$$

etc. In this way we obtain the representation

$$\text{si}(x) = \cos x \left(\frac{1}{x} - \frac{2!}{x^3} + - \cdots + (-1)^{n-1} \frac{(2n - 2)!}{x^{2n-1}} \right)$$

$$+ \sin x \left(\frac{1}{x^2} - \frac{3!}{x^4} + - \cdots + (-1)^{n-1} \frac{(2n - 1)!}{x^{2n}} \right) + (-1)^n (2n)! \, F_{2n+1}(x)$$

or, if we carry out one integration less, the remaining integral will be of the form

$$G_{2n}(x) = \int_x^\infty \frac{\cos t}{t^{2n}} \, dt.$$

To show that the development thus obtained is an asymptotic expansion, that is,

$$\text{si}(x) \sim \cos x \left(\frac{1}{x} - \frac{2!}{x^3} + \frac{4!}{x^5} - + \cdots \right) + \sin x \left(\frac{1}{x^2} - \frac{3!}{x^4} + \frac{5!}{x^6} - + \cdots \right),$$

we prove that $x^{2n} F_{2n+1}(x) \to 0$ as $x \to \infty$, the proof that $x^{2n-1} G_{2n}(x) \to 0$ as $x \to \infty$ being literally the same. For $t \geqq x$ we have

$$\frac{1}{t^{2n+\frac{1}{2}}} \leqq \frac{1}{x^{2n+\frac{1}{2}}}.$$

Using this inequality, we readily obtain

$$|F_{2n+1}(x)| = \left| \int_x^\infty \frac{\sin t}{t^{2n+1}} \, dt \right| \leq \frac{1}{x^{2n+1/2}} \left| \int_x^\infty \frac{\sin t}{\sqrt{t}} \, dt \right|.$$

Setting $t = \tau^2$, we have $dt/\sqrt{t} = 2d\tau$ and we see that the last integral equals $2s(\sqrt{x})$ where $s(x)$ is the complementary Fresnel integral (Sec. 14.2). From this, the proof follows. Therefore,

(16)
$$\operatorname{Si}(x) \sim \frac{\pi}{2} - \cos x \left(\frac{1}{x} - \frac{2!}{x^3} + \frac{4!}{x^5} - + \cdots \right)$$
$$- \sin x \left(\frac{1}{x^2} - \frac{3!}{x^4} + \frac{5!}{x^6} - + \cdots \right).$$

PROBLEMS

1. Apply the method illustrated by Ex. 1 for deriving the asymptotic expansion of erf x. *Hint:* show that the function $y = e^{x^2} \operatorname{erfc} x$ satisfies $y' - 2xy + 1 = 0$.

2. Prove the first statement in Theorem 1.

3. The function

$$\operatorname{li}(x) = \int_0^x \frac{dt}{\ln t}$$

is called the **logarithmic integral**. Show that $\operatorname{li}(e^{-x}) = -\operatorname{Ei}(x)$.

4. Find the asymptotic expansion of ci(x) by integrating by parts.

5. Show that $\operatorname{Ei}(ix) = \operatorname{ci}(x) - i \operatorname{si}(x)$. Then replace x by ix in (15) and separate the real and imaginary parts on both sides; show that this leads to the asymptotic expansions of ci(x) and si(x) as obtained in Prob. 4 and Ex. 2.

6. Find the asymptotic expansions of the Fresnel integrals. *Hint:* integrate the complementary functions by parts.

7. It can be shown that (16), with x replaced by $z = x + iy$ (z not pure imaginary) is an asymptotic expansion of the complex sine integral

$$\operatorname{Si}(z) = \int_0^z \frac{\sin t}{t} \, dt.$$

Conclude from this expansion that approximations for the zeros $z_n = x_n + iy_n$ of Si(z) are obtained from

$$\frac{\cos z}{z} = \frac{\pi}{2} \qquad \text{or} \qquad \cos z = \frac{\pi z}{2}.$$

Show that by separating the real and the imaginary parts [cf. (11), Sec. 10.12] and using $\cosh y \approx e^y/2$, $\sinh y \approx e^y/2$ (y large) we find

(17)   (a) $e^y \cos x = \pi x$ (b) $e^y \sin x = -\pi y$.

Let $x > 0$. Derive from (17)

$$\cos x = \pi x e^x \tan x$$

and conclude that, since $\cos x$ is relatively small in absolute value, x_n must be close to $2n\pi$, say, $x_n = 2n\pi + \delta_n$ where δ_n is small in absolute value, so that $\sin \delta_n \approx \delta_n$, $\cos \delta_n \approx 1$, and from (17),

$$(18) \qquad\qquad y_n \approx \ln (2n\pi^2), \qquad x_n \approx 2n\pi - \frac{\ln (2n\pi^2)}{2n\pi}$$

8. Show that from (18),

$$z_1 \approx 5.81 + 2.98i, \qquad z_2 \approx 12.27 + 3.68i, \qquad z_3 \approx 18.63 + 4.08i.$$

(Actually,

$$z_1 = 5.92 + 2.90i, \qquad z_2 = 12.34 + 3.67i, \qquad z_3 = 18.69 + 4.08i,$$

the given decimal places being correct.)

9. Apply the method illustrated by Ex. 1 for deriving the asymptotic expansion of the incomplete Gamma function $Q(\tfrac{1}{2}, x)$. *Hint:* consider $y = e^x \sqrt{x}\, Q(\tfrac{1}{2}, x)$.

10. Same task as in Prob. 9, for $Q(\alpha, x)$. *Hint:* consider $y = e^x x^{1-\alpha} Q(\alpha, x)$.

appendix **1**

REFERENCES

A General References

[A1] Courant, R., *Differential and Integral Calculus.* 2 vols. New York: Interscience, 1951, 1956.

[A2] Courant, R., and D. Hilbert, *Methods of Mathematical Physics.* New York: Interscience, 1955.

[A3] C.R.C. *Standard Mathematical Tables.* 11th ed. Cleveland: Chemical Rubber Pub. Co., 1957.

[A4] Dwight, H. B., *Mathematical Tables.* New York: McGraw-Hill, 1941.

[A5] Erdélyi, A., W. Magnus, F. Oberhettinger, and F. G. Tricomi, *Higher Transcendental Functions.* 3 vols. New York: McGraw-Hill, 1953 , 1955.

[A6] Fletcher, A., J. C. P. Miller, and L. Rosenhead, *An Index of Mathematical Tables.* New York: McGraw-Hill, 1946.

[A7] Jahnke, E., F. Emde, and F. Lösch, *Tables of Higher Functions.* 6th ed. New York: McGraw-Hill, 1960.

[A8] Kaplan, W., *Advanced Calculus.* 5th printing. Reading, Mass.: Addison-Wesley, 1959.

[A9] Knopp, K., *Infinite Sequences and Series.* New York: Dover, 1956.

[A10] Magnus, W., and F. Oberhettinger, *Formulas and Theorems for the Special Functions of Mathematical Physics,* New York: Chelsea, 1949.

[A11] Milne, W. E., *Numerical Calculus.* Princton, N. J.: Princeton University Press, 1949.

[A12] Taylor, A. E., *Advanced Calculus.* New York: Ginn, 1955.

[A13] Thomas, G. B., *Calculus and Analytic Geometry.* 2nd ed., 5th printing. Reading, Mass.: Addison-Wesley, 1953.

[A14] Whittaker, E. T., and G. N. Watson, *A Course of Modern Analysis.* New York: Macmillan, 1947.

[A15] Willers, F. A., *Practical Analysis.* New York: Dover, 1948.

B Ordinary Differential Equations (Chap. 1–4)

[A2], [A5], [A10], [A15].

[B1] Carslaw, H. S., and J. C. Jaeger, *Operational Methods in Applied Mathematics.* 2nd ed. London: Oxford University Press, 1948.

[B2] Churchill, R. V., *Operational Mathematics.* New York: McGraw-Hill, 1958.

[B3] Coddington, E. A., and N. Levinson, *Theory of Ordinary Differential Equations.* New York: McGraw-Hill, 1955.

[B4] Forsyth, A. R., *A Treatise on Differential Equations.* 6th ed. London: Macmillan, 1951.

[B5] Ince, E. L., *Ordinary Differential Equations.* New York: Dover, 1944.

[B6] Kamke, E., *Differentialgleichungen, Lösungsmethoden und Lösungen. I. Gewöhnliche Differentialgleichungen.* 4th ed. Leipzig: Akademische Verlagsgesellschaft, 1951. (This extremely useful book contains a systematic list of more than 1500 differential equations and their solutions.)

[B7] Levy, H., and E. A. Baggott, *Numerical Solutions of Differential Equations.* New York: Dover, 1950.

[B8] Morris, M., and O. E. Brown, *Differential Equations.* 3rd ed. New York: Prentice-Hall, 1952.

[B9] Watson, G. N., *A Treatise on the Theory of Bessel Functions.* 2nd ed. New York: Macmillan, 1944.

[B10] Widder, D. V., *The Laplace Transform.* Princeton, N.J.: Princeton University Press, 1941.

Tables

[A3].

[B11] Erdélyi, A., W. Magnus, F. Oberhettinger, and F. Tricomi, *Tables of Integral Transforms.* 2 vols. New York: McGraw-Hill, 1954.

C Vector Analysis and Integral Theorems (Chaps. 5 and 6)

[A1], [A8], [A12].

[C1] Brand, L., *Vector Analysis.* 3rd printing. New York: Wiley, 1961.

[C2] Brand, L., *Vectorial Mechanics.* New York: Wiley, 1930.

[C3] Kellog, O. D., *Foundations of Potential Theory.* New York: Dover, 1953.

[C4] Kreyszig, E., *Differential Geometry.* Toronto: Toronto University Press, 1959.

[C5] Lamb, H., *Hydrodynamics.* 6th ed. New York: Dover, 1945.

[C6] Struik, D. J., *Lectures on Classical Differential Geometry.* Reading, Mass.: Addison-Wesley, 1950.

[C7] Weatherburn, C. E., *Elementary Vector Analysis with Applications to Geometry and Physics.* London: Bell, 1921.

[C8] Weatherburn, C. E., *Advanced Vector Analysis with Applications to Mathematical Physics.* London: Bell, 1928.

D Matrices (Chap. 7)

[D1] Bodewig, E., *Matrix Calculus.* 2nd ed. Amsterdam: North Holland Pub. 1959.

[D2] Frazer, R. A., W. J. Duncan, and A. R. Collar, *Elementary Matrices.* Cambridge: University Press, 1938.

[D3] Gantmacher, F. R., *The Theory of Matrices.* 2 vols. New York: Chelsea, 1959.

[D4] McDuffee, C. C., *The Theory of Matrices.* New York: Chelsea, 1946.

[D5] Perlis, S., *Theory of Matrices.* Reading, Mass.: Addison-Wesley, 1952.

[D6] Schreier, O., and E. Sperner, *Introduction to Modern Algebra and Matrix Theory.* New York: Chelsea, 1951.

[D7] Schwerdtfeger, H., *Introduction to Linear Algebra and the Theory of Matrices.*
      Groningen: Noordhoff, 1950.

E Fourier Series and Integrals (Chap. 8)

[A9], [A14], [A15].
[E1] Carslaw, H. S., *Introduction to the Theory of Fourier's Series and Integrals.* 3rd ed.
      London: Macmillan, 1930.
[E2] Churchill, R. V., *Fourier Series and Boundary Value Problems.* New York:
      McGraw-Hill, 1941.
[E3] Rogosinski, W., *Fourier Series.* New York: Chelsea, 1950.
[E4] Sneddon, I. N., *Fourier Transforms.* New York: McGraw-Hill, 1951.
[E5] Szegö, G., *Orthogonal Polynomials.* Revised ed. New York: American Mathe-
      matical Society, 1959.
[E6] Titchmarsh, E. C., *Introduction to the Theory of Fourier Integrals.* Oxford:
      Clarendon, 1948.
[E7] Zygmund, A., *Trigonometric Series.* 2 vols. Cambridge: University Press, 1959.

Tables of Fourier Transforms
[B11], [E4].
[E8] Campbell, G. A., and R. M. Foster, *Fourier Integrals for Practical Applications.*
      Bell Telephone System Tech. Pub., 1942.

F Partial Differential Equations (Chap. 9)

[A2], [A14], [C3], [C5], [E2].
[F1] Bateman, H., *Partial Differential Equations of Mathematical Physics.* New York:
      Dover, 1944.
[F2] Bergman, S., and M. Schiffer, *Kernel Functions and Elliptic Differential Equations
      in Mathematical Physics.* New York: Academic Press, 1953.
[F3] Duff, G.F. D., *Partial Differential Equations.* Toronto: Toronto University Press,
      1956.
[F4] Lord Rayleigh, *The Theory of Sound.* 2 vols. New York: Dover, 1945.
[F5] Sagan, H., *Boundary and Eigenvalue Problems in Mathematical Physics.* New
      York: Wiley, 1961.
[F6] Sneddon, I. N., *Elements of Partial Differential Equations.* New York: McGraw-
      Hill, 1957.
[F7] Sommerfeld, A., *Partial Differential Equations in Physics.* New York: Academic
      Press, 1949.
[F8] Webster, A. G., *Partial Differential Equations of Mathematical Physics.* 2nd ed.
      New York: Hafner, 1947.

G Complex Analysis (Chap. 10–13)

[A9], [A14], [C5].
[G1] Ahlfors, L. V., *Complex Analysis.* New York: McGraw-Hill, 1953.
[G2] Bieberbach, L., *Conformal Mapping.* New York: Chelsea, 1953.
[G3] Churchill, R. V., *Complex Variables and Applications.* 2nd ed. New York:
      McGraw-Hill, 1960.
[G4] Hille, E., *Analytic Function Theory.* 2 vols. Boston: Ginn, 1959, 1962.
[G5] Knopp, K., *Theory of Functions.* 2 vols. New York: Dover, 1945.
[G6] Nehari, Z., *Conformal Mapping.* New York: McGraw-Hill, 1952.
[G7] Rothe, R., F. Ollendorf, and K. Pohlhausen, *Theory of Functions as Applied to
      Engineering Problems.* Cambridge, Mass.: Technology Press, 1933.

[G8]   Springer, G., *Introduction to Riemann Surfaces*. Reading, Mass.: Addison-Wesley, 1957.

[G9]   Titchmarsh, E. C., *The Theory of Functions*. 2nd ed. London: Oxford University Press, 1939.

H   Special Functions. Asymptotic Expansions (Chap. 14)

[A3]–[A7], [A9], [A10], [A14], [G5].

[H1]   Borel, E., *Leçons sur les séries divergentes*. 2nd ed. Paris: Gauthier-Villars, 1928.

[H2]   Erdélyi, A., *Asymptotic Expansions*. New York: Dover, 1956.

[H3]   Rainville, E. D., *Special Functions*. New York: Macmillan, 1960.

Tables

[A3], [A4], [A7].

[H4]   British Association for the Advancement of Science, *Mathematical Tables*. Vol. VII. *The Probability Integral*. Cambridge: University Press, 1939.

[H5]   Davis, H. T., *Tables of the Higher Mathematical Functions*. 2 vols. Bloomington, Ind.: Principia Press, 1933.

[H6]   National Bureau of Standards, *Tables of Probability Functions*. 2 vols. Washington, 1941 and 1948.

[H7]   Pearson, K., *Tables for Statisticians and Biometricians*. 2 parts. Cambridge: University Press, 1948.

ANSWERS TO ODD-NUMBERED PROBLEMS

Remark. In the case of more complicated problems, not only is the answer given but also the solution. Odd-numbered problems not occurring in this Appendix are those in which obvious graphical work, verifications of statements and formulas in the text, or simple proofs are required, or the answer is already given in the enunciation of the problem.

SECTION 0.1

1. Even   **3.** Neither even nor odd   **5.** Odd   **7.** Even

13. $\cosh^2 x - \sinh^2 x = \frac{1}{4}[(e^x + e^{-x})^2 - (e^x - e^{-x})^2] = \frac{1}{4} 4 e^x e^{-x} = 1$

15. $\cosh (x + y) - \cosh (x - y) = \frac{1}{2}[e^{x+y} + e^{-x-y} - (e^{x-y} + e^{-x+y})]$
$$= \frac{1}{2}(e^x - e^{-x})(e^y - e^{-y}) = 2 \ \sinh x \sinh y$$

SECTION 0.2

1. $f_x = x/\sqrt{x^2 + y^2}$ **3.** $f_x = -y/(x^2 + y^2), f_y = x/(x^2 + y^2)$

5. $f_x = -(x - a)[(x - a)^2 + (y - b)^2]^{-3/2}$ **7.** $f_{R_1} = -1/R_1^2, f_{R_2} = -1/R_2^2$

9. $4x/(x^2 + y^2)$ **11.** 0   **17.** 0, 0

19. $f_x = -2x/(x^2 + y^2 + z^2)^2$, $f_{xx} = 2(3x^2 - y^2 - z^2)/(x^2 + y^2 + z^2)^3$, etc.

SECTION 0.3

1. 14   **3.** 1   **5.** -400 **7.** 0   **9.** -27 **11.** $(b - a)(c - a)(c - b)$

13. $1 + a^2 + b^2 + c^2$ **15.** $abcd\left(\dfrac{1}{a} + \dfrac{1}{b} + \dfrac{1}{c} + \dfrac{1}{d}\right)$ **17.** $x = 1, y = 2$

SECTION 0.4

1. $14 + 8i$, $-0.1 - 0.8i$, $5 - 12i$, $-1.9 - 2.2i$, $5 + i$ **3.** $2i$, -1 **5.** $\pm 3i$
7. $-1 + 2i$, $-1 - 2i$ **15.** $(x_1 + iy_1)(x_2 + iy_2) = x_1 x_2 + ix_1 y_2 + iy_1 x_2 - y_1 y_2 = 0$
is equivalent to $x_1 x_2 - y_1 y_2 = 0$, $x_1 y_2 + y_1 x_2 = 0$. If x_2 and y_2 are not both zero,
the only solution of this system of linear equations is $x_1 = 0$, $y_1 = 0$.
17. $3x^2 y - y^3$ **19.** $2xy$, $4(x^2 - y^2) - 6y + 8$

SECTION 0.5

1. $\sqrt{8}\left(\cos\dfrac{\pi}{4} - i \sin\dfrac{\pi}{4}\right)$, $i \sin\dfrac{\pi}{2}$, $5\left(\cos 0.927 + i \sin 0.927\right)$

5. Geometrical interpretation: The distances from z and $\bar{z}$ to a point a on the real axis
are the same.
7. $2, 9, 3$ **9.** 1; this follows immediately from (6) and (8).
11. Circle of radius 1 with center at 0   **13.** Hyperbola $y^2 - x^2 = 1$
15. First quadrant of the complex z-plane

SECTION 0.7

1. $x_2 = 1.2308$, $x_3 = 1.2006$, $x_4 = 1.2000$ (exact: 1.2)
3. $x_2 = 2.9091$, $x_3 = 2.9001$, $x_4 = 2.9000$ (exact: 2.9)
5. $x_2 = 1.9$ (exact: 1.9)   **7.** $-1.3, 1.4$ **9.** $0.4, 1.6, 3$
11. 1.557 **13.** ± 1.189 **15.** $0, \pm 1.496$ **17.** $x_2 = -0.2$, $x_3 = -0.20032$

SECTION 0.8

9. 0.245 **11.** 0.26, $0 \leq E_T \leq 0.02$ **13.** 0.9466 (exact 0.9461)
15. 0.9458 **17.** 0.9461 **19.** $\ln 2 \approx 0.693\,25$ (exact 0.693 15), $M_4{}^* = 0.75$,
$M_4 = 24$, $0.000\,016 < E_S < 0.000\,53$ or $0.692\,72 < \ln 2 < 0.693\,24$

SECTION 1.1

13. $y(x) = -\frac{1}{2}\cos 2x + c$, $y(0) = -\frac{1}{2} + c = 1$, $c = \frac{3}{2}$, $y(x) = -\frac{1}{2}\cos 2x + \frac{3}{2}$
15. $y = \dfrac{x}{2} + \dfrac{1}{4}\sin 2x + \dfrac{\pi}{4}$ **17.** $y = 2x^2$ **19.** $y = 1 - e^{-x}$ **23.** $xy' = 4y$
25. $y' + y \tan x = 0$

SECTION 1.2

13. If f depends only on x or only on y, the isoclines are straight lines parallel to the y or
x axis, respectively.
15. The last integral has the value 0.75, approximately; it cannot be evaluated by
elementary methods and will be considered later (Sec. 14.2).
17. $y' = y/x^2$, $y' = e^{y/x^2}$, etc.
19. $s'(t) = 1/s(t)$. (The exact solution is $s(t) = +\sqrt{2t + 1}$, as the reader may verify.)

SECTION 1.3

1. Suppose you forgot $\tilde{c}$ in (4), wrote $\ln y = -x^2$, transformed this to $y = e^{-x^2}$
and then afterwards added a constant c, obtaining $y = e^{-x^2} + c$, which is not a solution
of $y' = -2xy$.
5. $dy \Big/ \left(y + \dfrac{b}{a}\right) = -a\,dx$, $y = ce^{-ax} - \dfrac{b}{a}$ **7.** $y = cx^{\frac{3}{2}}$; for $c \neq 0$ these are so-called
semicubical parabolas. Graph these curves.
9. $y^2 = 2 \arctan x + c$ **11.** $y = c \cosh x$ **13.** $y = c \cosh^4 x$

15. $y^3 = \frac{3}{2}(x + \frac{1}{2}\sin 2x) + c$ **17.** $y\,dy/(y^2 - 1) = -x\,dx/(x^2 - 1)$,
     $(y^2 - 1)(x^2 - 1) = c$
19. $y = c(x - 1)^2 \exp(\frac{2}{3}x^3 + x^2 + 2x)$ **21.** $y - 3\ln(y + 3) = 2\ln x + c$
23. $y = 2x^3$ **25.** $y = e^{-x^2}$ **27.** $y = 2\sin^2 x$ **29.** $y = x$
31. $y = \arcsin x$ **33.** $v^2 = v_0^2 + 2g(x - x_0)$ **35.** $y = -\frac{4}{9}x^2$
37. $pV = c = const.$ This is the law empirically found by Boyle (1662) and Mariotte (1676).
39. $y' = ky$, $y = y_0 e^{kt}$.   At $t = 1590$, $y = y_0/2$.   Consequently, $1590k = \ln\frac{1}{2}$,
$k = -0.000\,436$, $y(1) = y_0 e^{-0.000\,436}$. For small $|x|$, $e^x \approx 1 + x$. Thus, $y(1) \approx y_0 \times$
$(1 - 0.000\,436)$, $y_0 - y(1) \approx 0.000\,4$, that is, 0.04% will disappear.
41. $dp/dh = -kp$, $p = p_0 e^{-0.000\,038\,5\,h}$
43. $Y = 0.01 e^{-0.183 t}$
45. $y' = ky$, $y = y_0 e^{kt}$, $y(4) = y_0 e^{4k} = 2y_0$, $y(8) = y_0 e^{8k} = y_0(e^{4k})^2 = 4y_0$
47. $\Delta A = -kA\Delta x$ (A = amount of incident light, ΔA = absorbed light, Δx = thickness, $-k$ = constant of proportionality.) Let $\Delta x \to 0$. Then $A' = -kA$, so $A(x) = A_0 e^{-kx}$ is the amount of light in a thick layer at depth x from the surface of incidence.
49. $y(t) = (b - ace^{(b-a)kt})/(1 - ce^{(b-a)kt})$

SECTION 1.4

1. $y = cx^2 - 3x$ **3.** $y = \dfrac{x}{c - \ln x} + x$ **5.** $y = x\tan(\ln x + c) - x$

7. $y = \dfrac{x}{\sqrt{c - 2\ln x}} - x$ **9.** $y^2 + xy = cx^3$ **11.** $(y - x)^2 + 10y - 2x = c$

13. $\ln(x^2 + y^2) + 2\arctan\dfrac{y}{x} = c$ **15.** $\dfrac{2yy' + 2x}{y^2 + x^2} = 1$, $y^2 = ce^x - x^2$

17. $y = \ln(ce^{kx} - x)$
19. $r = l\exp(-\theta - \frac{1}{4}\pi)/\sqrt{2}$, etc., where l is the length of the table and r and θ are polar coordinates with center at the center of the table. Graph this logarithmic spiral.

SECTION 1.5

1. $y = c/(1 + x^2)$ **3.** Not exact, $y = cx^2$ **5.** $x^4 - e^{xy} = c$
7. $y^2 = c - 2e^x - x^2$ **9.** $\cosh x \cos y = c$ **11.** Not exact, $e^x \cos y = c$
19. $(x - 2)^2 + y^2 = 4$ **21.** $\dfrac{(x - 3)^2}{9} + (y - 1)^2 = 1$
27. $a = 2$, $x^2y + \sin y = c$ **29.** $a = \frac{3}{2}$, $x^2y^3 = c$

SECTION 1.6

1. $F = x$, $x^2y = c$ **3.** $F = e^x$, $e^x\cos y = c$ **5.** $F = y$, $y\cos xy = c$
7. $F = 1/xy$, $x^2y^2e^x = c$ **9.** $F = 1/xy$, $y = cx^2$
11. $F = 1/x(y - 1)$, $y = cx + 1$ **13.** $x^2 + y^2 = 9$
15. $y(x^2 - y^2) = -8$ **17.** $\dfrac{\partial P}{\partial y} = 4 = 1 + \dfrac{k}{x}x$, $k = 3$; thus, $4x^3y\,dx + x^4\,dy = 0$ is exact, and $x^4y = c$.
19. $xy^2 = c$. Hence, other factors are $xy^2F = xy^3$, $(xy^2)^2F = x^2y^5$, etc.

SECTION 1.7

3. $y = 5 + ce^{-x}$ **5.** $y = (3x + c)e^x$ **7.** $y = 2x^2 + \dfrac{c}{x^2}$

9. $y = \dfrac{x^4}{2} + cx^2$ **11.** $y = ce^{-x} + \frac{1}{2}(\sin x - \cos x)$ **13.** $y = ce^{-x^2/2} + 2$

15. $y = xe^x$ **17.** $y = \sin x + x^2$ **19.** $y = e^x x^3 - x$

23. $y_1' + fy_1 = r,\quad y_2' + fy_2 = r.$ By   subtraction, $(y_1 - y_2)' + f(y_1 - y_2) = 0$
or $y' + fy = 0.$

25. $y_1' + fy_1 = r,\quad y_2' + fy_2 = 0.$ By   addition, $(y_1 + y_2)' + f(y_1 + y_2) = r$
or $y' + fy = r.$

29. $y^{-4} = u,\ u' + \dfrac{2}{x} u = -20x^2,\ u = \dfrac{c}{x^2} - 4x^3,\ y = 1/\sqrt[4]{u}$

SECTION 1.8

1. $v = e^x,\ u = -3e^{-x} + c,\ y = ce^x - 3$ **3.** $y = \dfrac{x^4}{2} + cx^2$

5. $\ln y = z,\ z = c \csc x - \cot x,\ y = e^z$ **7.** $y^3 = z,\ z = ce^{-x^2/2} + 1$

9. $y = \sqrt{\dfrac{x}{2} e^x + cxe^{-x}}$

11. $y' = -f(x)y + r(x).$ At (x_0, y_0) this equals $-f(x_0)y_0 + r(x_0),$ and $\eta - y_0 = (\xi - x_0)[r(x_0) - f(x_0)y_0]$ represents the line through (x_0, y_0) with that slope. Similarly, $\eta - y_1 = (\xi - x_0)[r(x_0) - f(x_0)y_1)]$ represents the line through (x_0, y_1) whose slope is the value of y' at (x_0, y_1) given by (1). The point of intersection of these lines has the coordinates (ξ, η) given in the enunciation of the problem, and since these coordinates do not depend on y, the statement is proved.

15. $y' = \dfrac{dy}{dt}\dfrac{dt}{dx} = \dfrac{dy}{dt} \Big/ \dfrac{d\phi}{dt},\quad \dfrac{dy}{dt} + f[\phi(t)]\dfrac{d\phi}{dt} y = r[\phi(t)]\dfrac{d\phi}{dt}$

SECTION 1.9

5. 10^{-5} sec.   **7.** $I = 0.0035\,(\cos 314t + 314 \sin 314t - e^{-t}) \approx 1.1 \sin 314t$

9. From Prob. 8, first case, $RQ' + Q/C = E_0,$ and since $Q(0) = 0,$ we have $Q(t) = E_0 C(1 - e^{-t/RC}) = 1.2(1 - e^{-0.05t}).$ From this and (3*), $V(t) = Q/C = 12(1 - e^{-0.05t}).$

13. By differentiating (7), $RI' + \left(R' + \dfrac{1}{C}\right)I = 0,\ R' = -1,\ (100 - t)I' + 3I = 0,$
$I(t) = 10^{-6}(100 - t)^3$ when $0 \le t \le 100$ sec, $I = 0$ when $t > 100$ sec.

15. $I(t) = 2 - 2 \cdot 10^{-4}(100 - t)^2\ (0 \le t \le 100),\ I = 2\quad (t > 100)$

17. $I = 6\ (0 \le t \le 10),\ I = 6\,e^{1-0.1t}\quad (t > 10)$

19. From (5*), $I = I_1 = 1 - e^{-0.01t}\ (0 \le t \le 100),\ I = I_2 = c_2 e^{-0.01(t-100)}\ (100 \le t \le 200);\ I_1(100) = I_2(100)$ yields $c_2 = 1 - e^{-1} \approx 0.63.\ I = I_3 = 1 + c_3 e^{-0.01(t-200)}$ $(200 \le t \le 300);\ I_2(200) = I_3(200)$ yields $c_3 = (1 - e^{-1})e^{-1} - 1 \approx -0.77,$ etc. (Fig. 393).

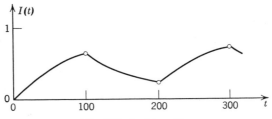

Fig. 393. Problem 19.

SECTION 1.10

9. Congruent semicubical parabolas   **11.** $y' = \dfrac{y}{x} \ln y$ **13.** $y' = (y^2 - 1)/xy$

15. $y' = \sqrt{1 - y^2}$ **17.** $y' = x^{-1} \arcsin y \sqrt{1 - y^2}$ **19.** $y = c * x^2$

21. $y = \sqrt{2x + c*}$ **23.** $y = -\dfrac{x}{2} - \tfrac{1}{4} \sin 2x + c*$ **25.** $y^2 - x^2 = c*$

27. $dg = 0$, that is $\dfrac{\partial g}{\partial x}\, dx + \dfrac{\partial g}{\partial y}\, dy = 0$. Thus $\dfrac{dy}{dx} = -\dfrac{\partial g/\partial x}{\partial g/\partial y}$. By replacing the right side by its negative reciprocal, the result follows.
29. $xy = c*$ **31.** Follows from $dy/dx = 1/(dx/dy)$.
33. Let $y(x)$ be such a curve. In Fig. 394, $OM = 2x$, $ON = 2y$, and the slope at (x, y) is $y' = -ON/OM = -y/x$. Thus $xy = c$.   **35.** $xy = c$ (hyperbolas)

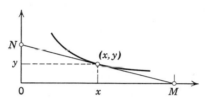

Fig. 394. Problem 33.

SECTION 1.11

1. $y_0 = 1$, $y_n = 1 + \displaystyle\int_0^x t y_{n-1}(t)\, dt$. Thus, $y_1 = 1 + \dfrac{x^2}{2}$, $y_2 = 1 + \dfrac{x^2}{2} + \dfrac{x^4}{8}$, $\cdots$,

$y_n = 1 + \dfrac{x^2}{2} + \dfrac{1}{2!}\left(\dfrac{x^2}{2}\right)^2 + \dfrac{1}{3!}\left(\dfrac{x^2}{2}\right)^3 + \cdots + \dfrac{1}{n!}\left(\dfrac{x^2}{2}\right)^n$. These are the first terms of the Maclaurin series of the exact solution $y = e^{x^2/2}$.

3. $y_n = \pi\left(1 + x^2 + \dfrac{x^4}{2!} + \cdots + \dfrac{x^{2n}}{n!}\right)$ **5.** $y_n = \dfrac{x^2}{2!} + \dfrac{x^3}{3!} + \cdots + \dfrac{x^{n+1}}{(n+1)!}$

7. $y_0 = 0$, $y_1 = x$, $y_2 = x + \dfrac{x^3}{3}$, $y_3 = x + \dfrac{x^3}{3} + \dfrac{x^5}{3 \cdot 5}$, $\cdots$

9. $y_0 = 0$, $y_1 = x^2 - \dfrac{x^4}{4}$, $y_2 = x^2 - \dfrac{x^6}{4 \cdot 6}$, $y_3 = x^2 - \dfrac{x^8}{4 \cdot 6 \cdot 8}$, $\cdots$

11. $y_1 = 1.125$, $y_2 = 1.132\,813$, $y_3 = 1.133\,138$

SECTION 1.13

7. $0.1, 0.202, 0.31008, 0.42869$ etc. Exact solution: $y = e^{x^2} \displaystyle\int_0^x e^{-t^2}\, dt$

11. The Runge-Kutta method is a fourth-order method.
13. $y = \tan x$

SECTION 2.1

7. Let $F(x, y', y'') = 0$ be the given equation. From $y' = z$ we obtain $y'' = z'$, and $F(x, z, z') = 0$, a first-order equation in z.
9. $y = c_1 e^{4x} + c_2$ **11.** $y = c_1 e^x + c_2$ **13.** $y = c_1 \ln x + c_2$
15. $y = c_1 \sinh x + c_2$ **17.** $y(t) = 2e^t + 4$, $y(3) \approx 44$, $\dot{y}(3) \approx 40$

19. $y(t) = \frac{1}{3}(2t + 4)^{\frac{3}{2}} - \frac{2}{3}$, $y(6) = \frac{62}{3}$, $\dot{y}(6) = 4$

21. $y' = z$, $y'' = \dfrac{dz}{dx} = \dfrac{dz}{dy}\dfrac{dy}{dx} = \dfrac{dz}{dy}z$, and the given equation reduces to the first order

equation $F\left(y, z, z\dfrac{dz}{dy}\right) = 0$.

SECTION 2.2

1. e^x, e^{-x} **3.** e^x, e^{2x} **5.** e^{4x}, e^{-2x} **7.** $1, e^{-x}$ **9.** e^{3ix}, e^{-3ix}
11. $e^{-(1+i)x}, e^{-(1-i)x}$ **13.** $a = -(\lambda_1 + \lambda_2), b = \lambda_1\lambda_2$ **15.** $y'' - 4y' + 3y = 0$
17. $y'' + 5y' = 0$ **19.** $y'' - 2y' + 2y = 0$

SECTION 2.3

1. $y = c_1e^{3x} + c_2e^{-2x}$ **3.** $y = c_1e^{2x} + c_2e^{-2x}$ **5.** $y = c_1e^{ix} + c_2e^{-ix}$
7. $y = c_1e^{(2+i)x} + c_2e^{(2-i)x}$ **9.** $y = c_1 + c_2e^{-3x}$ **11.** $y'' + 3y' - 4y = 0$
13. $y'' - 3y' = 0$ **15.** $y'' + 2y' + 2y = 0$ **17.** Independent   **19.** Dependent
21. Independent   **23.** Independent   **25.** No. On $-1 < x < 1$ the functions x^2
and $x|x|$ are linearly independent while on $0 < x < 1$ they are linearly dependent
(even identical).

SECTION 2.4

7. $y = A \cos x + B \sin x$ **9.** $y = e^x(A \cos x + B \sin x)$
11. $y = e^{-5x}(A \cos 3x + B \sin 3x)$
13. Eq. (4) may be written $y = c_1e^{\lambda_0 x} + c_2e^{\bar{\lambda}_0 x}$ where $\lambda_0 = p + iq$, $\bar{\lambda}_0 = p - iq$. Then
$\lambda^2 + a\lambda + b = (\lambda - \lambda_0)(\lambda - \bar{\lambda}_0) = \lambda^2 - (\lambda_0 + \bar{\lambda}_0)\lambda + \lambda_0\bar{\lambda}_0$. By comparison, we obtain
$a = -(\lambda_0 + \bar{\lambda}_0) = -2p$, $b = \lambda_0\bar{\lambda}_0 = p^2 + q^2$.
15. $y = A \cos 2x + B \sin 2x$ **17.** $y = c_1e^{5x} + c_2e^{-5x}$
19. $y = e^{-x}(A \cos 3x + B \sin 3x)$ **21.** $y = e^{2x}(A \cos 2x + B \sin 2x)$
23. $y = e^{-4x}(A \cos \sqrt{2}x + B \sin \sqrt{2}x)$ **25.** $y = A \cos \sqrt{3}x + B \sin \sqrt{3}x$
27. $y = 2 \sin 3x$ **29.** $y = e^x \cos 2x$ **31.** $y = e^{2x}(\cos x + \sin x)$
33. $y = 2 \sinh x$ **35.** $y = 2e^{-3x} \cos 4x$ **37.** $y = e^{-x}(\cos x - 2 \sin x)$
39. $y = 4 \cosh 2x$

SECTION 2.5

7. $y = (c_1 + c_2x)e^{x/2}$ **9.** $y = c_1e^{3x} + c_2e^{-3x}$ **11.** $y = (c_1 + c_2x)e^{-\pi x}$
13. $y = (x + 1)e^x$ **15.** $y = -6e^{-3x}$ **17.** $y = e^x - e^{-2x}$ **19.** $y = 0$
23. We have (1) $y'' + ay' + \dfrac{a^2}{4}y = 0$, $y_1 = e^{-ax/2}$. Set $y_2 = uy_1$. Substitute y_2 in (1)
and rearrange, finding

$$u\left[y_1'' + ay_1' + \frac{a^2}{4}y_1\right] + u'[2y_1' + ay_1] + u''y_1 = 0.$$

Since y_1 satisfies (1), the expression in the first bracket is zero. Differentiating y_1, we see
that the expression in the last bracket is zero. Hence $u'' = 0$. A solution is $u = x$, and
then $y_2 = uy_1 = xe^{-ax/2}$.

SECTION 2.6

1. $y = \cos t$ **3.** $y = e^{-0.5t}(\cos 0.87t + 0.57 \sin 0.87t)$ **5.** $y = (t + 1)e^{-t}$
7. $y = 1.01e^{-0.1t} - 0.01e^{-9.9t}$ **9.** It decreases as c increases.
11. $C = \sqrt{1 + 1/\omega^{*2}}$ is a monotone decreasing function of ω^*.

13. The positive solutions of $\tan t = -1$, that is, $3\pi/4$ (min.), $7\pi/4$ (max.), etc.

15. $\dot{y} = 0$ yields $(\omega^*B - \alpha A)\cos \omega^*t - (\alpha B + \omega^*A)\sin \omega^*t = 0$. Consequently, $(\omega^*B - \alpha A)/(\alpha B + \omega^*A) = \tan \omega^*t$. If t_0 is a solution, then the other solutions are $t_0 \pm T$, $t_0 \pm 2T$, $\cdots$, where $T = \pi/\omega^*$ is the period of $\tan \omega^*t$. Since the maxima and minima follow in alternating order, the statement is proved.

17. $A = y_0$, $B = (\alpha y_0 + v_0)/\omega^*$

19. From $y = 0$ [cf. (9)] we obtain $-c_1/c_2 = e^{-2\beta t}$. Since the left side is constant and the right side is monotone, the equation cannot have more than one solution.

21. From $y(0) = 0$ and (9) we have $y = c_1[e^{-(\alpha-\beta)t} - e^{-(\alpha+\beta)t}] \neq 0$ for all $t > 0$ because $c_1 \neq 0$ and $[\cdots] \neq 0$ for those t.

23. $\dot{y} = 0$ yields $t = t_0 = 1/\alpha - c_2/c_1$, and $t_0 > 0$ if $\alpha < c_1/c_2$ or (cf. Prob. 22) $\alpha < (v_0 + \alpha y_0)/y_0$, that is, $v_0/y_0 > 0$. Hence, a maximum or minimum arises if y_0 and v_0 have the same sign.

SECTION 2.7

1. $y = c_1x + c_2x^2$ **3.** $y = c_1x^3 + c_2x^{-2}$ **5.** $y = (c_1 + c_2 \ln x)x$

7. $y = c_1 + c_2 \ln x$ **9.** $y = (c_1 + c_2 \ln x)\sqrt{x}$ **11.** $y = x + 3x^4$

13. $y = x - x^3$ **15.** $y = (1 + \ln x)x^2$ **17.** $t = \ln x$, $dt/dx = 1/x$. Thus,

$$y' = \frac{dy}{dt}\frac{dt}{dx} = \frac{1}{x}\frac{dy}{dt},$$

$$y'' = \frac{d}{dx}\left(\frac{1}{x}\frac{dy}{dt}\right) = -\frac{1}{x^2}\frac{dy}{dt} + \frac{1}{x}\frac{d}{dt}\left(\frac{dy}{dt}\right)\frac{dt}{dx} = \frac{1}{x^2}\frac{d^2y}{dt^2} - \frac{1}{x^2}\frac{dy}{dt}.$$

Substitution into (1) yields the desired equation

$$\frac{d^2y}{dt^2} - \frac{dy}{dt} + a\frac{dy}{dt} + by = \frac{d^2y}{dt^2} + (a-1)\frac{dy}{dt} + by = 0.$$

19. Substitution of $y_2 = uy_1$, $y_2' = uy_1' + u'y_1$, $y_2'' = uy_1'' + 2u'y_1' + u''y_1$ into (1) gives $(x^2y_1'' + axy_1' + by_1)u + (2x^2y_1' + axy_1)u' + x^2u''y_1 = 0$. Since y_1 satisfies (1), the factor of u is zero. Since $y_1' = mx^{m-1}$ and $a = 1 - 2m$ in the critical case, the remaining expression is $u' + xu'' = 0$. Thus, $u' = 1/x$, $u = \ln x$, $y_2 = x^m \ln x$.

SECTION 2.8

1. $y'' - y = 0$, $W = -2$ **3.** $y'' + 2y' + 2y = 0$, $W = e^{-2x}$

5. $y'' - 4y' + 4y = 0$, $W = e^{4x}$ **7.** $x^2y'' + xy' - \dfrac{y}{4} = 0$, $W = -\dfrac{1}{x}$

9. $W = (\lambda_2 - \lambda_1)e^{(\lambda_1 + \lambda_2)x}$ **11.** $W = (m_2 - m_1)x^{m_1 + m_2 - 1}$

SECTION 2.9

1. Independent **3.** Dependent because $1 = \cos^2 x + \sin^2 x$ **5.** Independent
7. Dependent **9.** Dependent **13.** No

SECTION 2.10

1. $y = c_1e^x + c_2e^{2x} + c_3e^{3x}$ **3.** $y = (c_1 + c_2x + c_3x^2)e^{2x}$

5. $y = (c_1 + c_2x)e^x + c_3e^{-x}$ **7.** $y = A \cos x + B \sin x + C$

9. $y = A \cos x + B \sin x + Ce^x$ **13.** $y = \dfrac{c_1}{x} + c_2x + c_3x^2$

SECTION 2.11

1. $y = A \cos x + B \sin x + e^x$ **3.** $y = A \cos x + B \sin x + \sin 2x$
5. $y = A \cos x + B \sin x + 2 \sin 2x$ **7.** $y = A \cos 2x + B \sin 2x + 3x \cos 2x$

SECTION 2.12

1. $y = 3x - 2$ **3.** $y = x^4$ **5.** $y = 2x^3 + 2x$ **7.** $y = e^x + x$
9. $y = \cos x + 1$ **11.** $y = c_1 e^x + c_2 e^{-2x} + x^2 - 6$
13. $y = A \cos x + B \sin x + 2 \sin 2x$ **15.** $y = c_1 e^{-x} + c_2 e^x + xe^x$
17. $y = A \cos 2x + B \sin 2x + 3x \cos 2x$ **19.** $y = c_1 e^{3x} + c_2 e^x + 2xe^{3x}$
21. $y = x^2 + 2 \sin x$ **23.** $y = \sin x - \cos x + 3 \cos 2x$
25. $y = e^{-x} \sin x + \cos 2x$ **27.** $y = 2e^{-x} \sin x - \sin 2x$
29. $y = 3e^{-x} + 2 \sin x$

SECTION 2.13

1. $y = 4 \cos t + 2 \sin t$ **3.** $y = -\frac{1}{615} \cos 3t + \frac{1}{492} \sin 3t$
5. $y = A \cos \omega t + B \sin \omega t$ where

$$A = -b\omega c/D, \ B = bm(\omega_0{}^2 - \omega^2)/D, \ D = m^2(\omega_0{}^2 - \omega^2)^2 + \omega^2 c^2, \ \omega_0 = \sqrt{k/m}$$

7. $y = e^{-5t}(A \cos 2t + B \sin 2t) + \sin t$ **9.** $y = e^{-2t}(A \cos t + B \sin t) - 0.1 \cos 5t$
11. $y = \cos t - 6 \sin t + 3 \sin 2t$ **13.** $y = e^{-t} \sin t - 0.5 \sin 2t$
15. $y = e^{-3t}(4 \cos 2t + 5 \sin 2t) - 7 \cos 4t$
17. $y = \sin t - \frac{3}{13} \cos 2t + \frac{2}{13} \sin 2t$
19. $y = -\frac{1}{2} \cos t + \frac{1}{2} \sin t - \frac{1}{26} \cos 2t - \frac{5}{26} \sin 2t$

21. $y = \dfrac{1}{1 - \omega^2} (\cos \omega t - \cos t) = \dfrac{2}{1 - \omega^2} \sin \dfrac{1 + \omega}{2} t \sin \dfrac{1 - \omega}{2} t$

23. $\dot{y} = 0$ yields the equation $\frac{1}{2} \sin \dfrac{t}{2} = \sin t \left(= 2 \sin \dfrac{t}{2} \cos \dfrac{t}{2} \right)$, which is satisfied when

$\sin \dfrac{t}{2} = 0$ (solutions $0, 2\pi, 4\pi, \cdots$, corresponding to minima) and $\cos \dfrac{t}{2} = \dfrac{1}{4}$
(solutions near $\pi, 3\pi, 5\pi, \cdots$, corresponding to maxima).

SECTION 2.14

1. $I = 2 \sin 3t + \frac{11}{3} \cos 3t$ **3.** $I = \cos 2t + \frac{3}{10} \sin 2t$
7. $I = 10(\cos t - \cos 2t)$ **9.** $I = 50t \sin 4t$ **11.** $I = 1 - \cos t$

13. The discontinuity of $\dot{I}(t)$ follows from $L\dot{I} + \dfrac{q}{C} = E$ and the fact that the charge $q(t)$ in the capacitor is a continuous function of t. Continuity of $I(t)$ follows by integrating that equation, because $\int E \, dt$ is continuous.

15. $I = \begin{cases} I_1 \equiv A_1 \cos t + B_1 \sin t + 1 & \text{when } 0 < t < a, \\ I_2 \equiv A_2 \cos t + B_2 \sin t & \text{when } t > a. \end{cases}$

$I(0) = 0$, $q(0) = 0$, $E(0) = 0$ yields $\dot{I}(0) = 0$, $A_1 = -1$, $B_1 = 0$, and $I_1 = 1 - \cos t$. From this, $I_1(a) = 1 - \cos a$, $\dot{I}_1(a) = \sin a$. Thus $I_2(a) = I_1(a) = 1 - \cos a$, $\dot{I}_2(a) = \dot{I}_1(a) - a = -a + \sin a$, that is, $A_2 \cos a + B_2 \sin a = 1 - \cos a$, $-A_2 \sin a + B_2 \cos a = -a + \sin a$. Hence, $A_2 = \cos a + a \sin a - 1$, $B_2 = -\sin a - a \cos a$, and

$I = \begin{cases} 1 - \cos t & \text{when } 0 < t < a, \\ \cos(t - a) - a \sin(t - a) - \cos t & \text{when } t > a. \end{cases}$

17. $I = \begin{cases} \frac{1}{2}(e^{-t} - \cos t + \sin t) & \text{when } 0 < t < \pi \\ -\frac{1}{2}(1 + e^{-\pi}) \cos t + \frac{1}{2}(3 - e^{-\pi}) \sin t & \text{when } t > \pi \end{cases}$

21. $I = \begin{cases} 1 - e^{-t} & \text{when } 0 < t < a \\ (e^a - 1)e^{-t} & \text{when } t > a \end{cases}$ **23.** $I = \begin{cases} 1 & \text{when } 0 < t < a \\ -ae^{a-t} & \text{when } t > a \end{cases}$

SECTION 2.15

1. We regard the given equation as the real part of $y'' + 2y' + 2y = e^{2it}$. Substituting $y_p{}^* = Ke^{2it}$ into this equation, we obtain $(-4 + 4i + 2)Ke^{2it} = e^{2it}$. Thus, $K = 1/(-2 + 4i) = -\frac{1}{10} - \frac{i}{5}$. Hence, the steady-state output is

$$y_p = \text{Re}[y_p{}^*] = \text{Re}\left[\left(-\tfrac{1}{10} - \frac{i}{5}\right)(\cos 2t + i \sin 2t)\right] = -\tfrac{1}{10} \cos 2t + \tfrac{1}{5} \sin 2t.$$

3. $y_p = \frac{1}{6} \sin 4t$ **5.** $y_p = -\frac{30}{61} \cos 3t + \frac{36}{61} \sin 3t$

7. $I_p = -0.2006 \cos 10t + 0.1008 \sin 10t$

9. $I_p = -\frac{11}{73} \cos 4t + \frac{5}{73} \sin 4t$

SECTION 2.16

Using (8), we obtain

1. $y = A \cos 2x + B \sin 2x + \frac{1}{4} \cos 2x \ln (\cos 2x) + \frac{x}{2} \sin 2x$

3. $y = (c_1 + c_2 x)e^x + \dfrac{e^x}{x}$

5. $y = (c_1 + c_2 x)e^{-x} + x^2 e^{-x}(\frac{1}{2} \ln x - \frac{3}{4})$

7. $y = c_1 x + c_2 x^2 + x^4$. Note that in (8), $r = 6x^2$, because (8) was derived from (1), and the given equation assumes the form (1) by dividing it by x^2.

9. $y = \dfrac{c_1}{x} + c_2 x + xe^x$ **11.** $y = c_1 x + c_2 x^2 + x \cos x$

13. $y = c_1 x^2 + c_2 x^3 + x^2 \sin x$ **15.** $y = c_1 x^2 + c_2 x^3 + \dfrac{1}{x^4}$

SECTION 3.2

1. 2   **3.** ∞ **5.** $\frac{1}{4}$ **7.** ∞ **9.** 1   **11.** 3

15. If we multiply the two series term by term, the sum of the products for which $k + m = n$ is

$$\frac{x_1{}^n}{n!} + \frac{x_1{}^{n-1}}{(n-1)!} \frac{x_2}{1!} + \cdots + \frac{x_2{}^n}{n!} = \frac{1}{n!}\left[x_1{}^n + \binom{n}{1}x_1{}^{n-1} x_2 + \cdots + x_2{}^n\right] = \frac{(x_1 + x_2)^n}{n!}.$$

17. $y = c_0\left(1 - x + \dfrac{x^2}{2} - \dfrac{x^3}{6} - \frac{23}{24}x^4 + \frac{119}{120}x^5 + \cdots\right)$

19. $y = c_0 + c_1 x + (\frac{3}{2}c_1 - c_0)x^2 + (\frac{7}{6}c_1 - c_0)x^3 + \cdots$. Setting $c_0 = A + B$ and $c_1 = A + 2B$, this becomes $y = Ae^x + Be^{2x}$. This illustrates the fact that even if the solution of an equation is a known function, the power series method may not yield it immediately in the usual form.

21. $y = c_0 - \dfrac{c_0}{2}x^2 + (c_0 + 4)\left[\dfrac{x^4}{4!} - \dfrac{x^6}{6!} + - \cdots\right]$

$$+ c_1 x + (c_1 - 1)\left[-\dfrac{x^3}{3!} + \dfrac{x^5}{5!} - \dfrac{x^7}{7!} + - \cdots\right]$$

$$= (c_0 + 4) \cos x + (c_1 - 1) \sin x + 2x^2 + x - 4$$

23. $y = c_0 + c_1 x + c_0 x^2 + c_1 x^3$

25. $y = c_0 + c_1 x + \left(\dfrac{1}{2} - \dfrac{c_0}{2} - c_1\right) x^2 + \left(-\dfrac{1}{2} + \dfrac{c_0}{3} + \dfrac{c_1}{2}\right) x^3 + \cdots$

$= \left(\dfrac{x^2}{2} + (c_0 + c_1)x + c_0\right) e^{-x}$

27. $y = c_0 + c_1 x + c_0(x^2 + x^3 + \cdots) = \dfrac{c_0}{1-x} + (c_1 - c_0)x$

29. $y = c_0\left[1 + kt + \dfrac{(kt)^2}{2!} + \cdots\right] = c_0\left[1 + k(x-1) + \dfrac{k^2}{2!}(x-1)^2 + \cdots\right]$

SECTION 3.3

5. $y = P_3(z/a)$ **7.** Set $(x^2 - 1)^n = v(x)$. Since $v, v', v'', \cdots, v^{(n-1)}$ are zero at $x \pm 1$ and

$v^{(2n)} = (2n)!$, we obtain from (12) $(2^n n!)^2 \displaystyle\int_{-1}^{1} P_n{}^2\, dx = \int_{-1}^{1} v^{(n)} v^{(n)}\, dx = [v^{(n-1)} v^{(n)}]|_{-1}^{1}$

$- \displaystyle\int_{-1}^{1} v^{(n-1)} v^{(n+1)}\, dx = \cdots = (-1)^n \int_{-1}^{1} v v^{(2n)}\, dx = (-1)^n (2n)! \int_{-1}^{1} (x^2 - 1)^n\, dx$

$= 2(2n)! \displaystyle\int_{0}^{1} (1 - x^2)^n\, dx.$ Setting $x = \cos\beta$, the last expression takes the form

$2(2n)! \displaystyle\int_{0}^{\pi/2} \sin^{2n+1}\beta\, d\beta = 2(2n)!\, \dfrac{2\cdot 4 \cdots (2n)}{1\cdot 3\cdot 5 \cdots (2n+1)}.$

Since $2\cdot 4 \cdots (2n) = 2^n n!$ and $1\cdot 3\cdot 5 \cdots (2n+1) = (2n+1)!/2\cdot 4 \cdots (2n)$, the formula (13) follows.

11. Use (11') and equate the coefficients of each power of x on both sides, finding $f(x) = 6P_0 - 4P_1(x) + 2P_2(x)$.   **15.** $4P_3 - 2P_2 + P_1 - 2P_0$

SECTION 3.4

1. $y_1 = \dfrac{c_0}{x^2}\left[1 + \dfrac{x^2}{3!} + \dfrac{x^4}{5!} + \cdots\right] = \dfrac{c_0}{x^3}\sinh x,$ $y_2 = \dfrac{c_0{}^*}{x^3}\cosh x$

3. $y_1 = c_0(1 + x + x^2 + \cdots) = \dfrac{c_0}{1-x},$ $y_2 = \dfrac{c_0{}^*}{x}$

7. $y_1 = 1 + \dfrac{x^2}{2^2} + \dfrac{x^4}{(2\cdot 4)^2} + \dfrac{x^6}{(2\cdot 4\cdot 6)^2} + \cdots,$

$y_2 = y_1 \ln x - \dfrac{x^2}{4} - \dfrac{3x^4}{8\cdot 16} - \dfrac{11x^6}{64\cdot 6\cdot 36} - \cdots$ **9.** $y_1 = \sqrt{x}\, e^x, y_2 = (x+1)e^x$

13. $y_1 = \sqrt{x}, y_2 = e^x$ **15.** $y_1 = 1 + x, y_2 = (1+x)\ln x$

17. $y_1 = e^x, y_2 = e^x \ln x$ **19.** $y_1 = \sqrt{x}\, e^x, y_2 = e^{2x}$

31. $y = AF(\tfrac{1}{2}, \tfrac{1}{2}, \tfrac{1}{2}; x) + B\sqrt{x}\, F(1, 1, \tfrac{3}{2}; x)$

33. $y = AF(1, -\tfrac{1}{3}, \tfrac{1}{3}; x) + Bx^{2/3} F(\tfrac{5}{3}, \tfrac{1}{3}, \tfrac{5}{3}; x)$

SECTION 3.5

5. $J_0(x) = 1 - \dfrac{x^2}{4} + \dfrac{x^4}{64} - + \cdots;$ $1 - \dfrac{x^2}{4} = 0$ when $x = 2$, $1 - \dfrac{x^2}{4} + \dfrac{x^4}{64} = 0$

when $x = \sqrt{8}$. We clearly have $J_0(2) = \dfrac{1}{(2!)^2} - \dfrac{1}{(3!)^2} + - \cdots > 0$ and furthermore

$J_0(\sqrt{8}) = -\dfrac{2^3}{(3!)^2} + \dfrac{2^4}{(4!)^2} - + \cdots < 0$ because the terms decrease monotone in absolute value.

9. Differentiate the Maclaurin series of J_0 term by term.

11. $y = (A \cos x + B \sin x)/\sqrt{x}$ **15.** $y = AJ_\nu(\lambda x) + BJ_{-\nu}(\lambda x)$

17. $y = x^{-\nu}[AJ_\nu(x) + BJ_{-\nu}(x)]$ **19.** $y = AJ_\nu(\sqrt{x}) + BJ_{-\nu}(\sqrt{x})$

21. $y = AxJ_1(x)$ **23.** $y = x^\nu[AJ_\nu(x^\nu) + BJ_{-\nu}(x^\nu)]$

SECTION 3.6

5. From (2) and Rolle's theorem it follows that between two consecutive positive zeros of J_n there lies at least one zero of J_{n+1}. From (1) (with $\nu = n + 1$) and Rolle's theorem it follows that between two consecutive positive zeros of J_{n+1} there lies at least one zero of J_n. This proves the statement.

9. $\dfrac{8}{x}\left(\dfrac{6}{x^2} - 1\right)J_1 - \left(\dfrac{24}{x^2} - 1\right)J_0$ **21.** Cf. (1), (2).

25. Use (4) with $\nu = 1$ and integrate.

SECTION 3.7

3. $AJ_0(x) + BY_0(x)$ **5.** $x[AJ_1(x) + BY_1(x)]$ **7.** $x^{-1}[AJ_1(x) + BY_1(x)]$

9. $AJ_0(\sqrt{x}) + BY_0(\sqrt{x})$ **11.** $\sqrt{x}[AJ_0(x) + BY_0(x)]$ **17.** For $x \neq 0$ the terms of the Maclaurin series of $x^{-\nu}I_\nu(x)$ are positive.

SECTION 4.1

3. $\dfrac{a}{s^2} + \dfrac{b}{s}$ **5.** $\dfrac{12}{s^4} - \dfrac{6}{s^2} + \dfrac{8}{s}$ **7.** $\dfrac{3}{s^2 - 9}$ **9.** $\dfrac{1}{2s} - \dfrac{s}{2(s^2 + 4)}$

11. $\dfrac{\Gamma(3/2)}{s^{3/2}} = \dfrac{(1/2)\Gamma(1/2)}{s^{3/2}} = \dfrac{\sqrt{\pi}}{2s^{3/2}}$ **13.** $\dfrac{1}{s^2 + 4}$ **15.** $a\dfrac{s\cos\theta - \omega\sin\theta}{s^2 + \omega^2}$

17. $\dfrac{6}{(s + 3)^4}$ **19.** $\dfrac{s + a}{(s + a)^2 + \omega^2}$ **21.** $\dfrac{1}{2s - 2} - \dfrac{s}{2(s - 1)^2 + 8}$

23. By (1), $F(s) = \displaystyle\int_1^2 e^{-st}(t - 1)\,dt = \dfrac{e^{-s}}{s^2} - e^{-2s}\left(\dfrac{1}{s} + \dfrac{1}{s^2}\right)$

25. $\dfrac{t^{n-1}}{(n - 1)!}$ **27.** $2e^{-3t}$ **29.** $\cos\sqrt{\pi t}$ **31.** $\dfrac{t^{n-1}e^{at}}{(n - 1)!}$

SECTION 4.2

11. $(1 - \cos 2t)/4$ **13.** $(\sinh 2t - 2t)/8$ **15.** $2e^{-at} - 1$

17. $1 + e^{\pi t}$ **19.** $\sin \pi t + \dfrac{\pi^3 t^3}{6} - \pi t$ **21.** $\sin 2t - \cos 2t + 1 - 2t$

SECTION 4.3

1. $y = \cos t - \sin t$ **3.** $y = -2\cos 5t + 4\sin 5t$ **5.** $y = 2\cosh 2t$

7. $y = 3e^{-3t}$ **9.** $y = e^{-t}\sin t$ **11.** $y = e^{-2t}(\cos t - 2\sin t)$

13. $y = 3e^{-t}\sin 4t$ **15.** $y = e^{-t/2}\cos t$

SECTION 4.4

1. $3 - 2e^{-4t}$ **3.** $4e^{-4t} + 2e^{2t}$ **5.** $e^{-t} + 2e^{-2t} + 3e^{-3t}$ **7.** $1 - 2\sinh 5t$
9. $2\sinh 2t - 3\sinh t + 2$ **11.** $e^{-2t} - 2 + e^{t}$ **13.** $\cosh 3t + 2e^{t}$
15. $y = \frac{1}{2}e^{t} - e^{2t} + \frac{1}{2}e^{3t}$ **17.** $y = \frac{1}{3}e^{3t} + 2e^{-t} - \frac{4}{3}$ **19.** $y = e^{t} - e^{-2t} + \sin 3t$
21. $y = e^{-2t} + e^{2t} + e^{3t} + e^{-t}$

SECTION 4.5

1. $6\cos 3t - \frac{2}{3}\sin 3t$ **3.** $\frac{1}{4} + \frac{3}{4}\cos 2t$ **5.** $4e^{t}(\cos t + \sin t)$
7. $e^{-t}(\cos 2t - 2\sin 2t)$ **9.** $e^{3t}(3\cos t + 2\sin t)$
15. $\cosh t \sin t + \sinh t \cos t$ **17.** $e^{t}\cos t$ **19.** $e^{2t}\cos t + e^{t}\sin 2t$
21. $y = e^{t}\sin t$ **23.** $y = e^{t}\cos t$

SECTION 4.6

3. $e^{2t}(2t - 4)$ **5.** $e^{-t}(t^2 + t - 1)$ **7.** $1 + e^{-t}(t^2 + 1)$ **9.** $t + e^{3t}(t - 1)$
11. $\frac{1}{2}e^{-2t}(2 - t)^3$ **13.** $\frac{1}{2}t^2e^{t} - te^{2t}$ **15.** $y = e^{-4t}(3 - 2t)$
17. $y = e^{-t}(t - 1) + e^{-2t}$ **19.** $y = e^{-2t}(t - 2)^2$

SECTION 4.7

1. $e^{-t} t \cos t$ **3.** $e^{2t} t(\cos t - \sin t)$ **5.** $e^{-3t}(1 - t)\cos t$
7. $e^{-t}(\cos 2t - 2t\sin 2t)$ **9.** $e^{-2t}[(t + 2)\cos 3t - (2t + 3)\sin 3t]$
13. $y = t\sin t$ **15.** $y = t(\sin t - \cos t)$ **17.** $y = 2\cos 3t + t\sin 3t$
19. $y = \cos 5t + t(2\cos 5t + \sin 5t)$

SECTION 4.8

3. $\dfrac{1}{(s - 1)^2}$ **5.** $\dfrac{4s}{(s^2 - 4)^2}$ **7.** $\dfrac{2}{(s + 1)^3}$ **9.** $\dfrac{2s(s^2 - 3\omega^2)}{(s^2 + \omega^2)^3}$

11. $\dfrac{s^2 + 2s}{(s^2 + 2s + 2)^2}$ **13.** $\dfrac{s^2 + 2s + 5}{(s^2 + 2s - 3)^2}$ **15.** $\dfrac{t}{2}\sin t$ **17.** $\dfrac{t^2 e^{at}}{2}$

19. $\dfrac{e^{t} - 1}{t}$ **21.** $\dfrac{e^{-t}\sin t}{t}$ **23.** $\dfrac{1 - \cosh t}{t}$

SECTION 4.9

1. $2(1 - e^{-\pi s})/s$ **3.** $(e^{-s} - 2e^{-2s} + e^{-3s})/s$ **5.** $k/s(1 + e^{-as})$ **7.** $1/s(1 - e^{-s})$
9. $k/s(1 + e^{as})$ **11.** Apply Theorem 3, Sec. 4.2, to Prob. 3. The result is
$(e^{-s} - 2e^{-2s} + e^{-3s})/s^2$ **13.** $[2 - 2(\pi s + 1)e^{-\pi s}]/s^2$ **15.** $[1 - e^{-(s+1)\pi}]/(s + 1)$
17. $q(t) = CV_0 e^{-t/RC} (t \geq 0)$ **19.** $i(t) = \dfrac{V_0}{R}(1 - e^{-Rt/L})$
21. $f = 1$ when $2 < t < 4$ and 0 otherwise   **23.** $f = t - a$ when $t > a$ and 0 when
$0 < t < a$, cf. Theorem 3, Sec. 4.2.   **25.** $f = 0,\ t - 1,\ 2t - 3,\ 6 - t,\ 0$ when
$0 < t < 1, 1 < t < 2, 2 < t < 3, 3 < t < 6, t > 6$, respectively

SECTION 4.10

1. $1/s^2 e^{2s}$ **3.** $2/s^3 e^{s}$ **5.** $-se^{-\pi s}/(s^2 + 1)$ **7.** $e^{-s-2}/(s + 2)$
9. $(2s^{-3} + 2s^{-2} + s^{-1})e^{-s}$ **11.** $f = t - 2$ when $t > 2$ and 0 when $0 < t < 2$
13. $f = e^{2(t-2)}$ when $t > 2$ and 0 when $0 < t < 2$
15. $f = (-\sin \pi t)/\pi$ when $t > 1$ and 0 when $0 < t < 1$
17. $\mathscr{L}[f(at)] = \displaystyle\int_0^\infty e^{-st} f(at)\, dt = \frac{1}{a}\int_0^\infty e^{-s\tau/a} f(\tau)\, d\tau = \frac{1}{a} F\left(\frac{s}{a}\right)$
19. Use the result of Prob. 17 and Theorem 2, Sec. 4.1.

21. $e^{-3t/\pi}\cos t$ **23.** $f = K[\sin \omega t - u_{\pi/\omega}(t)\sin \omega t] = K[\sin \omega t + u_{\pi/\omega}\sin(\omega t - \pi)]$.
Ans. $K\omega(s^2 + \omega^2)^{-1}(1 + e^{-\pi s/\omega})$

25. $f = t - tu_a(t) = t - (t - a)u_a(t) - au_a(t)$. Ans. $[1 - (1 + as)e^{-as}]/s^2$

27. $i' + \displaystyle\int_0^t i(\tau)\,d\tau = t[1 - u_a(t)] = t - (t - a)u_a(t) - au_a(t)$. Consequently,

$$sI + \frac{1}{s}I = \frac{1}{s^2} - \frac{e^{-as}}{s^2} - \frac{a}{s}e^{-as}, \qquad I = \left[\frac{1}{s} - e^{-as}\left(\frac{1}{s} + a\right)\right]/(s^2 + 1).$$

Ans. $i = 1 - \cos t$ when $0 < t < a$, $i = \cos(t - a) - a\sin(t - a) - \cos t$ when $t > a$. Cf. Prob. 15, Sec. 2.14.

29. $i = \tfrac{1}{2}(e^{-t} - \cos t + \sin t)$ when $0 < t < \pi$,
$i = -\tfrac{1}{2}(1 + e^{-\pi})\cos t + \tfrac{1}{2}(3 - e^{-\pi})\sin t$ when $t > \pi$

SECTION 4.11

1. $\dfrac{\omega}{(s^2 + \omega^2)(e^{\pi s/\omega} - 1)}$ **3.** $\dfrac{\omega}{s^2 + \omega^2}\coth\dfrac{\pi s}{2\omega}$ **7.** $\dfrac{2\pi s + e^{-2\pi s} - 1}{s^2(1 - e^{-2\pi s})}$

9. $\dfrac{e^{2(1-s)\pi} - 1}{(1 - s)(1 - e^{-2\pi s})}$ **11.** $\left[\dfrac{\pi}{s}e^{-\pi s}(e^{-\pi s} - 1) + \dfrac{1}{s^2}(e^{-\pi s} - 1)^2\right]/(1 - e^{-2\pi s})$

13. $\left[\dfrac{1}{s^2}(1 - e^{-\pi s}) - \dfrac{\pi}{s}e^{-\pi s}\right]/(1 - e^{-2\pi s})$

17. $i' + \dfrac{R}{L}i = \dfrac{V_0}{L}[u_0(t) - u_a(t) + -\cdots], \quad I = \dfrac{V_0}{L}\dfrac{1}{s(s + k)}[1 - e^{-as} + e^{-2as} - +\cdots]$,

$$k = \frac{R}{L}, \quad \mathscr{L}^{-1}\left\{\frac{1}{s(s + k)}\right\} = 1 - e^{-kt}, \quad \mathscr{L}^{-1}\left\{\frac{e^{-as}}{s(s + k)}\right\} = (1 - e^{-k(t-a)})u_a(t), \quad \text{etc.},$$

$$i = \frac{V_0}{R}(1 - e^{-kt}) \qquad (t < a),$$

$$i = -\frac{V_0}{R}e^{-kt}(1 - e^{ka}) \qquad (a < t < 2a),$$

$$i = \frac{V_0}{R}[1 - e^{-kt}(1 - e^{ka} + e^{2ka}] \qquad (2a < t < 3a), \text{ etc.}$$

In general, by summing the finite geometric progression,

$$i = \frac{V_0}{R}\left[\delta - \frac{e^{-kt}}{1 + e^{ka}} - (-1)^n\frac{e^{-k[t-(n+1)a]}}{1 + e^{ka}}\right], \quad \delta = \begin{cases} 0 & (n \text{ odd}), \\ 1 & (n \text{ even}), \end{cases} \quad na < t < (n + 1)a.$$

The second term on the right dies out. Setting $t - na = \tau$, the remaining expression becomes

$$i = \begin{cases} \dfrac{V_0}{R}\left(1 - \dfrac{e^{-k\tau}}{1 + e^{-ka}}\right) & (n \text{ even}) \\[3mm] \dfrac{V_0}{R}\left(\dfrac{e^{-k\tau}}{1 + e^{-ka}}\right) & (n \text{ odd}) \end{cases} \qquad \begin{cases} \tau = t - na, \\ 0 < \tau < a, \\ k = R/L, \\ n = 0, 1, \cdots. \end{cases}$$

19. $Ri + \dfrac{1}{C}\displaystyle\int i\,dt = v(t)$, $RI + \dfrac{I}{Cs} = \dfrac{1 - e^{-s}}{s^2} - \dfrac{e^{-s}}{s}$,

$$i(t) = \begin{cases} C(1 - e^{-t/RC}) & \text{when } 0 < t < 1 \\[2mm] \left[\left(C - \dfrac{1}{R}\right)e^{1/RC} - C\right]e^{-t/RC} & \text{when } t > 1 \end{cases}$$

21. $\mathscr{L}(i') = s\mathscr{L}(i) - i(0) - je^{-s}$ where j is the jump of i at $t = 1$ (cf. Prob. 2, p. 214). To determine j, observe that Rj equals the jump -1 of the electromotive force at $t = 1$. Why?

23. $i(t) = \begin{cases} a \cos \omega t + b \sin \omega t - ae^{-t/RC} & \text{when } 0 < t < \pi/\omega \\ -a(1 + e^{\pi/\omega RC})e^{-t/RC} & \text{when } t > \pi/\omega \end{cases}$

where $a = \omega CK$, $b = \omega^2 RC^2 K$, $K = 1/[1 + (\omega RC)^2]$

25. $i(t) = \begin{cases} \dfrac{t}{R} + \dfrac{L}{R^2}(e^{-tR/L} - 1) & \text{when } 0 < t < 1 \\[2ex] \left[\dfrac{1}{R}e^{R/L}\left(1 - \dfrac{L}{R}\right) + \dfrac{L}{R^2}\right]e^{-tR/L} & \text{when } t > 1 \end{cases}$

27. $i(t) = \begin{cases} \dfrac{V_0}{\omega^* L} e^{-\alpha t} \sin \omega^* t & \text{when } 0 < t < a \\[2ex] \dfrac{V_0}{\omega^* L}[e^{-\alpha t} \sin \omega^* t - e^{-\alpha(t-a)} \sin \{\omega^*(t - a)\}] & \text{when } t > a \end{cases}$

where $\alpha = \dfrac{R}{2L}$, $\omega^{*2} = \dfrac{1}{LC} - \alpha^2$

29. Initial current 2 amperes, initial charge 0, $i = e^{-t/5}(2 \cos \frac{2}{5}t + \sin \frac{2}{5}t)$
35. Let ϕ_1 and ϕ_2 be the angular displacements of the wheels such that at $t = 0$, $\phi_1 = \phi_2 = 0$, $\phi_1' = \phi_2' = \omega$. Let c be the stiffness of the shaft (couple per radian relative twist of the wheels). Then at $t > 0$,

$$M_1\phi_1'' - c(\phi_2 - \phi_1) = -P, \qquad M_2\phi_2'' + c(\phi_2 - \phi_1) = 0.$$

Let $\Phi_1 = \mathscr{L}(\phi_1)$, $\Phi_2 = \mathscr{L}(\phi_2)$. Then the subsidiary equations are

$$(M_1 s^2 + c)\Phi_1 - c\Phi_2 = M_1\omega - \frac{P}{s}, \qquad -c\Phi_1 + (M_2 s^2 + c)\Phi_2 = M_2\omega.$$

Elimination of Φ_1 yields

$$\Phi_2 = \frac{\omega}{s^2} - \frac{cP}{s^3[M_1 M_2 s^2 + c(M_1 + M_2)]}, \text{ and } V = \mathscr{L}(v) = s\Phi_2.$$

Ans. $v = \omega - \dfrac{Pt}{M_1 + M_2} + \dfrac{P}{k(M_1 + M_2)} \sin kt$, $k^2 = c\left(\dfrac{1}{M_1} + \dfrac{1}{M_2}\right)$.

SECTION 5.2

1. 2,2,0, $|\mathbf{v}| = \sqrt{8}$ **3.** 1,1,0, $|\mathbf{v}| = \sqrt{2}$ **5.** $-1,5,0$, $|\mathbf{v}| = \sqrt{26}$
7. $2,-1,2$, $|\mathbf{v}| = 3$ **9.** $1,5,-1$, $|\mathbf{v}| = \sqrt{27}$ **11.** Q: $(2, 6, 3)$
13. Q: $(-0.5, 4.5, -2.5)$ **15.** Q: $(-3, -3, 1)$

SECTION 5.3

1. $\mathbf{i} + \mathbf{j} + 3\mathbf{k}$ **3.** $\sqrt{18}$ **5.** $-2\mathbf{i} - 5\mathbf{j} + 3\mathbf{k}$ **7.** $2\mathbf{i} + 7\mathbf{j} + 13\mathbf{k}$
9. $\sqrt{334}$ **11.** $-5\mathbf{i} - 2\mathbf{j} + 13\mathbf{k}$ **13.** $5\mathbf{j} + \mathbf{k}$ **15.** 0
17. The vector $\mathbf{r}$ from 0 to P is of the form $\mathbf{r} = k(\mathbf{a} + \mathbf{b})$. Also, $\mathbf{r} = \mathbf{a} + l(\mathbf{b} - \mathbf{a})$. Thus, $k\mathbf{a} + k\mathbf{b} = (1 - l)\mathbf{a} + l\mathbf{b}$. From this, $k = 1 - l$, $k = l$; hence $k = \frac{1}{2}$, $l = \frac{1}{2}$, and the proof is complete.

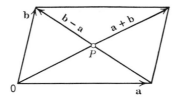

Fig. 395. Problem 17.

SECTION 5.4

1. 23,10,11   **3.** 34,12   **5.** $\sqrt{98}, \sqrt{52}$ **7.** 23/26   **9.** $-\sqrt{6/13}$ **11.** 6
13. 6   **15.** 0   **17.** -19 **19.** The angle β of the triangle at B is the angle between the vectors $\mathbf{c} = -2\mathbf{i}$ from B to A and $\mathbf{a} = -2\mathbf{i} + 2\mathbf{j}$ from B to C. Therefore $\cos \beta = \mathbf{a} \cdot \mathbf{c}/|\mathbf{a}||\mathbf{c}| = 1/\sqrt{2}, \beta = \pi/4$, etc.   **21.** Angle at A, $62°58'$, etc.

SECTION 5.6

1. $3\mathbf{k}, -3\mathbf{k}$ **3.** $2\mathbf{i} + \mathbf{j} - 7\mathbf{k}, \sqrt{54}, 4$ **5.** $3\mathbf{i} - 6\mathbf{k}$ **7.** $-\mathbf{i} - 2\mathbf{j} + 5\mathbf{k}$
9. $3\mathbf{k}$ **11.** $12\mathbf{i} + 6\mathbf{j} - 33\mathbf{k}$ **13.** $\mathbf{k}, -\mathbf{k}$ **15.** $\mathbf{i}, -\mathbf{i}$
17. $(\mathbf{i} + \mathbf{j} - 2\mathbf{k})/\sqrt{6}, (-\mathbf{i} - \mathbf{j} + 2\mathbf{k})/\sqrt{6}$ **19.** $\pm(3\mathbf{j} + 2\mathbf{k})/\sqrt{13}$
21. $\pm(3\mathbf{i} - 2\mathbf{j} + \mathbf{k})/\sqrt{14}$ **23.** Parallel   **25.** No   **27.** Parallel
29. $\sqrt{40}$ **31.** $\sqrt{3}$ **33.** 7   **35.** 11   **37.** 2   **39.** $\frac{1}{2}\sqrt{27}$
41. 7.516 65   **45.** $\sqrt{109}$ **47.** $\sqrt{35}$ **49.** 0   **51.** $8\sqrt{2}$ **53.** $\mathbf{v} = -4\sqrt{2}(\mathbf{i} + \mathbf{j})$
55. $(\mathbf{i} + \mathbf{j} + \mathbf{k})/\sqrt{3}$ **57.** $(15\mathbf{i} - 13\mathbf{j} + 6\mathbf{k})/\sqrt{430}$ **59.** $\mathbf{n} = 2\mathbf{i} + 3\mathbf{j} + 4\mathbf{k}$ and $\mathbf{p} = \mathbf{i} - \mathbf{j} + \mathbf{k}$ are normal vectors to the planes, and $\mathbf{v} = \mathbf{n} \times \mathbf{p} = 7\mathbf{i} + 2\mathbf{j} - 5\mathbf{k}$.

SECTION 5.7

1. 1   **3.** -1 **5.** 14   **7.** -133 **9.** 2   **11.** 5   **13.** 16   **15.** 42
17. 5/3   **19.** 1   **21.** Independent   **23.** Independent   **25.** Dependent
27. Dependent   **29.** Dependent   **31.** Independent   **33.** Dependent

SECTION 5.8

1. $28\mathbf{i} + 52\mathbf{j} - 42\mathbf{k}, 66\mathbf{i} + 36\mathbf{j} + 2\mathbf{k}$ **3.** $-792\mathbf{i} - 432\mathbf{j} - 24\mathbf{k}$
5. $98\mathbf{i} + 92\mathbf{j} - 42\mathbf{k}$ **7.** 0   **9.** 106   **11.** 624   **13.** $-60\mathbf{i} - 60\mathbf{j} + 30\mathbf{k}$
15. $-90\mathbf{i} - 60\mathbf{k}$ **19.** L is parallel to P.

SECTION 5.9

13. Concentric spheres   **15.** Parallel planes   **27.** Circles $x^2 + y^2 = c$, straight lines $2xy/(x^2 - y^2) = c$
29. Ellipses $y^2 + 16x^2 = c$, straight lines $y/x = c$

SECTION 5.10

1. $\mathbf{u}' = \mathbf{b}, \mathbf{u}'' = 0$ **3.** $\mathbf{u}' = -4 \sin t\, \mathbf{i} + 4 \cos t\, \mathbf{j}, \mathbf{u}'' = -\mathbf{u}$
5. $\mathbf{u}' = -6t \sin t^2\, \mathbf{i} + 6t \cos t^2\, \mathbf{j}$,
$\mathbf{u}'' = (-6 \sin t^2 - 12t^2 \cos t^2)\mathbf{i} + (6 \cos t^2 - 12t^2 \sin t^2)\mathbf{j}, |\mathbf{u}''| = 6\sqrt{1 + 4t^4}$
7. $\mathbf{u}' = -4 \sin 2t\, \mathbf{i} + 4 \cos 2t\, \mathbf{j} + 4\mathbf{k}, |\mathbf{u}'| = 4\sqrt{2}, |\mathbf{u}''| = 8$
9. $\mathbf{u}' = -3 \sin t\, \mathbf{i} + 2 \cos t\, \mathbf{j}, \mathbf{u}'' = -3 \cos t\, \mathbf{i} - 2 \sin t\, \mathbf{j}$
11. $\mathbf{u}' = \mathbf{i} + 2t\mathbf{j} + 3t^2\mathbf{k}, \mathbf{u}'' = 2\mathbf{j} + 6t\mathbf{k}$

17. $-6t - 3, (2t^3 + 9t)/\sqrt{t^4 + 9t^2}, 44t^3 + 3t^2$ **19.** $6t^2(32t^5 - 216t^3 - 4t - 3)$

27. $(-ti + j)(1 + t^2)^{-3/2}$ **29.** $\dfrac{\partial v}{\partial x} = 2xi - 2yj, \dfrac{\partial v}{\partial y} = -2yi - 2xj$

SECTION 5.11

1. $r(t) = (t + 1)i + (t + 4)j + (2t + 1)k$ **3.** $r(t) = -ti + 2tj$
5. $r(t) = (t + 1)i + 2j + (5t - 3)k$ **7.** $r(t) = (3t - 2)i - 2tj + (3t + 1)k$
9. By subtracting the last equation from the first we obtain $z = 5 - x$. By inserting this into the first equation we find $y = 2x - 3$. Setting $x = t$ the desired representation is $r(t) = ti + (2t - 3)j + (5 - t)k$.
11. $(0, 2, 1)$ **13.** $r(t) = (3 + \cos t)i + (2 + \sin t)j$
15. $r(t) = (1 + 2 \cos t)i + (2 + \sin t)j$

SECTION 5.12

1. $2\pi\sqrt{a^2 + c^2}$ **3.** $6a$ **5.** $8(10\sqrt{10} - 1)/27$

7. $s = a \displaystyle\int_0^{2\pi} (1 - \epsilon^2 \cos^2 t)^{1/2} \, dt = a \int_0^{2\pi} \left(1 - \tfrac{1}{2}\epsilon^2 \cos^2 t - \dfrac{1}{2 \cdot 4} \epsilon^4 \cos^4 t - \cdots \right) dt$

$$\int_0^{2\pi} \cos^{2n}t \, dt = 2\pi \frac{1 \cdot 3 \cdot 5 \cdots (2n - 1)}{2 \cdot 4 \cdot 6 \cdots (2n)}, \qquad n = 1, 2, \cdots,$$

$$s = 2\pi a \left[1 - \left(\frac{1}{2}\right)^2 \epsilon^2 - \frac{1}{3}\left(\frac{1 \cdot 3}{2 \cdot 4}\right)^2 \epsilon^4 - \frac{1}{5}\left(\frac{1 \cdot 3 \cdot 5}{2 \cdot 4 \cdot 6}\right)^2 \epsilon^6 - \cdots \right]$$

SECTION 5.13

1. $q(w) = (w + 2\sqrt{2})i + (w - 2\sqrt{2})j$ **3.** $q(w) = \sqrt{2}(1 - w)i + (1/\sqrt{2})(1 + w)j$
5. $q(w) = (1 + w)i + (1 + 2w)j + (1 + 3w)k$ **9.** For a straight line, $u' \equiv 0$.
11. Cf. (5).   **13.** $\dot{r} \cdot \dot{r} = a^2 \sin^2 t + b^2 \cos^2 t, \dot{r} \cdot \ddot{r} = (a^2 - b^2) \cos t \sin t,$
$\ddot{r} \cdot \ddot{r} = a^2 \cos^2 t + b^2 \sin^2 t$
17. u' is the rate of change of u. Hence, it lies in the plane of C, and the same is true for $p = u'/\kappa$.   **19.** By definition of a vector product, b' is perpendicular to u. Since b and b' are orthogonal, the result follows.   **21.** b is constant. Thus $b' \equiv 0$ and $\tau \equiv 0$.
23. $u = r', p = r''/\kappa, p' = (r'''/\kappa) - (r''/\kappa^2)\kappa'$ and the last term can be omitted when the determinant is simplified according to Rule F in Sec. 0.3.

SECTION 5.14

1. Positive x-axis, $3i$, 3 **3.** Positive z-axis, $8tk$, $8t$, $8k$
5. Segment $-1 \leq y \leq 1$ on the y-axis, $\cos t \, j$, $|\cos t|$, $-\sin t \, j$
7. Circle, $-6 \sin 2t \, i + 6 \cos 2t \, j$, 6, $-12 \cos 2t \, i - 12 \sin 2t \, j$ **9.** Circle,
$-2t \sin t^2 \, i + 2t \cos t^2 \, j$, $2t$, $(-2 \sin t^2 - 4t^2 \cos t^2)i + (2 \cos t^2 - 4t^2 \sin t^2)j$
11. $v = w \times r$, $w = \omega k$, $\dot{v} = w \times \dot{r} = w \times v$. Since v is tangent to the path, $w \times v$ has the direction opposite to r, and $|a| = |w||v| = \omega^2 R$, as before.

SECTION 5.15

3. $(e^{2t} + \sin t \cos t)/\sqrt{e^{2t} + \sin^2 t}$ **5.** $t^t (\ln t + 1)$
7. $(\cos t)^{\sin t - 1} [\cos^2 t \ln (\cos t) - \sin^2 t]$
11. $-t/(1 + t^2)^{3/2}$ **13.** $e^{2u} \sin 2v, e^{2u} \cos 2v$ **15.** $2, 0$

SECTION 5.16

1. $y\mathbf{i} + x\mathbf{j}$ **3.** $3(x^2 - y^2)\mathbf{i} - 6xy\mathbf{j}$ **5.** $[(y^2 - x^2)\mathbf{i} - 2xy\mathbf{j}]/(x^2 + y^2)^2$
7. $e^x \cos y\,\mathbf{i} - e^x \sin y\,\mathbf{j}$ **9.** $-(x\mathbf{i} + y\mathbf{j} + z\mathbf{k})/(x^2 + y^2 + z^2)^{3/2}$
11. $2xz\mathbf{i} - 2yz\mathbf{j} + (x^2 - y^2)\mathbf{k}$ **13.** $2x\mathbf{i} + 8y\mathbf{j} + 2z\mathbf{k}$ **15.** $yz\mathbf{i} + xz\mathbf{j} + xy\mathbf{k}$
17. $\mathbf{n} = \nabla f = -4x\mathbf{i} + \mathbf{j}$ where $f = y - 2x^2$. At A, $\mathbf{n} = -8\mathbf{i} + \mathbf{j}$.
19. $8\mathbf{i} + 6\mathbf{j}$ **21.** $-48\mathbf{i} - 16\mathbf{j}$ **23.** $-2\mathbf{i} - 2\mathbf{j} + \mathbf{k}$ **25.** $2\mathbf{i} + 4\mathbf{j} + 4\mathbf{k}$
27. $-3\mathbf{i} - 2\mathbf{j} + \mathbf{k}$
29. Let $fg = u$. Then $u_x = f_x g + fg_x$, $u_{xx} = f_{xx}g + 2f_x g_x + fg_{xx}$, etc.
33. $x^2 + y^2 + z^2$ **35.** $e^x \sin y$ **37.** $\arctan \dfrac{y}{x}$
39. $4, 4\sqrt{2}, 4, 0, -4, -4\sqrt{2}, -4, 0$ **41.** $-\sqrt{2}/9$ **43.** $1/3$ **45.** 0

SECTION 5.17

3. $a_{11} = a_{22} = a_{33} = 1$, $b_1 = 1$, $b_2 = 3$, $b_3 = -4$, all others zero
5. $a_{11} = 1$, $a_{22} = a_{33} = \cos\phi$, $a_{23} = -a_{32} = \sin\phi$, all others zero
7. $a_{12} = a_{23} = a_{31} = 1$, all others zero   **9.** 1 in Probs. 3–7, and -1 in Prob. 8

SECTION 5.18

1. No, because (1) involves coordinates.   **3.** $yz + zx + xy$ **5.** 0 **7.** 0
9. $6(x + z)$ **13.** 0 **15.** $f\nabla^2 g - g\nabla^2 f$ **19.** 220

SECTION 5.19

1. $3y\mathbf{k}$ **3.** $-y\mathbf{i} + 2x\mathbf{j}$ **5.** $-2z\mathbf{i} - 2x\mathbf{j} - 2y\mathbf{k}$ **7.** 0 **19.** $\operatorname{curl}\mathbf{v} = 4\mathbf{k}$,
$\operatorname{div}\mathbf{v} = 0$, incompressible. If $\mathbf{r}(t) = x\mathbf{i} + y\mathbf{j} + z\mathbf{k}$ represents a path, $\dot{\mathbf{r}} = \dot{x}\mathbf{i} + \dot{y}\mathbf{j} + \dot{z}\mathbf{k}$
$= -2y\mathbf{i} + 2x\mathbf{j}$, $\dot{x} = -2y$, $\dot{y} = 2x$, $x\dot{x} + y\dot{y} = 0$, $x^2 + y^2 = const$, $z = const$. The
paths are concentric circles.

SECTION 6.2

1. $2\sqrt{2}/3$ **3.** $5/3$ **5.** $\pi/2$ **7.** 16π **9.** $2/3$ **11.** $-4/3$ **13.** 0
15. $34/7$ **17.** 36 **19.** -30 **21.** 0

SECTION 6.3

1. $1/6$ **3.** $1/4$ **5.** $\ln 2$ **7.** $4/3$ **9.** $3\pi/4$ **11.** $a^3/3$ **13.** $\pi/2$ **15.** 1
17. $2,1$ **19.** $\bar{x} = \bar{y} = 4a/3\pi$ **21.** $I_x = bh^3/12$, $I_y = b^3h/4$
23. $I_x = (a + b)h^3/24$, $I_y = h(a^4 - b^4)/48(a - b)$

SECTION 6.4

3. 4 **5.** $\pi/2$ **7.** -8 **9.** 2 **11.** 0 **13.** 0 **15.** $1/4$ **17.** $\ln 2$
21. $(e^2 - 1)/2$

SECTION 6.5

1. The xy-plane, parallel straight lines
3. The xy-plane, concentric circles, straight lines through the origin
5. The cone $x^2 + y^2 = z^2$, circles, straight lines
7. $\dfrac{x^2}{a^2} + \dfrac{y^2}{b^2} + \dfrac{z^2}{c^2} - 1 = 0$ **9.** $\dfrac{x^2}{a^2} - \dfrac{y^2}{b^2} - z = 0$
13. $\mathbf{r} = u\mathbf{i} + u\mathbf{j} + v\mathbf{k}$ **15.** $\mathbf{r} = 2\cos u\,\mathbf{i} + \sin u\,\mathbf{j} + v\mathbf{k}$
17. $\mathbf{r} = 2\cos u\,\mathbf{i} + v\mathbf{j} + 2\sin u\,\mathbf{k}$

SECTION 6.6

1. $\mathbf{r}^*(p,q) = \mathbf{r} + p\mathbf{r}_u + q\mathbf{r}_v$, where $\mathbf{r}, \mathbf{r}_u, \mathbf{r}_v$ refer to P **3.** $(\mathbf{r}^* - \mathbf{r}) \cdot \operatorname{grad} f = 0$
5. $\mathbf{r}_u \cdot \mathbf{r}_v = 0$ **7.** $y = \sqrt{2} - x$ **9.** $z = 2\sqrt{2} + y$ **11.** $(1 + 4u^2)\,du^2 + dv^2$
13. $a^2 \cos^2 v\,du^2 + a^2\,dv^2$ **15.** $v^2\,du^2 + (1 + 4v^2)\,dv^2$
17. $ds^2 = (1 + z_x^2)\,dx^2 + 2z_x z_y\,dx\,dy + (1 + z_y^2)\,dy^2$ **21.** $\pi(\sqrt{125} - 1)/6$

SECTION 6.7

3. 4π **5.** $3\sqrt{5} + \frac{3}{2}\ln(2 + \sqrt{5})$ **11.** $ah\pi(a^2 + \frac{1}{3}h^2)$ **13.** $4\pi a^3 h$
15. $\pi h^4/\sqrt{2}$ **17.** $\pi(h_2^4 - h_1^4)/\sqrt{2}$ **19.** $2\pi^2 ab(4a^2 + 3b^2)$ **21.** Proof for a lamina
S of density σ. Choose coordinates so that A is the z-axis and B is the line $x = k$ in
the xz-plane. Then

$$J_B = \iint_S [(x - k)^2 + y^2]\sigma\,dA = \iint_S [x^2 - 2kx + k^2 + y^2]\sigma\,dA$$

$$= \iint_S (x^2 + y^2)\sigma\,dA - 2k\iint_S x\sigma\,dA + k^2\iint_S \sigma\,dA = J_A - 2k \cdot 0 + k^2 M.$$

SECTION 6.9

1. $1/6$ **3.** $abc/6$ **5.** $8/27$ **7.** $1/15$ **9.** $abc(b^2 + c^2)/12$ **11.** $\pi h a^4/2$
13. $8\pi a^5/15$ **15.** $1/2$ **17.** $4\pi a^2 h$ **19.** Put $f = 1$ in (9).   **21.** Use Prob. 20.
23. Cf. (10).

SECTION 6.11

1. ± 1 **3.** $\pm 3\pi/2$ **9.** $1/3$ **11.** $-18\pi\sqrt{2}$ **13.** 0 **17.** 21 **19.** 0

SECTION 6.12

1. Exact   **3.** Exact   **5.** Not exact   **7.** Exact   **9.** Not exact
11. $u = x + y + z + c$ **13.** $u = (x^2 + y^2)/2$ **15.** $u = e^{xyz} + c$
17. $u = xy + yz + xz + c$ **19.** 3 **21.** -5 **23.** $a^2 + bc$

SECTION 7.1

1. $\begin{pmatrix} 1 & -1 & 2 \\ 2 & 3 & 10 \end{pmatrix}$ **3.** $\begin{pmatrix} 6 & -14 & -1 \\ 0 & 11 & 9 \end{pmatrix}$ **5.** $\begin{pmatrix} -1 & 2 \\ 4 & -1 \\ 3 & 8 \end{pmatrix}$ **7.** A   **9.** No

11. $-\mathbf{K}$ **13.** 0 **15.** $\begin{pmatrix} 1 & 2.5 & 5.5 \\ 2.5 & 4 & 7.5 \\ 5.5 & 7.5 & 9 \end{pmatrix} + \begin{pmatrix} 0 & -0.5 & 0.5 \\ 0.5 & 0 & -0.5 \\ -0.5 & 0.5 & 0 \end{pmatrix}$

SECTION 7.2

1. $\mathbf{AB} = \begin{pmatrix} 9 & 20 \\ 4 & 16 \\ -3 & 12 \end{pmatrix}$, $\mathbf{BA}$ not defined   **3.** $\mathbf{AA}^\mathsf{T} = \begin{pmatrix} 53 & 10 & -13 \\ 10 & 13 & 13 \\ -13 & 13 & 30 \end{pmatrix}$,

$\mathbf{A}^\mathsf{T}\mathbf{A} = \begin{pmatrix} 26 & 22 & 7 \\ 22 & 40 & -16 \\ 7 & -16 & 30 \end{pmatrix}$ **5.** $(\mathbf{AB})^\mathsf{T} = \begin{pmatrix} 9 & 4 & -3 \\ 20 & 16 & 12 \end{pmatrix} = \mathbf{B}^\mathsf{T}\mathbf{A}^\mathsf{T}$

7. $CC^T = 14$, $C^TC = \begin{pmatrix} 9 & 3 & 6 \\ 3 & 1 & 2 \\ 6 & 2 & 4 \end{pmatrix}$ **15.** $AB = 0$, $BA = \begin{pmatrix} 10 & -8 & 28 \\ -5 & 4 & -14 \\ -5 & 4 & -14 \end{pmatrix}$

17. Dilatation in z_2-direction   **19.** $\begin{pmatrix} x_1 \\ x_2 \end{pmatrix} = \begin{pmatrix} 1 & 3 \\ 1 & -3 \end{pmatrix} \begin{pmatrix} z_1 \\ z_2 \end{pmatrix}$

SECTION 7.3

1. 180   **3.** 0   **5.** $4xyz$ **7.** $4a^2b^2c^2$ **9.** -9360 **11.** 0   **13.** 90

15. $\begin{vmatrix} 20 & 481 & 466 \\ 60 & 1443 & 1290 \\ 40 & 964 & 834 \end{vmatrix}$

SECTION 7.4

5. 2   **7.** 2   **9.** 3

SECTION 7.5

1. $x = 4$, $y = -2$ **3.** $x = 1$, $y = 3$ **5.** $x = 1$, $y = 2$, $z = 3$ **7.** $w = 0$, $x = 1$, $y = 2$, $z = 3$ **9.** $I_1 = (R_2 + R_3)F_0/D$, $I_2 = R_3E_0/D$, $I_3 = R_2E_0/D$ where $D = (R_1 + R_4)(R_2 + R_3) + R_2R_3$ **11.** $I_1 = \dfrac{R_4E_1 + R_5(E_1 + E_2)}{(R_1 + R_2 + R_3)(R_4 + R_5) + R_4R_5}$, etc.

SECTION 7.6

1. $x = 2z$, $y = -3z$, z arbitrary   **3.** $x = y = 0$ **5.** $x = z$, $y = -z$, z arbitrary
7. $y = 2w$, $z = 3x$ **9.** $w = z$, $x = 0$, $y = 0$
11. $ax + by + c = 0$ (The line L to be found.)
$ax_1 + by_1 + c = 0$ (P_1 on L.)
$ax_2 + by_2 + c = 0$ (P_2 on L.)
This homogeneous system in the unknowns a, b, c has a nontrivial solution if, and only if, the determinant of the coefficients is zero; this yields the desired result.

SECTION 7.7

1. $x = y + 1$, $z = 1$ **3.** $x = -z$, $y = 3z + 5$ **5.** $x = 3y + 2$, $z = 0$
7. $x = w + 1$, $z = 2y + 1$ **9.** $y = w - 5x + 9$, $z = 0$ **11.** $w = 2x + 1$, $y = 1$, $z = 2$ **13.** No solution

SECTION 7.8

3. Linearly dependent   **5.** Linearly dependent   **7.** Linearly independent
9. Linearly dependent   **11.** Linearly independent
13. For example, $\mathbf{x} = (0\ 0\ 0\ 1)$ **15.** k arbitrary

SECTION 7.9

1. $x = 1$, $y = 2$ **3.** $x = -2$, $y = 3$ **5.** $x = -4$, $y = 4$ **7.** $x = 1$, $y = 2$, $z = 4$ **9.** $x = -2$, $y = 0$, $z = 4$ **11.** $x = 2z$, $y = 3z$ **13.** $w = 1$, $x = 2$, $y = 3$, $z = 4$ **15.** $w = 1$, $x = 0$, $y = 4$, $z = 0$ **17.** $w = 0$, $x = 3z$, $y = 2z + 1$

SECTION 7.10

3. $\begin{pmatrix} 3 & -1 \\ -5 & 2 \end{pmatrix}$ **5.** $\dfrac{1}{a^2 - b^2}\begin{pmatrix} a & -b \\ -b & a \end{pmatrix}$ **7.** $\begin{pmatrix} 0.5 & -0.1 & 0.5 \\ 0 & 0.2 & 0 \\ -0.5 & 0.3 & -1.5 \end{pmatrix}$

9. $\begin{pmatrix} 0.4 & -0.2 & 0.2 \\ -0.2 & -0.4 & 0.4 \\ -0.4 & 0.2 & 0.8 \end{pmatrix}$ **11.** $\begin{pmatrix} 0 & 1 & 0 \\ 1 & 0 & 0 \\ 0 & 0 & 1 \end{pmatrix}$

$x = -2y^* + z^*$ $x = 19x^* + 2y^* - 9z^*$
13. $y = \frac{1}{2}(x^* + y^* - z^*)$ **15.** $y = -4x^* - y^* + 2z^*$
$z = -x^* + 2y^*$ $z = -2x^* \quad\quad + z^*$

17. This follows from (10). **27.** If $u_2 = 0$, (13) becomes $u_1 = t_{12}i_2$, $i_1 = t_{22}i_2$. In

this case, $u_1 = Z_2i_h = Z_1i_2$ (Fig. 396). Thus, $t_{12} = Z_1$, and $i_h = \dfrac{Z_1}{Z_2}i_2$. By applying

Kirchhoff's first law to A we thus have $i_1 = i_h + i_2 = \left(\dfrac{Z_1}{Z_2} + 1\right)i_2$. Hence, $t_{22} =$

$\dfrac{Z_1}{Z_2} + 1$. If $i_2 = 0$, (13) becomes $u_1 = t_{11}u_2$, $i_1 = t_{21}u_2$. Since $i_2 = 0$, $u_2 = u_1$ and

$t_{11} = 1$. Also $u_1 = Z_2i_1$ (Fig. 397). Thus $i_1 = \dfrac{u_1}{Z_2} = \dfrac{u_2}{Z_2}$ and $t_{21} = \dfrac{1}{Z_2}$. For a simpler

derivation see Prob. 32.

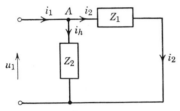

Fig. 396. Problem 27.

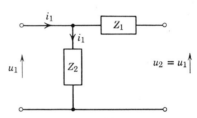

Fig. 397. Problem 27.

SECTION 7.11

1. $3, 2, \begin{pmatrix} 2 \\ 1 \end{pmatrix}, \begin{pmatrix} 1 \\ 1 \end{pmatrix}$ **3.** 0, any vector   **5.** $3, 9, \begin{pmatrix} 1 \\ 1 \end{pmatrix}, \begin{pmatrix} 1 \\ 4 \end{pmatrix}$

7. $1, -1, \begin{pmatrix} 1 \\ 1 \end{pmatrix}, \begin{pmatrix} 0 \\ 1 \end{pmatrix}$ **9.** $8, 4, -2, \begin{pmatrix} 1 \\ 0 \\ -1 \end{pmatrix}, \begin{pmatrix} 1 \\ -2 \\ -3 \end{pmatrix}, \begin{pmatrix} 1 \\ 0 \\ -3 \end{pmatrix}$

11. $20, 10, -5, \begin{pmatrix} -2 \\ 1 \\ 2 \end{pmatrix}, \begin{pmatrix} 1 \\ 2 \\ -1 \end{pmatrix}, \begin{pmatrix} 1 \\ 2 \\ 4 \end{pmatrix}$ **13.** $30, 25, 20, \begin{pmatrix} 1 \\ 2 \\ 4 \end{pmatrix}, \begin{pmatrix} -2 \\ 1 \\ 2 \end{pmatrix}, \begin{pmatrix} 1 \\ 2 \\ -1 \end{pmatrix}$

19. Proof by induction. For $m = 0$ and $m = 1$ the statement is true. Let $\mathbf{Ax}_j = \lambda_j\mathbf{x}_j$ where $\mathbf{x}_j$ is an eigenvector corresponding to λ_j. Suppose that the statement is true when $m = k$, that is, $\mathbf{A}^k\mathbf{x}_j = \lambda_j^k\mathbf{x}_j$. By premultiplying by $\mathbf{A}$ we obtain

$$\mathbf{A}^{k+1}\mathbf{x}_j = \mathbf{A}\lambda_j^k\mathbf{x}_j = \lambda_j^k(\mathbf{Ax}_j) = \lambda_j^{k+1}\mathbf{x}_j,$$

and the proof is complete.

21. The constant term of a polynomial of degree n with first coefficient $(-1)^n$ is the product of the zeros of the polynomial, as is known from algebra. The constant term of the characteristic polynomial is $\det \mathbf{A}$, as can be seen by developing $D(\lambda)$, given by (5). Since $\mathbf{A}$ is non-singular, $\det \mathbf{A} \neq 0$. From this the statement follows.

29. $y_1 = \sin \sqrt{2}t, y_2 = 2 \sin \sqrt{2}t$ **31.** The characteristic equation is

$$\lambda^2 + (a + b + c)\lambda + ac = 0$$

where $a = k_1/m_1$, $b = k_2/m_1$, $c = k_2/m_2$. The discriminant is

$$(a + b + c)^2 - 4ac = (a + b - c)^2 + 4bc > 0.$$

Thus the roots are real. Since their product equals ac (>0) and their sum equals $-(a + b + c)$, the statement follows.

33. $y_1 = 2e^{5t} - e^{-5t}$, $y_2 = e^{5t} + 2e^{-5t}$

35. $y_1 = 2 \cosh 2t$, $y_2 = 4 \sinh 2t$, $y_3 = 2 \cosh 2t$

SECTION 7.12

1. $\begin{pmatrix} 6 & -2 \\ -2 & 2 \end{pmatrix}$ **3.** $\begin{pmatrix} 0 & 4 \\ 4 & -1 \end{pmatrix}$ **5.** $\begin{pmatrix} 1 & 3 & -5 \\ 3 & 0 & 0 \\ -5 & 0 & 4 \end{pmatrix}$ **7.** $\begin{pmatrix} -1 & 3 & 4 \\ 3 & 2 & -2 \\ 4 & -2 & 5 \end{pmatrix}$

9. 0 **11.** 10 **13.** 42 **15.** 1 **17.** $2|x_1|^2 + |x_2|^2 + 2\text{Re}[(1 + i)\bar{x}_1 x_2]$

19. $|x_1|^2 + 3|x_2|^2 + 2\text{Re}[(2 + 5i)\bar{x}_1 x_2]$ **21.** $|x_1|^2 + 2\text{Re}[3\bar{x}_2 x_3 + i\bar{x}_1 x_2] + 2|x_3|^2$

25. $7i$ **27.** $32i$ **29.** $C^T = (aA + bB)^T = aA^T + bB^T = a\bar{A} + b\bar{B} = \overline{(aA + bB)} = \bar{C}$

33. If A is given, $H = (A + \bar{A}^T)/2$ is Hermitian, $S = (A - \bar{A}^T)/2$ is skew-Hermitian, and $A = H + S$.   **35.** The form in Prob. 2 is positive definite.

SECTION 7.13

1. Let A be unitary. Set $A^{-1} = B$. Then $B^T = (A^{-1})^T = (A^T)^{-1} = (\bar{A}^{-1})^{-1} = \bar{B}^{-1}$.

9. $A^{-1}A = A^T A = I$. Thus det $(A^{-1}A)$ = det $(A^T A)$ = det A^T det $A = 1$.

11. Let $Ax = \lambda x$ $(x \neq 0)$, $Ay = \mu y$ $(y \neq 0)$. Then $(Ax)^T = x^T A^T = x^T A = \lambda x^T$. Thus $\lambda x^T y = x^T Ay = \mu x^T y = \mu x^T y$. Hence, if $\lambda \neq \mu$, $x^T y = 0$ which proves orthogonality.

17. Using the result of Prob. 16, we have

$$\text{trace } \tilde{A} = \text{trace } [T^{-1}(AT)] = \text{trace } [(AT)T^{-1}] = \text{trace } (ATT^{-1}) = \text{trace } A.$$

19. $I = IT^{-1}T = T^{-1}IT$. Therefore det $(\tilde{A} - \lambda I)$ = det $(T^{-1}AT - T^{-1}\lambda IT)$ = det $[T^{-1}(A - \lambda I)T]$ = det T^{-1} det $(A - \lambda I)$ det T = det $(A - \lambda I)$. Hence, the characteristic determinants of $\tilde{A}$ and A are equal and so are the eigenvalues.

21. $Ax = \lambda x$ $(x \neq 0)$. Thus (a) $T^{-1}Ax = \lambda T^{-1}x = \lambda y$. Now $T^{-1}Ax = T^{-1}AIx = T^{-1}ATT^{-1}x = \tilde{A}T^{-1}x = \tilde{A}y$, and (a) becomes $\tilde{A}y = \lambda y$.

25. $\lambda = \pm 1$, $\begin{pmatrix} 1 \\ i - i\sqrt{2} \end{pmatrix}$, $\begin{pmatrix} 1 \\ i + i\sqrt{2} \end{pmatrix}$

31. $\lambda_1 = -k$, $\lambda_2 = -3k$, $x_1 = \begin{pmatrix} 1 \\ 1 \end{pmatrix}$, $x_2 = \begin{pmatrix} 1 \\ -1 \end{pmatrix}$, $y = x_1 \cos \sqrt{k}t + x_2 \sin \sqrt{3k}t$

33. Since A is symmetric and nonsingular its eigenvalues are real and none is zero. We have

$$\lambda^3 + a\lambda^2 + b\lambda + c = (\lambda - \lambda_1)(\lambda - \lambda_2)(\lambda - \lambda_3)$$
$$= \lambda^3 - (\lambda_1 + \lambda_2 + \lambda_3)\lambda^2 + (\lambda_1\lambda_2 + \lambda_2\lambda_3 + \lambda_3\lambda_1)\lambda - \lambda_1\lambda_2\lambda_3.$$

Straightforward calculation shows that $a > 0$, $b > 0$, $c > 0$. Thus

(α) $\lambda_1 + \lambda_2 + \lambda_3 < 0$, (β) $\lambda_1\lambda_2 + \lambda_2\lambda_3 + \lambda_3\lambda_1 > 0$, (γ) $\lambda_1\lambda_2\lambda_3 < 0$.

Suppose $\lambda_3 \leq \lambda_2 \leq \lambda_1$. Then by (γ) certainly $\lambda_3 < 0$, say $\lambda_3 = -\mu$ where $\mu > 0$, and (β) may be written $-\mu(\lambda_1 + \lambda_2) + \lambda_1\lambda_2 > 0$. From this, (δ) $\mu(\lambda_1 + \lambda_2) < \lambda_1\lambda_2$. We show that the assumption $\lambda_1 > 0$ leads to a contradiction. From (γ) we then have $\lambda_2 > 0$ and from (α), $\lambda_1 + \lambda_2 < \mu$ which implies $\lambda_2 < \mu$. Hence in (δ), $\lambda_1\lambda_2 < \mu\lambda_1$, and (δ) implies $\mu(\lambda_1 + \lambda_2) < \mu\lambda_1$ which is impossible because $\lambda_2 > 0$. Hence our assumption is false and the proof is complete. Then $\omega_j = \sqrt{\lambda_j}$ is purely imaginary, and the motion is harmonic.

SECTION 7.14

1. $5\sqrt{2}$ **3.** 10 **5.** 23.96 **11.** Centers at 5, radii 1, 2, 1 **13.** Centers at 8, 4, 0, -9, radii 2, 1, 3, 2 **17.** $26 \leq \lambda \leq 34$, $26 \leq \lambda \leq 34$, $28.66 \leq \lambda \leq 30$

19. We have (a) $\overline{\mathbf{B}}^\mathsf{T} = (\overline{\mathbf{U}^{-1}\mathbf{A}\mathbf{U}})^\mathsf{T} = \overline{\mathbf{U}^\mathsf{T}}\overline{\mathbf{A}}^\mathsf{T}(\overline{\mathbf{U}^{-1}})^\mathsf{T} = \mathbf{U}^{-1}\overline{\mathbf{A}}^\mathsf{T}\mathbf{U}$. Thus

$$\overline{\mathbf{B}}^\mathsf{T}\mathbf{B} = \mathbf{U}^{-1}\overline{\mathbf{A}}^\mathsf{T}\mathbf{U}\mathbf{U}^{-1}\mathbf{A}\mathbf{U} = \mathbf{U}^{-1}\overline{\mathbf{A}}^\mathsf{T}\mathbf{A}\mathbf{U} = \mathbf{U}^{-1}\mathbf{A}\overline{\mathbf{A}}^\mathsf{T}\mathbf{U}.$$

On the other hand, by (a),

$$\mathbf{B}\overline{\mathbf{B}}^\mathsf{T} = \mathbf{U}^{-1}\mathbf{A}\mathbf{U}\mathbf{U}^{-1}\overline{\mathbf{A}}^\mathsf{T}\mathbf{U} = \mathbf{U}^{-1}\mathbf{A}\overline{\mathbf{A}}^\mathsf{T}\mathbf{U}.$$

Hence $\overline{\mathbf{B}}^\mathsf{T}\mathbf{B} = \mathbf{B}\overline{\mathbf{B}}^\mathsf{T}$ and $\mathbf{B}$ is normal.

SECTION 7.15

1. $\mathbf{y} = \mathbf{A}\mathbf{x} = \lambda\mathbf{x}$, $m_1 = \mathbf{x}^\mathsf{T}\mathbf{y} = \lambda m_0$, $m_2 = \lambda^2 m_0$, $q = \lambda$, $\dfrac{m_2}{m_0} - q^2 = \lambda^2 - \lambda^2 = 0$ and $\epsilon = 0$ **5.** $q = 2$, $|\epsilon| \leq \sqrt{2}$ **7.** $q = 3$, $|\epsilon| \leq \sqrt{5} \approx 2.24$ **11.** $q = 3$, 5.774, $|\epsilon| \leq 2.55$, 1.337

SECTION 8.1

1. $\pi, \pi, 2, 2, 1, 1$ **17.** 0 (n even), $2/n$ (n odd) **19.** 0 ($n = 0$), $2\pi/n$ ($n = 1, 3, \cdots$), $-2\pi/n$ ($n = 2, 4, \cdots$) **21.** 0 **23.** $n[(-1)^n e^{-\pi} - 1]/(1 + n^2)$ **25.** $2\pi^3/3$ ($n = 0$), $(-1)^n 4\pi/n^2$ ($n = 1, 2, \cdots$)

SECTION 8.2

1. $\dfrac{1}{2} + \dfrac{2}{\pi}(\cos x - \tfrac{1}{3}\cos 3x + \tfrac{1}{5}\cos 5x - + \ldots)$

3. $\dfrac{1}{4} + \dfrac{1}{\pi}(\cos x - \tfrac{1}{3}\cos 3x + \tfrac{1}{5}\cos 5x - + \cdots)$

$\qquad + \dfrac{1}{\pi}(\sin x + \tfrac{2}{2}\sin 2x + \tfrac{1}{3}\sin 3x + \tfrac{1}{5}\sin 5x + \tfrac{2}{6}\sin 6x + \cdots)$

5. $\dfrac{2}{\pi}(\cos x - \tfrac{1}{3}\cos 3x + \tfrac{1}{5}\cos 5x - + \cdots + \sin 2x + \tfrac{1}{3}\sin 6x + \tfrac{1}{5}\sin 10x + \cdots)$

7. $\dfrac{1}{2} + \dfrac{4}{\pi}(\sin x - \tfrac{1}{2}\sin 2x + \tfrac{1}{3}\sin 3x + \tfrac{1}{5}\sin 5x - \tfrac{1}{6}\sin 6x + \cdots)$

9. $\dfrac{\pi^2}{3} - 4(\cos x - \tfrac{1}{4}\cos 2x + \tfrac{1}{9}\cos 3x - \tfrac{1}{16}\cos 4x + - \cdots)$

11. $a_0 = \pi^4/5$, $a_n = (-1)^n 8(\pi^2 n^2 - 6)/n^4$, $b_n = 0$ ($n = 1, 2, \cdots$)

13. $\dfrac{\pi}{2} + \dfrac{4}{\pi}(\cos x + \tfrac{1}{9}\cos 3x + \tfrac{1}{25}\cos 5x + \cdots)$

15. $a_0 = \pi^2/6$, $a_n = (-1)^n 2/n^2$, $b_n = \{2[(-1)^n - 1]/n^3\pi\} - \{\pi(-1)^n/n\}$

17. $\left(1 + \dfrac{2}{\pi}\right)\sin x - \dfrac{1}{2}\sin 2x + \left(\dfrac{1}{3} - \dfrac{2}{9\pi}\right)\sin 3x - \dfrac{1}{4}\sin 4x + \cdots$

19. $\dfrac{4}{\pi}\left(\sin x - \tfrac{1}{9}\sin 3x + \tfrac{1}{25}\sin 5x - + \cdots\right)$

SECTION 8.3

1. Neither even nor odd, even, odd, even, odd, neither even nor odd, even, even
3. Even   **5.** Even   **7.** Even   **9.** Odd   **19.** $\cosh x + \sinh x$

21. $\dfrac{1 + x^2}{1 - x^2} + \dfrac{2x}{1 - x^2}$

23. $\dfrac{\pi^2}{12} - \cos x + \dfrac{1}{4}\cos 2x - \dfrac{1}{9}\cos 3x + \dfrac{1}{16}\cos 4x - + \cdots$

25. $\dfrac{4}{\pi}\left(\dfrac{1}{2} - \dfrac{1}{1 \cdot 3}\cos 2x - \dfrac{1}{3 \cdot 5}\cos 4x - \dfrac{1}{5 \cdot 7}\cos 6x - \cdots\right)$

27. $-\pi - \dfrac{4}{\pi}(\cos x + \tfrac{1}{9}\cos 3x + \cdots) + 2(\sin x + \tfrac{1}{3}\sin 3x + \cdots)$

29. $\dfrac{4}{\pi}\left(\sin x - \tfrac{1}{9}\sin 3x + \tfrac{1}{25}\sin 5x - + \cdots\right)$

SECTION 8.4

7. $\dfrac{1}{2} + \dfrac{2}{\pi}\left(\cos\dfrac{\pi t}{2} - \dfrac{1}{3}\cos\dfrac{3\pi t}{2} + \dfrac{1}{5}\cos\dfrac{5\pi t}{2} - + \cdots\right)$

9. $\dfrac{1}{3} - \dfrac{4}{\pi^2}(\cos\pi t - \tfrac{1}{4}\cos 2\pi t + \tfrac{1}{9}\cos 3\pi t - \tfrac{1}{16}\cos 4\pi t + - \cdots)$

11. $\dfrac{4}{\pi}\left[\left(1 + \dfrac{2}{\pi}\right)\sin\dfrac{\pi t}{4} - \dfrac{1}{2}\sin\dfrac{\pi t}{2} + \left(\dfrac{1}{3} - \dfrac{2}{9\pi}\right)\sin\dfrac{3\pi t}{4} - \dfrac{1}{4}\sin\pi t + \cdots\right]$

13. $\dfrac{1}{4} + \dfrac{2}{\pi^2}(\cos 2\pi t + \tfrac{1}{9}\cos 6\pi t + \tfrac{1}{25}\cos 10\pi t + \cdots)$

15. $\dfrac{2}{\pi}(\sin\pi t - \tfrac{1}{2}\sin 2\pi t + \tfrac{1}{3}\sin 3\pi t - + \cdots)$

17. $\dfrac{4}{\pi}\left(\dfrac{1}{2} - \dfrac{1}{1 \cdot 3}\cos 2\pi t - \dfrac{1}{3 \cdot 5}\cos 4\pi t - \dfrac{1}{5 \cdot 7}\cos 6\pi t - \cdots\right)$

19. $-\dfrac{4}{\pi^2}(\cos\pi t + \tfrac{1}{9}\cos 3\pi t + \tfrac{1}{25}\cos 5\pi t + \cdots) + \dfrac{2}{\pi}(\sin\pi t + \tfrac{1}{3}\sin 3\pi t + \cdots)$

21. $\dfrac{1}{\pi}(\sin 4t - \tfrac{1}{9}\sin 12t + \tfrac{1}{25}\sin 20t - \tfrac{1}{49}\sin 28t + - \cdots)$

SECTION 8.5

1. $\dfrac{4}{\pi}(\sin x + \tfrac{1}{3}\sin 3x + \tfrac{1}{5}\sin 5x + \cdots)$

3. $2\left[\left(\pi - \dfrac{4}{1^3\pi}\right)\sin x - \dfrac{\pi}{2}\sin 2x + \left(\dfrac{\pi}{3} - \dfrac{4}{3^3\pi}\right)\sin 3x - \dfrac{\pi}{4}\sin 4x + - \cdots\right]$

5. $\left(1 + \dfrac{2}{\pi}\right)\sin x - \dfrac{1}{2}\sin 2x + \left(\dfrac{1}{3} - \dfrac{2}{9\pi}\right)\sin 3x - \dfrac{1}{4}\sin 4x + \cdots$

7. $\dfrac{4}{\pi}(\sin x - \tfrac{1}{2}\sin 2x + \tfrac{1}{3}\sin 3x + \tfrac{1}{5}\sin 5x - \tfrac{1}{6}\sin 6x + \tfrac{1}{7}\sin 7x + \cdots)$

9. $\dfrac{2}{\pi}(\sin \pi x - \tfrac{1}{2} \sin 2\pi x + \tfrac{1}{3} \sin 3\pi x - + \cdots)$

11. $\dfrac{1}{\pi}(\sin 4x - \tfrac{1}{9} \sin 12x + \tfrac{1}{25} \sin 20x - \tfrac{1}{49} \sin 28x + - \cdots)$

13. $f(x) = 1$

15. $\dfrac{l^2}{3} - \dfrac{4l^2}{\pi^2}\left(\cos \dfrac{\pi x}{l} - \dfrac{1}{4}\cos \dfrac{2\pi x}{l} + \dfrac{1}{9}\cos \dfrac{3\pi x}{l} - \dfrac{1}{16}\cos \dfrac{4\pi x}{l} + - \cdots\right)$

17. $\dfrac{1}{2} + \dfrac{2}{\pi}\left(\cos \dfrac{\pi x}{l} - \dfrac{1}{3}\cos \dfrac{3\pi x}{l} + \dfrac{1}{5}\cos \dfrac{5\pi x}{l} - + \cdots\right)$

19. $\dfrac{1}{2} + \dfrac{4}{\pi^2}\left(\cos \dfrac{\pi x}{l} + \dfrac{1}{9}\cos \dfrac{3\pi x}{l} + \dfrac{1}{25}\cos \dfrac{5\pi x}{l} + \cdots\right)$

21. $\dfrac{2}{\pi} - \dfrac{4}{\pi}\left(\dfrac{1}{1 \cdot 3}\cos \dfrac{2\pi x}{l} + \dfrac{1}{3 \cdot 5}\cos \dfrac{4\pi x}{l} + \dfrac{1}{5 \cdot 7}\cos \dfrac{6\pi x}{l} + \cdots\right)$

SECTION 8.6

15. $f = \dfrac{8}{\pi}\left(\sin x + \dfrac{1}{3^3}\sin 3x + \dfrac{1}{5^3}\sin 5x + \cdots\right)$

17. $f = 12\left(\sin x - \dfrac{1}{2^3}\sin 2x + \dfrac{1}{3^3}\sin 3x - + \cdots\right)$

19. Cf. Prob. 11, Sec. 8.2.

SECTION 8.7

1. $y = C_1 \cos \omega t + C_2 \sin \omega t + \dfrac{1}{\omega^2 - 1}\sin t$, the numerical values of the amplitude $A(\omega)$ of the last term being

ω	0.5	0.7	0.9	1.1	1.5	2.0	10.0
$A(\omega)$	-1.33	-0.20	-5.3	4.8	0.8	0.33	0.01

3. $y = C_1 \cos \omega t + C_2 \sin \omega t + B_1 \sin t + B_3 \sin 3t + B_5 \sin 5t$ where

ω	0.5	0.9	1.1	2.0	2.9	3.1	4.0	4.9	5.1	6.0	8.0
$B_1 = 1/(\omega^2 - 1)$	-1.33	-5.3	4.8	0.33	0.13	0.12	0.07	0.04	0.04	0.03	0.02
$B_3 = 1/9(\omega^2 - 9)$	-0.013	-0.014	-0.014	-0.02	-0.19	0.18	0.02	0.01	0.01	0.004	0.002
$B_5 = 1/25(\omega^2 - 25)$	-0.002	-0.002	-0.002	-0.002	-0.002	-0.003	-0.004	-0.04	0.04	0.004	0.001

5. $y = C_1 \cos \omega t + C_2 \sin \omega t$
$$+ \dfrac{4}{\pi}\left(\dfrac{1}{\omega^2 - 1}\sin t - \dfrac{1}{9(\omega^2 - 9)}\sin 3t + \dfrac{1}{25(\omega^2 - 25)}\sin 5t - + \cdots\right)$$

7. $y = C_1 \cos \omega t + C_2 \sin \omega t$
$$+ \dfrac{1}{\omega^2 - 1}\sin t - \dfrac{1}{2^3(\omega^2 - 4)}\sin 2t + \dfrac{1}{3^3(\omega^2 - 9)}\sin 3t - + \cdots$$

9. $y = C_1 \cos \omega t + C_2 \sin \omega t$
$$+ \dfrac{1}{2\omega^2} - \dfrac{1}{1 \cdot 3(\omega^2 - 4)}\cos 2t - \dfrac{1}{3 \cdot 5(\omega^2 - 16)}\cos 4t - \cdots$$

11. $y = -\dfrac{K}{c}\cos t$ **13.** $y = \dfrac{1 - n^2}{D}a_n \cos nt + \dfrac{nc}{D}a_n \sin nt$, $D = (1 - n^2)^2 + n^2 c^2$

15. $y = A_1 \cos t + B_1 \sin t + A_3 \cos 3t + B_3 \sin 3t + \cdots$ where
$A_n = -ncb_n/D$, $B_n = (1 - n^2)b_n/D$, $D = (1 - n^2)^2 + n^2 c^2$, $b_1 = 1$, $b_2 = 0$, $b_3 = -1/9$, $b_4 = 0$, $b_5 = 1/25$, $\cdots$

17. $I = \sum_{n=1}^{\infty} (A_n \cos nt + B_n \sin nt)$ where $A_n = (-1)^{n+1} \dfrac{120(10 - n^2)}{n^2 D_n}$,

$B_n = \dfrac{(-1)^{n+1} 1200}{n D_n}$, $D_n = (10 - n^2)^2 + 100n^2$,

$I = 5.97 \cos t + 6.63 \sin t - 0.41 \cos 2t - 1.38 \sin 2t + 0.01 \cos 3t + 0.44 \sin 3t + \cdots$

SECTION 8.8

3. $F = \dfrac{4}{\pi}\left[\sin x + \dfrac{1}{3}\sin 3x + \cdots + \dfrac{1}{N}\sin Nx\right]$ (N odd), cf. Ex. 1, Sec. 8.2

7. $F = \dfrac{\pi^2}{3} - 4\left(\cos x - \dfrac{1}{4}\cos 2x + \dfrac{1}{9}\cos 3x - \cdots + \dfrac{(-1)^{N+1}}{N^2}\cos Nx\right),$

$E^* = \dfrac{2\pi^5}{5} - \pi\left(\dfrac{2\pi^4}{9} + 16 + 1 + \dfrac{16}{81} + \dfrac{1}{16} + \cdots\right)$

SECTION 8.10

9. $\dfrac{2}{\pi}\displaystyle\int_0^{\infty} \dfrac{2\cos w - \cos 2w - 1}{w^2} \cos xw\, dw$

11. $\dfrac{6}{\pi}\displaystyle\int_0^{\infty} \dfrac{2 + w^2}{4 + 5w^2 + w^4} \cos xw\, dw$

13. $\dfrac{2}{\pi}\displaystyle\int_0^{\infty}\left[\dfrac{a\sin aw}{w} + \dfrac{\cos aw - 1}{w^2}\right]\cos xw\, dw$

15. Differentiating (10) we have

$$\dfrac{d^2 A}{dw^2} = -2\int_0^{\infty} f^*(v)\cos wv\, dv \qquad \text{where} \qquad f^*(v) = v^2 f(v),$$

and the result follows.

21. (17) follows from the fact that the integral in brackets is an odd function of w.

SECTION 8.11

1. $\dfrac{\sin x}{\sqrt{\pi}}, \dfrac{\sin 2x}{\sqrt{\pi}}, \cdots$ **3.** $\dfrac{1}{\sqrt{2\pi}}, \dfrac{\cos x}{\sqrt{\pi}}, \dfrac{\sin x}{\sqrt{\pi}}, \cdots$

5. $\sin \pi x, \sin 2\pi x, \cdots$ **7.** $\dfrac{1}{\sqrt{T}}, \sqrt{\dfrac{2}{T}}\cos\dfrac{2n\pi}{T}x, \sqrt{\dfrac{2}{T}}\sin\dfrac{2n\pi}{T}x$ $\quad (n = 1, 2, \cdots)$

11. $g_0 = 1/\sqrt{2}, g_1 = (\sqrt{3/2})\,x, g_2 = \sqrt{5/8}\,(3x^2 - 1)$

15. $p_0 = P_0, p_1(x) = P_1(2x - 1) = 2x - 1, p_2(x) = 6x^2 - 6x + 1$, etc.

17. $f = 1/\sqrt{x}$

19. If there is a function $h(x)$ which is orthogonal to every function of our closed set, then its Fourier constants with respect to that set are all zero, and by substituting h for f in Parseval's formula, $N(h) = 0$. Hence, the function h does not satisfy our general assumption, and this proves completeness of our set.

SECTION 8.12

5. $\sin \dfrac{2n + 1}{2l}\pi x, \ n = 0, 1, \cdots$ **7.** $y'' + \lambda y = 0, y'(0) = 0, y'(\pi) = 0$

9. $f = \dfrac{1}{2}P_0 + \dfrac{3}{4}P_1 - \dfrac{7}{16}P_3 + \cdots$ **11.** $f = \dfrac{1}{2}P_0 + \dfrac{5}{8}P_2 + \cdots$

21. $\displaystyle \int_0^\infty e^{-x} x^k L_n(x)\, dx = \frac{1}{n!} \int_0^\infty x^k \frac{d^n}{dx^n} (x^n e^{-x})\, dx = -\frac{k}{n!} \int_0^\infty x^{k-1} \frac{d^{n-1}}{dx^{n-1}} (x^n e^{-x})\, dx$

$\displaystyle = \cdots = (-1)^k \frac{k!}{n!} \int_0^\infty \frac{d^{n-k}}{dx^{n-k}} (x^n e^{-x})\, dx = 0 \text{ when } n > k.$

25. Differentiate the general formula in Prob. 22.

27. Denoting the generating function by $G(x, t)$ we have

$$\frac{\partial G}{\partial x} = \sum_{n=0}^\infty a_n{}'(x) t^n = \sum_{n=0}^\infty \frac{H_n{}'(x)}{n!} t^n.$$

On the other hand

$$\frac{\partial G}{\partial x} = tG = \sum_{k=0}^\infty \frac{H_k(x)}{k!} t^{k+1} = \sum_{n=1}^\infty \frac{H_{n-1}(x)}{(n-1)!} t^n.$$

Comparing corresponding coefficients the relation follows.

29. Abbreviate $e^{-x^2/2}$ by v, integrate by parts, and use the formula in Prob. 27. Then, for $n > m$,

$$\int_{-\infty}^\infty v H_m H_n\, dx = (-1)^n \int_{-\infty}^\infty H_m v^{(n)}\, dx = (-1)^{n-1} \int_{-\infty}^\infty H_m{}' v^{(n-1)}\, dx$$

$$= (-1)^{n-1} m \int_{-\infty}^\infty H_{m-1} v^{(n-1)}\, dx = \cdots = (-1)^{n-m} m! \int_{-\infty}^\infty H_0 v^{(n-m)}\, dx = 0:$$

here $v^{(n)} = d^n v/dx^n$, etc.

SECTION 8.13

3. By (1), Sec. 3.6, with $v = 1$,

$$c_m = \frac{2}{R^2 J_1{}^2(\alpha_{m0})} \int_0^R x J_0\left(\frac{\alpha_{m0}}{R} x\right) dx = \frac{2}{\alpha_{m0}{}^2 J_1{}^2(\alpha_{m0})} \int_0^{\alpha_{m0}} w J_0(w)\, dw = \frac{2}{\alpha_{m0} J_1(\alpha_{m0})},$$

$$f = 2\left(\frac{J_0(\lambda_{10} x)}{\alpha_{10} J_1(\alpha_{10})} + \frac{J_0(\lambda_{20} x)}{\alpha_{20} J_1(\alpha_{20})} + \cdots\right)$$

5. $c_m = \dfrac{2ak J_1(\alpha_{m0} a/R)}{\alpha_{m0} R J_1{}^2(\alpha_{m0})}$ **7.** $c_m = \dfrac{4 J_2(\alpha_{m0})}{\alpha_{m0}{}^2 J_1{}^2(\alpha_{m0})}$

9. $c_m = \dfrac{2R^2}{\alpha_{m0} J_1(\alpha_{m0})}\left[1 - \dfrac{2 J_2(\alpha_{m0})}{\alpha_{m0} J_1(\alpha_{m0})}\right]$

SECTION 9.1

25. By integration, $u = f(y)$ **27.** $u_x = f(y)$, $u = xf(y) + g(y)$
29. $u = A(y) \cos x + B(y) \sin x$ **31.** The solution of (a) is $u = xf(y) + g(y)$, cf. Prob. 27. From this and (b), $u_{yy} = xf''(y) + g''(y) = 0$ for all x. Thus, $f''(y) = 0$, $g''(y) = 0$, $f = ay + b$, $g = cy + k$, $u = xf + g = axy + bx + cy + k$.
33. $u = ax + by + c$ **35.** $p_y - p = 0$, $p = A(x)e^y$, $u = \int p\, dx = f(x)e^y + g(y)$
where $f(x) = \int A\, dx$ **37.** $u = 3 \ln(x^2 + y^2)/\ln 4$

SECTION 9.3

1. $u = 0.02 \cos t \sin x$ **3.** $u = k(\cos t \sin x - \cos 2t \sin 2x)$

5. $u = \dfrac{4}{5\pi}\left(\dfrac{1}{4} \cos 2t \sin 2x - \dfrac{1}{36} \cos 6t \sin 6x + \dfrac{1}{100} \cos 10t \sin 10x - + \cdots\right)$

7. $u = \dfrac{0.08}{\pi}\left(\cos t \sin x + \dfrac{1}{3^3}\cos 3t \sin 3x + \dfrac{1}{5^3}\cos 5t \sin 5x + \cdots\right)$

9. $u = 0.12\left(\cos t \sin x - \dfrac{1}{2^3}\cos 2t \sin 2x + \dfrac{1}{3^3}\cos 3t \sin 3x - + \cdots\right)$

11. $27,960/\pi^6 \approx 0.9986$ **13.** $u = ke^{c(x-y)}$ **15.** $u = ky^c e^{cx}$

17. $u = ke^{x^2+y^2+c(x-y)}$ **19.** $u = ke^{cx+y/c}$

SECTION 9.4

13. This follows immediately from the Euler formulas; note that t merely plays the role of a parameter, and the series is the Fourier sine series of the constant function 1, multiplied by $A \sin \omega t$.

15. Substitute $G_n(t)$ [Prob. 14] into $u(x, t)$ in Prob. 11 and use the given initial conditions. Then $G_n(0) = B_n = \dfrac{2}{l}\displaystyle\int_0^l f(x) \sin \dfrac{n\pi x}{l}\, dx,\ \dot{G}_n(0) = \lambda_n B_n{}^* + \dfrac{2A\omega(1 - \cos n\pi)}{n\pi(\lambda_n{}^2 - \omega^2)} = 0.$

17. $u = f_1(x) + f_2(x + y)$ **19.** $u = f_1(x + y) + f_2(2x - y)$

21. $u = xf_1(x + y) + f_2(x + y)$ **23.** $y'^2 - y' - 2 = (y' + 1)(y' - 2) = 0$, $y = -x + c,\ y = 2x + k,\ \Phi = x + y = const,\ \Psi = 2x - y = const$

27. $u = \dfrac{8l^2}{\pi^3}\left(\cos c\left(\dfrac{\pi}{l}\right)^2 t \sin \dfrac{\pi x}{l} + \dfrac{1}{3^3}\cos c\left(\dfrac{3\pi}{l}\right)^2 t \sin \dfrac{3\pi x}{l} + \cdots\right)$

29. $u(0, t) = 0,\ u(l, t) = 0,\ u_x(0, t) = 0,\ u_x(l, t) = 0$

31. $\beta l \approx (2n + 1)\dfrac{\pi}{2},\ n = 1, 2, \cdots$ (more exactly 4.730, 7.853, 10.996, $\cdots$)

33. $\beta l \approx (2n + 1)\dfrac{\pi}{2},\ n = 0, 1, \cdots$ (more exactly 1.875, 4.694, 7.855, $\cdots$)

SECTION 9.5

5. $u = \sin 0.1\pi x\, e^{-1.752\pi^2 t/100}$

7. $u = \dfrac{40}{\pi^2}\left(\sin 0.1\pi x\, e^{-0.01752\pi^2 t} - \dfrac{1}{9}\sin 0.3\pi x\, e^{-0.01752(3\pi)^2 t} + - \cdots\right)$

9. $u = \dfrac{800}{\pi^3}\left(\sin 0.1\pi x\, e^{-0.01752\pi^2 t} + \dfrac{1}{3^3}\sin 0.3\pi x\, e^{-0.01752(3\pi)^2 t} + \cdots\right)$

11. Since the temperatures at the ends are kept constant, the temperature will approach a steady-state (time-independent) distribution $u_I(x)$ as $t \to \infty$, and $u_I = U_1 + (U_2 - U_1)x/l$, the solution of (1) with $\partial u/\partial t = 0$, satisfying the boundary conditions.

13. $u(x, 0) = f(x) = 100,\ U_1 = 100,\ U_2 = 0,\ u_I = 100 - 10x,$

$B_n = -\dfrac{200}{n\pi}\cos n\pi = \dfrac{(-1)^{n+1}}{n} 63.66$ (cf. Prob. 12),

$u(x, t) = 100 - 10x + \dfrac{200}{\pi}\displaystyle\sum_{n=1}^{\infty}\dfrac{(-1)^{n+1}}{n}\sin\dfrac{n\pi x}{10} e^{-1.752(n\pi/10)^2 t},$

$u(5, t) = 50 + 63.66\left[e^{-0.1729 t} - \dfrac{1}{3}e^{-1.556 t} + \dfrac{1}{5}e^{4.323 t} - + \cdots\right].$

Obviously the sum of the first few terms is a good approximation of the true value at any $t > 0$. We find

t	1	2	3	10	50
$u(5, t)$	99	94	88	61	50

17. $u = \dfrac{\pi^2}{3} - 4\left(\cos x\, e^{-t} - \dfrac{1}{4}\cos 2x\, e^{-4t} + \dfrac{1}{9}\cos 3x\, e^{-9t} - + \cdots\right)$

19. $u = \dfrac{\pi}{8} + \left(1 - \dfrac{2}{\pi}\right)\cos x\, e^{-t} - \dfrac{1}{\pi}\cos 2x\, e^{-4t} - \left(\dfrac{1}{3} + \dfrac{2}{9\pi}\right)\cos 3x\, e^{-9t} + \cdots$

SECTION 9.6

5. The solution $\sin px\, e^{-c^2 p^2 t}$ of the heat equation satisfies the condition $u(0, t) = 0$, and (6) becomes

$$u(x, t) = \int_0^\infty B(p) \sin px\, e^{-c^2 p^2 t}\, dp, \qquad B(p) = \frac{2}{\pi}\int_0^\infty f(v) \sin pv\, dv$$

because $u(x, 0)$ must be the Fourier sine integral representation of $f(x)$. Since

$$2 \sin px \sin pv = \cos(px - pv) - \cos(px + pv)$$

we have

$$u(x, t) = \frac{1}{\pi}\int_0^\infty \int_0^\infty f(v)[\cos(px - pv) - \cos(px + pv)]e^{-c^2 p^2 t}\, dv\, dp.$$

Inverting the order of integration and evaluating the integral whose variable of integration is p as in the text, we obtain

$$u(x, t) = \frac{1}{2c\sqrt{\pi t}}\int_0^\infty f(v)\left[e^{-\frac{(x-v)^2}{4c^2 t}} - e^{-\frac{(x+v)^2}{4c^2 t}}\right]dv.$$

Writing this as the difference of two integrals and setting $\dfrac{v - x}{2c\sqrt{t}} = w$ and $\dfrac{v + x}{2c\sqrt{t}} = w$, respectively, the result follows.

13. $\operatorname{erf} x = \dfrac{2}{\sqrt{\pi}}\left(x - \dfrac{x^3}{1!\,3} + \dfrac{x^5}{2!\,5} - \dfrac{x^7}{3!\,7} + - \cdots\right)$

SECTION 9.8

5. $c\pi\sqrt{85}$ $(F_{29},\, F_{67},\, F_{76},\, F_{92})$, $c\pi\sqrt{221}$, $c\pi\sqrt{260}$, etc.

7. $B_{mn} = 0$ (m or n even), $\quad B_{mn} = -(-1)^{\frac{m+n}{2}}\dfrac{16ab}{\pi^4 m^2 n^2}$ (m and n both odd)

9. $B_{mn} = (-1)^{m+n}\dfrac{4ab}{mn\pi^2}$ $\quad$ **11.** $B_{mn} = 0$ (m or n even), $B_{mn} = \dfrac{64a^2 b^2}{\pi^6 m^3 n^3}$ (m, n both odd)

13. $u = \dfrac{0.64}{\pi^6}\displaystyle\sum_{\substack{m=1 \\ m,n\ \text{odd}}}^\infty \sum_{n=1}^\infty \dfrac{1}{m^3 n^3}\cos\left(\pi t\sqrt{m^2 + n^2}\right)\sin m\pi x \sin n\pi y$

15. $u = k\cos \pi\sqrt{5}t \sin \pi x \sin 2\pi y$

SECTION 9.10

3. u_2: $r = \alpha_1/\alpha_2 = 0.43565$, u_3: $r = \alpha_1/\alpha_3 = 0.27789$, $r = \alpha_2/\alpha_3 = 0.63788$

9. $u = 4k \displaystyle\sum_{m=1}^\infty \dfrac{J_2(\alpha_m)}{\alpha_m^2 J_1^2(\alpha_m)}\cos \alpha_m t\, J_0(\alpha_m r)$

SECTION 9.11

3. $u = 135 - \dfrac{250}{r}$ $\quad$ **5.** $u = \dfrac{100}{\ln 5}\ln \dfrac{r}{2} + 10$

11. $u = \dfrac{u_1 - u_0}{x_1 - x_0}x + \dfrac{x_1 u_0 - x_0 u_1}{x_1 - x_0}$ $\quad$ **13.** $u = \dfrac{(u_0 - u_1)r_0 r_1}{(r_1 - r_0)r} + \dfrac{u_1 r_1 - u_0 r_0}{r_1 - r_0}$,

where r is the distance from the center of the spheres.

SECTION 9.12

3. $u = 1$ **5.** $u = \frac{2}{3}r^2 P_2(\cos \phi) + \frac{1}{3} = r^2(\cos^2 \phi - \frac{1}{3}) + \frac{1}{3}$
7. $u = 4r^3 P_3(\cos \phi) - 2r^2 P_2(\cos \phi) + rP_1(\cos \phi) - 2$
9. $u = \frac{8}{5}r^3 P_3(\cos \phi) - \frac{3}{5}rP_1(\cos \phi)$

SECTION 10.1

1. 9/25   **3.** $x^4 - 6x^2y^2 + y^4$ **5.** $-2xy/(x^2 + y^2)^2$ **7.** 2   **13.** Consider $c = a + ib = z_1/(z_1 + z_2)$, assuming $z_1 + z_2 \neq 0$. From (1), $|a| \leq |c|$, $|a - 1| \leq |c - 1|$. Thus $|a| + |a - 1| \leq |c| + |c - 1|$. Clearly $|a| + |a - 1| \geq 1$, and the last inequality becomes

$$1 \leq |c| + |c - 1| = \left| \frac{z_1}{z_1 + z_2} \right| + \left| \frac{z_2}{z_1 + z_2} \right|.$$

Multiplication by $|z_1 + z_2|$ yields (2).   **15.** By (2), $|z_1| = |(z_1 + z_2) + (-z_2)| \leq |z_1 + z_2| + |z_2|$. Subtract $|z_2|$ on both sides.   **21.** The exterior of the circle of radius 1/2 with center at the origin   **23.** The y-axis   **25.** Ellipse with focal points at -1 and 1   **31.** Square both sides of both inequalities.

SECTION 10.2

1. $2 + 4i$, $-1 + 2i$, $20 - 20i$ **3.** $\mathrm{Re}\, f = x^2 - y^2 + 4x - 1$, $\mathrm{Im}\, f = 2xy + 4y$

5. $\mathrm{Re}\, f = \dfrac{1 - x}{(1 - x)^2 + y^2}$, $\mathrm{Im}\, f = \dfrac{y}{(1 - x)^2 + y^2}$ **7.** $-4\pi < \mathrm{Re}\, w < 2\pi$

9. $1 \leq |w| \leq 4$, $0 \leq \arg w < \pi$ **11.** The full plane   **13.** $6z(z^2 - 4)^2$

15. $\dfrac{10z}{(z^2 + 1)^2}$ **17.** $-44 - 196i$ **19.** $4 - 2i$

21. Use $\mathrm{Re}\, f(z) = \frac{1}{2}[f(z) + \overline{f(z)}]$, $\mathrm{Im}\, f(z) = \dfrac{1}{2i}[f(z) - \overline{f(z)}]$ and the result of Prob. 20.

23. For any $\epsilon > 0$ we must find a $\delta > 0$ such that $|z^2 - z_0^2| < \epsilon$ when $|z - z_0| < \delta$. Now $|z^2 - z_0^2| = |(z - z_0)[(z - z_0) + 2z_0]| \leq |z - z_0|^2 + 2|z_0|\,|z - z_0|$. Choose $\delta = \epsilon/(4\,|z_0| + \sqrt{2}\epsilon)$. Then $|z - z_0|^2 < \epsilon/2$ and $2|z_0|\,|z - z_0| < \epsilon/2$ when $|z - z_0| < \delta$. This proves the statement.
25. No, because $f(z) \to 0$ [$= f(0)$] as $z \to 0$ along the y-axis, but $f(z) \to 1$ [$\neq f(0)$] as $z \to 0$ along the positive x-axis.   **27.** Yes, because for $z \neq 0$, $|f| = x^2/\sqrt{x^2 + y^2} \leq |x| \leq |z|$ and, therefore, $|f| \to 0$ [$= f(0)$] as $|z| \to 0$.   **29.** By definition of continuity, for any $\epsilon > 0$ there is a $\delta > 0$ so that $|f(z) - f(a)| < \epsilon$ when $|z - a| < \delta$. Since $\lim_{n \to \infty} z_n = a$, for all sufficiently large n the points z_n lie in the disk $|z - a| < \delta$, i.e., $|f(z_n) - f(a)| < \epsilon$ for all these n.

SECTION 10.3

8.–13. Use (5).   **9.** Yes   **11.** No   **13.** Yes   **15.** $f = x + iy + c = z + c$, c real   **17.** $f = -iz^2/2 + ic$, c real   **19.** $f = e^z(\cos y + i \sin y) + ic$, c real

21. $v = 2 \arctan \dfrac{y}{x} + c$

23. $u_{xx} + u_{yy} = 2a + 2c = 0$, $c = -a$, $u = a(x^2 - y^2) + bxy$ **25.** Let $f = u + iv$ and $|f| = c$. Then $u^2 + v^2 = c^2$. By differentiation, $uu_x + vv_x = 0$, $uu_y + vv_y = 0$. By (5), $uu_x - vu_y = 0$, $uu_y + vu_x = 0$. Hence

$$(uu_x - vu_y)^2 + (uu_y + vu_x)^2 = (u^2 + v^2)(u_x^2 + u_y^2) = c^2(u_x^2 + u_y^2) = 0.$$

If $c = 0$, then $u = v = 0$. If $c \neq 0$, then $u_x^2 + u_y^2 = 0$, i.e., $u_x = u_y = 0$ and, by (5), $v_x = 0$, $v_y = 0$. Hence, $u = const$, $v = const$.

27. Let $f = u + iv$. By (3), $f' = u_x + iv_x = 0$. Hence, $u_x = 0$, $v_x = 0$. By (4) or (5), $u_y = 0$, $v_y = 0$. Hence, $u = const$, $v = const$, $f = u + iv = const$.

SECTION 10.4

1. $\frac{1}{2}, \frac{2}{3}, \frac{3}{4}, \frac{4}{5}, \cdots$ 3. $1 + 2\pi i$, $-1 + 4\pi i$, $\cdots$ 5. $1, 1, 2, 3, 5, 8, \cdots$
7. $2, 0, \frac{3}{2}, \frac{1}{2}, \frac{4}{3}, \frac{2}{3}, \frac{5}{4}, \frac{3}{4}, \cdots$ 9. Bounded, convergent with the limit 0, monotone
11. Not bounded, divergent, not monotone   13. Bounded, divergent, not monotone, limit points $0, \frac{1}{2}, 1$ 15. Bounded, convergent with the limit 1, not monotone
17. Bounded, convergent with the limit 0, monotone when $0 \leqq c \leqq 1/2$
21. $1, 3$ 23. 0 25. $1, -1$ 27. 0 29. $-1, 1$

SECTION 10.6

1. 6 terms   3. 2 terms   5. 5 terms   7. Divergent   9. Divergent
11. Convergent   13. Convergent [compare with (5)].   15. Convergent
17. Divergent (compare with the harmonic series).   19. Convergent; the sum is the decimal fraction $0.d_1 d_2 d_3 \cdots$.   21. Convergent   23. Divergent (by Theorem 1 in

Sec. 10.5)   25. $R_n = q^{n+1} + q^{n+2} + \cdots = q^{n+1}(1 + q + q^2 + \cdots) = \dfrac{q^{n+1}}{1 - q}$. When

$q = \frac{1}{4}$, $|R_n| = \dfrac{1}{3 \cdot 4^n} < 0.01$ for $n = 3$, i.e., 4 terms. When $q = \frac{1}{2}$ we need 8 terms.

When $q = 0.9$ we need 66 terms.

27. The test ratio is $\dfrac{(n + 2)n}{2(n + 1)^2} < \dfrac{1}{2}$. Thus, using $q = \dfrac{1}{2}$ we have

$$|R_n| \leqq \frac{|w_{n+1}|}{1 - q} = \frac{n + 2}{2^n(n + 1)} < 0.05 \qquad \text{for } n = 5.$$

Hence, 5 terms are needed, and $s \approx 1.657$.
29. This follows from Theorem 5, Sec. 10.4.

SECTION 10.8

1. 4   3. 1   5. $\frac{1}{3}$ 7. $2/\pi$ 9. 0   11. 1   15. 1   17. $\frac{1}{4}$ 19. 1

SECTION 10.9

11. 2   13. 3

SECTION 10.10

1. $(1 + i)/\sqrt{2}$, $-(1 + i)/\sqrt{2}$ 3. $\pm(1 - i)/\sqrt{2}$ 5. $\pm\frac{1}{2}(\sqrt{3} + i)$
7. $(\sqrt{3} + i)/2$, $(-\sqrt{3} + i)/2$, $-i$ 9. $\pm(1 + i)/\sqrt{2}$, $\pm(-1 + i)/\sqrt{2}$
11. $\pm(\sqrt{3} + i)/2$, $\pm i$, $\pm(\sqrt{3} - i)/2$ 13. -1, $\cos\dfrac{\pi}{5} \pm i\sin\dfrac{\pi}{5}$, $\cos\dfrac{3\pi}{5} \pm i\sin\dfrac{3\pi}{5}$
15. $\sqrt[6]{2}\left(\cos\dfrac{\pi}{12} + i\sin\dfrac{\pi}{12}\right)$, $\sqrt[6]{2}\left(\cos\dfrac{3\pi}{4} + i\sin\dfrac{3\pi}{4}\right)$, $\sqrt[6]{2}\left(\cos\dfrac{17\pi}{12} + i\sin\dfrac{17\pi}{12}\right)$
17. 4, $-2 \pm 2i\sqrt{3}$ 19. Quadratic equation in $p = z^2$. Ans. $z = \sqrt{p} = \pm 2, \pm 3i$
21. ± 1, $\pm\sqrt{2}(1 + i)$
23. Squaring $\sqrt{z} = w = u + iv$ we have $z = w^2$, that is, (1) $x = u^2 - v^2$, (2) $y = 2uv$.

Also (3) $|z| = |w^2| = |w|^2 = u^2 + v^2$. From (1) and (3), $u^2 = \frac{1}{2}(|z| + x)$, $v^2 = \frac{1}{2}(|z| - x)$. Taking square roots and noting that because of (2) the signs of these roots must be selected so that sign (uv) = sign y, the result follows.

25. $\pm(1 - i)$ **27.** $\pm(2 - i)$ **29.** $\pm(1 - 3i)$ **31.** $\pm(5 - 2i)$

33. $3 + 2i, 2 - i$ **35.** $\pm(1 + i), \pm(2 + i)$

SECTION 10.11

3. $(1 - i)/\sqrt{2}$ **5.** $(1 + i\sqrt{3})/2$ **7.** $(1 + i)\sqrt{e}/2$ **9.** $-e^2$

11. $e^{x^2-y^2} \cos 2xy$, $e^{x^2-y^2} \sin 2xy$ **13.** $e^{e^x \cos y} \cos (e^x \sin y)$, $e^{e^x \cos y} \sin (e^x \sin y)$

15. $e^{\pi i/4}$, $e^{-3\pi i/4}$; $e^{-\pi i/4}$, $e^{3\pi i/4}$; $5e^i$ arc tan $(4/3)$, $\sqrt{8}e^{-\pi i/4}$ **17.** $\sqrt[n]{r_1}e^{i(\theta_1 + 2k\pi)/n}$,

$k = 0, 1, \cdots, n - 1$ **19.** $3.992 + 6.218i$ **21.** $38.04 - 39.17i$ **23.** $2e^x \sin y + c$

25. $-e^{xy} \sin \dfrac{x^2 - y^2}{2} + c$ **27.** By (4), $e^z e^{-z} = e^0 = 1$ which implies $e^z \neq 0$ (and

$e^{-z} \neq 0$), cf. Prob. 15, Sec. 0.4.   **29.** $z = \ln 2 + (2n + 1)\pi i, n = 0, \pm 1, \pm 2, \cdots$

31. Let $g(z)$ be another analytic function for which $g' = g$. Consider $q = g/f$. Differentiation yields $q' = 0$. Thus, $q = k = const$ (Prob. 27, Sec. 10.3), and $g = qf = kce^z$. Hence, g has the same form as f.

33. $|e^z - 1| = |z + \dfrac{z^2}{2!} + \cdots| \leq |z| (1 + \dfrac{1}{2!} + \dfrac{1}{3!} + \cdots) = (e - 1) |z| < 2 |z|$ when

$0 < |z| < 1$

SECTION 10.12

5. $\sqrt{\sin^2 x + \sinh^2 y}$ **7.** $\sqrt{\dfrac{\sin^2 x + \sinh^2 y}{\cos^2 x + \sinh^2 y}}$ **9.** $\dfrac{\sin x \cos x}{\sin^2 x + \sinh^2 y}$

11. $\dfrac{\cos x \cosh y}{\cos^2 x + \sinh^2 y}$

17. $-0.303 - 2.112i$ **19.** $2.333 - 0.274i$ **21.** 11013

23. $\pi/2 \pm 2n\pi \pm 3i, n = 0, 1, 2, \cdots$ **25.** $\pm 2n\pi \pm 2.29i$

27. $\sin x \cosh y = 1000$, $\cos x \sinh y = 0$, $x = \pi/2 \pm 2n\pi$, $\cosh y = 1000$, $\cosh y \approx$ $e^y/2$ (y large), $e^y \approx 2000$, $y \approx 7.6$. Ans. $z = \pi/2 \pm 2n\pi \pm 7.6i$

35. $\pm(\pi/3)i \pm 2n\pi i, n = 0, 1, \cdots$ **37.** $0, \pm \pi i, \pm 2\pi i, \cdots$

39. $\cot z = i(e^{iz} + e^{-iz})/(e^{iz} - e^{-iz}) = i + 2i/(e^{2iz} - 1)$. $\cot z = i$ implies $2i/(e^{2iz} - 1) = 0$, which is impossible. $\cot z = -i$ implies $e^{2iz} = 0$, but $e^z \neq 0$ for all z.

SECTION 10.13

1. $\pm 2n\pi i, n = 0, 1, \cdots$ **3.** $2 \pm (2n + 1)\pi i, n = 0, 1, \cdots$

5. $1 + \left(\dfrac{\pi}{2} \pm 2n\pi\right)i, n = 0, 1, \cdots$ **7.** $(1 \pm 2n\pi)i, n = 0, 1, \cdots$

9. $\frac{1}{2} \ln 2 + \dfrac{\pi i}{4} \approx 0.347 + 0.785i$ **11.** $\ln 5 + \pi i \approx 1.609 + 3.142i$

13. $\ln 6 + \dfrac{\pi i}{3} \approx 1.792 + 1.047i$ **21.** $-i$

23. $e^{(2-i) \text{Ln} (1+i)} = e^{(2-i)\left(\ln \sqrt{2} + \frac{\pi i}{4}\right)} = e^{\ln 2 + \pi/4 + i\left(\frac{\pi}{2} - \ln \sqrt{2}\right)}$

$\qquad = 2e^{\pi/4}[\sin (\frac{1}{2} \ln 2) + i \cos (\frac{1}{2} \ln 2)] \approx 1.49 + 4.13i$

25. $e^{-\pi/4} [\cos (\ln \sqrt{2}) + i \sin (\ln \sqrt{2})]$

27. $\sqrt{2} e^{\pi/4}\left[\cos \left(\ln \sqrt{2} - \dfrac{\pi}{4}\right) + i \sin \left(\ln \sqrt{2} - \dfrac{\pi}{4}\right)\right]$

29. $\cos (\ln 4) + i \sin (\ln 4)$ **31.** $27 [\cos (\ln 3) - i \sin (\ln 3)]$

SECTION 11.1

1. $z = (1 - 4i)t, 0 \leq t \leq 3$ **3.** $z = 1 - i + (2 - i)t, 0 \leq t \leq 4$
5. $z = 4 + 2i + (-1 + 3i)t, 0 \leq t \leq 1$ **7.** $z = i + 2e^{it}, 0 \leq t \leq 2\pi$
9. $z = -4 + 6i + 6e^{it}, 0 \leq t \leq 2\pi$ **11.** $z = t + (4t^2 + 3)i, 1 \leq t \leq 3$
13. $z = t + \left(1 + \dfrac{2}{t}\right)i, 1 \leq t \leq 3$ **15.** $z = 2 - i + 2\cos t + 3i \sin t$
17. Straight line segment from $z = -4i$ to $z = 2$
19. Circle of radius 4 with center at $-2 + 3i$
21. $y = (x + 1)^4$ from $z = -2 + i$ to $z = i$
23. $z(t) = (2 + i)t, 0 \leq t \leq 1, z^2 = (2 + i)^2 t^2, dz = (2 + i) dt$. Ans. $\dfrac{2 + 11i}{3}$
25. $\dfrac{227}{3} + 23i$ **27.** $-\dfrac{88 + 16i}{3}$ **29.** (a) $2\pi i$, (b) $-2\pi i$ **31.** $r^2 \pi i$

SECTION 11.2

7. $2\pi e^2$ **9.** $2 \cosh 1$
11. For example, decompose C into the segments C_1 from i to $2 + i$, and C_2 from $2 + i$ to $4 + i$. On C_1 we have $1/|z^2| \leq 1$. On C_2 we have $1/|z^2| \leq \frac{1}{5}$. Hence, a better bound is $2 + \frac{2}{5}$.
13. $2\pi i$ **15.** $2 \cosh 1$ **17.** $-2\pi i$ **19.** 0

SECTION 11.3

1. If $z = 0$ lies exterior to C.   **3.** No   **5.** Does not apply.   **7.** Does not apply.
9. $-2(1 - i)/3$ **11.** $4\pi i/3$ **13.** (a) 0, (b) $-\pi$, (c) π **15.** 0 **17.** 0
19. $e^z/z = \dfrac{1}{z} + \left[1 + \dfrac{z}{2!} + \cdots\right]$. The integral of $1/z$ is equal to $2\pi i$, and the integral of the function in brackets, which is analytic, also at $z = 0$, is zero. Ans. $2\pi i$.
21. 0

SECTION 11.4

1. $-\frac{2}{3}(1 - i)$ **3.** $12i$ **5.** $-\dfrac{1566}{35}i$ **7.** -2 **9.** $4ie^{1/2}$
11. $\frac{1}{2} - \frac{1}{2} \cosh 2\pi$ **13.** $i/3$ **15.** $(\pi - \frac{1}{2} \sinh 2\pi)i$ **17.** 0

SECTION 11.5

1. $\dfrac{z^2 - 1}{z^2 + 1} = \dfrac{z^2 - 1}{(z + i)(z - i)} = \dfrac{f(z)}{z - z_0}$ where $f(z) = \dfrac{z^2 - 1}{z + i}$, $z_0 = i$. Ans. $2\pi i f(z_0) = 2\pi i f(i) = -2\pi$ **3.** 0 (by Cauchy's theorem)   **5.** $-\pi/2$ **7.** $-\pi i/2$ **9.** $2\pi i$
11. πi **13.** $2\pi i/\sqrt{e}$ **15.** $i\pi\sqrt{2}$ **17.** $-\pi$ **19.** $2i$

SECTION 11.6

1. Use $(1')$. Set $f = z^4 + z, z_0 = 1$. Then $f'(1) = 5$. Ans. $10\pi i$
3. By $(1'')$, πi **5.** $2\pi i$ **7.** $-10\pi i$ **9.** $(-1)^{n+1}2\pi i/(2n - 1)!$ **11.** $-6\pi i/5$
13. $16\pi ei$ **15.** $-8\pi i$ **17.** $2\pi i$
19. Let $f(z) = c_0 + c_1 z + \cdots + c_n z^n = z^n \left(c_n + \dfrac{c_{n-1}}{z} + \cdots + \dfrac{c_0}{z^n}\right)$, $c_n \neq 0, n > 0$.
Set $|z| = r$ and use Prob. 15, Sec. 10.1. Then
$$|f(z)| > r^n \left(|c_n| - \dfrac{|c_{n-1}|}{r} - \cdots - \dfrac{|c_0|}{r^n}\right).$$

Hence, for sufficiently large r, $|f(z)| > \frac{1}{2}r^n|c_n|$. From this the result follows.

21. If $f \neq 0$, then $g = 1/f$ would be analytic for all z, and there would be values of z exterior to every circle $|z| = R$ for which, say, $|g| > 1$ and thus $|f| < 1$ (cf. Prob. 18). This contradicts Prob. 19, and $f \neq 0$ cannot hold for all z.

SECTION 11.7

1. $1 + \left(z + \dfrac{\pi}{4}\right) - \dfrac{1}{2!}\left(z + \dfrac{\pi}{4}\right)^2 - \dfrac{1}{3!}\left(z + \dfrac{\pi}{4}\right)^3 + \cdots, \; R = \infty$

3. $-1 - (z + 1) - (z + 1)^2 - (z + 1)^3 - \cdots, \; R = 1$

5. $-1 - (z - \pi i) - \dfrac{1}{2!}(z - \pi i)^2 - \dfrac{1}{3!}(z - \pi i)^3 - \cdots, \; R = \infty$

7. $(z - 1) - \dfrac{(z - 1)^2}{2} + \dfrac{(z - 1)^3}{3} - + \cdots, \; R = 1$

9. $\dfrac{1+i}{2}\left[1 + \dfrac{1+i}{2}(z - i) + \left(\dfrac{1+i}{2}\right)^2(z - i)^2 + \cdots\right], \; R = \sqrt{2}$

11. $\cos^2 z = \dfrac{1}{2}(1 + \cos 2z) = \dfrac{1}{2}\left[2 - \dfrac{2^2}{2!}z^2 + \dfrac{2^4}{4!}z^4 - + \cdots\right], \; R = \infty$

13. $z + \dfrac{z^3}{3} + \dfrac{z^5}{2!\,5} + \dfrac{z^7}{3!\,7} + \cdots, \; R = \infty$

15. $z - \dfrac{z^3}{3!\,3} + \dfrac{z^5}{5!\,5} - \dfrac{z^7}{7!\,7} + - \cdots, \; R = \infty$

17. $z - \dfrac{z^5}{2!\,5} + \dfrac{z^9}{4!\,9} - \dfrac{z^{13}}{6!\,13} + - \cdots, \; R = \infty$

19. $z + \dfrac{1}{3}z^3 + \dfrac{2}{15}z^5 + \cdots, \; R = \dfrac{\pi}{2}$ **21.** $z + z^2 + \dfrac{z^3}{3} + \cdots, \; R = \infty$

SECTION 11.8

1. $1 - z^3 + z^6 - + \cdots, \; |z| < 1$ **3.** $1 - \dfrac{z^6}{2!} + \dfrac{z^{12}}{4!} - + \cdots, \; |z| < \infty$

5. $1 - 2z^2 + 3z^4 - 4z^6 + - \cdots, \; |z| < 1$

7. $4 + 5z + 6z^2 + 7z^3 + \cdots, \; |z| < 1$

9. $\dfrac{z^2}{1!\,3} - \dfrac{z^4}{3!\,7} + \dfrac{z^6}{5!\,11} - \dfrac{z^8}{7!\,15} + - \cdots, \; |z| < \infty$

11. $f' = 2zf + 1, f'' = 2(f + zf'), \text{ etc.}, f(0) = 0, f'(0) = 1, \text{ etc.}$

$f = z + \dfrac{2}{1\cdot 3}z^3 + \dfrac{2^2}{1\cdot 3\cdot 5}z^5 + \dfrac{2^3}{1\cdot 3\cdot 5\cdot 7}z^7 + \cdots, \; |z| < \infty$

13. $1 + \dfrac{3}{2}z^2 + \dfrac{29}{24}z^4 + \dfrac{511}{720}z^6 + \cdots, \; |z| < \dfrac{\pi}{2}$

15. $\dfrac{1}{1 - 3i} + \dfrac{3}{(1 - 3i)^2}[z - (1 + i)] + \dfrac{3^2}{(1 - 3i)^3}[z - (1 + i)]^2 + \cdots,$

$$|z - (1 + i)| < \tfrac{1}{3}\sqrt{10}$$

17. $\dfrac{i}{2}\left[1 - (1 + i)(z + i) + \tfrac{3}{4}(1 + i)^2(z + i)^2 - \dfrac{(1 + i)^3}{2}(z + i)^3 + \cdots\right], \; |z + i| < \sqrt{2}$

19. $\dfrac{5}{6} + \dfrac{17}{36}(z+1) + \dfrac{59}{216}(z+1)^2 + \dfrac{209}{1296}(z+1)^3 + \cdots, \; |z+1| < \dfrac{3}{2}$

21. $1 + 2\left(z - \dfrac{\pi}{4}\right) + 2\left(z - \dfrac{\pi}{4}\right)^2 + \dfrac{8}{3}\left(z - \dfrac{\pi}{4}\right)^3 + \cdots, \; \left|z - \dfrac{\pi}{4}\right| < \dfrac{\pi}{4}$

23. $e[1 + z + \tfrac{3}{2}z^2 + \tfrac{13}{6}z^3 + \cdots], \; |z| < 1$ **25.** $e[1 + z + z^2 + \tfrac{5}{6}z^3 + \cdots], \; |z| < \infty$

SECTION 11.9

1. Let $x \neq 0$. Given an $\epsilon > 0$, we can find an $N(\epsilon, x)$ such that $|s(x) - s_n(x)| = (1 + x^2)^{-n} < \epsilon$ for all $n > N(\epsilon, x)$. From this, $(1 + x^2)^n > \dfrac{1}{\epsilon}, n > \dfrac{\ln(1/\epsilon)}{\ln(1+x^2)}$. Since $\ln 1 = 0$, the right side can be made greater than any number by taking $|x|$ sufficiently small; that is, no $N(\epsilon)$ exists such that $N(\epsilon, x) \leq N(\epsilon)$ for *all* $x \neq 0$.

5. $s_n = x^n$; $s = \lim\limits_{n \to \infty} s_n = \begin{cases} 0 \text{ when } 0 \leq x < 1 \\ 1 \text{ when } x = 1 \end{cases}$ is discontinuous at $x = 1$ and, by Theorem 2, the statement follows.

7. Convergence follows from Theorem 1, Sec. 10.6. Let $R_n(z)$ and R_n^* be the remainders of (1) and (5), respectively. Since (5) converges, for given $\epsilon > 0$ we can find an $N(\epsilon)$ such that $R_n^* < \epsilon$ for all $n > N(\epsilon)$. Since $|f_n(z)| < M_n$ for all z in the region R we have $|R_n(z)| < R_n^*$ and therefore $|R_n(z)| < \epsilon$ for all $n > N(\epsilon)$ and all z in the region R. This proves that the convergence of (1) in the region R is uniform.

9. $|\cos^n x| \leq 1$, and $\Sigma(1/n^2)$ converges. **11.** $\dfrac{1}{|z| + n^2} \leq \dfrac{1}{n^2}$

13. $\left|\dfrac{z^n}{n^2}\right| = \dfrac{|z|^n}{n^2} \leq \dfrac{1}{n^2}$ in R **15.** Cf. Theorem 1.

17. By Theorem 2, Sec. 10.5, $|R_n(x)| \leq \dfrac{1}{x^2 + n + 1} < \dfrac{1}{n}$ for all x. Given an $\epsilon > 0$, we have $\dfrac{1}{n} < \epsilon$ for all $n > N(\epsilon) = \dfrac{1}{\epsilon}$, and $|R_n(x)| < \epsilon$ for all $n > N(\epsilon)$ and all x, which proves uniform convergence. Furthermore, for any fixed x, $\left|\dfrac{(-1)^{n-1}}{x^2 + n}\right| = \dfrac{1}{x^2 + n} > \dfrac{a}{n}$ where $n = 1, 2, \cdots$ and a is a suitable constant. Now $\Sigma \dfrac{a}{n} = a\Sigma\dfrac{1}{n}$ diverges, which proves that the series in Ex. 4 is not absolutely convergent.

SECTION 11.10

1. $\displaystyle\sum_{n=0}^{\infty} \dfrac{1}{n! \, z^{2n+4}}, \; (|z| > 0)$ **3.** $\displaystyle\sum_{n=0}^{\infty} \dfrac{(-1)^n 4^{2n+1}}{(2n+1)!} z^{2n-2}, \; (|z| > 0)$

5. $\displaystyle\sum_{n=0}^{\infty} (-1)^n z^{4(n-1)}, \; (0 < |z| < 1)$

7. $\dfrac{1}{1+z^2} = \dfrac{1}{(z-i)} \dfrac{1}{2i\left(1 + \dfrac{z-i}{2i}\right)} = \dfrac{1}{2i(z-i)} \displaystyle\sum_{n=0}^{\infty}\left(-\dfrac{z-i}{2i}\right)^n$

$= -\displaystyle\sum_{n=0}^{\infty}\left(\dfrac{i}{2}\right)^{n+1}(z-i)^{n-1}, \, 0 < |z-i| < 2, \quad \dfrac{1}{1+z^2} = \displaystyle\sum_{n=0}^{\infty} \dfrac{(-2i)^n}{(z-i)^{n+2}}, \; |z-i| > 2$

9. Represent $1/(1 - z^4)$ in terms of partial fractions. Develop each partial fraction in powers of $z + 1$. Add corresponding terms. Ans.

$$\frac{1}{4}\left[\frac{1}{z+1} + \sum_{n=0}^{\infty}\left(\frac{1}{2^{n+1}} + \frac{\sin[\frac{1}{4}(n+1)\pi]}{2^{(n-1)/2}}\right)(z+1)^n\right] \quad (0 < |z+1| < \sqrt{2})$$

and two other Laurent series valid for $\sqrt{2} < |z + 1| < 2$ and $|z + 1| > 2$.

11. $(1 - 4z)\sum_{n=0}^{\infty} z^{4n} = 1 - 4z + z^4 - 4z^5 + \cdots, \quad (|z| < 1),$

$$\left(\frac{4}{z^3} - \frac{1}{z^4}\right)\sum_{n=0}^{\infty}\frac{1}{z^{4n}} = \frac{4}{z^3} - \frac{1}{z^4} + \frac{4}{z^7} - \frac{1}{z^8} + -\cdots, \quad (|z| > 1)$$

13. $\frac{2}{z} + \sum_{n=0}^{\infty}\frac{(-1)^n - 4}{3^{n+1}}z^n, \quad (0 < |z| < 3), \quad \frac{2}{z} + \sum_{n=0}^{\infty}\frac{3^n(4 + (-1)^n)}{z^{n+1}}, \quad (|z| > 3)$

15. $\sum_{n=0}^{\infty}\frac{e}{n!}(z - 1)^{n-2}, \quad (|z - 1| > 0)$

17. $\sum_{n=0}^{\infty}\binom{-4}{n}(z - 1)^n, \, (|z - 1| < 1), \quad \sum_{n=0}^{\infty}\binom{-4}{n}\frac{1}{(z - 1)^{n+4}}, \quad (|z - 1| > 1)$

19. Let $\sum_{-\infty}^{\infty} A_n(z - a)^n$ and $\sum_{-\infty}^{\infty} B_n(z - a)^n$ be two Laurent series of the same function $f(z)$ in the same annulus. We multiply both series by $(z - a)^{-k-1}$ and integrate along a circle with center at a in the interior of the annulus. Since the series converge uniformly, we may integrate term by term. This yields $2\pi i A_k = 2\pi i B_k$. Thus, $A_k = B_k$ for all $k = 0, \pm 1, \cdots$.

SECTION 11.11

1. No   **3.** Yes   **5.** No   **7.** No   **9.** Yes

SECTION 11.12

1. $\pm 1, \pm i$ (simple)   **3.** $\pm n\pi, n = 0, 1, \cdots$ (third order)
5. $-1, \infty$ (simple)   **7.** $\pm 2n\pi i, n = 0, 1, \cdots$ (simple)   **9.** $\pm 1/n\pi$ (double)
11. $\pm 2, \infty$ (double)   **13.** ∞ (pole of the fourth order)
15. ∞ (essential singularity)   **17.** π (essential singularity)
19. ∞ (essential singularity)   **21.** $1, \infty$ (essential singularities), $\pm 2n\pi i, n = 0, 1, \cdots$
(simple poles)   **23.** $0, \infty$ (essential singularities)
25. If $f(z)$ has a pole of mth order at $z = a$, then

$$f(z) = \frac{c_m}{(z-a)^m} + \frac{c_{m-1}}{(z-a)^{m-1}} + \cdots = \frac{c_m}{(z-a)^m}\left[1 + \frac{c_{m-1}}{c_m}(z-a) + \cdots\right], c_m \neq 0.$$

For given $M > 0$, no matter how large, we can find a $\delta > 0$ so small that $\frac{|c_m|}{\delta^m} > 2M$ and

$$\left|\left[1 + \frac{c_{m-1}}{c_m}(z-a) + \cdots\right]\right| > \frac{1}{2} \text{ for all } |z-a| < \delta. \text{ Then } |f| > \frac{|c_m|}{\delta^m}\frac{1}{2} > M. \text{ Hence}$$

$|f| \to \infty$ as $z \to a$.

SECTION 11.13

1. $\operatorname*{Res}_{z=1} f(z) = -4$ **3.** $\operatorname*{Res}_{z=0} f(z) = \frac{1}{2}$ **5.** $\operatorname*{Res}_{z=-1} f(z) = -5, \operatorname*{Res}_{z=-2} f(z) = 9$

7. $\operatorname*{Res}_{z=1} f(z) = -\frac{1}{4}, \operatorname*{Res}_{z=i} f(z) = \frac{i}{4}, \operatorname*{Res}_{z=-1} f(z) = \frac{1}{4}, \operatorname*{Res}_{z=-i} f(z) = -\frac{i}{4}$

9. By (7), $\operatorname*{Res}_{z=n} f(z) = \dfrac{(-1)^n}{\pi}$ $(n = 0, \pm 1, \cdots)$ **11.** $\operatorname*{Res}_{z=n\pi} f(z) = 1$ $(n = 0, \pm 1, \cdots)$

13. $\operatorname*{Res}_{z=0} f(z) = 0$ **15.** $\operatorname*{Res}_{z=1} f(z) = -\dfrac{1}{4}$ $\operatorname*{Res}_{z=-1} f(z) = \dfrac{1}{4}$ **17.** $\operatorname*{Res}_{z=0} f(z) = 0$

19. $\operatorname*{Res}_{z=-4} f(z) = -\dfrac{3}{16}$, $\operatorname*{Res}_{z=-2} f(z) = \dfrac{1}{12}$, $\operatorname*{Res}_{z=4} f(z) = \dfrac{5}{48}$

21. $\operatorname*{Res}_{z=2n\pi i} f(z) = -1$ $(n = 0, \pm 1, \cdots)$ **23.** $\operatorname*{Res}_{z=n\pi} f(z) = 0$ $(n = 0, \pm 1, \cdots)$

25. $-\pi i$ **27.** $2\pi i$ **29.** $2\pi i$ **31.** $2\pi i$ **33.** 0   **35.** 0

SECTION 11.14

1. 0   **3.** $217\pi i/32$ **5.** $2\pi i$ **7.** $-4i$ **9.** $-4i$ **11.** $-4i \sinh \frac{1}{2}$

13. $-16\pi i/9$ **15.** The integrand may be written $\dfrac{1}{z^5} + \dfrac{2}{z} + \dfrac{3}{z - \frac{1}{2}}$. Ans. $10\pi i$

17. The integrand may be written $\dfrac{1}{z^3} + \dfrac{4}{z} - \dfrac{3}{z^2 + 4}$. Ans. $8\pi i$ **19.** 0

SECTION 11.15

1. $\dfrac{\pi}{2}$ **3.** $\dfrac{2\pi}{\sqrt{3}}$ **5.** $\dfrac{\pi}{\sqrt{k^2 - 1}}$ **7.** 0   **9.** $\cos 2\theta = \dfrac{1}{2}\left(z^2 + \dfrac{1}{z^2}\right)$,

$\displaystyle\int_0^{2\pi} \dfrac{\cos^2 \theta}{26 - 10 \cos 2\theta}\, d\theta = -\dfrac{1}{20i}\int_C \dfrac{(z^2 + 1)^2}{z(z^2 - \frac{1}{5})(z^2 - 5)}\, dz = \dfrac{\pi}{20}$ **11.** $\dfrac{2\pi}{1 - k^2}$

13. $I = \displaystyle\int_0^{2\pi} \dfrac{\cos^2 3\theta}{5 - 4\cos 2\theta}\, d\theta = \dfrac{1}{4}\int_C \dfrac{(z^3 + z^{-3})^2}{5 - 2(z^2 + z^{-2})}\, \dfrac{dz}{iz} = -\dfrac{1}{8i}\int_C \dfrac{(z^6 + 1)^2}{z^5(z^2 - 2)(z^2 - \frac{1}{2})}\, dz$

$= -\dfrac{2\pi i}{8i}\left[\operatorname*{Res}_{z=0} f(z) + \operatorname*{Res}_{z=\frac{1}{\sqrt{2}}} f(z) + \operatorname*{Res}_{z=-\frac{1}{\sqrt{2}}} f(z)\right]$. The second and the last residues are

$-27/8$. To determine the residue at $z = 0$, where $f(z)$ has a pole of the fifth order, we may develop $f(z)$, using the geometric series:

$$f(z) = \dfrac{(z^6 + 1)^2}{z^5}\, \dfrac{1}{(-2)(1 - z^2/2)}\, \dfrac{1}{(-\frac{1}{2})(1 - 2z^2)}$$

$$= \left(z^7 + 2z + \dfrac{1}{z^5}\right) \sum_{m=0}^{\infty}\left(\dfrac{z^2}{2}\right)^m \sum_{n=0}^{\infty}(2z^2)^n.$$

Multiplying term by term and collecting like powers of z, we find that $1/z$ has the coefficient $21/4$. Thus $I = 3\pi/8$. Ans. $I/2 = 3\pi/16$.

15. The integral is of the type considered in part B. The function $1/(1 + z^2)^3$ has a pole of the third order at $z = i$, and (8) in Sec. 11.13 yields the residue $3/16i$. Ans. $3\pi/8$.

17. 0   **19.** $2\pi/3$ **21.** $\pi/2$ **23.** $\pi/60$ **25.** $-(2\pi e^{-\sqrt{3}} \sin 1)/\sqrt{3}$

27. $\dfrac{\pi}{\sqrt{2}} e^{-1/\sqrt{2}}\left(\sin\dfrac{1}{\sqrt{2}} + \cos\dfrac{1}{\sqrt{2}}\right)$ **29.** π/e

31. The integral of e^{-z^2} along C is zero. Writing it as the sum of four integrals over the four segments of C we have

$$\int_{-a}^{a} e^{-x^2}\, dx + ie^{-a^2}\int_0^1 e^{y^2 - 2ayi}\, dy + e\int_a^{-a} e^{-x^2 - 2xi}\, dx + ie^{-a^2}\int_1^0 e^{y^2 + 2ayi}\, dy = 0.$$

Let $a \to \infty$. Then the terms having the factor e^{-a^2} approach zero. Taking the real part of the third integral, we thus obtain

$$-\int_{\infty}^{-\infty} e^{-x^2} \cos 2x \, dx = 2 \int_0^\infty e^{-x^2} \cos 2x \, dx = \frac{1}{e} \int_{-\infty}^\infty e^{-x^2} \, dx = \frac{\sqrt{\pi}}{e} . \quad \text{Ans.} \quad \frac{\sqrt{\pi}}{2e} .$$

33. $\int_C f(z) \, dz = 2\pi i \operatorname*{Res}_{z=i\sqrt{2}} f(z) = \pi \left(\frac{\sqrt{2}}{6} - \frac{i}{3} \right)$. Now $\int_C f(z) \, dz = \int_{-R}^{-1-\rho} f(x) \, dx$

$+ \int_{C_3} f(z) \, dz + \int_{-1+\rho}^{R} f(x) \, dx + \int_{C_1} f(z) \, dz$ where ρ is the radius of C_3. Let $R \to \infty$.

Then the last integral approaches zero. $\int_{C_3} f(z) \, dz = \frac{1}{3} \int_{C_3} \frac{dz}{z+1} - \frac{1}{3} \int_{C_3} \frac{z-1}{z^2+2} \, dz.$

The first integral on the right is equal to $-\pi i/3$. The value of the last integral depends on ρ and approaches zero as $\rho \to 0$. Thus,

$$\text{pr. v.} \int_{-\infty}^\infty f(x) \, dx = \lim_{\substack{\rho \to 0 \\ R \to \infty}} \left[\int_{-R}^{-1-\rho} f(x) \, dx + \int_{-1+\rho}^{R} f(x) \, dx \right]$$

$$= \frac{\pi i}{3} + 2\pi i \operatorname*{Res}_{z=i\sqrt{2}} f(z) = \frac{\pi\sqrt{2}}{6} .$$

SECTION 12.1

3. The positive and the negative v-axis, respectively

5. The parabola $v = \frac{1}{2}(1 - u^2)$ **7.** $|\arg w| < \frac{\pi}{2} , \; |w| > 1$

9. $4 < |w| < 9, |\arg z| < \frac{2\pi}{3}$ **19.** $-1 < u < 1, v > 1$

21. z^3 maps the given region onto the upper half plane. Multiplication by i rotates this half plane through the angle $\pi/2$, and addition of 1 carries the origin into the point 1. Thus, $w = iz^3 + 1$.

SECTION 12.2

1. No, the size is preserved, but the sense is reversed.   **9.** $-1, 1$ **11.** 0

SECTION 12.3

1. $w = u + iv = \dfrac{1}{z}, z = x + iy = \dfrac{1}{w}, x = \dfrac{u}{u^2 + v^2}, y = -\dfrac{v}{u^2 + v^2}$. By inserting this into $x^2 + y^2 + ax + by + c = 0$ $(a,b,c$ real) and multiplying by $u^2 + v^2$, we obtain $1 + au - bv + c(u^2 + v^2) = 0$.

3. $u^2 + (v + \frac{2}{3})^2 = \frac{1}{9}$ or $|w + \frac{2}{3}i| = \frac{1}{3}$ **5.** $\left| w + \dfrac{1+i}{2} \right| = \dfrac{1}{\sqrt{2}}$ **7.** $v = -\frac{1}{4}$

9. The image is bounded by the circles $|w - \frac{1}{2}| = \frac{1}{2}$ and $|w - \frac{1}{4}| = \frac{1}{4}$.

11. 0, 1   **13.** $0, e^{2k\pi i/n}, k = 0, 1, \cdots, n - 1$ **15.** $2 \pm \sqrt{6}$

17. For example, $w = 4/z, w = (z + 4)/(z + 1)$, etc.

19. $w = \dfrac{2z - 1}{z}, w = \dfrac{-1}{z - 2}$, etc.   **21.** $w = \dfrac{az + b}{bz + a}$, a and b arbitrary

23. $w_1 = iz, w_2 = w_1 + 4, w_3 = 1/w_2, w_4 = 5iw_3, w = w_4 - i$

SECTION 12.4

3. $w = \dfrac{z+1}{z-1}$　　**5.** $w = \dfrac{(1+i)z+1}{2z}$　　**7.** $w = \dfrac{i}{z}$　　**9.** $w = \dfrac{3z+4}{iz}$

11. $z = \dfrac{w+i}{iw+1} = \dfrac{u+i(v+1)}{1-v+iu}$. The real part is $x = c = \dfrac{2u}{(1-v)^2+u^2}$. Hence

$(v-1)^2 + \left(u - \dfrac{1}{c}\right)^2 = \dfrac{1}{c^2}$.　　**13.** $z = -\dfrac{iw+1}{w+i}$　　**15.** $z = \dfrac{-4w+1}{2w-1}$

17. If $|z| = 1$, then $z = \cos\theta + i\sin\theta$. A simple calculation shows that then $|z - z_0|^2 = |\bar{z}_0 z - 1|^2$. Thus, $|w| = 1$, that is, the unit circles correspond to each other. If $z = z_0$, then $w = 0$, and, since $|z_0| < 1$, z_0 lies inside $|z| = 1$, that is, the interior of $|z| = 1$ is mapped onto the interior of $|w| = 1$.

19. $t = z - 1 - 2i$ maps the given region R onto R_1. The function $p = t^4$ maps R_1 onto R_2, and R_2 can be mapped onto $|w| \le 1$ by a linear transformation, for example,

$w = \dfrac{p - i}{-ip + 1}$, cf. (3). By composing these mappings we see that R is mapped onto

$|w| \le 1$ by $w = \dfrac{(z - 1 - 2i)^4 - i}{-i(z - 1 - 2i)^4 + 1}$. Cf. Fig. 398.

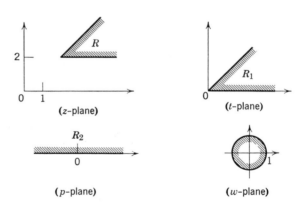

Fig. 398. Problem 19.

SECTION 12.5

1. $1 \le |w| \le e,\ 0 \le \arg w \le \dfrac{\pi}{2}$　　**3.** $\dfrac{1}{e^2} < |w| < \dfrac{1}{e},\ 0 < \arg w < \pi$

5. $t = z^2$ maps R onto the strip $0 < \operatorname{Im} t < \pi$, and $w = e^t$ maps this strip onto the upper half plane. Ans. $w = e^{z^2}$

7. $w' = \cos z = 0$ at $z = \pm(2n+1)\dfrac{\pi}{2},\ n = 0, 1, \cdots$

9. The region in the upper half-plane bounded by the ellipses

$$\frac{u^2}{\cosh^2 1} + \frac{v^2}{\sinh^2 1} = 1 \quad \text{and} \quad \frac{u^2}{\cosh^2 2} + \frac{v^2}{\sinh^2 2} = 1$$

11. Elliptical annulus bounded by the ellipses in Prob. 9 and cut along the positive imaginary axis

13. $\cosh z = \cos (iz) = \sin \left(iz + \dfrac{\pi}{2} \right)$ **19.** The exterior of $|w - \tfrac{1}{2}| = \tfrac{1}{2}$, Im $w > 0$

SECTION 12.6

5. 1, -1, two sheets   **7.** 0, 1, -1, two sheets which may be cut along the real axis from -1 to 0 and from 1 to infinity, and joined crosswise.

SECTION 13.1

1. $u(r) = 20 \dfrac{\ln r}{\ln 2} + 20 = 28.9 \ln r + 20$

3. $u(r) = -90 \dfrac{\ln r}{\ln 10} + 10 = -39.1 \ln r + 10$

5. $u = c \operatorname{Re} \ln (z^2 - a^2) = c \ln |z^2 - a^2|$

9. $u = \dfrac{1}{\ln 3} \operatorname{Re} \ln \dfrac{z + \frac{4}{3}}{z - \frac{4}{3}} = \dfrac{1}{\ln 3} \ln \left| \dfrac{z + \frac{4}{3}}{z - \frac{4}{3}} \right|$

SECTION 13.3

1. Parallel flow in the negative y-direction. $V = -i$
3. $V = 2x + 1 - 2iy$, $V_2 = 0$ on the x-axis. Cf. Fig. 399.

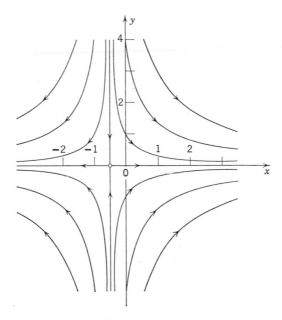

Fig. 399. Problem 3.

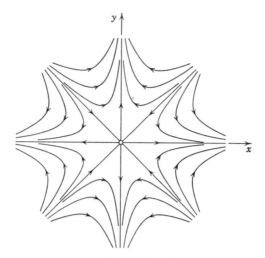

Fig. 400. Problem 5.

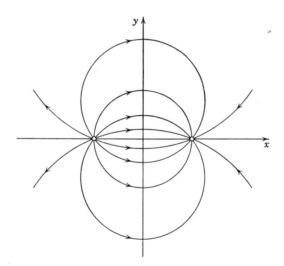

Fig. 401. Problem 11.

5. $V = 4x(x^2 - 3y^2) + 4iy(y^2 - 3x^2)$, $V_2 = 0$ on the x-axis and on the lines $y = \pm\sqrt{3}x$. Cf. Fig. 400.   **7.** $|F'(z)|^2 = \Phi_x{}^2 + \Phi_y{}^2 = const$

11. $F(z) = \dfrac{1}{2\pi} \ln \dfrac{z+a}{z-a}$. The streamlines are circles. Cf. Fig. 401.

15. The streamlines are circles $\dfrac{y}{x^2 + y^2} = c$ or $x^2 + (y - k)^2 = k^2$. Cf. Fig. 402.

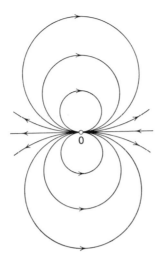

Fig. 402. Problem 15.

SECTION 13.4

3. $|f| = e^x$ is monotone. Hence its minimum lies at that point z (or those points) of R which has the smallest value of x among all points in R; clearly this is a point on the boundary. Similarly for the maximum.

5. This follows immediately from Theorem 3.

SECTION 13.5

1. Set $r = 0$ in (5).

9. $u = \dfrac{1}{2} + \dfrac{2}{\pi}\left(r \sin\theta + \dfrac{r^3}{3}\sin 3\theta + \dfrac{r^5}{5}\sin 5\theta + \cdots\right)$. Cf. Prob. 4.

11. $u = \dfrac{1}{3} - \dfrac{4}{\pi^2}\left(r\cos\theta - \dfrac{r^2}{4}\cos 2\theta + \dfrac{r^3}{9}\cos 3\theta - + \cdots\right)$

13. $u = \dfrac{2}{\pi}\left(r\cos\theta - \dfrac{r^3}{3}\cos 3\theta + \dfrac{r^5}{5}\cos 5\theta - + \cdots\right)$

$\qquad + \dfrac{2}{\pi}\left(r^2\sin 2\theta + \dfrac{r^6}{3}\sin 6\theta + \dfrac{r^{10}}{5}\sin 10\theta + \cdots\right)$

15. $u = 1 + r^2\cos 2\theta = \operatorname{Re}(1 + z^2)$ **17.** $u = r^3\sin 3\theta = \operatorname{Im} z^3$

SECTION 14.1

1.

k	1	2	3	4
$\Gamma(k + \tfrac{1}{2})$	$\dfrac{\sqrt{\pi}}{2} = 0.886$	$\dfrac{3\sqrt{\pi}}{4} = 1.329$	$\dfrac{15\sqrt{\pi}}{8} = 3.323$	$\dfrac{105\sqrt{\pi}}{16} = 11.632$

3. $\Gamma(2.1) = 1.1\Gamma(1.1) = 1.046$ **5.** $\Gamma(-1.5) = \dfrac{\Gamma(1.5)}{(-1.5)(-0.5)0.5} = 2.363$

7. -0.889 **15.** $1/60$ **17.** 1.077 **19.** The poles are simple. Hence by (6), Sec. 11.13, Res $\Gamma(\alpha) = \lim_{\alpha \to -k} (\alpha + k) \Gamma(\alpha)$. Now
$$\alpha = -k$$

$$\Gamma(\alpha) = \frac{\Gamma(\alpha + 1)}{\alpha} = \cdots = \frac{\Gamma(\alpha + k + 1)}{\alpha(\alpha + 1) \cdots (\alpha + k)} \quad \text{and, therefore,}$$

$$\underset{\alpha = -k}{\text{Res }} \Gamma(\alpha) = \lim_{\alpha \to -k} \frac{\Gamma(\alpha + k + 1)}{\alpha(\alpha + 1) \cdots (\alpha + k - 1)} = \frac{\Gamma(1)}{(-k)(-k + 1) \cdots (-2)(-1)}.$$

SECTION 14.2

7. Set $(t - \mu)/\sigma = \tau$. Then $dt = \sigma \, d\tau$ and

$$F(x) = \frac{1}{\sqrt{2\pi}} \int_{-\infty}^{(x-\mu)/\sigma} e^{-\tau^2/2} \, d\tau = \Phi\left(\frac{x - \mu}{\sigma}\right).$$

9. $C(x) = x - \dfrac{x^5}{2! \, 5} + \dfrac{x^9}{4! \, 9} - \dfrac{x^{13}}{6! \, 13} + - \cdots$

11. Since $Si(x)$ is odd, we may consider it for $x \geq 0$. Since $\sin x$ is periodic and $1/x$ decreases in a monotone fashion, we have

$$\left| \int_0^\pi \frac{\sin t}{t} \, dt \right| > \left| \int_\pi^{2\pi} \frac{\sin t}{t} \, dt \right| > \left| \int_{2\pi}^{3\pi} \frac{\sin t}{t} \, dt \right| > \cdots.$$

Since the first integral is positive, the second is negative, the third is positive, etc., the statement follows.

13. From (11), $C(x) + i S(x) = \displaystyle\int_0^x e^{it^2} \, dt$, $C(x) - i S(x) = \displaystyle\int_0^x e^{-it^2} \, dt$. Set $t^2 = i\tau^2$ and $t^2 = -i\tau^2$, respectively, and use $i = e^{i\pi/2}$. Then

$$C(x) + iS(x) = \frac{\sqrt{\pi}}{2} e^{i\pi/4} \operatorname{erf}(xe^{-i\pi/4}), \qquad C(x) - iS(x) = \frac{\sqrt{\pi}}{2} e^{-i\pi/4} \operatorname{erf}(xe^{i\pi/4}).$$

By addition and subtraction,

$$C(x) = \frac{\sqrt{\pi}}{4} [e^{i\pi/4} \operatorname{erf}(xe^{-i\pi/4}) + e^{-i\pi/4} \operatorname{erf}(xe^{i\pi/4})],$$

$$S(x) = \frac{\sqrt{\pi}}{4i} [e^{i\pi/4} \operatorname{erf}(xe^{-i\pi/4}) - e^{-i\pi/4} \operatorname{erf}(xe^{i\pi/4})].$$

17. The integrands are entire, so that their Maclaurin series have the radius of convergence $R = \infty$. From this and Theorem 4 in Sec. 10.9 the statement follows.

21. $S(x) = \dfrac{x^3}{1! \, 3} - \dfrac{x^7}{3! \, 7} + \dfrac{x^{11}}{5! \, 11} - + \cdots$. Let $x > 0$ and sufficiently small. Then the absolute values of the terms form a monotone decreasing sequence and, by Theorem 2 in Sec. 10.5, the absolute value of the error is less than $x^7/3! \, 7$. Hence, the absolute value of the relative error is less than $\dfrac{x^7/3! \, 7}{S(x)} \approx \dfrac{x^7/42}{x^3/3} = \dfrac{x^4}{14}$, and this is less than 0.01 when $|x| < 0.61$.

SECTION 14.3

1. Use (8), Sec. 14.3, for $x = 0, 0.5, 1.0, 1.5$, estimating the error by the use of Theorem 2, Sec. 10.5. The values are $0, 0.52, 0.84, 0.97$. The last value is also obtained from (7),

Sec. 14.3, which shows that the further values can be computed with the desired accuracy from this formula.

3. Consider the quotient $q_n = \left| \dfrac{c_n/x^n}{c_{n+1}/x^{n+1}} \right| = \left| \dfrac{c_n x}{c_{n+1}} \right|$. For n for which $q_n > 1$ the terms are still decreasing in absolute value until an n is reached for which $q_n < 1$ and the terms increase. Hence, the smallest n for which $q_n \leq 1$ is the subscript of the smallest term in absolute value. If some of the c_n are zero, the method must be modified in an obvious fashion.

5. Use the idea in Prob. 3.   **9.** Use (1).

11. $Q(0, x) = e^{-x}\left[\dfrac{1}{x} - \dfrac{1}{x^2} + \dfrac{2!}{x^3} - \cdots + (-1)^{n-1}\dfrac{(n-1)!}{x^n} \right] + (-1)^n n!\, I_n(x)$

where

$$I_n(x) = \int_x^\infty \frac{e^{-t}}{t^{n+1}}\, dt.$$

Denoting the expression in brackets by S_n, we have

$$|e^x Q(0, x) - S_n| = n!\, e^x I_n(x).$$

Since $1/t^{n+1} \leq 1/x^{n+1}$ for all $t \geq x$, we obtain

$$I_n(x) < \frac{1}{x^{n+1}} \int_x^\infty e^{-t}\, dt = \frac{e^{-x}}{x^{n+1}}.$$

Hence, for any fixed n,

$$|e^x Q(0, x) - S_n|x^n < \frac{n!\, e^x e^{-x}}{x} = \frac{n!}{x} \to 0 \qquad \text{as } x \to \infty,$$

that is,

$$e^x Q(0, x) \sim \frac{1}{x} - \frac{1}{x^2} + \frac{2!}{x^3} - + \cdots,$$

and the result follows.

13. Use the result of Prob. 12 and (13), Sec. 14.1.

SECTION 14.4

3. Set $p = -\ln t$. Then $t = e^{-p}$, $dt = -e^{-p}\, dp$, and

$$\text{li}(e^{-x}) = \int_0^{e^{-x}} \frac{dt}{\ln t} = \int_\infty^x \frac{-e^{-p}}{-p}\, dp = -\int_x^\infty \frac{e^{-p}}{p}\, dp = -\text{Ei}(x).$$

9. $y = e^x \sqrt{x}\, Q(\tfrac{1}{2}, x)$ satisfies $y' = \left(\dfrac{1}{2x} + 1 \right)y - 1$.   Ans.

$$\sqrt{x}\, e^{-x}\left(\frac{1}{x} - \frac{1}{2x^2} + \frac{1 \cdot 3}{4x^3} - \frac{1 \cdot 3 \cdot 5}{8x^4} + - \cdots \right).$$

INDEX

A

Absolute
  convergence 604, 617
  error 27
  value 24, 578
Acceleration 296
Addition
  of complex numbers 21
  of matrices 388
  of series 612
  of vectors 261
Alternating current 76, 151
Ampère 74
Amplification 149
Amplitude 145, 493
Analytic at infinity 692
Analytic continuation 626, 633
Analytic function
  definition 174, 585
  derivatives 666
  line integrals 646
  mapping by 719
  residues 698
  series representation 669, 685
  singularities 673, 694
  zeros 693
Analyzer, harmonic 501
Angle
  between curves 80, 351
  between vectors 264
Angular speed 297

Annulus 580
Approximate integration 34
Approximate solution
  of differential equations 51, 91, 159
  of eigenvalue problems 460
  of equations 29
Approximation, trigonometric 497
Arc length 291
Arc tan 25, 643
Area 342, 351
Argand diagram 20
Argument 24, 578
Asymptotic expansion 781
Atmospheric pressure 60
Augmented matrix 424
Average
  (*see* Mean value)

B

Beam 539
Beats 146
Bell-shaped curve 775
Bernoulli
  equation 72
  numbers 676
Bessel equation 190, 520, 563
Bessel functions
  of the first kind 192
  Hankel 203
  modified 204

Bessel functions (*Cont.*)
  Neumann 201
  orthogonality of 520
  of the second kind 201
  tables 194, 203, 565
  of the third kind 203
  zeros 194, 565
Bessel inequality 498, 512
Beta function 771
Bilinear form 445
Binomial series 675
Binormal vector 295
Bolzano-Weierstrass theorem 595
Borda 57
Boundary
  condition 514, 525
  point 581
  value problem 514, 569, 720
Bounded
  function 88
  region 333
  sequence 595
  set 581
Bounds for eigenvalues 455
Bound vector 257
Boyle 59
Branch point 739

C

Cantilever beam 539
Cantor-Dedekind axiom 598
Capacitance 75
Cardano 20
Cardioid 292
Cartesian coordinates 20, 258
Catenary 292
Cauchy 92
  convergence principle 596, 604
  equation 124, 137, 186
  -Hadamard formula 619
  inequality 669
  integral formula 664
  integral theorem 653
  principal value 704, 707
  product 621
  -Riemann equations 588
Center
  of gravity 336, 360
  of power series 170, 616

Centrifugal force 297
Centripetal acceleration 297
Chain rule 301
Change of variables 337
Characteristic
  determinant 441
  equation 105, 136, 441
  function 514, 531, 555
  polynomial 441
  value 439, 514, 532
  vector 439
Chebychev
  (*see* Tchebichef)
Circle of convergence 618
Circuit 74, 151, 240, 494
Circular
  disk 580
  helix 288, 292, 294, 296
  membrane 562
  ring 580
Circulation 376, 749
Closed
  disk 580
  interval 598
  point set 581
  set of orthogonal functions 513
Coefficients
  of a differential equation 101
  of a power series 166, 616
  of a system of equations 413
Cofactor 400
Collatz 458
Collinear 277
Collineatory transformation 453
Column
  of a determinant 400
  matrix 388
  of a matrix 387
  vector 388
Comparison test 605
Complementary
  error function 777
  Fresnel integrals 778
  sine integral 778
Complete 513
Complex
  exponential function 633, 642, 731
  Fourier integral 509
  Fourier series 485

Complex (*Cont.*)
  function 583
  hyperbolic functions 637, 734
  impedance 155
  integral 645
  line integral 645
  logarithm 639, 732
  number 20, 578
  number sphere 692
  plane 20
  plane, extended 691
  potential 736, 745, 752
  sequence 592
  series 599
  trigonometric functions 635, 732
  variable 583
Component 258, 264
Compressible fluid 317
Conditionally convergent 604
Conduction of heat 367, 540
Conformal mapping 717
Conjugate
  complex numbers 23
  harmonic functions 591
Connected set 581
Conservative field 310, 381
Continuity
  of a complex function 584
  equation 318
  of a function of two variables 300
  piecewise 209
  of a vector function 284
Continuously differentiable 290
Contour integral 659
Control mechanism 251
Convergence
  absolute 604, 617
  circle of 618
  conditional 604
  interval of 171, 619
  in the mean 513
  principle 596, 604
  radius of 618
  of a sequence 592
  of a series 171, 600
  tests for 601, 605
  uniform 679
Cooling 55

Coordinates
  Cartesian 20, 258
  cylindrical 569
  polar 24
  spherical 569
Coplanar 277
Coriolis acceleration 298
Cosecant 5, 636
Cosine
  of a complex variable 635
  hyperbolic 6, 637
  integral 779
  of a real variable 3
Cotangent 5, 636
Coulomb 74
  law 310
Cramer's rule 13, 15, 414
Critical
  damping 122
  point 719
Cross product 268
Curl 319, 372, 376
Curvature 294
Curve
  arc length of 291
  orientation of 291
  piecewise smooth 326
  plane 288
  rectifiable 290
  simple 289
  smooth 325, 646
  twisted 288
Cylinder, flow around 755
Cylindrical coordinates 569

D

D'Alembert 537
Damping
  constant 120
  critical 122
  force 120
Decreasing sequence 597
Decrement 124
Dedekind 598
Definite complex integral 645
Deformation of path 658
Delta, Kronecker 313
De Moivre's formula 26
Dependent 107, 133, 276

Derivative
  of a complex function 584, 666
  directional 305
  left-hand 472
  partial 9
  right-hand 472
  of a vector function 285
Descartes 20
Determinant
  characteristic 441
  definition 12, 400
  of a matrix 409
  of a system of equations 413
Development around different centers
  625
Diagonal matrix 391
Differentiable complex function 584
Differential
  exact 378
  form 378
  total 378
Differential equation
  Bernoulli 72
  Bessel 190, 520, 563
  Cauchy 124, 137, 186
  Cauchy-Riemann 588
  of circuits 74, 151
  with constant coefficients 104, 136
  elliptic 539
  Euler 124, 137
  exact 63
  homogeneous 61, 67, 101, 133
  hyperbolic 539
  hypergeometric 189
  Laguerre 518
  Laplace 309, 368, 568, 590
  Legendre 175, 573
  linear 67, 100, 133
  nonhomogeneous 67, 101, 133
  nonlinear 100, 133
  numerical methods for 91, 159
  order of 43
  ordinary 43
  parabolic 539
  partial 524
  Poisson 525
  separable 53
  series solution of 165
  Sturm-Liouville 514

Differential equation (*Cont.*)
  of vibrating beam 539
  of vibrating mass 117, 143, 443,
    492
  of vibrating membrane 550
  of vibrating string 527
  Weber 175, 519
Differential form 378
Differentiation
  analytic functions 666
  asymptotic series 790
  complex functions 584
  Laplace transforms 212, 232
  order of 11
  power series 626
  series 683
  vector functions 285
Directed line segment 256
Directional derivative 305
Direction field 51
Dirichlet
  discontinuous factor 505
  problem 761
Discharge of a source 754
Disk 580
Divergence
  theorem of Gauss 362
  of vector fields 315, 366
Division of complex numbers 22
Domain 301, 581
Dot product 263
Double
  Fourier series 557
  integral 333, 340
  point 289
Driving force 144
Dyne 117

E

Eigenfunction
  expansion 517
  of Sturm-Liouville problem 514
  of vibrating membrane 555
  of vibrating string, 531
Eigenvalue
  of matrix 439
  of Sturm-Liouville problem 514
  of vibrating membrane 555
  of vibrating string 531

Eigenvector 439
Electrical network 250, 416, 436
Electric circuit 74, 150, 238, 248
Electromechanical analogies 151
Electromotive force 74
Electrostatic field 744
Element
    of area 352
    of a determinant 400
    of a matrix 387
Elimination method 430
Ellipse 288, 292, 294
Ellipsoid 348
Elliptic
    differential equation 539
    paraboloid 348
Entire function 695
Equality
    of complex numbers 20
    of matrices 388
    of vectors 257, 259
Equation
    characteristic 105, 136, 441
    quadratic 29
    solution of 29
Equipotential
    lines 745, 751
    surfaces 744
Error 27
Error function 549, 774, 782
Escape from the earth 56
Essential singularity 695
Euler 92
    Beta function 771
    -Cauchy method 92, 94
    constant 201
    equation 124, 137
    formula 634, 636
    formulas for Fourier coefficients,
        469, 479
    numbers 677
Evaporation 60
Even function 3, 474
Exact
    differential 63, 378
    differential equation 63
Existence theorem
    differential equations 88, 127, 133
    Fourier integrals 504

Existence theorem (*Cont.*)
    Fourier series 472
    Laplace transforms 209
Exponential
    decay 48
    function, complex 633, 642, 731
    function, real 1
    integral 792
Extended
    complex plane 691
    power series method 181

F

Factor, integrating 65
Factorial function 769
Falling body 50
Family of curves 79
Field
    conservative 310, 381
    of force 282
    gravitational 282, 308, 568
    irrotational 751
    scalar 281
    vector 281
    velocity 282, 749
Finite complex plane 691
First
    fundamental form 350
    Green's formula 369
    shifting theorem 208
Fixed point 723
Fluid flow 317, 749
Flux 317
Folium of Descartes 290
Foot 117
Forced oscillations 143, 222, 245, 491
Form
    bilinear 445
    fundamental 350
    Hermitian 447
    quadratic 446
    skew-Hermitian 448
Fourier 464
    -Bessel series 522
    coefficients 469, 479, 489
    coefficients, complex 485
    constants 511
    cosine series 475
    double series 557

Fourier (*Cont.*)
half-range expansion 483
integral 504, 546, 706
integral, complex 509
series 469, 533
series, complex 485
series, generalized 511
sine series 475
transform 509
Four-terminal network 436
Fractional linear transformation 723
Free oscillations 117, 222
Frenet formulas 296
Frequency 119
Fresnel integrals 777
Frobenius
method of 181
theorem of 458
Full wave rectification 248
Function
analytic 585
Bessel
(*see* Bessel functions)
Beta 771
bounded 88
characteristic 514, 531, 555
complex 583
conjugate harmonic 591
entire 695
error 549, 774, 782
even 3, 474
exponential 1, 633, 731
factorial 769
Gamma 768
Hankel 203
harmonic 568, 590, 720
holomorphic 585
hyperbolic 6, 637, 734
Legendre 176
logarithmic 3, 639, 732
meromorphic 696
multi-valued 583
Neumann 201
odd 3, 474
orthogonal 510, 512
periodic 243, 465
rational 629
regular 585
scalar 281

Function (*Cont.*)
single-valued 583
staircase 237, 244
trigonometric, 3, 635, 732
unit step 235
vector 281
Fundamental
form 350
mode 532
system 108, 134, 428
theorem of algebra 669
triad 262
Funnel 57

G

Gamma function 191, 768, 771
Gauss 20
algorithm 431
divergence theorem 362
elimination method 430
hypergeometric equation 189
General
powers 641
solution 45, 106, 134
Generalized Fourier series 511
Geometric series 172, 605
Gershgorin 456
Gibbs phenomenon 506
Goursat 654
Gradient 305
Gravitational field 282, 308, 568
Green
formulas 369
theorem 340, 369, 376
Grouping 613
Guarding figures 28

H

Hadamard's formula 619
Hankel functions 203
Half-life time 59
Half-range Fourier series 483
Half-wave rectifier 243, 481
Harmonic
analyzer 501
conjugate 591
function 568, 590, 720, 760
oscillation 119
series 601

Heat
    equation 368, 541
    flow 367, 540, 735
Helix 288, 292, 294, 296
Helmholtz equation 571
Henry 74
Hermite polynomials 175, 519
Hermitian matrix 447
Hesse's normal form 267
High frequency line equations 575
Holomorphic function 585
Homogeneous
    differential equation 61, 67, 101, 133
    system of equations 13, 413
Höne (Wronski) 130
Hooke's law 117
Hyperbolic
    differential equation 539
    functions, complex 637, 734
    functions, real 6
    paraboloid 348
Hypergeometric
    differential equation 189
    functions 189
    series 189
Hypocycloid 292

I

Identity
    of Lagrange 280
    of power series 624
    transformation 722
Image 714
Imaginary
    axis 20
    part 20, 578
    unit 20
Impedance 152, 155
Improper integral 704, 707
Incomplete Gamma functions 771
Incompressible 318, 751
Increasing sequence 597
Indefinite
    integral 645
    integration 661
Independence
    linear 107, 133, 276
    of path 378, 657

Indicial equation 181
Inductance 75
Inductor 74
Inequality
    Bessel 498, 512
    Cauchy 669
    Schur 457
    triangle 579
Infinite
    sequence 592
    series 599
Infinity
    analytic at 692
    point at 691
Initial
    condition 55, 133, 525
    value problem 55, 111
Input 70, 144
Insertion of parentheses 613
Instrumental methods 34, 500
Integral
    contour 659
    cosine 779
    definite 645
    double 333, 340
    exponential 792
    Fourier 504, 546, 706
    Fresnel 777
    improper 704, 707
    line 326, 645
    logarithmic 793
    sine 778
    surface 355
    triple 362
Integral theorems
    complex 653, 664
    real 340, 362, 372
Integrating factor 65
Integration
    analytic functions 646
    asymptotic series 788
    Laplace transforms 213, 233
    power series 626
    series 682
Interval
    closed 598
    of convergence 619
    open 598

Inverse
  hyperbolic functions 643
  Laplace transform 206
  of a matrix 434
  trigonometric functions 643
Inversion 722
Irrotational 751
Isocline 50
Isolated
  point 694
  singularity 695
Iteration
  for eigenvalues 460
  for equations 32
  Picard 84

J

Jacobian 337, 720
Jukowski airfoil 742
Jump 486

K

Kirchhoff's laws 75
Kronecker delta 313
Kutta 95

L

Lagrange 72
  identity of 280
Laguerre polynomials 518
Lambert's law 60
Laplace 206
  equation 309, 368, 568, 590
  integrals 507
  operator 310
  transform 206
Laplacian 310, 344, 559
Laurent series 686
Law
  of cooling 55
  of mass action 60
  of the mean 302, 334, 366
Left-hand
  derivative 472
  limit 472
Left-handed
  coordinates 270
  triple of vectors 270

Legendre
  differential equation 175, 573
  functions 176
  polynomials 177, 517, 573
Leibniz 30
  test 601
Length
  of a curve 290
  of a vector 256
Level
  curve 714
  surface 307
Limit
  of complex function 583
  left-hand 472
  right-hand 472
  of sequence 592
  of vector function 284
Limit point 594, 694
Line integral
  complex 645
  real 326, 340, 372
Line of force 745
Lineal element 51
Linear
  combination 276
  dependence 107, 133, 276
  differential equation 67, 100, 133
  element 291
  independence 107, 133, 276
  mapping 723
  transformation 723
Liouville 514
  theorem of 669
Lipschitz condition 90
Logarithm 3, 639, 732
Logarithmic
  decrement 124
  integral 793

M

M-test 684
Maclaurin series 671
Mader-Ott analyzer 501
Magnitude of a vector 256
Mapping 714
  conformal 717
Mariotte 59

Mass action 60
Matrix 387
   addition 388
   augmented 424
   column 388
   diagonal 391
   Hermitian 447
   multiplication 394
   nonsingular 411
   normal 457
   null 391
   orthogonal 450
   scalar 397
   singular 411
   skew-Hermitian 448
   skew-symmetric 390, 451
   square 390
   symmetric 390, 451
   transpose of 389, 397, 412
   triangular 390
   unitary 449
   zero 391
Maximum
   modulus theorem 759
   principle 760
Mean value
   of analytic function 759
   of harmonic function 760
   of integral 749
   theorem 302, 334, 366
Membrane 550
Meromorphic function 696
Method
   Euler-Cauchy 92, 94
   of false position 31
   Frobenius 181
   of iteration 32, 84, 460
   of numerical integration 35
   power series 166
   Runge-Kutta 95, 161
   of undetermined coefficients 140
Minor 17, 400
Mixed triple product 274
Möbius strip 357
Modal matrix 452
Mode 532
Modified Bessel functions 204
Modular surface 638
Modulus 24

Moivre's formula 26
Moment
   of a force 272
   of inertia 336, 340, 356
Monotone
   decreasing 597
   increasing 597
   sequence 597
Morera's theorem 668
Moving trihedron
   (*see* Trihedron)
Multiple point 289
Multiplication
   asymptotic series 787
   complex numbers 21
   matrices 394
   power series 621
   vectors 261, 263, 268, 274
Multiplicity 442
Multiply connected 653
Multi-valued function 583
Mutual inductance 250

N

Nabla 305
Natural
   frequency 145
   logarithm 3, 639, 732
Neighborhood 284, 300, 580
Networks 416, 436
Neumann's function 202
Newton 30
   law of cooling 55
   law of gravitation 282
   method of 30
   second law 119
Nodal line 555
Node 532
Nonhomogeneous
   differential equation 67, 101, 133, 138
   system of equations 13, 413
Nonlinear differential equation 100, 133
Nonorientable surface 357
Nonsingular matrix 411
Norm 510, 512
Normal
   to a curve 294, 295
   matrix 457

Normal (*Cont.*)
    mode 532, 564
    to a surface 307, 349
    vector 266, 349
Null
    matrix 391
    vector 259
Number sphere 692
Numerical methods
    differential equations 91, 159
    eigenvalues 455
    equations 29
    Fourier coefficients 494
    integration 35
    linear equations 431
Nyström 161

O

Odd function 3, 474
Ohm 74
One-dimensional
    heat equation 541
    wave equation 529
One-to-one mapping 720
Open
    disk 580
    interval 598
    set 581
Operations on series 612
Order
    determinant 401
    differential equation 43
    differentiation 11
    eigenvalue 441
    square matrix 390
Ordinary differential equation 43
    (*see also* Differential equation)
Orientable surface 357
Orientation of a curve 291
Orthogonal
    curves 80
    functions 510, 512, 520
    matrix 450
    net 80
    trajectories 80
    triad 262
    vectors 262
Orthonormal 511, 512

Oscillations
    of beam 539
    in circuits 77, 151
    damped 119, 147, 493
    harmonic 119
    of mass on a spring 117, 143, 443, 455, 492
    of membrane 550
    of string 527
    undamped 118, 145
Output 71, 144
Overdamping 121

P

Pappus, theorem of 355
Parabola, semi-cubical 292
Parabolic differential equation 539
Parallel flow 753
Parallelepiped 275
Parallelogram law 21, 260
Parameters, variation of 72, 157
Parametric representation 287, 347
Parseval's formula 513
Partial
    derivative 9
    differential equation 524
    fraction 218
    sum 170, 599
Particular solution 45, 106, 134
Path of integration 326, 646
Periodic function 243, 465
Phase
    angle 149
    of complex number
        (*see* Argument)
    lag 149
Picard
    iteration method 84
    theorem of 696
Piecewise
    continuous 209
    smooth 326
Plane, complex 20
Plane curve 288
Planimeter 34
Point
    at infinity 691
    multiple 289

Point (*Cont.*)
   set 581
   source 754
Poisson
   equation 525
   integral formula 763
Polar
   coordinates 24
   form 24
   moment of inertia 336
Pole 695
Polynomial 629
   Chebychev 520
   Hermite 175, 519
   Laguerre 518
   Legendre 177, 517, 573
   Tchebichef 520
   trigonometric 497
Position vector 259
Positive definite 449
Postmultiplication 397
Potential
   complex 736, 745
   real 308, 568
Pound 117
Powers 629
Power series 170, 616, 680
Power series method 166
Premultiplication 397
Primitive period 465
Principal
   diagonal 390, 400
   normal vector 294
   part 694
   value 579, 630, 640, 707
Product
   of asymptotic series 787
   of complex numbers 21
   of matrices 394
   of power series 621
   of vectors 261, 263, 268, 274
Pure imaginary number 23

Q

Quadratic
   equation 29
   form 446
Quotient of complex numbers 22

R

Radiation of radium 47, 59
Radius of convergence 618
Range of values 583
Rank of a matrix 411
Rational function 629
Ratio test 606, 609
RC-circuit 77
Reactance 152
Real
   axis 20
   matrix 389
   part 20, 578
Rearrangement of series 614
Reciprocal of a matrix 434
Rectangular
   membrane 552
   rule 35
Rectifiable 290
Rectifier 243, 248, 481
Region 582
Regula falsi 31
Regular function 585
Relative error 27
Remainder 170, 599
Removable singularity 695
Representation, parametric 287, 347
Residue 698
Residue theorem 701
Resistance 74
Resonance 145, 230
Response 71, 144
Resultant of forces 260
Riemann
   equations 588
   number sphere 692
   surface 739
Right-hand
   derivative 472
   limit 472
Right-handed
   coordinates 270
   triple of vectors 268
RL-circuit 75
RLC-circuit 151
Rodrigues, formula of 179
Root 629
Root test 608, 610

Rotation 273, 297, 322, 750
Rounding error 28
Row
    of a determinant 400
    matrix 388
    of a matrix 387
    vector 388
Runge-Kutta method 95, 161

S

Saw-tooth wave 244
Scalar 256
    field 281
    function 281
    matrix 397
    product 263
    triple product 274
Schur's inequality 457
Secant 5, 636
Second Green's formula 369
Second shifting theorem 240
Sectionally continuous
    (*see* Piecewise continuous)
Semi-cubical parabola 292
Separation of variables 53, 529
Sequence 592
Series 599
    addition of 612
    asymptotic 781
    of Bessel functions 522
    binomial 675
    convergence 171, 600
    differentiation 683
    double Fourier 557
    of eigenfunctions 517
    Fourier 469, 533
    geometric 172, 605
    harmonic 601
    hypergeometric 189
    infinite 599
    integration 682
    Laurent 686
    Maclaurin 671
    multiplication of 621
    of orthogonal functions 517
    partial sums of 170, 599
    power 170, 616
    remainder of 170, 599
    Taylor 671
    trigonometric 466

Serret-Frenet formulas
    (*see* Frenet formulas)
Set of points 581
Shifting theorems 208, 240
Simple
    curve 289
    pole 695
Simply connected 382, 653
Simpson's rule 39
Simultaneous
    differential equations 439, 443
    linear equations 12, 412
Sine
    of complex variable 635, 732
    hyperbolic 6, 637, 734
    integral 505, 778, 792
    of real variable 3
Single-valued function 583
Singular
    at infinity 692
    matrix 411
    point 673, 694
    solution 46
Singularity 673, 694
Sink 317, 367, 751
Skew-Hermitian
    form 448
    matrix 448
Skew-symmetric matrix 390, 452
Sliding vector 257
Slug 117
Smooth
    curve 325, 646
    piecewise 326, 347, 646
    surface 347
Solution
    of differential equation 43, 101,
      133, 525
    of equations 29
    general 45, 106
    particular 45, 106
    of quadratic equation 29
    singular 46
    of systems of equations 413
Source 317, 367, 751
Spectral matrix 452
Spectrum 439, 532
Speed 296
    angular 297
Sphere 347

Spherical coordinates 569
Spring
  force 117
  modulus 118
Square
  error 497
  matrix 390
  wave 236, 240
Stagnation point 755
Staircase function 237, 244
Steady state 76, 147
Steiner's theorem 361
Step function 235
Stereographic projection 692
Stirling formula 770
Stokes's theorem 372
Straight line 265, 288
Stream function 752
Streamline 749
Strength of a source 754
String, vibrating 527
Sturm-Liouville
  equation 514
  problem 514
Submarine cable equations 576
Submatrix 410
Subsidiary equation 216
Subtraction
  of complex numbers 21
  of matrices 388
  of series 612
  of vectors 262
Sum
  of complex numbers 21
  of matrices 388
  of a series 600
  of vectors 261
Superposition principle 102
Surface 346
Surface integral 355
Symmetric matrix 390, 452
System
  of differential equations 439, 443
  of linear equations 12, 412

T

Tables of functions
  arc tan 25
  Bessel functions 194, 203, 565
  cosine integral 779

Tables of functions (*Cont.*)
  error function 776
  exponential function 7
  Gamma function 773
  hyperbolic functions 7
  natural logarithm 7
  sine integral 779
  tangent 7
  trigonometric functions 7
Table of Laplace transforms 251
Tangent 5, 636
  hyperbolic 8, 637
Tangent
  to a curve 286, 292
  plane 307, 349
  vector 293
Taylor series 671
Tchebichef polynomials 520
Telegraph equations 576
Tests for convergence 601, 605
Tetrahedron 276
Thermal conductivity 367
Time constant 78
Torricelli's law 57
Torsion of a curve 295
Torus 348, 352
Total
  differential 63, 378
  square error 497
Trace of a matrix 453
Trajectories 80
Transformation
  of Cartesian coordinates 314, 451
  by a complex function 714
  of integrals 340, 362, 372
  linear 723
  of vector components 312
Transient state 76, 147
Translation 722
Transmission line equations 575
Transpose of a matrix 389, 397, 412
Trapezoidal rule 36
Triangle inequality 579
Triangular matrix 390
Trigonometric
  approximation 497
  form of complex numbers 24
  functions, complex 635, 732
  functions, real 3

Trigonometric (*Cont.*)
    polynomial 497
    series 466
Trihedron 295
Triple integral 362
Triple of vectors 268
Trivial solution 415, 417
Truncation error 28
Twisted curve 288
Two-dimensional wave equation 552

U

Underdamping 121
Undetermined coefficients 140, 676
Uniform convergence 679
Uniqueness
    differential equations 89, 127, 133
    Laurent series 689
    power series 624
Unit
    binormal vector 295
    circle 580
    matrix 391
    normal vector 349
    principal normal vector 294
    step function 235
    tangent vector 293
    vector 257
Unitary
    matrix 449
    system of vectors 450

V

Variable, complex 583
Variation of parameters 72, 157

Vector 256
    addition 261
    field 281
    function 281
    moment 273
    product 268
Velocity
    of escape 56
    field 282, 749
    potential 751
    vector 296
Vibrations
    (*see* Oscillations)
Volta 74
Voltage drop 74
Volume 335
Vortex 754
Vorticity 750

W

Wave equation 529, 552
Weber's equation 175, 519
Weierstrass 588
    M-test 684
Weight function 512
Wessel 20
Wheatstone bridge 417
Work 265, 330
Wronskian 130, 135

Z

Zero
    of analytic function 693
    matrix 391
    vector 259